LIBRARY OF CONGRESS

CATALOGUE

OF

OPERA LIBRETTOS

PRINTED BEFORE 1800

PREPARED BY

OSCAR GEORGE THEODORE SONNECK

CHIEF OF THE DIVISION OF MUSIC

VOLUME II

AUTHOR LIST, COMPOSER LIST
AND ARIA INDEX

WASHINGTON
GOVERNMENT PRINTING OFFICE
1914

L. C. card, 13—35009

———

This work in two volumes is for sale by the
SUPERINTENDENT OF DOCUMENTS
Government Printing Office
Washington, D. C.

———

Price, $2.00 per set

AUTHOR LIST

AUTHOR LIST

[The name after the colon designates the composer. In case of translations, the name in parenthesis after composer's name is that of the original author]

Abbati, Giovanni Battista.
La virtù tra' nemici, Venezia, 1718: Boniventi.   Schatz 1193

Acanzio, Echille. *Arcadian* name of *marchese* Giovanni Piudemonte.

Achillini, Claudio.
Mercurio e Marte, Parma, 1628 (authorship doubtful): unknown.   Schatz 1448

Acciajuoli (Acciajoli), Filippo.
Chi e cagion del suo mal pianga se stesso, Roma, 1682: author.   ML 50.2.C43A2
Damira placata, Venetia, 1680: M. A. Ziani.   Schatz 11200
Il Girello, Venetia, 1682: Pistocchi.   Schatz 8198
L'Ulisse in Feaccia, Venetia, 1681: del Gaudio.   Schatz 3634

Addison, Joseph.
Rosamond, London, 1767: Arnold.   ML 50.2.R73A7

Adlerbeth, Gudmund Göran.
Cora och Alonzo: Naumann. For German versions of the text *see* Neumann, Joh. Leopold.
Procris och Cephal, Stockholm, 1778 (based on Marmontel): Johnsen (recitatives and a chorus only, the arias selected by Lalin).   Schatz 4967

Ageo Liteo. *Arcadian name of* Baldassare Galuppi's son, Antonio Galuppi.

Agosti, Giulio.
Artaserse, Napoli, 1708 (partly by Zeno and Pariati, with additions by Andrea del Pò): Orlandini and Mancini.   Schatz 7328

Alamanni, *marchese* **Vincenzio.**
L'arrivo d'Enea nel Lazio, Firenze, 1765: Galuppi.   Schatz 3443

Alcindo Isaurense, *P. A.*
La schiava riconosciuta, Venezia, 1766: Scolari.   Schatz 9805

Algarotti, *conte* **Francesco.**
Fetonte. *See* Graun's opera in Title catalogue.
Il giudizio di Paride. *See* Graun's opera in Title catalogue.
Iphigenie en Aulide (in his Saggio sopra l'opera in musica, Livorno, 1763).   ML 3858.A37
Iphigenia in Aulis (in his An essay on the opera, Glasgow, 1768).   ML 3858.A39

Alovar, Pietro.
Armida, ballet. *See* Casali's Antigona.
Le nozze di Perseo e d'Andromeda, ballet. *See* Casali's Antigona.

1175

Alzinger, Johann Baptist von.
Die gute mutter (Wien), 1795: Wranitzky.   SCHATZ 11110
Iphigenia in Tauris, Wien, 1781.   Tr. of Gluck's Iphigénie en
  Tauride (Guillard).   SCHATZ 3904
Iphigenia in Tauris.   Tr. of Gluck's L'Ifigenia in Tauride,
  Vienna, 1783 (Guillard-Da Ponte).   SCHATZ 3905

Amaranto Sciaditico.   *Arcadian name of* Girolamo Gigli.

Amarinzio, Nivildo.   *Arcadian name of* Gioacchino Pizzi.

Ancioni, Giovanni Batista.
Gli amori di Circe con Ulisse (Dresden, 1709): Badia.   SCHATZ 543
La costanza d'Ulisse, Vienna d'Austria (1700): Badia.   SCHATZ 544
—Second copy, with two folded plates, lacking in first copy.   ML 50.2.C69B2

Ancour, Claude Godard d', *called* Saint-Just.

André, Johann.
Der alte freyer, Frankfurt am Mayn, 1775: author.   SCHATZ 178
Der authomat, Hamburg, 1783: author.   SCHATZ 180
Das automat, Lübeck, 1784: author.   L. T. of the above.   SCHATZ 181
Der barbier von Sevilien, Offenbach am Mayn, 1776 (Tr. of
  Beaumarchais' Le barbier de Seville): translator.   SCHATZ 182
Die bezauberten, Berlin, 1777: author.   SCHATZ 184
Die colonie, Hamburg, 1780.   L. ed. of: SCHATZ 9230
Die kolonie, Frankfurt am Mayn, 1778.   Tr. of Sacchini's
  La colonie (Framery).   SCHATZ 9229
Felix oder Der findling, Riga, 1790.   Tr. of Monsigny's Felix
  ou L'enfant trouvé (Sedaine).   SCHATZ 6575
Der gleichgueltige ehemann, Hamburg, 1788.   Tr. of Schus-
  ter's Il marito indolente (Mazzolà).   SCHATZ 9748
Der hufschmied, Frankfurth und Leipzig, 1772.   Tr. of Phili-
  dor's Le maréchal ferrant (Quétant).   SCHATZ 8019
Im trueben ist gut fischen, Koeln am Rhein, 1786.   Tr. of
  Sarti's Fra i due litiganti il terzo gode (Goldoni).   SCHATZ 9460
Nina oder Wahnsinn aus liebe, Berlin, 1790.   Tr. of Dalayrac's
  Nina ou La folle par amour (Marsollier).   SCHATZ 2369
Richard Löwenherz, Berlin, n. d.   Tr. of Grétry's Richard,
  Coeur de Lion (Sedaine).   SCHATZ 4179
Die samnitische vermaehlungsfeier, Berlin, 1780 (together with
  Fr. L. W. Meyer).   Tr. of Grétry's Les marriage Samnites
  (Rozoy).   SCHATZ 4171
Die schoene Arsène, Hamburg, 1780.   Tr. of Monsigny's La
  belle Arsène (Favart).   SCHATZ 6564
Der töpfer, Frankfurt und Leipzig, 1774: author.   SCHATZ 191
Die unnütze vorsicht.   A. T. of his Der barbier von Sevilien.
Das urtheil des Midas, n. i., n. d.   (Together with v. Bonin.)
  Detached copy.   Tr. of Grétry's Le jugement de Midas
  (d'Hèle).   SCHATZ 4163

Andrei, Antonio.
L'avaro deluso, London, 1778 (only the alterations of Bertati's
  "Calandrano"): Sacchini.   SCHATZ 9209
Il convito or the banquet, London, 1782 (only the alterations,
  etc., in Livigni's text): Bertoni.   SCHATZ 910

Andrei, Antonio—Continued.

Il Don Calandrano, Firenze, 1781 (only the alterations of Bertati's text, which, as "L'avaro deluso," with the same alterations, had been performed in London, 1778): Sacchini.   Schatz 9245

Orpheus and Eurydice, London, 1785.   Tr. with alterations of Calsabigi's text for Gluck's Orfeo ed Euridice.   Schatz 3926

Andreucci, Bartolomeo.

Fabio vincitor di se stesso, Lucca, 1681: unknown.   *See* M. Curzio in Title catalogue.

Andrews, Miles Peter.

The baron Kinkvervankotsdorsprakingatchdern, London, 1781: Arnold (ascribed).   Longe 196
Belphegor; or, The wishes (Dublin), 1788: Barthélémon.   Longe 223
Fire and water, London, 1780: Arnold.   Longe 135
The mysteries of the castle, London, 1795: Shield.   Longe 229
Summer amusement or An adventure at Margate, London, 1781 (with Miles): Arnold.   Longe 91

Andrieux, François Guillaume Jean Stanislas.

L'enfance de Jean Jacques Rousseau, Paris, Seconde année [1794].   Schatz 2343

Anelli, Angelo.

Il barone di Moscabianca.   A. T. of his Oro non compra amore: Caruso.
Der braeutigam ohne braut.   A. T. of his Die vorgebildeten grafen: Cimarosa.
Il Castello d'Atlante, Brescia (1791): Martin y Soler.   Schatz 6029
Cinna, Milano (1793): Asioli.   Schatz 348
Il Cinna, Padova (1795): Paër.   Schatz 7560
I due supposti conti ossia Lo sposo senza moglie, Milano (1784): Cimarosa.   Schatz 1920
I due supposti conti ossia Lo sposo senza moglie, Dresda, 1787: Cimarosa.   Schatz 1921
Egelina, Milano (1793): Borghi.   Schatz 1231
Geld ist die loosung.   Tr. of his L'oro fa tutto, Dresda, 1795: Paër.   Schatz 7522
Der geraubte eimer.   Tr. of his La secchia rapita, Dresda, 1795: Zingarelli.   Schatz 11259
La Griselda, Venezia, 1793: Piccinni.   Schatz 8095
La Griselda (Vienna, 1794): Piccinni.   Schatz 8096
La lanterna di Diogene, Napoli, 1794: P. Guglielmi.   (Text also attributed to Giuseppe Palomba.)   Schatz 4250
La lanterna di Diogene—Die laterne des Diogenes, Dresda, 1796: P. Guglielmi.   Schatz 4251
L'oro fa tutto, Milano (1793): Paër.   Schatz 7521
L'oro fa tutto—Geld ist die loosung, Dresda, 1795: Paër.   Schatz 7522
Oro non compra amore o sia Il barone di Moscabianca, Venezia, 1794: Caruso.   Schatz 1649
La secchia rapita, Venezia, 1794: Bianchi.   Schatz 982
La secchia rapita, Milano (1793): Zingarelli.   Schatz 11258
La secchia rapita—Der geraubte eimer, Dresda, 1795: Zingarelli.   Schatz 11259

Anelli, Angelo—Continued.

Lo sposo senza moglie. A. T. of his I due supposti conti: Cimarosa.

Lo sposo senza moglie, Treviso, 1792: Cimarosa. L. T. of their I due supposti conti. SCHATZ 2006

La virtù al cimento, Parma (1798): Paër. SCHATZ 7545

Die vorgebildeten grafen oder Der braeutigam ohne braut. Tr. of his I due supposti conti ossia Lo sposo senza moglie, Dresda, 1787: Cimarosa. SCHATZ 1921

Anelli, Giuseppe.

Il geloso senza rivale, ballet. *See* P. Guglielmi's L'impresa d'opera.

Il matrimonio per concorso, ballet. *See* P. Guglielmi's L'impresa d'opera.

Il ratto della sposa, ballet. *See* Boroni's Artaserse.

Angelo, *conte* **Giacomo dall'.**

L'Aureliano, Venetia, 1666: Pallavicino. SCHATZ 7719

′ La Cleopatra, Venetia, 1662: Castrovillari. SCHATZ 1691

Il Demetrio, Venetia, 1666: Pallavicino. SCHATZ 7735

L'Euridamante, Venetia, 1654: Luccio. SCHATZ 5746

Angiolini, Gasparo (Gaspero).

Alessandro trionfante nell' Indie, ballet. *See* Salieri's La scuola de' gelosi.

L'amore e l'azzardo, ballet: author. *See* Rust's Gli antiquari in Palmira.

Amore e Psiche, ballet: author. *See* Bianchi's Nitteti.

Arianna nell' isola di Nasso, ballet. *See* Naumann's Armida.

Attila, ballet: author. *See* Anfossi's Antigono, 1781.

Il castigo de' bonzi, ballet: author. *See* Anfossi's Antigono, 1781.

Il diavolo a quattro ossia La doppia metamorfosi, ballet: author. *See* Calegari's Artemisia.

Il diavolo a quattro ossia La doppia metamorfosi, ballet: author. *See* Caruso's Il matrimonio in commedia.

Il diavolo a quattro ossia La doppia metamorfosi, ballet: author. *See* Gassmann's L'amore artigiano.

Il disertore francese, ballet: author. *See* Anfossi's Antigono.

Dorina e l'uomo selvatico, ballet: author. *See* G. Giordani's La disfatta di Dario.

Fedra, ballet: author. *See* Campobasso's Antigona.

I geni riuniti, ballet: author. *See* Caruso's Il matrimonio in commedia.

I geni riuniti, ballet: author. *See* Gassmann's L'amore artigiano.

Lauretia, ballet. *See* Bertoni's Cajo Mario.

La Lauretta, ballet: author. *See* Caruso's Il matrimonio in commedia.

La Lauretta, ballet: author. *See* Gassmann's L'amore artigiano.

Lauretta, ballet. *See* Tritto's L'Artenice.

Lorezzo, ballet: author. *See* Campobasso's Antigona.

Lorezzo, ballet: author. *See* V. Federici's L'Olimpiade.

Angiolini, Gasparo—Continued.

La morte di Cleopatra, ballet: author. *See* Rust's Gli antiquari in Palmira.

Le nozze de' Sanniti, ballet: author. *See* G. Giordani's La
disfatta di Dario.

L'orfano, ballet: author. *See* Tarchi's Giulio Sabino.

L'orfano della China, ballet. *See* Bertoni's Cajo Mario.

L'orfano nella China, ballet. *See* Bianchi's Eurione.

La partenza d'Enea, osia Didone abbandonata, ballet: unknown. *See* Gazzaniga's Zon-Zon principe di Kibin-
Kin-Ka.

La partenza di Berenice. A. T. of his ballet Tito: author.

Il rè alla caccia, ballet: author. *See* Naumann's Solimano.

Il rè alla caccia, ballet: author. *See* Tarchi's Giulio Sabino.

Sargine, ballet: author. *See* V. Federici's L'Olimpiade.

Semiramide, ballet: author. *See* Anfossi's Antigono.

Sidney e Silly, ballet. *See* Bianchi's Eurione.

Il Solimano Secondo, ballet: author. *See* Caruso's Il matrimonio in commedia.

Il Solimano secondo, ballet: author. *See* Gassmann's L'a-
more artigiano.

Solimano II, ballet: author. *See* P. Guglielmi's Le pazzie di
Orlando.

Il suffi e lo schiavo, ballet: author. *See* Calegari's Artemisia.

Tito o La partenza di Berenice, ballet: author. *See* Tarchi's
L'apoteosi d'Escole.

Il tutore sorpreso, ballet. *See* Tarchi's Giulio Sabino.

Angiolini, Pietro.

L'arrivo opportuno, ballet: *See* Zingarelli's Il mercato di
Monfregoso.

Ciro in Timbraja, ballet. *See* P. Guglielmi's Gli amanti della
dote.

Ciro in Timbraja, ballet. *See* Guglielmi's Lo sciocco poeta di
campagna.

Il disertor francese, ballet. *See* Gazzaniga's Il disertor
francese.

Gli finti filosofi, ballet. *See* P. Guglielmi's Gli amanti della
dote.

Li finti filosofi, ballet. *See* Guglielmi's Lo sciocco poeta di
campagna.

La morte di Attila, ballet. *See* Fioravanti's L'astuta in
amore ossia Il furbo malaccorto.

Rinaldo e Armida, ballet. *See* Salieri's La cifra.

Il solitario reso sociabile per amore, ballet. *See* Cimarosa's Il
convito.

Gli studi interotti, ballet. *See* Salieri's La cifra.

Il vero amico. A. T. of his ballet Zeboschi ed Esing.

Zeboschi ed Esing, ossia Il vero amico, ballet. *See* P. C.
Guglielmi's Dorval e Virginia.

Anseaume, Louis.

Les amans trompés, Paris, 1756 (possibly with Marcouville):
Laruette (?)   ML 50.2.A63

Anseaume, Louis—Continued.

Les amants trompés, Paris, 1756 (possibly with Marcou-
ville): Laruette (?)   SCHATZ 11478

Le Barnevelt français. A. T. of his L'école de la jeunesse:
Duni.

Bertholde à la ville. *See* Title catalogue.

Cendrillon, Paris, 1759: Laruette.   SCHATZ 5436

Le Chinois poli en France, Paris, 1754. Parody of Sellitti's
Il cinese rimpatriato.   SCHATZ 9828

La clochette, Paris, 1766: Duni.   SCHATZ 2836

La clochette, Paris, 1771: Duni.   SCHATZ 11692

La clochette, Paris, 1782: Duni.   SCHATZ 11693

Les deux chasseurs et la laitière, Paris, 1771: Duni.   SCHATZ 2838

Les deux chasseurs et la laitière, Paris, 1780: Duni.   SCHATZ 11694

Le docteur Sangrado, Paris, 1758: Duni and La Ruette.   SCHATZ 2859

L'école de la jeunesse ou Le Barnevelt françois, Paris, 1765:
Duni.   ML 50.2.E2D9

L'ecole de la jeunesse ou Le Barnevelt français, Paris, 1770:
Duni.   SCHATZ 2841

La fausse aventurière, Paris, 1757 (with Marcouville): Laruette.   SCHATZ 5437

L'isle des foux, Paris, 1762 (with Marcouville and Antilly):
Duni.   SCHATZ 2846

Die laecherliche werbung. A. T. of his Der militz: Duni.

Der letzte rausch, Mannheim, 1780. Tr. of his L'ivrogne
corrigé ou Le mariage du diable: Laruette-Gluck.   SCHATZ 3909

Le mariage du diable. A. T. of his L'ivrogne corrigé: Laruette-Gluck.

Mazet, Bruxelles, 1763: Duni.   ML 50.2.M48D9

Mazet, Paris, 1769: Duni.   SCHATZ 2847

Mazet, Paris, 1771: Duni.   SCHATZ 11696

Le medecin de l'amour, Paris, 1758 (partly by Marcouville):
Laruette.   SCHATZ 5438

Le medecin de l'amour, Bruxelles, 1766 (partly by de Marcouville): Van Maldere.   SCHATZ 5867

Das milchmaedchen und die beiden jaeger, Frankfurt am
Mayn, 1772. Tr. of his Les deux chasseurs et la laitière:
Duni.   SCHATZ 2839

Das milchmaedgen und die zween jaeger, n. i., n. d. Another
Tr.   SCHATZ 2840

Le milicien, Bruxelles, 1763: Duni.   SCHATZ 2848

Le milicien, Paris, 1774: Duni.   SCHATZ 11697

Der militz oder Die laecherliche werbung, Frankfurt am
Mayn, 1775. Tr. of his Le milicien: Duni.   SCHATZ 2849

Le peintre amoureux de son modèle, Paris, 1757: Duni.   ML 50.2.P32D9

Le peintre amoureux de son modèle, nouv. éd., Paris, 1767:
Duni.   SCHATZ 2853

Das redende gemaehlde, Mannheim, 1771. Tr. by Meyer of
his Le tableau parlant: Grétry.   SCHATZ 4189

Das redende gemaehlde, Hamburg, 1780. Reichard's Tr.   SCHATZ 4190

La ressource comique, Paris, 1772: Méreaux.   ML 50.2.R42M2

Le retour de tendresse, Paris, 1778: Mereaux.   ML 50.2.R4M3

Die schule der jugend, Frankfurt am Mayn, 1774.   Tr. of his
L'école de la jeunesse: Duni.   SCHATZ 2842

Anseaume, Louis—Continued.

Der soldat als zauberer, Mannheim, 1772. Tr. of his Le soldat
    magicien: Philidor.   SCHATZ 8025

Le soldat magicien, Paris, 1760: Philidor.   ML 50.2.S68P4

Le soldat magicien, Paris, 1775: Philidor.   SCHATZ 8024

Le tableau parlant, Paris, 1769: Grétry.   SCHATZ 4188

Der verliebte maler, Frankfurt am Mayn, 1773. Tr. of his Le
    peintre amoureux de son modèle: Duni.   SCHATZ 2854

L'yvrogne corrigé, Paris, 1759: Laruette.   SCHATZ 5434

Der zaubernde soldat (n. i., n. d.). Tr. of his Le soldat ma-
    gicien: Philidor.   SCHATZ 8026

Antilly, Louis Auguste Bertin d'.

L'isle des foux, Paris, 1762 (with Anseaume and Marcouville):
    Duni.   SCHATZ 2846

La vieillesse d'Annette et Lubin, Paris, 1790: Chapelle.   ML 50.2.V45C3

Apell, David Philipp von.

L'amour peintre ou Le jaloux dupé, Cassel, 1794: author.   SCHATZ 292

Apolloni, Apollonio.

L'Argia, Insprugg, 1655: Cesti.   SCHATZ 1777

L'Argia, Venetia, 1669: Cesti.   SCHATZ 1777a

Astiage, Venetia, 1677: Viviani. (Text modernized by Noris.)   SCHATZ 10783

La Dori, Venetia, 1663: Cesti.   SCHATZ 1778

La Dori, Venetia, 1666: Cesti.   SCHATZ 11683

La Dori, overo Lo schiavo reggio, Venetia, 1667: Cesti.   SCHATZ 1785

La Dori, Monaco, 1680: Cesti. (Text altered by Terzago.)   SCHATZ 1779

Il regio schiavo o sia La Dori, Mantova, 1672: Cesti. L. T. of
    their La Dori.   ML 50.2.D62C3

Arcoleo, Antonio.

Brenno in Efeso, Venetia, 1690: Perti.   SCHATZ 7947

Clearco in Negroponte, Venetia, 1685: Gabrieli.   SCHATZ 3402

La Rosaura, Venetia, 1689: Perti.   SCHATZ 7954

Ardia Rivarota. *Anagram of* Dario Varotari.

Arien, Bernhard Christian d'.

Antonius und Cleopatra (Litteratur und Theater Zeitung,
    1779): Kaffka.   SCHATZ 4772

Der baum der Diana, Hamburg, 1792. Tr. of Martin y Soler's
    L'arbore di Diana (Da Ponte).   SCHATZ 6002

Heinrich und Lyda, Leipzig, 1776: Neefe.   SCHATZ 7073

Das herrnrecht, Hamburg, 1789. Tr. of Martini's Le droit du
    seigneur (Desfontaines de la Vallée).   SCHATZ 6037

Koenig Theodor in Venedig, Hamburg, 1788. Tr. of Paisiello's
    Il rè Teodoro in Venezia (Casti).   SCHATZ 7653

Laura Rosetti, Leipzig, 1777: André.   SCHATZ 188

Nina oder Wahnsinn aus liebe, Hamburg, 1787. Tr. of Dalay-
    rac's Nina ou La folle par amour (Marsollier).   SCHATZ 2367

Die zwey vormuender, Hamburg, 1788. Tr. of Dalayrac's Les
    deux tuteurs (Fallet.)   SCHATZ 2341

Arnault, Vincent.

Mélidore et Phrosine, Paris, an second [1794]: Méhul.   SCHATZ 6277

Arne, Thomas Augustine.

    Artaxerxes, London, 1763: (Tr. of Metastasio's Artaserse):
        author.   ML 50.2.A81A7
    Artaxerxes, London, n. d.: author.   Longe 308
    Artaxerxes, London, 1792: author.   Longe 218
    The cooper (Collection of the most esteemed farces, Edin-
        burgh, 1792, t. vi): author.   Schatz 11753F
    Don Saverio, London, 1750: author.   Longe 241
    The guardian out-witted, London, 1764: author.   Longe 36
    The rose, London, 1773: Arne, who is the supposed author.   Longe 37
    The sot, London, 1775 (altered from Fielding): author.   Longe 274

Arnold, Samuel, *the younger*.

    Auld Robin Gray, London, 1794: Dr. S. Arnold.   Longe 239

Artale, Giuseppe.

    La Pasife o vero L'impossibile fatto possibile, Venetia, 1661:
        Castrovillari.   Schatz 1689

Arthur, John.

    The lucky discovery or The tanner of York, York, 1737: ballad
        opera.   Longe 152

Artino (Artimio) Corasio. *Arcadian name of* Metastasio.

Artolfi, Pietro.

    Il matrimonio per industria, Milano (1793) (authorship doubt-
        ful): Ferd. Rutini.   Schatz 9184
    Il matrimonio per industria, o sia Il servo astuto. O. T. of the
        above.

L'Assicurato. *Academic name of* conte Giacomo dall' Angelo.

Aston, Anthony.

    The fool's opera, or The taste of the town, London (ca. 1730):
        ballad farce.   Longe 291

Aston, Walter.

    The restauration of King Charles II or The life and death of
        Oliver Cromwell, London, 1732: ballad opera.   Longe 275

Atkinson, Joseph.

    A match for a widow or The frolics of fancy, London, 1788:
        Dibdin.   Longe 110

Aubert, Mrs.

    Harlequin-Hydaspes or The Greshamite, London, 1719.   Longe 200

Audinot, Nicolas Médard.

    Les bons et les méchans ou Philémon et Baucis, Paris, 1783.   ML 48.B2
    Dorothée, pantomime . . . précédée des Preux chevaliers,
        prologue-pantomime, Paris, 1782.   ML 48.B2
    Der fassbinder, Berlin, 1796. Tr. of his and Quétant's Le
        tonnelier: Audinot and Gossec.   Schatz 489
    Der fassbinder, Frankfurt am Mayn, 1773. Faber's Tr.   Schatz 488
    Philémon et Baucis. A. T. of his Les bons et les méchans.
    Les preux chevaliers. *See* his Dorothée.
    Le tonnelier, Paris, 1765: author, text revised by Quétant,
        music by Gossec and partly new.   ML 50.2.T68
    Le tonnelier, nouv. éd. augm., Paris, 1767 (rev. by Quétant):
        Audinot and Gossec.   Schatz 487

Audinot, Nicolas Médard—Continued.

Le tonnelier, Paris, 1768. Schatz 11672
Le tonnelier, Paris, 1768. "Nouv. éd." Schatz 11674
Le tonnelier, Paris, 1770. "Nouv. éd. augmentée." Schatz 11673

Auernbrugger, Leopold von.

Der rauchfangkehrer oder Die unentbehrlichen verraether
ihrer herrschaffen aus eigennutz, Wien, 1781: Salieri. Schatz 9313

Aureli, Aurelio.

Admetus, koenig in Thessalien (Hamburg, 1730). Tr. of his
Admeto: Hândel. Schatz 4470
Admetus, koenig in Thessalien (Hamburg, 1731). L. ed. of
this. Schatz 11713
L'Alcibiade, Venetia, 1680: M. A. Ziani. Schatz 11177
Second copy. ML 48.M2O
Alessandro Magno in Sidone, Venetia, 1679: M. A. Ziani. Schatz 11178
Alessandro Magno in Sidone, Vicenza, 1681: M. A. Ziani. ML 50.2.A515Z3
Amore spesso inganna. A. T. of his (?) Orfeo a torto geloso:
Sartorio.
Gl'amori d'Apollo e di Leucotoe, Venetia, 1663: Rovettino. Schatz 9107
Gl'amori infruttosi di Pirro, Venetia, 1661: Sartorio. Schatz 9480
L'Antigona delusa da Alceste, Milano, 1662: P. A. Ziani. Schatz 11212
L'Artaxerse ovvero L'Ormonda costante, Venétia, 1669:
Grossi. Schatz 4216
Circe abbandonata da Ulisse, Venetia, 1697: C. F. Pollaroli. Schatz 8324
Claudio Cesare, Venezia, 1672: Boretti. Schatz 1216
La costanza di Rosmonda, Venetia, 1659: Rovettino. Schatz 9108
La costanza di Rosmonda, Milano (1675): Rovettino. Schatz 11744
Creso tolto a le fiamme, Venezia, 1705: Polani. Schatz 8250
Demetrio, Parma, 1694: Sabadini. Schatz 9193
Diomede punito da Alcide, Venezia, 1701: Albinoni. Schatz 107
Diomede punito da Alcide, Parma, 1691: Sabadini. Schatz 9194
Le due rivali in amore, Venezia (1728): Albinoni. Schatz 108
Elena rapita da Paride, Venetia, 1687. L. T. of his Helena
rapita da Paride: Freschi, with new music by Navarra. Schatz 3358
Eliogabalo, Venetia, 1668: Boretti. Schatz 1219
L'Ercole in Tebe, Venetia, 1671 (rewrote Moniglia's text):
Boretti. Schatz 1222
L'Ercole trionfante, Parma, 1688: Sabadini. Schatz 9196
L'Erginda, Venetia, 1652: G. Sartorio. Schatz 9496
L'Erismena, Venetia, 1655: Cavalli. Schatz 1720
Le fatiche d'Ercole per Deianira, Venetia, 1662: P. A. Ziani. Schatz 11221
Il favore de gli Dei, Parma, 1690: Sabadini. ML 50.2.F237S2
Le fortune di Rodope e Damira, Bologna, 1658: P. A. Ziani. Schatz 11215
Gerone tiranno di Siracusa, Genova (1700): Gasparini. Schatz 3588
Gerone tiranno di Siracusa, Napoli, 1727 (L. T. of his Hierone,
tiranno di Siracusa): Hasse. ML 50.2.G3H2
La gloria d'Amore, Parma, 1690: Sabadini. Schatz 9198
Helena rapita da Paride, Venetia, 1677 (1st ed., 64 p.): Freschi. ML 50.2.H3F7
Helena rapita da Paride, Venetia, 1677: Freschi. Schatz 3351
Hierone tiranno di Siracusa, Parma, 1688: Sabadini. Schatz 9197
L'Ifigenia, Venezia, 1707 (alterations of Riva's text): Colletti. Schatz 2112
Lisimaco riamato da Alessandro, Venetia, 1682 (merely re-
wrote Sinibaldi's text): Legrenzi. Schatz 5545

Aureli, Aurelio—Continued.

Il Macedone continente.   A. T. of his La virtù sublimata dal
grande: M. A. Ziani.

Massimo Puppieno, Venetia, 1685: Pallavicino.   SCHATZ 7727

Medea in Atene, Venetia, 1678: Zannettini.   SCHATZ 11144

Il Medoro, Venetia, 1658: Luccio.   SCHATZ 5744

La ninfa bizzarra, Modona, 1701: M. A. Ziani.   SCHATZ 11190

Olimpia placata, Parma, 1687: Freschi and Sabadini.   L. T.
of his: SCHATZ 3359

Olimpia vendicata, Venetia, 1682: Freschi.   SCHATZ 3352

L'Orfeo, Venetia, 1673: Sartorio.   SCHATZ 9483

Orfeo a torto geloso overo Amore spesso inganna, Bologna,
1697.   (According to Schatz, this is a replica of his L'Orfeo
text, as set by Sartorio, but, as pointed out, the text is
almost entirely different.)   SCHATZ 9485

L'Ormonda.   A. T. of his L'Artaserse: Grossi.

Orpheus, Braunschweig, 1690: Sartorio.   Tr. of their L'Orfeo. SCHATZ 9484

Perseo, Venetia, 1665: Mattioli.   SCHATZ 6103

Pompeo Magno in Cilicia, Venetia, 1681: Freschi.   SCHATZ 3353

Prassitele in Gnido, Venezia, 1700: Colletti.   SCHATZ 2113

Prassitele in Gnido, Venetia, 1707: Polani.   SCHATZ 8255

La Rosilena, Venetia, 1664: Rovettino.   SCHATZ 9109

Gli scherzi di fortuna, Venetia, 1662: P. A. Ziani.   SCHATZ 11218

Teseo in Atene, Parma, 1688: Zannettini.   L. T. of their
Medea in Atene, with additional arias by Sabadini.   SCHATZ 11143

Teseo tra le rivali, Venezia, 1685: Freschi.   SCHATZ 3348

La virtù sublimata dal grande ovvero Il Macedone continente,
Venetia, 1683.   L. T. of his Alessandro Magno in Sidone:
M. A. Ziani.   SCHATZ 11209

Il vitio depresso e la virtù coronata, Venetia, 1687: Orgiani. SCHATZ 7299

Aureli, Girolamo.

La forza della pace, Roma, 1751 (authorship doubtful):
Rinaldo di Capua.   ML 50.2.F75R3

Il gran conte di Cordanova, Roma, 1754 (authorship doubtful):
Massi.   ML 50.2.G68M2

L'impazzito, Roma, 1748: Casali.   ML 50.2.I45C2

Autreau, Jacques.

Platée (Paris) 1745 (ballet, with Le Valois d'Orville): Rameau. ML 52.2.P5

Averara, A. D.

L'Ajace, Napoli, 1697: Lonati and Magni (more likely the
author was the abbate Pietro d'Averara).   SCHATZ 5682

Averara, Pietro d'.

Admeto rè di Tessaglia, Milano, 1702.   SCHATZ 5839

L'Ajace, Napoli, 1697: Lonati (but the t.-p. has plainly A. D.
Averara).   SCHATZ 5682

L'amante fortunato per forza, Venetia, 1684: Varischino.   SCHATZ 10594

Andromaca, Milano, 1701: unknown.   SCHATZ 11304

L'Aretusa, Venezia, 1709: Monari.   SCHATZ 6549

L'Arsiade (Mantova, 1700): Martinengo.   ML 50.2.A778M2

Arsiade, Torino, 1703: Martinengo.   SCHATZ 6032

Ascanio, Milano, 1702: C. F. Pollaroli.   SCHATZ 8274

Esione, Torino (1699): Ballarotti.   SCHATZ 592

Averara, Pietro d'—Continued.
Il Filindo, Venezia, 1720: Buini. SCHATZ 1382
Nerina, Venezia, 1728 (with alterations by Domenico Lalli):
    A. Pollaroli. SCHATZ 8263
Il pertinace, Venetia, 1689 (but authorship improbable):
    Biego. SCHATZ 1016
Pub. Elio Pertinace, Venetia, 1684: Legrenzi. SCHATZ 5538
                    Second copy. ML 48.M2O
Il trionfo della virtù, Venezia (1724): G. F. Brusa. SCHATZ 1375

Ayrenhoff.
Welche ist die beste nation?, Wien 1782: Umlauf. SCHATZ 10528

Ayres, James.
Sancho at court or The mock governor (London, 1742): ballad
    opera. LONGE 189

Azemar, d'.
Die beiden militzen, Frankfurt am Mayn, 1773. Tr. of his
    Les deux miliciens ou L'orpheline villageoise: Fridzeri. SCHATZ 3371
Les deux miliciens, ou L'orpheline villageoise, Paris, 1772:
    Fridzeri. SCHATZ 3370

Babo, Franz Joseph Marius von.
Armida und Rinaldo, Wien, 1793: Winter. L. T. of their
    Reinold und Armida. SCHATZ 11050
Kora und Alonzo (Muenchen, 1781): Winter. SCHATZ 11038
Das lustlager, Muenchen, 1784: Schubbauer. SCHATZ 9711
Reinold und Armida. O. T. of his Armida und Rinaldo:
    Winter.

Bacon, James.
The American Indian, or, Virtues of nature, London, 1795. LONGE 270

Baczko, Ludwig Adolph Franz Joseph von.
Die kantons-revision, Koenigsberg, 1794: Halter. SCHATZ 4449
Rinaldo und Alcina, Koenigsberg, 1794: Paradies. SCHATZ 7770
Die singschule, oder: Drei heirathen an einem tage, Koenigs-
    berg, 1794: Mühle. SCHATZ 6872

Badi, Paolo Emilio.
L'Argene, Venetia, 1689: Caldara. SCHATZ 1492
La Corilda overo L'amore trionfante della vendetta, Venezia,
    1688: Francesco Rossi. SCHATZ 8887
Le gare dell' inganno e dell' amore, Venetia, 1689: Orgiani. SCHATZ 7298
Il trionfo di Amore e di Marte, Venetia, 1689: Lombardini. SCHATZ 5679

Badini, Carlo Francesco.
Il disertore—The deserter, London, 1770: P. Guglielmi. SCHATZ 4242
Il disertore, Lisbona, 1772: P. Guglielmi. SCHATZ 4243
Il duca d'Atene, London, 1780: Bertoni. ML 48.M2K
Le pazzie di Orlando, Milano (1773): P. Guglielmi. SCHATZ 4301

Badoaro, Giacomo.
L'Helena rapita da Theseo, Venetia, 1653: Cavalli. SCHATZ 1735
Le Nozze d'Enea con Lavinia (manuscript): Monteverdi. SCHATZ 6596
L'Ulisse errante, Venetia, 1644: Sacrati. SCHATZ 9255

Badovero, *conte* **Camillo.**
Gl'amori fatali, Venetia, 1682 (L. T. of his Il Leandro): Pistocchi. SCHATZ 8199
Il Leandro, Venetia, 1679: Pistocchi. SCHATZ 8196
Sesto Tarquinio, Venetia, 1679: Tomasi. SCHATZ 10359

Baggesen, Jens Emanuel.
Erik Eiegod, Kiøbenhavn, 1798: Kunzen. SCHATZ 5316
Holger Danske (Cramer's Musik, 1789): Kunzen. ML 4.M3
Second copy. SCHATZ 5321

Bagliacca, Pietro Antonio.
La dama immaginaria (Venezia, 1777): Astaritta. SCHATZ 370
I pazzi per disimpegno, Venezia (1782): Andreozzi. SCHATZ 222
Rosina consolata ossia L'innocenza protetta, Venezia, 1781: Valentini. SCHATZ 10584

Bailly, Jacques.
Armide (Les parodies du Nouveau Théâtre italien, Paris, 1738, t. iii) (parody of Lully's opera). ML 48.P3

Baker, Robert.
The mad-house, London, 1737: ballad opera. LONGE 192

Balbis.
Tancredi, Torino (1767): Bertoni. SCHATZ 930

Baldinotti.
La Lodoiska, Lisbona, 1796. Tr. of Kreutzer's Lodoiska (Jaure) with additional music by others. SCHATZ 5269

Ballani, Francesco.
Lisandro, Genova (1790): Isola. SCHATZ 4906
Il podestà di Tufo antico o sia Il tutore burlato, Roma (1786): Accorimboni. SCHATZ 17
Tullo Ostilio, Roma, 1784: Gazzaniga. SCHATZ 3685

Ballani, Mario.
La conquista di Granata, Firenze, 1796: Curcio. L. T. of their La presa di Granata. SCHATZ 2306
La presa di Granata, (Livorno, 1795): Curcio. SCHATZ 2305

Ballerini, *barone* **Francesco.**
Il trionfo dell' amore & della costanza.—Der triumph der liebe und bestaendigkeit, Hamburg (1718): Conti. SCHATZ 2199
Vespetta e Milo, Dresda, 1717. (Intermezzi in Lotti's Giove in Argo): I–II by A. Scarlatti (text by Stampiglia), III by Conti (text by the above). SCHATZ 5719
Vespetta e Milo, Dresde, 1717 (with S. Stampiglia): A. Scarlatti and F. B. Conti. SCHATZ 9522

Ballon, Domenico.
Amazili e Telesco. A. T. of his ballet La conquista del Perù.
L'Americana in Europa, ballet. *See* Gazzaniga's La disfatta de' Mori.
Angelica e Wilton, ballet: Nucci. *See* Isola's La conquista del vello d'oro.
Le bizzarie del bel sesso. A. T. of his ballet La vedova ingegnosa.

Ballon, Domenico—Continued.

La conquista del Perù ossia Amazili e Telesco, ballet. *See* Tarchi's Ademira.

La distruzione di Cartagine, ballet: Trento. *See* Andreozzi's Amleto.

I due cacciatori e la venditrice di latte, ballet: Nucci. *See* Isola's La conquista del vello d'oro.

L'incoronazione di Uladislao, rè di Polonia in rè d'Ungheria, ballet: Nucci. *See* Isola's La conquista del vello d'oro.

Ino e Temisto, ballet. *See* Nasolini's La Calliroe.

Le ninfe di Diana, ballet. *See* Bianchi's Calto.

Orfeo ed Euridice, ballet: Gluck and Pugnani. *See* Gazzaniga's La disfatta de' Mori.

Sardanapalo, rè degli Assirj, ballet. *See* Andreozzi's Agesilao.

Il trionfo di Arianna, ballet. *See* Tarchi's La Virginia.

La vedova ingegnosa ossia Le bizzarie del bel sesso, ballet. *See* Tarchi's Ademira.

Ballot de Sauvot.

Pigmalion, Paris, 1772. (Rev. version of De La Motte's La sculpture): Rameau.   ML 48.B2

Banti, Giuseppe.

Adelaide di Ghesclino, ballo eroico. *See* Fabrizj's L'amore per interesse.

La contadina astuta, ballet. *See* Paër's L'oro fa tutto.

La costanza coniugale, ballet: Canavasso. *See* Andreozzi's Teodelinda.

Il disertore francese, ballet: Canavasso. *See* G. Giordani's Ariarate.

La fiera di Sinigaglia, ballet: Canavasso. *See* Andreozzi's Teodelinda.

Il Gastaldo burlato, ballet: Canavasso. *See* Andreozzi's Teodelinda.

Mastino della Scala, ballet: Trento. *See* Paër's L'oro fa tutto.

L'Olimpiade, ballet: Astaritta. *See* Meucci's Telemaco.

Il Posilipo di Napoli, ballet. *See* P. Guglielmi's Lo sciocco poeta di campagna.

Il riconoscimento di Teseo ossia Teseo e Medea, ballet: Canavasso. *See* G. Giordani's Ariarate.

Il trionfo improvviso, ballet: Canavasso. *See* Pugnani's Demetrio a Rodi.

Zima, ballet. *See* P. Guglielmi's Lo sciocco poeta di campagna.

Zima, ballet. *See* Zingarelli's La secchia rapita.

Banzy.

Ballet dansé a Ville-Neuve-Saint-George (Recueil général des opéra, Paris, 1703, t. 4): Colasse.   Schatz 2104

Barbapiccola, N. (*pseud.*?).

L'Irene, Napoli, 1704 (only interpolations in conte Roberti's text): G. B. Pullaroli and D. Scarlatti.   Schatz 9539

Barbetta, Carlo.

L'Amorosa libertà, Macerata, 1647: Ferrari, F.   Schatz 3076

72251°—VOL 2—14——2

Barbier, Marie Anne.

Les festes de l'été (Recueil général des opéra, Paris, 1734, t. xii) (with Pellegrin): Montéclair. SCHATZ 6589

Le jugement de Paris (Recueil général des opéra, Paris, 1734, t. xii) (with Pellegrin): Bertin de la Doué. SCHATZ 880

Les plaisirs de la campagne (Recueil général des opéra, Paris, 1734, t. xii) (with Pellegrin): Bertin de la Doué. SCHATZ 881

Bardella, Francesco.

Il figlio delle selve, Mannheim (1753) (only the alterations in Capece's text): Holzbauer. SCHATZ 4781

Il figlio delle selve, Genova (1755): Mazzinghi and others. SCHATZ 6217

Bardotti, Luigi.

Carolina e Mexicow, ballet. *See* Sarti's Giulio Sabino.

Baretti, Giuseppe.

Fetonte sulle rive del Po (Torino, 1750): Giai. SCHATZ 3818

Barlocci, Giovanni.

L'ambizione delusa, Torino (1747). L. T. of his Madonna Ciana: Latilla. SCHATZ 5462

L'ambizione delusa. Also O. T. of his Il vecchio amante (composed under this title by Latilla).

L'ambizione delusa, Venezia (1744). L. T. of his La commedia in commedia: Rinaldo di Capua. SCHATZ 8802

Ciana, Monaco, 1749. L. T. of his Madama Ciana: Latilla. SCHATZ 5448

La commedia in commedia, Ferrara (1747): Latilla. SCHATZ 5457

La commedia in commedia, Venezia, 1749: Rinaldo di Capua. SCHATZ 8803

La finta cameriera—Das verstellte kammermaedgen (Bronseviga, 1751): Galuppi. SCHATZ 3454

La finta cameriera, Venezia, 1743: Latilla. SCHATZ 5445

La libertà nociva, Venezia (1744): Rinaldo di Capua. SCHATZ 8798

Madama Ciana, Venezia, 1744: Latilla. SCHATZ 5447

Il vecchio amante, Torino (1747): Latilla. SCHATZ 5463

Das verstellte kammermaedgen. Tr. of his La finta cameriera (Bronseviga, 1751): Galuppi. SCHATZ 3454

Baroni, Bartolomeo.

Marco Manlio Capitolino, Lucca, 1777. *See* M. Curzio in Title catalogue.

Barré, Pierre Yves.

Aristote amoureux ou Le philosophe bridé, Paris, 1780 (with de Piis): unknown. ML 50.2.A746

Les amours d'été, Paris, 1784 (with de Piis): unknown. SCHATZ 11480

La matinée et la veillée villageoisie ou Le sabot perdu, Paris, 1784 (with de Piis): unknown. SCHATZ 11499

L'opéra en province, Paris, 1778 (with Piis): parody of Gluck's Armide. ML 50.2.A76G5

Le printemps, Paris, 1784 (with de Piis): Prot. SCHATZ 8471

Renaud d'Ast, Paris, Prault, 1788 (with Radet): Dalayrac. ML 50.2.R39D21

Renaud d'Ast, Paris, Brunet, 1788 (withRadet): Dalayrac. ML 50.2.R39D22

La vallée de Montmorency ou Jean Jacques Rousseau dans son hermitage, pasticcio. *See* Title catalogue.

Les vendangeurs ou Les deux baillis, Paris, 1781 (with de Piis): unknown. SCHATZ 11221

Barsanti, Giov. Nicolao.
Il Temistocle, Lucca, 1678.   *See* M. Curzio in Title catalogue.

Bartoli, Giuseppe.
La vittoria d'Imeneo, Torino (1750): Galuppi.   SCHATZ 3500

Bartolini, Nicolao.
Gli avantaggi della concordia, Lucca, 1672.   *See* M. Curzio in Title catalogue.

Bartolini, Niccolò Enea.
Venere gelosa, Padova, 1643: Sacrati.   SCHATZ 9251

Bartolamei (Bartolommei) Giuseppe.
Il generoso perdono, ballet.   *See* Cimarosa's Lo sposo senza moglie.
La scuola di scultura, ballet.   *See* Cimarosa's Lo sposo senza moglie.
Bacco e Arianna, ballet.   *See* Sarti's I due litiganti.

Bartolommei Smeducci, Girolamo.
Drammi musicali morali di Girolamo Bartolommei già Smeducci . . .
Firenze, G. A. Bonardi, 1656.   2 v. in 1:   viii, 288; 2 p. l., 371 p. 23 cm.
Title of v. 2 reads: "Drammi musicali sacri . . ." These are: L'Eufrasia—Il sacrifizio d'Isac—L'innocenza di Susanna—L'annunziazione della B. Vergine—Maddalena al Sepolcro—La vendita di Gioseffo—Il figliuol prodigo—Le selve ad onore di S. Andrea Corsini. As these *drammi musicali* more properly belong to the category of oratorios, they have not been entered here.
The dramas in the first volume are: Cerere racconsolata—Il natale di Minerva—Perseo trionfante—Il trionfo di Maggio, vincitor della peste—Amore gastigato—La gloria d'Orfeo.
No composers recorded.
ML 49.A2B3

Bartolotti, Giovanni Francesco.
Scipione il giovane, Venezia (1731): Predieri.   SCHATZ 8458

Barton, Andrew (*pseud.?*)
The disappointment or The force of credulity, New York, 1767: ballad opera.   ML 50.6.D52
The disappointment or The force of credulity, Philadelphia, 1796.   (Second ed.)   ML 50.6.D54

Barziza, *conte* **Pietro Giorgio.**
Filippo rè della Grecia, Venezia, 1706: C. F. Pollaroli.   SCHATZ 8289
Il Germanico, Venezia, 1716: C. F. Pollaroli.   SCHATZ 8294

Bassi, Carlo.
L'Andromeda, Piacenza (1662): Tortona.   SCHATZ 10374

Bate, *Rev.* **Henry.**   *See later name* Dudley, *Sir* Henry Bate.

Batsch, August Johann Georg Carl.
Erano, n. i., 1779: unknown.   ML 50.2.E58

Baugé.   *See* Beaugé.

Baumgarten, Gotthilf von.
Zemire und Azor, Breslau, 1775 (with Schubert): author.   SCHATZ 658

Baurans.

Le maître de musique, Bruxelles, 1758.   Parody of Pergo-
lesi's Il maestro di musica.   ML 50.2.M3P3

Le maître de musique, Paris, 1784.   SCHATZ 5467

La servante maitresse, Paris, 1754.   Parody of Pergolesi's La
serva padrona (Federico).   SCHATZ 7895

La servante maitresse, Paris, 1771.   SCHATZ 7895a

La servante maitresse, La Haye, 1755.   ML 48.A4

La servante maîtresse, Bruxelles, n. d.   ML 50.2.S51P3

Beauchamp, Pierre François Godard de.

Le jaloux puni (Le nouveau théâtre italien, Paris, 1753, t. iii):
Mouret.   PQ 1231.I5N6

Beaugé (Baugé), Daniel Paul Chappuzeau de.

Coronis (Amsterdam), 1692: Gatti.   ML 50.2.C67G2

Coronis (Recueil général des opéra, Paris, 1703, v. 4): Gatti.   SCHATZ 3632

Beaumarchais, Pierre Augustin Caron de.

Axur, koenig von Ormus, Hamburg und Altona, 1799.   Tr. of
his Tarare: Salieri.   SCHATZ 9332

Axur re d'Ormus (Praga), 1788.   Practically independent
Italian version by Da Ponte of his Tarare: Salieri.   SCHATZ 9326

The barber of Seville, or The useless precaution, London,
1776.   Tr. of his Le barbier de Seville.   LONGE 318

Der barbier von Sevilien, Offenbach am Mayn, 1776: André.
Tr. of his Le barbier de Seville.   SCHATZ 182

Der barbier von Seville oder Die vergebliche vorsicht, Leipzig, 1784: F. L. Benda.   Tr. of his Le barbier de Seville.   SCHATZ 764

Tarar, Hamburg, 1791.   Tr. of his Tarare (and partly of Da
Ponte's Axur, rè d'Ormus): Salieri.   SCHATZ 9330

Tarare, London, 1787.   Tr. of his Tarare: Salieri.   LONGE 299

Tarare, Amsterdam, 1787: Salieri.   SCHATZ 9325

Die unnütze vorsicht.   A. T. of his Der barbier von Sevilien:
André.

Die vergebliche vorsicht.   A. T. of his Der barbier von Seville:
F. L. Benda.

Beaumont, Francis, *and* Fletcher, John.

Bonduca, or, The British heroine, London, 1696: Purcell, H.   LONGE 208

The prophetess or The history of Dioclesian, London, 1690
(altered by Betterton): H. Purcell.   ML 48.M2D

The prophetess or The history of Dioclesian, London, 1759
(partly new text, with new music, but suppression of
Purcell's).   LONGE 72

Beaunoir, *Mme* de.   *See* Robineau, Alexandre Louis Bertrand.

Beckau, Joachim.

Das ende der babylonischen monarchie oder Belsazer, Ham-
burg (1723): Telemann.   SCHATZ 10258

———— The same.   IIter theil, Hamburg (1723): Telemann.   SCHATZ 10259

Oriana (Hamburg, 1717).   Tr. of Händel's Amadigi di Gaula
(Heidegger).   SCHATZ 4474

Der thrazische printz Floridantes, Hamburg, 1723.   Tr. of
Händel's Floridante (Rolli).   SCHATZ 4477

Becker, Wilhelm Gottlieb.
Die drei pächter, Wien, 1785. Tr. of Dezède's Les trois
    fermiers (Monvel).   SCHATZ 2524
Das liebesgrab, Heydelberg, 1779: Schwindel.   SCHATZ 9779

Bédéno, Jean Claude. *See* Dejaure.

Beffroy de Reigny, Louis Abel (*called* Cousin Jacques).
Le club des bons-gens, ou La reconciliation, Marseille, cin-
    quième année [1796–97]: author.   SCHATZ 704
Les deux charbonniers ou Les contrastes, Paris, an VIII
    [1799–1800]: author.   SCHATZ 705
Magdelon, Paris, an VIII [1799–1800]: author.   SCHATZ 706
Nicodème dans la lune ou La révolution pacifique, Paris,
    1791: author.   SCHATZ 707
La petite Nannette, Paris, an V–1797: author.   SCHATZ 703

Bellamy, Thomas.
The benevolent planters, London, 1789.   LONGE 195

Bellini, Serafino.
L'amore volubile, Bologna (1779): Caruso.   SCHATZ 1666

Belmuro, Andrea.
La contadina. O. T. of his Don Tabarrano: Hasse.
Don Tabarrano (Dresda, 1737): Hasse. (L. T. of La con-
    tadina.)   SCHATZ 4529
Don Tabarrano—Don Tabarrano (Dresda, 1747): Hasse.   SCHATZ 4530
Il Tabarano—Der Tabaran, Braunschweig (1749). L. T. of
    his Don Tabarrano: Hasse.   SCHATZ 4531

Bencini, Carlo.
Lauretta, ballet. *See* P. Guglielmi's La serva innamorata.

Benedetti, Domenico.
La moda, Venezia, 1754: Bertoni.   SCHATZ 922

Benincasa, Bartolomeo.
Il disertore, Venezia, 1784: Bianchi.   SCHATZ 978
Il disertore, Genova, Anno II (1799): **Tarchi.**   SCHATZ 10235

Benserade, Isaac de.
[L'amour malade, Paris, 1657]: Lully.   ML 52.2.B15
Ballet du temps, Paris, 1654: Lully.   ML 52.2.B17
Les festes de l'Amour et de Bacchus (Recueil général des
    opéra, t. i, Paris, 1703) (supposed joint-author with Quin-
    ault and Molière): Lully.   SCHATZ 5766
Les nopces de Pelée et de Thetis, Paris, 1654: ballet, part of
    which is accredited to J. B. de Lully.   ML 52.2.N67
Le triomphe de l'amour, ballet (Recueil général des opéra, t.
    ii, Paris, 1703) (jointly with Quinault): Lully.   SCHATZ 5774

Benson.
Britain's glory; or, A trip to Portsmouth, London (1794):
    Arnold.   LONGE 246
Love and money or The fair Caledonian, London (1795):
    Arnold.   LONGE 246

Bentivoglio, *marchese* **Ippolito.**

L'Achille in Sciro, Venetia, 1663: Legrenzi.   SCHATZ 5532

L'Achille in Sciro, Venetia, 1664: Legrenzi.   SCHATZ 11720

Tiridate, Venetia, 1668: Legrenzi (text in part possibly by
    Minato).   SCHATZ 5539

Beregani, *conte* **Nicolo.**

L'Annibale in Capua, Venetia, 1661: P. A. Ziani.   SCHATZ 11225

Il Genserico, Venetia, 1669: Cesti.   SCHATZ 1780

Il Giustino, Bologna (1711): Albinoni. (Text modernized by
    Pariati.)   SCHATZ 129

Giustino, Venetia, 1683: Legrenzi.   SCHATZ 5544

Giustino, Roma, 1724: Vivaldi.   SCHATZ 10769

L'Heraclio, Venetia, 1671: P. A. Ziani.   SCHATZ 11217

Ottaviano Ces. Augusto, Venetia, 1682: Legrenzi.   SCHATZ 5537

Il Tito, Venetia, 1666: Cesti.   SCHATZ 1784

Beretta, Giuseppe.

La fede ne tradimenti, Venezia, 1705 (originally by Girolamo
    Gigli): C. F. Pollaroli.   SCHATZ 8288

Beretti, Filippo.

Andronico e Ramira, ballet. *See* Borghi's Egilina.

Andronico e Ramira, ballet. *See* Nasolini and Trento's Gli
    innamorati.

Andronico e Ramira, ballet. *See* Sarti's Le nozze di Dorina.

Andronico e Ramira, ballet. *See* Winter's I fratelli rivali.

La bella Arsene, ballet: Canavasso. *See* Martin y Soler's
    Andromaca.

La caccia d'Isabella, regina di Spagna, ballet. *See* Tarchi's
    Ezio.

Il calzolajo, ballet. *See* Cristiani's La città nuova.

I comici Italiani alla China, ballet. *See* Cimarosa's I due
    supporti conti.

La contadina filosofa, ballet. *See* Alessandri's Il vecchio
    geloso.

Una cosa rara. A. T. of his ballet Lilla e Lubino.

Li due sposi sfortunati, ballet. *See* Prati's Demofoonte.

L'esilio di Tarquinio il Superbo, VII. rè di Roma, ballet:
    Trento. *See* Zingarelli's La morte di Mitridate.

Una festa villereccia, ballet. *See* Tarchi's L'Arminio.

Il giudice, e padre, ballet. *See* Borghi's Egilina.

Giulietta e Romeo, ballet. *See* Tarchi's Antioco.

Giulietta e Romeo, fatto patrio Veronese, ballet. *See* Tarchi's
    L'Arminio.

L'innocenza scoperta, ballet. *See* Cimarosa's I due supposti
    conti.

Ipermestra ossia La morte di Danao, ballet. *See* Giordani's
    Nicomede.

L'Italia rigenerata, ballet. *See* Zingarelli's Meleagro.

Lilla e Lubino ossia Una cosa rara, ballet. *See* Tarchi's An-
    tioco.

La moglie virtuosa, ballet. *See* Cristiani's La città nuova.

Padre e figlio rivali sconosciuti. A. T. of his ballet Tamar e
    Selimo: Trento.

Il pastor fido, ballet. *See* Alessandri's Il vecchio geloso.

Beretti, Filippo—Continued.

Il reclutamento nel villaggio, ballet. *See* Zingarelli's Meleagro.

Gli Sciti, ballet. *See* Asioli's Cinna.

Gli Sciti, ballet. *See* Paisiello's Ipermestra.

Tamar e Selimo, ossia Padre e figlio rivali sconosciuti, ballet: Trento. *See* Isola's Lisandro.

Teatro italiano alla China, Il: Canavasso. *See* Martin y Soler's Andromaca.

Il tempio della morte, Verona (1794), ballet.   ML 52.2.T32

Vertunno e Pomona, ballet. *See* Anfossi's La forza delle donne.

Il volubile assodato, ballet: Canavasso. *See* Ottani's Arminio.

Bergalli, Luisa.

Agide rè di Sparta, Venezia (1725): Porta.   Schatz 8387

L'Elenia, Venezia, 1730: Albinoni.   Schatz 105

Berger, Christian August.

Bitten und erhoerung (Litteratur und Theater Zeitung, Berlin, 1783): Kaffka.   Schatz 4772

Berger, Traugott Benjamin.

Achills zuernender schatten, Leipzig, 1777.   Schatz 11595

Bergobzoom, Johann Baptist.

Graf von Waltron, oder Die subordination, Hamburg, 1792: Walter.   Schatz 10860

Berling, Theodor.

Der zauber-hain oder Das land der liebe, n. i., 1799: Bierey.   Schatz 1032

Bernard, Pierre Joseph Justin (*called* Gentil-Bernard).

Castor et Pollux (Paris) 1737: Rameau.   ML 50.2.C29R2

Castor et Pollux (Recueil général des opéra, Paris, 1745, t. xvi): Rameau.   ML 48.R4

Castor et Pollux—Castore e Polluce (Parma, 1758): Rameau.   Schatz 8589

Castor e Pollux, Paris, 1764: Rameau.   Schatz 8590

Castor et Pollux, Bordeaux, 1782: Rameau.   ML 48.M2L

Castor e Pollux, Paris, An V (1796–97) (31 p.): Rameau.   Schatz 8586

Castor et Pollux, Paris, an V (1796–97) (29 p.): Rameau.   Schatz 11751

Castore e Polluce (Monaco) 1788. Tr. from the French "Castor e Pollux" by Frugoni and reduced from five to three acts by the composer, Georg Jos. Vogler.   Schatz 10800

Bernardini, Marcello (*known also as* Marcello di (da) Capua).

Le burle per amore, Venezia (1784): Martin y Soler.   Schatz 6007

Li cinque pretendenti, Trieste (1794): author. L. T. of his La donna di spirito.   Schatz 849

Il conte di bell' umore, Roma (1783): author.   Schatz 844

Il conte di bell' umore—Der graf bey guter laune (Praga, 1783): author.   Schatz 831

Il conte di bell' umore—O conde de bello humor, Lisbona, 1791: author.   Schatz 843

La donna bizarra, Napoli, 1791: author. (Supposedly later version of his La donna di spirito.)   Schatz 832

La donna di spirito, Milano (1791): author.   Schatz 842

Bernardini, Marcello—Continued.

Le donne bisbetiche o sia L'antiquario fanatico, Orvieto
(1791): author.   L. T. of his La finta Galatea o sia L'antiquario fanatico.   ML 50.2.D61B2

Il fonte d'acqua gialla o sia Il trionfo della pazzia, Roma
(1786): author.   ML 50.2.F7B2

Le quattro nazioni, Firenze, 1793: author.   L. T. of his La
donna di spirito.   Schatz 833

La schiava amorosa, Roma (1770): Borghi.   ML 50.2.S41B6

La sposa polacca, Venezia (1799): author.   Schatz 852

Il trionfo della pazzia.   A. T. of his Il fonte d'acqua gialla.

Bernardon.   *See real name:* Johann Joseph Felix von Kurz.

Bernardoni, Pietro Antonio.

Poemi drammatici di Pietro Antonio Bernardoni Poeta Cesareo
. . . Parte terza . . .

Vienna, Gio. Van Ghelen, 1707.   195 p.   16½ cm.

Dedication dated Vienna, September 15, 1707, and prefatory note followed
by these "poemi drammatici": Introduzione al balletto dell' opera
in prosa, intitolata Il Demetrio—L'enigma del fato, sciolto da Giove—
La concordia della virtù e della fortuna—L'oracolo di Velleda—Enea
ne gli Elisi—Proteo sul Reno—Numa Pompilio—La Psiche—Il Danubio consolato—Andromeda.

Meleagro, Venezia, 1718: Albinoni.   Schatz 122

Il Meleagro, Brescia, 1710: M. A. Ziani.   Schatz 11202

Berni, *conte* **Francesco.**

La Filo overo Giunone repacificata con Ercole, Parma (1660):
Manelli.   Schatz 5889

La gara de gli elementi, Parma, 1660: Ferrari.   Schatz 3070

I sei gigli, Parma, 1660: Manelli.   Schatz 5891

L'esiglio d'Amore, Ferrara, 1651: Mattioli and Laurenzi.   Schatz 6106

La palma d'amore, Ferrara, 1650: Mattioli.   Schatz 6104

Bertati, Giovanni.

Alcines oe, Kiøbenhavn, 1777.   Tr. of his L'isola d'Alcina:
Gazzaniga.   Schatz 3667

Gli amanti alla prova.   O. T. of his Gli amanti dispettosi:
Caruso.

Gli amanti alla prova—Die liebhaber auf der probe, Dresda,
1784: Piticchio.   Schatz 8201

Gli amanti dispettosi, Napoli, 1787: Caruso.   L. T. of their
Gli amanti alla prova.   Schatz 1653

L'amor bizzarro o sia La gelosa di se stessa, Venezia, 1775:
Rust.   Schatz 9167

Amor l'astuzia insegna, Venezia, 1797: Gardi.   Schatz 3536

L'Amore costante, Venezia (1787): Gazzaniga.   Schatz 3683

L'Amore per interesse, Parma (1787): Fabrizj.   Schatz 2971

Andromeda (Venezia, 1796): Zingarelli.   Schatz 11265

L'anello incantato (Lisbona, 1772): Bertoni.   Schatz 929

Armida, Venezia, 1773: Naumann.   Schatz 7039

Armide (Leipzig, 1782).   Tr. of his Armida: Naumann.   Schatz 7040

Gli astrologi imaginari.   O. T. of his I filosofi imaginari.

L'avaro, Firenze (1777): Anfossi.   Schatz 228

L'avaro—Den giaerrige, Kiobenhavn, 1776: Anfossi.   Schatz 229

L'avaro—Der geizige (Dresden, 1780): Anfossi.   Schatz 230

L'avaro, Ferrara (1776): Astaritta.   Schatz 381

Bertati, Giovanni—Continued.

L'avaro deluso, London, 1778 (his "Calandrano" as altered by
Andrei): Sacchini. SCHATZ 9209

Azor, rè di Kibinga, Venezia (1779): Anfossi. SCHATZ 265

La bella Lauretta, Venezia, 1795: Gardi. SCHATZ 3537

Die beständigkeit in der liebe. A. T. of his Isabella und Rodrigo: Anfossi.

Calandrano, Venezia (1771): Gazzaniga. SCHATZ 3658

I campi Elisi ossia Le spose ricuperate, Milano (1788): Caruso. SCHATZ 1662

Il capriccio drammatico, Venezia (1787): Valentini (?) and
others. SCHATZ 10580

Il cavaliere errante, Parma (1780): Traetta. SCHATZ 10389

Il cavaliero errante—Der irrende ritter (Vienna, 1780): Traetta. SCHATZ 10390

Chi sta ben, non si muova, Firenze, 1787: Robuschi. SCHATZ 8843

Der civilisirte bauer. Tr. of his Il zotico incivilito, Dresda,
1792: Anfossi. SCHATZ 253

La contessa di Amalfi—Die graefinn von Amalfi, Dresda, 1794:
Weigl. L. T. of their La principessa di Amalfi. SCHATZ 10945

La contessa di Bimbinpoli (Lisbona, 1773): Astaritta. SCHATZ 368

La contessa di Novaluna, Venezia (1786): Fabrizj. SCHATZ 2975

Il convitato di pietra. A. T. of his Don Giovanni: Gazzaniga.

La costanza in amor rende felice, Trieste (1787): Gazzaniga. SCHATZ 3686

La costanza in amore. A. T. of his Isabella e Rodrigo: Anfossi.

Il curioso accidente, Venezia, 1789: Astaritta. SCHATZ 385

Il divertimento in campagna—Der zeitvertreib auf dem lande,
Dresda, 1783. L. T. of his La contessa di Bimbinpoli:
Astaritta. SCHATZ 369

Dom João, ou O convidado de pedra. Tr. of his Il Don Giovanni ossia Il convitato di pietra, Lisbonna, 1792: Gazzaniga. SCHATZ 3682

Il Don Calandrano, Firenze, 1781: Sacchini (as "L'avaro
deluso," with the same alterations by Andrei, performed
1778 at London, though Bertati's original title was "Calandrano"). SCHATZ 9245

Don Giovanni o sia Il convitato di pietra: Gazzaniga. Forms
second act of his Il capriccio dramatico, Venezia (1787):
Valentini and others. SCHATZ 10580

Don Giovanni, ossia Il convitato di pietra—Dom João ou O
convidado de pedra, Lisbonna, 1792: Gazzaniga. SCHATZ 3682

La donna di genio volubile, Venezia, 1796: Portugal. SCHATZ 8404

La donna di genio volubile, Lisbona, 1798: Portugal. ML 48.C6 IV

La donna di genio volubile—Die wankelmuethige, Dresda,
1798: Portugal. SCHATZ 8405

La donna innamorata, Venezia, 1796: Nicolini. SCHATZ 7142

La donna instabile, Venezia (1776): Borghi. SCHATZ 1229

Li due amanti rivali, Venezia, 1779: Caruso. L. T. of their
La virtuosa alla moda. SCHATZ 1663

Die eifersucht auf der probe, Gera, 1791: Anfossi. Tr. of
their Il geloso in cimento. SCHATZ 237

Die eingebildeten philosophen (Wien) 1781. Tr. of his I
filosofi imaginari: Paisiello. SCHATZ 7617

Das entfuehrte bauernmaedchen. Tr. of his La villanella
rapita: Bianchi. SCHATZ 987

Bertati, Giovanni—Continued.

Die erdichteten lehnserben. Tr. of his I finti eredi, Dresda,
 1787: Sarti.   Schatz 9434

Der eyfersuechtige bauer. Tr. of his Il villano geloso, Dresda,
 1770: Naumann.   Schatz 7060

Il fanatico in berlina, Torino (1792): Paisiello. L. T. of his
 La locanda.   Schatz 7635

La fata capricciosa, Venezia, 1789: Gardi.   Schatz 3548

La fedeltà tra le selve, Roma (1789): Bianchi. L. T. of their
 La villanella rapita, with some arias by V. Fioravanti.   Schatz 992

I filosofi immaginarj (Lisbona, 1775): Astaritta. L. T. of their
 I visionari.   Schatz 379

I filosofi immaginari, Napoli, 1784: Paisiello. L. T. of his
 "Gli astrologi imaginari."   Schatz 7616

I filosofi immaginarii—Os filosofos imaginarios, Lisboa, 1790:
 Paisiello.   ML 48.C6 II

Os filosofos imaginarios. Tr. of his I filosofi immaginarii,
 Lisboa, 1790: Paisiello.   ML 48.C6 II

I finti eredi—Les héritiers supposés, Pietroburgo (1785):
 Sarti.   Schatz 9433

I finti eredi—Die erdichteten lehnserben, Dresda, 1787:
 Sarti.   Schatz 9434

I finti eredi, Lisbona, 1794: Sarti.   Schatz 9467

La forza delle donne. O. T. of his Ogus o sia Il trionfo del
 bel sesso.

La forza delle donne (Venezia, 1778): Anfossi.   Schatz 267

Der geizige. Tr. of his L'avaro, (Dresden, 1780): Anfossi.   Schatz 230

La gelosa di se stessa. A. T. of his L'amor bizzarro: Rust.

Le gelosie di Pippo. A. T. of his La villanella rapita, Lisbona, 1796: Bianchi.

Il geloso in cimento, Venezia, 1774: Anfossi.   Schatz 236

Den giaerrige. Tr. of his L'avaro, Kiobenhavn, 1776: Anfossi. Schatz 229

Die graefinn von Amalfi. Tr. of his La contessa di Amalfi,
 Dresda, 1794: Weigl.   Schatz 10945.

Die heimlich geschlossene ehe. Tr. of his Il matrimonio
 segreto, Dresda, 1792: Cimarosa.   Schatz 1948

Les héritiers supposés. Tr. of his I finti eredi, Pietroburgo,
 (1785): Sarti.   Schatz 9433

Die heyrath durch betrug. Tr. of his Il matrimonio per
 inganno, Brunsevic, 1782: Anfossi.   Schatz 245

Der hypocondriste. Tr. of his L'ipocondriaco, Dresda, 1776:
 Naumann.   Schatz 7050

Le industrie amorose. O. T. of his Il matrimonio per inganno.

Le industrie amorose (Venetia, 1778): Ottani.   Schatz 7365

L'inimico delle donne, Venezia (1771): Galuppi.   Schatz 3455

L'innocenza vendicata. A. T. of his La morte di Dimone:
 Tozzi.

Die insel der Alcina, Berlin, 1794. Tr. of his L'isola d'Alcina: A. Bianchi.   Schatz 972

Die insel der Alcina. Tr. of his L'isola di Alcina (Dresda,
 1773): Gazzaniga.   Schatz 3666

L'intrigo amoroso, Venezia, 1795: Paër.   Schatz 7505

L'intrigo amoroso, Lisboa, 1798: Paër.   Schatz 7559

L'intrigo amoroso—Die liebes intrigue, Dresda, 1799: Paër.   Schatz 7506

Bertati, Giovanni—Continued.

L'ipocondriaco—Der hypochondriste, Dresda, 1776: Naumann. SCHATZ 7050

Der irrende ritter. Tr. of his Il cavaliero errante (Vienna, 1780): Traetta. SCHATZ 10390

Isabella e Rodrigo o sia La costanza in amore, Venezia, 1776: Anfossi. SCHATZ 241

Isabella e Rodrigo o sia La costanza in amore—Isabella und Rodrigo oder Die beständigkeit in der liebe, Dresda, 1784: Anfossi. SCHATZ 242

L'isola d'Alcina, Bologna (1779): Gazzaniga. ML 48.A5 v.30

L'isola d'Alcina—Alcines oe, Kiøbenhavn, 1777: Gazzaniga. SCHATZ 3667

L'isola della fortuna, Lisbona, 1767: Luchesi. SCHATZ 5742

L'isola di Alcina, Venezia, 1772: Gazzaniga. SCHATZ 3665

L'isola di Alcina—Die insel der Alcina (Dresda, 1773): Gazzaniga. SCHATZ 3666

Die lächerlichen gelehrten. Tr. of his I visionari, Dresda, 1774: Astaritta. SCHATZ 376

Die liebesintrigue. Tr. of his L'intrigo amoroso, Dresda, 1799: Paër. SCHATZ 7506

Die liebhaber auf der probe. Tr. of his Gli amanti alla prova, Dresda, 1784: Piticchio. SCHATZ 8201

La locanda, Venezia, 1771: Gazzaniga. SCHATZ 3668

La locanda (altered by Girolamo Tonioli), Vienna (1792): Paisiello. SCHATZ 7634

La locanda (altered by Girolamo Tonioli), London, 1792: Paisiello. SCHATZ 7672

Il maestro geloso, Venezia (1781): Caruso. SCHATZ 1645

Il marito che non ha moglie, Venezia, 1774: Astaritta. SCHATZ 373

Il matrimonio per inganno, Vicenza (1780): Anfossi. (Text same as Le industrie amorose.) SCHATZ 244

Il matrimonio per inganno—Die heyrath durch betrug, Brunsevic, 1782: Anfossi. SCHATZ 245

Il matrimonio segreto—Die heimlich geschlossene ehe, Dresda, 1792: Cimarosa. SCHATZ 1948

Melinda, Venezia, 1798: Nasolini. SCHATZ 7022

La morte di Dimone o sia L'innocenza vendicata, Venezia, 1763 (Italian version of J. F. von Kurtz' drama): Tozzi. SCHATZ 10385

Il nemico delle donne (Vienna, 1775). L. T. of his L'inimico delle donne: Galuppi. SCHATZ 3456

Le nozze disturbate, Dresda, 1774. L. T. of his La villanella incostante: Naumann. SCHATZ 7059

Le nozze in contrasto, Venezia, 1779: Valentini. SCHATZ 10582

Le nozze in contrasto—Die streitige heurath, Dresda, 1782: Valentini. SCHATZ 10583

Le nozze in contrasto, Firenze, 1785: Valentini. ML 48.A5 v.24

Ogus o sia Il trionfo del bel sesso—Ogus oder Der triumph des schoenen geschlechts, Dresda, 1796: Winter. SCHATZ 11058

L'opera nuova, Venezia (1781): Rauzzini. SCHATZ 8613

L'orfanella americana, Venezia (1787): Anfossi. SCHATZ 270

L'orfanella americana—Die verwaiste Amerikanerin (Dresda, 1790): Gestewitz. SCHATZ 3796

Osmanns serail. Tr. of his Il serraglio di Osmano, Dresda, 1787: Ghinassi. SCHATZ 3803

Bertati, Giovanni—Continued.

Il palazzo d'Osmano, Lisbona, 1795. L. T. of his Il seraglio
. di Osmano: Gazzaniga.   Schatz 3680

Il pazzo glorioso, Casalmaggiore (1790): Bernardini.   Schatz 850

Die phantasten. Tr. of his I visionari, Dresda, 1793: Paisiello.   Schatz 7619

Die philosophen (n. pl., n. d.). Same as his Die eingebildeten
philosophen.   Schatz 7618

Il più bel dono, inutile (Venezia, 1779): Rossetti.   Schatz 8884

La principessa di Amalfi. O. T. of his La contessa di Amalfi:
Weigl.

La principessa di Amalfi, Berlino (1796): Weigl.   Schatz 10946

I quaqueri (Venezia, 1779): Rossetti.   Schatz 8883

Li rivali ridicoli, Venezia (1780): Mortellari.   Schatz 6691

Saed ossia Il serraglio, Torino (1798). Tr. of his L'intrigo
amoroso: Paer.   Schatz 7507

La scola di musica. A. T. of his Le tre orfanelle: Bernardini.

Il seraglio di Osmano, Venezia, 1785: Gazzaniga.   Schatz 3676

Il serraglio. A. T. of his Saed.

Il serraglio di Osmano—Osmanns serail, Dresda, 1787: Ghinassi.   Schatz 3803

Le sorelle rivali, Milano (1782): Valentini and others. L. T.
of their La statua matematica.   Schatz 10586

Lo sposalizio per dispetto, Venezia (1782): Monti.   Schatz 6600

Le spose ricuperate. A. T. of his I campi Elisi: Caruso.

Lo sposo disperato (Venezia, 1777): Anfossi.   Schatz 252

La statua matematica. L. T. of his Le sorelle rivali: Valentini and others.

Lo strambo in berlina, Lisbona, 1795. L. T. of his La locanda:
Paisiello.   Schatz 7685

Die streitige heurath. Tr. of his Le nozze in contrasto,
Dresda, 1782: Valentini.   Schatz 10583

Il tamburo notturno. See this under Lorenzi.

La tomba di Merlino, Venezia, 1772: Gazzaniga.   Schatz 3673

Le tre orfanelle o sia La scola di musica, Venezia, 1798: Bernardini.   Schatz 847

Gli tre pretendenti, Bologna (1777): Borghi.   Schatz 1230

Il trionfo del bel sesso. A. T. of his Ogus: Winter.

Der triumph des schoenen geschlechts. Tr. A. T. of his Ogus:
Winter.

Gli umori contrari, Venezia (1798): Nasolini.   Schatz 7030

Il valore delle donne, Casale (1783): Anfossi.   Schatz 268

La vedova bizzarra, Napoli, 1788: Anfossi.   Schatz 261

La vendemmia, Vienna (1779): Gazzaniga.   ML 50.2.V28G3

La vendemmia—Die weinlese, Dresda, 1783: Gazzaniga.   Schatz 3675

La vendemmia, Lisbona, 1794: Gazzaniga.   Schatz 3674

Die verwaiste Amerikanerin. Tr. of his L'orfanella americana (Dresda, 1790): Gestewitz.   Schatz 3796

Il vilanello geloso. O. T. of his I finti eredi.

La villanella incostante, Venezia, 1773: Naumann.   Schatz 7058

La villanella rapita, Venezia, 1783: Bianchi.   Schatz 986

La villanella rapita—Das entfuehrte bauernmaedchen, Dresden, 1785: Bianchi.   Schatz 987

La villanella rapita, Milano (1785): Bianchi.   ML 48.A5v.12

Bertati, Giovanni—Continued.

La villanella rapita, London, 1790: Bianchi.   ML 48.M2V

La villanella rapita o sia Le gelosie di Pippo, Lisbona, 1796:
Bianchi.   Schatz 990

Il villano geloso, Venezia, 1769: Galuppi.   Schatz 3472

Il villano geloso, Dresda, 1770—Der eyfersuechtige bauer:
Naumann.   Schatz 7060

La virtuosa alla moda, Siena, 1777: Caruso.   Schatz 1648

I visionari. O. T. of his Gli astrologi imaginari and his I
filosofi immaginari.

I visionarj, Venezia, 1772: Astaritta.   Schatz 375

I visionari—Die lächerlichen gelehrten, Dresda, 1774: Astaritta.   Schatz 376

I visionari—Die phantasten, Dresda, 1793. L. T. of his I
filosofi imaginari: Paisiello.   Schatz 7619

Die wankelmuethige. Tr. of his La donna di genio volubile,
Dresda, 1798: Portugal.   Schatz 8405

Die weinlese. Tr. of his La vendemmia, Dresda, 1783: Gazzaniga.   Schatz 3675

Der zeitvertreib auf dem lande. Tr. of his Il divertimento in
campagna, Dresda, 1783: Astaritta.   Schatz 369

Zon-Zon principe di Kibin-Kinka, Milano (1773): Gazzaniga.   Schatz 3688

Il zotico incivilito—Der civilisirte bauer, Dresda, 1792: Anfossi. L. T. of their Lo sposo disperato.   Schatz 253

Berthaud.

Ballet du Dereiglement des passions, de l'interest, de l'amour,
& de la gloire (Paris, 1648): Lambert(?).   ML 52.2.B12

Berti, Antonio.

Duglas ed Ernestina, ballet. *See* Spontini's Adelina Senese.

Fata Alcinoe ossia Amore ed innocenza, ballet. *See* Mayr's
Avviso ai maritati.

Il matrimonio inaspettato, ballet. *See* Valentini's Le sorelle
rivali.

Le pastorelle difese, ballet. *See* Valentini's Le sorelle rivali.

Berti, Domenico.

I giganti abbattuti. *See* M. Curzio in Title catalogue.

Berti, Domenico.

Marc' Antonio, Lucca, 1687: unknown. *See* M. Curzio in
Title catalogue.

Berton, Henri Montan.

Ponce de Léon, Paris (1797): author.   Schatz 896

Bertrand.

La fortune au village. *See* Mad. Favart.

Bertrand, Friedrich Anton Franz.

Pyramus und Thisbe, Halle, 1787: Türk.   Schatz 10512

Bertuch, Friedrich Justin.

Das grosse loos, Weimar, 1774: Wolf.   Schatz 11080

Polyxena, Weimar, 1793: Schweitzer.   Schatz 11757

Polyxena, Hamburg, 1794: Schweitzer.   Schatz 9778

Betterton, Thomas.

The prophetess or The history of Dioclesian, London, 1690
(altered from Beaumont and Fletcher): H. Purcell.　　ML 48.M2D

Beverini, Bartolomeo.

Bruto costante, Lucca, 1660. *See* M. Curzio in Title catalogue.
Hercole perseguitata, Lucca, 1657: Stiava. *See* M. Curzio in
Title catalogue.
Il porto della libertà, Lucca, 1654: Stiava. *See* M. Curzio in
Title catalogue.
La prudenza vittoriosa, Lucca, 1669. *See* M. Curzio in Title
catalogue.

Beverini, Francesco.

Dario in Babilonia, Venetia, 1671: Boretti.　　　Schatz 1217
Il Demofonte, Roma, 1669: unknown.　　　ML 50.2.D38

Biancardi, Bastiano. *See his pseudonym* Domenico Lalli.

Biancardi, Carlo.

Le preziose umiliate, ballet. *See* Winter's Belisa.

Bianchi, Antonio.

L'amore in ballo, Venezia, 1765: Paisiello.　　Schatz 7587
Le villeggiatrici ridicole, Venezia, 1765: Boroni.　　Schatz 1253

Bianchini, *dottor.*

Le contese di Pallade e Venere sopra il bando d'Amore,
Bologna, [16—]: Colonna.　　　ML 50.2.C66C6

Biancolelli, Pierre François. *Better known as* Dominique.

Bickerstaffe (Bickerstaff), Isaac.

The captive, London, 1769: Dibdin and others.　　Longe 37
Daphne and Amintor, London, 1766: pasticcio from Shalon,
Vento, Cocchi, Piccinni, Monsigny.　　Longe 26
Daphne and Amintor (Collection of the most esteemed
farces, Edinburgh, 1792, t. v).　　Schatz 11753E
The Ephesian matron, London, 1769: Dibdin.　　Longe 306
The Ephesian matron (Collection of the most esteemed farces,
Edinburgh, 1792, t. vi): Dibdin.　　Schatz 11753F
He wou'd if he cou'd or An old fool worse than any, London,
1771: Dibdin.　　Longe 251
He would if he cou'd or An old fool worse than any (Collection
of the most esteemed farces, Edinburgh, 1792, t. v):
Dibdin.　　Schatz 11753E
Lionel and Clarissa, London, 1768: Dibdin and others.　　Longe 14
Lionel and Clarissa. A. T. of his The school for fathers (Bell,
British theatre, London, 1791, t. 1): Dibdin and others. PR 1241.B4
Love in a village, London, 1763: Arne and others.　　Longe 42
Love in a village, London, 1781: Arne and others.　　Longe 322
Love in a village, London, 1791 (J. Bell, British theatre,
1791–97, v. 1).　　PR 1241.B4
Love in a village, Philadelphia, 1794: Arne and others.　　ML 50.6.L72
Love in the city, London, 1767, 2d ed.: Dibdin (but largely
selected). O. T. of The romp.　　Longe 32
The maid of the mill, London, 1765: pasticcio, selected by
the author and Samuel Arnold and partly composed by
the latter.　　Longe 46

Bickerstaffe, Isaac—Continued.

The maid of the mill, London, 1791 (J. Bell, British theatre, 1791–97, v. 1).   PR 1241.B4

An old fool worse than any. A. T. of his He wou'd if he cou'd: Dibdin.

The padlock, London (1768): Dibdin.   LONGE 46

The padlock (Collection of the most esteemed farces, Edinburgh, 1792, t. iii): Dibdin.   SCHATZ 11753C

A peep into the seraglio. A. T. of his The sultan.

The recruiting sergeant, London, 1770: Dibdin.   LONGE 37

The recruiting sergeant (Collection of the most esteemed farces, Edinburgh, 1792): Dibdin.   SCHATZ 11753F

The romp, London, 1786: Dibdin, who assisted in the compilation of the text.   LONGE 97

The romp (Collection of the most esteemed farces, Edinburgh, 1792, t. vi).   SCHATZ 11753F

The royal garland, London, 1768: Arnold.   LONGE 36

The school for fathers; or Lionel and Clarissa, London, 1791 (J. Bell, British theatre, London, 1791–97, t. i): Dibdin and others. *See* title catalogue under O. T. Lionel and Clarissa.   PR 1241.B4

The spoil'd child, Boston, 1796: unknown.   PR 1241.D7   v.7

The sultan or A peep into the seraglio (London), 1787: unknown.   LONGE 98

The sultan or A peep into the seraglio (Collection of the most esteemed farces, Edinburgh, 1792, t. i).   SCHATZ 11753A

Thomas and Sally or The sailor's return, London, n. d.: Arne.   LONGE 37

Thomas and Sally or The sailor's return, Dublin, 1773: Arne.   AC 901.T5

Thomas and Sally (Collection of the most esteemed farces, Edinburgh, 1792, v. 2): Arne.   SCHATZ 11753B

Biehl, Charlotta Dorothea.

Kierligheds-brevne, Kiøbenhavn, 1774: Sarti.   SCHATZ 9446

Orpheus og Euridice, Kiøbenhavn, 1790: Naumann.   SCHATZ 7052

Orpheus und Euridice (Cramer's Magazin der Musik, 1786, p. 1085–1145). C.'s Tr. of the above.   ML4.M2

Orpheus und Euridice, Kiel und Hamburg (179–). Tr. of the above.   SCHATZ 7053

Soliman den Anden (Copenhagen, 1778): Th. C. Walter.   SCHATZ 10867

Binder von Krieglstein, Johann Friedrich, *freiherr von.*

Bellerofon, Muenchen, 1785: Winter.   SCHATZ 11022

Birch, Samuel.

The adopted child, London, 1795: Attwood.   LONGE 230

The mariners, London, 1793: Attwood.   LONGE 227

The smugglers, London, 1796: Attwood.   LONGE 238

Bisaccioni, *conte* **Maiolino.**

Ercole in Lidia, Venetia, 1645: Rovetta.   SCHATZ 9105

Orithia, Venetia, 1650: G. Sartorio.   SCHATZ 9497

La Semiramide in India, Venetia, 1648: Sacrati.   SCHATZ 9254

Veremonda l'Amazzone di Aragona, Venetia, 1652: Cavalli.   SCHATZ 1742

Bissari, *conte* **Enrico.**

La Silvia, Venezia (1730): Cordans.   SCHATZ 2228

Bissari, *conte* **Pietro Paolo.**

  Angelica in India, Vicenza, 1656: unknown.   Schatz 11307

  La Bradamante, Venetia, 1650: Cavalli.   Schatz 1731

  L'Erinto, Monaco, 1671: Kerl.   Schatz 5141

  Euridice di Tessaglia, Vicenza, 1658: unknown.   Schatz 11327

  La Romilda, Vicenza, 1659: Grossi.   Schatz 4219

  La Torilda, Venetia, 1648: Cavalli.   Schatz 1733

Bladen, Martin.

  Orpheus and **Euridice, masque.** *See* Title catalogue

Blèck, Riccardo.

  L'Indiana a Londra, ballet. *See* Santi's Il marito indolente.

  Il pentimento amoroso, ballet. *See* Astaritta's L'isola di Begodi.

  Lo sposo deluso, ballet. *See* Astaritta's L'isola di Begodi.

Blümner, Heinrich.

  Die dorffeyer (Leipzig, 1790): unknown.   Schatz 11451

Blumhofer, Max.

  Die luftschiffer oder Der strafplanet der erde, Leipzig und Koeln, 1787: author.   ML 50.2.L9B4

Boaden, James.

  Aurelio and Miranda, London, 1799.   Longe 266

  Cambro-Britons, London, 1798: Arnold.   Longe 248

Boccardi di Mazzera, *cav.* **Michel Angelo (Angiolo).**

  Amore e sdegno, Venezia, 1726: Tavelli. (Text is Silvani's Amore e sdegno, partly rewritten.)   Schatz 10253

  Cleofide—Cleofide, Berlino (1777): Hasse. (The text is merely an altered version of Metastasio's L'Alessandro nell' Indie.)   Schatz 4573

  Il regno galante, Venezia, 1727: Reali.   Schatz 8619

Boccella, Cristoforo.

  Partenope sul lido etrusco, Lucca, 1785: Andreozzi.   Schatz 197

Boccella, Michele.

  La libertà gelosa di se stessa in persona di Annibale amante di patria, Lucca, 1684: unknown. *See* M. Curzio in Title catalogue.

Boccella Pier Francesco.

  Decio sacrificato alla patria, Lucca, 1684: unknown. *See* M. Curzio in Title catalogue.

Boccherini, Giovanni Antonio Gastone.

  Don Chisciotte alle nozze di Gamace, Vienna, 1770: Salieri.   Schatz 9286

  Le donne letterate (Vienna), 1770: Salieri.   Schatz 9335

  La fiera di Venezia—Der markt von Venedig, Dresda, 1775: Salieri.   Schatz 9293

  La fiera di Venezia—Markedet i Venedig, Kiøbenhavn (1777): Salieri.   Schatz 9295

  La fiera di Venezia, Milano (1779): Salieri.   Schatz 9291

  Der geraubte eymer, Mannheim (1774). Tr. of his La secchia rapita: Salieri.   Schatz 9320

  Der geraubte eymer. Tr. of his La secchia rapita, Dresda, 1775: Salieri.   Schatz 9321

Boccherini, Giovanni Antonio Gastone—Continued.

Der jahrmarkt zu Venedig, Berlin, 1799. Tr. of his La fiera
di Venezia: Salieri. SCHATZ 9294

Markedet i Venedig. Tr. of his La fiera di Venezia, Kiøbenhavn (1775): Salieri. SCHATZ 9295

Der markt von Venedig, Dresda, 1775. Tr. of his La fiera di
Venezia: Salieri. SCHATZ 9293

Die messe zu Venedig, Mannheim (1772). Tr. of his La fiera
di Venezia: Salieri. SCHATZ 9292

La secchia rapita (Vienna) 1772: Salieri. SCHATZ 9319

La secchia rapita—Der geraubte eymer, Dresda, 1775: Salieri. SCHATZ 9321

Turno re de Rutoli, Vienna, 1767: unknown. ML 50.2.T9

Bock, Johann Christoph.

Armide, Stuttgart (1786): Zumsteeg. SCHATZ 11292

Clarisse oder Das unbekannte dienstmaedgen, Leipzig, 1772:
Roellig. SCHATZ 8856

Der eifersuechtige mann (Komische opern der Italiener,
Leipzig, 1782): Piccinni. Perhaps Tr. of his "Gelosia per
gelosia." SCHATZ 8119

Der glueckswechsel oder Mutter Natur in ihren kindern
(Komische opern der Italiener, Leipzig, 1782). Tr. of
Piccinni's Le vicende della sorte (Petrosellini). SCHATZ 8120

Das herbstabentheuer oder Wer wagt, gewinnt, n. i., 1790:
Accorimboni. SCHATZ 11678

Das herbstabentheuer oder Wer wagt, gewinnt (Komische
opern der Italiener, th. II, no. 3): Accorimboni. SCHATZ 15

Ist's nicht die eine, so ist's die andere. A. T. of his Der
kapellmeister: Lorazi.

Die Italienerin zu London, Hamburg, 1789. Tr. of Cimarosa's
L'Italiana in Londra. SCHATZ 1940

Der kapellmeister; oder Ist's nicht die eine, so ist's die andere,
(Komische opern der Italiener, Leipzig, 1781, Bd. I):
Lorazi. (Tr. of his Il maestro di cappella burlato). SCHATZ 5684

Das maedchen im Eichthale, Hamburg, 1785: Lampe. SCHATZ 5384

Mutter Natur in ihren kindern. A. T. of his Der glueckswechsel.

Bocquet de Liancourt.

Myrtil et Lycoris (Paris) 1778 (with Boutellier): Desormery. ML 50.2.M92D2

Boehm, Johann.

Der Koenig Theodor in Venedig, Koeln, 1785. Tr. of Paisiello's Il rè Teodoro in Venezia. SCHATZ 7651

Theodor in Venedig, Berlin, 1799. L. T. of his Der koenig
Theodor in Venedig: Paisiello (Casti). SCHATZ 7652

Boggio, Gian-Domenico.

L'amante democratico, Torino (1799): Cristiani. SCHATZ 2293

Argea, Torino (1799): Andreozzi. SCHATZ 215

La conquista del vello d'oro, Torino (1791): Isola. SCHATZ 4905

Demetrio a Rodi, Torino (1789): Pugnani. SCHATZ 8503

La disfatta de' Mori, Torino (1791): Gazzaniga. SCHATZ 3662

Teodelinda, Torino (1789): Andreozzi. SCHATZ 211

Volodomiro, Torino (1787): Cimarosa. SCHATZ 2000

Boissel.

Le nouveau Don-Quichotte, Nantes (Bruxelles), 1792: Champein.   ML 50.2.N62C3

Boldini, Giovanni.

Massimiano. *See* this under Zeno.

La ninfa Apollo, Venezia (1734) (originally by Lemene): Galuppi.   Schatz 3488

Onorio, Venezia (1729) (with Lalli): F. Ciampi.   Schatz 1874

Sulpizia fedele, Venezia (1729): A. Pollaroli.   Schatz 8261

Bonacossi, *conte* **Ercole.**

La Calciope, autograph ms., 16—: unknown.   ML 95.B6

Bonarelli, *conte* **Prospero.**

Intramezzi da rappresentarsi nella Filli di Sciro, Ancona, 1639: unknown.   ML 50.2.I6

Bonatti, Lorenzo Mario.

Il contrasto de fiumi Serchio di Lucca; Tebro di Roma; Ronco di Ravenna, Bologna, 1674: Fioriti.   ML 48.A5   v.5

Bonechi, Giuseppe.

Bellerophon, St. Petersburg, 1757. Tr. of his Bellerofonte: Araya.   ML 50.2.B35A7

Bonin, Christian Friedrich *freiherr* **von.**

Das fest Germaniens, Neustrelitz, 1789: Zeller.   Schatz 11165

Das urtheil des Midas, n. i., n. d. (together with André, Johann). (Detached copy.) Tr. of Grétry's Le jugement de Midas (d'Hèle).   Schatz 4163

Der zauberspiegel, n. i., n. d. Tr. of Grétry's La fausse magie (Marmontel).   Schatz 4156

Bonis, Giovanni Antonio.

Il Dario ravivato, Venetia, 1675: unknown.   Schatz 11318

Bonis, Novello.

La Flora, Venetia, 1681: A. Sartorio and M. A. Ziani.   Schatz 9495

L'Odoacre, Venetia, 1680: Varischino.   Schatz 10593

Bonneval, Michel de.

Le ballet des romans, Lyon, 1742: Niel. (Contains only "La Bergerie," the first entrée.)   Schatz 7161

Lindor et Ismène: L. J. Francoeur. Entrée in Les fêtes liriques, Paris, 1766.   ML 52.2.F46

Les romans (Recueil général des opéra, Paris, 1745, t. xvi): Niel.   ML 48.R4

Bontempi, Giovanni Andrea Angelini.

Il Paride—Paris, Dresda, 1662: author.   Schatz 1209

Borghesi, Ambrosio.

Lo scialaquatore alla fiera, Venezia, 1745: Orlandini and others.   Schatz 7347

La vedova accorta, Venezia, 1746: Bertoni, but only the recitatives and nine arias.   Schatz 927

Borgo, Pio dal.

I trionfi di Goffredo in Gerusalemme, Pisa, 1739: Fini.   Schatz 3106

Il trionfo dell' Arno (Pisa, 1766): Brunetti.   Schatz 1366

Bos, Salomon.

Het feest der Braminen, Amsteldam, 1798. Tr. of Wenzel
Müller's Das sonnenfest der Braminen (Hensler). Schatz 6966

Bossi, Giuseppe.

La burla di D. Pacconio a Parigi, ballet. *See* Anfossi's La
maga Circe.

La filosofa olandese, ballet. *See* Anfossi's La maga Circe.

Il generoso perdono, ballet: Giuliani. *See* Anfossi's La maga
Circe.

Bostel, Lucas von.

Der hochmuethige, gestuerzte und wieder erhabne Croesus,
Hamburg (1711): Keiser. Schatz 5124

— Same title (Hamburg, 1730): Keiser. Schatz 5096

Bottarelli, F.

Il Cid, London, 1773. Tr. of Sacchini's opera into English,
Italian text by G. G. Bottarelli. Schatz 9246

La clemenza di Scipione, London, 1778: Bach. (English
text only.) Schatz 528

Creso, London, 1767. Tr. of Sacchini's opera. Schatz 9216

Motezuma, London, 1775. English tr. of Sacchini's opera. Schatz 9232

Bottarelli, Giovanni Gualberto.

Il Cid, London, 1773: Sacchini. Schatz 9246

La conquista del Messico—The conquest of Mexico, London,
1767: Vento. ML 50.2.C65V2

The father and the son rivals. Tr. of his Il padre e il figlio
rivali, London, 1769: Giordani, T. Schatz 3851

Motezuma, London, 1775: Sacchini. Schatz 9232

Il Padre e il figlio rivali—The father and the son rivals, London, 1769: T. Giordani. Schatz 3851

Rodelinda, regina de' Longobardi (altered from Salvi)—
Rodelinde königinn der Longobarden (Berlino) 1741:
Graun.

— Same title, Berlino, 1778: Graun. Schatz 4117

La schiava, London, 1772. Alterations of Piccinni's Gli
stravaganti. ML 50.2.S85P4

Sesostri, London, 1768: P. Guglielmi. (A modernization of
Zeno's and Pariati's text.) Schatz 4267

Botturini (Butturini), Mattia.

L'apoteosi d'Ercole, Venezia, 1790: Tarchi. Schatz 10212

Gl'Indiani, Venezia, 1796: Nasolini. Schatz 7004

Bianca de' Rossi, Venezia, 1797: Trento. Schatz 10418

Merope, Venezia, 1796: Nasolini. Schatz 7005

Il ratto di Proserpina, Venezia (1791): Cimador. Schatz 1902

Seleuco, rè di Siria, Venezia, 1791: Bianchi. Schatz 1000

Zaira, Venezia, 1797: Nasolini. Schatz 7018

Boullault.

L'acteur dans son ménage, Paris, an VIII [1799–1800]: probably Saint-Amans. ML 48.M2L

Bouilly, Jean Nicolas.
L'amour conjugal.   A. T. of his Léonore: Gaveaux.
La famille américaine, Blois, an IV [1796]: Dalayrac.   ML 50.2.F17D2
Léonore, ou L'amour conjugal, Paris, an septième [1798–99]:
    Gaveaux.   SCHATZ 3649

Boulton, Thomas.
The sailor's farewell or The Guinea outfit, Liverpool, n. d.   LONGE 323

Bounce, Benjamin.   *pseud. of* Henry Carey.

Bouqueton.
Cephal und Procris, ballet: Cannabich or Toeschi.   *See* Holz-
    bauer's Hadrian in Syrien.
Reinald und Armide, ballet: Cannabich or Toeschi.   *See*
    Holzbauer's Hadrian in Syrien.

Bourlin, Antoine Jean.   *See* Dumaniant.

Boutellier, Maximilien Jean.
Myrtil et Lycoris (Paris) 1778: Desormery.   ML 50.2.M92D2

Boutet, Jacques Marie, *better known as* Monvel.

Boyce, Samuel.
The rover or Happiness at last, London, 1752.   LONGE 160

Boyd, Elizabeth.
Don Sancho: or, The students whim (London, 1739).   LONGE 59

Boyer, Claude.
Méduse (Recueil général des opéra, Paris, 17 03, t. v.): Gervais.   SCHATZ 3792

Braccioli, Grazio.
Alessandro fra' le Amazoni, Venezia, 1715: Chelleri.   SCHATZ 1812
Armida in Damasco, Venezia, 1711: G. Rampini.   SCHATZ 8595
Arsinoe vendicata, Venezia, 1712: Ruggeri.   SCHATZ 9134
Calfurnia, Venezia, 1713: Heinichen.   SCHATZ 4701
Calpurnia.   A. T. of his Die roemische grossmuth: Heinichen.
La costanza in cimento con la crudeltà, Venetia, 1712: Aresti.   SCHATZ 313
Crisippo, Ferrara (1710): Aresti.   ML 50.2.C85A7
La gloria trionfante d'amore, Venezia, 1712: G. Rampini.   SCHATZ 8596
Orlando, Venezia, 1727: Vivaldi.   SCHATZ 10776
Orlando finto pazzo, Venetia (1714): Vivaldi.   SCHATZ 10777
Orlando furioso, Mantova (1725): O. Polarolli.   SCHATZ 8257
Orlando furioso, Venezia, 1713: Ristori.   SCHATZ 8818
Rodomonte sdegnato, Venezia, 1714: M. A. Gasparini.   SCHATZ 3601
Die roemische grossmuht oder Calpurnia, Hamburg (1716).
    Tr. of his Calfurnia: Heinichen.   SCHATZ 4702

Brambilla, Antonio.
Il tempo fa giustizia a tutti, Milano (1797): Paër.   SCHATZ 7537

Branchi, Silvestro.
La coronatione d'Apollo per Dafne conversa in lauro, Bologna,
    1623: Vernizzi.   *See also his* Trattenimento, etc.   SCHATZ 10715
Stratira, Bologna, 1617: Vernizzi.   SCHATZ 10714
Trattenimento musicale d'Apollo con il Reno . . ., Bologna,
    1621. (Consists in addition, of "La coronatione d'Apollo
    per Dafne conversa in lauro," music probably by Vernizzi,
    and "Amore guerriero per la Rocca incantata").   ML 52.2.T7

Brandes, Johann Christian.[1]
Ariadne auf Naxos, Gotha, 1775: G. Benda.   SCHATZ 768
Ariadne auf Naxos, Leipzig, 1790: Benda, G.   ML 50.2.A737
Ino, Leipzig, 1790: Reichardt.   ML 52.2.I5
Ino (Melodramen, Pilsen, 1791): Reichardt.   SCHATZ 8643

Braun, Heinrich.
Der dorfbader, Muenchen, 1783: unknown.   SCHATZ 11605
Die dorfschule, n. i., 1783: unknown.   SCHATZ 11606
Das hirtenmaegdchen, Muenchen, 1784: Winter.   SCHATZ 11037

Bredal, Niels Krog.
Bondepigen ved hoffet, Kjøbenhavn, 1776. Tr. of Ciampi's
    Le caprice amoureux ou Ninette à la cour (Favart).   SCHATZ 2852
Den Forstilte tvistighed (Kjøbenhavn, 1777). Tr. of Mon-
    signy's Rose et Colas (Sedaine).   SCHATZ 6585

Brender à Brandis, G.
Het vernietigd verdrag, Amsteldam, 1799. Tr. of Gaveaux'
    Le traité nul (Pigault-Lebrun).   SCHATZ 3644

Breni, Lodovico.
La libertà trionfante, Lucca, 1654: Bigongiari. *See* M. Curzio
    in Title catalogue.

Bressand, Friedrich Christian.
Die biss in und nach dem todt unerhoerte treue des Orpheus,
    Hamburg (1709): Keiser. (Five-act version of their
    Orpheus.)   SCHATZ 5105
Circe oder des Ulisses erster theil, Hamburg, 1702: Keiser. SCHATZ 5082
Echo ·~nd Narcissus (Hamburg, 1694): Bronner.   SCHATZ 1334
Hercules unter denen Amazonen, Hamburg (1694): Krieger.   SCHATZ 5272
———— Anderer theil: Krieger.   SCHATZ 5273
Jason, oder Die eroberung des gueldenen fluesses (Hamburg,
    1720): Keiser.   SCHATZ 5097
Orpheus, ander theil, Hamburg (1702): Keiser. (First part
    was then called Die sterbende Eurydice oder Orpheus.)   SCHATZ 5107
Penelope und Ulysses, ander theil, Hamburg, 1702: Keiser.   SCHATZ 5109
Procris and Cephalus, Hamburg, 1701: Bronner.   SCHATZ 1333
Die sterbende Eurydice oder Orpheus, Hamburg (1702):
    Keiser. L. T. of their Orpheus.   SCHATZ 5106
Die wiederkehr der gueldenen zeit (Hamburg) 1699: Keiser.   SCHATZ 5131

Bretzner, Christoph Friedrich.
Adrast und Isidore, n. i., 1787: von Kospoth.   SCHATZ 5217
Adrast und Isidore oder Die nachtmusik, Wien, 1780: Mitscha. SCHATZ 6535
Adrast und Isidore oder Die serenate (Operetten, bd. I, Leip-
    zig, 1779): Preu.   SCHATZ 11680
Der aepfeldieb, Wien, 1781: Jost (Jast).   SCHATZ 4979
Der aepfeldieb, oder Der schatzgraeber (Operetten, Leipzig,
    1779): Kaffka.   SCHATZ 4982
Belmont und Constanze oder Die entfuehrung aus dem serail,
    Leipzig, 1781: André.   SCHATZ 183
Belmont und Constanze oder Die entfuehrung aus dem serail,
    Stuttgart, 1784: Dieter.   SCHATZ 2574

---

[1] For some reason, unknown to me, Schatz enters Brandes as Joseph Jacob Christian.

Bretzner, Christoph Friedrich—Continued.

Belmonte und Konstanze, Berlin, 1788. L. T. of his Die entführung aus dem Serail: Mozart.   ML 50.2.E5M8

Belmonte und Konstanze, Berlin, 1798: Mozart.   Schatz 6812

Endlich fand er Sie. A. T. of his: Der irrwisch: Dieter.

Endlich fand er sie. A. T. of his Der irrwisch: von Kospoth.

Endlich fand er sie. A. T. of his Der irrwisch: Preu.

Endlich fand er sie. A. T. of his Das irrlicht: Umlauf, also of the L. T. of this, Der irrwisch.

Die entfuehrung aus dem serail. A. T. of his Belmont und Constanze: André.

Die entfuehrung aus dem serail. A. T. of his Belmont und Constanze: Dieter.

Die entfuehrung aus dem serail, Kaufbeuren [1790]: Knecht.   Schatz 5197

Die entfuehrung aus dem serail, Wien, 1782 (retouched by Stephanie d. Jüng.): Mozart.   Schatz 6811

Die entführung aus dem serail, Warschau (1783): Mozart.   Schatz 6856

Das irrlicht oder Endlich fand er sie, Wien, 1785: Umlauf.   Schatz 10526

Der irrwisch oder Endlich fand er sie, Riga (1786): Umlauf.   Schatz 10527

Der irrwisch oder Endlich fand er sie, Stuttgart, 1782: Dieter.   Schatz 2579

Der irrwisch, n. i., 1784: Kospoth.   ML 50.2.I68K6

Der irrwisch oder Endlich fand er sie, n. i., 1787: von Kospoth.   Schatz 5218

Der irrwisch oder Endlich fand er sie (Operetten, Leipzig, 1779): Preu.   Schatz 11680

Der irrwisch oder Endlich fand er sie, Leipzig, 1788: Preu.   Schatz 8464

Das mädchen im Thurme. A. T. of his Das wütende heer.

Die maedchen sind von Flandern. A. T. of his Weibertreue: Mozart.

Maedchenlist und liebe. A. T. of his Die wette: Mozart.

Das maedgen im thurme. A. T. of his Das wuetende heer: Schweitzer.

Die nachtmusik. A. T. of his Adrast und Isidore: Mitsha.

Opera buffa (Singspiele, Leipzig, 1796): Kallenbach.   Schatz 4999

Rosemunde (Litteratur und Theater Zeitung, 1780): Kaffka.   Schatz 4772

Schattenspiel an der wand (Singspiele, Leipzig, 1796): Kallenbach.   Schatz 5000

Der schatzgraeber. A. T. of his Der aepfeldieb: Kaffka.

Der schlaftrunk, Breslau (179–?): Bierey.   Schatz 1028

Der schlaftrunk, Altona, n. d.: Kallenbach.   Schatz 5001

Die schoene muellerin, Berlin (1793). Tr. of Paisiello's L'amor contrastato (Palomba).   Schatz 7594

Die serenate. A. T. of his Adrast und Isidore: Preu.

Weibertreue oder Die maedchen sind von Flandern, Leipzig, 1794. Tr. of Mozart's Cosi fan tutte (Da Ponte).   Schatz 6766

Die wette oder Maedchenlist und liebe, Hamburg (1796). L. T. of his Weibertreue: Mozart.   Schatz 6767

Das wuetende heer oder Das maedchen im thurme (Wien, 1787) (remodeled by Ruprecht): Ruprecht.   Schatz 9162

Das wütende heer oder Das mädchen im thurme (Operetten, Leipzig, 1779, bd. I): Schweitzer.   Schatz 11680

Das wuetende heer oder Das maedgen im thurme, Leipzig, 1788: Schweitzer.   Schatz 9777

Breval, John.

The rape of Helen, London, 1737: ballad opera.   Longe 52

Brewer, George.
Bannian day, London, 1796: S. Arnold. LONGE 234

Breymann.
Il fido amico, oder Der getreue freund Hercules und Theseus (Hamburg, 1708): Graupner. SCHATZ 4123
La grandezza d'animo oder Arsinoe (Hamburg, 1710): Keiser. SCHATZ 5093
Der morgen des europaeischen glueckes oder Aurora, Hamburg (1710): Keiser. SCHATZ 5104

Briani, Francesco.
Isacio tiranno, Venezia, 1710: Lotti. SCHATZ 5721
Il vincitor generoso, Venezia, 1708: Lotti. SCHATZ 5726

Bridges, Thomas.
Dido, London, 1771: unknown. LONGE 32
The Dutchman, London, 1775: unknown. LONGE 116

Brinkman, N. C.
Camille of Het onderaardsch gewelf, Amsterdam, 1796 (with van Streek). Tr. of Dalayrac's Camille ou Le souterrain (Marsollier). SCHATZ 2392

Brooke, Frances.
Rosina, London, 1783: Shield. LONGE 91

Brooke, Henry.
Little John and the giants, n. i., n. d. (from his Collected works?): ballad opera. LONGE 131

Broughton, Thomas.
Hercules, London, 1745: Händel. LONGE 306

Brunetti, Pasquale.
La selvaggia ovvero Adelia e Roberto, ballet: unknown. *See* Paër's L'intrigo amoroso.

Brunner, Gottfried Samuel.
Poltis oder Das gerettete Troja, Leipzig, 1773: Joh. Ad. Hiller. (Text is an amplification and revision of a ms. by Steinel). SCHATZ 4731

Brusa, Francesco.
Le statue, Venezia, 1757: author. SCHATZ 1378

Bürde, Samuel Gottlieb.
Don Sylvio von Rosalva oder Der sieg der natur ueber die schwaermerey (Schleswig, 1796?): Phanty. SCHATZ 8004
Don Sylvio von Rosalva oder Der sieg der natur ueber die schwaermerey, Koenigsberg, 1795: Sander. SCHATZ 9371
Die liebe unter den gondolieren. A. T. of his Die regata zu Venedig.
Die regata zu Venedig oder Die liebe unter den gondoliren, Berlin, 1798: Fliess. SCHATZ 3247
Die regata zu Venedig oder Die liebe unter den gondolieren, Koenigsberg, 1795: Sander. SCHATZ 9372
Der sieg der natur ueber die schwaermerey. A. T. of his Don Sylvio von Rosalva.

Buganza, Giovanni Battista.
Il tributo campestre, Mantova, 1768: Traetta. SCHATZ 10401

Buini, Giuseppe Maria.

Albumazar, Venezia, 1727: author.   SCHATZ 1387
Armida delusa, Venezia, 1720: author.   SCHATZ 1389
Artanaganamenone, Venezia (1731): author. L. T. of his
  Malmosor.   SCHATZ 1397
Chi non fà, non falla, Venezia (1732): author.   SCHATZ 1391
Fidarsi è bene, ma non fidarsi è meglio, Venezia (1731):
  author.   SCHATZ 1396
Le frenesie d'amore, Venezia, 1726: author. L. T. of his
  Il Savio delirante.   SCHATZ 1386
Malmosor. O. T. of his Artanaganamenone.
Il protettore alla moda, Venezia, 1749: author, with additions
  by Galuppi.   SCHATZ 3520
Il Savio delirante, Bologna (1726): author.   SCHATZ 1385
La Zanina maga per amore, Bologna (1737): author.   SCHATZ 1398
Zanina maga per amore, Bologna, 1745: author.   SCHATZ 1399

Buonacossa, Borso.

L'Alarico, Bologna (1716): G. B. Bassani.   SCHOTZ 633

Buonarroti, Michelangelo.

Il natal d'Ercole, Firenze, 1605: Peri.   SCHATZ 7920

Burchi, Gaspero.

I divertimenti dei Calabresi, ballet. *See* Gagni's I matti
  gloriosi.

Burgoyne, John.

The lord of the manor, London, 1781: Jackson.   LONGE 91
The lord of the manor, Philadelphia, 1790: Jackson.   ML 50.6.L62
The lord of the manor, Philadelphia, 1791: Jackson.   ML 50.6.L63
The maid of the oaks, London, 1774: Barthelemon (partly
  selected from Rousseau, Philidor, and La Borde).   LONGE 48
Richard Coeur de Lion, London, 1786. Tr. of Grétry's opera,
  music adapted by Linley.   LONGE 98

Buri, Ernst Karl Ludwig Ysenburg von.

Das gespenst, Neuwied, 1789: author.   SCHATZ 1421
Der kohlenbrenner, Neuwied, 1789: author.   SCHATZ 1422
Die matrosen, n. i., n. d. (detached copy): author.   SCHATZ 1423

Burlini, Lorenzo.

La forza d'amore, Venetia, 1697: C. F. Pollaroli.   SCHATZ 8292
La Mariamme, Venetia, 1696: Ruggeri.   SCHATZ 9139

Burney, Charles.

The cunning man, London, 1766. Tr. of Rousseau's Le devin
  du village; Rousseau.   LONGE 257
The cunning man, London, 1766 (2d ed.).   LONGE 26
The cunning man (Collection of the most esteemed farces,
  Edinburgh, 1792, v. ii).   SCHATZ 11753B

Buschmann, Ehrenfried Engelbert.

Die strassenraeuber, Hamburg und Bremen, 1770: unknown. ML 50.2.S746

Busenello, Giovanni Francesco.

Gli amori d'Apollo e di Dafne, Venetia, 1656 [!]: Cavalli.   SCHATZ 1716
La Didone, Venetia, 1656: Cavalli.   SCHATZ 1718
L'incoronazione di Poppea, Venetia, 1656: Monteverdi.   SCHATZ 6593

Busenello, Giovanni Francesco—Continued.

La prosperità infelice di Giulio Cesare dittatore, Venetia, 1656: Cavalli.   Schatz 1726

La Statira principessa di Persia, Venetia, 1655: Cavalli.   Schatz 1728

La Statira, principessa di Persia, Venetia, 1656: Cavalli.   Schatz 11682

Busius, H. H.

Der cavalier durch die liebe. Tr. of Piccinni's Il cavaliere per amore (Petrosellini).   Schatz 8081

Die in verwirrung lebende familie. Tr. of Scolari's La famiglia in scompiglio (Dresda, 1766).   Schatz 9795

Der jahrmarkt zu Magerndorf. Tr. of Fischietti's Il mercato di Malmantile, Dresda (1766), (Goldoni).   Schatz 3232

Bussani, Giacomo Francesco.

Anacreonte tiranno, Venetia, 1678: Sartorio.   Schatz 9490

Antonino e Pompeiano, Venetia, 1677: Sartorio.   Schatz 9491

—— 2d copy.   ML 48.M2O

Cesare in Egitto (Venezia, 1744): Colombo.   Schatz 2115

Cesare in Egitto, Milano (1735): Giacomelli.   Schatz 3806

César en Egipte, Strassbourg, 1751. Tr. of Cesare in Egitto,   Schatz 4902

Argentina, 1751: Jommelli.   Schatz 4848

Cesare in Egitto, Milano, 1770 (retouched by Goldoni): Piccinini.   Schatz 8083

Cesare in Egitto—Julius Caesar in Aegypten, Kiøbenhavn (1763): Sarti.   Schatz 9427

Enea in Italia, Venetia, 1675: Pallavicino.   Schatz 7723

Ercole su'l Termodonte, Venetia, 1678: Sartorio.   Schatz 9493

Ercole sul Termodonte—Hercules am Thermodon (Dresda, 1747): Schürer.   Schatz 9732

Ercole su'l Termidonte, Roma, 1723: Vivaldi.   ML 50.2.E61V4

Giulio Cesare in Egitto, Venetia, 1677: Sartorio.   Schatz 9489

Hercules am Thermodon. Tr. of his Ercole sul Termodonte (Dresda, 1747): Schürer.   Schatz 9732

Julius Caesar i Aegypten. Tr. of his Cesare in Egitto, Kiøbenhavn (1763): Sarti.   Schatz 9427

Massenzio, Venetia, 1673: Sartorio.   Schatz 9494

Il ratto delle Sabine, Venetia, 1680: Agostini.   Schatz 65

Buti, Francesco.

The nuptials of Peleus and Thetis, London, 1654: Caproli. Tr. of their Le nozze di Peleo e di Theti.   Longe 241

Butturini, Maria. *See* Botturini.

C.

La resource des théâtres, Paris, 1760 (Theatre de M. Favart, Paris, Duchesne, 1763–77, t. viii). (Only final vaudeville written and composed by Favart.)   ML 49.A2F1

C., L. L. von.

Der chinesische held, Wienn, 1755. Tr. of Bonno's L'eroe cinese (Metastasio).   Schatz 1197

Cahusac, Louis de.

Anacréon: Rameau. Entrée in Les fêtes liriques, Paris, 1766. ML 52.2.F46

Les fêtes de l'Himen et de l'Amour ou Les dieux d'Egipte, Paris, 1765: Rameau.   ML 52.2.F42R2

Cahusac, Louis de—Continued.

Les fêtes de l'Hymen et de l'Amour, Paris, 1778: Rameau.　ML 52.2.F42R3

Naïs, Paris, 1764: Rameau.　ML 52.2.N22

Zoroastre (Paris), 1749: Rameau.　ML 50.2.Z7R2

Zoroastro, Dresda (1752): Adam (with pieces by Rameau).
Tr. of his French text.　Schatz 55

Cailhava d'Estandoux, Jean François.

La buona figliuola, Paris, Didot, 1771 (French parody, on p.
47–48 music): Piccinni.　Schatz 8073

La buona figliuola, Paris, Didot, 1771 (French parody, on p.
47–48 text): Piccinni.　ML 48.M2M

La buona figliuola, Paris, Duchesne, 1772 (French parody):
Piccinni.　Yudin PQ

Les étrennes de l'amour, Paris, 1769: Boyer.　ML 50.2.E75

Le nouveau marié ou Les importuns, Paris, 1771: Bacelli.　Schatz 520

Ziste et Zeste ou Les importuns, Paris, an V (1796) (with
Leger): partly by Leger.　ML 48.M2E

Cajani, Giuseppe.

L'amante in cimento, ballet.　*See* Portugal's Non irritare le
donne.

L'amor per interesse, ballet.　*See* Fioravanti's L'amor per
interesse.

Armida e Rinaldo, ballet: author.　*See* Cimarosa's Il pittor
parigino.

Berilowitz in Tartaria, ballo eroico pantomimo: author.　*See*
Fioravanti's L'amor per interesse.

Caterina e Blech, ballet: author.　*See* Bernardini's Furberia
e puntiglio.

Elisabetta e Blech, ballet: author.　*See* Curcio's Le nozze a
dispetto.

Isola piacevole, ballet.　*See* Gardi's La semplice.

Nicola e Cirilla, ballet.　*See* Gardi's Il finto Stregone.

Calindo Grolo.　*Anagram of* Carlo Goldoni

Calsabigi, Ranieri de'.

Alceste, Milano, 1768: P. Guglielmi.　Schatz 4233

Alceste, Vienna, 1767: Gluck.　Schatz 3885

Alceste, Bologna (1778): Gluck.　ML 48.A25 v.29

Alceste, Paris, 1779: Gluck.　(Du Roullet's French version.)　Schatz 3888

Alceste, Paris, 1786: Gluck.　Schatz 3940

Alceste (Mainz?) 1792: Gluck.　Schatz 3889

La critica teatrale, Venezia, 1775: Astaritta.　(C.'s text
originally called L'opera seria).　Schatz 378

L'Elfrida, Firenze, 1795: Paisiello.　ML 48.A5 v.14

Elfrida, Venezia, 1796: Paisiello.　Schatz 7615

L'Elfrida, Parma, 1798: Paisiello.　Schatz 7703

[Elvira] (Naples, 1794): Paisiello.　Schatz 7695

L'opera seria.　O. T. of his La critica teatrale.

L'opera seria (Firenze, 1771): Gassmann.　Schatz 3623

Orfeo—Orpheus, Berlino (1788) (with additions): Bertoni,
additions by Reichardt.　L. T. of Orfeo ed Euridice.　Schatz 917

Orfeo: Gluck.　Abbr. T. of his Orfeo ed Euridice, forming the
third part of Gluck's Le feste d'Apollo, Parma (1769).　Schatz 3897

Calsabigi, Ranieri de'—Continued.

Orfeo ed Euridice: Bertoni. *See* for first ed. Bertoni's Aristo
e Temira e Orfeo ed Euridice, Venezia, 1776. Schatz 934–935

Orfeo ed Euridice, Venezia, 1776: Bertoni. Schatz 916

Orfeo, ed Euridice, Vienna (1762): Gluck. ML 50.2.O7G4

Orfeo ed Euridice e Aristo e Temira, Bologna (1771): Gluck;
the second by Monza. Schatz 3934

Orphée et Euridice, Paris, 1775: Gluck. Moline's Tr. of Orfeo
ed Euridice. ML 50.2.O7G45

Orphée et Euridice, Paris, 1782: Gluck. ML 48.M2H

Orpheus and Eurydice, London, 1785. Tr. of his Orfeo ed
Euridice: Gluck (with music also of J. Chr. Bach, Händel,
and Anfossi.) Schatz 3926

Orpheus and Euridice (Cramer's Magazin der musik, Feb.
1785): Gluck. Tr. by Eschenburg. Schatz 3912

Paride ed Elena, Napoli, 1777: Gluck. ML 50.2.P27G5

Cambi, Bartolommeo (Bortolamio).

I dei del mare (Venezia, 1776): Sarti. Schatz 9477

Le peregrine erranti, ballet. *See* Salari's Il marchese Car-
bonari.

Camidio Matiaglauro. *Arcadian name of* Pietro Antonio
Bagliacca.

Campeggi, *conte* **Ridolfo.**

L'Aurora ingannata (intermedii in his Filarmindo, Venezia,
1628): Giacobbi. PQ

Prosperpina rapita, Bologna, 1613: Giacobbi(?). ML 50.2.P68

Reno sacrificante, Bologna, 1617: Giacobbi. Schatz 3804

Campilli, Leopoldo.

Il divertimento de' Quaquerinella China, ballet. *See* Gagni's
I matti gloriosi.

Campion, Thomas.

A relation of the late royall entertainment . . . whereunto is
annexed . . . the Lords maske, London, 1613. *See* Title
catalogue. ML 52.2.R38

Campistron, Jean Galbert de.

Achille et Polixene (Amsterdam) 1687: Colasse and Lully. ML 49.A2L9

Achille et Polixene (Amsterdam) 1701: Colasse and Lully. ML 50.2.A25L9

Achille et Polixene (Recueil général des opéra, t. iii, Paris,
1703): Colasse and Lully. Schatz 5781

Acis et Galatée (Amsterdam) 1686: Lully. ML 49.A2L9

Acis et Galatée (Recueil général des opéra, t. iii, Paris, 1703):
Lully. Schatz 5756

Acis und Galatée, Stuttgart, 1698: Lully. Schatz 5757

Alcide (Recueil général des opéra, t. iv, Paris, 1703): L. de
Lully and Marais. Schatz 5785

La mort d'Hercule, Paris, 1705. L. T. of his Alcide: L. de
Lully and Marais. ML 50.2.A51L9

Canciani, Giuseppe. *See* Canziani.

Candeille, Julie.

Catherine ou La belle fermière, Paris, 1793: author. ML 50.2.C31C2

Candi, Giovanni Pietro.

    Gli amanti generosi, Venetia, 1703: Vinacese.   SCHATZ 10739

    Idaspe, Venezia, 1730: Broschi.   SCHATZ 1339

    Il tradimento premiato, Venetia, 1709: Polani.   SCHATZ 8252

Canicà, Domenico.

    Il governadore, Napoli, 1747: Logroscino.   SCHATZ 5673

Canziani (Canciani), Giuseppe.

    Alceste e Admeto, ballet: Le Messier. *See* Monza's Cleopatra.

    L'amante generosa, ballet. *See* Bertoni's Telemaco ed Eurice.

    L'amante travestita, ballet: Le Messier. *See* G. M. Rutini's Sicotencal.

    L'arrivo di Venere nell' isola di Cipro, ballet. *See* Radicchi's Medonte rè di Epiro.

    Cleopatra, ballet. *See* Borghi's Eumene.

    Cupido trionfatore o sia Apollo e Dafne, ballet: Canobio. *See* Pio's Nettuno ed Egle.

    La disgrazia opportuna, ballet: Le Messier. *See* Monzas's Cleopatra.

    Le dissensioni d'amore nel campo, ballet: Le Messier. *See* G. M. Rutini's Sicotencal.

    Ines di Castro, ballet. *See* P. Guglielmi's Il Demetrio.

    Le jugement de Paris—Das urtheil des Paris, ballet. *See* Tozzi's Zenobia.

    Linceo, ballet. *See* Mortellari's Antigona.

    La maggior impresa d'Ercole o sia Admeto ed Alceste, ballet: Canobio. *See* Pio's Nettuno ed Egle.

    Pigmalione, ballet. *See* Mortellari's Arsace.

    Piramo e Tisbe, ballet. *See* Piccinni's La Griselda.

    Porzia, ballet. *See* Alessandri's Calliroe.

    Lo sbarco de' Spagnuoli nell' America, ballet: Le Messier. *See* G. M. Rutini's Sicotencal.

    Il tradimento punito, ballet. *See* Piccinni's La Griselda.

    Il trionfo di Cesare in Egitto, ballet: Le Messier. *See* Monza's Cleopatra.

Capece, Carlo Sigismondo.

    Amor d'un ombra e gelosia d'un aura (with alterations by Carlo de Palma), 1725: Sellitti.   SCHATZ 9829

    L'Amor vince Fortuna, Roma, 1686: unknown.   ML 50.2A67

    Il figlio delle selve, Modona (1701): Boni.   SCHATZ 1181

    Il figlio delle selve, Mannheim (1753) (partly rewritten by Bardella): Holzbauer.   SCHATZ 4781

    Il figlio delle selve (retouched by Francesco Bardella), Genova (1755): Felice Mazzinghi and others.   SCHATZ 6217

    Il figlio delle selve, Torino, 1699: A. Scarlatti.   SCHATZ 9530

    Telemaco, Roma, 1718: A. Scarlatti.   SCHATZ 9532

    Tetide in Sciro, Vicenza, 1715: C. F. Pollaroli.   SCHATZ 8319

Capistron.

    See Campistron.

Caramondani, Antonio de' Filistri da.   *See* Filistri.

Caravita, Giuseppe.

Didone, Lisbona, 1799 (Metastasio's text with alterations):
Marino. Schatz 5968

L'esilio d'Apollo. *See* Portugal's La donna di genio volubile,
Lisbona, 1798. ML 48.C6IV

Rinaldo d'Aste, Lisbona, 1799. (Versification and alteration
of Carpani's text): Portugal. Schatz 8429

Carcajus, Domenico.

Amor fa l'uomo cieco. *See* Title catalogue.

Carey, George Saville.

The cottagers (together on p. 47–75 with his The inoculator,
London, 1766.) Longe 151

The old woman weatherwise, London, 1788: unknown. Longe 251

The noble pedlar or The fortune hunter, 2d ed., London, 1771:
Barthelemon. Longe 213

Carey, Henry.

The dramatick works of Henry Carey.
*London, Printed by S. Gilbert, 1743. 8 p. l. (incl. port.), 254,
[2] p. 22cm.*

In the preface Carey expresses his thanks to his subscribers for having ena-
bled him to "exhibit" his "dramatick works, not only free from the
errors of false and spurious editions, publish'd without my knowledge
or consent, but (upon this occasion) revised and improv'd even from
my own original copies."
The collection contains: Amelia—Terraminta—The dragon of Wantley—
The dragoness—Chrononhotonthologos—The contrivances—The honest
Yorkshire-man—Nancy or The parting lovers.

ML 49.A2C2

Amelia, London, 1732: Lampe. Longe 105

Chrononhotonthologos, London, 1770: ballad burlesque. *See
also* The tragedy of . . . Longe 54

Chrononhotonthologos (Collection of the most esteemed farces,
Edinburgh, 1792, t. ii). Schatz 11753B

The contrivances, London, 1765: author. Longe 69

The contrivances (Collection of the most esteemed farces,
Edinburgh, 1792, t. iv). Schatz 11753D

The dragon of Wantley, London, 1738 (12th ed.): Lampe. ML 50.2.D67L2

The dragon of Wantley, London, 1770. ML 50.2.D67L3

The dragon of Wantley, London, n. d. Longe 69

The honest Yorkshire-man, London, 1736: partly ballad opera,
partly Carey. (L. T. and better known than O. T., The
Wonder! An honest Yorkshireman.) ML 50.5.H65

The honest Yorkshire-man, London, 1763. Longe 73

Margery or A worse plague than the dragon, London, 1738 (3d
ed.): Lampe. Longe 153

The tragedy of Chrononhotonthologos, London, n. d.: ballad
burlesque. *See also* Chrononhotonthologos. ML 50.2.C47

The Wonder! An honest Yorkshireman. *See* L. T. The honest
Yorkshire-man.

Carini (*pseud. of* Carey, Henry).

Carli Ottavio.

Il Fetonte, Lucca, 1675. *See* M. Curzio in Title catalogue.

Caro, Maria de'.

Oscar e Malvina, ballet: Nucci. *See* Trento's Bianca de' Rossi.

Carolet.

L'allure (Le théâtre de la foire, Paris, 1737, t. ix, 2): Gillier.   ML 48.L2X

L'amour descœuvré, ou, Les vacances de Cythère (Le théâtre de la foire, Paris, 1737, t. ix, 2).   ML 48.L2X

Les audiences de Thalie (Le théâtre de la foire, Paris, 1737, t. ix, 2): Corrette.   ML 48.L2X

L'isle du mariage (Le théâtre de la foire, Paris, 1737, t. ix): Corrette.   ML 48.L48X

La lanterne veridique (Le théâtre de la foire, Paris, 1737, t. ix, 2): Gillier.   ML 48.L2X

La mère jalouse (Le théâtre de la foire, Paris, 1737, t. ix, 2): Gillier.   ML 48.L2X

Le parterre merveilleux (Le théâtre de la foire, Paris, 1737, t. ix, 2): Gillier.   ML 48.L2X

Le père rival (Le théâtre de la foire, Paris, 1737, t. ix, 2): Corrette.   ML 48.L2X

Les petites maisons (Le théâtre de la foire, Paris, 1737, t. ix, 2): Travenol.   ML 48.L2X

Le retour d' l'opéra comique au faubourg S. Germain (Le théâtre de la foire, Paris, 1737, t. ix, 2): Corrette.   ML 48.L2X

Le reveil de l'opéra-comique (Le théâtre de la foire, Paris, 1737, t. ix, 2): Gillier.   ML 48.L2X

Le rival de lui-même (with his Le parterre merveilleux, Le théâtre de la foire, Paris, 1737, t. ix, 2): Gillier.   ML 48.L2X

Carpani, Giuseppe.

Gli antiquari in Palmira, Milano (1780): Rust.   Schatz 9176

Camilla ossia La sepolta viva, Lisbona, 1799. Tr. of Dalayrac's Camille (Marsollier).   Schatz 2332

La caravana del Cairo, Milano (1795). Tr. of Grétry's, La caravane du Caire (comte de Provence and Morel de Chefdeville).   Schatz 4200

Raollo, signore di Crequi, Lisbona, 1795. Tr. of Dalayrac's Raoul, sire de Créqui (Monvel).   Schatz 2376

Rinaldo d'Aste, Venezia, 1794: Portugal.   Schatz 8428

Rinaldo d'Aste, Lisbona, 1799: Portugal. (Text altered by Caravita.)   Schatz 8429

Lo spazzacamino principe, Milano (1790): Tarchi.   Schatz 10238

Carstens, A. G.

Aglae eller Støtten (Copenhagen, 1774) (with Claus Fasting): Sarti.   Schatz 9423

Casali, Giuseppe.

La disfatta di Dario, Alessandria (1779) (originally by duca S. Angiolo Morbilli): Ferrero.   Schatz 3081

Casanova de Seignalt, Giacomo.

Zoroastro, Dresda (1752): Adam. Tr. of Cahusac's text.   Schatz 55

Casari, Filippo.

Il matrimonio per scomessa ossia La guerra aperta, Venezia, 1795: Della Maria.   Schatz 2494

Cascina, Pietro.
Alfea reverente, Pisa, 1639: Pisani. — SCHATZ 8191

Caselli, Francesco.
Vertunno e Pomona, ballet. *See* Rust's Il conte Baccelone.

Casòli, Francesco.
La vergine del sole (1799): Andreozzi. — SCHATZ 203

Casori, Ferdinando.
Mesenzio rè d'Etruria, Firenze, 1782: Cherubini. — SCHATZ 1846

Casor(r)i, Gaetano.
L'amore industrioso, Dresda, 1769: Ottani. — SCHATZ 7357
L'amore industrioso, Venezia, 1765: G. M. Rutini. — SCHATZ 9186

Cassani, Vincenzo.
Cleomene, Venezia, 1718: Albinoni. — SCHATZ 128
Filandro, Venezia (1729). L. T. of his L'incostanza schernita:
    Albinoni. — SCHATZ 109
Filandro—Philander (Dresda, 1747): Porpora. — SCHATZ 8357
L'incostanza schernita, Venezia, 1727: Albinoni. — SCHATZ 95
Niņo, Venezia (1732) (only the alterations in Zanelli's text):
    Courcelle. — SCHATZ 2283
Plautilla, Venezia, 1721: A. Pollaroli. — SCHATZ 8264
Romolo e Tazio, Venezia, 1722: Pietragrua. — SCHATZ 8166
Il tiranno eroe, Venezia, 1710: Albinoni. — SCHATZ 127

Castet.
Le bucheron, ou Les trois souhaits, Paris, 1763 (with Gui-
    chard): Philidor. — SCHATZ 8010
Le bucheron ou Les trois souhaits, Copenhague, 1767 (with
    Guichard): Philidor. — YUDIN PQ
Le bucheron ou Les trois souhaits, Paris, 1771 (with Guichard):
    Philidor. — SCHATZ 11736
Le bucheron ou Les trois souhaits, Paris, 1782: Philidor. — SCHATZ 11737
Die drey wuensche. A. T. of his and Guichard's Der holz-
    hauer: Philidor.
Der holzhauer oder Die drey wuensche, Frankfurt am Mayn,
    1773. Tr. of his and Guichard's Le bucheron: Philidor. — SCHATZ 8011
Skoohuggeren eller De tre ønsker (Copenhagen, 1782). Tr. of
    his and Guichard's Le bucheron: Philidor. — SCHATZ 8013
De tre ønsker. A. T. of his and Guichard's Skovhuggeren:
    Philidor.
Les trois souhaits. A. T. of his and Guichard's Le bucheron:
    Philidor.

Castelli, Girolamo.
L'Almerico in Cipro, Venetia, 1675: del Gaudio. — SCHATZ 3635

Casti, Giambattista.
La grotta di Trofonio—Die hoehle des Trophonius, Dresda,
    1786: Salieri. — SCHATZ 9297
La grotta di Trofonio, Parma (1791): Salieri. — SCHATZ 9296
Die hoehle des Trophonius. Tr. of his La grotta di Trofonio,
    Dresda, 1786: Salieri. — SCHATZ 9297
Der koenig Theodor, (n. pl.), 1792, and — SCHATZ 7683
Der koenig Theodor in Venedig, Koeln, 1785. Tr. of his Il
    rè Teodoro in Venezia: Paisiello. — SCHATZ 7651

Casti, Giambattista—Continued.

Koenig Theodor in Venedig, Hamburg, 1788.   Another Tr.   SCHATZ 7653

Der Koenig Theodor zu Venedig, Stuttgart, 1785. Another Tr. SCHATZ 7682

Il rè Teodoro in Venezia, Milano (1788): Paisiello.   ML 50.2.R3P22

Il re Teodoro in Venezia, Paris, 1789: Paisiello.   ML 50.2.R3P27

Le roi Théodore à Venise, Versailles, 1787.   French version of
   his Il rè Teodoro in Venezia: Paisiello.   ML 50.2.R3P25

Theodor in Venedig, Berlin, 1799. L. T. of his Koenig Theodor
   in Venedig: Paisiello.   SCHATZ 7652

Trofons zauberhoele, Riga, 1794. Tr. of his La grotta di Trofonio: Salieri.   SCHATZ 9299

Die zauberhoele des Trofonius (Wien), 1789. Tr. of his La
   grotta di Trofonio: Salieri.   SCHATZ 9298

Castoreo, Giacomo.

Giocasta, regina d'Armenia, Venetia, 1677 (additions to
   Moniglia's text): Grossi.   SCHATZ 4217

La guerriera Spartana, Venetia, 1654: P. A. Ziani.   SCHATZ 11216

Pericle effeminato, Venetia, 1653: Luccio.   SCHATZ 5747

Cataneo, *conte* Domenico di.

Teseo in Sicilia, Venezia, 1754: Tiepolo.   SCHATZ 10352

Cavalieri, Bortolamio.

L'impresa d'opera, Venezia, 1769: P. Guglielmi.   SCHATZ 4282

Cavazza, Gherardo.

La scoperta d'un isola nell' America del capitano Durson
   Inglese, ballet. *See* Crippa's Le confusioni per la somiglianza.

L'uomo effeminato, ballet. *See* Crippa's Le confusioni per somiglianza.

Cazotte, Jacques.

Les sabots, Paris, 1769 (with Sedaine): Duni.   ML 50.2.S2D9

Les sabots, Paris, 1770: Duni.   SCHATZ 2855

Les sabots, Paris, 1777: Duni.   SCHATZ 11698

Cerilo Orcomeno, P. A.

Amor per oro—Liebe aus haabsucht, Dresda, 1790: Seydelmann.   SCHATZ 9840

Il capitan Tenaglia, o sia La muta per amore, Firenze, 1784:
   Moneta.   SCHATZ 6556

Liebe aus haabsucht.   Tr. of his Amor per oro, Dresda, 1790:
   Seydelmann.   SCHATZ 9840

La muta per amore.   A. T. of his Il capitan Tenaglia: Moneta.

La muta per amore, Venezia, 1783: Mortellari.   SCHATZ 6693

Cerlone, Francesco.

Le astuzie amorose, Venezia (1775): Mortellari.   SCHATZ 6688

Le astuzie amorose, Firenze, 1777: Paisiello.   SCHATZ 7675

La Bellinda, Napoli, 1781: Tritto.   SCHATZ 10461

Li Napoletani in America, Lisbona (1775): Piccinni.   SCHATZ 8133

Le trame per amore, Napoli, 1783: Paisiello.   SCHATZ 7681

Cesari, Gaetano.

Li amori di Tirsi ed Eurilla interrotti dalla maga Falsirena
   ballet. *See* Galuppi's Cajo Mario.

Il giudizio di Paride ballet: *See* Galuppi's Cajo Mario.

Chabannes, Marc Antoine Jacques Rochon de.

Les prétendus, Paris, 1789: Le Moine. SCHATZ 5487

Le seigneur bienfaisant, Paris, 1782 (consisting of "Le retour du seigneur dans ses terres," "Le Pressoir," "Les fêtes de l'automne" and "L'incendie"): Floquet. SCHATZ 3249

Chabanon de Maugris, Michel Paul Gui de.

Sabinus (Paris) 1773: Gossec. SCHATZ 4011

Chancel de Lagrange, François Joseph de. *See* Lagrange-Chancel.

Chanfort, de.

Palmire, ballet, Paris, 1765 (Journal des spectacles, 1766, t. ii): de Bury. ML 48.J7

La vengeance de l'amour, ou Diane et Endimion (with his Palmire, Journal des spectacles, Paris, 1766, t. ii): de Bury.

Zenis et Almasie (Paris), 1765 (Journal des spectacles, t. ii, Paris, 1766): de La Borde. ML 48.J7

Chatterton, Thomas.

The revenge, London, 1795: Arnold. LONGE 296

Checchi, Giovanni Battista.

Alessandro e Campaspe, ballet. *See* Mayr's Un pazzo ne fa cento.

Apelle e Campaspe. A. T. of his ballet La generosità d'Alessandro.

La generosità d'Alessandro ossia Apelle e Campaspe, ballet. *See* Zingarelli's Il Pirro.

Chetwood, William Rufus.

The generous Free-mason or The constant lady, London, 1731: ballad opera, partly composed by Carey, Clarke, Sheeles. ML 50.5.G4

The lovers opera, 2d ed., London, 1729: ballad opera. LONGE 49

The lovers opera, 3d ed., London, 1730. ML 50.5.L72

Chevalier.

La fête d'amour ou Lucas et Colinette. *See* Mad. Favart.

Chiabrera, Gabriello.

Il rapimento di Cefalo, Firenze, 1600: Caccini and others. SCHATZ 1449

Chiari, Pietro.

Alcimena principessa dell' Isole Fortunate o sia L'amore fortunato ne' suoi disprezzi, Venezia, 1750: Galuppi. SCHATZ 3479

Amor lunatico, Venezia, 1770: Galuppi. SCHATZ 3436

L'amore fortunato ne' suoi disprezzi. A. T. of his Alcimena principessa dell' Isole Fortunate: Galuppi.

Amore in Trappola, Venezia, 1768: Traetta. SCHATZ 10405

L'amore senza malizia, Venezia, 1768: Ottani. SCHATZ 7358

L'amore senza malizia (Lisbona, 1774): Ottani. ML 48.C6I

L'amore senza malizia—Die liebe ohne bosheit, Dresda, 1768: Ottani. SCHATZ 7359

L'astrologa, Torino, 1762: Piccinni. SCHATZ 8147

La bella Girometta, Venezia, 1761: Bertoni. SCHATZ 937

Il caffè di campagna, Torino (1762): Celoniat. SCHATZ 1772

Il caffè di campagna, Venezia, 1761: Galuppi. SCHATZ 3501

72251°—VOL 2—14——4

Chiari, Pietro—Continued.

O casamento inesperado. A. T. of his O marquez de Tulipano.

Le contadine furlane, Venezia, 1771: Boroni.   SCHATZ 1252

La donna Girandola, Venezia, 1763: Perillo.   SCHATZ 7924

Le donne sempre donne, Venezia, 1767: Luchesi.   SCHATZ 5741

Den flanevurne kone. Tr. of his version of La moglie bizzarra, Kiøbenhavn, 1763: Galuppi.   SCHATZ 3434

La Francese a Malghera, Venezia, 1764: Traetta.   SCHATZ 10411

Der geadelte landmann. A. T. of his Das witzige land-maedchen.

Die getreue braut. Tr. of his La sposa fedele, Dresda, 1771: P. Guglielmi.   SCHATZ 4272

L'ingannatore ingannato, Venezia, 1764: Bertoni   SCHATZ 939

La lavandara, Torino (1770). L. T. of his Il marchese villano: Galuppi.   SCHATZ 3515

La lavandara astuta, Mantova (1771). L. T. of his Il marchese villano: Galuppi.   SCHATZ 3505

Die liebe ohne bosheit. Tr. of his L'amore senza malizia, Dresda, 1768: Ottani.   SCHATZ 7359

Il marchese di Tulipano o sia Il matrimonio inespetato—O marquez de Tulipano ou O casamento inesperado, Lisbona, 1790. L. T. and Tr. of his Il matrimonio inaspettato: Paisiello.   SCHATZ 7688

Il marchese villano, Vienna (1767): Galuppi.   SCHATZ 3458

O marquez de Tulipano ou O casamento inesperado. Tr. of his Il matrimonio inaspettato, Lisbona, 1790: Paisiello.   SCHATZ 7688

Il matrimonio inaspettato (St. Petersburg, 1779?): Paisiello.   SCHATZ 7636

Il matrimonio per inganno, Venezia, 1771. L. T. of his Il marchese villano: Galuppi.   SCHATZ 3506

La moglie bizzarra—Den flanevurne kone, Kiøbenhavn, 1763. His version of Galuppi's "L'amante di tutte" (Ant. Galuppi).   SCHATZ 3434

Le nozze di Paride, Venezia, 1756: Galuppi.   SCHATZ 3489

Le orfane svizzere, Venezia, 1770: Boroni.   SCHATZ 1248

I raggiri fortunati, Venezia, 1795: Nasolini.   SCHATZ 7029

Robert und Kalliste oder Der triumph der treue, Breslau und Leipzig, 1776. Tr. of his La sposa fedele: P. Guglielmi.   SCHATZ 4273

Le serve rivali, Venezia, 1767: Traetta.   SCHATZ 10397

La sposa fedele (Lisbona, 1773): P. Guglielmi.   SCHATZ 4270

La sposa fedele—Den troe brund, Kiøbenhavn, 1768: P. Guglielmi.   SCHATZ 4271

La sposa fedele—Die getreue braut, Dresda, 1771: P. Guglielmi.   SCHATZ 4272

La sposa fedele, Cremona, n. d.: (?) Guglielmi.   ML 50.2.S72

Der triumph der treue. A. T. of his Robert und Kalliste: P. Guglielmi.

Den troe brund. Tr. of his La sposa fedele, Kiøbenhavn, 1768: P. Guglielmi.   SCHATZ 4271

Das witzige landmaedchen, oder Der geadelte landmann, Nuernberg, 1787. Tr. of his Il matrimonio inaspettato: Paisiello.   SCHATZ 7638

Chiaveri, Luigi.

La villanella socorsa, ballet. *See* Bianchi's La villanella rapita, Lisbona, 1796.

Chirrap, Terentio. *Anagram of* Pietro Trinchera.

Choudard, Pierre Jean Baptiste. *Better known under his pseud.* Desforges.

Chudy, Joseph.
Der docktor, Pressburg (1779): author.   SCHATZ 1872

Cialli, Rinaldo.
Ariberto e Flavio, regi de Longobardi, Venetia, 1684[!]: Lonati.   SCHATZ 5680
Creonte, Venetia, 1691: M. A. Ziani.   SCHATZ 11181
La Falsirena, Venetia, 1690: M. A. Ziani.   SCHATZ 11196
La fortuna tra le disgratie, Venetia, 1688: Biego.   SCHATZ 1014
Le generose gare tra Cesare e Pompeo, Venetia, 1686: Gabrieli.   SCHATZ 3403
Marte deluso, Venetia, 1691. L. T. of his La Falsirena: M. A. Ziani.   SCHATZ 11197
Il trionfo della innocenza, Venetia, 1692: Lotti.   SCHATZ 5724

Cianfanelli, Giovanni Antonio.
La diserzione per equivoco, ballet. *See* Curcio's La conquista di Granata.
La disfatta di Dario. A. T. of his ballet Il trionfo di Alessandro: Stabingher.
Il trionfo di Alessandro o sia La disfatta di Dario, ballet: Stabingher. *See* Cimarosa's Oreste.
Il trionfo di Alessandro o sia La disfatta di Dario, ballet: Stabingher. *See* Sarti's Medonte.

Cibber, Colley.
Capocchio and Dorina. *See* The happy captive *in* Title catalogue.
Damon and Phillida, London, 1765. (Based on his "Love in a riddle"): ballad opera.   ML 50.5.D17
Damon and Phillida: Dibdin.   LONGE 322
Damon and Phillida, (Collection of the most esteemed farces, Edinburgh, 1792, t. v.)   SCHATZ 11753E
Flora, London, 1729: ballad opera.   LONGE 197
Flora or Hob in the well, 7th ed., London, 1768: Bates.   LONGE 73
Flora or Hob in the well (Dramatic works, London, 1777)   PR 3347.A1
Flora or Hob in the well (Collection of the most esteemed farces, Edinburgh, 1792, t. iv)   SCHATZ 11753D
Love in a riddle, London, 1719 [! instead of 1729]: ballad opera.   ML 50.5.B3
Myrtillo. *See his* Venus and Adonis, London, 1736.
A sequel to the opera of Flora, London, 1732: ballad opera.   ML 50.5.S3
The temple of dullness. With the humour of Signor Capocchio and Signora Dorinna, London, 1745: Th. A. Arne.   ML 50.2.T39A7
Venus and Adonis . . . and Myrtillo, London, 1736: Pepusch.   ML 52.2.V47

Cibber, Theophilus.
Patie and Peggy or The fair foundling, London, 1730: ballad opera.   ML 50.5.P18

Cicognini, Giacinto (Hiacinto) Andrea.

L'Alessandro amante, Venetia, 1667 (L. T. of Gli amori di Alessandro e di Rossane):   Boretti.   SCHATZ 1215

Gl'amori di Alessandro Magno e di Rossane, Venetia, 1651: Luccio.   SCHATZ 5745

Celio, Roma, 1664: unknown.   ML 50.2.C34

Il D. Gastone overo La più costante tra le maritate, Roma, 1675: unknown.   ML 50.2.D59

Giasone, Venetia, 1649: Cavalli.   SCHATZ 1751

Il Giasone, Venetia, 1664: Cavalli.   SCHATZ 1722

Il Giasone, Venetia, 1666: Cavalli.   ML 50.2.G36C1

Il Giasone, Milan, n. d.: Cavalli.   ML 50.2.G36C2

Il novello Giasone, Roma, 1671: Cavalli. (*See their* Giasone.) SCHATZ 1750

Orontea, regina d'Egitto, Torino, 1662: Cesti.   SCHATZ 1781

Orontea, regina d'Egitto, Venetia, n. publ., n. d.: Cesti.   ML 50.2.O73C2

Cigna-Santi, Vittorio Amedeo.

Alcina e Ruggero, Torino (1775): Alessandri.   SCHATZ 141

Andromeda, Torino (1755): Cocchi.   SCHATZ 2051

Andromeda, Torino (1772): Colla.   SCHATZ 2106

Enea nel Lazio, Torino (1760): Traetta.   SCHATZ 10391

Ercole sul Tago (Lisbona, 1785): Santos.   SCHATZ 9395

Ifigenia in Aulide, Torino (1762): Bertoni.   SCHATZ 914

Ifigenia [in Aulide], Roma (1766): Franchi.   ML 50.2.I4F7

Issea, Torino (1771): Pugnani.   SCHATZ 8507

Mitridate rè di Ponto, Torino (1767): Gasparini.   SCHATZ 3604

Motezuma, Venezia, 1772: Galuppi.   SCHATZ 3463

Motezuma, Torino (1780): Insanguine.   SCHATZ 4835

Motezuma, Torino (1765): G. F. de Majo.   SCHATZ 5858

Tamas Kouli-Kan nell' India, Torino (1772): Pugnani.   SCHATZ 8506

Ciliberti, Gaetano.

L'incognito fortunata, Napoli, 1782: Rust.   SCHATZ 9172

L'inganno, Napoli, 1782: Caruso.   SCHATZ 1652

Cini, Giovanni Battista.

Descrizione dell' apparato . . . [Psiche ed Amore, intermedii], Fiorenza, 1566: Striggio and Corteccia. (The description by Cini)   ML 52.2.D3

Descrizione de gl'intermedii . . . [Psiche ed Amore], Firenze, 1593: Striggio and Corteccia. (The description by Il Lasca.)   PQ.

Cini, Vincenzo.

Gl' amori politici della libertà raminga, Lucca, 1666. *See* M. Curzio in Title catalogue.

Cipretti, Pietro.

Die haeuslichen zwistigkeiten. A. T. of his Die mode: Salieri and others.

La moda, Venezia, 1769: Boroni.   SCHATZ 1249

Die mode, oder Die haeuslichen zwistigkeiten (Wien, 1771): Salieri and others. Pasticcio Tr. from his La moda ossia I scompigli domestici.   SCHATZ 9337

Claudius, Georg Carl, *called* Franz Ehrenberg.

Der fuerst und sein volk, n. i., 1794: Pitterlin, with interpolations from Dittersdorf and Bertoni.   SCHATZ 11613

Claudius, Georg Carl—Continued.

Der fuerst und sein volk, Leipzig, n. d.: same composers.   SCHATZ 8204

Der onkel aus Amsterdam, Riga und Mitau, 1796. Tr. of
Cimarosa's Il pittore parigino (Petrosellini).   SCHATZ 1970

Cleofonto Doriano. *Arcadian name* of *conte* Antonio Papi.

Clerico, Francesco.

Amleto, ballet. *See* Tarchi's Alessandro nell' Indie.

Amleto, ballet. *See* Zingarelli's Apelle e Campaspe.

Le avventure del carnovale, ballet: Canavasso. *See* Rispoli's
Idalide.

I barbari sacrifizi distrutti, ballet: Canavasso. *See* Rispoli's
Idalide.

La caduta di Troia, ballet: Canavasso. *See* Monza's Erifile.

La caduta di Troja, ballet. *See* Pio's Medonte.

La conquista del vello d'oro, ballet. *See* Nasolini's Tito e
Berenice.

Il convalescente innamorato, ballet. *See* Martin y Soler's La
capricciosa corretta.

Il convalescente innamorato, ballet. *See* Pio's Medonte.

I due vedovi, ballet. *See* Tarchi's Alessandro nell' Indie.

Ercole e Dejanira, ballet. *See* Bianchi's Daliso e Delmita.

Ercole e Dejanira, ballet. *See* Paër's La virtù al cimento.

Gabriella di Vergy, ballet. *See* Anfossi's La Nitteti.

Gustavo Vasa, ballet. *See* Rust's L'isola capricciosa.

Li montanari nel Perù, ballet: Canavasso. *See* Rispoli's
Idalide.

La morte d'Agamemnone, ballet. *See* Andreozzi's Ines de
Castro.

La morte d'Ercole, ballet. *See* Metastasio's Adriano in Siria.

Olimpia, ballet. *See* Winter's Catone in Utica.

Il ritorno d'Agamemnone, ballet. *See* P. Guglielmi's Arsace.

I sacrifizi di Tauride, ballet. *See* P. Guglielmi's Rinaldo.

Lo sposo burlato, ballet: author. *See* Caruso's Il vecchio
burlato.

La superba innamorata, ballet. *See* Nasolini's Adriano in
Siria.

La vanità corretto dal disprezzo, ballet: Canavasso. *See*
Monza's Erifile.

La virtù al cimento, ballet. *See* Paër's La virtù al cimento.

Zemira e Azor, ballet: author. *See* Andreozzi's Giovanna
d'Arco.

Zemira e Azor, ballet: author. *See* Caruso's Il vecchio
burlato.

Zorei e Ozai, ballet: author. *See* G. Giordani's Erifile.

Clive, *Mrs.* Catherine.

The rehearsal or Boys in petticoats, London, 1753: Boyce.   LONGE 270

Cobb, James.

The Cherokee, London, 1795: Storace.   LONGE 233

The doctor and the apothecary, London, 1788. Tr. of Ditterr-
dorf's Der apotheker und der doctor, with additions by
Storace (Stephanie d. jüng.).   SCHATZ 2586

The haunted tower, London, 1789: Storace.   LONGE 203

The haunted tower, London, 1791: Storace.   LONGE 218

The haunted tower, Dublin, n. d.: Storace.   SCHATZ 10081

Cobb, James—Continued.

Love in the East or Adventures of twelve hours, London, 1788:
Linley. Longe 110

The pirates, London, 1792: Storace. Longe 220

The siege of Belgrade, London, 1791: Storace, partly utilizing
Martin y Soler's "Una cosa rara." Longe 207

The siege of Belgrade, Dublin (179–). Longe 233

The siege of Belgrade, London (ca. 1796). Longe 263

The strangers at home, London, 1786: Linley. Longe 96

Coffey, Charles.

The beggar's wedding, 5th ed., London, 1733: ballad opera.
L. T. of his Phebe. ML 50.5.B4

The beggar's wedding, London, 1763. Longe 102

The boarding-school, or, The sham captain: ballad opera. Longe 50

The boarding-school, or, The sham captain (Collection of the
most esteemed farces, Edinburgh, 1792, t. v.). Schatz 11753E

The devil to pay, or, The wives metamorphos'd, London,
1732: ballad opera. ML 50.5.D37

The devil to pay, or, The wives metamorphos'd, London,
1748. ML 50.5.D39

[Same title] London, 1771. Longe 69

[Same title] (Collection of the most esteemed farces, Edinburgh, 1792, t. II). Schatz 11753B

The female parson, or, Beau in the sudds, London, 1730:
ballad opera. Longe 47

The merry cobler or The second part of The devil to pay, London, 1735: ballad opera. ML 50.5.M3

Phebe or The beggar's wedding (London, 1729?). O. T. of
The beggar's wedding, both ballad operas. Longe 151

Colatelli, Girolamo.

Armida regina di Damasco, Verona, 1711: Orgiani. L. T. of
his Gli amori di Rinaldo con Armida. Schatz 7296

L'honor al cimento, Venezia, 1703: Orgiani. L. T. of his Gli
amori di Rinaldo con Armida. Schatz 7295

Il trionfo d'Armida, Venezia (1726): Albinoni. Schatz 132

Collé, Charles.

L'isle sonnante, Paris, 1768: Monsigny. Schatz 6576

L'isle sonnante, Paris, 1771: Monsigny. Schatz 11727

A collection of the most esteemed farces and entertainments
performed on the British stage [vignette].

*Edinburgh, Printed for Silvester Doig and William Anderson,
1792. 6 v. 19 cm.*

Contains the following librettos: *v. 1:* Florizel and Perdita—The mock doctor—The sultan—The chaplet. *v. 2:* The reprisal—The devil to pay—
The virgin unmask'd—The cunning man—Thomas and Sally—Chrononhotonthologos—The lottery—Midas. *v. iii:* The golden pippin—
The intriguing chambermaid—The padlock—Cymon. *v. 4:* The deserter—Edgar and Emmeline—The rival candidates—Comus—The
contrivances—Flora. *v. 5:* The dragon of Wantley—The boarding
school—Damon and Phillida—He wou'd if he cou'd—Daphne and
Amintor. *v. 6:* The Ephesian matron—The waterman—May-day—
The theatrical candidates—The cooper—The romp—Amintas—The
recruiting sergeant.

Our copy lacks, in v. 5, p. 49-72, which contain also "The dragon of
Wantley" complete.

ML 48S11753A–F

A collection of the most esteemed farces, etc.—Continued.

L. of C. has also:

— A collection of the most esteemed farces and entertainments, performed on the British stage. New ed.

Edinburgh, C. Elliot, 1786. 4 v. fronts. 18 cm.

The contents of these four vols. are identical with the contents of vols. 1–4 of the 1792 edition, and the 1786 ed. evidently was identical with the first ed. of 1782–1783. In the prefatory advertisement of fourth volume of the latter (reprinted in the 1786 ed.) the publisher announced that this fourth volume would "terminate the publication for the present," but that he is "determined at some future period to add two or three volumes."

The librettos in the 1786 ed. have not been entered in the main (title) catalogue, in order to avoid needless duplication.   PR 1251.C6

Collet de Messine, Jean Baptiste.

Sara ou La fermière ecossaise, Paris, 1774: Vachon.   Schatz 10571

Collier, *Sir* George.

Selima & Azor, London, 1784 (imitation of Marmontel's Zémire et Azor, with alterations by Sheridan): Linley, utilizing Grétry.   Longe 95

Colman, George, 1732–94.

Achilles in petticoats, London, 1774 (alterations of Gay's Achilles): Arne.   Longe 26

Comus. *See* Milton.

Elfrida, London, 1796 (J. Bell, British theatre, London, 1791–97, v. 35) (his dramatization of Mason's poem): Th. A. Arne.   PR 1241.B4

The fairy prince, London, 1771: Th. Aug. Arne.   Longe 52

A fairy tale, London, 1777: M. Arne, Dibdin, Burney, etc.   Longe 243

The giant's causeway. A. T. of his Harlequin Teague: Arnold.

Harlequin Teague or The giant's causeway, London, 1782: Arnold.   ML 52.2.H2A7

The portrait, London, 1370 [! instead of 1770]: Arnold.   ML 50.2.P59A7

The portrait, London, 1370 [! instead of 1770]: Arnold.   Longe 26

The Spanish barber, London, 1783: Arnold.   Longe 91

Colman, George, 1762–1836.

The battle of Hexham, Dublin, 1790: Arnold.   Longe 233

The banquet-gallery. A. T. of his Feudal times: Kelly.

Blue-beard, or, Female curiosity, London, 1798: Kelly.   Longe 246

The castle of Sorrento. Only revised Heartwell's text.

Female curiosity. A. T. of his Blue-beard.

Feudal times or The banquet-gallery, London (1799): Kelly.   Longe 249

Inkle and Jarico, London, n. d.: Arnold.   Longe 99

The iron chest, London, 1796: Storace.   Longe 236

The mountaineers, London, 1793: Arnold.   Longe 227

The mountaineers, London, 1795: Arnold.   Longe 231

The surrender of Calais, Dublin, 1792: Arnold.   Longe 233

Two to one, Dublin, 1785: Arnold.   PR

Coltellini, Marco.

L'Almeria, Livorno, 1761: de Majo.   ML 50.2.A54M3

Amore e Psiche, Vienna, 1767: Gassmann.   Schatz 3626

Antigona, Milano (1789): Campobasso d'Alessandro.   Schatz 1538

Armida-Armide, Berlino (1797): Righini.   Schatz 8778

Coltellini, Marco—Continued.

Armida (n. i., n. d.): Salieri.   SCHATZ 9274

Armida, Lueneburg, 1786: Salieri.   SCHATZ 9275

Il conte Baccelone, Venezia, 1774 (with alterations): Rust.   SCHATZ 9178

La contessina, Roma (1773): Bernardini.   ML 50.2.C665B3

La contessina, Brescia, 1774: Gassmann and others.   SCHATZ 3613

La contessina—Den unge grevinde, Kiobenhavn, 1778: Gassmann.   SCHATZ 3614

La contessina, Verona, 1775: Piccinni.   SCHATZ 8149

Ifigenia in Tauride, Vienna (1763): Traetta.   SCHATZ 10393

Ifigenia in Tauride, Livorno, 1763: Traetta.   SCHATZ 10393a

Ifigenia in Tauride, Mantova (1777): Traetta.   ML 48.A5 v.24

Piramo e Tisbe—Piramus und Thisbe, Berlino, 1771: Hasse.   SCHATZ 4555

Il superbo deluso (Lisboa, 1774): Gassmann. L. T. of their
La contessina.   SCHATZ 3621

Den unge grevinde. Tr. of his La contessina, Kiobenhavn,
1778: Gassmann.   SCHATZ 3614

Venere placata, Livorno (1760): Campion.   SCHATZ 1536

Coluzzi, Niccolò.

Arminio, Torino (1781): Ottani.   SCHATZ 7363

Germanico, Torino (1744): Bernasconi.   SCHATZ 865

Germanico in Germania, Roma, 1770: Monza.   SCHATZ 6609

Germanico in Germania, Roma (1732): Porpora.   SCHATZ 8358

Comante Eginetico. *Arcadian name of* Carlo Innocente Frugoni.

Conradi, Johann Melchior.

Freud und Liebesstreitt, Oettingen, 1699 author.   SCHATZ 2181

Constantini, Angelo de.

Les amours d'Ulisse e de Circe. Tr. of Badia's Gli amori di
Circe con Ulisse (Dresden, 1709) (Ancioni).   SCHATZ 543

Contini, Domenico Filippo.

La donna ancora è fedele, Roma, 1676: Pasquini.   ML 50.2.D6P2

Gli equivoci del sembiante, Milano (1703): Caldara.   ML 48.A5 v.12

Gl'equivoci nel sembiante, Roma, 1679: A. Scarlatti.   SCHATZ 9527

Convò, Giulio.

Il più fedel tra vasalli, Napoli, 1705 (substitute arias only.
Mainly by Silvani): Aldrovandini.   SCHATZ 138

Cooke, Thomas.

The battle of the poets, or, The contention of the laurel,
London, 1731.   LONGE 321

Penelope, London, 1728 (with J. Mottley): ballad opera.   LONGE 152

Coppola, Giovanni Carlo.

Le nozze degli Dei, Firenze, 1637: unknown.   SCHATZ 11351

Corancez, Olivier de.

Daphnis et Chloé (2 p. l. in the score of Rousseau's "Fragmens de Daphnis et Chloé," Paris, 1779.   M 1500.R89

Corebio, Epitide. *Arcadian name of* Gaetano Ciliberti.

Corio, *marchese* **Gioseffo Gorini.**

L'Ipolito, Milano, 1745: Gluck.   SCHATZ 3931

Corneille, Thomas.

    Bellerophon, Paris, 1679: Lully.   ML 50.2.B35L7

    Bellerophon, (Amsterdam) 1679: Lully.   ML 50.2.B35L8

    Bellerophon (Amsterdam) 1682 (with de Fontenelle and per-
haps Boileau): Lully.   ML 49.A2L9

    Bellerophon (Recueil général des opéra, Paris, 1703, t. ii).   Schatz 5762

    Medée, Amsterdam, 1695: Charpentier.   ML 50.2.M5C2

    Medée (Recueil général des opéra, Paris, 1703, t. iv): Char-
pentier.   Schatz 1801

    Psyché (Amsterdam) 1688: Lully.   ML 50.2.P8L92

    Psyché (Recueil général des opéra, t. ii, Paris, 1703) (pos-
sibly Fontenelle collaborated): Lully.   Schatz 5771

Corradi, Giulio Cesare.

    L'Alboino in Italia, Venetia, 1691: Tosi and C. F. Pollaroli.   Schatz 10382

    L'Alvilda, regina de' Goti.   A. T. of his L'Amazone corsara:
Pallavicino.

    Amage, regina de' Sarmati, Venetia, 1694: C. F. Pollaroli.   Schatz 8270

    L'Amazone corsara, overo L'Alvilda, regina de Goti, Venetia,
1686: Pallavicino.   Schatz 7716

    L'amor di Curzio per la patria, Venetia, 1690: Algisi.   Schatz 160

    L'Aristeo, Venezia, 1700: A. Pollaroli.   Schatz 8260

    L'Atanagilda, regina di Gottia.   A. T. of his L'inganno reg-
nante: M. A. Ziani.

    Gli avvenimenti d'Erminia e di Clorinda sopra il Tasso,
Venetia, 1693: C. F. Pollaroli.   Schatz 8275

    Il Creso, Venetia, 1681: Legrenzi.   Schatz 5542

    La divisione del mondo, Venetia, 1675: Legrenzi.   Schatz 5534

    Il Domizio, Venetia, 1696: M. A. Ziani.   Schatz 11182

    I due Cesari, Venetia, 1683: Legrenzi.   Schatz 5543

    L'Egisto rè di Cipro, Venetia, 1698: M. A. Ziani.   Schatz 11184

    Germanico sul Reno, Venetia, 1676: Legrenzi.   Schatz 5536

    La Gierusalemme liberata, Venetia, 1687: Pallavicino.   Schatz 7725

    Il gran Tamerlano, Venetia, 1689: M. A. Ziani.   Schatz 11189

    L'inganno regnante overo L'Atanagilda regina di Gottia,
Venetia, 1688: M. A. Ziani.   Schatz 11205

    Iole, regina di Napoli, Venetia, 1692: C. F. Pollaroli.   Schatz 8323

    Il Nerone, Venetia, 1679: Pallavicino.   Schatz 7729

    La pastorella al soglio, Venezia, 1702: unknown.   Schatz 11355

    Primislao, primo rè di Boemia, Venetia, 1697: Albinoni.   Schatz 124

    La schiava fortunata, Venetia, 1674 (modernization of Mo-
niglia's text): Cesti and M. A. Ziani.   Schatz 1782

    Il Tigrane rè d'Armenia, Venezia, 1697: Albinoni.   Schatz 126

    Il trionfo della continenza, Venetia, 1691: Algisi.   Schatz 161

    Il Vespasiano, Venetia, 1678: Pallavicino.   Schatz 7732

Corte, Giovanni Battista.

    Doriclea ripudiata da Creso, Venezia, 1729: Porta.   Schatz 8378

Corticelli, Luigi.

    Adelaide, ballet.   *See* Paisiello's Il Sismano nel Mogol.

    Il tutore ingannato, ballet.   *See* Paisiello's Il Sismano nel
Mogol.

Cousin Jacques.   *See* Beffroy de Reigny.

Cramer, Carl Friedrich.

Aline, königinn von Golconda (in his Musik, 1789). Tr. of
Schulz' Aline, reine de Golconde (Sedaine).　　ML 4.M3

Armida (Magazin der Musik, 1783) Tr. of Salieri's opera
(Coltellini).

Athalia, Kiel, n. d. Tr. of Schulz' Athalie (Racine).　　SCHATZ 9719

Holger Danske (Cramer's Musik, 1789). Tr. of Kunzen's
opera (Baggesen).　　ML 4.M3

Orpheus und Euridice (Magazin der Musik, Hamburg, 1786,
p. 1085–1145). Cramer's Tr. of Naumann's Orpheus og
Euridice (Biehl).　　ML 4.M2

Orpheus und Euridice, Kiel und Hamburg (179–). Tr. of
Naumann's Orpheus og Euridice (Biehl).　　SCHATZ 7053

Cross, James C.

The apparition, London, 1794: Reeve.　　LONGE 239

British fortitude and Hibernian friendship, or, An escape
from France, London, 1794: Reeve.　　LONGE 308

The purse, or, Benevolent tar, London, 1794: Reeve.　　LONGE 227

The raft or Both sides of the water, London, 1798: Reeve.　　LONGE 246

Crowne, John.

Calisto: or, The chaste nimph, London, 1675: Staggins.　　LONGE 106

Cumberland, Richard.

Amelia, London, 1771: Dibdin, Piccinni, Potenza, and
others. (Altered from his "The summer's tale.)　　LONGE 298

Calypso, London, 1779: Butler.　　LONGE 102

The summer's tale, London, 1765: pasticcio: Arne, Arnold,
Joh. Chr. Bach, Cocchi, etc.　　LONGE 40

Cupeda, Donato.

Gli affetti più grandi, vinti dal più giusto, Vienna d'Austria
(1701): G. B. Bononcini.　　SCHATZ 1199

L'amar per virtù, Venezia, 1699: Draghi and others.　　SCHATZ 2806

La finta cecità di Antioco il Grande, Vienna d'Austria (1695):
Draghi.　　SCHATZ 2797

Il Gordiano Pio, Vienna d'Austria (1700): M. A. Ziani.　　SCHATZ 11188

Il Romolo, Vienna d'Austria (1702): M. A. Ziani.　　SCHATZ 11193

Curtz, Daniele.

Il feudatorio ingannato, ballet. *See* Fioravanti's La disfatta
di Dario.

Cuvelier de Trye, Jean Guillaume Antoine.

Les faux monnoyeurs ou La vengeance, Paris, an cinquième
[1797–98]: Gresnich.　　SCHATZ 4131

Le génie Asouf ou Les deux coffrets, Paris, an VIII [1799–1800]:
pasticcio, made up from Pleyel, Cherubini, Paisiello,
Grétry, Le Sueur, etc.　　SCHATZ 10591

Les Quiproquo nocturnes, Paris (1798) an VI: Morange.　　SCHATZ 6627

Dalberg, Wolfgang Heribert, *freiherr* von.

Elektra, Mannheim, 1780: Cannabich.　　SCHATZ 1574

Dalton, John.

Comus. *See* Milton.

Danchet, Antoine.

Achille et Deidamie (Recueil général des opéra, t. xv, Paris,
1739): Campra.   SCHATZ 1539

Achille et Deidamie (Théâtre, Paris, 1751, t. iii): Campra.   PQ 1792.D2

Alcine (Recueil général des opéra, Paris, t. viii, 1706):
Campra.   SCHATZ 1541

Alcine, Amsterdam, 1707: Campra.   ML 50.2.A512C2

Alcine (Théâtre, t. 2, Paris, 1751): Campra.   PQ 1972.D2

Amarillis (Recueil général des opéra, Paris, 1706, t. viii):
Campra. (Substitute pastorale in their Les Muses.)   SCHATZ 1542

Amarillis (Théatre, Paris, 1751, t. ii): Campra. (Substitute
pastorale in their ballet Les Muses.)   PQ 1972.D2

Les amours de Mars et de Venus, ballet (Recueil général des
opéra, Paris, 1714, t. x): Campra.   SCHATZ 1543

Les amours de Venus (Théâtre, Paris, 1751, t. iii): Campra.
L. T. of his Les amours de Mars et Vénus.   PQ 1972.D2

Apollon et Daphné, Amsterdam, 1699: L. de Lully.   ML 50.2.A73L9

Apollon et Daphné (Théâtre, Paris, 1751, t. ii).   PQ 1972.D2

Arethuse (Recueil général des opéra, Paris, 1703, t. vii):
Campra.   SCHATZ 1544

Arethuse (Théâtre, Paris, 1751, t. ii): Campra.   PQ 1972.D2

Le bal interrompue: Campra. *See their* Trois nouvelles
entrées.

Le bal interrompu (Théatre, Paris, 1751, t. ii). Entrée in
Fragments de Monsieur Lully.   PQ 1972.D2

Camille, reine des Volsques, Paris, 1717: Campra.   ML 50.2.C253C2

Camille, reine des Volsques (Recueil général des opéra, Paris,
1734, t. xii): Campra.   SCHATZ 1546

Camille, reine des Volsques (Théâtre, Paris, 1751, t. iii):
Campra.   PQ 1972.D2

Cariselli. *See* Fragments de Mr Lully.

Diane (Théâtre, Paris, 1751, t. iii): Campra.   PQ 1972.D2

Les festes vénitiennes (Recueil général des opéra, Paris, 1714,
t. x): Campra.   SCHATZ 1549

Les fêtes vénitiennes (Théâtre, Paris, 1751, t. iii): Campra. PQ 1972.D2

Fragments de Mr de Lully (Recueil général des opéra, t. vii,
Paris, 1703).   SCHATZ 5767

Hesione (Recueil général des opéra, Paris, 1703, t. vii):
Campra.   SCHATZ 1555

Hesione (Théâtre, Paris, 1751, t. ii): Campra.   PQ 1972.D2

Idomenée (Recueil général des opéra, Paris, 1714, t. x):
Campra.   SCHATZ 1557

Idoménée (Théâtre, Paris, 1751, t. iii): Campra.   PQ 1972.D2

Iphigénie en Tauride. *See* this under Duché.

Le jaloux trompé (Théâtre, Paris, 1751, t. ii). Entrée in
Fragments de Monsieur Lully.   PQ 1972.D2

Les Muses (Recueil général des opéra, Paris, 1706, t. viii):
Campra.   SCHATZ 1558

Les Muses (Théâtre, Paris, 1751, t. ii): Campra.   PQ 1972.D2

Prologue de la tragédie d'Iphigénie (Théâtre, Paris, 1751,
t. ii): Demarets.   PQ 1972.D2

La sérénade vénitienne: Campra. *See their* Trois nouvelles
entrées.

Danchet, Antoine—Continued.

Tancrede (Recueil général des opéra, Paris, 1706, t. viii):
Campra. SCHATZ 1560

Tancrede (Théâtre, Paris, 1751, t. ii): Campra. PQ 1972.D2

Télémaque, Amsterdam, 1705: pasticcio arr. by Campra. ML 50.2.T34C3

Télémaque (Recueil général des opéra, Paris, 1706, t. viii). SCHATZ 1561

Telemaque (Théâtre, Paris, 1751, t. ii). PQ 1972.D2

Telephe (Recueil général .des opéra, Paris, 1720, t. xi):
Campra. SCHATZ 1562

Telephe (Théâtre, Paris, 1751, t. iii): Campra. PQ 1972.D2

Le triomphe de Vénus: Campra. *See their* Trois nouvelles
entrées.

Trois nouvelles entrées ajoutées aux Fragments (Recueil
général des opéra, Paris, 1703, t. vii): Campra. SCHATZ 1563

Venus (Théâtre, Paris, 1751, t. ii). PQ 1972.D2

Dancourt, Florent Carton.

Ballet de la jeunesse (Amsterdam) 1686: La Lande. ML 49.A2L9

Dancourt, L. H.

Le combat nocturne ou Les morts vivans, La Haye, 1770:
Le Petit. SCHATZ 5489

Les morts vivans. A. T. of his Le combat nocturne.

La rencontre imprévue, Paris, 1776: Gluck. SCHATZ 3919

Die pilgrime von Mecca (Mekka). A. T. of his Die unvermuthete zusammenkunft.

Det uventede møde (Kiobenhavn, 1776?). Tr. of his La rencontre imprévue: Gluck. SCHATZ 3922

Die unvermuthete zusammenkunft oder Die pilgrime von
Mecca, Frankfurt am Mayn, 1772. Tr. of his La rencontre
imprévue: Gluck. SCHATZ 3920

Daniel, Samuel.

The vision of the twelve goddesses, London, 1717. LONGE 201

Da Ponte, Lorenzo.

L'ape musicale rinnuovata, Vienna (1791): pasticcio. SCHATZ 11308

L'arbore di Diana, Milano (1788): Martin y Soler. SCHATZ 5999

Axur, koenig von Ormus, Wien, 1788. Tr. of his Axur re
d'Ormus: Salieri. SCHATZ 9327

Axur, koenig von Ormus, Pressburg, 1788. Another Tr. of the
above. SCHATZ 9328

Axur, koenig von Ormus. Tr. of his Axur, rè d'Ormus,
Dresda, 1789: Salieri. SCHATZ 9329

Axur, koenig von Ormus, n. i., n. d. (after 1800?). Tr. of his
Axur, rè d'Ormus: Salieri. SCHATZ 9334

Axur re d'Ormus (Praga), 1788: Salieri. Practically independent Italian version of his Tarare. SCHATZ 9326

Axur, re d'Ormus—Axur, koenig von Ormus, Dresda, 1789:
Salieri. SCHATZ 9329

Axur rè d'Ormus, Milano (1792): Salieri. SCHATZ 9331

Der baum der Diana, Wien, 1787: Martin y Soler. Tr. of
their L'arbore di Diana as are the following. SCHATZ 6000

Der baum der Diana, Wien, 1788. SCHATZ 6001

Der baum der Diana, Hamburg, 1792. SCHATZ 6002

Da Ponte, Lorenzo—Continued.

Der baum der Diana, Oels (1795).   Schatz 6003

Bellezza ed onestà. A. T. of his Una cosa rara: Martin y
Soler.

Bellezza ed onestà, Venezia (1788). L. T. of the same.   Schatz 6030

Il Bertoldo, Firenze (1788): Brunetti.   Schatz 1363

Bertoldo e Bertoldino, Genova (1791). L. T. of the above.   Schatz 1364

Bertoldo, Wien, 1787: Piticchio.   Schatz 8202

Il burbero di buon cuore, Venezia, 1789: Martin y Soler.   Schatz 6005

Il burbero di buon cuore—Der gutherzidge polterer, Dresda,
1789: Martin y Soler.   Schatz 6006

La caffettiera bizzarra—Die launige kaffeeschenkinn, Dresda,
1796: Weigl.   Schatz 10930

La capricciosa corretta—So bessert sie sich, Dresda, 1796:
Martin y Soler.   Schatz 6008

La Cifra, Milano (1790): Salieri (only alteration of Petrosellini's text).   Schatz 9281

La cifra, Lisbona, 1796: Salieri.   ML 48.C6II

Una cosa rara o sia Bellezza ed onestà, Vienna (1787): Martin
y Soler.   Schatz 6015

Una cosa rara o sia Bellezza ed onestà—Die seltenheit oder
Schoenheit und tugend, Dresda, 1787: Martin y Soler.   Schatz 6017

Una cosa rara osia Bellezza ed onestà. Die seltne sache oder
Schoenheit und tugend, Wien, 1787: Martin y Soler.   Schatz 2587

La cosa rara, London, 1789: Martin y Soler.   ML 48.M2M

Una cosa rara o sia Bellezza ed onestà, Firenze, 1791: Martin
y Soler.   ML 48 A5 v.16

Cosa rara oder Der seltne fall, n. i., 1797. Tr. of his Una cosa
rara: Marin y Soler.   Schatz 6019

Cosi fan tutte o sia La scuola degli amanti, Vienna (1790):
Mozart.   Schatz 6762

Cosi fan tutte o sia La scuola degli amanti—Eine wie die
andere oder Die schule der liebhaber, Dresda, 1791:
Mozart.   Schatz 6763

Cosi fan tutte—Eine machts wie die andere oder Die schule
der liebhaber, Breslau (1795): Mozart.   Schatz 6764

Il dissoluto punito o sia Il D. Giovanni, Praga (1787): Mozart. Schatz 6788

Il Don Giovanni. A. T. of his Il dissoluto punito: Mozart.

Don Juan, Frankfurt, 1789. Tr. of his Il dissoluto punito o
sia Il Don Giovanni: Mozart.   Schatz 6789

Don Juan oder Die redende statue, n. i., 1793. Tr. of his Il
Don Giovanni: Mozart.   Schatz 6859

Don Juan oder Der steinerne gast, n. i., 1795. Another Tr.   Schatz 6790

Eine ist wie die andere. A. T. of his Die schule der liebhaber.

Eine machts wie die andere oder Die schule der liebhaber,
Breslau (1795): Mozart. Preceded by Italian title: Cosi
fan tutte.   Schatz 6764

Eine wie die andere oder Die schule der liebhaber. Tr. of his
Cosi fan tutte, Dresda, 1791: Mozart.   Schatz 6763

Elskernes skole. A. T. of his Veddemaalet: Mozart.

Gli equivoci, Vienna (1787): Storace.   Schatz 10079

Gli equivoci—Die irrthuemer, Dresda, 1797: Storace.   Schatz 10080

Etwas seltsames oder Schoenheit und ehrbarkeit, Wien, 1787.
Tr. of his Une cosa rara: Martin y Soler.   Schatz 6016

Da Ponte, Lorenzo—Continued.

Figaro's heyrath, Hamburg, 1791. Tr. of his Le nozze di
 Figaro: Mozart.   SCHATZ 11396

Figaro's hochzeit oder Der tolle tag. Tr. of his Le nozze di
 Figaro o sia La folle giornata, Berlino, 1790: Mozart.   SCHATZ 6827

Figaro's hochzeit oder List über list, Passau, 1793. Another Tr. SCHATZ 6860

La folle giornata. L. A. T. of his Le nozze di Figaro: Mozart.

Der gutherzige polterer. Tr. of his Il burbero di buon cuore,
 Dresda, 1789: Martin y Soler.   SCHATZ 6006

Die hochzeit des Figaro, Wien 1798. Tr. of his Le nozze di
 Figaro: Mozart.   SCHATZ 6828

Die hochzeit des Figaro, Leipzig, 1794. Another Tr.   SCHATZ 6829

L'Ifigenia in Tauride, Vienna, 1783. Tr. of Gluck's Iphigénie
 en Tauride (Guillard).   SCHATZ 3905

Die irrthuemer. Tr. of his Gli equivoci, Dresda, 1797:
 Storace.   SCHATZ 10080

L'isola piacevole, Venezia, 1797: Martin y Soler.   SCHATZ 6011

L'isola piacevole, Firenze, 1797: Martin y Soler.   ML 48.A5v. 15

Die launige kaffeeschenkinn. Tr. of his La caffettiera bizzarra, Dresda, 1796: Weigl.   SCHATZ 10930

List über list. A. T. of his Figaros hochzeit, Passau, 1793:
 Mozart.

Die maedchen sind von Flandern. A. T. of his Weibertreue.

Maedchenlist und liebe. A. T. of his Die wette: Mozart.

Le nozze di Figaro, Vienna (1786): Mozart.   SCHATZ 6826

Le nozze di Figaro o sia La folle giornata—Figaro's hochzeit
 oder Der tolle tag, Berlino, 1790: Mozart.   SCHATZ 6827

Il nuovo Figaro, Parma, 1794: Paër.   SCHATZ 7565

Die redende statue. A. T. of his Don Juan: Mozart.

Schoenheit und ehrbarkeit. A. T. of his Etwas seltsames.

Schoenheit und tugend. A. T. of his Die seltenheit.

Schoenheit und tugend. A. T. of his Die seltne sache: Martin
 y Soler.

Die schule der liebhaber. A. T. of his Eine (machts) wie die
 andere.

Die schule der liebhaber oder Eine ist wie die andere, Augsburg, 1794: Mozart. Tr. of their Cosi fan tutte.   SCHATZ 6765

La scuola degli amanti. A. T. of his Cosi fan tutte: Mozart.

Die seltenheit oder Schoenbeit und tugend. Tr. of his Una
 cosa rara o sia Bellezza ed onestà, Dresda, 1787: Martin y
 Soler.   SCHATZ 6017

Der seltne fall, n. i., 1797. Tr. of his Una cosa rara: Martin y
 Soler.   SCHATZ 6019

Die seltne sache oder Schoenbeit und tugend, Wien, 1787:
 Martin y Soler. Tr. of their Una cosa rara.   SCHATZ 2587

The siege of Belgrade, Dublin, n. d. Adaptation of his Una
 cosa rara: Martin y Soler, with additions by Storace.   SCHATZ 6021

La serva onorata, Napoli, 1792. (A condensation by Lorenzi
 of his Le nozze di Figaro): Piccinni.   SCHATZ 8129

So bessert sie sich. Tr. of his La capricciosa corretta, Dresda,
 1796: Martin y Soler.   SCHATZ 6008

Der steinerne gast. A. T. of his Don Juan: Mozart.

Der talisman, Wien, 1789. Tr. of Goldoni's Il Talismano, as
 partly rewritten by the above: Salieri.   SCHATZ 9322

Da Ponte, Lorenzo—Continued.

Der talisman oder Die zigenner (n. i.) 1790. Another Tr. of
the above.   SCHATZ 9323

Der talisman, Berlin, 1798. Another Tr.   SCHATZ 9324

Tarar, Hamburg, 1791. Tr. of his Axur, rè d'Ormus (and
partly of Beaumarchais's Tarare): Salieri.   SCHATZ 9330

Der tolle tag. A. T. of his Figaro's hochzeit: Mozart.

Veddemaalet eller Elskiernes skole, Kiøbenhavn, 1798. Tr.
of his Cosi fan tutte: Mozart.   SCHATZ 6768

Weibertreue oder Die maedchen sind von Flandern, Leipzig,
1794. Tr. of his Cosi fan tutte: Mozart.   SCHATZ 6766

Die wette, oder Maedchenlist und liebe, Hamburg (1796).
Tr. of his Cosi fan tutte: Mozart.   SCHATZ 6767

Die zigenner. A. T. of Der talisman: Salieri.

Davenant, Charles.

Circe, London, 1703: Banister.   LONGE 128

D'Avenant, *Sir* William.

The history of St Francis Drake, London, 1659: unknown.   ML 52.2.H4

The siege of Rhodes, London, 1663: Henry Lawes, Henry
Cook, Matthew Locke, Charles Coleman, and George
Hudson.   ML 50.2.S62

Davesne.

Les jardiniers, Paris, 1772: Prudent.   SCHATZ 8475

David, Domenico.

L'amante eroe, Venetia, 1691: M. A. Ziani.   SCHATZ 11198

Amor e dover, Venezia, 1697: C. F. Pollaroli.   SCHATZ 8271

Creonte tiranno di Tebe, Napoli, 1699: Pollaroli and Scarlatti:
L. T. of his La forza della virtù. Pollaroli.   ML 50.2.C78P7

La forza della virtù, Bologna, 1694: Perti.   SCHATZ 7948

La forza della virtù, Venetia, 1693: C. F. Pollaroli.   SCHATZ 8293

Decker, Thomas.

The sun's darling, London, 1656 (with J. Ford): unknown.   LONGE 242

Defranceschi, Carlo Prospero.

Dreymahl angefuehrt. A. T. of his Falstaff: Salieri.

Falstaff, Berlino, 1799. Tr. of his Falstaff o sia Le tre burle:
Salieri.   SCHATZ 9290

Falstaff oder Dreymahl angefuehrt, Dresda, 1799. Tr. of his
Falstaff o sia Le tre burle: Salieri.   SCHATZ 9289

Falstaff o sia Le tre burle—Falstaff oder Dreymahl angefuehrt,
Dresda, 1799: Salieri.   SCHATZ 9289

Le tre burle. A. T. of his Falstaff: Salieri.

De Jaure (Dejaure) (Bédéno, Jean Claude, *known as*).

La dot de Suzette, Paris, an VI (1798): Boieldieu.   ML 50.2.D64B6

Le Franc Breton ou Le négociant de Nantes, Paris, 1791:
Kreutzer and Solié.   ML 50.2.F8K7

Lodoiska, Paris, 1792: Kreutzer.   SCHATZ 5265

La Lodoiska, Lisbona, 1796. Tr. of the above, with additional
music by other composers.   SCHATZ 5269

Le nouveau d'Assas, Paris, 1790: Berton.   ML 50.2.N6B2

Dejouy.
　　Comment faire? ou, Les épreuves de misanthropie et repentir,
　　　　Paris, an VII, [1799] (wïth Longchamps).　　　　ML 48.M2L

Delaribardiére.　*See* La Ribardière, de.

Demoustier, Charles Albert.
　　L'amour filial, Paris, an second [1793–94]: Gaveaux.　　ML 50.2.A7G2
　　Apelle et Campaspe, Paris, an VI [1798]: Eler.　　　　Schatz 2912
　　Kindliche liebe, Frankfurt a/M., 1798.　Tr. of his L'amour
　　　　filial: Gaveaux.　　　　　　　　　　　　　　　Schatz 3637

Dent, John.
　　The bastille, London, 1790.　　　　　　　　　　　Longe 318
　　Too civil by half, London, 1783.　　　　　　　　　Longe 92

Dercy (Dercis), Alphonse François.
　　La caverne, Liège, 1795: Le Sueur.　　　　　　　　ML 50.2.C34L2
　　Telemaque dans l'isle de Calypso, Paris, an. IV [1796]: Le
　　　　Sueur.　　　　　　　　　　　　　　　　　　　ML 50.2.T35L3

Derrick, Samuel.
　　Sylla, London, 1753.　Tr. of Graun's Silla (Tagliazucchi).　Longe 262

Des Boulmiers.　(Julien, Jean Auguste, *known as*)
　　Anton und Antonette (Muenchen, 1778).　Tr. of his Toinon et
　　　　Toinette: Gossec.　　　　　　　　　　　　　　Schatz 4014
　　Toinon et Toinette, Paris, 1768: Gossec.　　　　　Schatz 4013
　　Toinon et Toinette, Paris, 1781: Gossec.　　　　　Schatz 11703

Deschamps, Jacques Marie.
　　Claudine ou Le petit commissionnaire, Paris, an II (1794):
　　　　Bruni.　　　　　　　　　　　　　　　　　　ML 50.2.C57B7

Desfontaines de la Vallée.　(Fouques-Deshayes, François Guil-
　　　　laume, *better known as*)
　　L'amant statue, Paris, 1786: Dalayrac.　　　　　　ML 50.2.A64D2
　　L'aveugle de Palmyre, Paris, 1767 (39 p.): Rodolphe.　　Schatz 11752
　　L'aveugle de Palmyre, Paris, 1767 (54 p.): Rodolphe.　　Schatz 8851
　　L'aveugle de Palmyre, Paris, 1776: Rodolphe.　　　ML 48.M2M
　　Les chouans de vitré, Paris, an deuxième [1793–94]: unknown.　ML 48.M2L
　　La dot, Paris, 1784: Dalayrac.　　　　　　　　　ML 50.2.D63D2
　　La dot, Paris, 1786: Dalayrac.　　　　　　　　　ML 50.2.D63D22
　　Le droit du seigneur, Amsterdam, 1784: Martini.　　Schatz 6036
　　La fête de l'égalité, Paris, an III [1795] (with Radet): un-
　　　　known.　　　　　　　　　　　　　　　　　　ML 48.M2L
　　Das herrnrecht, Hamburg, 1789.　Tr. of his Le droit du
　　　　seigneur: Martini.　　　　　　　　　　　　　Schatz 6037
　　De minnaer standbeeld, Amsterdam, 1794: Dalayrac.　Tr. of
　　　　their L'amant statue.　　　　　　　　　　　　Schatz 2388
　　Nanine, soeur de lait de la reine de Golconde, Genève, 1773:
　　　　Rodolphe.　　　　　　　　　　　　　　　　ML 50.2.N2R7
　　Das recht des lehnsherren, Oels (1796).　Tr. of his Le droit du
　　　　seigneur: Martini.　　　　　　　　　　　　　Schatz 6038
　　La vallée de Montmorency ou Jean Jacques Rousseau dans
　　　　son hermitage, pasticcio.　*See* Title catalogue.

Desforges. (Choudard, Pierre Jean Baptiste, *better known as*)

Alisbelle ou Les crimes de la féodalité, Paris, an II (1794):
Jadin. SCHATZ 4949

L'épreuve villageoise, Paris, 1784: Grétry. ML 50.2.E55G7

L'epreuve villageoise, Paris, 1785: Grétry. SCHATZ 4149

Les promesses de mariage, Paris, 1788: Berton. SCHATZ 902

Théodore et Paulin. O. T. of his L'épreuve villageoise:
Grétry.

Desriaux.

Démophon, Paris, de Lormel, 1789: Vogel. ML 50.2.D4V6

Démophon, Paris, Ruault, 1789: Vogel. ML 50.2.D4V62

La toison d'or, Paris, 1786: Vogel. ML 50.2.T67V7

Destouches, Philippe Néricault.

Les amours de Ragonde. n. i., n. d.: Mouret. SCHATZ 6738

Devisse, Eligio.

L'arrivo d'Europa nell' isola di Creta, ballet: Le Messier. *See*
Bertoni's Ifigenia in Aulide.

Dezède, Nicolas. (*Sometimes called* Desaides, Des Aides, etc.)

Auguste et Théodore, ou, Les deux pages, Paris, 1790: author.
Text in collaboration with baron de Mantauffeld. SCHATZ 2525

Dian, Antonio.

La caccia d'Enrico IV, Venezia, 1783 (authorship doubtful):
Rust. SCHATZ 9177

Dibdin, Charles.

Annette and Lubin, London, 1778: author. LONGE 102

The Chelsea prisoner, London, 1779: author. LONGE 164

The cobler or A wife of ten thousand, London, 1774: author. LONGE 32

The deserter, London, 1773. Tr. of Monsigny's Le deserteur
(Sedaine) with additional music by the above and
Philidor. LONGE 13

The deserter (Collection of the most esteemed farces, Edinburgh, 1792, t. iv). SCHATZ 11753D

The deserter, New York, 1787: author. ML 50.6.D36

Favourite songs . . ., London (*ca.* 1790): author. LONGE 214

The first of August. A. T. of his The waterman.

The gipsies, London, 1778: Arnold. LONGE 102

The Graces, London, 1782: author. LONGE 256

Harlequin everywhere. A. T. of his The mirror.

Harvest-home, London, 1787: author. LONGE 99

Liberty-hall or A test of good fellowship, London, 1785: author. LONGE 95

The marriage act, London, 1781 (reduced version of his The
islanders): author. LONGE 91

The metamorphoses, London, 1776: author. LONGE 214

The mirror or Harlequin everywhere, London, 1779: author. LONGE 102

Poor Vulcan, London, 1778: author. LONGE 87

The quaker, London, 1777: author. LONGE 87

The romp. *See* Bickerstaffe.

Rose and Colin, London, 1778: author. LONGE 87

The seraglio, London, 1776: author (partly by Arnold). LONGE 124

The seraglio, airs, chorusses, London, 1776. ML 50.2.S48

The shepherd's artifice, London, 1765: author. LONGE 52

Dibdin, Charles—Continued.

The shepherdess of the Alps, London, 1780: author.	LONGE 126
A test of good fellowship. A. T. of his Liberty-hall.	
The touchstone or Harlequin traveller, London, 1779: author.	LONGE 102
The waterman or The first of August, London, 1783: author.	LONGE 121
The waterman or The first of August. (Collection of the most esteemed farces, Edinburgh, 1792, t. vi.)	SCHATZ 11753F
The wedding ring, London, 1773: author.	LONGE 28
A wife of ten thousand. A. T. of his The cobler.	
The wives revenged, London, 1778: author.	LONGE 87

Dibdin, Thomas.

The mouth of the Nile or The glorious first of August, London, 1798 (2d ed.): Attwood.	LONGE 254
The naval pillar, London, 1799: Moorehead.	LONGE 258

Dieu-la-Foy.

Le quart-d'heure de Rabélais, Paris, an VII [1798–99] (with Prévôt-d'Iray): unknown.	ML 48.M2K

Diodati, Agostino.

Amor piaga ogni core, Ferrara, 1690: Chierici.	ML 50.2.A65C3

Diodati, Giuseppe Maria.

Gli amanti in puntiglio, Napoli, 1794: Tritto.	SCHATZ 10465
L'apprensivo raggirato, Napoli, 1798: Cimarosa.	SCHATZ 1904
Le astuzie in amore, Napoli, 1790: Tritto.	SCHATZ 10460
Il Cartesiano fantastico, Napoli, 1790: Tritto.	SCHATZ 10467
Il Corrivo, Napoli, 1787: G. Giordani.	SCHATZ 3839
Il credulo con farsa La baronessa Stramba, Napoli, 1786: Cimarosa. (Text of the farsa by Mililotti.)	SCHATZ 1977 **and** 1985
Il credulo con farsa L'impresario in angustie, Napoli, 1786: Cimarosa.	SCHATZ 1916 **and** 1929
Entrepreneuren i knibe, Kjøbenhavn, 1795: Cimarosa. Tr. of their L'impresario in angustie.	SCHATZ 1933
L'impegno superato, Napoli, 1795: Cimarosa.	SCHATZ 1996
L'impostore smascherato, Napoli, 1794: Tritto.	SCHATZ 10472
L'impresario in angustie, Napoli, 1786: Cimarosa. *See their* Il credulo.	SCHATZ 1929
L'impresario in angustie, Lisbona, 1792: Cimarosa.	ML 48.C6 II
L'impresario in angustie—Der schauspieldirektor in der Klemme, Dresda, 1794: Cimarosa.	SCHATZ 1930
L'impresario in angustie ed Il convitato di pietra, Milano (1789): Cimarosa.	SCHATZ 11755
L'impresario in angustie ou Le directeur dans l'embarras, Paris (Bruxelles) 1792: Cimarosa.	ML 50.2.I5C3
A noiva fingida, Lisboa 1790: Portugal. Tr. of his Le trame deluse.	SCHATZ 8431
Le nozze in garbuglio, Napoli, 1793: Tritto.	SCHATZ 10473
Penelope (Livorno, 1795): Cimarosa.	SCHATZ 1967
Der schauspieldirektor in der klemme. Tr. of his L'impresario in angustie, Dresda, 1794.	SCHATZ 1930
I sposi in Rissa, Napoli, 1791: Fraja.	SCHATZ 3314
Le trame deluse. O. T. of his A noiva fingida.	
Le trame deluse, Vienna (1787): Cimarosa.	SCHATZ 1972

Diodati, Giuseppe Maria—Continued.

Le trame deluse—Die vereitelten raenke, Dresda, 1788: Ci-
rosa. SCHATZ 1973

Die vereitelten raenke. Tr. of his Le trame deluse, Dresda,
1788. SCHATZ 1973

Dittersdorf, Carl Ditters von.

Don Quixote der zweite, Oels, 1795: author. SCHATZ 2589

Der eiserne mann. A. T. of his Gott Mars: Dittersdorf.

Der gedemuethigte stolz. A. T. of his Terno secco: author.

Der gefoppte braeutigam, Hall am Kocher, n. d.: author. Tr.
of his Lo sposo burlato. SCHATZ 2590

Der gefoppte braeutigam, n. i., n. d.: author. SCHATZ 2590A

Gott Mars oder Der eiserne mann, Oels (1795): author. SCHATZ 2592

Hieronimus Knicker, Hamburg, 1792: author. ML 50.2.H35D4

Hieronymus Kniker [!], Passau, 1793 (with Vulpius' alterations): author. SCHATZ 2593

Hieronimus Knicker, n. i., 1793: author. SCHATZ 2594

Hilft's nicht, so schadt's nicht. A. T. of his Das rothe
kaeppchen: Dittersdorf.

Das rothe kaeppchen oder Hilft's nicht, so schadt's nicht,
Koeln am Rheine, 1791: author. SCHATZ 2603

Das rothe kaeppchen, Weimar, 1792 (altered by Vulpius):
author. SCHATZ 2604

Terno secco, oder Der gedemuethigte stolz, Oels (1797): author. SCHATZ 2609

Dodsley, Richard.

The blind beggar of Bethnal Green, London, 1741: Th. A.
Arne. LONGE 124

Rex et pontifex, London, 1745. ML 52.2.R4

The triumph of peace, London, 1749: Th. A. Arne. AC 901.M5 v.519

Doering, Johann Wilhelm.

Die bezauberte insel. A. T. of his Der sturm: Ritter.

Inkle und Yariko, oder, Er war nicht ganz barbar, Cassel,
1798: Ebers. SCHATZ 2890

Der sturm oder Die bezauberte insel, Cassel, 1798: Ritter. SCHATZ 8831

Dolfin, Giovanni.

La villeggiatura di Mestre, Venezia (1770): Perillo. SCHATZ 7923

Dolfino, Pietro.

L'Adelaide, Venetia, 1672: Sartorio. SCHATZ 9488

L'Ermengarda regina de' Longobardi, Venetia, 1670: Sartorio. SCHATZ 9482

Dominique. (Biancolelli, Pierre François, *better known as*)

Alceste. (Les parodies du Nouveau théâtre italien,
Nouv. éd., Paris, 1738, t. iv) (parody with Romagnesi of
Lully's opera.) ML 48.P3

Arlequin Bellerophon (Les parodies du Nouveau théâtre italien, Nouv. éd., Paris, 1738, t. iv) (with Romagnesi.
Parody of Lully's Bellérophon). ML 48.P3

Arlequin Phaëton (Les parodies du Nouveau théâtre italien,
Nouv. éd., Paris, 1738, t. iv) (with Romagnesi. Parody
of Lully's Phaëton). ML 48.P3

Dominique—Continued.

Arlequin Roland (Les parodies du Nouveau théâtre italien, Nouv. éd., Paris, 1738, t. iii) (with Romagnesi. Parody of Lully's Roland.) ML 48.P3

Arlequin Tancrede (Les parodies du Nouveau théâtre italien, Nouv. éd., Paris, 1738, t. iv) (with Romagnesi. Parody of Campra's Tancrède). ML 48.P3

La bonne femme (Les parodies du Nouveau théâtre italien, Nouv. éd., Paris, 1738, t. iv) (with Romagnesi. Parody of Gervais' Hipermnestre). ML 48.P3

Don Micco e Lesbina (Les parodies du Nouveau théâtre italien, Nouv. éd., Paris, 1738, t. iv) (with Romagnesi). ML 48.P3

Hesione (Les parodies du Nouveau Théâtre italien, Nouv. éd., Paris, 1738, t. iv) (with Romagnesi. Parody of Campra's opera). ML 48.P3

Le joueur (Les parodies du Nouveau Théâtre italien, Nouv. éd., Paris, 1738, t. iv) (with Romagnesi. Parody of Il giocatore): Mouret. ML 48.P3

Medée et Jason (Les parodies du Nouveau Théâtre italien, Nouv. éd., Paris, 1738, t. iii) (with Riccoboni the younger and Romagnesi). Parody of Salomon's Medée et Jason. ML 48.P3

Les noces d'Arlequin et de Silvia ou Thetis et Pelée déguisés (Les parodies du Nouveau Théâtre italien, Paris, 1738, t. ii). (Parody of Colasse's Thétis et Pelée.) ML 48.P3

Pirame et Thisbé (Les parodies du Nouveau Théâtre italien, Nouv. éd., Paris, 1738, t. iii) (with Romagnesi and Riccoboni). Parody of Francoeur and Rebel's Pirame et Thisbé. ML 48.P3

Donzel.

Calipso, Torino (1777): Ottani. SCHATZ 7360

Dorman, Joseph.

The female rake or Modern fine lady, London, 1736: ballad opera. LONGE 150

Dossie, Robert.

The statesman foil'd, London, 1768: Rush. LONGE 37

Douberral.

Alessio ed Eloisa o sia Il disertore, ballet. *See* Astaritta's Ipermestra.

Draghi, Antonio.

Apollo deluso, Vienna, 1669: Sances and Leopold I. ML 48.M2D

Drais und Sauerbronn, Karl Wilhelm Ludwig Friedrich *freiherr* **von.**

Elmine, Nürnberg, 1781: André. SCHATZ 185

Drury, Robert.

The devil of a duke, or, Trapolin's vagaries, London, 1732: ballad opera. LONGE 120

The fancy'd queen, London, 1733: ballad opera. LONGE 189

The mad captain, London, 1733: ballad opera. LONGE 50

The rival milliners or The humours of Covent Garden, London, 3d ed. (173–): ballad opera. LONGE 76

Dryden, John.
Albion and Albanius, London, 1685: Grabut.   ML 50.2.A43
Amphitryon; or, The two Sosias, London, 1691 (The songs, 1690): H. Purcell.   ML 50.2.A705P9
Amphitryon: or The two Sosias, London, 1756 (as altered by Hawkesworth, practically dropping all of Purcell's numbers).   PR 3415.A5   1756
King Arthur or The British worthy, London, 1691: H. Purcell.   ML 50.2.K54
King Arthur or The British worthy, London, 1781 (altered by Garrick): Purcell and Th. A. Arne.   Longe 251
The state of innocence, and fall of man, London, 1684: unknown.   ML 50.2.S745

Dubois, *Lady* **Dorothea.**
The divorce, London, 1771: Hook.   Longe 184

Du Boulay (Boullay), Michel.
Orphée (Amsterdam) 1690: L. de Lully.   ML 50.2.O75L9
Orphée (Recueil général des opéra, t. iv, Paris, 1703): L. de Lully.   Schatz 5783
Zephire et Flore (Amsterdam) 1688: L. and J. L. de Lully.   ML 50.2.Z4L9
Zephire et Flore, Paris (Anvers) 1689: L. and J. L. de Lully.   ML 50.2.Z4L9
Zephire et Flore (Recueil général des opéra, t. iii, Paris, 1703): L. de Lully and J. L. de Lully.   Schatz 5784

Dubreuil.
Iphigénie en Tauride, Paris, 1783: Piccinni.   ML 50.2.I65P3

Du Buisson, Paul Ulric.
L'impresario in angustie ou Le directeur dans l'embarras, Paris (Bruxelles) 1792. Tr. of Cimarosa's L'Impresario in angustie.   ML 50.2.I5C3
Le roi Théodore à Venise, Versailles, 1787.   French version of Paisiello's Il rè Teodoro in Venezia.   ML 50.2.R3P25
Zelia, Paris, 1793: Deshayes.   ML 50.2.Z33D2

Du Buisson de Chalandray.
La coquette de village, ballet. *See* Bernasconi's Didone abbandonata.
Le prie del' oiseau ou du papagie, ballet. *See* Bernasconi's Didone abbandonata.
Urtheil des Paris, ballet. *See* Bernasconi's Temistokles.

Duché, Joseph François, *sieur* **de Vancy.**
Ballet des Amours de Momus, Amsterdam, 1696: Desmarets.   ML 52.2.A4D2
Les amours de Momus (Recueil général des opéra, Paris, t. v, 1703): Desmarets.   Schatz 2529
Céphale et Procris (Recueil général des opéra, t. iv, Paris, 1703): de La Guerre.   Schatz 5376
Les festes galantes (Recueil général des opéra, Paris, t. vi, 1703): Desmarets.   Schatz 2532
Iphigénie en Tauride (Recueil général des opéra, t. viii, Paris, 1706) (partly by Danchet): Desmarets and Campra.   Schatz 2537
Scylla (Recueil général des opéra, t. vii, Paris, 1703): Gatti.   Schatz 3633
Téagene et Cariclée, Amsterdam, 1695: Desmarets.   ML 50.2.T3D3
Téagene et Cariclée (Recueil général des opéra, t. v, Paris, 1703): Desmarets.   Schatz 2534

Dudley, *Sir* **Henry Bate** (*originally Rev*. Henry Bate).
The flitch of bacon, Dublin, 1779: Shield.　　LONGE 118
The rival candidates, London, 1775: Carter.　　LONGE 32
The rival candidates (Collection of the most esteemed farces,
Edinburgh, 1792, t. iv): Carter.　　SCHATZ 11753D
The travellers in Switzerland, London, 1794: Shield.　　LONGE 227
The woodman, Songs, duets, etc., London, 1791: Shield.　　LONGE 218
The woodmann, London, 1791: Shield.　　LONGE 215

Duffet, Thomas.
Epilogue . . . Macbeth (in his Empress of Morocco, London,
1674).　　LONGE 271
The mock-tempest or The enchanted castle, London, 1675:
unknown.　　LONGE 194

Dumaniant. (Bourlin, Antoine Jean, *better known as*)
La belle esclave ou Valcour et Zéila, Paris, 1787: Philidor.　　ML 50.2.B3P3

Duncombe, William.
Athaliah, London, 1746. Tr. of Racine's Athalia.　　LONGE 70

Dunlap, William.
The archers or Mountaineers of Switzerland, New York, 1796:
Carr.　　ML 50.6.A72
Darby's return (New York magazine, 1790): unknown.　　AP2.A2M5

Dupaty, Emanuel.
L'opéra comique, Paris, an VI [1797–98] (with Ségur le jeune):
Della Maria.　　ML 50.2.O6D2
L'opéra comique, Toulouse, an VII [1798–99]: Della Maria.　　ML 50.2.O6D22

Dupen, Luigi.
La distruzione d'Aquileja fatta da Attila rè degli Unni, ballet:
Scannavino. *See* Guglielmi's Enea e Lavinia.
La Nina pazza per amore, ballet. *See* Guglielmi's Enea e
Lavinia.
La turca in cimento, ballet. *See* Andreozzi's Angelica e
Medoro.

Duplessis.
Orphée et Euridice (Parma, 1791): Paër.　　SCHATZ 7550

Duquesny (Duquesney) Lauchelin (Lauchlin).
Ahtor ed Erma, ballet: Trento. *See* G. Nicolini's Artaserse.
Ahtor ed Erma, ballet: Trento. *See* Prota's I studenti.
Cook, ossia Gl'Inglesi in Othaiti, ballet. *See* Mayr's Lodoiska.
Egle e Cloco o siano I satiri puniti: Haydn. *See* Tritto's La
fedeltà tra le selve.
Ernesto ed Elisa, ballet: unknown. *See* Prota's I studenti.
La famiglia riunita. A. T. of his ballet Orlina: Ercolani.
L'inutile precauzione, ballet. *See* Mayr's Lauso e Lidia.
L'inutile precauzione, ballet. *See* Tritto's Il barone in
angustie.
Il mercato di Pozzuolo ossia Il speciale ingannato, ballet.
See Mayr's Lodoiska.
Obert e Melina, ballet: Trento. *See* Mayr's cantata Temira
e Aristo.

Duquesny (Duquesney) Lauchelin (Lauchlin)—Continued.

Orlina ossia La famiglia riunita, ballet: Ercolani. *See* Zingarelli's Carolina e Mexicow.

I satiri puniti. A. T. of his ballet Egle e Cloco: Haydn.

Zulima o sia La famiglia riunita, ballet: Pleyel. *See* Farinelli's Il nuovo savio della Grecia.

Durandi, Jacopo.

Annibale in Torino, Torino, 1771: Paisiello.	Schatz 7692
Annibale in Torino, Torino (1792): Zingarelli.	Schatz 11239
Armida, Torino (1770): Anfossi.	Schatz 226
Armida, Verona (1771): Manfredini.	Schatz 5893
Berenice, Torino (1771): Platania.	Schatz 8214
Ecuba, Torino (1769): Celoniat.	Schatz 1771

Durfey, Thomas.

Cinthia and Endimion, or, The loves of the deities, London, 1697: D. Purcell.	Longe 224
The comical history of Don Quixote, London, 1729 (3 parts): H. Purcell, H. Eccles, Courteville, and others.	Longe 68
The fool turn'd critick, London, 1678.	Longe 112
A fool's preferment or The three dukes of Dunstable (London) 1688: H. Purcell.	M 3.3.P9ii, 11
—— Second copy, lacking the music.	Longe 132
The two queens of Brentford or Bayes no poetaster, London, 1721: unknown.	Longe 169
Wonders in the sun or, The kingdom of the birds, London, 1706: pasticcio.	Longe 194

Duronceray, Marie Justine Benoîte. *See* Favart, Mme.

Du Roullet, François Louis Gaud Lebland, *marquis.*

Alceste, Paris, 1779: Gluck.	Schatz 3888
Alceste, Paris, 1786: Gluck.	Schatz 3940
Les Danaides, Paris, 1784 (with baron von Tschudi): Salieri.	Schatz 9285
Iphigénie en Aulide, Paris, 1774: Gluck.	Schatz 3898
Iphigénie an Aulide, Nouv. éd., Bordeaux, 1783: Gluck.	ML 48.M2L

Duval, Alexandre.

Der arrestant, Frankfurt am Main, 1799: Della Maria. Tr. of their Le prisonnier.	Schatz 2486
The castle of Sorrento, London, 1799. (English adaptation of his Le prisonnier): Della Maria-Attwood.	Longe 256
The prisoner or The resemblance, London, 1799. Tr. of his Le prisonnier ou La ressemblance: Della Maria.	Longe 254
Le prisonnier ou La ressemblance, Amsterdam, 1798: Della Maria.	Schatz 2485
La recontre. A. T. of his Le vieux château: Della Maria.	
La ressemblance. A. T. of his Le prisonnier: Della Maria.	
Le vieux château ou La rencontre, Paris, an vi (1798): Della Maria.	ML 50.2.V49

Dyk, Johann Gottfried.

Der neue gutsherr, n. i., n. d. (detached copy): Joh. Ad. Hiller. (The "ausführung der gesaenge" of the text by J. Fr. Juenger.)	Schatz 4730

Eaco Panellenio. *Arcadian name* of *conte* Jacopo Antonio Sanvitale.

Eberl, Ferdinand.
Der baum der Diana. Tr. of Martin y Soler's L'arbore di
Diana (Da Ponte).
Betrug durch aberglauben, Wien (1786): Dittersdorf.   Schatz 2587
Cosa rara oder Der seltne fall, n. i., 1797. Tr. of Martin y
Soler's Una cosa rara (Da Ponte).   Schatz 6019
Der talisman, Wien, 1789. Tr. of Salieri's Il talismano
(Goldoni and Da Ponte).   Schatz 9322

Echille Acanzio. *Arcadian name* of *marchese* Giovanni Piudemonte.

Ecclestone, Edward.
Noah's flood or The destruction of the world, London, 1679.   ML 50.2.N74

Eckartshausen, Carl von.
Fernando und Yariko, Muenchen, 1784: Neubauer.   Schatz 7092

Egisippo Argolide. *Arcadian name of* Carlo Giuseppe Lanfranchi Rossi.

Ehrenberg, Franz. *See his real name*, Claudius, G. C.

Eichholz, Friedrich Wilhelm.
Sanko Panssa, Halberstadt, 1776. Tr. of Philidor's Sancho
Pança dans son isle (Poinsinet le jeune).   Schatz 8023

Einsiedel, Friedrich Hildebrand von.
Die bestrafte eifersucht, Berlin, 1794. Tr. of Cimarosa's Il
marito disperato (Lorenzi).   Schatz 1943
Ceres, n. i. (1773): Wolf.   Schatz 11076

Engel, Carl Christian.
Biondetta (Schwerin, 1790): Friedr. Adam Hiller.   Schatz 4715
Der jahrmarkt, Leipzig, 1778: G. Benda (only additions to
Gotter's text and composed by Joh. Adam Hiller).   Schatz 772

Engel, Johann Jakob.
Die apotheke, Leipzig, 1772: Neefe.   Schatz 7070
Die apotheke, Wien, 1778: Umlauf.   Schatz 10523

Ensildo Prosindio. *Arcadian name of* Giuseppe Petrosellini.

Epitide Corebio. *Arcadian name of* Gaetano Ciliberti.

Erdmann, Ludwig.
Ich heisse Theiss, oder Der aepfeldieb, Regensburg, 1778:
Gaertner.   Schatz 3553

Ermelinda Talèa. *Arcadian name of* Maria Antonia Walpurgis,
princess of Saxony.

Errico (Herrico), Scipione.
La Deidamia, Venetia, 1644: Cavalli.   Schatz 1745

Eschenburg, Johann Joachim.
Der deserteur, Frankfurt am Mayn (1773). Tr. of Monsigny's
Le déserteur (Sedaine).   Schatz 6570
Die eifersucht auf der probe, Gera, 1791. Tr. of Anfossi's Il
geloso in cimento (Bertati).   Schatz 237
Erast und Lucinde, Muenster, 1777. Tr. of Grétry's Silvain
(Marmontel).   Schatz 4187

Eschenburg, Johann Joachim—Continued.

Der grossmuethige seefahrer, n. i., n. d.   Tr. of Piccinni's La
  schiava riconosciuta, and A. T. of his Die sklavin.   Schatz 8117

Das gute maedchen, Leipzig, 1783.   Tr. of Piccinni's La
  buona figliuola (Goldoni).   Schatz 8075

Das gute maedchen, Hamburg, 1791.   L. ed. of the above.   Schatz 8076

Lukas und Hannchen, Braunschweig, 1768: Beckmann.   Schatz 685

Die nacht, Hamburg (ca. 1780).   Tr. of Piccinni's Notte
  critica (Goldoni).   Schatz 8101

Orpheus und Euridice (Cramer's Magazin der musik, 1785).
  Tr. of Gluck's Orfeo ed Euridice (Calsabigi).   Schatz 3912

Robert und Kalliste, oder Der triumph der treue, Breslau und
  Leipzig, 1776.   Tr. of P. Guglielmi's La sposa fedele
  (Chiari).   Schatz 4273

Die sclavin und der grossmuethige seefahrer, Mannheim, 1773.
  Tr. of Piccinni's La schiava riconosciuta (unknown).   Schatz 8115

Der triumph der treue.   A. T. of his Robert und Kalliste: P.
  Guglielmi.

Die unruhige nacht, Wien, 1783.   Tr. of Gassmann's La notte
  critica (Goldoni).   Schatz 3616

Der zaubernde soldat, n. i., n. d.   Tr. of Philidor's Le soldat
  magicien (Anseaume).   Schatz 8026

Estcourt, Richard.

Prunella, London, n. d.: pasticcio.   ML 50.2.P74

Ewald, Johannes (Evald, Johan).

Balders død, n. i., n. d.: Hartmann.   Schatz 4463

Balders tod, Kopenhagen, 1785.   **Tr. of the above.**   Schatz 4464

Fiskerne, n. i., n. d.: Hartmann.   Schatz 4465

Ewald, Schack Hermann.

Heyrath aus liebe, Gotha, 1781: Hönicke.   Schatz 4787

Faber, Johann Heinrich.

Anton und Antonette (Muenchen, 1778).   Tr. of Gossec's
  Toinon et Toinette (Des Boulmiers).   Schatz 4014

Die beiden geizigen, Frankfurt am Mayn, 1772.   Tr. of
  Grétry's Les deux avares (Fenouillot de Falbaire de
  Quingey).   Schatz 4146

Die beiden militzen, Frankfurt am Mayn, 1773.   Tr. of Fridzeri's Les deux miliciens.   Schatz 3371

La bella Arsena, Augsburg, 1781.   Tr. of Monsigny's La belle
  Arsene (Favart).   Schatz 6565

Der fassbinder, Frankfurt am Mayn, 1773.   Tr. of Audinot and
  Gossec's Le tonnelier (Audinot and Quétant).   Schatz 488

Die fee Urgele oder Was den damen gefällt, Frankfurt am
  Mayn (1776).   Tr. of Duni's La fée Urgèle (Favart).   Schatz 2844

Das fest der weiblichen tugend.   A. T. of his Das rosenmaedchen.

Die freundschaft auf der probe, Frankfurt am Mayn, 1772.
  Tr. of Grétry's L'amitié à l'epreuve (Favart).   Schatz 4135

Der gaertner von Sidon, Frankfurt am Mayn, 1773.   Tr. of
  Philidor's Le jardinier de Sidon (de Pleinchêne).   Schatz 8016

Hanns der schuhflicker, Frankfurt am Mayn, 1772.   Tr. of
  Philidor's Blaise le savetier (Sedaine).   Schatz 8008

Faber, Johann Heinrich—Continued.

Der hausfreund, Frankfurt am Mayn, 1774. Tr. of Grétry's
 L'ami de la maison (Marmontel).   Schatz 4133

Der holzhauer, oder Die drey wuensche, Frankfurt am Mayn,
 1773. Tr. of Philidor's Le bucheron (Guichard and
 Castet).   Schatz 8011

Julie, Frankfurt am Mayn, 1774. Tr. of Dezède's Julie
 (Monvel).   Schatz 2521

Der koenig und der pachter, Frankfurt am Mayn, 1773. Tr.
 of Monsigny's Le roi et le fermier (Sedaine).   Schatz 6582

Die laecherliche werbung. A. T. of his Der militz.

Lucile, Frankfurt am Mayn, 1772. Tr. of Grétry's Lucile
 (Marmontel).   Schatz 4166

Man sieht niemals alles voraus, Frankfurt am Mayn, 1772. Tr.
 of Monsigny's On ne s'avise jamais de tout (Sedaine). Schatz 6579

Melide oder Der schiffer, Riga (1786). Tr. of Philidor's Mélide ou Le navigateur (Fenouillot de Falbaire de Quingey). Schatz 8035

Der militz oder Die lächerliche werbung, Frankfurt am Mayn,
 1775. Tr. of Duni's Le milicien (Anseaume).   Schatz 2849

Die muellerin, Frankfurt am Mayn, 1773. Tr. of de la Borde's
 La meunière de Gentilly (Lemonnier).   Schatz 5347

Der praechtige freygebige, Frankfurt am Mayn, 1774. Tr. of
 Grétry's Le magnifique (Sedaine).   Schatz 4168

Roschen und Colas, Frankfurt am Mayn, 1772. Tr. of Monsigny's Rose et Colas (Sedaine).   Schatz 6584

Das rosenfest zu Salenci, Frankfurt am Mayn, 1775. Tr. of
 Grétry's La rosière de Salenci (Masson).   Schatz 4183

Das rosenmädchen, oder Das fest der weiblichen tugend,
 Frankfurt am Mayn, 1772. Tr. of La rosière de Salenci
 (Favart): Blaise, Philidor, and Duni.   Schatz 2860

Der schiffer. A. T. of his Melide: Philidor.

Der schlosser, Frankfurt am Mayn, 1772. Tr. of Kohault's
 Le serrurier (Quétant).   Schatz 5206

Die schnitter, Frankfurt am Mayn (1769) Tr. of Duni's Les
 moissonneurs (Favart)   ML 50.2.M75D94

Die schnitter, Frankfurt am Mayn, 1772. Tr. of Duni's Les
 moissonneurs (Favart).   Schatz 2851

Die schoene Arsene, Frankfurt am Mayn, 1776. Tr. of Monsigny's La belle Arsene (Favart).   Schatz 6563

Die schule der jugend, Frankfurt am Mayn, 1774. Tr. of
 Duni's L'école de la jeunesse (Anseaume).   Schatz 2842

Silvain, Frankfurt am Mayn, 1772. Tr. of Grétry's Silvain
 (Marmontel).   Schatz 4185

Tom Jones, Frankfurt am Mayn, 1773. Tr. of Philidor's Tom
 Jones (Poinsinet le jeune).   Schatz 8030

Die unvermuthete zusammenkunft oder Die pilgrime von
 Mecca, Frankfurt am Mayn, 1772. Tr. of Gluck's La
 rencontre imprévue (Dancourt).   Schatz 3920

Der verkleidete liebhaber oder Der verstellte gaertner, Frankfurt am Mayn, 1774. Tr. of Philidor's L'amant deguisé
 (Favart and de Voisenon).   Schatz 8006

Was den damen gefällt. A. T. of his Die fee Urgele: Duni.

Der zauberer, Regensburg, 1781 (Tr. of Poinsinet's Le sorcier):
 Croes.   Schatz 2294

Faber, Johann Heinrich—Continued.
Der zauberer, Frankfurt am Mayn, 1772. Tr. of Philidor's
Le sorcier (Poinsinet le jeune). Schatz 8028
Zemire und Azor, Frankfurt am Mayn, 1775. Tr. of Grétry's
Zémire et Azor (Marmontel). Schatz 4192

Faber, P. D.
Eremiten paa Formentara, Kiøbenhavn, 1791. Tr. of Wolf's
Der eremit auf Formentara (Kotzebue). Schatz 11082

Fabian, R.
Trick for trick, London, 1735: ballad opera. ML 50.5.T84

Fabiani. (*Same as* Giuseppe?)
Ariadne and Theseus, ballet. *See* Piccinni's Cato in Utica.
Der bezauberte kranz, ballet. *See* Piccinni's Das artige
maedgchen.
Die liebe und Psiche, ballet. *See* Piccinni's Catone in Utica.

Fabiani, Giuseppe.
Amore e Psiche, ballet. *See* Fischietti's La molinara.
I prodigi d'amore, ballet: unknown. *See* Sarti's Il militare
bizzaro.

Fabiani, Michele.
Amore e Psiche, ballet: Curcio. *See* Robuschi's Briseide.
Enea nel Lazio, ballet. *See* Giordani's Tito Manlio.
Il trionfo d'Arbace, ballet: d'Anglois. *See* Nasolini's La
morte di Semiramide.
Il trionfo di Alessandro ossia La prigionia di Dario, ballet:
Bertoja. *See* Paisiello's Elfrida.

Fabri, *the younger,* **Gottfried Lebrecht.**
Piramus und Tisbe, n. i., 1788. (Altered by the composer):
Spindler. Schatz 9977

Fagan, Christophe Barthelemy.
La servante justifiée, Paris, 1744 (Theatre de M. Favart, Paris,
Duchesne, 1763–77, t. vi): unknown. ML 49.A2F1
La servante justifiée, Paris, 1766 (with Favart): unknown. Schatz 11513

Falbaire de Quingey, Charles Georges Fenouillot de. *See*
Fenouillot de . . .

Falier, Giorgio Antonio.
Circe delusa, Venetia, 1711: Boniventi. Schatz 1186
Non son quella, è la difesa, Venezia, 1710: Ruggeri. Schatz 9132

Fallet.
Die zwey vormuender, Hamburg, 1788. Tr. of his Les deux
tuteurs: Dalayrac. Schatz 2341

Falsen, Enevold de.
Naturens røst, Kiøbenhavn, 1799: Kunzen. Schatz 5327

Fanzaglia, Antonio.
Bradamante nell' isola d'Alcina, Parma, 1729: Broschi. Schatz 1342

Fasting, Claus.
Aglae eller Støtten (Copenhagen, 1774) (with A. G. Carstens):
Sarti. Schatz 9423

Fattorini, Tebaldo.

Adone in Cipro, Venetia, 1676 (Alterations in Giannini's text):
Legrenzi.   Schatz 5540

Eteocle e Polinice, Venetia, 1675: Legrenzi.   Schatz 5535

Faur.

La fête de la Cinquantaine, Paris, 1796: Dezède.   Schatz 2527

Faustini, Giovanni.

L'Alciade, Venetia, 1667: P. A. Ziani.   Schatz 11211

La Calisto, Venetia, 1651: Cavalli.   Schatz 1744

La Doriclea, Venetia, 1645: Cavalli.   Schatz 1737

L'Egisto, Venezia, 1643: Cavalli.   Schatz 1719

L'Egisto, Firenze, 1646: Cavalli.   Schatz 1719a

L'Eritrea, Venetia, 1652: Cavalli.   Schatz 1721

L'Ersilla, Venetia, 1648: unknown.   Schatz 11326

L'Eupatra, Venetia, 1655: P. A. Ziani.   Schatz 11214

L'Euripo, Venetia, 1649: Cavalli.   Schatz 1738

Il Meraspe. A. T. of his Il tiranno humiliato: Pallavicino.

L'Oristeo, Venetia, 1651: Cavalli.   Schatz 1752

L'Oristeo travestito, Bologna, 1656 (much altered): Cavalli.   Schatz 1724

L'Ormindo, Venetia, 1644: Cavalli.   Schatz 1725

Il tiranno humiliato d'amore, overo Il Meraspe, Venetia, 1667:
Pallavicino.   Schatz 7737

Il Titone, Venetia, 1645: Cavalli.   Schatz 1749

La virtù de' strali d'amore, Venetia, 1642: Cavalli.   Schatz 1729

Favart, Charles Simon.

Theatre de M. Favart, ou recueil des comedies, parodies &
opera-comiques qu'il a donnés jusqu'à ce jour, avec les
airs, rondes & vaudevilles notés dans chaque pièce . . .
*Paris, Du Chesne, 1763–[77] 10 v. fronts. (v. 1–8, incl. 2
port.) plates. 19½ cm.*   ML 49.A2F1
Title vignette.
Each comedy has special t.-p. (or half-title) and separate paging.
Vol. 1–8 published 1763 (v. 2 and 6 dated 1743 by printer's error) Vol. 9 and
10 have imprint date 1772 on general t.-p., but the special title-pages
of two of the comedies are dated 1776 and 1777 respectively.

Acajou, Paris, 1744: unknown.   ML 50.2.A23

Acajou, Paris, 1753 (Theatre de M. Favart, Paris, Duchesne,
1763–77, t. vii).   ML 49.A2F1

L'amant déguisé ou Le jardinier supposé, Paris, 1769 (Theatre
de M. Favart, Paris, Duchesne, 1763–77, t. x) (with
Voisenon): Philidor.   ML 49.A2F1

L'amant déguisé, ou Le jardinier supposé, Paris, 1772 (with
Voisenon): Philidor.   Schatz 8005

L'amant déguisé, ou Le jardinier supposé, Paris, 1785 (with
Voisenon): Philidor.   Schatz 11735

Les amans inquiets, Paris, 1751 (parody of Colasse's Thetis et
Pelée).   ML 48.P2

Les amants inquiets, Paris, Sec. ed., 1751 (Theatre de M.
Favart, Paris, 1763–77, t. i). Parody of Colasse's Thetis
et Pelée.   ML 49.A2F1

L'amitié à l'épreuve, Paris, 1771: Grétry.   Schatz 4134

L'amitié à l'épreuve, Paris, 1776 (Theatre de M. Favart,
Paris, Duchesne, 1763–77, t. x). (One-act version):
Grétry.   ML 49.A2F1

Favart, Charles Simon—Continued.

L'amitié a l'épreuve, Paris, 1777: Grétry.　　　　　ML 48.M2M

L'amour au village, Paris, 1762 (Theatre de M. Favart, Paris,
　　Duchesne, 1763–77, t. vii).　　　　　　　　　　　ML 49.A2F1

L'amour impromptu, Paris, 1756 (Theatre de M. Favart,
　　Paris, Duchesne, 1763–77, t. viii) and.　　　　　ML 49.A2F1

L'amour impromptu, Paris, 1767. Parody of an entrée in
　　Rameau's Les fêtes d'Hébé.　　　　　　　　　　　Schatz 11479

Les amours champêtres, Troisième ed., Paris, 1759 (Theatre de
　　M. Favart, Paris, 1763–77, t. I.)　　　　　　　　ML 49.A2F1

Les amours de Bastien et Bastienne. *See* Madame Favart.

Les amours grivois, n. i., 1751 (Theatre de M. Favart, Paris,
　　Duchesne, 1763–77, t. vii) (with Lagarde and Lesueur.
　　The O. T. was L'ecole des amours grivois).　　　　ML 49.A2F1

Annette et Lubin. *See* Madame Favart.

Arsene Leipzig, 1778 (German imitation by Meissner):
　　Seydelmann.　　　　　　　　　　　　　　　　　　Schatz 9841

Arsene, n. i., n. d.: Seydelmann.　　　　　　　　　　Schatz 11748

Baiocco et Serpilla, Nouv. ed., Paris, 1760 (Theatre de M.
　　Favart, Paris, 1763–77, t. ii): Sodi.　　　　　　　ML 49.A2F1

Baiocco et Serpilla, Paris, 1771: Sodi. (Parody of Il marito
　　giogatore e la moglie bacchettona.)　　　　　　　Schatz 9929

Le bal de Strasbourg, Paris, 1744: en vaudevilles (with de La
　　Garde and Lesueur).　　　　　　　　　　　　　　ML 48.P2

Le bal de Strasbourg, Paris, 1744 (Theatre de M. Favart, Paris,
　　Duchesne, 1763–77, t. vii) (with Lagarde and Lesueur).　ML 49.A2F1

Le bal bourgeois, Paris, 1762 (Theatre de M. Favart, Paris,
　　Duchesne, 1763–77, t. viii).　　　　　　　　　　ML 49.A2F1

Les bateliers de Saint Cloud, Bruxelles, 1744 (Theatre de M.
　　Favart, Paris, Duchesne, 1763–77, t. vi).　　　　ML 49.A2F1

Les bateliers de Saint Cloud, Paris, 1766. L. T. of his La fête
　　de Saint Cloud.　　　　　　　　　　　　　　　　Schatz 11483

La bella Arsena, Augsburg, 1781. Tr. of his La belle Arsène. Schatz 6565

La belle Arsène, Paris, 1775: Monsigny.　　　　　　Schatz 6562

La belle Arsène, n. i., n. d. (1775) (Theatre de M. Favart, Paris,
　　Duchesne, 1763–77, t. x) (four-act version): Monsigny.　ML 49.A2F1

La Bohémienne, La Haye, 1758. Parody of Rinaldo di
　　Capua's La Zingara.　　　　　　　　　　　　　　Schatz 8797

La Bohemienne, Paris, Duchesne, 1759 (Theatre de M. Favart,
　　Paris, 1763–77, t. ii). Parody of Rinaldo di Capua's La
　　Zingara.　　　　　　　　　　　　　　　　　　　ML 49.A2F1

Bon depigen ved hoffet (Copenhagen, 1776). Tr. of his Le
　　caprice amoureux ou Ninette à la cour: Ciampi and
　　others.　　　　　　　　　　　　　　　　　　　　Schatz 2852

Le caprice amoureux ou Ninette à la cour, Paris, 1758 (three
　　act version): pasticcio: Parody of Ciampi's Bertoldo,
　　Bertoldino e Cacasenno.　　　　　　　　　　　　ML 50.2.B37C33

Le caprice amoureux ou Ninette à la cour, Nouv. éd., Paris,
　　1759 (two act version): pasticcio. Parody of Ciampi's
　　Bertoldo, Bertoldino e Cacasenno.　　　　　　　Schatz 1877

Le caprice amoureux ou Ninette a la cour, n. i., n. d. (Two
　　act version) (Theatre de M. Favart, Paris, Duchesne,
　　1763–77, t. iii).　　　　　　　　　　　　　　　　ML 49.A2F1

Favart, Charles Simon—Continued.

Ce qui plaît aux dames. A. T. of his La fée Urgèle: Duni.

La chercheuse d'esprit, suivant la copie imprimée à Paris, 1744.   ML 50.2.C4

La chercheuse d'esprit, Paris, 1756 (Theatre de M. Favart, Paris, Duchesne, 1763–77, t. vi).   ML 49.A2F1

La chercheuse d'esprit, Paris, 1772.   ML 48.M2N

Les Chinois, Paris, 1759 (Theatre de M. Favart, Paris, Duchesne, 1763–77, t. iii) (with Naigeon): parodied mainly from Sellitti's "Il Cinese rimpatriato."   ML 49.A2F1

Les Chinois, Amsterdam, 1760 (with Naigeon, who alone is mentioned in the title).   Schatz 9825

Le cocq de village, Nouv. éd., Paris, 1752.   ML 50.2.C605

Le cocq de village, n. i., n. d. (Theatre de M. Favart, Paris, Duchesne, 1763–77, t. vi).   ML 49.A2F1

La coquette sans le savoir, Paris (Toulon) 1772 (with P. Rousseau).   ML 48.M2M

La coquette trompée, n. i., n. d. (Theatre de M. Favart, Paris, 1763–77, t. i): Dauvergne.   ML 49.A2F1

Cythere assiégée, Paris, 1760 (also forms part of Theatre de M. Favart, Paris, Duchesne, 1763–77, t. vii. ML 49.A2F1).   ML 50.2.C95

Le depart de l'opera-comique, Paris, 1759 (Theatre de M. Favart, Paris, Duchesne, 1763–72, t. viii).   ML 49.A2F1

Le départ de l'Opéra comique, Paris, 1766.   Schatz 11489

Don Quichote chez la duchesse, Paris, 1760 (Theatre de M. Favart, Paris, Duchesne, 1763–77, t. vi): Boismortier.   ML 49.A2F1

The Englishman out of Paris. A. T. of his The reapers.

Les ensorcelés ou Jeannot et Jeannette. *See* Madame Favart.

Die erdichtete luft-geister. A. T. of his Isabella und Gertraude: Blaise.

La famille réunie, Paris, 1790: Chapelle.   ML 50.2.F174C3

Fanfale, Paris, 1759 (Theatre de M. Favart, Paris, 1763–77, t. i) (with Marcouville) Parody of Destouches' Omphale.   ML 49.A2F1

La fée Urgele (Paris) 1765 (Journal des spectacles, Paris, 1766, t. ii): Duni.   ML 48.J7

La fée Urgele ou Ce qui plait aux dames, Paris, veuve Duchesne, 1765 (Theatre de M. Favart, Paris, Duchesne, 1763–77, t. ix): Duni.   ML 49.A2F1

La fée Urgèle ou Ce qui plaît aux dames, Paris, 1768: Duni.   Schatz 2843

La fée Urgèle ou Ce qui plaît aux dames, Paris, 1781: Duni.   Schatz 11695

La fée Urgele ou Ce qui plait aux dames, Copenhague, 1770: Duni.   Yudin PQ

Die fee Urgele oder Was den damen gefällt, Frankfurt am Mayn (1776). Tr. of his La fée Urgèle ou Ce qui plait aux dames: Duni.   Schatz 2844

La fête d'amour ou Lucas et Colinette. *See* Mad. Favart.

Les festes de la paix, Nouv. éd., augmentée, Paris, 1763 (Theatre de M. Favart, Paris, Duchesne, 1763–77, t. ix): Philidor.   ML 49.A2F1

La fête du château, Paris, 1766 (76 p.) (also forms part of Theatre de M. Favart, Paris, Duchesne, 1763–77, t. ix. ML 49.A2F1).   ML 50.2.F33

La fête du château, Paris, 1766 (52 p.).   ML 50.2.F331

La fête du château, Paris, 1767.   Schatz 11491

Favart, Charles Simon—Continued.

La fille mal gardée ou Le pédant amoureux. *See* Mad. Favart.

La fortune au village. *See* Mad. Favart.

Die freundschaft auf der Probe, Frankfurt am Mayn, 1772.
Tr. of his L'amitié à l'épreuve: Grètry. Schatz 4135

Die freundschaft auf der probe, Wien, 1780. Schatz 4136

Hippolite et Aricie, Nouv. ed., Paris, 1759 (Theatre de M.
Favart, Paris, 1763–77, t. i) Parody of Rameau's Hippolite et Aricie. ML 49.A2F1

Les Indes dansantes, Paris, 1751 (parody of Rameau's Les
Indes galantes): unknown. ML 50.2.I56

Les Indes dansantes, Paris, 1759 (Theatre de M. Favart, Paris,
1763–77, t. i). Parody of Rameau's Les Indes galantes. ML 49.A2F1

Isabelle et Gertrude ou Les sylphes supposés, Paris, 1765:
Blaise. Schatz 1064

Isabelle et Gertrude ou Les sylphes supposés—Isabella und
Gertraude oder Die erdichtete luft-geister, Mannheim,
1767: Blaise. Schatz 1065

Isabelle et Gertrude ou Les sylphes supposés, n. i., n. d.
(Theatre de M. Favart, Paris, Duchesne, 1763–77, t. ix). ML 49.A2F1

Isabelle et Gertrude ou Les sylphes supposés, Paris, 1784:
Blaise. Schatz 11677

Le jardinier supposé. A. T. of his and de Voisenon's L'amant
supposé: Philidor.

Les jeunes mariés, La Haye, 1751. (Title page attributes the
play to Parmentier.) Schatz 11715

Les jeunes mariés, Paris, 1757 (Theatre de M. Favart, Paris,
Duchesne, 1763–77, t. vii). ML 49.A2F1

Les jeunes mariés, Paris, 1767. Schatz 11495

Le mariage par escalade, Paris, 1757 (Theatre de M. Favart,
Paris, Duchesne, 1763–77, t. viii). ML 49.A2F1

Le mariage par escalade, Paris, 1777. Schatz 11497

Les moissonneurs, Paris, veuve Duchesne, 1768 (61 p.): Duni. Schatz 2850

Les moissonneurs, Paris, veuve Duchesne, 1768 (91, [4] p.)
(Theatre de M. Favart, Paris, Duchesne, 1763–77, t. x):
Duni. ML 49.A2F1

Moulinet, Paris, 1739 (Theatre de M. Favart, Paris, Duchesne,
1763–77, t. vi). ML 49.A2F1

Nannerl bei hofe. A. T. of his Der verliebte eigensinn.

Ninette à la cour. A. T. of his La caprice amoureux.

La noce interrompue, Paris, 1758 (Theatre de M. Favart, Paris,
Duchesne, 1763–77, t. iv). Parody of Lully's Alceste. ML 49.A2F1

Les nymphes de Diane, Paris, 1755: Moulinghen. ML 50.2.N9M6

Les nymphes de Diane, Paris, Duchesne, 1755 (Theatre de
M. Favart, Paris, Duchesne, 1763–77, t. viii). ML 49.A2F1

Les nymphes de Diane, Paris, 1766. Schatz 11502

La parodie au Parnasse, Paris, Duchesne, 1759 (Theatre de
M. Favart, Paris, Duchesne, 1763–77, t. viii). ML 49.A2F1

Le pédant amoureux. A. T. of his La fille mal gardée: Duni.

Le petit-maitre malgré lui. A. T. of his La répétition interrompue.

Petrine, Paris, 1759 (Theatre de M. Favart, Paris, Duchesne,
1763–77, t. iv). (Some couplets by Sedaine in this much
altered version of Favart's parody Farinette of Lully's
Proserpine.) ML 49.A2F1

Favart, Charles Simon—Continued.

Le prix de Cythere, Paris, 1761 (Theatre de M. Favart, Paris, Duchesne, 1763–77, t. vi) (with the marquis de Paulme).   ML 49.A2F1

Raton et Rosette, Troisième éd., Paris, 1759 (Theatre de M. Favart, Paris, Duchesne, 1763–77, t. ii). (Parody of Mondonville's Titon et l'Aurore.)   ML 49.A2F1

The reapers or The Englishman out of Paris, London, 1770. Tr. of his Les moissonneurs: Duni.   Longe 204

La répétition interrompue (C. F. Pannard, Théâtre, Paris, 1763, v. 2) (jointly with Pannard).   PQ 2019.P3

La répétition interrompue ou Le petit-maitre malgré lui, Paris, 1758 (Theatre de M. Favart, Paris, Duchesne, 1763–77, t. viii). (F.'s altered version of the preceding title.)   ML 49.A2F1

La ressource des théâtres. *See* Title catalogue.

Le retour de l'opera-comique, Paris, 1759 (Theatre de M. Favart, Paris, 1763–77, t. viii).   ML 49A2F1 .

Das rosenfest, Weimar, 1774: Wolf. Tr. of his La rosière de Salenci.   Schatz 11083

Das rosenfest (Weimar) 1776: Wolf. Tr. of his La rosière de Salenci.   ML 50.2R75W6

Das rosenmädchen oder Das fest der weiblichen tugend, Frankfurt am Mayn, 1772. Tr. of his La rosière de Salenci: Blaise, Philidor, and Duni.   Schatz 2860

La rosiere de Salenci, Paris, veuve Duchesne, 1770 (Theatre de Favart, Paris, Duchesne, 1763–77, t. x): Blaise, Duni, Philidor.   ML 49.A2F1

Sansonnet et Tonton. O. T. of his L'amour impromptu.

Die schnitter, Frankfurt am Mayn (1769) Faber's Tr. of his Les moissonneurs: Duni.   ML 50.2.M75D94

Die schnitter, Frankfurt am Mayn, 1772. Tr. of his Les moissonneurs: Duni.   Schatz 2851

Die schoene Arsene, Frankfurt am Mayn. Tr. by Faber of his La belle Arsène: Monsigny.   Schatz 6563

Die schoene Arsene, Hamburg, 1780. André's Tr.   Schatz 6564

De schoone Arsène, Amsteldam, 1789. Ruloffs' tr.   Schatz 6586

Die schöne Arsene: Seydelmann. *See* his Arsene.

De schoone Arsène, Amsteldam, 1789. Tr. of his La belle Arsène: Monsigny.   Schatz 6586

La servante justifiée, Paris, 1744 (Theatre de M. Favart, Paris, Duchesne, 1763–77, t. vi) (with Fagan): Moulingen (?)   ML 49.A2F1

La servante justifiée, Paris, 1766 (with Fagan): Moulingen (?)   Schatz 11513

Den skiønne Arsene (Kiøbenhavn, 1781). Tr. of his La belle Arsène: Monsigny.   Schatz 6566

La soirée des boulevards, Paris, 1759.   Schatz 11514

La soirée des boulevards, Nouv. éd., Paris, 1759 (Theatre de M. Favart, Paris, Duchesne, 1763–77, t. iv).   ML 49.A2F1

Soliman Second, Paris, 1762 (Theatre de M. Favart, Paris, Duchesne, 1763–77, t. iv): Gilbert.   ML 49.A2F1

Soliman second ou Les trois sultanes, Paris, 1772: Gilbert.   ML 48.M2N

Supplément de la Soirée des boulevards, Paris, 1760 (Theatre de M. Favart, Paris, Duchesne, 1763–77, t. iv). (Text partly by Panard and Guérin.)   ML 49.A2F1

Favart, Charles Simon—Continued.

Les sylphes supposés. A. T. of his Isabelle et Gertrude: Blaise.

Thesée, n. i., n. d. (Theatre de M. Favart, Paris, Duchesne, 1763–77, t. vii) (with Laujon and Parvi. Parody of Lully's Thesée).   ML 49.A2F1

Tircis et Doristée, Paris, 1759 (Theatre de M. Favart, Paris, Duchesne, 1763–77, t. ii). Parody of Lully's Acis et Galatée.   ML 49.A2F1

Les trois sultanes. A. T. of his Soliman Second.

Der verkleidete liebhaber oder Der verstellte gaertner, Frankfurt am Mayn, 1774. Tr. of his and de Voisenon's L'amant déguisé ou Le jardinier supposé: Philidor.   SCHATZ 8006

Der verliebte eigensinn oder Nannerl bei hofe, Pressburg, 1778. Tr. of his Le caprice amoureux.   SCHATZ 1878

Der verstellte gaertner. A. T. of his and de Voisenon's Der verkleidete liebhaber: Philidor.

Zéphire et Fleurette, Paris, 1754 (Theatre de M. Favart, Paris, Duchesne, 1763–77, t. ii) (Laujon and Panard's parody of Rebel and Francoeur's Zelindor, as retouched by Favart).   ML 49.A2F1

Favart, *Madame,* *née* **Marie Justine Benoite Du Ronceray (Duronceray).**

Les amours de Bastien et Bastienne, La Haye, 1755 (with Harny and her husband). Parody of Rousseau's Le devin du village.   ML 48.A4

Les amours de Bastien et Bastienne, Nouv. éd., Paris, 1759 (Theatre de M. Favart, Paris, Duchesne, 1763–77, t. v).   ML 49.A2F1

Les amours de Bastien et Bastienne, Paris, 1770.   SCHATZ 11481

Les amours de Bastien et Bastienne, Avignon, 1768.   ML 48.M2M

Annette et Lubin, Paris, 1763 (with her husband, Lourdet de Santerre, but probably not Voisenon): Blaise.   SCHATZ 1063

Annette et Lubin, Paris, Duchesne, 1763 (78, [2] p.) (Theatre de M. Favart, Paris, Duchesne, 1763–77, t. v): Blaise.   ML 49.A2F1

Annette et Lubin, Paris, 1770: Blaise.   SCHATZ 11675

Annette et Lubin, Avignon, 1774: Blaise.   ML 48.M2M

[Annette et Lubin] (imperfect copy).   SCHATZ 11676

Les ensorcelés ou Jeannot et Jeannette, Paris, 1757 (with her husband, Guerin de Frémicour and Harny de Guerville, who principally selected and arranged the music).   SCHATZ 4454

Les ensorcelés ou Jeannot et Jeannette, Paris, 1758 (Theatre de M. Favart, Paris, Duchesne, 1763–77, t. v).   ML 49.A2F1

La fête d'amour ou Lucas et Colinette (Theatre de M. Favart, Paris, Duchesne, 1763–77, t. v) (with her husband and Chevalier).   ML 49.A2F1

La fille mal gardée ou Le pédant amoureux, Paris, 1759 (with her husband and Lourdet de Santerre): Duni.   SCHATZ 2845

La fille mal gardée ou Le pedant amoureux, Paris, 1758 (Theatre de M. Favart, Paris, Duchesne, 1763–77, t. v) (with her husband and Lourdet de Santerre): Duni. Parody of the entrée La Provençale in Mouret's Les festes de Thalie.   ML 49.A2F1

Favart, *Madame,* *née* **Marie Justine Benoite Du Ronceray (Duronceray)**—Continued.

La fortune au village, Paris, Duchesne, 1761 (Theatre de M. Favart, Paris, Duchesne, 1763–77, t. v) (with her husband and Bertrand): Gilbert.   ML 49.A2F1

Jeannot et Jeannette. A. T. of her Les ensorcelés.

Lucas et Colinette. A. T. of her La fête d'amour.

Le pédant amoureux. A. T. of her La fille mal gardée.

Favier, Charles Auguste (Carlo Augusto).

La contadina spiritosa, ballet. *See* Zingarelli's Quinto Fabio.

Ezio, ballet. *See* Zingarelli's Quinto Fabio.

Matrimonio per gratitudine, Il, ballet. *See* Marinelli's L'interesse gabba tutti.

Favier, Giacomo.

Le nozze americane, ballet: Le Messier. *See* Colla's Andromeda.

Il ritorno della primavera, ballet: Le Messier. *See* Colla's Andromeda.

Favier, Jean (Giovanni).

Le Danaidi. A. T. of his ballet L'Ipermestra.

Iffigenia in Tauride, ballet. *See* Paisiello's Il Demofoonte.

L'Ipermestra o Le Danaidi, ballet. *See* Anfossi's L'Olimpiade.

I Panduri accampati, ballet: Gebhard. *See* Pugnani's Tamas Kouli-Kan nell' India.

Zefiro e Flora, ballet. *See* Manfredini's Armida.

Favières, Etienne Guillaume François.

Elisca ou L'amour maternel, Paris, an VII (1799): Grétry.   ML 50.2.E33G7

Lisbeth, Paris, an VIII [1799–1800]: Grétry.   Schatz 4197

Paul et Virginie, Hamburg, 1796: Kreutzer.   Schatz 5266

Fedeli, Ruggiero.

Silvia, Ratisbona, 1690: author.   Schatz 3038

Federico, Gennaro Antonio.

Die als magd gewordene frau. Tr. of his La serva padrona, Braunschweig (1749): Pergolesi.   Schatz 7894

Amor vuol sofferenza. O. T. of his libretto Li matti per amore.

Il fantastico. O. T. of his Il nuovo D. Chisciotte: Leo and Gomes.

Lo frate nnammorato, Napole (1734): Pergolesi.   Schatz 7903

Gl'ingannati, Napoli, 1734: Latilla.   Schatz 5454

L'Ippolita, Napoli (1733): N. Conti.   Schatz 2207

Die magd als frau im hause (Dresden, 1740): Pergolesi.   Schatz 7892

Li matti per amore, Venezia, 1754 (L. T. of his libretto Amor vuol sofferenza): Cocchi.   Schatz 2035

Li matti per amore—Die narren für liebe, Berlino, 1764: Cocchi.   Schatz 2036

De meid meesteres. A. T. of his Pandolfus en Zerbina: Pergolesi.

Il nuovo D. Chisciotte, Napoli, 1748: Leo and Gomes. L. T. of his Il fantastico: Leo.   ML 50.2.F178L3

L'Ottavio, Napoli (1733): Latilla.   Schatz 5452

Federico, Gennaro Antonio—Continued.

Pandolfus en Zerbina of De meid meesteres, Amsteldam, 1793.
Tr. of his La serva padrona: Pergolesi. SCHATZ 7896

La Rosaura, Napoli, 1736: Sarro. SCHATZ 9419

La serva padrona, Venezia, 1748: Pergolesi. SCHATZ 7892

La serva padrona—Die als magd gewordene frau, Braunschweig (1749): Pergolesi. SCHATZ 7894

La serva padrona (Frankfurt a/M, 1755): Pergolesi (Soralli's version of the text). SCHATZ 7902

La serva padrona, Venezia, 1795: Trento. SCHATZ 10429

La servante maitresse, Paris, 1754. Parody of his La serva padrona: Pergolesi. SCHATZ 7895

La servante maitresse, Paris, 1771. SCHATZ 7895a

La servante maîtresse, Bruxelles, n. d. ML 50.2S51P3

Feind, Barthold.

Almira, koenigin in Castilien. A. T. of his Der durchlauchtige secretarius: Keiser.

L'amore ammalato. Die kranckende liebe. Oder: Antiochus und Stratonica (Deutsche gedichte, Stade, 1708): Graupner. ML 49.A2F2

L'amore ammalato. Italian T. of his Die kranckende liebe oder Antiochus und Stratonica (Hamburg, 1708): Graupner. SCHATZ 4120

L'amore verso la patria, Die liebe gegen das vaterland oder Der sterbende Cato, Hamburg (1715). SCHATZ 5075

Der angenehme betrug oder Der carneval von Venedig (Hamburg, 1707): Keiser. SCHATZ 5076

Der angenehme betrug oder Der carneval von Venedig, Hamburg, 1716: Keiser. SCHATZ 5118

Der angenehme betrug oder Der carneval von Venedig, Hamburg (1723): Keiser. SCHATZ 5119

Antiochus und Stratonica. A. T. of his Die kranckende liebe: Graupner.

Bellerophon oder Das in die preussische krone verwandelte wagengestirn (Hamburg, 1708): Graupner. SCHATZ 4118

Der carneval von Venedig. A. T. of his Der angenehme betrug: Keiser.

La costanza sforzata. Die gezwungene bestaendigkeit oder Die listige rache des Sueno (Hamburg, 1706): Keiser. SCHATZ 5084

La costanza sforzata. Die bezwungene bestaendigkeit [etc.] (Feind, Deutsche gedichte, Stade, 1708): Keiser. ML 49.A2F2

Desiderius, koenig der Longobarden (Hamburg, 1709): Keiser. SCHATZ 5085

Der durch den fall des grossen Pompejus erhoehete Julius Caesar (Hamburg, 1710): Keiser. SCHATZ 5086

Der durchlauchtige secretarius oder Almira, koenigin in Castilien (Hamburg, 1706) (revision of Feustking's text): Keiser. SCHATZ 5122

Die edelmuehtige Octavia. A. T. of his Die roemische unruhe: Keiser.

Die gezwungene bestaendigkeit oder Die listige rache des Sueno. *See his* La costanza sforzata: Keiser.

Das in die preussische krone verwandelte wagengestirn. A. T. of his Bellerophon: Graupner.

Feind, Barthold—Continued.

Die kleinmuehtige selbst-moerderin Lucretia oder Die staats-
thorheit des Brutus (Hamburg, 1705): Keiser.   Schatz 5099

—[Same title] (Feind, Deutsche gedichte, Stade, 1708).   ML 49.A2F2

Die kranckende liebe, oder Antiochus und Stratonica. German title of L'amore ammalato . . . (Hamburg, 1708):
Graupner.   Schatz 4120

Die liebe gegen das Vaterland oder Der sterbende Cato. *See
his* L'amore verso la patria.

Die listige rache des Sueno. A. T. of his Die gezwungene bestaendigkeit.

Masagniello furioso oder Die neapolitanische fischer-empoerung (Deutsche gedichte, Stade, 1708): Keiser.   ML 49.A2F2

Masagniello furioso . . . Die neapolitanische fischer-empoerung, Hamburg (date cut off): Keiser.   Schatz 5125

— [Same title, but with port.], Hamburg, 1714: Keiser.   Schatz 5126

Masagniello furioso oder Die neapolitanische fischer-empoerung (Hamburg, 1727): Keiser.   Schatz 5102

Die neapolitanische fischer-empoerung. A. T. of his Masagniello furioso: Keiser.

Rinaldo, Hamburg (1715). Tr. of Händel's Rinaldo (Rossi
and Hill).   Schatz 4489

Rinaldo (Hamburg, 1723). L. ed. of the above.   Schatz 4501

Das roemische April-fest, Hamburg (1716): Keiser.   Schatz 5127

Die roemische unruhe oder Die edelmuehtige Octavia (Hamburg) 1705: Keiser.   Schatz 5128

— [Same title] (Feind, Deutsche gedichte, Stade, 1708).   ML 49.A2F2

Die staatsthorheit des Brutus. A. T. of his Die kleinmuethige
selbst-moerderin Lucretia: Keiser.

Der sterbende Cato. A. T. of his Die liebe gegen das vaterland.

Fenouillot de Falbaire de Quingey, Charles George.

Die beiden geizigen, Frankfurt am Mayn, 1772. Tr. of his
Les deux avares: Grétry.   Schatz 4146

Les deux avares, Paris, 1770: Grétry.   ML 50.2.D48G7

Les deux avares, Paris, Ballard, 1771: Grétry.   Schatz 4143

Les deux avares, Paris, Delalain, 1771: Grétry.   Schatz 11704

Das grab des Mufti oder Die zwey geitzigen, Stettin, 1778.
Tr. of his Les deux avares: Grétry.   Schatz 4144

Das grab des Mufti oder Die zwey geizigen, Leipzig, 1776:
Joh. Ad. Hiller. (Based on his Les deux avares.)   Schatz 4720

Melide oder Der schiffer, Frankfurt, 1778. And   Schatz 8034

— [Same title] Riga (1786). Tr. of: Schatz 8035

Mélide ou Le navigateur, Paris, 1774: Philidor.   Schatz 8033

Die zwei (zwey) geizigen. A. T. of his Das grab des Mufti.

Feralintizco, *col'* **Antuono.** *Pseud. of* Tulli, Francesco Antonio.

Ferlotti, Niccolò.

Nina pazza per amore, ballet. *See* Andreozzi's Amelia ed
Ottiero.

Fermelhuis, N.

Pirrhus (Recueil général des opéra, t. xiv, Paris, 1734): Royer. Schatz 9110

Ferrari, Benedetto.
 L'Andromeda, Venetia, 1637: Manelli.   Schatz 5887
 L'Armida, Venezia, 1639: author.   Schatz 3065
 L'Armida (Poesie drammatiche, Milano, 1644): author.   Schatz 11699
 L'inganno d'amore—Liebs betrug (Regensburg, 1653): Bertali. Schatz 874
 La maga fulminata (Poesie drammatiche, Milano, 1644):
  Manelli.   Schatz 5888
 La ninfa avara (Poesie drammatiche, Milano, 1644): author.   Schatz 3066
 Il pastor regio, Venetia, 1640: author.   Schatz 3067
 Il pastor regio (Poesie drammatiche, Milano, 1644): author.   Schatz 11700
 Il prencipe giardiniero (Poesie drammatiche, Milano, 1644):
  author.   Schatz 3068
 Proserpina rapita (Poesie drammatiche, Milano, 1644): author. Schatz 3069

Ferrière(s), Alexandre, *baron* **de.**
 Les souliers mors-dorés, ou La cordonnière allemande, Paris,
  1776: Fridzeri.   Schatz 3372

Fesanio, Merindo. *Arcadian name of* Benedetto Pasqualigo.

Feustking, Friedrich Christian.
 Die betrogene staats-liebe, oder Die unglueckselige Cleopatra,
  koenigin von Egypten, Hamburg, 1704: Mattheson.   Schatz 6101
 Die durch blut und mord erlangete liebe oder Nero (Hamburg,
  1705): Händel.   Schatz 4475
 Der in krohnen erlangte gluecks wechsel oder Almira, koenigin
  von Castilien (Hamburg, 1704): Händel.   Schatz 4479
 Der in cronen erlangte gluecks wechsel oder Almira, koenigin
  von Castilien (Hamburg), 1732. L. ed. of the above.   Schatz 4500

Fianello, Giuseppe.
 Il finto Esaù, overo Gli odii fraterni, Venetia, 1698: Pacelli.   Schatz 7377

Fiedler, Gottlieb.
 Der grossmuethige Scipio Africanus (Hamburg, 1694) (based
  on conte Minato's Scipione Affricano): Kusser.   Schatz 2285

Fielding, Henry.
 The author's farce; and The pleasures of the town, London,
  1730: ballad opera.   ML 50.5.A82
 Don Quixote in England, London, 1754: ballad opera.   Longe 53
 The genuine Grub-street opera, London, 1731: ballad opera,
  O. T. of which was The Welsh opera.   ML 50.5.G79
 The grey mare the better horse. A. T. of his The Welsh opera.
 The intriguing chambermaid, London, 1750: ballad opera.   ML 50.5.I5
 The intriguing chambermaid (Collection of the most esteemed
  farces, Edinburgh, 1792, t. iii).   Schatz 11753C
 The lottery, 3d. ed., London, 1732: ballad opera, but music
  partly by Seedo.   ML 50.5.L68
 The lottery (Collection of the most esteemed farces, Edin-
  burgh, 1792, t. ii).   Schatz 11753B
 Miss Lucy in town, London, 1742: ballad opera.   ML 50.5.M4
 The mock doctor or The dumb lady cur'd (Collection of the
  most esteemed farces, Edinburgh, 1792, t. i).   Schatz 11753A
 The mock doctor or The dumb lady cur'd, 4th éd., London,
  1753. Tr. of Molière's Le medecin malgré lui.   ML 50.5.M58
 The mock doctor or The dumb lady cur'd, London, 1761.   ML 50.5.M6

Fielding, Henry—Continued.

An old man taught wisdom or The virgin unmask'd, 2d. ed., London, 1735: ballad opera.   ML 50.5.O42

The virgin unmasked, London, 1786.   L. T. of his An old man taught wisdom.   Longe 97

The virgin unmask'd (Collection of the most esteemed farces, Edinburgh, 1792, t. ii).   Schatz 11753B

The Welsh opera or The grey mare the better horse, London (1731): ballad opera.   Longe 262

Fiévée, Joseph.

Les rigeurs du cloitre, Paris, 1793: Berton.   Schatz 898

Filistri da Caramondani, Antonio de'.

Aeneas in Latium.   Tr. of his Enea nel Lazio, Berlino (1793): Righini.   Schatz 8782

Andromeda, Berlino, 1788: Reichardt.   Schatz 8634

Atalanta e Meleagro—Athalante und Meleager, Berlino (1797): Righini.   Schatz 8779

— Same, Berlino, 1799.   Schatz 8780

Brenno-Brennus, Berlino, 1789: Reichardt.   ML 50.2.B8R3

Brennus, Berlin, 1798.   Tr. of his Brenno: Reichardt.   Schatz 8637

La compagnia d'opera a Nanchino—Die operisten in Nanking, Berlino, 1790: Alessandri.   Schatz 143

Dario—Darius, Berlino (1791): Alessandri.   Schatz 144

Enea nel Lazio—Aeneas in Latium, Berlino (1793): Righini.   Schatz 8782

Die operisten in Nanking.   Tr. of his La compagnia d'opera a Nanchino, Berlino, 1790: Alessandri.   Schatz 143

Il ritorno di Ulisse a Penelope—Ulysses rückkunft zur Penelope, Berlino (1790): Alessandri.   Schatz 149

Il trionfo d'Arianna—Der triumph der Ariadne, Berlino, 1796: Righini.   Schatz 8788

Ulysses rückkunft zur Penelope.   Tr. of his Il ritorno di Ulisse a Penelope, Berlino (1790): Alessandri.   Schatz 149

Vasco di Gama, Berlino (1792): pasticcio.   Schatz 11374

Filostrato Lucàno Cinnèo. *Supposed pseud.* of Antonio Soliva, but more probably *anagram of* Francesco Antonio Tullio.

Fioravanti, Valentino.

Il furbo contro al furbo, Venezia (1797): author.   Schatz 3131

Fiorillo, Carlo.

L'equivoco ricompensato, ballet.   *See* Robuschi's Li raggiri fortunati.

Gl'uccellatori, ballet.   *See* Robuschi's Li raggiri fortunati.

Fiorini, Giacomo.

Il proseguimento del Chiarlone—Proceguimento ou segunda parte do Falador, Lisbona (1766): Marescalchi.   Schatz 5947

Fiorini, Giovanni.

L'opera in prova alla moda—La répétition ordinaire de l'opéra (followed by) Urganostocor, Amsterdam, 1753: Latilla.   Schatz 5450

Urganostocor.   *See his* L'opera in prova alla moda.

Fiorio, Gaetano.

L'arrivo del Burchello da Padova in Venezia, Venezia, 1779: Caruso.   Schatz 1660

Fletcher, John.
The prophetess or The history of Dioclesian. *See* Beaumont.

Fleury.
Biblis (Recueil général des opéra, t. xv, Paris, 1739): La Coste. Schatz 5352
Les genies (Paris) 1736: Duval. ML 52.2.G3
Les génies, ballet (Recueil général des opéra, Paris, 1745, t. xvi): Duval. ML 48.R4

Florian, Jean Pierre Claris de.
Blanche et vermeille, Paris, 1781: Rigel. ML 50.2.B4R3

Florimondo Ermionèo. *Arcadian name of* Giovanni **Greppi.**

Förg, Carl J.
Der baron vom vesten thurme (Muenchen) 1777. **Tr. of** Michl's "Il barone di Torreforte. Schatz 6488
Helena und Paris, Muenchen, 1782: Winter. Schatz 11035
Helena und Paris, Berlin, 1797: Winter. Schatz 11036

Fontenelle, Bernard Le Bovier de.
Bellerophon. *See* Corneille.
Endymion (Recueil général des opéra, Paris, 1739, **t. xv**): Colin de Blamont. Schatz 1066
Enée et Lavinie (Amsterdam) 1696: Colasse. ML 50.2.E4C6
Enée et Lavinie (Recueil général des opéra, Paris, 1703, **t. 4**): Colasse. Schatz 2099
Enée et Lavinie, Paris, 1758: Dauvergne. ML 50.2.E4D2
Le jardinier de Sidon. *See* Title catalogue.
Thetis et Pelée, Paris, 1699 [!]: Colasse. ML 50.2.T48C6
Thetis et Pelée (Amsterdam), 1689: Colasse. ML 50.2.T48C62
Thetis et Pelée (Recueil général des opéra, Paris, 1703, **t. iii**): Colasse. Schatz 2103
Thétis et Pélée (Paris) 1765 (Journal des spectacles, Paris, 1766, t. i): La Borde. ML 48.J7

Foppa, Giuseppe.
Aci e Galatea, Venezia, 1792: F. Bianchi. Schatz 993
Alonso e Cora, Venezia, 1786: F. Bianchi. Schatz 994
Amleto, Padova (1792): Andreozzi. Schatz 212
Il barone Spazzacamino, Lisbona, 1799. **L. T. of his Lo** spazzacamino principe: Portugal. Schatz 8433
Calto, Venezia, 1788: Bianchi. Schatz 996
I capricci (Venezia, 1795): Trento. Schatz 10442
Il chiamantesi filosofo. A. T. of his Non **irritare le donne:** Portugal.
Il contravveleno, Venezia, 1799: Gardi. Schatz 3547
Le donne cambiate—Die verwandelten weiber, **Dresda, 1799:** Portugal. Schatz 8406
Dorval e Virginia, Lisbona, 1795: P. C. Guglielmi. Schatz 4344
Dorval e Virginia, Venezia, 1792: Tarchi. Schatz 10219
I due sordi. A. T. of his Il matrimonio improviso.
Eugenia, Venezia, 1792: Nasolini. Schatz 7000
Eugenia—Eugenie, Dresda, 1794: Nasolini. Schatz 7001
Il finto Stregone, Venezia, 1798: Gardi. Schatz 3549
Furberia e puntiglio, Venezia, 1798: Bernardini. Schatz 834
Giulietta e Romeo, Milano (1796): Zingarelli. Schatz 11247
Giulietta e Romeo, Lisboa, 1798: Zingarelli. ML 50.2.G43Z3

Foppa, Giuseppe—Continued.

L'impresario di Smirne (Trieste, 1798): Rampini. SCHATZ 8592

Gli innamorate, Venezia, 1793: Nasolini and Trento. SCHATZ 7031

L'intrigo della lettera, Venezia, Anno primo [1797]: Mayr. SCHATZ 6154

L'intrigo della lettera, Lisboa, 1798: Mayr. ML 50.2.I65M2

Julie und Romeo, Botzen (1798): Zingarelli. **Tr. of their** Giulietta e Romeo. SCHATZ 11248

Laodicea. O. T. of his Tegene e Laodicea.

Lauso e Lidia, Venezia (1798): Mayr. SCHATZ 6156

Il matrimonio improviso (Venetia, 1794): Paër. SCHATZ 7563

Il matrimonio improviso o I due sordi, Barcellona (1798): Paër. SCHATZ 7564

Os moleiros, Lisboa, 1795: Paër. Tr. of: SCHATZ 7558

I molinari, Venezia, 1794: Paër. SCHATZ 7515

Il muto per astuzia (Venezia, 1799): Bernardini. SCHATZ 851

Non irritare le donne ovvero Il chiamantesi filosofo, Venezia, 1798: Portugal. SCHATZ 8438

Un pazzo ne fa cento, Venezia (1796): Mayr. SCHATZ 6176

Rinaldo, Venezia, 1789: P. Guglielmi. SCHATZ 4303

Der schorsteinfeger Peter, oder Das spiel des ohngefaehrs, Pirna, 1799. Tr. of his Lo spazzacamino principe: Portugal. SCHATZ 8419

Il secreto: Mayr. *Printed with* Cimarosa's I duello per complimento, Venezia, Anno primo [1797]. SCHATZ 2002

La semplice ovvero La virtù premiata, Venezia, 1798: Gardi. SCHATZ 3541

Lo spazzacamino, Dresda, 1794. L. T. of his Lo spazzacamino principe: Portugal. SCHATZ 8418

Lo spazzacamino principe, Venezia, 1794: Portugal. SCHATZ 8417

Das spiel des ohngefaehrs. A. T. of his Der schorsteinfeger Peter: Portugal.

Tegene e Laodicea, Firenze, 1799: Paër (O. T. of the text was Laodicea). SCHATZ 7508

La testa riscaldata, Venezia, 1799: Paër. SCHATZ 7540

Tito e Berenice, Venezia, 1793: Nasolini. SCHATZ 7017

Die verwandelten weiber. Tr. of his Le donne cambiate, Dresda, 1799: Portugal. SCHATZ 8406

La virtù premiata. A. T. of his La semplice: Gardi.

Ford (Foard), John.

The sun's darling, London, 1656 (with Decker): **unknown.** LONGE 242

Forgeot, Nicolas Julien.

Les dettes, Paris, 1787: Champein. SCHATZ 1794

Les pommiers et le moulin, Paris, 1791: Lemoine. ML 50.2.P56L2

Le rival confident, Paris, 1788: Grétry. ML 50.2.R58G7

De schulden, Amsterdam, 1791: Champein. Tr. of their Les dettes. SCHATZ 1795

Forrest, Ebenezer.

Momus turn'd fabulist or Vulcan's wedding, London, 1729: ballad opera. ML 50.5.M63

Forrest, Theodosius.

The weathercock, London, 1775. LONGE 86

Forrest, Thomas.

See The disappointment in Title catalogue.

Fouques-Deshayes, François Guillaume. *Better known as* Desfontaines de la Vallée.

Framery, Nicolas Etienne.

Le barbier de Séville, Amsterdam, 1786: Paisiello.   SCHATZ 7600

La colonie, Paris, 1776: Sacchini. (Parody of his "L'isola .
    d'amore.")   SCHATZ 9228

Die colonie, Hamburg, 1780: Sacchini. Tr. of the above.   SCHATZ 9230

L'Indienne, Paris, 1771: Cifolelli.   SCHATZ 1897

L'infante de Zamora, La Haye, 1783 (French parody of La
    Frascatana): Paisiello.   ML 50.2.F84P22

Die kolonie, Frankfurt am Mayn, 1778. Tr. of his La colonie:
    Sacchini.   SCHATZ 9229

Nanette et Lucas ou La paysanne curièuse, Paris, 1754 [*recte*
    1764]: d'Herbain.   ML 50.2.N17H3

Nanette et Lucas, ou La paysanne curieuse, Paris, 1775:
    d'Herbain.   SCHATZ 4644

L'Olympiade ou Le triomphe de l'amitié, Paris, 1777. Par-
    ody of Sacchini's L'Olimpiade (Metastasio).   SCHATZ 9239

La paysanne curieuse. A. T. of his Nanette et Lucas: d'Her-
    bain.

Le triomphe de l'amitié. A. T. of his L'Olympiade: Sac-
    chini.

Frances.

The enchanted wood, London, 1792: not mentioned.   LONGE 220

Franceschi, Antonio.

La Didone delirante, Venetia, 1686: Pallavicino.   SCHATZ 7736

Franceschi, Francesco.

Leonida rè di Sparta, Lucca, 1783. *See* M. Curzio in Title
    catalogue.

Franchi, Paolino (Paolo).

L'Albagia in fumo, ballet. *See* Tarchi's La congiura Piso-
    niana.

Alfredo il Grande, rè degli Anglo-Sassoni, ballet: Trento. *See*
    Bianchi's Seleuco.

L'amore in contrasto, ballet. *See* Anfossi's Zemira.

Gli amori di Angelica e Medoro, ballet. *See* Paër's La Rossana.

Il bottaro di Svezia, ballet. *See* Paisiello's Le gare generose.

Il calzettaro ossia Tanto va la gatta al lardo che si lascia lo
    zampino, ballet. *See* Paisiello's Gli schiavi per amore.

La capricciosa, ballet. *See* Sarti's Adriano in Siria.

La disfatta di Vario. A. T. of his ballet La Tusnelda: Cana-
    vasso.

Don Pietro, rè di Castiglia, ballet. *See* Anfossi's Zemira.

Li due avari, ballet: Canavasso. *See* Anfossi's Gengis-Kan.

I due avari, ballet. *See* Zingarelli's Ifigenia in Aulide.

Il feudatorio, ballet. *See* Monza's Ifigenia in Tauride.

Il finto giardiniere, ballet. *See* Monza's Enea in Cartagine.

La Galzeuca ossia Golconda liberata dalla tirannide di Scour-
    Malou, ballet: Canavasso. *See* Pugnani's Achille in
    Sciro.

Gioconda, ballet: Canavasso. *See* Cimarosa's Artaserse.

Franchi, Paolino (Paolo)—Continued.

Guatimozin ossia La conquista del Messico, ballet. *See* Zingarelli's Ifigenia in Aulide.

Gustavo Vaza, ballet. *See* Sarti's Adriano in Siria.

Hurtado e Miranda, ballet. *See* Luchesi's Ademira.

Hurtado e Miranda, ballet. *See* Monza's Ifigenia in Tauride.

Inkle e Jariko, ballet. *See* Paisiello's Gli schiavi per amore.

Inkle e Jariko, ballet. *See* Prati's La morte di Semiramide.

Lauso e Lidia, ballet. *See* Monza's Cajo Mario.

Lodoiska, ballet. *See* Paër's La Rossana.

Lucio Giunio Bruto, ballet. *See* Tarchi's La congiura Pisoniana.

Il matrimonio cinese, ballet: Canavasso. *See* Anfossi's Gengis-Kan.

Il matrimonio per concorso, ballet: Canavasso. *See* Pugnani's Achille in Sciro.

Il matrimonio per concorso, ballet. *See* Zingarelli's Ifigenia in Aulide.

La pianella perduta, ballet. *See* Paër's La Rossana.

Padmani e Mirda, ballet. *See* Minoja's Tito nelle Gallie.

Padmani e Mirda, ballet. *See* Monza's Enea in Cartagine.

La pianella perduta, ballet. *See* Paisiello's Le gare generose.

Il primo navigatore, ballet. *See* Minoja's Tito nelle Gallie.

La principessa di Tingi, ballet: Giordani. *See* Insanguine's Calipso.

Pulcinella, cavaliere d'industria, ballet. *See* Monza's Ifigenia in Tauride.

Raol de Crequi, ballet: Winter and Pichl.

Il rè pastore, ballet: Canavasso. *See* Anfossi's Gengis-Kan.

Il rè pastore, ballet. *See* Borghi's Creso rè di Lidia.

Solimano II, ballet. *See* Bianchi's Selenco.

Gli sposi delusi dalle astuzie di Crespino, ballet: Canavasso. *See* Cimarosa's Artaserse.

Tito e Berenice, ballet. *See* Borghi's Arbace.

La tranquillità disturbata, ballet. *See* Borghi's Creso rè di Lidia.

La Tusnelda o sia La disfatta di Vario, ballet: Canavasso. *See* Cimarosa's Artaserse.

Urtado e Miranda, ballet. *See* Curcio's La Ñitteti.

Frankenau, Rasmus.

Arvire og Evelina, Kiøbenhavn (1799). Tr. of Sacchini's Armire et Evelina. (The title of the printed score is "Evelina.") Schatz 9208

Franklin, Andrew.

A trip to the Nore, London, 1797. Longe 244

Fransky, Franz Joseph.

Der bestrafte hochmuth, oder: Liebe macht alle staende gleich, Hamburg, 1798: Gerl. L. T. of their Graf Balbarone oder Die maskerade. Schatz 3785

Frederick the Great, *king of Prussia.*

See in Title catalogue—

Coriolano: Graun.

Fetonte: Graun.

Frederick the Great—Continued.

    See in Title catalogue—

        I fratelli nemici: Graun.

        Il giudizio di Paride: Graun.

        Ifigenia in Aulide: Graun.

        Merope: Graun.

        Montezuma: Graun.

        Silla: Graun.

Freeman, Mark.

    The downfall of bribery: or, The honest men of Taunton, London (173–).   LONGE 168

Friggieri, Domenico.

    La festa interrotta o sia Il trionfo della virtù—Das unterbrochene fest oder Der triumph der tugend, Regensburg, n. d.: von Schacht.   SCHATZ 9563

    I furori di Orlando—Die rasereyen des Rolands (Ratisbona, 1777): Touchemolin.   SCHATZ 10383

    Il trionfo della virtù. A. T. of his La festa interrotta.

    Der triumph der tugend. A. T. of his Das interbrochene fest: von Schacht.

    Il tutore deluso o sia La semplice (Regensburg, ca. 1780). (Merely altered this text by an unknown author for von Schacht, the composer.)   SCHATZ 9564

    Das unterbrochene fest oder Der triumph der tugend. Tr. of his La festa interotta o sia Il trionfo della virtù, Regensburg, n. d.: von Schacht.   SCHATZ 9563

Frisari, Girolamo.

    Antioco il Grande, Venetia, 1681: Legrenzi.   SCHATZ 5533

    L'Aurora in Atene, Venetia, 1678: Zannettini.   SCHATZ 11146

    Il Pausania, Venetia, 1682: Legrenzi.   SCHATZ 5546

Froelich, F. H. W.

    Das erndte-fest, Altona, 1795. Tr. of Schulz' Høst-gildet (Thaarup).   SCHATZ 9722

Frugoni, Carlo Innocenzio (Innocente).

    Aristeo (second act of his Le feste d'Apollo).

    Bauci e Filemone (1st act of his Le feste d'Apollo).

    Castore e Polluce (Monaco) 1788. (Tr. of Bernard's "Castor et Pollux."). Reduced from five to three acts by the composer, Georg Jos. Vogler.   SCHATZ 10800

    Egle. Act in his Le feste d'Imeneo: Traetta.

    Fedra, Napoli, 1788: Paisiello. L. T. of his "Ippolito ed Aricia" as altered by Salvioni.   SCHATZ 7668

    Le feste d'Apollo, Parma (1769) (with exception of third act which was from Calsabigi's Orfeo): Gluck.   SCHATZ 3897

    Le feste d'Imeneo (Parma, 1760): Traetta.   SCHATZ 10392

    I fratelli riconosciuti, Parma, 1726 (Only the alterations in Silvani's La verità nell' inganno): Capello.   SCHATZ 1590

    Gl'Incà del Perù, Parma (1757). Tr. of Rameau's Les Incas du Pérou (Fuzelier).   SCHATZ 8588

    Ippolito ed Aricia, Mannheim (1759): Holzbauer.   SCHATZ 4784

    Iride. Act in his Le feste d'Imeneo: Traetta.

Frugoni, Carlo Innocenzio (Innocente)—Continued.

Medea riconosciuta, Die wiedererkannte Medea, Wien (1735):
    Vinci. Altered version of their Medo.   SCHATZ 10753
Medo, Torino, 1753: Abos.   SCHATZ 10
Medo, Parma, 1728: Vinci.   SCHATZ 10748
Saffo. Act in his Le feste d'Imeneo: Traetta.
Scipione in Cartagine nuova, Parma (1730): Giacomelli.   SCHATZ 3808
I Tintaridi (Firenze, 1768): Traetta.   SCHATZ 10400
Il trionfo d'amore. Prologue to his Le feste d'Imenco:
    Traetta.
Die wieder erkannte Medea. Tr. of his Medea riconosciuta,
    Wien (1735): Vinci.   SCHATZ 10753

Frugoni, Francesco Fulvio.

L'Epulone, Venetia, 1675: unknown.   PQ

Fusconi, Giovanni Battista.

Amore innamorato, Venetia, 1642: Cavalli.   SCHATZ 1734
Argiope, Venezia, 1649 (together with an anonymous author,
    possibly Pietro Michieli): Rovetta and Leardini (?).   SCHATZ 9106

Fuzelier (Fuselier), Louis.

Achmet et Almanzine. *See* Le Sage.
Les ages (Recueil général des opera, Paris, 1734, t. xii):
    Campra.   SCHATZ 1540
Amadis le cadet (Les parodies du Nouveau théâtre italien,
    Nouv. éd., Paris, 1738, t. ii). Parody of Destouches'
    Amadis de Grèce.   ML 48.P3
L'amour marin. *See* Le Sage.
Les amours déguisez (Recueil général des opéra, Paris, 1720,
    t. xi): Bourgeois.   SCHATZ 1272
Les amours des déesses (Recueil général des opéra, t. xiv,
    Paris, 1734): Quinault.   SCHATZ 8530
Les amours des dieux (Recueil général des opéra, t. xiv, Paris,
    1734): Mouret.   SCHATZ 6739
Les amours des dieux, Paris, 1757.   ML 52.2.A5
Les animaux raisonnables (Le théâtre de la foire, Paris, 1737,
    t. iii) (with Le Grand): Gillier.   ML 48.L2 III
Arion (Recueil général des opéra, Paris, t. xi, 1720): Matho.   SCHATZ 6097
Arlequin défenseur d'Homère (Le théâtre de la foire, Paris,
    1737, t. ii): Gillier.   ML 48.L2 I
Arlequin Endymion. *See* Le Sage.
Arlequin Persée (Les parodies du Nouveau théâtre italien,
    Nouv. éd., Paris, 1738, t. ii) (parody of Lully's Persée).   ML 48.P3
Les comediens corsaires. *See* Le Sage.
L'école des amans. *See* Le Sage.
L'enchanteur Mirliton. *See* Le Sage.
Les enragez. *See* Le Sage.
L'espérance. *See* Le Sage.
Les festes grecques et romaines (Recueil général des opéra,
    Paris, 1734, t. xiii): Colin de Blamont.   SCHATZ 1067
La forêt de Dodone. *See* Le Sage.
Fragments, composés du Prologue des Amour des dieux, etc.
    (Paris), 1765: Mouret, Dauvergne and Rameau.   ML 48.J7
La grand-mère amoureuse (Le théâtre de la foire, Paris, 1731,
    t. viii) (with d'Orneval): Gillier.   ML 48.L2 VIII

Fuzelier (Fuselier), Louis—Continued.

Hercule filant (Les parodies du Nouveau théatre italien, Nouv. éd., Paris, 1738, t. ii). ML 48.P3

Gl'Incà del Perù, Parma (1757). Tr. of his Les Incas du Pérou: Rameau. SCHATZ 8588

Les Incas du Perou (Paris) 1765 (Journal des spectacles, Paris, 1766, t. i): Rameau. ML 52.2.I5

Les Indes galantes (Paris) 1743: Rameau. ML 52.2.I4R2

Les Indes galantes (Recueil général des opéra, Paris, 1745, t. xvi): Rameau. ML 48.R4

L'indifférence. *See* Le Sage.

L'industrie. *See* Le Sage.

Le jeune vieillard. *See* Le Sage.

Momus exilé (Les parodies du Nouveau théatre italien, Nouv. éd., Paris, 1738, t. iii) (parody of the ballet Les élémens). ML 48.P3

L'ombre du cocher poète. *See* Le Sage.

Parodie, tragi-comedie (Les parodies du Nouveau théatre italien, Nouv. éd., Paris, 1738, t. ii). ML 48.P3 .

La Penelope moderne. *See* Le Sage.

Le Pharaon (Le théâtre de la foire, Paris, 1737, t. ii): Gillier. ML 48.L2 ii

Le Pharaon (Théâtre de la foire, Paris, 1737, t. ii): Gillier. ML 48.L2 ii

Pierrot Romulus ou Le ravisseur poli. *See* Le Sage.

Prologue des Indes galantes (Paris), 1765 (Journal des spectacles, Paris, 1766, t. i): Rameau. (Entrée in their Les Indes galantes.) ML 48.J7

Le ravisseur poli. A. T. of his Pierrot Romulus.

Le régiment de la Calotte. *See* Le Sage.

La reine des Péris (Recueil général des opéra, Paris, 1734, t. xiii): Aubert. SCHATZ 486

Le remouleur d'amour. *See* Le Sage.

Les routes du monde. *See* Le Sage.

Les sauvages (Paris), 1765 (Journal des spectacles, t. i, Paris, 1766): Rameau. (Entrée in their Les Indes galantes.) ML 48.J7

Le serdeau des théatres (Les parodies du Nouveau théatre italien, Nouv. éd., Paris, 1738, t. ii) (parody of Pirithoüs). ML 48.P3

Le tableau du mariage. *See* Le Sage.

Le temple de l'ennuy. *See* Le Sage.

Le temple de mémoire. *See* Le Sage.

Zemine et Almanzor. *See* Le Sage.

G * *

Zwo komische operetten, Chemnitz, 1773 ("Das vornehme Suschen" and "Das testament"): unknown. SCHATZ 11655

G., G. S.

Farsa per musica [Imene ed Armonia], Firenze, 1762: Meli. ML 48.M2F

Gabrieli, Giacomo.

Amalasunta, Venezia, 1719: Chelleri. SCHATZ 1811

Gabrielli, Diamante.

Psiche, Mantova, 1649: Leardini. ML 50.2.P78L3

Theti . . . Niobe, Mantova, 1652: Bertali. SCHATZ 872–873

Gaizzardi, Giovanni Battista.

Laomedonte, Venezia, 1715: Baseggio. SCHATZ 619

Galiani, Ferdinando.

Socrate immaginario—Der eingebildete Sokrates (with G. Lorenzi), Dresda, 1781: Paisiello. Schatz 7658

Galleotti (Galeotti), Vincenzo.

Amore e Psiche, ballet: Le Messier. *See* Bertoni's Tancredi.

La caccia d'Enrico Quarto, ballet. *See* Anfossi's Demofoonte.

Il convitato di pietra, ballet: Le Messier. *See* Bertoni's Tancredi.

La dolce vendetta, ballet. *See* Anfossi's Demofoonte.

Gallet, Sebastien (Sebastiano).

Aci e Galatea, ballet: Canavasso. *See* Curzio's Solimano.

Amor può tutto ossia Il trionfo del valore, ballet: pasticcio. *See* P. Guglielmi's Ademira.

L'amor vincitore ossia Diana ed Endimione, ballet. *See* Bianchi's La villanella rapita.

L'amor vincitore, ballet. *See* Salieri's Il talismano.

L'amore maestro di scuola, ballet. *See* Rispoli's Ipermestra.

Annibale in Torino, ballet: Canavasso. *See* Tarchi's Bacco ed Arianna.

Bacchus et Ariane, Paris (1791): Rochefort. ML 52.2.B1R6

Bacco ed Arianna, ballet. *See* Insanguine's Motezuma.

Il Bajram de' Turchi, ballet. *See* Salieri's Il talimano.

Il Beiram o sia Il carnevale turco, ballet: Canavasso. *See* Curzio's Solimano.

Chi ne fa ne aspetta, ballet. *See* Cimarosa's Volodomiro.

La conquista del Perù. A. T. of his ballet Pizarro nell' America.

La contatina nel palazzo signorile. A. T. of his ballet Ninetta: Canavasso.

Diana ed Endimione. A. T. of his ballet L'amor vincitore.

Di rado l'uom sa giudicar se stesso, ballet. *See* P. Guglielmi's Alessandro nell' Indie.

Il disertore, ballet. *See* P. Guglielmi's L'impostore punito.

Enea e Turno, ballet: Canavasso. *See* Bianchi's Briseide.

L'enlevement des Sabines, ballet: Alessandri. *See* Ferrero's La disfatta di Dario.

La fiera di Batavia, ballet: Canavasso. *See* Curzio's Solimano.

Il guerrier generoso, ballet. *See* Insanguine's Motezuma.

L'incoronazione di Siroe, ballet: Canavasso. *See* Sarti's Siroe.

Lauso e Lidia, ballet: Canavasso. *See* Rust's Adriano in Siria.

Ludovico il Moro, ballet. *See* Rispoli's Ipermestra.

Ludovico Sforza detto Il Moro, ballet. *See* Cimarosa's Volodomiro.

Il manescalco, ballet: Canavasso. *See* Rust's Adriano in Siria.

Il maniscalco francese, ballet. *See* Mortellari's Semiramide.

Il maniscalco francese, ballet. *See* Zingarelli's Alsinda.

Ninetta o sia La contadina nel palazzo signorile, ballet: Canavasso. *See* Sarti's Siroe.

Le pazzie amorose, ballet. *See* Bianchi's La villanella rapita.

Le pazzie amorose, ballet. *See* P. Guglielmi's L'impostore punito.

Il Pizarro nell' America, ossia La conquista del Perù, ballet. *See* Tarchi's Demofoonte.

Gallet, Sebastien (Sebastiano)—Continued.

Popolo d'Argo, ballet. *See* Rispoli's Ipermestra.

Porzia, ballet. *See* Alessandri's Calliroe.

Le rapt des Sabines, ballet. *See* P. Guglielmi's L'impostore punito.

Il ratto delle Sabine, ballet. *See* Mortellari's Semiramide.

Telemaco nell' isola di Calipso, ballet: Pietro Dutillieu. *See* P. Guglielmi's Alessandro nell' Indie.

Il rè pastore, ballet. *See* Sarti's Giulio Sabino.

Rinaldo nella Selva incantata, ballet: Canavasso. *See* Sarti's Siroe.

Il signore benefico, ballet. *See* Salieri's Il talismano.

Il signore benefico, ballet: Canavasso. *See* Tarchi's Il trionfo di Clelia.

Il signore benefico, ballet. *See* Zingarelli's Alsinda.

Gli sventurati amori di Cleide ed Almindo o sia Il trionfo de' Goti, ballet: Ercolano. *See* Bianchi's La vendetta di Nino.

Il tempio della pazzia, ballet. *See* Insanguine's Motezuma.

Il trionfo de' Goti. A. T. of his ballet Gli sventurati amori di Cleide ed Almindo: Ercolano. *See* Bianchi's La vendetta di Nino.

Il trionfo del valore. A. T. of his Amor può tutto.

Il trionfo dell' Amore fra i pastori, ballet. *See* Sarti's Giulio Sabino.

La viaggiatrice o sia Le circostanze imbarazzanti, ballet: Canavasso. *See* Bianchi's Briseide.

Il Vologeso, ballet. *See* Gazzaniga's Circe.

Galuppi, Antonio.

L'amante di tutte, Urbino, 1761: Bald. Galuppi.	SCHATZ 3432
L'amante di tutte, Firenze, 1764: Bald. Galuppi.	ML 48A v.20
L'amante di tutte—Der liebhaber von allen, Dresda, 1770: Bald. Galuppi.	SCHATZ 3433
Den flanevurne kone. Tr. of his L'amante di tutte, Kiøbenhavn (1763) (as retouched by Chiari under the title La moglie bizzarra): Bald. Galuppi.	SCHATZ 3434
Der liebhaber von allen. Tr. of his L'amante di tutte, Dresda, 1770: Bald. Galuppi.	SCHATZ 3433
La moglie bizzarra—Den flanevurne kone, Kiøbenhavn (1763). L. T. of his L'amante di tutte (as retouched by Chiari): Bald. Galuppi.	SCHATZ 3434
Li tre amanti ridicoli, Gubbio (1765): Bald. Galuppi.	SCHATZ 3471
Il vecchio geloso (Vienna, 1767). L. T. of his L'amante di tutte: Bald. Galuppi.	SCHATZ 3510

Gambino, Francesco Sebastiano.

Briseide, Torino (1784): F. Bianchi.	SCHATZ 1002

Gambuzzi, Innocenzo.

I baccanali, ballet. *See* Bianchi's Il disertore.

La donna militare. A. T. of his ballet Il seguito tra l'armi.

Enea nel Lazio, ballet: Bonazzi. *See* Sarti's Il trionfo della pace.

La favola d'Apollo e Dafne, ballet: Canssoava. *See* Rispoli's Nitteti.

Gambuzzi, Innocenzo—Continued.

Le gelosie villane in Montefosco, ballet: Canavasso. *See* Martin y Soler's Vologeso.

Germanico in Germania, ballet: Gatti. *See* Rossetti's Olimpiade.

Giaccona, ballet. *See* Rossetti's Olimpiade.

Il macchinista ossia La susta matematica, ballet: Canavasso. *See* Martin y Soler's Vologeso.

Il matrimonio de' Groelandesi, ballet: Canavasso. *See* Rispoli's Nitteti.

Il matrimonio de' Groenlandesi, ballet. *See* Rossetti's Olimpiade.

Medonte, ballet: Mattei. *See* Cavi's La prepotenza delusa.

Medonte, ballet: Mattei. *See* Salari's L'amore rammingo.

Il mercato d'Amacari Danase, ballet. *See* Boroni's Le orfane svizzere.

Il pellegrinaggio o sia La vindemmia fiamminga, ballet: Bonazzi. *See* Sarti's Il trionfo della pace.

La pescatrice fedele, ballet. *See* Boroni's Le orfane svizzere.

Il seguito tra l'armi o sia La donna militare, ballet. *See* Salari's L'amore rammingo.

La sposa peruviana, ballet: Canavasso. *See* Martin y Soler's Vologeso.

Le vendemmie fiamminghe, ballet. *See* Bianchi's Il disertore.

La vindemmia fiamminga. A. T. of his ballet Il pellegrinaggio: Bonazzi.

Gamerra, Giovanni de (di).

Adrasto rè d'Egitto, Milano (1792): Tarchi.	Schatz 10233
Gli amanti in Tempe, Firenze, 1792: Andreozzi.	Schatz 216
L'amor marinaro—Die liebe im matrosenkleide, Dresda, 1798: Weigl.	Schatz 10926
L'Armida, Milano (1771): unknown.	Schatz 11309
Armida, Milano (1772): Sacchini.	Schatz 9205
Armida, Piacenza (1786): Sacchini.	Schatz 11745
Arsace, Venezia, 1788. (L. T. of his Medonte rè di Epiro): P. Guglielmi.	Schatz 4297
Arsace, Venezia, 1775: Mortellari.	Schatz 6685
La calamita de cuori (Vienna, 1774): Salieri.	Schatz 9276
La calamita de cuori—Der magnetstein der herzen, Dresda, 1776: Salieri.	Schatz 9277
Cleomene, Bologna (1789): Sarti.	Schatz 9428
Cleomene, Perugia, 1791: Sarti.	ML 48.A5 v.7
Daliso e Delmita, Padova (1789). (L. T. of his Delmita e Daliso): Bianchi.	Schatz 997
Daliso e Delmita (Vienna, 1776): Salieri. L. T. of their Delmita e Daliso.	ML 48. A5v.45
Delmita e Daliso. O. T. of his Daliso e Delmita.	
I due vedovi—Der wittwer und die wittwe, Dresda, 1798: Winter.	Schatz 11029
Eraclito e Democrito—Heraclit und Democrit, Berlino (1795): Salieri.	Schatz 9287
Erifile, Modena (1781): Bianchi.	Schatz 989
Erifile, Genova (1783): G. Giordani.	Schatz 3844

Gamerra, Giovanni de (di)—Continued.

Erifile, Torino (1786): Monza.	SCHATZ 6614
Erifile regina di Lacinto, Sassari, 1784: Sacchini.	SCHATZ 9244
Il flauto magico (Dresda) 1794. Tr. of Mozart's Die zauber-flote (Schikaneder).	SCHATZ 6850
Giulietta e Pierotto, Vienna (1794): Weigl.	SCHATZ 10934
Giulietta e Pierotto—Julchen und Peter, Dresda, 1796: Weigl.	SCHATZ 10935
Heraclit und Democrit. Tr. of his Eraclito e Democrito, Berlino (1795): Salieri.	SCHATZ 9287
Julchen und Peter. Tr. of his Giulietta e Pierotto, Dresda, 1796: Weigl.	SCHATZ 10935
Die liebe im matrosenkleide. Tr. of his L'amor marinaro, Dresda, 1798: Weigl.	SCHATZ 10926
Lucio Silla, Venezia (1774): Anfossi.	SCHATZ 243
Lucio Silla, Mannheim (1773): Bach. (Text altered by Verazi.)	SCHATZ 529
Lucius Silla, Mannheim (1774) (altered by Verazi): Bach. Tr. of their Lucio Silla.	SCHATZ 530
Lucio Silla, Torino (1779): Mortellari.	SCHATZ 6682
Der magnetstein der herzen. Tr. of his La calamita de cuori, Dresda, 1776: Salieri.	SCHATZ 9277
Medonte, Torino (1778): Bertoni.	SCHATZ 923
Medonte, Napoli, 1779: Insanguine.	SCHATZ 4836
Medonte, rè di Epiro. O. T. of his Arsace.	
Medonte rè di Epiro, Milano (1790): Pio.	SCHATZ 8187
Medonte re di Epiro, Venezia, 1778: Radicchi.	SCHATZ 8539
Medonte, Napoli, 1783: Sarti (with interpolations).	SCHATZ 9447
Medonte, rè di Epiro. O. T. of this opera.	
Il Moro—Der mohr, Dresda, 1797: Salieri.	SCHATZ 9303
Palmira, Stuttgart, 1797. Tr. of his Palmira regina di Persia: Salieri.	SCHATZ 9307
Palmira regina di Persia, Vienna (1795): Salieri.	SCHATZ 9305
Palmira regina di Persia—Palmira koenigin von Persien, Dresda, 1797: Salieri.	SCHATZ 9306
Pirro, rè di Epiro, Milano (1792). L. T. of the above, with alterations.	SCHATZ 11261
Il Pirro, Parma, 1799: Zingarelli.	SCHATZ 11253
Il Sismano nel Mogol, Cremona (1785): Paisiello.	SCHATZ 7697
Der wittwer und die wittwe. Tr. of his I due vedovi, Dresda, 1798: Winter.	SCHATZ 11029

Gandini, Carlo.

La caduta d'Amulio, Venezia, 1747: Pampani.	SCHATZ 7757

Gardel, Maximilien Léopold Philippe Joseph.

La chercheuse d'esprit, Paris, 1777, ballet: unknown.	ML 52.2.C28
Les Graces (Paris) 1779: unknown.	ML 52.2.G7
Mirsa, Paris, 1779.	ML 52.2.M4
Ninette à la cour, (Paris) 1777: unknown.	ML 52.2.N4
Le premier navigateur ou Le pouvoir de l'amour, Paris, 1785: pasticcio from Grétry.	ML 52.2.P6
La Rosiere, Paris, 1783: unknown.	ML 48.B2

Gardel, Pierre (*called* **Cadet**).

    Le jugement de Paris, Paris, an VI [1797–98] ballet: Haydn,
        Pleyel, Méhul.   ML 52.2J9

    Télémaque dans l'isle de Calipso, Paris, 1790, ballet: Miller.   ML 48.B2

Garrick, David.

    A Christmas tale, London, 1774: Dibdin.   Longe 16

    Cymon, London, 1767: M. Arne.   Longe 46

    Cymon (Collection of the most esteemed farces, Edinburgh,
        1792, t. iii).   Schatz 11753C

    Cymon (I. Bell's British Theatre, 1791–97, v. 29).   PR 1241.B4

    The enchanter, or, Love and magic, London, 1760: Smith.   Longe 306

    The fairies, London, 1755: Smith. (G.'s authorship doubtful.)   ML 50.2.F14

    The fairies, 2d ed., London, 1755: Smith.   ML 50.2.F142

    King Arthur or The British worthy, London, 1781. (Altered
        from Dryden): Purcell and Arne.   Longe 251

    May-day or The little gipsy, London, 1775: Arne.   Longe 78

    May-day or The little gipsy (Collection of the most esteemed
        farces, Edinburgh, 1792, t. vi): Arne.   Schatz 11753F

    A peep behind the curtain or The new rehearsal (incl. the
        musical burletta "Orpheus") London, 1767: Barthé-
        lemon.   ML 50.2.P31

    A peep behind the curtain or The new rehearsal (incl. the
        musical burletta "Orpheus") new ed., London, 1772:
        Barthélemon.   Longe 27

    The theatrical candidates (together with his May-day) Lon-
        don, 1775: Bates.   Longe 78

    The theatrical candidates (Collection of the most esteemed
        faces, Edinburgh, 1792, t. vi): Bates.   Schatz 11753F

    The theatrical candidates, n. i., n. d. (detached).   Longe 239

Garzia, Urbano.

    Gli amanti ridicoli ossia La capricciosa umiliata, ballet. *See*
        Tritto's Le avventure galanti.

    Le Amazoni moderne o sia Il ribello per amore, ballet. *See*
        Sarti's Cleomene.

    Il Bruto milanese ossia La congiura contro Galeazzo Maria
        Sforza Visconti, ballet. *See* Nasolini's Il trionfo di Clelia.

    La capricciosa umiliata. A. T. of his ballet Gli amanti
        ridicoli.

    Carlo e Carolina, ballet. *See* Cimarosa's Li amanti comici.

    La cosa rara, ballet. *See* Tarchi's Lo spazzacamino principe.

    Emirena e Sigismondo, ballet. *See* Tritto's Le avventure
        galanti.

    L'equivoco fortunato, ballet: *See* Gnecco's L'indolente

    Federico II, rè di Prussia, ballet. *See* Salieri's Axur, rè
        d'Ormus, Milan, 1792.

    Ginevra di Scozia, ballet. *See* Gnecco's L'indolente.

    Giulia e Blinval, ballet. *See* Bianchi's Il chinese in Italia

    Gonzalvo in America, ballet. *See* G. Nicolini's Gli Sciti.

    Il marito umiliato ossia La moglie di spirito, ballet. *See*
        Cimarosa's Li amanti comici.

    I matrimonj per inganno, ballet. *See* Nicolini's Gli Sciti.

    Il matrimonio per astuzia, ballet. *See* Bianchi's Il chinese
        in Italia.

Garzia, Urbano—Continued.

L'oracolo, ballet. *See* Nasolini's Il trionfo di Clelia.

Il quadro animato, ballet. *See* Portugal's Lo spazzacamino principe.

Il ribello per amore. A. T. of his ballet Le Amazoni moderne.

Il tutor medico deluso, ballet. *See* Sarti's Cleomene.

La villeggiatura in scompiglio, ossia Il falso amico, ballet. *See* G. Giordani's Cajo Mario.

Gasbarri, Gaetano.

L'amor per interesse, Napoli, 1797: Fioravanti.　　　SCHATZ 3112

Gasparini, Marc' Antonio.

L'Alciade overo La violenza d'amore, Milano, 1709 (originally overo L'eroico amore): F. Gasperini, C. F. Polaroli, and Ballarotti.　　　SCHATZ 3597

L'amante impazzito, Venetia (1714). L. T. of his L'Alciade overo La violenza d'amore: Gasparini, Polaroli and Ballarotti.　　　SCHATZ 3598

Zenocrate, ambasciatore a' Macedoni, Venetia, 1687: Porfiri. SCHATZ 8356

Gataker, Thomas.

The jealous clown or The lucky mistake, London, 1730: ballad opera.　　　LONGE 136

Gay, John.

Achilles, London, 1733: ballad opera.　　　ML 50.5.B3

Achilles, London, 1777: ballad opera.　　　SCHATZ 11469

The beggar's opera, London, 1728 (1st ed.): arr. by Pepusch (ballad opera).　　　ML 50.5.B3

The beggar's opera, London, 1729.　　　ML 50.5.B33

The beggar's opera, Fifth ed., London, 1742.　　　AC 901.M5 v.519

The beggar's opera, London, 1765.　　　ML 50.5.B35

The beggar's opera, London, 1777.　　　SCHATZ 7864

The beggar's opera, London, 1791 (Bell's British theatre, London, 1791–97, t. 2).　　　PR 1241.B4

The beggar's opera, London, Cooke (before 1800?).　　　PR 3473.B4C6

Polly, London, 1729: ballad opera, arr. by Pepusch.　　　ML 50.5.P74

Polly, London, n. d.　　　ML 50.5.B3

Polly, London, 1777.　　　SCHATZ 7865

Gazal, D.

Cloris und Tirsis—Clori e Tirsi (Hamburg): 1719. Tr. and L. T. of Conti's I satiri in Arcadia.　　　SCHATZ 2196

Gemmingen, Otto Heinrich, *reichsfreiherr* **von.**

Pygmalion, Mannheim, 1778. Tr. of Pygmalion: Coignet and Rousseau (Rousseau).　　　SCHATZ 2096

Gentili, Giacomo.

Aci e Galatea, ballet. *See* Tarchi's Il matrimonio per contrattempo.

Gl'amanti delusi, ballet. *See* Sarti's Cleomene.

Il bottaro, ballet. *See* P. Guglielmi's Arsinoe e Breno.

Esione liberata, ballet. *See* Sarti's Cleomene.

La felicità nata dalle sventure, ballet. *See* P. Guglielmi's Arsinoe e Breno.

Il tutore in scompiglio, ballet. *See* Tarchi's Il matrimonio per contrattempo.

Gentleman, Francis.
Cupid's revenge, London, 1772: Hook.   LONGE 244

Gerstenberg, Heinrich Wilhelm von.
Minona oder Die Angelsachsen, Hamburg, 1785: Schulz.   SCHATZ 9724

Geysbeck, P. C. Witsen.
Eufrosine, Amsteldam, 1798. Tr. of Méhul's Euphrosine (Hoffmann).   SCHATZ 6274

Ghelardini, Gaetano.
L'inverno ossia La pianella perduta, ballet. *See* P. Gugliel-mi's Le due gemelle.
La pianella perduta. A. T. of his ballet L'inverno.
La villanella rapita. A. T. of his ballet Le vendemmie.
Le vendemmie, o sia La villanella rapita, ballet. *See* Sarti's Fra i due litiganti il terzo gode, Lisboa, 1793.

Ghelen, Johann Anton, *edler* von.
Alcides an der doppel-strasse (Wien, 1760). Tr. of Hasse's Alcide al bivio (Metastasio).   SCHATZ 4506
Artaxerxes, Wien (1763). Tr. of Gius. Scarlatti's Artaserse (Metastasio).   SCHATZ 9541
Die baeurinn bey hofe, Wienn (1767). Tr. of Sacchini's La contadina in corte (unknown).   SCHATZ 9214
Hypsipile (Wien, 1760). Tr. of Gius. Scarlatti's Issipile (Metastasio).   SCHATZ 9549
Merope, Wien (1749). Tr. of Jommelli's Merope (Zeno).   SCHATZ 4866
Die triumphierende Claelia (Wien, 1762). Tr. of Hasse's Il trionfo di Clelia (Metastasio).   SCHATZ 4567

Ghigi (Ghisi), Stefano.
Flavio Bertarido rè de Longobardi, Venezia, 1706: C. F. Pol-laroli.   SCHATZ 8290
Flavius Bertaridus, koenig der Longobarden (Hamburg, 1729): Telemann. (Tr. of his Flavio Bertarido, rè de' Longo-bardi.)   SCHATZ 10260

Gianni, Nicola.
L'annore resarciuto, Napole, 1727: Orefice.   ML 50.2.A715O7

Giacomini, Giuseppe.
Il Corindo, Firenze, 1680: unknown.   SCHATZ 11316

Giannini, Giovanni Battista (Giambattista).
Aci e Galatea, ballet. *See* Cimarosa's Il fanatico burlato.
Annetta e Fierillo, ballet: Capuzzi. *See* Millico's La Zelinda.
L'amanti schiavi, ballet. *See* Piccinni's Ercoleal Terme-donte.
Astarbea ossia Pimmalione vendicato, ballet: Dutillieu. *See* Anfossi's Il matrimonio per fanatisimo.
L'Aurora vendicata, ballet. *See* P. Guglielmi's La pastorella nobile.
La calzolaja tedesca, ballet. *See* Fioravanti's Le cantatrici villane.
Il difficile per inganno facile, ballet. *See* Andreozzi's Il dis-prezzo vinto.
La disfatta de' Marocchini. A. T. of his Il trionfo de' Spag-noli: Dutillieu.

Giannini, Giovanni Battista (Giambattista)—Continued.

Gli Europei nell' isola de' canibali, ballet. *See* Piccinni's Ercole al Termedonte.

La fata benefica, ballet: Paisiello and Ercolani. *See* Cimarosa's I nemici generosi.

La fata benefica, ballet. *See* P. Guglielmi's Admeto.

La Ginevra degli Almieri, ballet. *See* Cimarosa's L'apprensivo raggirato.

L'infedeltà sorpresa, ballet. *See* Tritto's La vergine del sole.

Inganno ed amor van sempre insieme, ballet. *See* Ruggi's La guerra aperta.

Gl'inglesi in America, ballet: Ercolano. *See* Bianchi's Il ritratto.

L'isola de' cannibali, ballet. *See* Tritto's La molinara spiritosa.

Il maestro di cappella o sia Il tutore deluso, ballet. *See* Cimarosa's Il fanatico burlato.

Magia contro magia, ballet: Dutillieu. *See* Bernardini's L'ultima che si perde è la speranza.

Magia contra magia, ballet: Dutillieu. *See* P. Guglielmi's L'Azzardo.

Il moro di corpo bianco o sia Lo schiavo del proprio onore, ballet: Ercolano. *See* P. Guglielmi's La sposa contrastata.

Lo moro di corpo bianco o sia Lo schiavo del proprio senso, ballet. *See* Marinelli's Amore aguzza l'ingegno.

La morte di Meleagro, ballet: Ercolano. *See* Tritto's L'equivoco.

Orbecch, ballet: Dutillieu. *See* Fioravanti's Gl'inganni fortunati.

Pimmalione vendicato. A. T. of his ballet Astarbea: Dutillieu.

Il pittor burlato, ballet. *See* Anfossi's Zenobia in Palmira.

Il quacquero burlato, ballet. *See* Caruso's Gli amanti dispettosi.

Le reclute villane, ballet. *See* Caruso's Gli amanti dispettosi.

Lo schiavo del proprio onore. A. T. of his ballet Il moro di corpo bianco: Ercolano.

Il Tancredi, ballet. *See* Tritto's La vergine del sole.

Il trionfo de' Spagnoli o sia La disfatta de' Marrocchini, ballet: Dutillieu. *See* Bernardini's Amore per incanto.

Il trionfo de' Spagnoli o sia La disfatta de' Marocchini, ballet: Dutillieu. *See* Bernardini's La donna bizarra.

Il tutore deluso. A. T. of his ballet Il maestro di cappella.

Il Zorilan, ballet. *See* Anfossi's Zenobia in Palmira.

Zorilan, ballet: mainly from Paisiello's compositions. *See* Cimarosa's L'impegno superato.

Giannini, Giovanni Matteo (Gianmatteo).

Adone in Cipro, Venetia, 1676: Legrenzi.	Schatz 5540

Almansore o sia Il pregiudizio che nasce dal mancare di parola. O. T. of his:

L'Almansore in Alimena, Venetia (1703): C. F. Pollaroli.	Schatz 8269
Il Nicomede in Bitinia, Venetia, 1677: Grossi.	Schatz 4218
Onorio in Roma, Venetia, 1692: C. F. Pollaroli.	Schatz 8305

Il pregiudizio che nasce dal mancare di parola. A. T. of his Almansore: C. F. Pollaroli.

Gieseke, Johann Georg Carl Ludwig.

Der travestirte Hamlet (Vienna) 1799: Tuczek. SCHATZ 10506
Die zauberflöte. *See* Title catalogue.
Die zwölf schlafenden jungfrauen, Wien, 1798: Stegmayer. SCHATZ 10052

Gigli, Girolamo.

L'amor fra gl'impossibili, Ancona, 1727: Mastini. SCHATZ 6095
Amore dottorato, con le Conclusioni difese da lui nel Tempio
della Virtù, Siena (1691): unknown. ML 48.A5 v.46
Amore fra gl'Impossibili, Roma & Siena, 1693: Campelli. SCHATZ 1532
Anagilda, Venezia, 1749: unknown. SCHATZ 11302
L'Anagilda, Roma (1711): Caldara. SCHATZ 1491
Dorina e Grullo, intermezzi: Caldara. *In their* L'Anagilda,
Rome (1711). SCHATZ 1491
La fede ne' tradimenti, Faenza (1723): Buini. ML 48.A5 v.4
La fede ne' tradimenti, Siena, 1689: Fabbrini. SCHATZ 2962
La fede ne' tradimenti, Siena, 1689 (3 p. l., 48 p.): Fabbrini. ML 50.2.F24F2
La fede ne' tradimenti, Venezia, 1721: Pietragrua. SCHATZ 8165
La fede ne tradimenti, Venezia, 1705 (with alterations by
Giuseppe Beretta): C. F. Pollaroli. SCHATZ 8288
La fede ne' tradimenti, Napoli, 1718: Sarro. SCHATZ 9415
La forza d'amore, Siena (*ca.* 1690): Fabbrini. ML 48.A5 v.46
La forza del sangue e della pietà, Siena, 1686: Fabbrini. SCHATZ 2963
La Geneviefa, Siena (1685): Fabbrini. ML 50.2.G29
Lodovico Pio, Siena, 1687: Fabbrini. ML 50.2.L4F2

Gilbert, Gabriel.

Les peines et les plaisirs (Recueil général des opéra, Paris,
1703, t. i): Cambert. SCHATZ 1520

Gioanetti, Rocco.

Le feste di Flora, ballet. *See* Jommelli's Bajazet.

Gioja, Gaetano.

La contadina impertinente. A. T. of his ballet La vin-
demmia.
Cora o La vergine del sole, ballet. *See* Tarchi's La Danaidi.
La costanza premiata o sia Il genio tutelare, ballet. *See* An-
dreozzi's Arsinoe.
La disfatta di Abdurahamel, tiranno di Trabacca, ballet. *See*
Andreozzi's Argea.
Elfrida, ballet. *See* Zingarelli's Artaserse.
Il feudatorio pentito, ballet. *See* Zingarelli's Artaserse.
Nina pazza per amore, ballet. *See* Andreozzi's Argea.
Gli Orazi e i Curiazi, ballet. *See* Basili's Il ritorno d'Ulisse.
La vergine del sole. A. T. of his ballet Cora.
La volubile, ballet. *See* Andreozzi's Argea.
La volubile, ballet. *See* Basili's Il ritorno d'Ulisse.
La vindemmia o La contadina impertinente, ballet. *See*
Tarchi's Le Danaidi.

Giotti, Cosimo.

Ines de Castro, Firenze, 1793: Andreozzi. SCHATZ 213

Giovannini, Pietro.

Epponina. O. T. of his Giulio Sabino.
Giulio Sabino, Venezia, 1781: Sarti. SCHATZ 9438
Giulio Sabino, Genova (1781): Sarti. SCHATZ 9440

Giovannini, Pietro—Continued.

Giulio Sabino—Julius Sabinus, Vienna, 1785: Sarti.   SCHATZ 9439

Giulio Sabino, Firenze, 1785: Sarti.   SCHATZ 11747

Giulio Sabino, London, 1788: Sarti.   SCHATZ 9441

Giulio Sabino, Lisbona, 1798: Sarti.   ML 48.C6 XXII

Giulio Sabino, Torino (1790): Tarchi.   SCHATZ 10220

Julius Sabinus. Tr. of his Giulio Sabino, Vienna, 1785:
Sarti.   SCHATZ 9439

Julius Sabinus, Pressburg, 1785. Tr. of his Giulio Sabino:
Sarti.   SCHATZ 9442

Julius Sabinus, Nuernberg, 1791. Tr. of his Giulio Sabino:
Sarti.   SCHATZ 9479

Giržick, Franz Xavier.

Axur, Koenig von Ormus, Pressburg, 1788. Tr. of Salieri's
Axur rè d'Ormus (Da Ponte).   SCHATZ 9328

Die christliche Judenbraut, Augsburg, 1793: Panek.   SCHATZ 7762

Gisberti, Domenico.

Amor tiranno, Bologna, 1649: D. Pellegrini.   SCHATZ 7859

Le barbarie del caso, Venetia, 1664: Molinari.   SCHATZ 6548

Il Caligola, Roma, 1674: Pagliardi. L. T. of: SCHATZ 7586

Caligula delirante, Venetia, 1672: Pagliardi. (The O. T. of
the text (not of the opera) had been "La pazzia in trono
ovvero Caligola delirante."   SCHATZ 7582

La pazzia in trono, ovvero Caligola delirante. O. T. of his
Caligula delirante.

Giudice, Pietro.

La caccia d'Enrico IV, ballet: unknown. *See* P. Guglielmi's
Le due gemelle.

Giunti, Antonio.

Das hochzeitsfest des Amors und der Norizia, Monaco (1765).
Tr. of Sales' Le nozze di Amore e di Norizia (Eugenio
Giunti).   SCHATZ 9268

Giunti, Eugenio.

Das hochzeitsfest des Amors und der Norizia, Muenchen
(1765). Tr. of his Le nozze di Amore e di Norizia: Sales.   SCHATZ 9268

(Le nozze di Amore e di Norizia)—Das hochzeitsfest des Amors
und der Norizia, Monaco (1765): Sales.   SCHATZ 9268

Scipione, Venezia, 1778: Sarti.   SCHATZ 9474

Scipione in Cartagena—Scipio in Kartagena, Monaco (1770):
Sacchini.   SCHATZ 9240

Semiramide—Semiramis, Monaco, 1765 (only the licenza):
Bernasconi.   SCHATZ 860

Giusti, Alvise.

Argenide, Venezia, 1738: Chiarini.   SCHATZ 1853

Argenide, Venezia, 1733: Galuppi.   SCHATZ 3481

Motezuma, Venezia (1733): Vivaldi.   SCHATZ 10773

Giusti, Girolamo.

Belmira in Creta, Venezia, 1729: Galeazzi.   SCHATZ 3419

Giuvo, Nicolò.

La Cassandra indovina, Napoli, 1713: Fago.   SCHATZ 2980

Il Radamisto, Venezia, 1707: Fago.   SCHATZ 2981

Glauche.

Otto (Hamburg, 1726).   Tr. of Pallavicino-Haym's Ottone:
Händel.   Schatz 4482

Glodoci, Loran, *anagram of* Carlo Goldoni.

Gnecco, Francesco.

Auretta e Masullo, ossia Il contratempo, Genova (1792): author.   Schatz 3958

Godi, Giovanni Cesare.

Eraclea, Venetia, 1696: Sabadini.   Schatz 9195

Goethe, Johann Wolfgang von.

Claudine af Villa Bella, Kiøbenhavn (1787): Schall.   Tr. of
his Claudine von Villa Bella.   Schatz 9584
Claudine von Villa Bella, Leipzig, Göschen, 1788 (Ächte aus-
gabe—"Pedro von Rovero").   PT 1915.C2
Claudine von Villa Bella, Wien, 1780: von Becke.   Schatz 677
Claudine von Villa Bella, Berlin, 1789: Reichardt.   Schatz 8640
Erwin und Elmire, Frankfurt und Leipzig, 1775.   Schatz 186
Erwin und Elmire, Leipzig, Göschen, 1788 (Ächte ausgabe). PT 1915.E8   1788
Erwin und Elmire, Regensburg, n. d.   Schatz 11453
Die fischerinn, n. i., 1782: Schröter.   Schatz 9696
Jery und Bätely, Leipzig, Göschen, 1790. ("Ächte aus-
gabe"—"zurück tretend" in two words.)   PT 1958.J5   1790
Jery und Bätely, Leipzig, Göschen, 1790. ("Ächte aus-
gabe"—"zurücktretend" in one word.)   PT 1958.J5   1790a
Scherz, list und rache, Leipzig, Göschen, 1790. ("Ächte
ausgabe"—"Er ist bitter").   PT 1958.S4   1790
Scherz, list und rache, Leipzig, Göschen, 1790. ("Ächte
ausgabe"—"Es ist bitter.")   PT 1958.S4   1790a

Goetz, Joseph Fr. *baron* **von.**

Lenardo und Blandine (Augsburg, 1785): Winter.   Schatz 11040

Gogel, I. J. A.

De apothecar en de doctor, Amsteldam, 1796.   Tr. of Dittersdorf's Der apotheker und der doktor (Stephanie d. jüng.) Schatz 2611

Goldoni, Carlo.

Opere drammatiche giocose del Signor dottore Carlo Goldoni
fra gli Arcadi Polisseno Fegejo.
*Torino, Nella Stamperia reale, a spese di A. Olzati, 1757.   4 v.
16½cm.*   ML 49.A2 G6
Opere teatrali.
Venezia, Antonio Zatta e figli, 1788–1795.   44 v.   18½cm.
Vols. 35–44 have the title "Drammi giocosi per musica."   They were pub-
lished 1794–95.   PQ

The accomplish'd maid, London, 1767.   Tr. of his La buona
figliuola: Piccinni.   Longe 32
The accomplish'd maid, Philadelphia, 1777: Piccinni.   Tr.
of their La buona figliuola.   ML 50.6 A2
L'amante cabala (Opere drammatiche giocose, t. iv, Torino,
1757).   ML 49.A2G6
L'amante cabala (Opere teatrali, Venezia, Zatta e figli, 1788–
95, t. 35).   PQ

Goldoni, Carlo—Continued.

L'amor artigiano (Venezia, 1776): Schuster.	Schatz 9759
Amor contadino, Venezia, 1760: Lampugnani.	Schatz 5386
L'amor contadino—Bønderfolks elskov, Kiøbenhavn (1763): Lampugnani.	Schatz 5387
Amor fa l'uomo cieco (Opere teatrali, Venezia, Zatta e figli, 1788–95, v. 35).	PQ
Amore artigiano (Opere teatrali, Venezia, Zatta e figli, 1788–95, v. 37).	PQ
L'amore artigiano, Roma, 1788: Accorimboni.	Schatz 16
L'amore artigiano, Firenze, 1770: Gassmann.	Schatz 3608*
L'amore artigiano, Milano (1782): Gassmann.	Schatz 3608
L'amore artigiano—Die liebe unter den handwerks leuten, Dresda, 1770: Gassmann.	Schatz 3609
L'amore artigiano—Die liebe bey den handwerkern, Regensburg (178–?): Gassmann.	Schatz 3610
L'amore artigiano, Venezia, 1761: Latilla.	Schatz 5442
L'amore artigiano—De forelskte haandverksfolk, Kiøbenhavn (1762): Latilla.	Schatz 5443
Amore contadino (Opere teatrali, Venezia, Zatta e figli, 1788–95, v. 37).	PQ
Amore in caricatura (Opere teatrali, Venezia, Zatta e figli, 1788–95, v. 37).	PQ
Amore in caricatura, Venezia, 1761: Ciampi.	Schatz 1888
L'amore in musica (t.-p. wanting): Boroni.	ML 50.2.A69B6
L'amour en musique. Tr. of his L'amore in musica (Stuttgart) 1770: Boroni.	Schatz 1245
Der apotheker. Tr. of his Lo speziale: Pallavicini and Fischietti.	Schatz 7715
L'Arcadia in Brenta (Opere drammatiche giocose, t. ii, Torino, 1757).	ML 49.A2G6
L'Arcadia in Brenta (Opere teatrali, Venezia, Zatta e figli, 1788–95, v. 43).	PQ
L'Arcadia in Brenta, Milano, 1750: Galuppi.	Schatz 3440
L'Arcadia in Brenta, Monaco, 1759: Galuppi.	Schatz 3518
L'Arcadia in Brenta, Lisbona (1764): J. C. da Silva.	Schatz 9885
Arcifanfano, re de' matti (Opere drammatiche giocose, t. i, Torino, 1757).	ML 49.A2G6
Arcifanfano rè dei matti (Opere teatrali, Venezia, Zatta e figli, 1788–95, v. 40).	PQ
L'Arcifanfano, Lisbona (1768): Scolari.	Schatz 9801
Arcifanfano, rè dei matti, Venezia, 1750: Galuppi.	Schatz 3442
Arcifanfano, rè dei matti, Torino (1759): Galuppi.	Schatz 3497
Aristide (Opere drammatiche, t. iii, Torino, 1757).	ML 49.A2G6
Aristide (Opere teatrali, Venezia, Zatta e figli, 1788–95, v. 35).	PQ
Aristide, Venezia, 1735: Macari.	Schatz 5808
Die artigen zufaelle zwischen liebe und eifersucht. Tr. of his Li vaghi accidenti fra amore e gelosia (Leipzig, 1756): Galuppi.	Schatz 3450
Gli artigiani, Milano (1795): Anfossi.	Schatz 227
L'astuzia felice (Opere teatrali, Venezia, Zatta e figli, 1788–95, v. 41).	PQ
L'astuzia felice, Venezia, 1767: Gherardesca.	Schatz 3800

Goldoni, Carlo—Continued.

I bagni d'Abano (Opere drammatiche giocose, Torino, 1757, t. iii).   ML 49.A2G6

I bagni d'Abano (Opere teatrali, Venezia, Zatta e figli, 1788–95, v. 44).   PQ

I bagni d'Abano, Venezia, 1753: Galuppi and Bertoni.   Schatz 3519

La bella verità (Opere teatrali, Venezia, Zatta e figli, 1788–95, v. 39).   PQ

La bella verità (n. i., 1762): Piccinni.   Schatz 8069

Bertoldo, Argentina, 1751: Ciampi. L. T. of their Bertoldo, Bertoldino e Cacasenno.   Schatz 1876

Bertoldo, Bertoldino e Cacasenno (Opere drammatiche giocose, Torino, 1757, t. i).   ML 49.A2G6

Bertoldo, Bertoldino e Cacasenno (Opere teatrali, Venezia, Zatta e figli, 1788–95, v. 39).   PQ

Bertoldo, Bertoldino e Cacasenno, Venezia, 1749: Ciampi.   Schatz 1882

Bertoldo, Bertoldino e Cacasenno—Bertoldus, Bertoldinus und Cacasennus (Bronsevico, 1750): Ciampi.   Schatz 1879

Bertoldo in corte, Ferrara (1755): Ciampi. L. T. of the above.   Schatz 1887

La birba (Opere drammatiche giocose, Torino, 1757, t. iv).   ML 49.A2G6

La birba (Opere teatrali, Venezia, Zatta e figli, 1788–95, v. 35).   PQ

Il bottanico novellista, Venezia, 1770: Fischietti.   Schatz 3241

La bottega da caffè (Opere drammatiche giocose, Torino, 1757, t. iv).   ML 49.A2G6

La bottega del caffè (Opere teatrali, Venezia, Zatta e figli, 1788–95, v. 35).   PQ

La buona figliuola (Opere teatrali, Venezia, Zatta e figli, 1788–95, v. 38).   PQ

La buona figliuola, Torino, 1758: Duni.   Schatz 2834

La buona figliuola, Venezia, 1760: Perillo.   Schatz 7921

La buona figliuola, Roma, 1760: Piccinni.   ML 50.2.B9P4

La buona figliuola, Vienna (1768): Piccinni.   Schatz 8070

La buona figliuola—Den fromme pige, Kiøbenhavn, 1770: Piccinni.   Schatz 8071

La buona figliuola, Paris, Didot, 1771: Piccinni. (French parody, no music on p. 47–48.)   ML 48.M2M

La buona figliuola, Paris, Didot, 1771: Piccinni. (French parody, music on p. 47–48.)   Schatz 8073

La buona figliuola, Paris, Duchesne, 1772: Piccinni (French parody).   Yudin PQ

La buona figliuola, Napoli, 1778: Piccinni.   Schatz 8131

La buona figliuola—Das gute maedel, Dresda, 1781: Piccinni.   Schatz 8074

La buona figliuola maritata (Opere teatrali, Venezia, Zatta e figli, 1788–95, v. 38).   PQ

La buona figliuola maritata, Vienna (1764): Piccinni.   Schatz 8135

La buona figliola maritata, Roma (1769): Piccinni.   Schatz 8136

Buovo d'Antona (Opere teatrali, Venezia, Zatta e figli, 1788–95, v. 41).   PQ

Buovo d'Antona, Venezia, 1759: Traetta.   Schatz 10388

La calamita de' cuori (Opere drammatiche giocose, Torino, 1757, t. i).   ML 49.A2G6

La calamita de' cuori (Opere teatrali, Venezia, Zatta e figli, 1788–95, v. 43).   PQ

Goldoni, Carlo—Continued.

La calamita de' cuori, Venezia, 1753: Galuppi. Schatz 3476

La cascina (Opere teatrali, Venezia, Zatta e figli, 1788–95,
v. 41). PQ

La cascina, Venezia (1756): Scolari. Schatz 9789

La cascina—Der meyerhof, Berlino, 1763: Scolari. Schatz 9790a

La cascina, Lisbona (1766): Scolari. ML 50.2.C27S2

Cesare in Egitto, Milano, 1770 (revision of Bussani's text):
Piccinni. Schatz 8083

Il ciarlatano, Venezia, 1759: Scolari. Schatz 9793

Il conte Caramella (Opere drammatiche giocose, Torino, 1757,
t. iii). ML 49.A2G6

Il conte Caramella (Opere teatrali, Venezia, Zatta e figli,
1788–95, v. 40). PQ

Il conte Caramella, Vicenza, 1759: Galuppi. Schatz 3446

Il conte Caramella—Der graf Caramella (Dresden, 1755):
Galuppi. Schatz 3447

La contessina (Opere drammatiche giocose, Torino, 1757,
t. iv). ML 49.A2G6

La contessina (Opere teatrali, Venezia, Zatta e figli, 1788–95,
v. 38). PQ

La contessina, Venezia (1743): Macari. Schatz 5809

La conversazione (Opere teatrali, Venezia, Zatta e figli, 1788–
95, v. 42). PQ

La conversazione, Venezia, 1758: Scolari. Schatz 9794

Il credulo deluso, Napoli, 1776: Paisiello. Schatz 7666

Die critische nacht.   Tr. of his La notte critica, Dresda, 1768:
Boroni. Schatz 1247

De gustibus non est disputandum (Opere teatrali, Venezia,
Zatta e figli, 1788–95, v. 38). PQ

De gustibus non est disputandum, Venezia, 1754: Scarlatti,
Gius. Schatz 9543

La diavolessa (Opere teatrali, Venezia, Zatta e figli, 1788–95,
v. 43). PQ

La diavolessa, Venezia (1755): Galuppi. Schatz 3449

La donna di governo (Opere teatrali, Venezia, Zatta e figli,
1788–95, v. 44). PQ

La donna di governo, Venezia, 1764: Galuppi. Schatz 3451

Le donne che comandono.   A. T. of his Il mondo alla roversa.

Le donne che comandono.   A. T. of his Il mondo al rovescio.

Le donne vendicate (Opere drammatiche giocose, Torino,
1757, t. i). ML 49.A2G6

Le donne vendicate (Opere teatrali, Venezia, Zatta e figli,
1788–95, v. 43). PQ

Le donne vendicate, Venezia, 1751: Cocchi. Schatz 2043

Le donne vendicate, Roma, 1763: Piccinni. Schatz 8090

Le donne vendicate, Venezia, 1764: Piccinni. Schatz 8091

I due litiganti, Padova (1792): Sarti. (Same as their Fra i
due litiganti il terzo gode.) Schatz 9456

La favola de' tre gobbi (Opere drammatiche giocose, Torino,
1757, t. iv). ML 49.A2G6

La favola de' tre gobbi (Opere teatrali, Venezia, Zatta e figli,
1788–95, v. 35). PQ

Il festino (Opere teatrali, Venezia, Zatta e figli, 1788–95, v. 38). PQ

Goldoni, Carlo—Continued.

La fiera di Sinigaglia (Opere teatrali, Venezia, Zatta e figli, 1788–95, v. 41).	PQ
La fiera di Sinigaglia, Roma, 1760: Fischietti.	SCHATZ 3239
Filosofia ed amore (Opere teatrali, Venezia, Zatta e figli, 1788–95, v. 38).	PQ
Filosofia ed amore, Venezia, 1760: Gassmann.	SCHATZ 3615
Il filosofo (Opere drammatiche giocose, Torino, 1757, t. iv).	ML 49.A2G6
Il filosofo (Opere teatrali, Venezia, Zatta e figli, 1788–95, v. 35).	PQ
Il filosofo di campagna (Opere teatrali, Venezia, Zatta e figli, 1788–95, v. 43).	PQ
Il filosofo di campagna, Venezia, 1754: Galuppi.	SCHATZ 3452
Il filosofo di campagna—Der landmann ein philosoph (Dresden, 1755): Galuppi.	SCHATZ 3453
Il filosofo di campagna, Mannheim (1756): Holzbauer.	SCHATZ 4782
La finta semplice (Opere teatrali, Venezia, Zatta e figli, 1788–95, v. 41).	PQ
La finta semplice, Venezia, 1764: Perillo.	SCHATZ 7926
Il finto principe, Opere drammatiche giocose, Torino, 1757, t. iii).	ML 49.A2G6
Il finto principe (Opere teatrali, Venezia, Zatta e figli, 1788–95, v. 39).	PQ
Der fischer im trueben, Stuttgart, 1785. Tr. of his Fra i due litiganti il terzo gode: Sarti.	SCHATZ 9458
La fondazion di Venezia (Opere drammatiche giocose, Torino, 1757, t. iii).	ML 49.A2G6
La fondazion di Venezia, Venezia (1736): Macari.	SCHATZ 5810
La fondazione di Venezia (Opere teatrali, Venezia, Zatta e figli, 1788–95, v. 36).	PQ
De forelskte haandverksfolk. Tr. of his L'amore artigiano, Kiøbenhavn (1762): Latilla.	SCHATZ 5443
Fra i due litiganti il terzo gode—Unter zwey streitenden siegt der dritte, Dresda, 1784: Sarti. (Same as I pretendenti delusi.)	SCHATZ 9457
Fra i due litiganti il terzo gode, Lisbona, 1793: Sarti.	SCHATZ 9468
Fra i due litiganti il terzo gode, Milano, 1795: Sarti.	SCHATZ 9454
Den fromme pige. Tr. of his Là buona figliuola, Kiøbenhavn, 1770: Piccinni.	SCHATZ 8071
La gara tra la commedia e la musica (Opere teatrali, Venezia, Zatta e figli, 1788–95.	PQ
La generosità politica, Venezia, 1736 (with Domenico Lalli): Marchi.	SCHATZ 5936
Germondo (Opere teatrali, Venezia, Zatta e figli, 1788–95, v. 36).	PQ
Il gondoliere ossia Gli sdegni amorosi (Opere teatrali, Venezia, Zatta e figli, 1788–95, v. 35).	PQ
Der graf Caramella. Tr. of his Il conte Caramella, (Dresden, 1755): Galuppi.	SCHATZ 3447
Gustavo Primo, rè di Svezia, Venezia (1740): Galuppi. O. T. of the next.	SCHATZ 3474
Gustavo Vasa (Opere teatrali, Venezia, Zatta e figli, 1788–95, v. 36).	PQ
Das gute maedchen, Leipzig, 1783. Tr. of his La buona figliuola: Piccinni.	SCHATZ 8075

Goldoni, Carlo—Continued.

Das gute maedchen, Hamburg, 1791. Another ed. of the above.   SCHATZ 8076

Das gute maedel. Tr. of his La buona figliuola, Dresda, 1781: Piccinni.   SCHATZ 8074

Das gute maegdchen, Mannheim (1769). Tr. of his La buona figliuola: Piccinni.   SCHATZ 8072

Der herr doctor. Tr. of his Il signor dottore, Dresda (1768): Fischietti.   SCHATZ 3237

Im trueben ist gut fischen, Hamburg (1785). Tr. of his Fra i due litiganti il terzo gode: Sarti.   SCHATZ 9459

Im trueben ist gut fischen, Koeln am Rhein, 1786. Another Tr. of the above.   SCHATZ 9460

L'innocenza protetta dal Cielo o siano Li portentosi effetti della gran madre Natura, Venezia (1762) (L. T. of his I portentosi effetti della madre Natura): unknown.   SCHATZ 11385

L'ipocondriaco (Opere drammatiche giocose, Torino, 1757, t. iv).   ML 49.A2G6

L'ippocondriaco (Opere teatrali, Venezia, Zatta e figli, 1788–95, v. 35).   PQ

L'isola di Bengodi (Venezia, 1777) (modernization of his Il paese della Cuccagna): Astaritta.   SCHATZ 382

L'isola disabitata (Opere teatrali, Venezia, Zatta e figli, 1788–95, v. 42).   PQ

L'isola disabitata, Venezia, 1757: Gius Scarlatti.   SCHATZ 9547

L'isola disabitata—Die unbewohnte insel, Dresda, 1767: Scarlatti.   SCHATZ 9547

Der jahrmarkt zu Magerndorf. Tr. of his Il mercato di Malmantile (Dresda, 1766): Fischietti.   SCHATZ 3232

Der jahrmarkt zu Malmantile. Tr. of his Il mercato di Malmantile (Hannover, 1770): Fischietti.   SCHATZ 3238

Der land-mann ein philosoph. Tr. of his Il filisofo di campagna (Dresden, 1755): Galuppi.   SCHATZ 3453

Die liebe bey den handwerkern. Tr. of his L'amor artigiano, Regensburg (178–?): Gassmann.   SCHATZ 3610

Die liebe unter den handwerksleuten. Tr. of his L'amore artigiano, Dresda, 1770: Gassmann.   SCHATZ 3609

Die liebe unter den handwerksleuten, Dresden, 1779. Another Tr.   SCHATZ 3611

Die liebe unter den handwerksleuten, Hamburg, 1782.   SCHATZ 3612

Lucrezia Romana (Opere teatrali, Venezia, Zatta e figli, 1788–95, v. 43).   PQ

Lugrezia Romana in Costantinopoli (Opere drammatiche giocose, Torino, 1757, t. iii).   ML 49.A2G6

Lugrezia Romana in Constantinopoli, Venezia, 1737: Macari.   SCHATZ 5811

O lunatico illudido, Lisboa, 1791 (Tr. of his Il mondo della luna): Portugal.   ML 50.2.L95P7

La mascherata (Opere drammatiche giocose, Torino, 1757, t. i).   ML 49.A2G6

La mascherata (Opere teatrali, Venezia, Zatta e figli, 1788–95, v. 42).   PQ

La mascherata, Venezia, 1751: Galuppi or Cocchi.   SCHATZ 3487

Il mercato di Malmantile (Opere teatrali, Venezia, Zatta e figli, 1788–95, v. 44).   PQ

Il mercato di Malmantile, Venezia, 1758: Fischietti.   SCHATZ 3231

Goldoni, Carlo—Continued.

Il mercato di Malmantile—Der jahrmarkt zu Magerndorf (Dreda, 1766). Tr. of the above.	SCHATZ 3232
Il mercato di Malmantile—Der jahrmarkt zu Malmantile (Hannover, 1770). Another Tr.	SCHATZ 3238
Il mercato di Malmantile, Venezia, 1758: Scarlatti, Gius.	SCHATZ 9550
Il mercato di Monfregoso, Milano (1792) (altered version of his Il mercato di Malmantile): Zingarelli.	ML 50.2.M55Z2
Il mercato di Monfregoso, Lisboa, 1795: Zingarelli.	ML 50.2.M55Z3
Der meyerhof. Tr. of Scolari's La cascina, Berlino, 1763: Sarti.	SCHATZ 9790a
Il mondo al rovescio o sia Le donne che comandono (Opere drammatiche giocose, Torino, 1757, t. i).	ML 49.A2G6
Il mondo alla roversa, ossia Le donne che comandono (Opere teatrali, Venezia, Zatta e figli, 1788–95, v. 41).	PQ
Mondo alla roversa, o sia Le donne che comandono, Venezia, 1753: Galuppi.	SCHATZ 3459
Il mondo alla roverscia—Die verkehrte welt (Dresda, 1768): Galuppi. L. T. of the above.	SCHATZ 3460
Il mondo della luna (Opere drammatiche giocose, Torino, 1757, t. ii).	ML 49.A2G6
Il mondo della luna (Opere teatrali, Venezia, Zatta e figli, 1788–95, v. 40).	PQ
Il mondo della luna, Venezia, 1775: Astaritta.	SCHATZ 383
Il mondo della luna, Lisbona (1765): Avondano.	SCHATZ 510
Il mondo della luna, Venezia, 1750: Galuppi.	SCHATZ 3461
Il mondo della luna, Napoli (1792). L. T. of Il credulo deluso: Paisiello.	SCHATZ 7667
Il mondo nella luna, London, 1760: pasticcio, chiefly by Galuppi.	ML 48.M2H
Monsieur Petiton (Opere drammatiche giocose, Torino, 1757, t. iv).	ML 49.A2G6
Monsieur Petiton (Opere teatrali, Venezia, Zatta e figli, 1788–95, v. 35).	PQ
Der nachlaessige, n. i., n. d. Tr. of his Il negligente: Ciampi.	SCHATZ 1889
Die nacht, Hamburg (ca. 1780). Tr. of his Notte critica: Piccinni.	SCHATZ 8101
Il negligente (Opere drammatiche giocose, Torino, 1757, t. ii).	ML 49.A2G6
Il negligente (Opere teatrali, Venezia, Zatta e figli, 1788–95, v. 44).	PQ
Il negligente, Venezia, 1749: Ciampi.	SCHATZ 1886
Il negligente—Der nachlaessige, n. i., n. d.: Ciampi. (Altered version and Tr.)	SCHATZ 1889
La notte critica (Opere teatrali, Venezia, Zatta e figli, 1788–95, v. 39).	PQ
La notte critica, Venezia, 1766: Boroni.	SCHATZ 1246
La notte critica—Die critische nacht, Dresda, 1768: Boroni.	SCHATZ 1247
La notte critica, Pisa, 1769: Gherardesca.	SCHATZ 3801
Notte critica, Lisbona (1767): Piccinni (Niccolò, not Luigi).	SCHATZ 8100
Le nozze (Opere teatrali, Venezia, Zatta e figli, 1788–95, v. 37).	PQ
Le nozze. O. T. of his I pretendenti delusi and Fra i due litiganti il terzo gode.	
Le nozze, Venezia, 1757: Galuppi.	SCHATZ 3465

Goldoni, Carlo—Continued.

Le nozze di Dorina, London (1787): Sarti. L. T. of their I pretendenti delusi. — ML 48.M2K

Le nozze di Dorina, Torino (1796): Sarti. (Same as their Fra due litiganti il terzo gode and I pretendenti delusi.) — Schatz 9455

Le nozze in campagna, Venezia, 1768: Sciroli. — Schatz 9782

I oprørt vand er godt at fiske, Kiøbenhavn, 1795. Tr. of his Fra i due litiganti il terzo gode: Sarti. — Schatz 9462

Oronte (Opere teatrali, Venezia, Zatta e figli, 1788–95, v. 36). — PQ

Il paese della Cucagna (Opere drammatiche giocose, Torino, 1757, t. iii). — ML 49.A2G6

Il paese della Cuccagna (Opere teatrali, Venezia, Zatta e figli, 1788–95, v. 44). — PQ

Il paese della Cuccagna, Vienna, 1770: unknown. — Schatz 11354

Il paese della Cuccagna, Venezia, 1750: Galuppi. — Schatz 3492

Il pazzo glorioso, Venezia, 1753 (alterations only, in Villano's Lo stravagante): Cocchi. — Schatz 2053

Il pazzo glorioso, Monaco, 1758: Cocchi. — Schatz 2037

Pelarina (Opere drammatiche giocose, Torino, 1757, t. iv). — ML 49.A2G6

La pelerina (Opere teatrali, Venezia, Zatta e figli, 1788–95, v. 35). — PQ

Le pescatrici (Opere drammatiche giocose, Torino, 1757, t. iii). — ML 49.A2G6

Le pescatrici (Opere teatrali, Venezia, Zatta e figli, 1788–95, v. 44). — PQ

Le pescatrici, Venezia, 1752: Bertoni. — Schatz 921

Le pescatrici (Torino, 1754): Gioanetti. — Schatz 3831

Pisistrato (Opere teatrali, Venezia, Zatta e figli, 1788–95, v. 36). — PQ

Li portentosi effetti della gran madre Natura. A. T. of his L'innocenza protetta dal Cielo.

I portentosi effetti della madre Natura (Opere drammatiche giocosi, Torino, 1757, t. ii). — ML 49.A2G6

I portentosi effetti della madre Natura (Opere teatrali, Venezia, Zatta e figli, 1788–95, v. 42). — PQ

I portentosi effetti della madre Natura, Venezia, 1752: Scarlatti, Gius. — Schatz 9554

I portentosi effetti della madre Natura, Monaco (1758): Scarlatti, Gius. — Schatz 9553

Il povero superbo, Venezia, 1755: Galuppi. (Text based on his Castalda.) — Schatz 3467

I pretendenti delusi, Venezia, 1782: Sarti. (O. T. of the text "Le nozze." The opera was first performed as Fra i due litiganti il terzo gode.) — Schatz 9453

La pupilla (Opere drammatiche giocose, Torino, 1757, t. iv). — ML 49.A2G6

La pupilla (Opere teatrali, Venezia, Zatta e figli, 1788–95, v. 35). — PQ

Il quartiere fortunato (Opere teatrali, Venezia, Zatta e figli, 1788–95, v. 35). — PQ

Il re alla caccia (Opere teatrali, Venezia, Zatta e figli, 1788–95, v. 37). — PQ

Il rè alla caccia, Venezia (1763): Galuppi. — Schatz 3475

Il regno delle donne. L. T. of his Il mondo alla roversa o sia Le donne che comandono: Galuppi.

Goldoni, Carlo—Continued.

La ritornata di Londra (Opere teatrali, Venezia, Zatta e figli, 1788–95, v. 44).   PQ

La ritornata di Londra, Venezia (1756): Fischietti.   Schatz 3234

La ritornata di Londra—Die zurueckkunft aus London (Dresden, 1756): Fischietti.   Schatz 3235

La scuola moderna (Opere teatrali, Venezia, Zatta e figli, 1788–95, v. 42).   PQ

La scuola moderna o sia La maestra di buon-gusto, Venezia, 1748 (retouched version of A. Palomba's La maestra): Cocchi.   Schatz 2048

Gli sdegni amorosi (Opere drammatiche giocose, Torino, 1757, t. iv). L. T. and A. T. of his Il gondoliere.   ML 49.A2G6

La serva astuta o sia Il filosofo in campagna, Venezia (1761). L. T. of his Il filosofo di campagna: Galuppi.   Schatz 3513

Il signor dottore (Opere teatrali, Venezia, Zatta e figli, 1788–95, v. 40).   PQ

Il signor dottore (Monaco, 1760): Fischietti.   Schatz 3236

Il signor dottore—Der herr doctor, Dresda (1768): Fischietti.   Schatz 3237

Lo speziale (Opere teatrali, Venezia, Zatta e figli, 1788–95, v. 42).   PQ

Lo speziale, Venezia, 1755: Pallavicini and Fischietti.   Schatz 7714

Lo speziale—Der apotheker, Dresden (1755): Pallavicini and Fischietti.   Schatz 7715

Statira (Opere teatrali, Venezia, Zatta e figli, 1788–95, v. 36).   PQ

Statira, Venezia, 1751: Maggiore and others.   Schatz 5832

Statira, Venezia (1756): Scolari.   Schatz 9799

Il talismano (Opere teatrali, Venezia, Zatta e figli, 1788–95, v. 37).   PQ

Der talisman, Wien, 1789. Tr. of his Il talismano (partly rewritten by Da Ponte): Salieri.   Schatz 9322

Der talisman oder Die zigeuner, n. i., 1790. Another Tr. of the above.   Schatz 9323

Der talisman, Berlin, 1798. Another Tr.   Schatz 9324

Il talismano, Milano (1785): Salieri (1st act) and Giacomo Rust (2d and 3d acts).   Schatz 9336

Il Tigrane. (Goldoni merely retouched and modernized Silvani's text, La virtù trionfante dell' amore e dell' odio).

I tre gobbi rivali, Napoli, 1783: Fabrizj.   Schatz 2972

Gli uccellatori (Opere teatrali, Venezia, Zatta e figli, 1788–95, v. 42).   PQ

Li uccellatori, Venezia, 1759: Gassmann.   Schatz 3617

Gl'uccellatori, Vienna (1768): Gassmann.   Schatz 3627

Die unbewohnte insel. Tr. of his L'isola disabitata, Dresda, 1767: Scarlatti, Gius.   Schatz 9547

Die unruhige nacht, Wien, 1783. Tr. of his La notte critica: Gassmann.   Schatz 3616

Unter zwey streitenden siegt der dritte. Tr. of his Fra i due litiganti il terzo gode, Dresda, 1784: Sarti.   Schatz 9457

Unter zwey streitenden zieht der dritte den nutzen, Salzburg, 1787. Tr. of his Fra i due litiganti il terzo gode: Sarti.   Schatz 9461

Li vaghi accidenti fra amore e gelosia—Die artigen zufaelle zwischen liebe und eifersucht (Leipzig, 1756). L. T. of his La diavolessa: Galuppi.   Schatz 3450

Goldoni, Carlo—Continued.

Die verkehrte welt. Tr. of his Il mondo alla roverscia (Dresda,
    1768): Galuppi.   SCHATZ 3460

Il viaggiator ridicolo (Vienna, 1766): Gassmann.   SCHATZ 3618

Il viaggitor ridicolo, Venezia, 1761: Perillo.   SCHATZ 7922

Il viaggiatore ridicolo (Opere teatrali, Venezia, Zatta e figli,
    1788–95, v. 40).   PQ

Il viaggiatore ridicolo, Brescia (1771): Caramanica.   SCHATZ 1619

Il viaggiatore ridicolo, Lisbona (1770): Scolari and others.   ML 50.2.V42S2

Le virtuose ridicole (Opere drammatiche giocose, Torino,
    1757, t. ii).   ML 49.A2G6

Le virtuose ridicole (Opere teatrali, Venezia, Zatta e figli,
    1788–95, v. 43).   PQ

Le virtuose ridicole, Venezia, 1752: Galuppi.   SCHATZ 3512

Vittorina (Opere teatrali, Venezia, Zatta e figli, 1788–95,
    v. 36).   PQ

I volponi (Opere teatrali, Venezia, Zatta e figli, 1788–95,
    v. 39).   PQ

Die welt im monde. Tr. of his Il mondo della luna, Oels
    (17—): Galuppi.   SCHATZ 3462

Die zigeuner. A. T. of his Der talisman: Salieri.

Die zurueckkunft aus Londen. Tr. of his La ritornata di
    Londra (Dresden, 1756): Fischietti.   SCHATZ 3235

Gonella, Francesco.

Aviso aos casados, Lisboa, 1796. Tr. of his L'avviso ai mari-
    tati: Isouard.   SCHATZ 4944

L'avviso ai maritati—Die schule der ehemaenner, Dresda,
    1795: Isouard.   SCHATZ 4908

Avviso ai maritati, Venezia (1798): Mayr.   SCHATZ 6188

La Lodoiska, Venezia (1796): Mayr.   SCHATZ 6158

Lodoiska, Milano (1799): Mayr. (Text altered by Rossi.)   SCHATZ 6159

L'Oreste, Pisa (1798): Moneta.   SCHATZ 6555

Die schule der ehemaenner. Tr. of his L'avviso ai maritati,
    Dresda, 1795: Isouard.   SCHATZ 4908

Zulima, Firenze, 1796: Portugal.   ML 48.A5 v.14

Goodenough, Richard Joceline.

The cottagers, London, 1768: unknown. O. T. of his Wil-
    liam and Nanny.   LONGE 119

William and Nanny; or, The cottagers, London, 1779: un-
    known. L. T. of his The cottagers.   LONGE 214

Goodwin, Thomas.

The loyal shepherds or The rustic heroine (London, n. d.).   LONGE 303

Gori. *See his real name,* Rigo.

Gosse, Etienne.

L'auteur dans son ménage, Paris, an VII [1799]: Bruni.   ML 50.2.A93 B8

Gotter, Friedrich Wilhelm.

Die dorfgala, Gotha, 1774: Schweitzer.   SCHATZ 9770

Die dorfgalla, Hamburg, 1778: Schweitzer.   SCHATZ 9771

Der dorfjahrmarkt, n. i., 1790: G. Benda. L. T. of their Der
    jahrmarkt.   SCHATZ 773

Die drey wuensche. A. T. of his Der holzhauer: G. Benda.

Gotter, Friedrich Wilhelm—Continued.

Die geisterinsel, Berlin, 1798: Reichardt.   SCHATZ 8641

Die geisterinsel, Altona, n. d.: Zumsteeg.   SCHATZ 11294

Der holzhauer oder Die drey wuensche, Berlin, 1772: G. Benda.   SCHATZ 770a

Der holzhauer, Riga (1785): G. Benda.   SCHATZ 770b

Der jahrmarkt, Leipzig, 1778: G. Benda (two acts, with Engel's additions to the text, as composed by Joh. Adam Hiller).   ML 50.2.J2B2

        Second copy. SCHATZ 772

Julie und Romeo, Berlin, 1796: G. Benda. L. T. of their Romeo und Julie.   SCHATZ 777

Lukas und Bärbchen. L. T. of his Der jahrmarkt.

Medea, Hamburg, 1776: G. Benda.   SCHATZ 774

Medea (Melodramen, Pilsen und Klattau, Joseph Johann Morgensaeuler, 1791, iii): G. Benda.   SCHATZ 774a

Pygmalion (Melodramen, Pilsen und Klattau, Joseph Johann Morgensaeuler, 1791, i): G. Benda. (Text transl. from Rousseau.)   SCHATZ 775

Romeo und Julie, Leipzig, 1779: G. Benda.   SCHATZ 776

Das tartarische gesez, Leipzig, 1779: André.   SCHATZ 190

Tom Jones, Hamburg (1779). Tr. of Philidor's Tom Jones (Poinsinet le jeune).   SCHATZ 8031

Walder, Gotha, 1778: G. Benda.   SCHATZ 778

Gozzi, Carlo *or* **Gaspare.**

Il puntiglio amoroso, Venezia (1763) (authorship of either doubtful): Galuppi.   SCHATZ 3507

Grandi, Tommaso.

Eifersucht auf dem lande. Tr. of his Le gelosie vilane, Berlino, 1791: Sarti.   SCHATZ 9437

Le gelosie villane, Casale, 1779: Anfossi.   SCHATZ 280

Le gelosie villane—Die eyfersucht der bauern, Dresda, 1778: Sarti.   SCHATZ 9436

Le gelosie villane, Napoli, 1784: Sarti.   SCHATZ 9435

Le gelosie villane—Eifersucht auf dem lande, Berlino, 1791: Sarti.   SCHATZ 9437

Die eyfersucht der bauern. Tr. of his Le gelosie villane, Dresda, 1778: Sarti.   SCHATZ 9436

Il militare bizzaro, Venezia, 1778: Sarti.   SCHATZ 9448

Granget, Pierre.

L'Asiatico generoso, ballet. *See* Galuppi's L'Ipermestra.

I due vergognesi da nozze, ballet. *See* Galuppi's L'Ipermestra.

Granville, George (*Lord* **Lansdowne**).

The British enchanters, or, No magick like love, London, 1732.   LONGE 75

Graziolli, Giovanni.

Le due pastorelle smarrite, ballet. *See* Baini's Il finto Pariggino.

Grazzini, Giulio Cesare.

La Ginevra infanta di Scozia, Ferrara (1690): Bassani.   SCHATZ 632

Greene, Robert.
Luminalia or The festivall of light, London, 1637 (authorship doubtful): Laniere (also doubtful). ML 52.2.L92

Grenier.
La mélomanie, Nouv. éd., Toulon, 1787: Champein. ML 50.2.M52C4

Greppi, Giovanni.
Castrini padre e figlio, Venezia, 1787: Robuschi. SCHATZ 8840
Li raggiri fortunati, Bologna (1792). L. T. of his Castrini, padre e figlio: Robuschi. SCHATZ 8846
Lo stravagante Inglese, Bronsvic, 1788: Bianchi. SCHATZ 983

Griffiths, *Mrs.*
The barber of Seville, or, The useless precaution, London, 1776. Tr. of Beaumarchais' Le barbier de Seville. LONGE 318

Grimani, Giovanni.
Sigismondo primo al diadema, Venetia, 1696: Pignatta. SCHATZ 8171

Grimani, Vincenzo.
Agrippina, Venezia, 1709: Händel. SCHATZ 4471
Agrippina—Agrippina, Hamburg (1718). Tr. of the above. SCHATZ 4472
Elmiro, rè di Corinto, Venetia, 1686: Pallavicino. SCHATZ 7722
Orazio, Venetia, 1788: Tosi. SCHATZ 10377
Teodosio—Theodosius, Hamburg (1718): Fux, Gasparini, and Caldara. SCHATZ 3392
Il Teodosio, Venezia, 1699: M. A. Ziani. SCHATZ 11194

Gross, J.
Die illumination (Wien) 1787: Kuerzinger. SCHATZ 5338

Grolo, Calindo. *Anagram of* Carlo Goldoni.

Grossmann, Gustav Friedrich Wilhelm.
Adelheit von Veltheim, Leipzig, 1781: Neefe. SCHATZ 7068
Adelheit von Veltheim, n. i., n. d.: Neefe. SCHATZ 11734
Der barbier von Sevilla oder Die unnütze vorsicht, Koeln, 1786. Tr. of Paisiello's Le barbier de Seville. SCHATZ 7601
Der barbier von Seville oder Die vergebliche vorsicht, Leipzig, 1784: F. L. Benda. Tr. of Beaumarchais' Le barbier de Seville with added songs. SCHATZ 764
Eigensinn und launen der liebe, Frankfurt und Leipzig, 1783. Tr. of Deller's Le contese per amore. SCHATZ 2495
Der kurze irrthum, n. i., 1790. Tr. of Dezède's L'erreur d'un moment (Monvel). SCHATZ 2518
Melide oder Der schiffer, Frankfurt, 1778 (with Neefe). Tr. of Philidor's Mélide ou Le navigateur (Fenouillot de Falbaire de Quingey). SCHATZ 8034
Die reue vor der that, Frankfurt und Leipzig, 1783. Tr. of Dezède's L'erreur d'un moment (Monvel). SCHATZ 2519
Der schiffer. A. T. of his and Neefe's Melide: Philidor.
Die unnütze vorsicht. A. T. of his Der barbier von Sevilla.
Was einem recht, ist dem andern billig, Frankfurt und Leipzig, 1783. Tr. of Dezède's Julie (Monvel). SCHATZ 2522

Grugnanelli, Francesco.
Merope. Tr. of Graun's Merope, Berlino, 1756 (Tagliazucchi). SCHATZ 4105
Montezuma. Tr. of Graun's Montezuma, Berlino, 1771 (Tagliazucchi). SCHATZ 4108

Grugnanelli, Francesco—Continued.

Silla. Tr. of Graun's Silla, Berlino, 1753 (Tagliazucchi). SCHATZ 4116

Die uneinigen brueder. Tr. of Graun's I fratelli nemici, Berlino (1756) (Tagliazucchi). SCHATZ 4100

Gualazzi, Fulgenzio Matteo.

Il prodigio dell' innocenza, Venetia, 1695: Albinoni. SCHATZ 104

La schiavitù fortunata, Venetia, 1694: C. F. Pollaroli. SCHATZ 8317

Guarini, Battista.

Il pastor fido, Padoa, 1721 (altered by Pasqualigo): Pietragrua. SCHATZ 8164

Guerin de Frémicour, Jean Nicolas.

Les ensorcelés ou Jeannot et Jeannette, Paris, 1757 (with Mad. Favart and Harny de Guerville, who principally selected and arranged the music). SCHATZ 4454

— Same title, Paris, 1758 (Theatre de M. Favart, Paris, Duchesne, 1763–77, t. v). ML 49.A2F1

Supplément de la Soirée des boulevards. See Favart.

Guglielmi, Alessandro.

La costanza guerriera, ballet: Canavasso. See Ottani's Fatima.

Il disertore francese, ballet. See Caruso's Il cavalier magnifico.

Li pescatori, ballet. See Sarti's La giardiniera brillante.

Guichard, Henri.

Ulysse (Recueil général des opéra, t. viii, Paris, 1706): Rebel. SCHATZ 8622

Guichard, Jean François.

Le bucheron, ou Les trois souhaits, Paris, 1763 (with Castet): Philidor. SCHATZ 8010

Le bucheron ou Les trois souhaits, Copenhague, 1767 (with Castet): Philidor. YUDIN PQ

Le bucheron ou Les trois souhaits, Paris, 1771 (with Castet): Philidor. SCHATZ 11736

Le bucheron ou Les trois souhaits, Paris, 1782: Philidor. SCHATZ 11737

Die drey wuensche. A. T. of his and Castet's Der holzhauer: Philidor.

Der holzhauer oder Die drey wuensche, Frankfurt am Mayn, 1773. Tr. of his and Castet's Le bucheron: Philidor. SCHATZ 8011

Skovhuggeren eller De tre ønsker (Copenhagen, 1782). Tr. of his and Castet's Le bucheron: Philidor. SCHATZ 8013

De tre ønsker. A. T. of his and Castet's Skovhuggeren: Philidor.

Les trois souhaits. A. T. of his and Castet's Le bucheron: Philidor.

Guillard, Nicolas François.

Arvire et Evelina, Paris, 1788: Sacchini, completed by J. B. Rey. SCHATZ 9207

Arvire og Evelina, Kiøbenhavn (1799). Tr. of his Arvire et Evelina: Sacchini. SCHATZ 9208

Chimene ou Le Cid, Paris, 1783: Sacchini. SCHATZ 9224

Dardanus, Paris, 1784 (utilizing de La Bruère's text): Sacchini. SCHATZ 9217

Dardanus, Paris, 1786. The same reduced to three acts. SCHATZ 9248

Les Horaces (Paris) 1786: Salieri. ML 50.2.H6S2

Guillard, Nicolas François—Continued.

L'Ifigenia in Tauride, Vienna, 1783. Tr. of his Iphigénie en
Tauride: Gluck.   Schatz 3905

Iphigenia in Tauris, Wien, 1781. Tr. of his Iphigénie en
Tauride: Gluck.   Schatz 3904

Iphigénie en Tauride (Paris) 1779: Gluck.   Schatz 3903

Oedipe à Colone, n. i. (Paris, ca. 1792): Sacchini.   Schatz 9234

Oedip zu Colonos, Berlin, 1798. Tr. of his Oedipe à Colone:
Sacchini.   Schatz 9235

Olimpie, Paris, an VII [1798–99]: Kalkbrenner.   Schatz 4998

Guldberg, Frederik Hoegh.

Aftenen, Kiøbenhavn, 1795: Schall.   Schatz 9581

Guy, Jean Henri.

Anacréon chez Polycrate, Paris (1797): Grétry.   Schatz 4137

Le baiser donné et rendu, Paris, 1796: Gresnich.   ML 50.2.B2G7

Sophie et Moncars ou L'intrigue portugaise, Paris, an VI
(1797): Gaveaux.   ML 50.2.S7G2

Haffner, W. Philipp.

Maegera, n. i., 1774: Böhm.   Schatz 1115

Hahn, Ludwig Philipp.

Wallrad und Evchen oder Die parforsjagd, Zweibruecken,
1782: Maier.   Schatz 5844

Halbe, Johann August.

Die zauberhoele des Trofonius (Wien) 1789. Tr. of Salieri's
La grotta di Trofonio (Casti).   Schatz 9298

Hamann, Johann Georg.

Judith, gemahlin Kayser Ludewigs des Frommen oder Die
siegende unschuld, Hamburg (1732). Tr. only the recitatives for this pasticcio by Händel, Chelleri, and Telemann. Schatz 4481

Margaretha, koenigin in Castilien (Hamburg, 1730): Telemann.   Schatz 10263

Der streit der kindlichen pflicht und der liebe oder Die flucht
des Aeneas nach Latien (Hamburg), 1731: Porpora, recitatives by Telemann. Tr. of Metastasio's Didone abbandonata.   Schatz 8365

Der weiseste in Sidon, Hamburg (1733): Telemann.   Schatz 10268

Harny de Guerville.

Les amours de Bastien et Bastienne. *See* Madame Favart.

Les ensorcelés ou Jeannot et Jeannette, Paris, 1757 (with Mad.
Favart and Guérin de Frémicour. The music selected
and arranged principally by the above).   Schatz 4454

— Same title, Paris, 1758 (Theatre de M. Favart, Paris, Duchesne, 1763–77, t. v).   ML 49.A2F1

Georget et Georgette, Avignon, 1768: Alexandre.   Yudin PQ

Le petit-maître en province, Paris, 1765: Alexandre.   ML 50.2.P337A4

Le petit-maître en province, Paris, veuve Duchesne, 1771:
Alexandre.   Schatz 159

Harris, James.

Daphnis and Amaryllis, Exon, 1766: pasticcio, *Händel* and
others. (Text the same as of next entry).   Longe 293

The spring, London (1762): Händel and others.   ML 50.2.S743H2

Harris, Joseph.
 Love's a lottery and a woman the prize. With a new masque,
  call'd Love and riches reconcil'd, London, 1699.   Longe 240

Hatchett, William.
 The Chinese orphan, London, 1741.   Longe 125

Hautemer.
 Bertholde à la ville. *See* Title catalogue.

Hawker, Essex.
 The country-wedding and Skimmington, London, 1729.
  Same as his The wedding.   Longe 275
 The wedding, London, 1729: Pepusch (ballad opera). Longe 33
 The wedding, London, 1734 (2d ed.).   Longe 306

Hawkesworth, John.
 Edgar and Emmeline (Collection of farces, Edinburgh, 1792,
  t. iv): M. Arne.   Schatz 11753 **D**

Haym, Nicola Francesco.
 Julius Cæsar in Aegypten (Hamburg, 1725): Händel. Tr.
  of their Giulio Cesare in Egitto, German recitatives, etc.,
  by Linike.   Schatz 4478
 Julius Cæsar in Aegypten (Hamburg, 1733). L. ed. of above. Schatz 11690
 Otto (Hamburg, 1726). Tr. of his and Pallavicini's Ottoue:
  Händel.   Schatz 4482
 Rodelinda, koenigin in der Lombardey (Hamburg, 1734). Tr.
  of his and Salvi's Rodelinda: Händel.   Schatz 4490
 Tamerlan (Hamburg, 1725). Tr. of his and Piovene's Tamer-
  lano: Händel (interpolated intermezzo by Telemann). Schatz 4492
 Tamerlano—Tamerlane, London, 1724 (adaptation of Pio-
  vene's text): Händel.   ML 50.2.T23
 Zenobia oder Das muster rechtschaffener ehelichen liebe
  (Hamburg, 1726). Tr. of his Radamisto: Händel. Schatz 4502

Heard, William.
 The snuff-box or A trip to Bath, London, 1775: Hook. Longe 310

Heartwell, Henry.
 The castle of Sorrento, London, 1799. (English adaptation of
  Duval's text "Le prisonnier"): Attwood. Text revised
  by George Colman, the younger.   Longe 256
 The prisoner or The resemblance, London, 1799. Tr. of Della
  Maria's Le prisonnier ou La ressemblance (Duval). Longe 254

Heermann, Gottlob Ephraim.
 Der abend im walde, Weimar, 1774: Wolf.   Schatz 11075
 Die dorfdeputirten, Berlin, 1796: Schuhbauer. Schatz 9710
 Die dorfdeputirten, n. i., 1792: Teyber.   Schatz 10295
 Die dorfdeputirten, Weimar, 1773: Wolf.   Schatz 11077
 Die dorfdeputirten, Riga, n. d.: Wolf.   Schatz 11077a
 Das rosenfest, Weimar, 1774: Wolf.   Schatz 11083
 Das rosenfest (Weimar) 1776: Wolf.   ML 50.2.R75W6
 Die treuen köhler, Muenchen (1786): Schuhbauer. Schatz 9712
 Die treuen köhler, Kaufbeuren (1789): Knecht. Schatz 5198
 Die treuen koehler, Weimar, 1773: Wolf.   Schatz 11085

Heiberg, Peter Andreas.
 Chinafarerne (n. i., n. d.): Schall.   Schatz 9583
 Indtoget (Skuespil, 3. bind): Schulz.   Schatz 9723
 Selim og Mirza, Kiøbenhavn, 1790: Zink.   Schatz 11272

Heidegger, John James.
 Oriana, Hamburg (1717). Tr. of his Amadigi di Gaula:
  Händel.   Schatz 4474

Heiden, Nicolaus Adam.
 Julius Sabinus, Nuernberg, 1791. Tr. of Sarti's Giulio Sabino
  (Giovannini).   Schatz 9479

Hêle, Thomas d'.
 L'amant jaloux. A. T. of his Les fausses apparences: Grétry.
 L'amant jaloux, ou Les fausses apparences, Toulouse, 1780:
  Grétry. Inverted T. of their Les fausses apparences. ML 50.2.F235G7
 Der eifersuechtige liebhaber, Wien, 1780. Tr. of his Les
  fausses apparences: Grétry.   Schatz 4158
 Les evènements imprévues, Paris, 1780: Grétry.   Schatz 4151
 Les fausses apparences ou L'amant jaloux, Paris, 1779:
  Grétry.   ML 50.2.F235G6
 Les fausses apparences, ou L'amant jaloux, Paris, 1780: Grétry. Schatz 4157
 Le jugement de Midas, Paris, 1778: Grétry.   ML 50.2.J9G7
 Le jugement de Midas, Paris, 1779: Grétry.   Schatz 4161
 Die unvermutheten zufaelle, Wien, 1781. Tr. of his Les
  evènements imprévues: Grétry.   Schatz 4152
 Das urtheil des Midas, Muenster, 1781. Rothmann's Tr. of
  his Le jugement de Midas: Grétry.   Schatz 4162
 Das urtheil des Midas, Mitau, 1783. Neefe's Tr.   Schatz 4164
 Das urteil des Midas, n. i., n. d. (detached copy). Bonin's Tr. Schatz 4163

Hempel, Caroline Luise.
 Die Grazien (Theater Journal fuer Deutschland, Gotha, 1778):
  André.   Schatz 11754

Henisch, Carl Franz.
 Der bassa von Tunis, Berlin u. Leipzig, 1774: Holly. Schatz 4768
 Das testament. *See* Title catalogue.
 Das vornehme Suschen. *See* Title catalogue.
 Der zaubrer, Prag, 1772: Holly.   Schatz 4773

Hennequin, Louis.
 Le bon fils, Paris, an quatrième (1795–96): Lebrun. ML 50.2.B7L3

Hensel, Johann Daniel.
 Singspiele von Johann Daniel Hensel . . .
 Hirschberg, W. Pittschiller und komp., 1799. 2 v. in 1. 17½ᶜᵐ.
  Part I has special t.-p. and part 2 has two special title-pages, the second
   one reading ". . . Ein singspiel . . . nach Shakespear, Gotter und
   J. W. D. umgearbeitet . . ."
  Contents.—1. bdchen. Die geisterbeschwörung, eine operette. Daphne,
   oder Die frühlingsfeier in Arkadien, eine oper.—2. bdchen. Die geis-
   terinsel, von Gotter, umgearb. nach Shakespear und J. W. D. und in
   4 akte gebracht.   ML 49.A2H3
 Daphne oder Die fruehlingsfeier in Arkadien, Hirschberg,
  1799. (Singspiele, erstes baendchen): author. Schatz 4635
 Die geisterbeschwoerung, Hirschberg, 1799 (Singspiele, erstes
  baendchen): author.   Schatz 4635

Hensel, Johann Daniel—Continued.

Die geisterinsel, Hirschberg, 1799: author.   Schatz 4637

Der alte ueberall und nirgends (I–II ter theil), Wien, 1796: Schatz 6906 and Müller.   6907

Das aufgeboth. A. T. of his Die getreuen Oesterreicher: W. Müller.

Das faustrecht in Thueringen. Erster theil, Wien, 1797: Kauer.   Schatz 5027

— Zweyter theil, Wien, 1797: Kauer.   Schatz 5028

— Dritter theil, Wien, 1797: Kauer.   Schatz 5029

Het feest der Braminen, Amsteldam, 1798. Tr. of his Das sonnenfest der Braminen: Müller.   Schatz 6966

Die getreuen Oesterreicher oder Das aufgeboth, Wien, 1797: Müller.   Schatz 6929

Das goldene gefaess. A. T. of his Ritter Willibald: Kauer.

Gute menschen lieben ihren fuersten oder Die Jakobiner in Deutschland, Wien, 1799: Kauer.   Schatz 5032

Der invalide (Wien, 1786): Müller.   Schatz 6934

Die jagd, Wien, 1799: Schenck.   Schatz 9597

Die Jakobiner in Deutschland. A. T. of his Gute menschen lieben ihren fuersten: Kauer.

Die loewenjagd. A. T. of his Die verschwoerung der Odaliken: W. Müller.

Die loewenritter, Wien, 1799: Krauer.   ML 50.2.L5K2

Das Petermaennchen. Erster theil, Wien, 1794: Weigl.   Schatz 10942

— Zweiter theil, Wien, 1794: Weigl.   Schatz 10943

Ritter Willibald oder Das goldene gefaess, Wien, 1794: Kauer. Schatz 5053

Das schlangenfest in Sangora, Wien, 1797: Müller.   Schatz 6959

Die schoene marketenderinn, Wien, 1795: Müller.   Schatz 6961

Die schoene marketenderin (Wien) 1798: Müller.   Schatz 6961a

Das sonnenfest der Braminen, Wien, 1790: Müller.   Schatz 6965

Der sturm, Wien, 1798: Müller.   Schatz 6967

Taddaedl, der dreyssigjaehrige A. B. C. Schuetz, Wien, 1799: Müller.   Schatz 6968

Die verschwoerung der Odalisken, oder Die loewenjagd, Wien, 1792: Müller.   Schatz 6974

Der waffenschmied, Wien, 1797: Kauer.   Schatz 5065

Wer den schaden hat, darf fuer den spott nicht sorgen, Wien, 1798: Müller.   Schatz 6976

Die zwoelf schlafenden jungfrauen (IIter theil) Wien, 1798: Müller.   Schatz 6979

Hensler, Carl Friedrich.

Die marionettenbude oder Der jahrmarkt zu Gruenwald, Salzburg, 1797: Th. Weigl.   ML 50.2.M455W3

Herbst, C. A.

Die ruinen von Portici, Breslau, 1798: Fischer, F.   Schatz 3216

Herdlitzka, Giuseppe.

Le reclute del villaggio, ballet. *See* Martin y Soler's L'accorta cameriera.

Il ritorno opportuno, ballet. *See* Martin y Soler's L'accorta cameriera.

La schiava americana, ballet. *See* Paisiello's Le vane gelosie.

La vindemmia, ballet. *See* Paisiello's Le vane gelosie.

Herklots, Carl Alexander.

Die boese frau (Operetten, IV, Berlin, 1792): Walter. SCHATZ 10858

Dido, Berlin, 1799. Tr. of Piccinni's Didon (Marmontel). SCHATZ 8089

Falstaff, Berlin, 1799. Tr. of Salieri's Falstaff o sia Le tre burle (Defranceschi). SCHATZ 9290

Das inkognito (Operetten, Berlin, 1793): Gürrlich. SCHATZ 4372a

Die insel der Alcina, Berlin, 1794: A. Bianchi. Tr. of Bertati's text L'isola d'Alcina. SCHATZ 972

Kindliche liebe, Frankfurt a. M., 1798. Tr. of Gaveaux's L'amour filial (Demoustier). SCHATZ 3637

Der mädchenmarkt (Operetten, Berlin, 1793): Dittersdorf, 1797. SCHATZ 3601

Der maedchenmarkt, Hamburg, 1793: von Kospoth. SCHATZ 5220

Oedip zu Colonos, Berlin, 1798. Tr. of Sacchini's Oedipe à Colone (Guillard). SCHATZ 9235

Philipp und Georgette, Hamburg, 1798. Tr. of Dalayrac's Philippe et Georgette (Marsollier). SCHATZ 2372

Pigmalion oder Die reformation der liebe, Berlin, 1794: unknown. ML 50.2.P411

Schwarz und weiss (Operetten, Berlin, 1793): unknown. SCHATZ 11649

Verwirrung durch aehnlichkeit (Berlin) 1795. Tr. of Portugal's Le confusioni della somiglianza (Mazzini). SCHATZ 8401

Herrico, Scipione. *See* Errico.

Heywood, Thomas.

Loves mistresse or The Queens masque, 2d ed., London, 1640. LONGE 61

Hiesberger, Leopold.

Im finstern ist nicht gut tappen (Wien) 1787: Schenck. SCHATZ 9596

Ein singspiel ohne titel (n. i., n. d., before 1800?): Schenck. SCHATZ 9594

Hill, Aaron.

Daraxes (Dramatick works, 1760, v. 2). LONGE 326

Merlin in love or Youth against magic (Dramatic works, 1760, v. I). LONGE 325

The Muses in mourning (Dramatic works, 1760, v. 2). LONGE 326

Rinaldo (Dramatic works, London, 1760, v. I) (plan by Hill, Italian text by Rossi, tr. back into English by Hill): Händel. LONGE 325

Rinaldo, Hamburg (1715). Tr. of his and Rossi's Rinaldo: Händel. SCHATZ 4489

Rinaldo (Hamburg, 1723). L. ed. of the above. SCHATZ 4501

Rinaldo, Napoli, 1718: Händel, added arias by Leo. SCHATZ 4495

The snake in the grass (Dramatic works, London, 1760, v. 2). LONGE 326

Hinsch.

Der beglueckte Florindo (Hamburg) 1708: Händel. SCHATZ 4476

Berenice (Hamburg) 1702: Bronner. SCHATZ 1332

Claudius, roemischer kaeyser (Hamburg, 1726): Keiser. L. T. of their Die verdammte staatsucht. SCHATZ 5083

Dido, Koenigin von Carthago (Hamburg) 1707: Graupner. SCHATZ 4122

La fedeltà coronata oder Die gekroente treue (Hamburg, 1706): Keiser. SCHATZ 5089

Lucius Verus oder Die siegende treue (Hamburg, 1728): Keiser. SCHATZ 5101

Hinsch—Continued.

　　Die verdammte staat-sucht, oder Der verfuehrte Claudius,
　　　　Hamburg, 1703: Keiser.　　　　　　　　　　　　　SCHATZ 5130

　　Die verwandelte Daphne (Hamburg) 1708: Händel.　Second
　　　　part of their Der beglueckte Florindo.　　　　　　SCHATZ 4493

　　Victor, hertzog der Normannen (Hamburg) 1702: Schiefer-
　　　　decker, Mattheson and Bronner.　　　　　　　　SCHATZ 9605

Hippesley, John.

　　Flora or Hob in the well, 7th ed., London, 1768: Bates.　(Text
　　　　really by Cibber.)　　　　　　　　　　　　　　LONGE 73

Hoadley, James.

　　Phoebe, London, 1748: Greene.　　　　　　　　　　LONGE 274

Hoare, Prince.

　　The captive of Spilburg, London, 1799 (based on Marsollier's
　　　　Camille ou Le souterrain): Dussek.　　　　　　LONGE 249

　　Lock and key, London, 1796: Shield.　　　　　　　LONGE 238

　　Mahmoud (London) 1796: Storace, Sarti, Haydn, etc., and
　　　　Kelly.　　　　　　　　　　　　　　　　　　　LONGE 234

　　My grandmother, n. i., 1794: Storace.　　　　　　LONGE 233

　　No song no supper, n. i., 1790: Storace (chiefly) and Pleyel,
　　　　Grétry, Dr. Harington, Giordani, Gluck, etc.　LONGE 206

　　No song no supper, Dublin, 1792: Storace, etc.　SCHATZ 10085

　　The prize or 2, 5, 3, 8, Dublin, 1793: Storace.　LONGE 233

Hochkirch.　*Original name of* Franz von Loë.

　　Die geister-burg, 1799: P. Ritter.　　　　　　　SCHATZ 8823

Hoë, Johann Joachim.

　　Die durch verstellung und grossmuth uber die grausamkeit
　　　　siegende liebe oder Julia, Hamburg (1717): Keiser.　SCHATZ 5087

　　Die grossmuethige Tomyris, Hamburg (1717): Keiser.　SCHATZ 5094

　　Geheimen begebenheiten Henrico IV, koenigs von Castilien
　　　　und Leon, oder: Die getheilte liebe, Hamburg (1711):
　　　　Mattheson.　　　　　　　　　　　　　　　　SCHATZ 6100

　　Il trionfo dell' amore & della costanza—Der triumph der
　　　　liebe, Hamburg (1718): Conti.　　　　　　　　SCHATZ 2199

　　Das zerstoerte Troja oder Der durch den tod Helenen ver-
　　　　soehnte Achilles, Hamburg (1716): Keiser.　　SCHATZ 5117

Hoffman(n), François Benoît.

　　Adrien, Paris, an VII (1799): Méhul.　　　　　　SCHATZ 6276

　　Callias, ou Nature et patrie, Paris, Troisième année (1794–95):
　　　　Grétry.　　　　　　　　　　　　　　　　　SCHATZ 4202

　　Eufrosine, Amsteldam, 1798.　Tr. of his Euphrosine et le
　　　　tyran corrigé: Méhul.　　　　　　　　　　　SCHATZ 6274

　　Euphrosine et le tyran corrigé, ou Le pouvoir de l'amour,
　　　　Liège [1794–95]: Méhul.　　　　　　　　　　SCHATZ 6242

　　Le jockei, Paris, an IV (1796): Solié.　　　　　ML 50.2.J6S6

　　Léon ou Le château de Montenero, Paris, an 7 ʹ1798): Da-
　　　　layrac.　　　　　　　　　　　　　　　　　ML 50.2.L26D2

　　Médée, Paris, an V, 1797: Cherubini.　　　　　ML 50.2.M5C3

　　Nature et patrie.　A. T. of his Callias: Grétry.

　　Phèdre, Bordeaux, 1786: Le Moine.　　　　　　ML 50.2.P35L2

　　Le pouvoir de l'amour.　A. T. of his Euphrosine et le tyran
　　　　corrigé: Méhul.

Holcroft, Thomas.
The choleric fathers, London, 1785: Shield. LONGE 96
The noble peasant, London, 1784: Shield (and Cooke, Smith,
Duni, Sacchini). LONGE 93

Holman, Joseph George.
Abroad and at home, London, 1796: Shield. LONGE 237

Hook, *Mrs.* James (Harriet Horncastle Hook).
The double disguise, London, 1784: Hook. LONGE 95

Hotter.
Stoertebecker und Joedge Michaels, erster theil, Hamburg,
1701: Keiser. SCHATZ 5111
—, zweyter theil, Hamburg, 1701: Keiser. SCHATZ 5112

Hough, J.
Second thought is best (London), 1788: unknown. LONGE 270

Howell, James.
The nuptials of Peleus and Thetis, London, 1654. Tr. of
Caproli's Le nozze di Teti e Peleo (Buti). LONGE 241

Huber, Franz Xaver.
Die drei sultaninnen. A. T. of his Soliman der Zweite:
Süssmayer.
Die edle rache, n. i., n. d.: Suessmayer. SCHATZ 10177
Myrrha und Elvira oder Das opferfest, Hamburg, 1797. Vul-
pius' version of his Das unterbrochene opferfest: Winter. SCHATZ 11060
Das opferfest. A. T. of Vulpius' Myrrha und Elvira, which
is but his version of Huber's Das unterbrochene opferfest:
Winter.
Das opferfest, Hamburg (1798). The same, with this as main
title. SCHATZ 11062
Il sacrifizio interrotto, Dresda, 1798: Winter. Tr. of their
Das unterbrochene opferfest. SCHATZ 11061
Soliman der zweite, oder Die drei Sultaninnen, Wien, 1799:
Süssmayer. SCHATZ 10182
Das unterbrochene opferfest: Winter. O. T. of their Myrrha
und Elvira, oder Das opferfest, Il sacrifizio interrotto,
Das opferfest, etc.
Der wildfang (Wien) 1790: Süssmayer. SCHATZ 10185

Huber, Johann Ludwig (*or* Ludwig Ferdinand).
Tamira, Tuebingen, 1791: Zumsteeg. SCHATZ 11295

Huber, Leopold.
Auf dem land kennt man die rache nicht. A. T. of his Der
unshuldige betrug: Kauer.
Der unschuldige betrug, oder Auf dem land kennt man die
rache nicht, Wien, 1790: Kauer. SCHATZ 5061

Huber, Ludwig Ferdinand (*or* Johann Ludwig).
Tamira, Tuebingen, 1791: Zumsteeg. SCHATZ 11295

Hübner, Lorenz.
Semiramis. Tr. of Salieri's Semiramide (Munich, 1782)
(Metastasio) ML 50.2.S48S2
Tankred. Tr. of Holzbauer's Tancredi (München, 1783). SCHATZ 4786

Hull, Thomas.

The fairy Favour, London, 1766.   Longe 109
Love finds the way, London, 1777.   ML 50.2.L6
Pharnaces, London, 1765: Bates.   Longe 50
The royal merchant, London, 1768: Linley.   Longe 197
The Spanish lady, London (1769).   Longe 150

Hunold, Christian Friedrich.

Theatralische / galante und geistliche gedichte / von Menantes [*pseud.*].

*Hamburg / G. Liebernickel, 1706.   7 p. l., 241 (i. e. 269), 80,
[6] p., 1 l. front.   16½ cm.*

No. 207-208 omitted in paging; pages 257-271 numbered 227-241. On
p. [137]-196:

"Der gestûrtzte und wieder erhôhte Nebucadnezar, kônig zu
Babylon unter dem grossen propheten Daniel, in einem
singe-spiel auf dem grossen hamburgischen schau-platze
vorgestellet im jahr 1704": Keiser.   ML 49.A2H9

Der bestuerzte und wiedererhoehte Nebucadnezar, Koenig
zu Babylon unter dem grossen propheten Daniel (Hamburg, 1704): Keiser.   Schatz 5092

Die ueber die liebe triumphirende weissheit, oder Salomon
(Hamburg, 1703): Keiser.   Schatz 5113

Hurlstone, Thomas.

Just in time, London (1792): Carter.   Longe 220
To arms! or The British recruit, London, 1793: Shield and
Giordani.   Longe 221

Hus, J. B. Eugène.

Lise et Colin ou La surveillance inutile, Paris, an IV (1796):
Gaveaux.   ML 50.2.L4G2

Huss, Augusto.

Le allegrezze per le vittorie di Scipione, ballet: Le Messier.
   See Galuppi's Sofonisba.
Amore custode del giardino di Armida, ballet: Le Messier.
   See Anfossi's Armida.
L'amore vinto dall' amicizia, ballet: Le Messier.   *See* G. F.
de Majo's Catone in Utica.
La contribuzione sforzata, ballet: Le Messier.   *See* Galuppi's
Sofonisba.
La costanza affricana soccorsa dall' arte magica, ballet: Le
Messier.   *See* Galuppi's Sofonisba.
Le donne Ateniesi e i loro compagni, ballet: Le Messier.   *See*
Pasque's Arianna e Teseo.
Le fontane incantate, ballet: *See* Gluck's Il trionfo di Clelia.
Le fontane incantate, ballet: Le Messier.   *See* Pasque's
Arianna e Teseo.
Il guoco dell' arco, ballet: Le Messier.   *See* Pasque's Arianna
e Teseo.
La morte d'Orfeo, ballet: Le Messier.   *See* Gius. Scarlatti's
Pelopida.
Il rapimento di Proserpina, ballet: Le Messier.   *See* G. F.
de Majo's Catone in Utica.
Il riposo interotto, ballet.   *See* Gluck's Il trionfo di Clelia.
I selvatici, ballet: Le Messier.   *See* Gius. Scarlatti's Pelopida.

Ihlée, Johann Jakob.
　Der arrestant, Frankfurt am Main, 1799.　Tr. of Della Maria's
　　Le prisonnier (Duval).　　　　　　　　　　　　SCHATZ 2486
　Das fest der winzer, n. i., n. d.　L. T. of his Die weinlese:
　　Kunzen.　　　　　　　　　　　　　　　　　　SCHATZ 5332
　Das fest der winzer, oder Wer fuehrt die braut nach hause,
　　n. i., n. d.　L. T. of his Die weinlese: Kunzen.　SCHATZ 5333
　Die weinlese, Frankfurt am Main, 1793: Kunzen.　SCHATZ 5331
　Wer fuehrt die braut nach hause?　A. T. of his Das fest der
　　winzer: Kunzen.

Ilgener, P. F.
　Die schnitter, Rostock, 1779: unknown.　　　　SCHATZ 11462

Imbert, Barthélémy.
　Les deux sylphes, Paris, 1781: Désaugiers.　　　ML 50.2.D5D2

Imer, Giuseppe.
　Il Trojano schernito in Cartagine nascente e moribonda,
　　Venezia, 1743: pasticcio.　　　　　　　　　　ML 48.A5 v.10

Inalbo Laerzio, P. A.
　Seila, Faenza (1787): Scolart.　　　　　　　　SCHATZ 9807

Ivanovich, Cristoforo.
　L'amor guerriero, Venetia, 1663: P. A. Ziani.　SCHATZ 11220
　Circe, Venetia, 1679: Freschi.　　　　　　　　SCHATZ 3347
　La costanza trionfante, Venetia, 1673: Partenio.　SCHATZ 7777
　Lisimacco, Venetia, 1674: Pagliardi.　　　　　SCHATZ 7583

Jackman, Isaac.
　The Milesian, London, 1777: Carter.　　　　　LONGE 86

Jackson, William.
　Lycidas, London, 1767: author.　　　　　　　　LONGE 198

Jacoby, Johann Georg.
　Apollo unter den hirten (Hannover, 1770): Schweitzer.　SCHATZ 9769
　Elysium (Hannover, 1770): Schweitzer.　　　　SCHATZ 9772
　Phaedon und Naide oder Der redende baum (Theatralische
　　Schriften, Nachtrag zu seinen sämtlichen werken, Leip-
　　zig, 1792): Boeklin von und zu Boeklinsau.　SCHATZ 1113
　Der tod des Orpheus (Theater schriften, Leipzig, 1792):
　　Bachmann.　　　　　　　　　　　　　　　　SCHATZ 537

Janquières, Jean Baptiste de.
　Le Guy de Chesne, ou La feste des Druides, Paris, 1763:
　　Laruette.　　　　　　　　　　　　　　　　　SCHATZ 5439

Jester, Ernst Friedrich.
　Louise, Riga, 1794: F. L. Benda.　　　　　　　SCHATZ 765
　Der triumpf der liebe, Hamburg, 1796: Stegmann.　SCHATZ 10044

Jodrell, Richard Paul.
　Who's afraid? (Select dramatic pieces, London, 1787).　LONGE 203

Johnson, Charles.
　The village opera, London, 1729 (70 p.): ballad opera.　ML 50.5.B3
　The village opera, London, 1729 (76 p.).　　　ML 50.5.V45

Jolly, Antoine François.
　Méléagre (Recueil général des opéra, t. x, Paris, 1714): Stuck.　SCHATZ 10124

Journal des spectacles, représentés devant Leurs Majestés, sur les théâtres de Versailles & de Fontainebleau, pendant l'anné 1765 ...

[*Paris*], *P. R. C. Ballard, 1766. 2 v. 21*ᶜᵐ.

CONTENTS.—t. 1. Intermedes d'amour pour amour. Les Incas du Perou. Prologue des Indes galantes. Les sauvages, entrée ajoutée aux Indes galantes. Fragments, composés du prologue des Amours des dieux, de l'acte de L'amour enjoué, et de celui de La danse. Thétis et Pélée. Renaud d'Ast.—t. 2. Silvie. Palmire. La vengeance de l'amour, ou Diane et Endimion, pantomime héroïque. La fée Urgele. Programme du ballet d'Églé. Le triomphe de Flore. Zenis et Almasie. Thesée. Erosine.

ML 48.J7

Juenger, Johann Friedrich.

Der neue guts herr, n. i., n. d. (a detached copy): Joh. Ad. Hiller (only "die ausfuehrung der gesaenge" in Dyk's text).   SCHATZ 4730

Der schiffspatron oder Der gutsherr, Hamburg, 1794: Dittersdorf.   SCHATZ 2608

Der schiffspatron oder Der neue gutsherr, Leipzig, 1793. Rev. of the above.   SCHATZ 2607

Julien, Jean Auguste. *Better known as* Des Boulmiers.

Kaffka, Johann Christoph.

Der guckkasten, oder Das beste komt zulezt (Sammlung auserlesener Theaterstücke, Breslau, 1784): author.   SCHATZ 4984

So prellt man alte fuechse (Sammlung auserlesener Theaterstücke, Breslau, 1784): author.   SCHATZ 4987

Keate, George.

The monument in Arcadia, London, 1773.   LONGE 186

Keiser, Reinhard.

Die blut-durstige rache oder Heliates und Olympia (Hamburg) 1709: author.   SCHATZ 5080

La forza dell' amore, Die macht der liebe oder Die von Paris entfuehrte Helena, Hamburg, 1709: author.   SCHATZ 5090

Kellgren, Johan Henrik.

Gustaf Adolph och Ebba Brahe (Stockholm) 1788: G. J. Vogler.   SCHATZ 10795

Kelly, John.

The plot, London, 1735: ballad opera.   LONGE 293

Kemble, John Philipp.

Lodoiska, London (1794): pasticcio (Storace, Cherubini, Kreutzer, and Andreozzi).   LONGE 228

Kempel.

Andromeda und Perseus, Wien, 1780: Zimmermann.   SCHATZ 11234

Kendrick, *Dr.*

The lady of the manor, London, 1778: Hook.   LONGE 85

King, Thomas.

Love at first sight, London, 1763: ballad opera.   LONGE 36

Klein, Anton.

Günther von Schwarzburg (1777): Holzbauer.   SCHATZ 4783

Knapp, Henry.
Hunt the slipper (Dublin) 1792: Arnold. LONGE 223

Knigge, Adolf Friedrich, *freyherr von.*
Figaro's heyrath, Hamburg, 1791. Tr. of Mozart's Le nozze
di Figaro (Da Ponte). SCHATZ 11396
Die hochzeit des Figaro, Wien, 1798. His and Philippine
Eregine, freiin von Knigge's Tr. of Mozart's Le nozze
di Figaro, Wien, 1798 (Da Ponte). SCHATZ 6828
Der talismann, Berlin, 1798. Tr. of Salieri's Il talismano. SCHATZ 9324

Knight, Thomas.
The turnpike gate, London, 1799: Mazzinghi and Reeve. LONGE 258

Knudsen, Lars.
Den besnaerede cadi, n. i., n. d. Tr. of Monsigny's Le cadi
dupé (Lemonnier). SCHATZ 6568
Elskovs magt, Kiøbenhavn, 1791. Tr. of Naumann's Tutto
per amore (Mazzolà). SCHATZ 7063
I oprørt vand er godt at fiske, Kiøbenhavn, 1795. Tr. of
Sarti's Fra i due litiganti il terzo gode (Goldoni). SCHATZ 9462
Skovhuggeren eller De tre ønsker (Copenhagen, 1782). Tr. of
Philidor's Le bucheron (Guichard and Castet). SCHATZ 8013

Koch, Friedrich.
Der lahme husar, Dresden und Leipzig, 1784: Seydelmann. SCHATZ 9845

Koenig, Johann Ulrich.
Cadmus, Hamburg (1725): Kuntze. SCHATZ 5314
Die entdeckte verstellung oder Die geheime liebe der Diana,
Hamburg (1712): Keiser. SCHATZ 5088
Fredegunda, Hamburg, 1716: Keiser. SCHATZ 5123
Fredegunda, Hamburg (1736): Keiser. SCHATZ 5091
Der gedultige Socrates, Hamburg (1721): Telemann. (Text
is a Tr. of conte Niccolò Minato's "La patienza di Socrate
con due moglie.") SCHATZ 10261
Das neu-beglueckte Sachsen (Hamburg, 1730): Telemann. SCHATZ 10272
Die oesterreichische grossmuht oder Carolus V (Hamburg,
1712): Keiser. SCHATZ 5108
Die roemische grossmuht oder Calpurnia, Hamburg (1716).
Tr. of Heinichen's Calfurnia (Braccioli). SCHATZ 4702
Sancio, oder Die siegende grossmuth (Hamburg, 1727): Tele-
mann. SCHATZ 10266
Der sich raechende Cupido, Hamburg (1724). L. T. of his
Die entdeckte verstellung: Keiser with interpolated
Italian arias. SCHATZ 5129
Die wieder-hergestellte ruh oder Die gecroente tapferkeit des
Heraclius (Hamburg, 1712): Keiser. SCHATZ 5115

Komareck, Johann Nepomuk.
Marie von Montalban oder Lanassa's zweyter theil, n. i., 1794:
Winter. SCHATZ 11633

Korb, Christian Gottlieb.
Der ehrliche raeuber, Neubrandenburg, 1785: Zeller. SCHATZ 11164
Das muendel, Altona, 1783. ML 50.2.M86

Kotzebue, August Friedrich Ferdinand von.

Das dorf im gebuerge, Wien (1798): Weigl.   Schatz 10932

Der eremit auf Formentara (Mannheim?) 1790: P. Ritter.   Schatz 8822

Der eremit auf Formentara, n. i. (1790): Wolf.   Schatz 11081

Eremiten paa Formentara, Kiøbnehavn, 1791.   Tr. of Wolf's opera.   Schatz 11082

Schach Wampum oder Die wuensche, Hamburg, 1792.   L. T. of his Sultan Wampum oder Die wuensche: Stegmann.   Schatz 10043

Der spiegelritter, Hamburg, 1795: Walter.   Schatz 10865

Der spiegelritter, n. i., n. d.: Walter.   Schatz 10865a

Sultan Wampum, oder Die wuensche, n. i., 1794: Stegmann.   Schatz 10042

Sultan Wampum oder, Die wuensche, n. i., n. d. (detached copy): Stegmann.   Schatz 11749

Die wuensche.   A. T. of his Sultan Wampum: Stegmann, and of the L. T. of this, Schach Wampum.

Kraus, Wilhelm.

Das testament.   *See* Title catalogue.

Das vornehme Suschen.   *See* Title catalogue.

Kuntze, Johann Paul.

Die uber eyffersucht und list triumphirende bestaendige liebe, Wittenberg (ca. 1720): author.   Schatz 5315

Kurz, Johann Joseph Felix von, *called* **Bernardon.**

Asmodeus der krumme teufel, Wien, 1770: Haydn.   L. T. of Der neue krumme teufel.   Schatz 4609

Li creduti spiriti, Venezia, 1764: Naumann.   Schatz 7064

La morte di Dimone o sia L'innocenza vendicata, Venezia, 1763 (Italian version by Giov. Bertati): Tozzi.   Schatz 10385

L.

Der einsiedler, Leipzig, 1780: unknown.   Schatz 11452

L., A.

La locandiera, Lucca, 1798: La Motte Foucher.   Schatz 5358

La Bruère, Charles Antoine Le Clerc de.

Bacchus et Erigone, n. i., n. d. (printed 1769 together with "L'Amour et Psyché): Mondonville.   ML 52.2.B105M6

Dardanus, Paris, 1761: Rameau.   ML 50.2.D27R2

Dardanus, Paris, 1784 (largely rewritten by Guillard): Sacchini.   Schatz 9217

Dardanus, Paris, 1786.   The same, reduced to three acts.   Schatz 9248

Les voyages de l'amour (Recueil général des opéra, Paris, 1745, t. xvi): Boismortier.   ML 48.R4

La Chabeaussière, Ange Etienne Xavier Poisson de.

– Azémia, ou Les sauvages, Paris, 1787: Dalayrac.   ML 50.2.A98D2

– Azémia, ou Les sauvages, Toulouse, 1787: Dalayrac.   ML 50.2.A98D12

– Azémia, ou Les sauvages, Paris, 1788: Dalayrac.   ML 48.M2L

Les deux tuteurs, Paris, 1784: Dalayrac.   ML 50.2.D51D2

Les deux tuteurs, Paris, 1785: Dalayrac.   ML 50.2.D51D22

– L'éclipse totale, Paris, 1782: Dalayrac.   Schatz 2342

– Die wilden, Frankfurt am Main, 1791: Dalayrac.   Tr. of their Azémia.   Schatz 2371

Lafont, Joseph de.

Les amours de Protée (Recueil général des opéra, t. xiii, Paris, 1734): Gervais. — SCHATZ 3790a

Les amours de Protée, Lyon, 1742: Gervais. — SCHATZ 3790b

Le ballet des XXIV heures, Paris, 1723 (prologue only): Aubert. — ML 52.2B11

La critique des Festes de Thalie. *See his* Les festes de Thalie.

Les festes de Thalie—La critique des Festes de Thalie (Recueil général des opéra, Paris, t. xi, 1720): Mouret. — SCHATZ 6741 and 6742

Hypermnestre (Recueil général des opéra, Paris, t. xii, 1734): Gervais. — SCHATZ 3791a

Hypermnestre, Lyon, 1742: Gervais. — SCHATZ 3791b

Orion (Recueil général des opéra, t. xiv, Paris, 1734) (with de Pellegrin): La Çoste. — SCHATZ 5355

La Provençale (Paris, 1755): Mouret. — ML 52.2.F3

La querelle des théâtres. *See* Le Sage.

Le triomphe de Thalie. A. T. of his Les festes de Thalie: Mouret.

La Fontaine, Jean de.

Astrée (Amsterdam), 1692: Colasse. — ML 50.2.A86C6

Astrée (Recueil général des opéra, Paris, 1703, t. 4): Colasse. — SCHATZ 2097

Lagarde (La Garde), de.

Les amours grivois. *See* Favart.

Le bal de Strasbourg. *See* Favart.

Lagrange.

Cassandra: or, The virgin prophetess, London [1692]. An English version of Lagrange-Chancel's Cassandre? — LONGE 180

Lagrange-Chancel. (Chancel de Lagrange, François Joseph de, *known also as* **La Grange.,**

Ariane, Paris, 1717 (with Roy): Mouret. — ML 50.2.A739M6

Ariane (Recueil général des opéra, Paris, v. xii, 1734) (with Roy): Mouret. — SCHATZ 6694

Cassandre, Amsterdam, 1707: Bouvard and Bertin de la Doué. — ML 50.2.C28B6

Cassandre (Recueil général des opéra, Paris, 1710, t. ix): Bouvard and Bertin de la Doué. — SCHATZ 1275

Medus, roy des Mèdes (Recueil général des opéra, Paris, 1703, t. vii): Bouvard. — SCHATZ 1274

La Jonchère, Venard de.

Théatre lyrique, de M. de La J . . .

Paris, Chez Barbou [etc.] 1772. 2 v. 18½cm.

Title-vignette. Half-title of v. I bound after p. 144 "Essai sur l'Opéra": v. 1, p. 1–178.

CONTENTS.—Alexandre et Thalestris—Amphitryon—Antiope—Massilie ou La foundation de Marseille—Sapho—Scamandre—Le siège de Tyr—Tésée.

Composers are not recorded.

ML 49.A2L2

Lalin, Lars Samuel.

Acis och Galatea, Stockholm, 1773: Händel, Johnsen, and others. — SCHATZ 4494

Lalli, Domenico, *pseud. of* **Bastiano Biancardi.**

L'amor di figlia, Venezia, 1718: Corta. (A revised version of
G. A. Moniglia's text "La pietà di Sabina.") Schatz 8395

L'amor di figlio non conosciuto, Venecia, 1715: Albinoni. Schatz 102

L'amor tirannico, Venezia, 1722: Chelleri and G. Porta (third
act). Schatz 1819

L'Amor tirannico, Venezia, 1710: Gasparini. Schatz 3558

Argeno, Venezia, 1728: Leo. Schatz 5552

L'Argippo, Milano, 1722 (retouched by Claudio Nicola
Stampa): Fiorè. Schatz 3191

L'Argippo, Venezia, 1717: Porta. Schatz 8388

Arsilda, regina di Ponto, Venezia, 1716: Vivaldi. Schatz 10760

Camaide, imperatore della China o vero Li figliuoli rivali del
padre, Salisburgo (1722): Caldara. Schatz 1479

Cambise, Napoli, 1719: A. Scarlatti. Schatz 9526

Candace, Venezia, 1738 (alterations only in Silvani's text):
Lampugnani. Schatz 5392

Dalisa, Venezia (1730): Hasse. (Text by conte Minato,
altered by Lalli.) Schatz 4577

Gl'eccessi della gelosia, Venezia, 1722: Albinoni. Schatz 116

Elisa, Venetia, 1711: Ruggeri. Schatz 9129

Epaminonda, Venezia (1732): Giacomelli. Schatz 3811

Euristeo, Venezia, 1732: Hasse. (Text by Zeno, altered by
Lalli.) Schatz 4580

Evergete. *See* Silvani, Francesco.

Farnace, Venezia, 1718: C. F. Pollaroli. Schatz 8287

Li figliuoli rivali del padre. A. T. of his Camaide, imperatore
della China.

Filippo rè di Macedonia, Venezia, 1721: Act I–II Boniventi,
act III Vivaldi. Schatz 1196

La generosità politica, Venezia, 1736 (with Goldoni?): Marchi. Schatz 5936

Die im betruge vertheidigte unschuld. Tr. of his L'innocenza difesa nell' inganno, Copenhagen, 1753. Schatz 11342

Il Gran Mogol, Napoli, 1713 (buffo scenes and certain designated arias by Serino): Mancini. Schatz 5879

Il gran Mogol. O. T. of his L'innocenza difesa nell' inganno.

L'innocenza difesa nell' inganno—Die im betruge vertheidigte
unschuld, Copenhagen, 1753: unknown. (L. T. of his
Il gran Mogol.) Schatz 11342

Il Lamano, Venezia, 1719: M. A. Gasperini. Schatz 3600

La marchesina di Nanchin ed il conte di Pelusio: Caldara.
Intermezzi in their Camaide, imperatore della China.

La Mariane, Venezia (1724): Albinoni and Porta. L. T. of
his text Gl'eccessi della gelosia. Schatz 117

La Mariane, Firenze (1726): Albinoni, Porta, and others. ML 48.A5 v.18

Nerina, Venezia, 1728 (supposed revision of Pietro d'Averara's
text): A. Pollaroli. Schatz 8263

Onorio, Venezia (1729) (with G. Boldini): F. Ciampi. Schatz 1874

Il pentimento generoso, Venezia, 1719: Fiorè. Schatz 3194

Timocrate, Venezia, 1723: Leo. Schatz 5560

Tropotipo, Venezia, 1726: Pescetti. Schatz 7963

Turia Lucrezia, Venezia, 1726: A. Pollaroli. Schatz 8265

Ulisse, Venezia (1725): Porta. Schatz 8394

Lalli, Domenico, *pseud, of* **Bastiano Biancardi**—Continued.

Ulisses (Breslau, 1726): Treu. SCHATZ 10444

I veri amici, Monaco (1722) (with Silvani): Albinoni. SCHATZ 99

I veri amici, Venezia, 1713 (with Francesco Silvani): Paulati. SCHATZ 7786

Viriate, Venezia, 1739: Hasse. (Merely alterations in Metastasio's text.) SCHATZ 4581

La Marre, de.

Zaïde, reine de Grenade, Lyon, 1749: Royer. ML 52.2.Z2R7

Lambrecht, Matthias Georg.

Der quasi-mann, Muenchen, 1789: Danzi. SCHATZ 2410

La Motte, Antoine Houdart de.

Alcione, Amsterdam, 1707: Marais. ML 50.2.A513M2

Alcione (Recueil général des opéra, t. ix, Paris, 1710): Marais. SCHATZ 5919

Amadis de Grece, Amsterdam, 1699: Destouches. ML 50.2.A595D2

Amadis de Grece (Recueil général des opéra, Paris, 1703, t. vi). SCHATZ 2543

Canente (Recueil général des opéra, Paris, 1703, t. 7): Colasse. SCHATZ 2098

Le carnaval et la folie (Recueil général des opéra, t. viii,
Paris, 1706): Destouches. SCHATZ 2545

L'Europe galante (Recueil général des opéra, Paris, 1703, t.
vi): Campra. SCHATZ 1548

Issé (Recueil général des opéra, t. vi, Paris, 1703): Destouches. SCHATZ 2546

Issé (Recueil général des opéra, t. ix, Paris, 1710): Destouches. SCHATZ 2547

Issé (Paris) 1773: Destouches, altered by Berton. ML 50.2.I75D2

Marthesie, première reine des Amazones (Recueil général des
opéra, t. vi, Paris, 1703): Destouches. SCHATZ 2548

Omphale (Recueil général des opéra, t. vii, Paris, 1703): Destouches. SCHATZ 2549

Omphale, Paris, 1752: Destouches. SCHATZ 2549A

Omphale (Hamburg, 1724): Telemann. (Tr. of the above's
Omphale.) SCHATZ 10265

Pigmalion, Paris, 1772 (Ballot de Sauvot's version of his La
sculpture): Rameau. ML 48.B2

Scanderberg (Recueil général des opéra, Paris, 1745, t. xvi)
(finished by de La Serre): Rebel and Francoeur. ML 48.R4

Scanderberg (Paris) 1763: Rebel and Francoeur. ML 50.2.S34R2

Sémélé (Recueil général des opéra, t. ix, Paris, 1710): Marais. SCHATZ 5921

Titon et L'Aurore, Paris, 1763: Mondonville. ML 50.2.T59M7

Titon et L'Aurore, Marseille, 1775: Mondonville. ML 50.2.T59M73

Le triomphe des arts (Recueil général des opéra, t. vii, Paris,
1703): La Barre. SCHATZ 5344

La Venitienne (Recueil général des opéra, t. viii, Paris, 1706):
La Barre. SCHATZ 5345

Landi, Antonio.

I Greci in Tauride—Die Griechen in Taurica, Berlino, 1772:
Agricola. (Revised version of their Oreste e Pilade.) SCHATZ 68

Landi, Lelio Maria.

Gl'inganni amorosi scoperti in villa, Bologna (1696): Aldrovandini. SCHATZ 135

Langford, Abraham.

The lover his own rival, London, 1736: ballad opera. ML 50.5.L7

The lover his own rival, London, 1753. LONGE 198

Lanfranchi-Rossi. *See* Rossi, Carlo Giuseppe Lanfranchi.

Lantino, Liviano, *anagram of* Villano, Antonio.

Lany, Bartolomeo.
Piramo e Tisbe, ballet: Ghebhard. *See* Colla's Didone.

Lanzoni, *marchese* **Annibale.**
L'Almadero, Mantova, 1667: unknown. SCHATZ 11298

La Ribadière, de.
Les aveux indiscrets, Paris, 1759: Monsigny. ML 50.2.A95M7
Les deux cousines ou La bonne amie, Bruxelles, 1764: Des-
brosses. SCHATZ 2528
Les deux soeurs rivales, Paris, 1762: Desbrosses. ML 50.2.D495D2

La Roque, Antoine de.
Medée et Jason (Recueil général des opéra, t. x, Paris, 1714)
(with de Pellegrin, according to Schatz): Salomon. SCHATZ 9343
Theonoé, Paris, 1715: Salomon. ML 50.2.T43S2
Théonoé (Recueil général des opéra, t. xi, Paris, 1720):
Salomon. SCHATZ 9344

La Salle, Adrien Nicolas, *marquis* **de.**
Les pêcheurs, Avignon, 1766: Gossec. ML 50.2.P305G7
Les pêcheurs, Paris, 1767: Gossec. SCHATZ 4010
Les pêcheurs, Paris, 1771: Gossec. SCHATZ 11702
Les pêcheurs, Paris, 1782: Gossec. SCHATZ 11701
De visschers, Amsterdam, 1793. Tr. of his Les pêcheurs:
Gossec. SCHATZ 4015

La Serre, Jean Louis Ignace de, *sieur* **de l'Anglade.**
Diomède (Recueil général des opéra, Paris, 1714, t. x): Bertin
de la Doué. SCHATZ 879
Pirame et Thisbé (Recueil général des opéra, t. xiv, Paris,
1734): Francoeur and Rebel. SCHATZ 3336
Pirame et Thisbé (Lyon) 1741. ML 50.2.P43R2
Pirithous (with Seguineau) (Recueil général des opéra, t. xiii,
Paris, 1734): Mouret. SCHATZ 6743
Polidore (Recueil général des opera, t. xiii, Paris, 1734):
Stuck. SCHATZ 10125
Polixene et Pirrhus (Recueil général des opéra, t. ix, 1710):
Colasse. SCHATZ 2102
Scanderberg (Recueil général des opéra, Paris, 1745, t. xvi):
Rebel and Francoeur. (La Motte's text finished by La
Serre.) ML 48.R4
Tarsis et Zélie (Recueil général des opéra, t. xiv, Paris, 1734):
Francoeur and Rebel. SCHATZ 3337

Latteignant (Lattaignan), Gabriel Charles de.
Bertholde à la ville. *See* Title catalogue.
Le rossignol, Paris, 1753 (with another author). ML 48.A4

Lauchery, Stephan.
Achilles und Ulysses auf der insel Scyros, ballet: Cannabich.
See Bach's Lucius Silla.
Acis und Galatea, ballet: Toeschi. *See* Bach's Lucius Silla.
Medea und Jason, ballet. *See* Bach's Themistocles.

Lauchery, Stephan—Continued.

Rogerius auf der insel der Alcine, ballet: Toeschi. *See* Bach's Themistocles.

Der tod des Hercules, ballet: pasticcio. *See* Salieri's Die mésse zu Venedig.

Laujon, Pierre.

L'amoureux de quinze ans, ou La double fête, Paris, veuve Duchesne, 1771 (68 p.): Martini. — Schatz 6034

L'amoureux de quinze ans ou La double fête, Paris, veuve Duchesne, 1771 (64 p.): Martini. — Yudin PQ

Le bal de Strasbourg. *See* Favart.

La double fête. A. T. of his L'amoureux de quinze ans: Martini.

Ismene et Ismenias, Paris, 1770: La Borde. — ML 50.2.I7L2

Der liebhaber von funfzehn jahren, Wien, 1778. Tr. of his L'amoureux de quinze ans: Martini. — Schatz 6035

Matroco, Paris, 1778: Grétry. — ML 50.2.M465G7

Le poète supposé ou Les préparatifs de fête, 2d ed., Paris (1782): Champein. — ML 50.2.P5C3

Silvie (Paris) 1765 (Journal des spectacles, t. ii, 1766): P. M. Berton and Trial. — ML 48.J7

Thesée. *See* Favart.

Zéphire et Fleurette. *See* Favart.

Leacock, John.

See The disappointment in Title catalogue.

Leboeuf, Jean Joseph.

Renaud, Paris, 1783: Sacchini (French version of his Armida). — Schatz 9206

Renaud, Bruxelles, 1783: Sacchini. — ML 50.2.R38S2

Renaud, Paris, 1786: Sacchini. — ML 50.2.R38S3

Lebreton. *Same as* Berton.

Lediard, Thomas.

Julius Caesar in Aegypten (Hamburg, 1725). Tr. of Händel's Giulio Cesare in Egitto (Haym). — Schatz 4478

Julius Caesar in Aegypten (Hamburg, 1733). Later ed. of above. — Schatz 11690

Lee, Henry.

Throw physick to the dogs, London, 1798 (also known as "Caleb Quotem and his wife"): Arnold. — ML 50.2.T52

Le Fèvre, Domenico.

Adriano in Siria, ballet. *See* Bertoni's Eumene.

Alcina ed Astolfo, ballet. *See* Zingarelli's Annibale in Torino.

Alessandro nell' Indie, ballet: principally Stabinger. *See* P. Guglielmi's Enea e Lavinia.

Gli amori di Mirtello con Silvanzia, ballet. *See* Antonelli's Catone in Utica.

Gli amori di Mirtillo e con Silvanzia, ballet. *See* Giordani's Osmane.

Apollo e Dafne, ballet. *See* G. Giordani's Atalanta.

Colombo nell' Indie, ballet: Rossetti. *See* Tritto's L'Artenice.

Le Fèvre, Domenico—Continued.

Il Cristoforo Colombo nell' Indie, ballet. *See* Brunetti's Bertoldo.

La cuccagna, ballet: pasticcio. *See* Zingarelli's Annibale in Torino.

La discesa d'Ercole all' inferno o sia Alceste ed Admeto, ballet: Canobbio. *See* Antonelli Torre's Catone in Utica.

La discesa d'Ercole all' inferno, ballet. *See* Cherubini's Ifigenia in Aulide.

D. Pedro, infante di Portogallo, ballet: Rossetti. *See* Sacchini's Lucio Vero.

La festa di flora, ballet. *See* Sacchini's Lucio Vero.

La feste di Flora, ballet. *See* Cherubini's Ifigenia in Aulide.

Le figlie astute, ballet. *See* Brunetti's Bertoldo.

Le figlie astute, ballet. *See* P. Guglielmi's Enea e Lavinia.

Il finto giardiniere, ballet. *See* Zingarelli's Annibale in Torino.

Giasone e Medea, ballet. *See* Martin y Soler's L'arbore di Diana.

Il Pigmalione, ballet. *See* G. Giordani's Atalanta.

Il ritorno di Rinaldo presso Armida o sia La vendetta di Armida vinta dall' amore, ballet: Rossetti. *See* Bianchi's Cajo Mario.

Le sultane, ballet. *See* G. Giordani's Atalanta.

Tancredi ossia Il padre crudele, Verona (1793), ballet.　　ML 52.2.T22

La vendetta di Armida vinta dall' amore. A. T. of his Il ritorno di Rinaldo presso Armida: Rossetti.

Venere con Adone ossia Le gelosie di Diana e di Marte, ballet. *See* Paër's Ero e Leandro.

Le Franc, Jean Jacques, *marquis* **de Pompignan.**

Le triomphe de l'harmonie (Recueil général des opéra, Paris, 1745, t. xvi): Grenet.　　ML 48.R4

Leger, F. P. A.

Belle et bonne, Paris, an VI, 1798: author.　　ML 48.M2L

Ziste et Zeste ou Les importuns, Paris, an V (1796) (with Cailhava): partly by Leger.　　ML 48.M2E

Legrand.

Die artige schaefer, ballet. *See* Piccinni's Das gute maegdchen.

Die eifersuechtige faunen, ballet. *See* Piccinni's Das gute maegdchen.

Le Grand, Alexandre.

Les animaux raisonnables. *See* Fuzelier.

Le Grand, Marc Antoine.

Le ballet des xxiv heures, Paris, 1723 (the prologue by de Lafont): Aubert.　　ML 52.2.B11

Le cahos (Les parodies du Nouveau théâtre italien, Nouv. éd., Paris, 1738, t. iii). (Parody of Destouches and Lalande's ballet Les élémens.)　　ML 48.P3

Lelio *fils*. *See* Riccoboni, Francesco.

Lemene, *conte* **Francesco de.**

L'inganno felice, Venezia, 1730: unknown. L. T. of his La
Ninfa Apollo.   Schatz 11341
Il Narciso, Lodi (1676): Bortio.   Schatz 1254
La ninfa Apollo, Venezia, 1734 (retouched by Giovanni
Boldoni): Galuppi.   Schatz 3488
La ninfa Apollo, Venezia, 1709: Gasparini.   Schatz 3574
La ninfa Apollo, Venezia, 1726 (modernized): Francesco
Rossi.   Schatz 8888
Tirsi, Venezia (1734): unknown.   Schatz 11371

Lemonnier, Guillaume Antoine, *real name of* De Vaux.

Antoine Masson. O. T. of his Le bon fils: Philidor.
Le bon fils, Paris, 1773: Philidor.   Schatz 8009
Den besnaerede cadi, n. i., n. d. Tr. of his Le cadi dupé:
Monsigny.   Schatz 6568
Le cadi dupé, Vienne, 1768: Gluck.   Schatz 3924
Le cadi dupé, Paris, 1761: Monsigny.   ML 50.2.C2M7
Le cadi dupé, Paris, 1766: Monsigny.   Schatz 11725
Le cadi dupé, Paris, 1782: Monsigny.   Schatz 6567
Le maître en droit, Paris, 1762: Monsigny.   ML 50.2.M31M6
Le maître en droit, Paris, 1764: Monsigny.   Schatz 6577
La meuniere de Gentilly, Paris, 1768: de La Borde.   ML 50.2.M63L2
La meuniere de Gentilly, Avignon, 1768: de La Borde.   ML 50.2.M63L22
La meunière de Gentilly, Paris, 1770: de La Borde.   Schatz 5346
La meunière de Gentilly, Paris, 1779: de La Borde.   Schatz 11718
Die muellerin, Frankfurt am Mayn, 1773: de La Borde. Tr.
of their La meunière de Gentilly.   Schatz 5347
Renaud d'Ast (Paris) 1765 (Journal des spectacles, t. i, 1766):
Trial and Vachon.   ML 48.J7
L'union de l'amour et des arts (Paris), 1774: Floquet.   ML 52.2.U5

Lemontey, Pierre Edouard.

Palma ou Le voyage en Grèce, Paris, an VII [1798–99]: Plantade.   ML 50.2.P2P4

Lendenesi, Giacomo.

L'amante contrastata, Venezia, 1768: Felici.   Schatz 3053

Lenox, Charlotte.

Philander, London, 1758.   Longe 52

Leonardi, Donato Antonio.

Mutio Scevola, Lucca, 1675. *See* M. Curzio.

Leopold, Carl Gustav af.

Frigga, Stockholm, 1787: Åhlström.   Schatz 69

Lepicq, Charles (Carlo).

Adelaide di Guesclin, ballet. *See* Cafaro's Il natal d'Apollo.
Gli amanti protetti dall' Amore, ballet. *See* Borghi's Siroe.
Griselda, ballet. *See* Martin y Soler's Ifigenia in Aulide.
Orfeo sul Monte Rodope, ballet. *See* Insanguine's Medonte.
La Semiramide, ballet. *See* Jommelli's Armida abbandonata.
I tre Orazj e i tre Curiazj, ballet. *See* Bertoni's Telemaco ed
Eurice.

Lereno Secinuntino, *Arcade Romano.* (Real name unkown to Wotquenne and Schatz.)

A vingança da Cigana, Lisboa (1794): Moreira.   Schatz 6634

                       Second copy. ML 48.C6 1

Le Sage, Alain René.

Le theatre de la foire, ov l'opera-comique. Contenant les meilleures pie'ces qui ont été représentées aux foires de S. Germain & de S. Laurent. Enrichies d'estampes en taille-douce, avec une table de tous les vaudevilles & autres airs gravez-notez à la fin de chaque volume. Recueillies, revûës, & corrigées. Par Mrs. Le Sage & d'Orneval . . .

Paris, P. Gandouin, 1724–37. 9 v. in 10. plates. 17½^{cm}.

Added t.-p., engr.

Imprint varies: vol. 1–3, 7–10, Chez P. Gandouin, 1737 (v. 7–8, 1731); v. 4–5, Chez E. Ganeau, 1724; v. 6, Chez la veuve Pissot, 1728.

Tome ix, ii, ptie., by Carolet, has title: Le theatre de la foire, ov l'opera comique, contenant une partie des piéces qui ont été représentées aux foires de S. Germain & de S. Laurent, pendant les années 1732, 1733, & 1734.   ML 48.L2

— — Second set.

Approbation [2] p., wanting in v. 4.   ML 48.L22

Vol. 6–10 different issues from those of first set:

Vol. 6 has imprint: Paris, Chez P. Gandouin, 1731. Arrangement of type different. The "Table des airs" is a duplicate of that in vol. 5. That belonging to vol. 6 is wanting in this set.

Vol. 7–8 have on last page of text, "De l'imprimerie de la veuve Delatour," instead of, "De l'imprimerie de la veuve Carnier."

Vol. 9 has different arrangement of type. "Les trois comères," listed in table of contents, wanting.

Title of v. 10 reads: Avec une table des vaudevilles [etc.] Composées revûes & corrigées par Monsieur Carolet. Tome x. Paris, Chez la veuve Gandouin, 1734.

Achmet et Almanzine (Le théâtre de la foire, Paris, 1728, t. vi) (text with d'Orneval and Fuzelier): Gillier   ML 48.L2 vi

L'amour marin. *See* L'indifférence.

Les amours de Nanterre (Le théâtre de la foire, Paris, 1737, t. iii) (with d'Orneval): Gillier.   ML 48.L2 iii

Les amours de Protée (Le théâtre de la foire, Paris, 1731, t. vii) (with d'Orneval. Parody of Gervais's opera): Gillier.   ML 48.L2 vii

Arlequin Colombine. *See his* Colombine Arlequin.

Arlequin Endymion (Le théâtre de la foire, Paris, 1724, t. iv) (with Fuzelier and d'Orneval).   ML 48.L2 iv

Arlequin Hulla ou La femme repudiée (Le théâtre de la foire, Paris, 1737, t. ii) (with d'Orneval): Aubert.   ML 48.L2 ii

Arlequin invisible (Le théâtre de la foire, Paris, 1737, t. i): Gillier.   ML 48.L2 1

Arlequin Mahomet (Le théâtre de la foire, Paris, 1737, t. i): Gillier.   ML 48.L2 1

Arlequin, roy de Serendib (Le théâtre de la foire, t. i, Paris, 1737): Gillier.   ML 48.L2 1

Arlequin Thétis (Le théâtre de la foire, Paris, 1737, t. i): Gillier.   ML 48.L2 1

La ceinture de Venus (Le théâtre de la foire, Paris, 1737, t. i): Gillier.   ML 48.L2 1

Colombine Arlequin, ou Arlequin Colombine (Le théâtre de la foire, Paris, 1737, t. ii): Gillier.   ML 48.L2 ii

Le Sage, Alain René—Continued.

Les comediens corsaires—L'obstacle favorable—Les amours déguisez (Le théâtre de la foire, Paris, 1728, t. vi) (with d'Orneval and Fuzelier): Gillier.   ML 48.L2 vi

Le corsaire de Salé (Le théâtre de la foire, Paris, 1731, t. vii) (with d'Orneval).   ML 48.L2 vii

Les couplets en procès (Le théâtre de la foire, Paris, 1731, t. vii) (with d'Orneval): Gillier.   ML 48.L2 vii

Les desesperés (Le théâtre de la foire, Paris, 1737, t. ix) (with d'Orneval): Gillier.   ML 48.L2 ix

Les eaux de Merlin (Le théâtre de la foire, Paris, 1737, t. ii): Gillier.   ML 48.L2 ii

L'école des amans (Le théâtre de la foire, Paris, 1737, t. ii): Gillier.   ML 48.L2 ii

L'enchanteur Mirliton (Le théâtre de la foire, Paris, 1728, t. vi) (with Fuzelier and d'Orneval): Gillier.   ML 48.L2 vi

Les enragez (Le théâtre de la foire, Paris, 1728, t. vi) (with Fuzelier and d'Orneval).   ML 48.L2 vi

L'esperance. *See his* L'indifférence.

La foire de Guibray (Le théâtre de la foire, Paris, 1737, t. i).   ML 48.L2 i

La forêt de Dodone (Le théâtre de la foire, Paris, 1724, t. iv) (with Fuzelier and d'Orneval): Gillier.

Les funerailles de la Foire (Le théâtre de la foire, Paris, 1737, t. iii) (with d'Orneval): Gillier.   ML 48.L2 iii

L'indifférence—L'amour—L'esperance (Le théâtre de la foire, Paris, 1731, t. viii) (with Fuzelier and d'Orneval): Gillier.   ML 48.L2 viii

L'industrie—Zemine et Almanzor—Les routes du monde (Le théâtre de la foire, Paris, 1731, t. viii) (with Fuzelier and d'Orneval): Gillier.   ML 48.L2 viii

L'isle des Amazones (Le théâtre de la foire, Paris, 1737, t. iii) (with d'Orneval): Gillier.   ML 48.L2 iii

Le jeune vieillard (Le théâtre de la foire, Paris, 1724, t. v) (with Fuzelier and d'Orneval): Mouret.   ML 48.L2 v

Le mari préferé (Le théâtre de la foire, Paris, 1737, t. ix): Gillier.   ML 48.L2 ix

Les mariages de Canada (Le théâtre de la foire, Paris, 1734, t. ix): Gillier.   ML 48.L2 ix

Le monde renversé (Le théâtre de la foire, Paris, 1737, t. iii) (with d'Orneval): Gillier.   ML 48.L2 iii

L'ombre du cocher poète (Le théâtre de la foire, Paris, 1724, t. v) (with Fuzelier and d'Orneval): Gillier.   ML 48.L2 v

L'opéra-comique assiegé (Le théâtre de la foire, Paris, 1731, t. vii) (with d'Orneval): Gillier.   ML 48.L2 vii

Parodie de l'opera de Telemaque (Le théâtre de la foire, Paris, 1737, t. i): Gillier.   ML 48.L2

Les pelerins de la Mecque (Le théâtre de la foire, Paris, 1728, t. vi) (with d'Orneval): Gillier.   ML 48.L2 vi

La Penelope moderne (Le théâtre de la foire, Paris, 1731, t. vii) (with Fuzelier and d'Orneval): Gillier.   ML 48.L2 vii

Pierrot Romulus ou Le ravisseur poli. *See his* L'ombre du cocher poète in the Title catalogue.

La premiere representation (Le théâtre de la foire, Paris, 1737, t. ix): Gillier.   ML 48.L2 ix

Le Sage, Alain René—Continued.

La princesse de Carizme (Le théâtre de la foire, Paris, 1737, t. iii): Gillier.   ML 48.L2 III

La princesse de la Chine (Le théâtre de la foire, Paris, 1731, t. vii) (with d'Orneval): Gillier.   ML 48.L2 VII

La querelle des théâtres (Le théâtre de la foire, Paris, 1737, t. iii) (with de La Font): Gillier.   ML 48.L2 III

Le rappel de la foire à la vie (Le théâtre de la foire, Paris, 1737, t. iii) (with d'Orneval): Gillier.   ML 48.L2 III

Le régiment de la Calotte (Le théâtre de la Foire, Paris, 1724, t. v) (with Fuzelier and d'Orneval): Gillier.   ML 48.L2 V

La reine du Barostan (Le théâtre de la foire, Paris, 1731, t. vii) (with d'Orneval): Gillier.   ML 48.L2 VII

Le rémouleur d'amour. *See* L'ombre du cocher poète in the Title catalogue.

Roger de Sicile, surnommé Le roi sans chagrin (Le théâtre de la foire, Paris, 1737, t. ix) (with d'Orneval): Gillier.   ML 48.L2 IX

Les routes du monde. *See his* L'industrie.

La sauvagesse (Le théâtre de la foire, Paris, 1737, t. ix) (with d'Orneval): Gillier.   ML 48.L2 IX

Sophie et Sigismond (Le théâtre de la foire, Paris, 1737, t. ix) (with d'Orneval): Gillier.   ML 48.L2 IX

Les spectacles malades (Le théâtre de la foire, Paris, 1731, t. vii) (with d'Orneval): Gillier.   ML 48.L2 VII

La statue merveilleuse (Le théâtre de la foire, Paris, 1724, t. iv) (with d'Orneval): Gillier.   ML 48.L2 IV

Le tableau du mariage. *See his* Le temple de l'ennuy.

Der tempel des gedaechtnisses, Frankfurt und Leipzig, 1770: Elmer. Tr. of Le temple de mémoire.   SCHATZ 2917

Le temple de l'ennuy—Le tableau du mariage (Le théâtre de la foire, Paris, 1737, t. ii): Gillier.   ML48 L2 II

Le temple de mémoire (Le théâtre de la foire, Paris, 1728, t. vi) (with Fuzelier and d'Orneval): Gillier.   ML 48.L2 VI

Le temple du destin (Le théâtre de la foire, Paris, 1737, t. i): Gillier.   ML 48.L2 I

Le tombeau de Nostradamus (Le théâtre de la foire, Paris, 1737, t. i): Gillier.   ML 48L.2 I

Les trois comères (Le théâtre de la foire, Paris, 1737, t. ix) (with d'Orneval): Gillier.   ML 48.L2 IX

Die verkehrte welt (Hamburg, 1728): Telemann. Tr. of Le monde renversé.   SCHATZ 10267

Zemine et Almanzor. *See his* L'industrie.

Lesueur.

Les amours grivois. *See* Favart.

Le bal de Strasbourg. *See* Favart.

Le Tellier.

Arlequin, sultane favorite (Le théâtre de la foire, t. i, Paris, 1737).   ML 48.L2I

Le Valois d'Orville, Adrien Joseph.

Platée (Paris) 1745 (with Autreau): Rameau.   ML 52.2.P5

Leveridge, Richard.

Pyramus and Thisbe, London, 1716: author.   LONGE 54

Lichtenberg, Georg Christoph.
    Lampedo, Darmstadt (1779): G. J. Vogler.   Schatz 10798

Lichtenstein, Carl August, *freiherr* **von.**
    Die steinerne braut, Dessau, 1799: author.   Schatz 5599

Licurio, Palemone. *Arcadian name of* Silvio Stampiglia.

Lillo, George.
    Britannia and Batavia, London, 1740: Carey.   ML 50.2.B86
    Silvia or The country burial, London, 1731: ballad opera.   Longe 262

Liprandi, Nicolo. *See* Angelo Anelli, *his real name.*

Liviano Lantino, *anagram of* Antonio Villano.

Livigni, Filippo.
    The banquet. Tr. of his Il convito, London, 1782: Bertoni.   Schatz 910
    Die betrogenen kastellane. Tr. of his Li castellani burlati:
      Dresda, 1788; Fabrizj.   Schatz 2967
    La cameriera per amore (Lisbona, 1776): Alessandri.   Schatz 152
    Li castellani burlati—Die betrogenen kastellane, Dresda,
      1788: Fabrizj.   Schatz 2967
    I castellani burlati, Venezia (1785): Valentini.   Schatz 10581
    Chi la fa, l'aspetta, Milano (1788): Fabrizj.   Schatz 2968
    Il convito or The banquet, London, 1782: Bertoni.   Schatz 910
    Il convito—Das gastmahl, Dresda, 1783: Cimarosa.   Schatz 1915
    Il convito, Lisbona, 1796: Cimarosa.   Schatz 1914
    Li due castellani burlati, Lisbona, 1797: Fabrizi. L. T. of
      I castellani burlati.   ML 50.2.D7F2
    Li due fratelli ridicoli. A. T. of his La finta baronessa:
      Alessandri.
    Die eigensinnige ehefrau. Tr. of his La moglie capricciosa
      (Dresda, 1786): Gazzaniga.   Schatz 3672
    La finta baronessa o Li due fratelli ridicoli, Lisbona, 1795:
      Alessandri. L. T. of their La finta principessa.   Schatz 150
    La finta principessa, Genova (1783): Alessandri.   Schatz 146
    La finta principessa, Venezia, 1796: Marinelli.   Schatz 5967
    La Frascatana, Siena (1776): Paisiello.   Schatz 7620
    La Frascatana—Die Frascatanerin, Dresda, 1776: Paisiello.   Schatz 7621
    La Frascatana—Landsbye-pigen fra Frascati, Kiøbenhavn,
      1776: Paisiello.   Schatz 7623
    La Frascatana, n. i., 1782 (German Tr.): Paisiello.   ML 50.2.F84P2
    La Frascatana oder Das maedchen von Fraskati, n. i., 1782:
      Paisiello.   Schatz 7624
    La Fraschetana, London, 1776: Paisiello.   Schatz 7622
    Der fuerst von Taranto. Tr. of his Il principe di Taranto,
      Dresda, 1798: Paër.   Schatz 7524
    Das gastmahl. Tr. of his Il convito, Dresda, 1783: Cimarosa.   Schatz 1915
    Le gelosie fortunate, Venezia, 1786: Anfossi.   Schatz 269
    Giannina e Bernadone—Hannchen und Bernardon, Dresda,
      1785: Cimarosa.   Schatz 1926
    Giannina e Bernadone, Napoli, 1795: Cimarosa.   ML 50.2.G33C3
    Die glueckliche unschuldige. Tr. of his L'innocente fortu-
      nata, Dresda (1780): Paisiello.   Schatz 7633
    Die gluecklichen reisenden. Tr. of his I viaggiatori felici,
      Dresda, 1781.   Schatz 255

Livigni, Filippo—Continued.

Die gluecklichen reisenden. Tr. of his I viaggiatori felici
(Vienna, 1783).   Schatz 256

Hannchen und Bernardon. Tr. of his Giannina e Bernardone,
Dresda, 1785: Cimarosa.   Schatz 1926

L'innocente fortunata, Firenze, 1774: Paisiello.   Schatz 7631

L'innocente fortunata—Die glueckliche unschuldige, Dresda
(1780).   Schatz 7633

Landsbye-pigen fra Frascati, Kiøbenhavn, 1776. Tr. of his
La Frascatana: Paisiello.   Schatz 7623

Das maedchen von Fraskati. A. T. of his La Frascatana,
n. i., 1782: Paisiello.   Schatz 7624

Das maedchen von Fraskati, Luebeck, 1785. Tr. of his La
Frascatana: Paisiello.   Schatz 7625

Il marchese Carbonaro, Venezia (1776): Salari.   Schatz 9267

La moglie capricciosa, Firenze, 1791: Gazzaniga.   ML 48.A5 v.24

La moglie capricciosa—Die eigensinnige ehefrau (Dresda,
1786): Gazzaniga.   Schatz 3672

La moglie capricciosa, Pisa, 1795: Gazzaniga.   Schatz 3671

La molinara, Venezia, 1788: Fischietti.   Schatz 3233

A mulher caprichosa, Lisboa, 1791. Tr. of his La moglie
capricciosa: Gazzaniga.   Schatz 3678

Il principe di Taranto—Der fuerst von Taranto, Dresda, 1798:
Paër. (Text is merely an altered version of La finta
principessa.)   Schatz 7524

I puntigli gelosi, Venezia, 1783: Alessandri.   Schatz 154

La semplice fortunata, Napoli, 1773. L. T. of his L'innocente
fortunata: Paisiello.   Schatz 7632

Serva per amore, Venezia, 1773: Galuppi.   Schatz 3508

Lo sposo di tre, e marito di nessuna, Venezia (1783): Cherubini.   Schatz 1848

I viaggiatori felici, London, 1782: Anfossi.   Schatz 254

I viaggiatori felici—Die gluecklichen reisenden, Dresda, 1781:
Anfossi.   Schatz 255

I viaggiatori felici—Die gluecklichen reisenden (Vienna,
1783).   Schatz 256

Lloyd, Robert.

Arcadia, or, The shepherd's wedding, London, 1761: Stanley.   Longe 52

The capricious lovers, London, 1765: Rush.   Longe 26

Phillis at court, London, 1767: T. Giordani. (Altered version of his The capricious lovers.)   Longe 36

Loccatelli, Fabio.

Cesare al Rubicone, Faenza, 1725: Masini.   Schatz 6063

Lockman, John.

Rosalinda, London, 1740: Smith.   ML 50.2.R72

Lodge, Thomas.

Luminalia or The festivall of light, London, 1637 (authorship
doubtful): Laniere (also doubtful).   ML 52.2.L92

Loë, Franz von. *Originally* **Hochkirch.**

Loeuillart-Davrigni, J.

La lettre, Paris, an 3 (1794–95).   ML 48.M2L

Lonati, Carlo Ambrogio.
Antioco principe della Siria, Ger ova (1690): author.   SCHATZ 5681

Longchamps.
Comment faire? ou, Les épreuves de misanthropie et repentir.
 See Dejouy.

Lonsdale, Mark.
The Spanish rivals, London, 1784: Linley.   LONGE 95

Loran Glodoci, *anagram of* Carlo Goldoni.

Lorber, Johann Christoph.
Orpheus, Braunschweig, 1690. Tr. of Sartorio's L'Orfeo
 (Aureli).   SCHATZ 9484

Lorenzi, Giambattista (Giovanni Battista).
Gli amanti comici o sia D. Anchise Campanone, Napoli, 1794:
 Paisiello.   SCHATZ 7588
Gli amanti ridicoli, Napoli, 1797: di Palma.   SCHATZ 7746
L'apparenza inganna o sia La villeggiatura, Napoli, 1784:
 Cimarosa.   SCHATZ 1980
Die bestrafte eifersucht, Berlin, 1794. Tr. of his Il marito
 disperato: Cimarosa.   SCHATZ 1943
Il convitato di pietra. A. T. of his Don Giovanni Tenorio:
 Fabrizj.
Il convitato di pietra (p. 69–167 of La finta amalata, Lisboa,
 1796): Fabrizi.   ML 48.C6 III
Il convitato di pietra (printed together with L'impresario in
 angustie, music by Cimarosa), Napoli, 1793: Tritto.   SCHATZ 10466
La Corsala, Napoli, 1771: Piccinni.   SCHATZ 8121
Don Anchise Campanone (Vienna) 1775. Same as his "Gli
 amanti comici"): Paisiello.   SCHATZ 7589
D. Anchise Campanone. A. T. of his Gli amanti comici,
 Napoli, 1794.
D. Chisciotte della Mancia, Napoli, 1769: Paisiello.   SCHATZ 7611
Don Giovanni Tenorio ossia Il convitato di Pietra, Bologna
 (1791): Fabrizj.   SCHATZ 2973
Don Quischott von Mancia, Wien (1771). Tr. of Paisiello's D.
 Chisciotte della Mancia (third act and several arias in
 acts 1–2 by Florian Gassmann).   SCHATZ 7612
D. Taddeo in Barcellona, Napoli, 1774: Pio.   SCHATZ 8185
Li due gemelli e La scuffiara, Napoli, 1784: (both operas) Tritto. SCHATZ 10456
Le duel comique (Paris) 1777. Tr. of his Il duello: Paisiello,
 with add. music by Méreaux.   ML 50.2.D8P2
Il duello, Napoli, 1774: Paisiello.   SCHATZ 7676
Der eingebildete Sokrates. Tr. of his and Galiani's Socrate
 immaginario, Dresda, 1781: Paisiello.   SCHATZ 7658
Le fallaci apparenze, Venezia, 1793 (adapted by A. Valli
 from L.'s Gelosia per gelosia): Astaritta.   SCHATZ 386
La finta zingara: P. Guglielmi. (Forms p. 33–71 of his Le
 sventurate fortunate, Napoli, 1785).   SCHATZ 4274
La finta zingana ossia Il solachianello, Napoli, 1791: P.
 Guglielmi. L. T. of the above.   SCHATZ 4245
Fra i due litiganti il terzo gode. O. T. of his Gli amanti
 comici o sia Don Anchise Campanone.
La fuga, Napoli, 1777: Monti.   SCHATZ 6603

Lorenzi, Giambattista (Giovanni Battista)—Continued.

Il furbo malaccorto, Napoli, 1782: Paisiello.	SCHATZ 7677
L'idolo cinese, Napoli, 1783: Paisiello.	SCHATZ 7670
L'idolo cinese, Venezia, 1773: Rust.	SCHATZ 9179
L'infedeltà fedele, Napoli, 1779: Cimarosa.	SCHATZ 1936
L'infedeltà fedele—Treu in der untreue, Dresda, 1782: Cimarosa.	SCHATZ 1937
Il marito disperato, Napoli, 1785: Cimarosa.	SCHATZ 1942
La modista ossia La scuffiaja, Gorizia (1790). L. T. of his La modista raggiratrice: Paisiello.	SCHATZ 7643
La modista raggiratrice, Napoli, 1787: Paisiello.	SCHATZ 7642
Nina o sia La pazza per amore, Napoli, 1790: Paisiello.	SCHATZ 7645
Nina, o sia La pazza per amore—Nina, oder Wahnsinn aus liebe, Dresda, 1791: Paisiello.	SCHATZ 7646
La pazza per amore. A. T. of his Nina: Paisiello.	
La pietra simpatica, Napoli, 1796: di Palma.	ML 50.2.P4P2
La scuffiaja. A. T. of his La modista: Paisiello.	
La scuffiara, Napoli, 1784: Tritto. (Published together with their Li due gemelli.)	SCHATZ 10456
La serva onorata, Napoli (1792). (Really only a condensation of da Ponte's Le nozze di Figaro): Piccinni.	SCHATZ 8129
Socrate immaginario—Der eingebildete Sokrates (with F. Galiani), Dresda, 1781: Paisiello.	SCHATZ 7658
Il solachianello. A. T. of his La finta zingana: P. Guglielmi.	
Il tamburo, Napoli, 1784: Paisiello.	SCHATZ 7659
Il tamburo notturno, Parma, 1778. L. T. of the above, with alterations by Bertati: Paisiello.	SCHATZ 7660
Il tamburo notturno (Vienna, 1774). Boccarini's version of the above.	SCHATZ 7661
Li tre Eugenj, Napoli, 1778: Lenzi.	SCHATZ 5551
Treu in der Untreue. Tr. of his L'infedeltà fedele, Dresda, 1782: Cimarosa.	SCHATZ 1937
Le vane gelosie, Milano (1791): Paisiello.	SCHATZ 7701
La villeggiatura. A. T. of his L'apparenza inganno: Cimarosa.	
Wahnsinn aus liebe. A. T. of his Nina.	

Lotti, Lotto.

Didio Giuliano, Parma, 1687: Sabadini.	SCHATZ 9199
L'idea di tutte le perfezioni, Piacenza, 1690: Tosi.	SCHATZ 10379
Milziade, Venetia, 1699: Ruggeri.	SCHATZ 9140
La saggia pazzia di Giunio Bruto, Venetia, 1698: Ruggeri.	SCHATZ 9141

Love, James.

The village wedding or The faithful country maid, London, 1767: unknown.	LONGE 198

Luchesi, Pompeo.

L'Oreste in Sparta, Reggio, 1697: C. F. Pollaroli.	SCHATZ 8306

Luchini (Lucchini), Antonio Maria.

L'Adaloaldo furioso, Venezia (1727): Macari.	SCHATZ 5807
Dorilla in Tempe, Venezia, 1726: Vivaldi.	SCHATZ 10765
L'Ermengarda, Venezia (1723): Albinoni.	SCHATZ 91
Farnace (Bronsevico, 1754): unknown.	SCHATZ 11329
Farnace, Brusselle (1729): Cortona.	ML 50.2.F21C6

Luchini, (Lucchini) Antonio Maria—Continued.

Farnace, Torino (1751): Perez.   SCHATZ 7878

Farnace, Firenze (1749): Pescetti.   SCHATZ 7966

Farnace, Venezia, 1739: Rinaldo di Capua.   SCHATZ 8796

Farnace, Monaco (1740): Porta.   SCHATZ 8379

Farnace, Venezia, 1776: Sarti.   SCHATZ 9473

Farnace, Venezia, 1726: Vivaldi.   SCHATZ 10766

Foca Superbo, Venezia, 1716: Lotti.   SCHATZ 5717

Giove in Argo—Jupiter en Argos, Dresda (1717): Lotti.   SCHATZ 5719

La haine vaincue par la force du sang. Tr. of his Gl'odj delusi dal sangue, Dresda (1718): Lotti.   SCHATZ 5707

L'inganno tradito dall' amore, Salisborgo (172–?): Caldara.   SCHATZ 1485

Jupiter en Argos. Tr. of his Giove in Argo, Dresda (1717): Lotti.   SCHATZ 5719

Gl'odj delusi dal sangue, Venezia, 1728: Galuppi and Pescetti.   SCHATZ 3521

Gl'odj delusi dal sangue—La haine vaincue par la force du sang, Dresda (1718): Lotti.   SCHATZ 5707

Selin. Gran signor de' Turchi, Venezia, 1730: pasticcio.   SCHATZ 11361

Li sforzi d'ambizione e d'amore, Venezia (1724): Porta.   SCHATZ 8392

Tieteberga, Venezia, 1717: Vivaldi.   SCHATZ 10781

Lucini, Giovanni Battista.

Gli equivoci in amore overo La Rosaura, Roma, 1690: Scarlatti.   SCHATZ 9535

Lüderwald, Georg Ernst.

Der freybrief, Berlin, 1788: music selected from Haydn, Mozart, von Weber. In its original one-act version also composed by Ernst Lange (1792), Julius Miller (1802).   SCHATZ 4610a

Der freybrief (Nuernberg?) 1797. The two-act version.   SCHATZ 4610

Lully, Jean Baptiste de.

Le carnaval (Recueil des opéra, t. i, Paris, 1703) (with Molière and Quinault): Lully.   SCHATZ 5765

Lungi, Angelo.

Madama Prudenza, Roma, 1749 (authorship doubtful): Sciroli.   ML 50.2.M2S2

Luzzi, Eusebio.

Chi la fa l'aspetta, ballet. *See* Astaritta's Il curioso accidente.

Il convitato, ballet: Gluck. *See* Calvi's Ezio.

Il convitato di pietra, ballet: *See* Ferd. Rutini's Il matrimonio per industria.

Il diavolo a quattro, ballet: Angiolini. *See* Calvi's Ezio.

Il geloso in cimento, ballet. *See* Bianchi's Le villanelle astute.

Il geloso in cimento, ballet. *See* Ferd. Rutini's Il matrimonio per industria.

Giulietta e Romeo, ballet. *See* Bianchi's Le villanelle astute.   SCHATZ 1010

Mario e Felice, ballet: Trento. *See* Bianchi's Ines de Castro.

Nina pazza per amore, ballet. *See* Astaritta's Il curioso accidente.

Rossana, ballet. *See* Caruso's Li sposi in commedia.

Lo spazzacamino, ballet. *See* Bianchi's Ines de Castro.

M., C.

Il trionfo di Scipione in Cartagine, Firenze, 1795: Curcio.   SCHATZ 2307

Mabille.
 Cécile, Paris, 1781: Dezède.   SCHATZ 2516

M'Donald (MacDonald), A.
 Love and loyalty (Miscellaneous works, London, 1791).   LONGE 282
 The princess of Tarento (Miscellaneous works, London, 1791):
  pasticcio from Corelli, Vanhall, Gluck, etc.   LONGE 282

Maclaren (M'Laren), Archibald.
 The coup de main or The American adventuress, London,
  1784: ballad opera.   ML 50.2.C74
 The humours of the times or What news now?, London. 1799. LONGE 323

MacNally, Leonard.
 The apotheosis of Punch, London, 1779.   LONGE 102
 Critic upon critic, London, 1792: ballad opera.   LONGE 232
 Robin Hood or Sherwood forest, London, 1784: Shield.   LONGE 93
 Robin Hood or Sherwood forest, 5th ed., London, 1787.   ML 50.2.R62S3

MacSwinny (MacSwiney), Owen.
 Camilla, London, 1706.   Tr. of M. A. Bononcini's Il trionfo di
  Camilla (Stampiglia).   LONGE 132
 Pyrrhus and Demetrius, London, 1709: Scarlatti and Haym. ML 50.2.P95

Maderni, Carlo.
 Sardanapalo, Venetia, 1679: Freschi.   SCHATZ 3354

Maffei, *marchese,* **Scipione.**
 La fida ninfa (Verona, 1730): Orlandini.   ML 50.2.F4O7
 La fida ninfa (Poesie, Verona, 1752, t. ii): Orlandini.   PQ

Maggi, Carlo Maria.
 Il trionfo d'Augusto in Egitto, Milano (1672): unknown.   SCHATZ 11372

Maggi, Giacomo.
 Mitridate in Sebastia, Firenze (1704): Albinoni.   SCHATZ 139

Magni, Giuseppe.
 La vedova scaltra, ballet.   *See* Alessandri's Il matrimonio per
  concorso.
 Le vedova sealtra, ballet.   *See* Guglielmi's La sposa fedele.

Maillé de Marencour.
 L'amour quéteur, Nouv. éd., Paris, 1782: unknown.   ML 50.2.A702
 La ruse d'amour ou L'épreuve, Paris, 1786: Chardiny.   ML 50.2.R9C3

Malipiero, Francesco.
 L'innocenza riconosciuta, Venezia, 1717: C. F. Pollaroli.   SCHATZ 8298

Mallet, David.
 Alfred, London, 1740: Arne.   *See* Thompson, James.   AC 901.M5 v.596
 Alfred, London, 1773: Arne.   LONGE 36

Malvezzi, *conte* **Ottavio.**
 La Rosaura overo Amore figlio della gratitudine, **Insprugg**
  (1692): Badia.   SCHATZ 542

Mandelli, *conte* **Otto.**
 Pallade trionfante in Arcadia, Venezia, 1714: Ristori.   SCHATZ 8819
 Il trionfo di Pallade in Arcadia, Bologna, 1715: Aresti.   SCHATZ 312

Manfredi, Eustachio.
Caio Ostilio, Firenze, 1794: G. Giordani.   Schatz 3850
Nicomede, Genova (1790): G. Giordani.   Schatz 3847
Il tempio della gloria—O templo da gloria, Lisboa, 1790:
     Spontoni.   Schatz 10017

Manfredi, Eustacchio.
Dafni, Bologna (1696): Aldrovandini.   ML 50.2.D2

Manley (Mary De la Rivière Manley), *Mrs.*
The court legacy, London, 1733.   Longe 275

Mantauffeld, Ernest, *baron* de.
Auguste et Théodore, ou, Les deux pages, Paris, 1790 (together
     with the composer): Dezède.   Schatz 2525

Mantile, Domenico.
L'isola di Bellamarina, Napoli, 1792: De Blasis.   Schatz 2420
La nuovo savio della Grecia, Napoli, 1796: Farinelli.   Schatz 3019

Maraffi, Antonio.
Il principe di Lago Nero ossia La contadina in corte, ballet.
     See di Palma's Gli amanti della dote.

Marcello, Benedetto.
Arato in Sparta, Venezia, 1709: Ruggeri.   Schatz 9130

Marchesini, Carlo Antonio.
L'Alcatrasso geloso, Vicenza, 1672: Spinazzari.   Schatz 9975

Marchesini, Marcello.
Artemisia regina di Caria, Napoli, 1797: Cimarosa.   Schatz 1990

Marchi, Antonio.
Alcina, London, 1736: Händel.   Schatz 4496
Alcina delusa da Rugero, Venezia, 1725: Albinoni.   Schatz 113
Artabene rè de Parti, Venezia, 1718: Vivaldi. L. T. of their
     La costanza trionfante degl' amori e degl' odii.   Schatz 10762
La costanza trionfante degl' amore e degl' odii, Venezia, 1716:
     Vivaldi.   Schatz 10761
Demetrio e Tolomeo, Venezia, 1702: A. Pollaroli.   Schatz 8258
L'Erginia imascherata, Venezia, 1710: unknown.   Schatz 11324
Gl'evenimenti di Rugero, Venezia, 1732: Albinoni. L. T. of
     their Alcina delusa da Rugero.   Schatz 113
L'ingannator ingannato, Venezia, 1710: Ruggeri.   Schatz 9138
L'odio vinto dalla costanza, Venezia, 1731. L. T. of his La
     costanza trionfante degl' amori e degl' odii (with altera-
     tions by Bartolomeo Vitturi): Vivaldi (with new music
     by Galeazzi).   Schatz 10763
Radamisto, Venetia, 1698: Albinoni.   Schatz 97
La Rosalinda, Venetia, 1693: M. A. Ziani.   Schatz 11210
Il vinto trionfante del vincitore, Venezia, 1717: pasticcio.
     O. T. of text was Zenobia regina dei Palmireni.   Schatz 11379
Zenobia regina dei Palmireni. O. T. of his Il vinto trionfante
     del vincitore.
Zenobia, regina de Palmireni, Venetia, 1694: Albinoni.   Schatz 112
Zenone, imperator d'Oriente, Venetia, 1696: Albinoni.   Schatz 101

Marconi, Francesco.

Le confusioni per la somiglianza, Milano (1792): Crippa.   SCHATZ 2290

Marcouville, Pierre Augustin Lefebvre de.

Les amans trompés, Paris, 1756 (with Anseaume): Laruette (?) ML 50.2.A63

Les amants trompés, Paris, 1756 (with Anseaume): Laruette (?).   SCHATZ 11478

Fanfale, Paris, 1759 (Théatre de M. Favart, Paris, 1763–77,
t. i) (with Favart). Parody of Destouches' Omphale.   ML 49.A2F1

La fausse aventurière, Paris, 1757 (with Anseaume): Laruette. SCHATZ 5437

L'isle des foux, Paris, 1762 (with Anseaume and d'Antilly):
Duni.   SCHATZ 2846

Le medecin de l'amour, Paris, 1758 (mostly by Anseaume):
Laruette.   SCHATZ 5438

Le medecin de l'amour, Bruxelles, 1766 (with Anseaume):
van Maldere.   SCHATZ 5867

Mari, Francesco.

Die waescherinnen, n. i., n. d.: Zannetti. Tr. of their Le
lavarandine.   SCHATZ 11139

Die waeschermaedchen (Komische opern der Italiener, hrsg.
von J. C. Bock, Leipzig, 1781): Zannetti. Tr. of their
Le lavarandine.   SCHATZ 11138

Maria Antonia Walpurgis, *princess of Saxony* (=**Ermelinda
Talèa,** *Pastorella Arcada*).

Talestri regina delle Amazoni, Monaco, 1760: authoress.   SCHATZ 5950

Talestri, regina delle Amazzoni, Dresda, 1770: authoress.   SCHATZ 5948

Il trionfo della fedeltà, Dresda, 1754: authoress.   SCHATZ 5949

Mariani, Tommaso.

Lo co. di Scrignano, Napoli (1729): Roberto (2d act, the two
other acts anonymous).   SCHATZ 8837

Il finto pazzo per amore. O. T. of his Il soldato per forza
impazzito per amore.

Il finto pazzo, Brunsviga, [1749]. L. T. of his Livietta e
Tracollo o sia La contadina astuta: Pergolesi.   SCHATZ 7891

Il ladro convertito per amore, Venezia, 1750. L. T. of his
Livietta e Tracollo o sia La contadina astuta: Pergolesi. SCHATZ 7906

Livietta e Tracollo o La contadina astuta: Pergolesi. O. T.
of "La contadina astuta," "Il finto pazzo," "Il ladro
convertito per amore," "La finta Polacca," "Tracollo,"
etc.

La schiava per amore, Roma, 1746: Paci.   SCHATZ 7379

Il soldato per forza impazzito per amore, Pavia (1774 or 1775):
Sacchini.   SCHATZ 9221

La vedova ingegnosa (Dresda, 1747): Leo or Prota or Sellitti. ML 50.2.V25L2

Der verstellte narr aus liebe, Wien, 1779. Tr. of his Il soldato
per forza impazzito per amore: Sacchini.   SCHATZ 9222

Mariottini, Gaetano.

L'incostanza degli amanti, ballet. *See* Insanguine's Medonte.

Mariscotti, Bernardino.

Le api riverite, Bologna, 1628: unknown.   ML 48.M2 1

Markoe, Peter.

The reconciliation or The triumph of nature, Philadelphia,
1790.   ML 50.6.R28

Marliani, Antonio.

Gli amanti protetti da Amore, ballet. *See* Traetta's Cavaliere errante.

La festa di ballo disturbata dalla famiglia dei Covielli, ballet. *See* Traetta's Cavaliere errante.

Marmontel, Jean François.

Die abgeredete zauberey, Wien, 1778. Tr. of his La fausse magie: Grétry.   SCHATZ 4154

—L'ami de la maison, Paris, 1772: Grétry.   SCHATZ 4132

L'ami de la maison, Paris, 1776: Grétry.   ML 48.M2M

L'amour conjugal. A. T. of his Céphale et Procris: Grétry.

—Atys (Paris) 1780 (after Quinault): Piccinni.   SCHATZ 8067

Atys, Paris, 1783: Piccinni.   SCHATZ 11743

—La bergère des Alpes, Avignon, 1766: Kohault.   ML 48.M21

La bergère des Alpes, Bruxelles, 1770: Kohault.   SCHATZ 5204

Das blendwerk, Gotha, 1781. Tr. of his La fausse magie: Grétry.   SCHATZ 4155

—Céphale et Procris ou L'amour conjugal, Paris, 1773: Grétry.   SCHATZ 4198

Dido, Berlin, 1799. Tr. of the following: SCHATZ 8089

—Didon, Paris, 1783: Piccinni.   SCHATZ 8088

Erast und Lucinde, Muenster, 1777. Tr. of his Silvain: Grétry.   SCHATZ 4187

—La fausse magie, Paris, 1775 (48 p.): Grétry.   SCHATZ 4153

La fausse magie, Paris, 1775 (72 p.): Grétry.   ML 50.2.F23G7

Der hausfreund, Frankfurt am Mayn, 1774. Tr. of his L'ami de la maison: Grétry.

—Le Huron, Paris, 1768: Grétry.   ML 50.2.H8G6

Le Huron, Paris, 1770: Grétry.   SCHATZ 4159

Le Huron, Paris, 1772: Grétry.   ML 50.2.H8G7

Le Huron, Paris, 1779: Grétry.   SCHATZ 11705

—La leçon ou La tasse de glaces, Paris, an V (1797): Dalayrac.   ML 50.2.L23D2

—Lucile, Paris, veuve Duchesne, 1769: Grétry.   ML 50.2.L8G7

Lucile, Paris, Merlin, 1769: Grétry.   SCHATZ 4165

Lucile, Paris, 1770: Grétry.   SCHATZ 11706

Lucile, Paris, 1774: Grétry.   SCHATZ 11707

Lucile, Frankfurt am Mayn, 1772. Tr. of the above.   SCHATZ 4166

Selima & Azor, London, 1784. English version of his Zémire et Azor: Linley, utilizing Grétry.   LONGE 95

—Silvain, Paris, Merlin, 1770 (40 p.): Grétry.   SCHATZ 4184

Silvain, Paris, Merlin, 1770 (55 p.): Grétry.   ML 50.2.S63

Silvain, Frankfurt am Mayn, 1772. Tr. of the above.   SCHATZ 4185

Silvain, Wien, 1778. Another Tr.   SCHATZ 4186

La tasse de glaces. A. T. of his La leçon: Dalayrac.

Der zauberspiegel, n. i., n. d. Tr. of his La fausse magie: Grétry.   SCHATZ 4156

Zemira e Azore, London, 1779. Tr. of his Zémire et Azor: Grétry.   SCHATZ 4196

—Zémire et Azor, Paris, 1772: Grétry.   YUDIN PQ

Zemire et Azor, Berlin, 1773: Grétry.   SCHATZ 11709

Zemire et Azor, Paris, 1774: Grétry.   SCHATZ 4191

Zemire et Azor (imperfect copy): Grétry.   ML 52.2.Z45

Zemire und Azor (detached copy): Grétry.   SCHATZ 11710

Zemire und Azor, Frankfurt am Mayn, 1775. Tr. of his Zémire et Azor: Grétry.   SCHATZ 4192

Marmontel, Jean François—Continued.
   Zemire und Azor, Muenster, 1777. Another Tr.   SCHATZ 4195
   Zemire und Azor, Breslau und Leipzig, 1779. Another Tr.   SCHATZ 4193
   Zemire und Azor, Mitau, 1782. Another Tr.   SCHATZ 4194

Marsollier des Vivetières, Benoît Joseph.
   Adolphe et Clara ou Les deux prisonniers, Paris, an VII (1799):
      Dalayrac.   ML 50.2.A33D2
   Alexis, ou L'erreur d'un bon père, Paris, 1798: Dalayrac.   ML 50.2.A52D2
   Die beyden kleinen Savoyarden, Leipzig, 1795. Tr. of his
      Les deux petits Savoyards: Dalayrac.   SCHATZ 2338
   Camilla ossia La sepolta viva, Lisbona, 1799: Dalayrac. Tr.
      of their Camille.   SCHATZ 2332
   Camille of Het onderaardsch gewelf, Amsterdam, 1796: Da-
      layrac. Tr. of their Camille ou Le souterrain.   SCHATZ 2392
   Camille ou Le souterrain, Paris, 1791: Dalayrac.   ML 50.2.C25D2
   Camille ou Le souterrain, Paris, 1793: Dalayrac.   ML 50.2.C25D22
   The captive of Spilburg, London, 1799. (Tr. with alterations
      of his Camille ou Le souterrain): Dussek.   LONGE 249
   Les deux petits Savoyards, Paris, 1789: Dalayrac.   SCHATZ 2336
   Les deux petits Savoyards, Hambourg, 1795: Dalayrac.   ML 50.2.D49D2
   Les deux petits Savoyards, Hamburg (179–): Dalayrac.   SCHATZ 11688
   L'erreur d'un bon père. A. T. of his Alexis: Dalayrac.
   La fausse peur, Paris, 1775: d'Arcis.   SCHATZ 2411
   La folle par amour. A. T. of his Nina: Dalayrac.
   The love distracted maid. A. T. of his Nina: Dalayrac.
   La maison isolée ou Le vieillard des Vosges, Paris, An cin-
      quième [1797]: Dalayrac.   SCHATZ 2363
   Marianne, Paris, Vente (1796) (55 p.): Dalayrac.   ML 50.2.M45D2
   Marianne, Paris, Vente (?1796) (44 p.): Dalayrac.   ML 50.2.M45D21
   Nina or The love distracted maid, London, 1787. Tr. of his
      Nina ou La folle par amour: Dalayrac.   LONGE 99
   Nina ou La folle par amour, Paris, 1788: Dalayrac.   ML 50.2.N4D2
   Nina oder Wahnsinn aus liebe, Hamburg, 1787: Dalayrac.
      d'Arien's Tr.   SCHATZ 2367
   — Same title, Mainz, 1787. Schmieder's Tr.   SCHATZ 2368
   — Same title, Berlin, 1790. André's Tr.   SCHATZ 2369
   Nina oder Was vermag die liebe nicht, Berlin, 1789. Another
      Tr.   SCHATZ 2370
   La pauvre femme, Paris, An V. [1796–97]: Dalayrac.   ML 50.2.P295D2
   La sepolta viva. A. T. of his Camilla: Dalayrac.
   Le traité nul, Paris, an V (ou 1797): Gaveaux.   ML 50.2.T77G2
   Le traité nul, Paris, an VII (1799): Gaveaux.   ML 50.2.T77G22
   Het vernietigd verdrag, Amsteldam, 1799. Tr. of his Le
      traité nul: Gaveaux.   SCHATZ 3644
   Le vieillard des Vosges. A. T. of his La maison isolée:
      Dalayrac.
   Wahnsinn aus liebe. A. T. of his Nina: Dalayrac.
   Was vermag die liebe nicht? A. T. of his Nina: Dalayrac.
   Die zween Savoyarden, Wien, 1792. Tr. of his Les deux
      petits Savoyards: Dalayrac.   SCHATZ 2340

Martelli, Pietro Jacopo.
   Gli amici, Bologna (1699): Albergati.   SCHATZ 77

Marten (Martein), Giovanni Battista.

Amor corsaro, ballet: Le Messier. *See* Monza's Oreste.

Bradamante e Ruggero, ballet: Le Messier. *See* Monza's
Oreste.

La forza dell' amore e dell' amicizia, ballet. *See* P. Guglielmi's Tamerlano.

Il naufragio felice, ballet. *See* Borghi's La donna instabile.

La rete di Vulcano, ballet. *See* Sacchini's Creso.

Martinelli, Gaetano.

Adrasto rè degli Argivi (Lisboa, 1784): Carvalho.	SCHATZ 1670
Alcione, (Lisbona, 1787): Carvalho.	SCHATZ 1674
Archelao, (Lisboa, 1785): I. C. da Silva.	SCHATZ 9887
Artemisia regina di Caria, (Lisbona, 1787): Moreira.	SCHATZ 6629
Ati e Sangaride, (Lisboa, 1779): Santos.	SCHATZ 9398
Le avventure di Cleomede, Lisboa (1772): Jommelli.	SCHATZ 4889
Bauce e Palemone (Lisboa, 1789): J. C. da Silva.	SCHATZ 9883
Die befreyte sklavinn. Tr. of his La schiava liberata, Dresda, 1777: Schuster.	SCHATZ 9754
Die befreyte sklavin (Kaffka, Sammlung auslaendischer theaterstuecke, Breslau, 1784). Another Tr.	SCHATZ 9755
Il cacciatore deluso, Lisbona (1771): Jommelli.	SCHATZ 4897
Cadmo (Lisboa, 1784): A. da Silva.	SCHATZ 9881
La conversazione. *See* Title catalogue.	
Creusa in Delfo (Lisbona, 1774): Perez.	SCHATZ 7880
La critica. *See* Title catalogue.	
Edalide e Cambise (Lisboa, 1780): J. C. da Silva.	SCHATZ 9886
L'eroe coronato (Lisbona, 1775): Perez.	SCHATZ 7881
Gli eroi spartani (Lisboa, 1788): Moreira.	SCHATZ 6630
L'eroina lusitana, Lisbona, 1795: Moreira.	SCHATZ 6635
De forsonede medbeylere. Tr. of his I rivali placati, Kiøben-havn, 1777: P. Guglielmi.	SCHATZ 4262
Il giuoco di picchetto. *See* Title catalogue.	
L'imenei di Delfo (Lisbona, 1785): Moreira.	SCHATZ 6631
Lindane e Dalmiro (Lisboa, 1789).	SCHATZ 9882
—— 2d copy.	ML 48.C6 1
Il matrimonio per concorso (Lisbona, 1773): Alessandri.	SCHATZ 148
Il matrimonio per concorso, Milano, (1768): Jommelli.	SCHATZ 4864
Il natale augusto, Lisbona, 1783: Moreira.	SCHATZ 6637
Le nozze disturbate, Venezia, 1766: Paisiello.	SCHATZ 7696
Numa Pompilio II, rè de Romani (Lisbona, 1789): Carvalho.	SCHATZ 1672
Palmira di Tebe (Lisbona, 1781): Santos.	SCHATZ 9399
Penelope nella partenza da Sparta (Lisbona, 1782): Carvalho.	SCHATZ 1673
Il ratto della sposa, Venezia, 1765: P. Guglielmi.	SCHATZ 4280
Il ratto della sposa, Lisbona (1767): P. Guglielmi.	ML 50.2.R27G9
Il ratto di Proserpina (Lisboa, 1784): J. C. da Silva.	SCHATZ 9884
Li rivali placati, Bonn, 1774: P. Guglielmi.	SCHATZ 4261
I rivali placati—Den forsonede medbeylere, Kiøbenhavn, 1777: P. Guglielmi.	SCHATZ 4262
La schiava liberata, Lisbona, 1770: Jommelli.	SCHATZ 4898
La schiava liberata—Die befreyte sklavinn, Dresda, 1777: Schuster.	SCHATZ 9754
Semiramide in bernesco. Same as his Il cacciatore deluso: Jommelli.	
Siface e Sofonisba, Lisbona, 1783: Moreira.	SCHATZ 6632

Martinelli, Gaetano—Continued.

Lo spirito di contradizione, Venezia, 1766: P. Guglielmi. SCHATZ 4305
Lo spirito di contradizione, Lisbona (1772): de Lima. SCHATZ 5616
Teséo (Lisbona, 1783): de Lima. SCHATZ 5619
Testoride Argonauta (Lisboa, 1780): Carvalho. SCHATZ 1669
Tomiri (Lisbona, 1783): Carvalho. SCHATZ 1675

Martini, Francesco.

Diogene tentato, ma non vinto dall' amore, ballet. *See* Rust's
Il conte Baccelone.

Martoscelli, Giuseppe.

Patro Tonno d'Isca, Mmenezia, 1714: Veneziano. ML 50.2.P29V2

Mason, William.

Caractacus, London, 1759: Arne. LONGE 42
Caractacus, York, 1777: Arne. PR 3548.M2A65
Caractacus, London, 1796 (Bell's British theatre, 1791–97, v.
34): Arne. PR 1241.B4
Elfrida, London, 1752. LONGE 44
Elfrida, London, 1796 (J. Bell, British theatre, London, 1791–
97, v. 35): Arne. (Colman's dramatization of the text.) PR 1241.B4

Massip.

Les festes nouvelles (Recueil général des opéra, t. xv, Paris,
1739): Duplessis, le jeune. SCHATZ 2861

Masson, Alexandre Frédéric Jacques, *marquis* **de Pézay.**

Das rosenfest zu Salenci, Frankfurt am Mayn, 1775. Tr. of
his La rosière de Salenci: Grétry. SCHATZ 4183
La rosière de Salenci, Paris, 1774: Grétry (67 p.). ML 50.2.R8G71
La rosière de Salenci, Paris, 1775: Grétry. SCHATZ 4182
La rosière de Salenci, Paris, 1785 (54 p.). ML 50.2.R8G73

Matiaglauro, Camidio. *Arcadian name of* Bagliacca, Pietro
Antonio.

Mattei, Saverio.

Il natal d'Apollo, Napoli, 1775: Cafaro. ML 48.M2G

Matthesius, Jacob.

Hannchen Robert, Gotha, 1779: unknown. SCHATZ 11615

Mattheson, Johann.

Aesopus bey hofe (Hamburg, 1729): Telemann. SCHATZ 10255
Der ehrsuechtige Arsaces (Hamburg, 1722) (based on Salvi's
Amore e maestà): Orlandini and Amadei. SCHATZ 7354
Nero (Hamburg, 1729). Tr. of Orlandini's Nerone (Piovene). SCHATZ 7344
Zenobia oder Das muster rechtschaffener ehelichen liebe
(Hamburg, 1726). Tr. of Händel's Radamisto (Haym). SCHATZ 4502

Mauricius, Johann.

Circe (Hamburg) 1734: Keiser (composed Praetorius's translation. Italian arias were interpolated). SCHATZ 5081

Mauro, Antonio.

Il curioso accidente della caccia. A. T. of his ballet Dove
entrò cervo, esce donna.
Dove entrò cervo, esce donna, o sia Il curioso accidente della
caccia, ballet. *See* Rust's La caccia d'Enrico IV.
La serietà in conflitto, ballet. *See* Rust's La caccia d'Enrico
IV.

Mauro, Ortensio.

Der grossmuethige Roland (Hamburg, 1695). Tr. of his Orlando generoso: Steffani.   Schatz 10034

Orlando generoso. O. T. of his Der grossmuethige Roland: Steffani.

Le rivali concordi. O. T. of his Die vereinigten mit-buhler oder Die siegende Atalanta: Steffani.

Il trionfo del fato o Le glorie d'Enea. O. T. of his: Schatz 10037

Il triumfo del fato oder Das maechtige geschick bei Lavinia und Dido (Hamburg, 1699): Steffani.

Die vereinigten mit-buhler oder Die siegende Atalanta (Hamburg, 1698). Tr. of his Le rivali concordi: Steffani.   Schatz 10035

Mazzarà, Francesco.

L'ambizione castigata, Venezia, 1717: unknown. (Same as his "Umor di principessa o sia L'ambizione castigata.")   Schatz 11299

Endimion (Breslau, 1727): Bioni. (Tr. and Italian text of their Endimione.)   Schatz 1043

L'Endimione, Venetia, 1709: Boniventi.   Schatz 1190

Paride in Ida, Venezia, 1706: Manza and Colletti.   Schatz 5917

Mazzini, Cosimo.

Die buckeligen. A. T. of his Die taeuschende aehnlichkeit.

Le confusioni della somiglianza ossiano I due gobbi. O. T. of his La somiglianza, ossiano I gobbi: Portugal.

I due gobbi. A. T. of his Le confusioni della somiglianza.

I due gobbi, Padova (1793). L. T. of his Le confusioni della somiglianza ossiano I due gobbi: Portugal.   Schatz 8445

I gobbi. A. T. of his La somiglianza: Portugal.

L'interesse gabba tutti, Firenze, 1795: Marinelli.   Schatz 5961

La somiglianza ossiano I gobbi—Die taeuschende aehnlichkeit oder Die buckeligen, Dresda, 1793. L. T. of his Le confusioni della somiglianza ossiano I due gobbi: Portugal.   Schatz 8400

Die taeuschende aehnlichkeit oder Die buckeligen. Tr. of his La somiglianza ossiano I gobbi, Dresda, 1793: Portugal.   Schatz 8400

Verwirrung durch aehnlichkeit (Berlin?) 1795. Tr. of his Le confusioni della somiglianza: Portugal.   Schatz 8401

Mazzolà, Caterino.

Die abenteurer. Tr. of his Gli avventurieri, Dresda, 1791: Paisiello.   Schatz 7057

Alles aus liebe. Tr. of his Tutto per amore, Dresda, 1785: Naumann.   Schatz 7057

L'amor perfetto. A. T. of his Il servo padrone: Piccinni.

L'amor perfetto. A. T. of his Il servo padrone: Schuster.

Amore giustificato—Die gerechtfertigte liebe, Dresda, 1792: Naumann.   Schatz 7037

Gli avari in trappola—Die geizigen in der falle, Dresda, 1787: Schuster.   Schatz 9743

Gli avventurieri—Die abenteurer, Dresda, 1791: Paisiello.   Schatz 7654

Il capriccio corretto—Der eigensinn der liebe, Dresda, 1783: Seydelmann.   Schatz 9843

La capricciosa ravveduta, Venezia, 1794 (L. T. of his Il turco in Italia): Bianchi.   Schatz 976

Mazzolà, Caterino—Continued.

La dama soldato, Venezia, 1792: Gazzaniga.   SCHATZ 3660

La dama soldato—Die dame als soldat, Dresda, 1791: Naumann.   SCHATZ 7043

Der eigensinn der liebe. Tr. of his Il capriccio corretto, Dresda, 1783: Seydelmann.   SCHATZ 9843

Elisa—Elise, Dresda, 1781: Naumann.   SCHATZ 7047

Elskovs magt, Kiøbenhavn, 1791. Tr. of his Tutto per amore: Naumann.   SCHATZ 7063

Er soll und muss ein narr seyn. Tr. of his Il pazzo per forza, Dresda, 1783: Schuster.   SCHATZ 9751

A escola dos ciosos, Lisboa, 1795. Tr. of his La scuola de' gelosi: Salieri.   SCHATZ 9318

Der geist des widerspruchs. Tr. of his Lo spirito di contraddizione, Dresda, 1785: Schuster.   SCHATZ 9757

Die geizigen in der falle. Tr. of his Gli avari in trappola, Dresda, 1787: Schuster.   SCHATZ 9743

Die gerechtfertigte liebe. Tr. of his Amore giustificato, Dresda, 1792: Naumann.   SCHATZ 7037

Der gleichgueltige ehemann. Tr. of his Il marito indolente, Dresda, 1782: Schuster.   SCHATZ 9747

Der gleichgueltige ehemann, Hamburg, 1788. Another Tr.   SCHATZ 9748

Il governatore dell' isole Canarie, Roma (1785): Accorimboni.   ML 50.2.G6A2

Il governatore dell isole Canarie—Der gouverneur der canarischen inseln (Dresda, 1785): Ghinassi.   SCHATZ 3802

Da gratitudine amore. A. T. of his Il mostro: Seydelmann.

Der herr als bedienter oder Die wahre liebe. Tr. of his Il servo padrone ossia L'amor perfetto, Dresda, 1792: Schuster.   SCHATZ 9756

L'isola capricciosa, Venezia, 1780: Rust.   SCHATZ 974

Liebe aus dankbarkeit. A. T. of his Das ungeheuer: Seydelmann.

Liebe hasst allen zwang. A. T. of his Die schule der eifersucht: Salieri.

Il marito indolente (Venetia, 1778): Santi.   SCHATZ 9393

Il marito indolente—Der gleichgueltige ehemann, Dresda, 1782: Schuster.   SCHATZ 9747

Il mostro ossia Da gratitudine amore—Das ungeheuer, oder Liebe aus dankbarkeit, Dresda, 1786: Seydelmann.   SCHATZ 9846

Osiride—Osiris, Dresda, 1781: Naumann.   SCHATZ 7054

Il pazzo per forza—Er soll und muss ein narr sein, Dresda, 1783: Schuster.   SCHATZ 9751

Rübenzahl, o sia Il vero amore—Ruebenzahl oder Die wahre liebe, Dresda, 1789: Schuster.   SCHATZ 9752

Ruggiero, Venezia, 1769: P. Guglielmi.   SCHATZ 4304

Die schule der eifersuechtigen, Hamburg, 1787. Tr. of his La scuola de' gelosi: Salieri.   SCHATZ 9317

Die schule der eifersuechtigen. Tr. of his La scola de gelosi, Brunsvic, 1782: Salieri.   SCHATZ 9315

Die schule der eifersucht, oder Liebe hasst allen zwang, Koeln am Rhein, 1787. Another Tr. of the above.   SCHATZ 9316

La scola de' gelosi (Venezia), 1779: Salieri.   SCHATZ 9314

La scola de gelosi—Die schule der eifersuechtigen, Brunsvic, 1782: Salieri.   SCHATZ 9315

Mazzolà, Caterino—Continued.

La scuola de 'gelosi, Verona (1780): Salieri. ML 50.2.S46S2

Il servo padrone ossia L'amor perfetto, Venezia, 1794: Piccinni. SCHATZ 8152

Il servo padrone ossia L'amor perfetto—Der herr als bedienter oder Die wahre liebe, Dresda, 1792: Schuster. SCHATZ 9756

Lo spirito di contraddizione—Der geist des widerspruchs, Dresda, 1785: Schuster. SCHATZ 9757

Il Turco in Italia. O. T. of his La cappricciosa ravveduta.

Tutto per amore—Alles aus liebe, Dresda, 1785: Naumann. SCHATZ 7057

Das ungeheuer oder Liebe aus Dankbarkeit. Tr. of his Il mostro, ossia Da gratitudine amore, Dresda, 1786: Seydelmann. SCHATZ 9846

Il vero amore. A. T. of his Rübenzahl: Schuster.

Die wahre liebe. A. T. of his Der herr als bedienter: Schuster.

Die wahre liebe. A. T. of his Ruebenzahl: Schuster.

Was thut die liebe nicht, Leipzig, 1793. Tr. of his La dama soldato: Naumann. SCHATZ 7044

Medley, Mat., *pseud. of* Aston, Anthony.

Medolago, Antonio.

Tomiri, Venetia, 1680: Vitali. SCHATZ 10758

Tullia Superba, Venetia, 1678: Freschi. SCHATZ 3356

Meissner, August Gottlieb.

Operetten von A. G. Meissner. Nach dem französischen [vignette].

Leipzig, Im verlage der Dykischen buchhandlung, 1778. 5 p. l., 95, [1]; 79; 3 p. l., 73 p. 17cm.

CONTENTS.—Das grab des mufti—Der liebesteufel oder der Alchymist—Arsene.

No composers mentioned. ML 49.A2M3

Der alchymist. A. T. of his Der liebesteufel.

Der alchymist, Leipzig, 1778 (no composer mentioned). SCHATZ 9742

Der alchymist (Berlin) 1778: André. SCHATZ 177

Der alchymist, Hamburg, 1779: Schuster. SCHATZ 9742a

Arsene, Leipzig, 1778: Seydelmann, not mentioned. (German version of Favart's "La belle Arsène" text.) SCHATZ 9841

Arsene, n. i., n. d.: Seydelmann. SCHATZ 9842

Arsene, n. i., n. d.: Seydelmann. SCHATZ 11748

Das grab des Mufti, oder Die zwey geizigen, Leipzig, 1776: Joh. Ad. Hiller. SCHATZ 4720

Der liebesteufel oder Der alchymist (O. T. of his Der alchymist.)

Sophonisbe, Leipzig, 1776: Neefe. SCHATZ 7072

Sophonisbe, n. i., n. d. (detached copy): Neefe. SCHATZ 11724

Die zwey geizigen. A. T. of his Das grab des Mufti: Joh. Ad. Hiller.

Melosio, Francesco.

L'Orione, Venetia, 1653: Cavalli. SCHATZ 1740

Sidonio e Dorisbe, Venetia (1642): Fontei. SCHATZ 3290

Menantes. *See his real name*, Hunold, Christian Friedrich.

Mendez, Moses.

The chaplet, London, 1750: Boyce.   AC 901.M5 v.519

The chaplet, London, 1767: Boyce.   Longe 73

The chaplet (A collection of the most esteemed farces, Edinburgh, 1792, v. 1): Boyce.   Schatz 11753A

The double disappointment, London, 1760.   ML 50.5.D79

Robin Hood, London, 1751: The Society of the Temple of Apollo (?Burney).   AC 901.M5 v.519

The shepherds lottery, London, 1751: Boyce.   Longe 54

Mennesson.

Ajax (Recueil général des opéra, t. xi, Paris, 1720): Bertin de la Doué.   Schatz 878

Ajax, Lyon, 1742: Bertin de la Doué.   Schatz 11668

Manto la fée (Recueil général des opéra, t. x, Paris, 1714): Stuck.   Schatz 10123

Les plaisirs de la paix (Recueil général des opéra, Paris, 1720, t. xi): Bourgeois.   Schatz 1273

Merindo Fesanio. *Arcadian name of* Pasqualigo, Benedetto.

Merry, Robert.

The picture of Paris. Taken in the year 1790, London, 1790: Shield.   Longe 207

Messink.

The choice of Harlequin or The Indian chief, London, 1782: M. Arne.   Longe 102

The choice of Harlequin, n. i., n. d.: M. Arne.   ML 52.2.C3

Metastasio, Pietro Antonio Domenico Bonaventura.

Opere drammatiche del Sig. abate Pietro Metastasio . . . Volume primo [—quarto].

Venezia, Giuseppe Bettinelli, 1733–37. 4 v. 19 cm.

Vignettes. Fol. port. of Metastasio in first vol.

    ML 49.A2M4

— Poesie del Signor abate Pietro Metastasio. Tomo primo [—ix].

Parigi, vedova Quillau, 1755. 16 cm.

Edited with "Dissertazione su le poesie drammatiche del abate P. Metastasio," by Ranieri de' Calsabigi. Our set lacks the vols. after v. 9.

    ML 49.A2M42

— Opere.

Parigi, vedova Herissant, 1780–1782. 12 v. 26cm.   ML 49.A2M44

— Tragedies-opera, de l'abbé Metastasio. Traduites en françois, par M. . . .

Vienne, 1751. 5 v. 14 cm.

Tr. by César Pierre Richelet.

Contents.—t. 1. Cyrus. Zenobie.—t. 2. Adrien. Titus.—t. 3. Siroës. Aëtius.—t. 4. Les Graces vengées. Démophon.—t. 5. Hypsipile. Regulus.   ML 49.A2M47

Achille in Sciro (Opere drammatiche, Venezia, 1733–37, v. 4).   ML 49.A2M4

— Achille in Sciro (Poesie, Parigi, vedova Quillau, 1755, t. iv).   ML 49.A2M42

— Achille in Sciro (Opere, Parigi, 1780–82, t. v).   ML 49.A2M44

Achille in Sciro—Achilles in Scirus, Berlino, 1765: Agricola.   Schatz 66

Achille in Sciro, Venezia, 1794: Bernardini.   Schatz 829

Achille in Sciro, Venezia, 1764: Bertoni.   Schatz 903

Metastasio, Pietro Antonio Domenico Bonaventura—Continued.

Achille in Sciro, Vienna d'Austria (1736): Caldara.	SCHATZ 1476
Achille in Sciro, Venezia, 1739: Chiarini.	SCHATZ 1852
Achille in Sciro, Venezia, 1766: Gassmann.	SCHATZ 3607
Achille in Sciro, Torino (1785): Pugnani.	SCHATZ 8505
Achille in Sciro (Venezia, 1747): Runcher.	SCHATZ 9151
Achille in Sciro—Achilles in Sciro, Wolffenbüttel (1746): Verocai.	SCHATZ 10717
Achilles in Sciro. Tr. of his Achille in Sciro, Wolffenbüttel (1746): Verocai.	SCHATZ 10717
Achilles in Scirus. Tr. of his Achille in Sciro, Berlino, 1765: Agricola.	SCHATZ 66
Achilles in Scyro, Wien, 1735: Caldara. Tr. of their Achille in Sciro.	SCHATZ 1477
Adrian in Syrien. Tr. of his Adriano in Siria, Monaco (1755): Bernasconi.	SCHATZ 854
L'Adriano (Venice, 1748): Ciampi.	SCHATZ 1875
Adriano en Syria. Tr. of his Adriano in Siria, Madrid (1757): Conforto.	SCHATZ 2121
L'Adriano in Siria (Opere drammatiche, Venezia, 1733–37, t. 1).	ML 49.A2M4
— Adriano in Siria (Poesie, Parigi, vedova Quillau, 1755, t. 1) ("Nella forma in cui sono stati ridotti dall' autore. *See* note on p. 169 of t. vi).	ML 49.A2M42
— Same, t. vi. ("Come . . . nell' altre edizioni.")	
— Adriano in Siria (Opere, Parigi, 1780–82, t. 1).	ML 49.A2M44
Adriano in Siria, Venezia, 1780: Alessandri.	SCHATZ 153
Adriano in Siria—Adrian in Syrien, Monaco (1755): Bernasconi.	SCHATZ 854
Adriano in Siria—Der in Syrien triumphirende kayser Hadrianus (Stuggarda, 1737): Broschi.	SCHATZ 1338
Adriano in Siria, Venezia, 1757: F. Brusa.	SCHATZ 1376
Adriano in Siria, Vienna d'Austria (1732): Caldara.	SCHATZ 1478
Adriano in Siria—Adriano en Syria, Madrid (1757): Conforto.	SCHATZ 2121
Adriano in Siria, Venezia, 1760: Galuppi.	SCHATZ 3473
Adriano in Siria, Venezia, 1733: Giacomelli.	SCHATZ 3805
Adriano in Siria, Venezia, 1740: Giai.	SCHATZ 3819
Adriano in Siria, Venezia (1766): P. Guglielmi.	SCHATZ 4232
Adriano in Siria, Dresda (1752): Hasse.	SCHATZ 4503
Adriano in Siria—Adrianus in Syrien, Dresda (1752): Hasse.	SCHATZ 4504
Adriano in Siria, Mannheim (1769): Holzbauer.	SCHATZ 4778
Adriano in Siria, Venezia, 1760: Mazzoni.	SCHATZ 6225
Adriano in Siria, Pavia (1777): Misliweczek.	SCHATZ 6533
L'Adriano in Siria, Modena (1775): Monti.	SCHATZ 6605
Adriano in Siria, Roma (1758): Rinaldo di Capua.	ML 50.2.A36R4
Adriano in Siria, Torino (1782): Rust.	SCHATZ 9166
Adriano in Siria, Milano (1790): Nasolini.	SCHATZ 6998
Adriano in Siria, Venezia, 1771: Sacchini.	SCHATZ 9204
Adriano in Siria, Roma, 1779: Sarti.	SCHATZ 9470
L'Adriano in Siria (Venezia, 1752): Scarlatti, Gius.	SCHATZ 9540
Adriano in Siria, Venezia (1754): Scolari.	SCHATZ 9802
Adrien (Tragédies-opera, Vienne, 1751, t. ii). Tr. of his Adriano in Siria.	ML 49.A2M47
Aetius (Tragédies opera, Vienne, 1751, t. iii). Tr. of his Ezio.	ML 49.A2M47

Metastasio, Pietro Antonio Domenico Bonaventura—Continued.

Aetius. Tr. of his Ezio, Berlino, 1755 (as altered by Taglia-
    zucchi): Graun.　　　　　　　　　　　　　　　　　　Schatz 4096
Aetius. Tr. of his Ezio, Stutgart, 1758: Jommelli.　　　Schatz 4858
Gli affetti generosi. A. T. of his L'Atenaide.
Alcide al bivio (Opere, Parigi, 1780–82, t. viii).　　　ML 49.A2M44
Alcide al bivio (Vienna, 1760): Hasse.　　　　　　　　Schatz 4505
Alcides an der doppel-strasse (Wien, 1760): Hasse. Tr. of
    the above.　　　　　　　　　　　　　　　　　　　Schatz 4506
Alcide al bivio—Alcides ved te to veie, Kiøbenhavn, 1774:
    Hasse.　　　　　　　　　　　　　　　　　　　　　Schatz 4507
Alessandro e Poro—Alexander und Porus, Berlino, 1744:
    Graun.　　　　　　　　　　　　　　　　　　　　　Schatz 4087
L'Alessandro nell' Indie (Opere drammatiche, Venezia, 1733–
    37, v. 2).　　　　　　　　　　　　　　　　　　　ML 49.A2M4
— Alessandro [nell' Indie] (Poesie, Parigi, vedova Quillau,
    1755, t. iv). ("Nella forma in mi sono stati ridotti dall'
    autore." See note, t. vi, p. 169.)　　　　　　　ML 49.A2M42
— Same, t. vi. ("Come . . . nell' altre edizioni.")
Alessandro nell' Indie (Opere, Parigi, 1780–82, t. iv).　ML 49.A2M44
Alessandro nell' Indie, Roma (1772): Anfossi.　　　　Schatz 282
Alessandro nell' Indie, St. Pietroburgo, 1759: Araya.　Schatz 304
Alessandro nell' Indie, Bologna (1787): F. Bianchi.　ML 50.2.A517B25
Alessandro nell' Indie, Venezia, 1792: F. Bianchi.　　Schatz 974
Alessandro nell' Indie—Alexander in Indien, Wolffenbüttel,
    1752: Fiorillo.　　　　　　　　　　　　　　　　　Schatz 3198
Alessandro nell' Indie, Venezia (1755): Galuppi, also:　Schatz 3430
Alessandro nell' Indie—Alexander in Indien, Monaco (1755).　Schatz 3431
Alessandro nell' Indie, Napoli, 1789: P. Guglielmi.　　Schatz 4234
L'Alessandro nell' Indie, Venezia, 1736: Hasse.　　　Schatz 4508
L'Alessandro nell' Indie, Venezia, Presburgo, 1741: Hasse.　Schatz 4509
Alessandro nell' Indie (Venezia, 1743): Hasse.　　　　Schatz 4593
L'Alessandro nell' Indie—Alexander in Indien, Stutgart,
    1760: Jommelli.　　　　　　　　　　　　　　　　Schatz 4841
Alessandro nell' India (Lisbona, 1776): Jommelli.　　Schatz 4899
Alessandro nell' Indie, Venezia, 1753: Latilla and others.　Schatz 5455
L'Alessandro nell' Indie, Venezia, 1778: Marescalchi.　Schatz 5946
Alessandro nell' Indie, Lucca (1783): Mortellari.　　Schatz 6683
Alessandro nell' Indie, Lisbona, 1755: Perez.　　　　Schatz 7882
Alessandro nell' Indie, Venezia (1732): Pescetti.　　Schatz 7960
Alessandro nell' Indie, Firenze (1777): Piccinni.　　Schatz 8137
Alessandro nell' Indie, Venezia, 1775: Rust.　　　　Schatz 9175
Alessandro nell' Indie, Venezia, 1763: Sacchini.　　Schatz 9243
Alessandro nell' Indie, Torino (1766): Sacchini.　　Schatz 11746
Alessandro nell' Indie, Bologna (1764): Sciroli.　　Schatz 9781
Alessandro nell' Indie, Venezia, 1759: Scolari.　　Schatz 9786
Alessandro nell' Indie (Livorno, 1791): Tarchi.　　Schatz 10228
Alessandro nell' Indie, Vicenza, 1750: Tiraboschi.　Schatz 10355
Alessandro nell' Indie, Roma (1730): Vinci.　　　　Schatz 10742
Alessandro nell' Indie, Monaco (1735): Vinci.　　　Schatz 11297
Alexander in Indien. Tr. of his Alessandro nell' Indie,
    Wolffenbüttel, 1752: Fiorillo.　　　　　　　　Schatz 3198
Alexander in Indien. Tr. of his Alessandro nell' Indie,
    Monaco (1755): Galuppi.　　　　　　　　　　Schatz 3431

Metastasio, Pietro Antonio Domenico Bonaventura—Continued.

Alexander in Indien. Tr. of his L'Alessandro nell' India,
Stutgart, 1760: Jommelli.   SCHATZ 4841

Alexander und Porus. Tr. of his Alessandro e Poro, Berlino,
1744: Graun.   SCHATZ 4087

Amintas, London, 1769: Rush, Guglielmi, etc. Altered version of The royal shepherd.   LONGE 37

Amintas (Collection of the most esteemed farces, Edinburgh,
1792, t. vi).   SCHATZ 11753

L'Amor prigioniero (Poesie, Parigi, vedova Quillau, 1755,
t. vii).   ML 49.A2M42

L'amor prigioniero (Opere, Parigi, 1780–82, t. ii).   ML 49.A2M44.

L'Angelica (Opere drammatiche, Venezia, 1733–37, v. 3).   ML 49.A2M4

— L'Angelica (Poesie, Parigi, vedova Quillau, 1755, t. ix).   ML 49.A2M42

— L'Angelica (Opere, Parigi, 1780–82, t. x).   ML 49.A2M44

La Angelica, n. i., n. d.: unknown.   SCHATZ 11306

L'Angelica (Lisbona, 1778): Carvalho.   ML 50.2.A71C2

Antigono (Poesie, Parigi, vedova Quillau, 1755, t. v).   ML 49.A2M42

Antigono (Opere, Parigi, 1780–82, t. vi).   ML 49.A2M44

Antigono, Venezia, 1773: Anfossi.   SCHATZ 225

Antigono, Milano (1781): Anfossi and Gatti.   SCHATZ 283

Antigono, Venezia, 1794: Caruso.   SCHATZ 1659

Antigono, Venezia, 1762: Galuppi.   SCHATZ 3439

Antigono, Roma (1756): Gluck.   ML 50.2.A72G5

Antigono (Dresda, 1744): Hasse.   ML 50.2.A72H2

Antigono, Lucca, 1744: Hasse.   ML 48.M2M

Antigono, Venezia, 1768: G. F. de Majo.   SCHATZ 5854

Antigono, Roma (1772): Monza.   SCHATZ 6620

Antigono-Antigonus, Monaco (1769): Sales.   SCHATZ 9269

Antigono, Padova, 1764: Traetta.   SCHATZ 10406

L'Antigono, Mantova (1786): Zingarelli.   ML 50.2.A72Z4

Antigonus. Tr. of his Antigono, Monaco (1769): Sales.   SCHATZ 9269

L'ape (Opere, Parigi, 1780–82, t. xi).   ML 49.A2M44

L'Artaserse (Opere drammatiche, Venezia, 1733–37, v. i).   ML 49.A2M4

— Artaserse (Poesie, Parigi, vedova Quillau, 1755, t. i).   ML 49.A2M42

— Artaserse (Opere, Parigi, 1780–82, t. i).   ML 49.A2M44

Artaserse, Cagliari, 1750: unknown.   SCHATZ 11310

Artaserse, Pisa, 1770: pasticcio.   ML 48.A5 v.30

Artaserse, Torino (1741): Arena.   SCHATZ 308

Artaserse, Torino (1761): J. Chr. Bach.   SCHATZ 532

[Artaserse]—Artaxerxes, Muenchen (1763): Bernasconi.   SCHATZ 863

Artaserse, Milano (1777): Bertoni.   SCHATZ 905

Artaserse, London, 1779: Bertoni.   SCHATZ 906

Artaserse, Genova (1788): Bertoni.   SCHATZ 907

Artaserse, Venezia, 1776: Borghi.   SCHATZ 1227

Artaserse, Verona (1770): Boroni.   SCHATZ 1250

Artaserse, Padova, 1738: Brivio.   SCHATZ 1325

L'Artaserse (Firenze, 1780): Caruso.   SCHATZ 1656

Artaserse, Verona (1741): Chiarini.   SCHATZ 1854

Artaserse, Torino (1785): Cimarosa.   SCHATZ 1905

L'Artaserse (Vienna, 1749): Galuppi.   SCHATZ 3444

Artaserse—Artaxerxes, Stutgart (1751): Graun.   SCHATZ 4090

Artaserse, Bologna (1789): P. Guglielmi.   SCHATZ 4298

Artaserse, Venezia, 1730: Hasse.   SCHATZ 4576

Metastasio, Pietro Antonio Domenico Bonaventura—Continued.

Artaserse—Artaxerxes (Dresda, 1740): Hasse (second version).   SCHATZ 4513

Artaserse, Ferrara (1765): Hasse (third version?).   SCHATZ 4590

Artaserse—Artaxerxes, Stutgart, 1756: Jommelli.   SCHATZ 4843

Artaserse, Venezia, 1762: G. F. de Majo.   SCHATZ 5861

Artaserse, Venezia, 1772: Manfredini.   SCHATZ 5892

Artaserse, Venezia (1795): Nicolini.   SCHATZ 7140

Artaserse, Venezia (1750): Pampani.   SCHATZ 7754

Arteserse, Venezia (1742): Paganelli.   SCHATZ 7572

Artaserse, Venezia (1761): Ponzo.   SCHATZ 8356

Artaserse, Perugia, 1781: Rust.   ML 50.2.A8R8

Artaserse, Firenze, 1783: Rust.   SCHATZ 9165

Artaserse, Roma (1768): Sacchini.   ML 50.2.A8S2

Artaserse, Copenhagen (1752): Scalabrini and others.   SCHATZ 9515

Artaserse—Artaxerxes (Ratisbona, n. d.): von Schacht.   SCHATZ 9562

Artaserse, Venezia, 1758: Scolari.   SCHATZ 9787

Artaserse (Venezia, 1744): Teradellas.   SCHATZ 10283

Artaserse, Roma (1730): Vinci.   SCHATZ 10743

Artaserse—Artaxerxes (Dresda, 1746): Vinci.   SCHATZ 10744

Artaserse, Milano (1794): Zingarelli.   SCHATZ 11240

Artaserse Longimano, Venezia, 1737 (L. T. of his "Temistocle"): Pampino.   SCHATZ 7753

Artaxerxes, London, n. d. (Tr. of his Artaserse): Arne, Th. A.   LONGE 308

Artaxerxes, London, 1792: Arne.   LONGE 218

Artaxerxes, Muenchen (1763) Tr. of his Artaserse: Bernasconi.   SCHATZ 863

Artaxerxes.   Tr. of his Artaserse, Stutgart (1751): Graun.   SCHATZ 4090

Artaxerxes.   Tr. of his Artaserse (Dresda, 1740): Hasse (second version).   SCHATZ 4513

Artaxerxes.   Tr. of his Artaserse, Stutgart, 1756: Jommelli.   SCHATZ 4843

Artaxerxes, Wien (1763).   Tr. of his Artaserse: Scarlatti,
Gius.   SCHATZ 9541

Artaxerxes.   Tr. of his Artaserse (Ratisbona, n. d.): von
Schacht.   SCHATZ 9562

Artaxerxes.   Tr. of his Artaserse (Dresda, 1746): Vinci.   SCHATZ 10744

L'asilio d'Amore (Opere drammatiche, Venezia, 1733–37, v. 2).   ML 49.A2M4

— L'asilio d'amore (Poesie, Parigi, vedova Quillau, 1755,
t. v).   ML 49.A2M42

— L'asilio d'amore (Opere, Parigi, 1780–82, t. iii).   ML 49.A2M44

Astrea placata (Poesie, Parigi, vedova Quillau, 1755, t. vii).   ML 49.A2M42

Astrea placata (Opere, Parigi, 1780–82, t. v).   ML 49.A2M44

Astrea placata ovvero La felicità della terra—Astrea tilfredsstillet eller Jordens lyksalighed, Copenhagen, 1760: Sarti.   SCHATZ 9426

Astrea placata ovvero La felicità della terra, Dresda (1753):
Schürer.   SCHATZ 9730

Astrea tilfredsstillet eller Jordens lyksalighed.   Tr. of his
Astrea placata ovvero La felicità della terra, Copenhagen,
1760: Sarti.   SCHATZ 9426

L'Atenaide o vero Gli affetti generosi (Opere, Parigi, 1780–82,
t. xi).   ML 49.A2M44

Attilio Regolo (Poesie, Parigi, vedova Quillau, 1755, t. vi).   ML 49.A2M42

Attilio Regolo (Opere, Parigi, 1780–82, t. viii).   ML 49.A2M44

Attilio Regolo, Friedrichstadt (1750): Hasse.   SCHATZ 4518

Attilio Regolo—Attilius Regulus, Friedrichstadt (1750):
Hasse.   SCHATZ 4519

Metastasio, Pietro Antonio Domenico Bonaventura—Continued.

Attilio Regolo, Roma, 1753: Jommelli. SCHATZ 4844

Ballo cinese (Opere drammatiche, Venezia, 1733–37, v. 4).
(Same as "Le Cinesi.") ML 49.A2M4

Cato in Utica. Tr. of his Catone in Utica, Berlino, 1743:
Graun. SCHATZ 4092

Der Cato in Utica. Tr. of his Il Catone in Utica, Stutgart,
1754: Jommelli. SCHATZ 4847

Cato in Utica, Mannheim (1770). Tr. of his Catone in Utica:
Piccinni. SCHATZ 8079

Cato in Utika. Tr. of his Il Catone in Utica (Bronsevigo,
1768): Bach. SCHATZ 527

Il Catone in Utica (Opere drammatiche, Venezia, 1733–37,
v. 2). ML 49.A2M4

— Catone in Utica (Poesie, Parigi, vedova Quillau, 1755,
t. iii). ML 49.A2M42

— Catone in Utica (Opere, Parigi, 1780–82, t. iv). ML 49.A2M44

Catone in Utica, Livorno (1789): Andreozzi. SCHATZ 195

Catone in Utica, Napoli, 1784: Antonelli Torre. SCHATZ 289

Il Catone in Utica, Pavia (1763): Bach. SCHATZ 526

Il Catone in Utica—Cato in Utika (Bronsevigo, 1768): Bach. SCHATZ 527

Catone in Utica, Venezia, 1757: Ciampi. SCHATZ 1884

Il Catone in Utica, Lucca, 1749: Duni. SCHATZ 2835

Catone in Utica, Venezia, 1761: Gassmann. SCHATZ 3625

Catone in Utica—Cato in Utica, Berlino, 1743: Graun. SCHATZ 4092

Catone in Utica, Torino, 1731: Hasse. SCHATZ 4586

Il Catone in Utica—Der Cato in Utica, Stutgart, 1754: Jommelli. SCHATZ 4847

Catone in Utica, Roma, 1747: Latilla. SCHATZ 5456

Catone in Utica, Sec. ed., Venezia (1729): Leo. SCHATZ 5557

Catone in Utica, Torino (1763): G. F. de Majo. SCHATZ 5860

Catone in Utica, Mannheim (1770): Piccinni. SCHATZ 8078

Catone in Utica, Roma, 1728: Vinci. SCHATZ 10746

Il Catone in Utica (Venice, 1747): Vinci, Jommelli, and
others. SCHATZ 10754

Catone in Utica, Venetia, 1791: Winter. SCHATZ 11027

Die Chineser (Mannheim, 1756). Tr. of his Le Cinesi: Holzbauer. SCHATZ 4780

Der chinesische held, Wienn, 1755: Bonno. Tr. of their
L'eroe cinese. SCHATZ 1197

Der chinesische held. Tr. of his L'eroe cinese, Berlino, 1773:
Hasse. SCHATZ 4538

Der chinesische held. Tr. of his L'eroe cinese, Monaco (1771):
Sacchini. SCHATZ 9219

Den chinesiske helt. Tr. of his L'eroe cinese, Kiøbenhavn,
1773. SCHATZ 9220

Il Ciclope (Poesie, Parigi, vedova Quillau, 1755, t. vii). ML 49.A2M42

Il Ciclope (Opere, Parigi, 1780–82, t. ii). ML 49.A2M44

Le Cinesi (Poesie, Parigi, vedova Quillau, 1755, t. iv). ML 49.A2M42

Le Cinesi (Opere, Parigi, 1780–82, t. ii). ML 49.A2M44

Il Ciro riconosciuto (Opere drammatiche, Venezia, 1733–37,
v. 4). ML 49.A2M4

Ciro riconosciuto (Poesie, Parigi, vedova Quillau, 1755, t. iv). ML 49.A2M42

Ciro riconosciuto (Opere, Parigi, 1780–82, t. v). ML 49.A2M44

Metastasio, Pietro Antonio Domenico Bonaventura—Continued.

Ciro riconosciuto, Venezia, 1737: Galuppi and Caldara.	SCHATZ 3517
Ciro riconosciuto, Milan (1746): Galuppi.	ML 50.2.C53G3
Ciro riconosciuto, Roma (1759): Galuppi.	SCHATZ 3445
Il Ciro riconosciuto—Der erkennte Cyrus, Stuttgart (1752): Hasse.	SCHATZ 4525
Ciro riconosciuto, Bologna, 1744: Jommelli.	SCHATZ 4879
Ciro riconosciuto, Roma, 1737: Rinaldo di Capua.	SCHATZ 8795
Il Ciro riconosciuto—Der wiedererkannte Cyrus, Braunschweig (1746): Verocai.	SCHATZ 10718
The clemency of Titus, London, 1737. Tr. of his La clemenza di Tito: Veracini.	SCHATZ 10618
La clemenza di Tito (Opere drammatiche, Venezia, 1733–37, v. 4).	ML 49.A2M4
— La clemenza di Tito (Poesie, Parigi, vedova Quillau, 1755, t. iii).	ML 49.A2M42
— La clemenza di Tito (Opere, Parigi, 1780–82, t. iii).	ML 49.A2M44
La clemenza di Tito, Napoli, 1772: Anfossi.	SCHATZ 273
La clemenza di Tito, Torino (1739): Arena.	SCHATZ 309
La clemenza di Tito—Die guetigkeit des Titus, Monaco (1768): Bernasconi.	SCHATZ 856
La clemenza di Tito, Vienna d'Austria (1734): Caldara.	SCHATZ 1498
La clemenza di Tito—Die guetigkeit des Titus, Monaco (1747): Camerlocher.	SCHATZ 1523
La clemenza di Tito, Reggio (1759): Ciampi.	SCHATZ 1880
La clemenza di Tito, Genova, 1736: Ciochetti.	SCHATZ 2011
La clemenza di Tito, Camerino (1757): Cristiani.	SCHATZ 2291
La clemenza di Tito, Torino (1760): Galuppi.	SCHATZ 3498
La clemenza di Tito, Verona (1738): Hasse. (O. T. of the opera: Tito Vespasiano ovvero La clemenza di Tito.)	SCHATZ 4526
La clemenza di Tito, Hamburg, 1748: Hasse.	SCHATZ 4528
La clemenza di Tito—Die mildigkeit des Titus, Stutgart, 1753: Jommelli.	SCHATZ 4849
La clemenza di Tito, Lisbona, 1771: Jommelli.	SCHATZ 4884
La clemenza di Tito, Venezia, 1735: Leo.	SCHATZ 5553
La clemenza di Tito, Milano, 1738: Marchi.	SCHATZ 5937
La clemenza di Tito, Lisbona, 1755: Mazzoni.	SCHATZ 6229
La clemenza di Tito (Venetia, 1748): Pampani.	SCHATZ 7758
La clemenza di Tito, Venezia, 1760: Scarlatti, Gius.	SCHATZ 9542
[La clemenza di Tito]—The clemency of Titus, London, 1737: Veracini.	SCHATZ 10618
Cleofide, Berlino (1754): Agricola.	SCHATZ 67
Cleofide—Cleofide, Berlino (1777): Hasse. (The text is "L'Alessandro nelle Indie," as altered by Michel Angelo Boccardi.)	SCHATZ 4573
Cleonice, Venezia, 1740: Hasse. (Partly based on their Demetrio, by Bartolomeo Vitturi.)	SCHATZ 4578
Il conclave del MDCCLXXIV, Roma (1775)—Das conclave von MDCCLXXIV. (Fictitious imprint, author, and composer. Satire written by Sertori): Piccinni.	SCHATZ 8084
Das conclave von MDCCLXXIV, Rom (1775). Separate ed. of the above.	SCHATZ 8085
Il conclave del 1774, Venezia, 1797. L. ed. of the above.	SCHATZ 8132

Metastasio, Pietro Antonio Domenico Bonaventura—Continued.

La contesa de' Numi (Opere drammatiche, Venezia, 1733–37,
v. 2). ML 49.A2M4

— La contesa de' Numi (Poesie, Parigi, vedova Quillau, 1755,
t. vi). ML 49.A2M42

— La contesa de' Numi (Opere, Parigi, 1780–82, t. iv). ML 49.A2M44

La corona (Opere, Parigi, 1780–82, t. xi). ML 49.A2M44

Cyrus (Tragédies-opéra, Vienne, 1751, v. i). Tr. of his Il Ciro
riconosciuto. ML 49.A2M47

La danza (Poesie, Parigi, vedova Quillau, 1755, t. ii). ML 49.A2M42

La danza (Opere, Parigi, 1780–82, t. i). ML 49.A2M44

Il Demetrio (Opere drammatiche, Venezia, 1733–37, v. i). ML 49.A2M4

— Demetrio (Poesie, Parigi, vedova Quillau, 1755, t. i). ML 49.A2M42

— Demetrio (Opere, Parigi, 1780–82, t. i). ML 49.A2M44

Il Demetrio, Livorno (1785): unknown. Schatz 11319

Demetrio, Monaco (1772): Bernasconi. Schatz 857

Il Demetrio, Venezia, 1780: Bianchi. Schatz 1008

Demetrio (Roma, 1732): Giai. Schatz 3816

Demetrio, Venezia (1742): Gluck. Schatz 3929

Il Demetrio, Venezia (1775): P. Guglielmi. Schatz 4310

Demetrio, Venezia, 1732: Hasse. Schatz 4532

Il Demetrio—Demetrius, Dresda, 1740: Hasse (second version). Schatz 4533

Il Demetrio, Mannheim (1753): Jommelli. Schatz 4850

Il Demetrio, Venezia, 1768: Pampani. Schatz 7761

Demetrio, Venezia, 1751: Perez. Schatz 7876

Demetrio, Torino (1762): Ponzo. Schatz 8354

Demetrio—Demetrius, Hamburg, 1744: Scalabrini and others. Schatz 9516

Demetrio, Padova, 1752: Scarlatti, Gius. Schatz 9544

Demetrio—Demetrio, Bologna, 1739: Schiassi. ML 50.2.D37S3

Il Demetrio, Lodi (1764): Wagenseil. ML 48.A5 v.10

Il Demetrio rè della Siria, Wolfenbuettel (1734): Caldara. Schatz 1480

Demetrius. Tr. of his Il Demetrio, Dresda, 1740: Hasse. Schatz 4533

Demetrius, Mannheim (1753). Tr. of his Demetrio: Jommelli. Schatz 4851

Demetrius, London, 1737: Pescetti. Schatz 7964

Demetrius. Tr. of his Demetrio, Hamburg, 1744: Scalabrini
and others. Schatz 9516

Demofonte, Venezia, 1754: Cocchi. Schatz 2042

Il Demofoonte (Opere drammatiche, Venezia, 1733–37, v. 2). ML 49.A2M4

— Demofoonte (Poesie, Parigi, vedova Quillau, 1755, t. iii). ML 49.A2M42

— Demofoonte (Opere, Parigi, 1780–82, t. iv). ML 49.A2M44

Demofoonte, Genova (1774): Anfossi and others. Schatz 274

Demofoonte—Demophoon, Monaco (1766): Bernasconi. Schatz 864

Demofoonte, London, 1778: Bertoni. Schatz 911

Demofoonte, Milano (1759): Ferradini. Schatz 3063

Il Demofoonte, Padova, 1758: Galuppi. Schatz 3063

Demofoonte—Demophontes, Berlino, 1774: Graun. Schatz 4094

Demofoonte—Demophoon (Dresda, 1748): Hasse. Schatz 4534

Demofoonte, Venezia, 1749: Hasse. Schatz 4582

Il Demofoonte, Malta (1765): Hasse (second version). Schatz 4574

Demofoonte, Padova (1743): Jommelli. ML 50.2.D39J5

Demofoonte, Milano (1753): Jommelli. ML 50.2.D39J6

Metastasio, Pietro Antonio Domenico Bonaventura—Continued.

Demofoonte—Demophon, Stutgart, 1764: Jommelli.	SCHATZ 4852
Demofoonte, Lisbona (1775): Jommelli.	SCHATZ 4853
Demofoonte, Venezia (1738): Latilla.	SCHATZ 5458
Demofoonte, Torino (1754): Manna.	SCHATZ 5903
Il Demofoonte, Venezia, 1769: Misliweczek.	SCHATZ 6529
Il Demofoonte, Venezia, 1775: Paisiello.	SCHATZ 7698
Demofoonte, Venezia, 1764: Pampani.	SCHATZ 7752
Demofoonte, Modenà (1783): Pio.	ML 48.A5 v.30
Demofoonte, Milano (1794): Portugal.	SCHATZ 8403
Demofoonte, Venezia, 1787: Prati.	SCHATZ 8454
Demofoonte, Torino (1788): Pugnani.	SCHATZ 8504
Demofoonte, Venezia (1735): Schiassi.	SCHATZ 9600
Demofoonte, Pavia (1777): Schuster.	SCHATZ 9760
Demofoonte, Milano (1786): Tarchi.	SCHATZ 10218
Demofoonte, Mantova (1770): Traetta.	SCHATZ 10408
Demofoonte—Demophoon, Wolffenbuttel (1742): Verocai.	SCHATZ 10719
Demofoonte, Lucca, 1741: Vinci.	SCHATZ 10745
Demofoonte, rè di Tracia—Demophontes, koenig in Thracien, Berlino, 1745: Graun.	SCHATZ 4113
Demophon (Tragédies-opera, Vienne, 1751, t. iv). (Richelet's Tr. of Demofoonte.)	ML 49.A2M47
Demophon. Tr. of his Demofoonte, Stutgart, 1764: Jommelli.	SCHATZ 4852
Demophontes. Tr. of his Demofoonte, Berlino, 1774: Graun.	SCHATZ 4094
Demophontes, king of Thrace, London, 1737. Tr. of his Demofoonte: Duni.	SCHATZ 2837
Demophontes, koenig in Thracien. Tr. of his Demofoonte rè di Tracia, Berlino, 1745: Graun.	SCHATZ 4113
Demophoon. Tr. of his Demofoonte (Dresda, 1748): Hasse.	SCHATZ 4534
Demophoon. Tr. of his Demofoonte, Wolffenbuttel (1742): Verocai.	SCHATZ 10719
Dido (Breslau, 1726): Albinoni. Tr. of their Didone abbandonata.	SCHATZ 90
Didon abandonnée. Tr. of his La Didone abbandonata, Stuttgart, 1763: Jommelli.	SCHATZ 4855
Didone, Torino (1773): Colla.	SCHATZ 2107
La Didone, Forli (1779): Ottani.	SCHATZ 7364
Didone, Lisbona, 1799 (as altered by Giuseppe Caravita): Marino.	SCHATZ 5968
La Didone, Firenze, 1795: Paisiello.	SCHATZ 7699
Didone, Torino, 1750: Terradellas.	SCHATZ 10285
La Didone abbandonata (Opere drammatiche, 1733–37, v. i).	ML 49.A2M4
— Didone abbandonata (Poesie, Parigi, vedova Quillau, 1755, t. ii) ("Nella forma in cui sono stati ridotti dall' autore." *See* note, t. vi, p. 169).	ML 49.A2M42
— Same, t. vi. ("Come . . . nell' altre edizioni.")	
— Didone abbandonata (Opere, Parigi, 1780–82, t. iii).	ML 49.A2M44
Didone abbandonata (Roma, 1732): unknown.	SCHATZ 11380
Didone abbandonata, Venezia, 1747: Adolfati.	SCHATZ 57
Didone abbandonata, Venezia (1775): Albinoni.	SCHATZ 89
Didone abbandonata, Lucca, 1775: Anfossi.	SCHATZ 233
La Didone abbandonata, Monaco (1760): Bernasconi	SCHATZ 858

Metastasio, Pietro Antonio Domenico Bonaventura—Continued.

La Didone abbandonata—Die verlassene Dido, Bronsevigo
    (1751): Fiorillo.   Schatz 3200

La Didone abbandonata, Milano, 1755: Fioroni.   Schatz 3206

Didone abbandonata, Venezia (1764): Galuppi.   Schatz 3503

[La Didone abbandonata]—Die verlassene Dido, Dresden,
    1742: Hasse.   Schatz 4535

Didone abbandonata—Die verlassene Dido, Berlino, 1769:
    Hasse.   Schatz 4536

La Didone abbandonata—Die verlassene Dido, Stutgart, 1751:
    Jommelli.   Schatz 4854

La Didone abbandonata—Didon abandonnée, Stuttgart, 1763:
    Jommelli.   Schatz 4855

Didone abbandonata, Venezia, 1770: G. F. de Majo.   Schatz 5855

Didone abbandonata, Venezia (1751): Manna.   Schatz 5901

Didone abbandonata, London (1775–76): Sacchini and others.   Schatz 11321

Didone abandonata, Napoli, 1724: Sarro.   ML 50.2.D55S2

Didone abbandonata, Venezia (1730): Sarro.   Schatz 9422

Didone abbandonata—Den forladte Dido, København (1762):
    Sarti.   Schatz 9432

La Didóne abbandonata, Ferrara (1763): Scolari.   Schatz 9806

Didone abbandonata, Venezia, 1757: Traetta.   Schatz 10402

Didone abbandonata, Roma (1726): Vinci.   ML 50.2.D55V4

La Didone abbandonata, Perugia (1781): Zanetti.   ML 48.A5 v.5

Egeria (Opere, Parigi, 1780–82, t. viii).   ML 49.A2M44

Egeria (Vienna, 1764): Hasse.   Schatz 4537

L'Endimione (Opere drammatiche, Venezia, 1733–37, v. 3).   ML 49.A2M4

— L'Endimione (Poesie, Parigi, vedova Quillau, 1755, t. ix).   ML 49.A2M42

— L'Endimione (Opere, Parigi, 1780–82, t. x).   ML 49.A2M44

Endimione, Venezia (1742): Bernasconi.   Schatz 869

L'Endimione ovvero Il trionfo d'amore, Stutgart (1759):
    Jommelli.   Schatz 4856

L'Endimione (Lisbona, 1780): Jommelli.   Schatz 4895

L'Enea negli Elisi ovvero Il tempio dell' eternità (Opere
    drammatiche, Venezia, 1733–37, v. 2).   ML 49.A2M4

Die entdeckte Semiramis. Tr. of his La Semiramide ricono-
    sciuta (Dresda, 1747): Hasse.   Schatz 4560

Der entsatz Bethuliens. A. T. of Judith: Demler. Tr. of his
    "Betulia liberata," by unknown translator.

Der erkennte Cyrus. Tr. of his Il Ciro riconosciuto, Stuttgart
    (1752): Hasse.   Schatz 4525

L'eroe cinese (Poesie, Parigi, vedova Quillau, 1755, t. vi).   ML 49.A2M42

L'eroe cinese (Opere, Parigi, 1780–82, t. vii).   ML 49.A2M44

L'eroe cinese, Venezia (1753): unknown.   Schatz 11325

L'eroe cinese—Der chinesische held, Berlino, 1773: Hasse.   Schatz 4538

L'eroe cinese—Der chinesiche held, Monaco (1771): Sacchini.   Schatz 9219

L'eroe cinese—Den chinesiske helt, København, 1773: Sac-
    chini.   Schatz 9220

L'eroica gratitudine. A. T. of his Il Ruggiero.

L'eroica gratitudine. A. T. of his Il Ruggiero: Hasse.

L'Ezio (Opere drammatiche, Venezia, 1733–37, v. i).   ML 49.A2M4

— Ezio (Poesie, Parigi, vedova Quillau, 1755, t. ii).   ML 49.A2M42

— Ezio (Opere, Parigi, 1780–82, t. ii).   ML 49.A2M44

Metastasio, Pietro Antonio Domenico Bonaventura—Continued.

Ezio, Brescia, 1742: pasticcio.	ML 50.2.E9
Ezio, London, 1764–65: pasticcio from Pescetti, Bach, Galuppi, etc.	ML 48.M2N
Ezio, Lucca (1782): Alessandri.	Schatz 145
Ezio, Venezia (1778): Anfossi.	Schatz 275
Ezio, Roma (1729): Auletta.	Schatz 498
Ezio, Venezia, 1767: Bertoni.	Schatz 912
Ezio, Torino (1731): Broschi.	Schatz 1340
Ezio, Pavia (1784): Calvi.	Schatz 1518
Ezio, Verona (1740): Cortona and others.	Schatz 2264
Ezio, Venezia, 1772: Gazzaniga.	Schatz 3687
Ezio-Aëtius, Berlino, 1755 (altered by Tagliazucchi): Graun.	Schatz 4096
Ezio, Dresda (1755): Hasse. (Second version.)	Schatz 4539
Ezio, Bologna (1741): Jommelli.	Schatz 4857
Ezio-Aetius, Stutgart, 1758: Jommelli.	Schatz 4858
Ezio, Lisbona (1772): Jommelli.	Schatz 4894
Ezio, Venezia (1737): Lampugnani.	Schatz 5388
Ezio, Venetia (1743): Lampugnani.	Schatz 11719
Ezio (Venezia, 1747): Pescetti.	Schatz 7965
Ezio, Venezia (1728): Porpora.	Schatz 8370
Ezio, Venezia (1754): Scarlatti, Gius.	Schatz 9545
Ezio, Vicenza (1792): Tarchi.	Schatz 10239
Ezio, Padova (1765): Traetta.	Schatz 10410
La felicità della terra. A. T. of his Astrea placata: Sarti.	
La felicità della terra. A. T. of his Astrea placata: Schürer.	
Fernando nel Messico. (Tarducci used verses by Metastasio for the text of Giordani's opera of this title.)	
Die flucht des Aeneas nach Latien. A. T. of his Der streit der kindlichen pflicht und der liebe: Porpora-Telemann.	
Den forladte Dido. Tr. of his Didone abbandonata, Kiøbenhavn (1762): Sarti.	Schatz 9432
La Galatea (Opere drammatiche, Venezia, 1733–37, v. 3).	ML 49.A2M4
— La Galatea (Poesie, Parigi, vedova Quillau, 1755, t. ix).	ML 49.A2M42
— La Galatea (Opere, Parigi, 1780–82, t. x).	ML 49.A2M44
La gara (Opere, Parigi, 1780–82, t. xi).	ML 49.A2M44
Il Giustino (Opere drammatiche, Venezia, 1733–37, v. 3).	ML 49.A2M4
— Giustino (Poesie, Parigi, vedova Quillau, 1755, t. ix).	ML 49.A2M42
— Giustino (Opere, Parigi, 1780–82, t. x).	ML 49.A2M44
Die gnade des Titus. Tr. of his La clemenza di Tito, Hamburg, 1748: Hasse.	Schatz 4528
Les Graces vengées (Tragedies-opera, Vienne, 1751, t. iv). Tr. of his Le Grazie vendicate.	ML 49.A2M47
Le Grazie vendicate (Opere drammatiche, Venezia, 1733–37, v. 4).	ML 49.A2M4
— Le Grazie vendicate (Poesie, Parigi, vedova Quillau, 1755, t. vii).	ML 49.A2M42
— Le Grazie vendicate (Opere, Parigi, 1780–82, t. iii).	ML 49.A2M44
Die guetigkeit des Titus. Tr. of his La clemenza di Tito, Monaco (1768): Bernasconi.	Schatz 856
Die guetigkeit des Titus. Tr. of his La clemenza di Tito, Monaco (1747): Camerlocher.	Schatz 1523
Die guetigkeit des Titus, Wolfenbuettel (1744). Tr. of his La clemenza di Tito: Hasse.	Schatz 4527

Metastasio, Pietro Antonio Domenico Bonaventura—Continued.

Hadrian in Syrien, Mannheim, 1768. Tr. of his Adriano in
    Siria: Holzbauer.   SCHATZ 4779

Hadrianus. *See his* Der in Syrien triumphirende . . .

Hypermenestra. Tr. of his Ipermestra (Bronsevico, 1759):
    Fiorillo.   SCHATZ 3201

Hypermenestra. Tr. of his Ipermestra (Friedrichsstadt,
    1751): Hasse.   SCHATZ 4543

Hypsipile (Tragedies, Vienne, 1751, t. v). Tr. of his Issipile.   ML 49.A2M47

Hysipile (Mannheim, 1754). Tr. of his Issipile: Holzbauer.   SCHATZ 4785

Hypsipile (Wien, 1760). Tr. of his Issipile: Scarlatti, Gius.   SCHATZ 9549

Der im schaefer verborgene koenig. Tr. of his Il rè pastore,
    Berlino, 1770: Hasse.   SCHATZ 4557

L'impresario—The master of the opera, Londra, 1737: Sarro.
    (Originally the intermezzi in Metastasio's La Didone
    abbandonata.)   SCHATZ 9411

L'impresario dell' Isole Canarie, Vienna (1747): Leo.   SCHATZ 5558

L'impresario dell' Isole Canarie—Der impresarius oder Opern-
    verwalter von den Canarischen inseln, Postdam, 1748:
    Leo.   SCHATZ 5559

Der impresarius oder Opernverwalter von den Canarischen
    inseln. Tr. of his L'impresario dell' isole Canarie, Pots-
    dam, 1748: Leo.   SCHATZ 5559

Der in Syrien triumphirende kayser Hadrianus. Tr. of his
    Adriano in Siria (Stuggarda, 1737): Broschi.   SCHATZ 1338

Ipermestra (Poesie, Parigi, vedova Quillau, 1755, t. v).   ML 49.A2M42

Ipermestra (Opere, Parigi, 1780–82, t. vi).   ML 49.A2M44

Ipermestra, Venezia, 1789: Astaritta.   SCHATZ 387

Ipermestra (Venezia, 1748): Bertoni.   SCHATZ 926

Ipermestra-Hypermenestra (Bronsevico, 1759): Fiorillo.   SCHATZ 3201

L'Ipermestra, Venezia, 1761: Galuppi.   SCHATZ 3457

Ipermestra (Venezia, 1744): Gluck.   SCHATZ 3930

L'Ipermestra, Vienna (1744): Hasse (the licenza with final
    chorus by Predieri).   SCHATZ 4542

Ipermestra—Hypermenestra (Friedrichsstadt, 1751): Hasse
    (second version).   SCHATZ 4543

Ipermestra, Venezia, 1774: Naumann.   SCHATZ 7049

Ipermestra, Padova (1791): Paisiello.   SCHATZ 7702

Ipermestra, Alessandria (1755): Re.   SCHATZ 8618

Ipermestra, Milano (1786): Rispoli.   SCHATZ 8815

L'isola disabitata (Poesie, Parigi, vedova Quillau, 1755, t. iv).   ML 49.A2M42

L'isola disabitata (Opere, Parigi, 1780–82, t. ii).   ML 49.A2M44

L'isola disabitata—Die unbewohnte insel (Stutgart, 1761):
    Jommelli.   SCHATZ 4863

L'isola disabitata, Venezia, 1775: Naumann.   SCHATZ 7061

L'isola disabitata, Lisbona, 1799: Paisiello.   SCHATZ 7693

L'isola disabitata, Bologna (1768): Traetta.   SCHATZ 10394

L'isola disabitata—Den ubeboede øe, Kiøbenhavn, 1772:
    Traetta.   SCHATZ 10395

L'Issipile (Opere drammatiche, Venezia, 1733–37, v. i).   ML 49.A2M4

— Issipile, Metastasio (Poesie, Parigi, vedova Quillau, 1755,
    t. ii).   ML 49.A2M42

— Issipile (Opere, Parigi, 1780–82, t. ii).   ML 49.A2M44

Issipile, Roma, 1732: no composer.   ML 50.2.I78

Metastasio, Pietro Antonio Domenico Bonaventura—Continued.

L'Issipile, Vienna d'Austria (1732): Conti.	SCHATZ 2205
Issipile, Torino, 1738: Galuppi.	SCHATZ 3499
Issipile, Parma (1756): Galuppi.	SCHATZ 3514
L'Issipile, Venezia, 1758: Gassmann.	SCHATZ 3622
Issipile, Venezia (1796): Marinelli.	SCHATZ 5956
L'Issipile, Macerata, 1748: Mazzoni.	SCHATZ 6226
L'Issipile, Venezia (1732): Porta.	SCHATZ 8391
I'Issipile, Vienna (1760): Scarlatti, Gius.	SCHATZ 9548

Jordens lyksalighed. A. T. of his Astrea tilfredsstillet: Sarti.

Judith oder Der entsatz Bethuliens. (Tr. of his "Betulia liberata," by unknown translator): Demler. Forms p. [3–14] of Die niederlage der Hunnen vor Augsburg (Augsburg, 1780).   SCHATZ 2507

Die mildigkeit des Titus. Tr. of his La clemenza di Tito, Stutgart, 1753.   SCHATZ 4849

Narbale, Venezia, 1774 (much altered version of his L'eroe cinese): Bertoni.   SCHATZ 940

Il natal di Giove (Poesie, Parigi, vedova Quillau, 1755, t. ii).	ML 49.A2M42
Il natal di Giove (Opere, Parigi, 1780–82, t. i).	ML 49.A2M44
Nitetis. Tr. of his La Nitteti, Kiøbenhavn (1761): Sarti.	SCHATZ 9452
Nitteti (Opere, Parigi, 1780–82, t. viii).	ML 49.A2M44
La Nitteti, Napoli, 1756: no composer.	ML 50.2.N46
La Nitteti, Venezia (1780): Anfossi.	SCHATZ 276
Nitteti, Venezia, 1789: Bertoni.	SCHATZ 941
Nitetti, Milano (1789): Bianchi.	SCHATZ 1003
La Nitteti, Napoli, 1783: Curcio.	SCHATZ 2300
La Nitteti, Firenze (1758): Hasse.	SCHATZ 4547
La Nitteti, Lisbona (1770): Jommelli.	SCHATZ 4891
Nitetti—Nitetis, St. Pietroburgo (1788): Paisiello.	ML 50.2.N46P2
La Nitteti, Napoli, 1764: Mazzoni.	SCHATZ 6227
La Nitteti, Milano, 1771: Monza.	SCHATZ 6615
Nitteti, Torino (1783): Rispoli.	SCHATZ 8812
La Nitteti—Nitetis, Kiøbenhavn (1761): Sarti.	SCHATZ 9452
La Nitteti, Venezia, 1765: Sarti.	SCHATZ 9475
La Nitteti, Reggio (1757): Traetta.	SCHATZ 10403
L'Olimpiade (Opere drammatiche, Venezia, 1733–37, v. i).	ML 49.A2M4
— Olimpiade (Poesie, Parigi, vedova Quillau, 1755, t. ii).	ML 49.A2M42
— Olimpiade (Opere, Parigi, 1780–82, t. ii).	ML 49.A2M44
L'Olimpiade, Venezia, 1744: Anfossi.	SCHATZ 246
L'Olimpiade, Venezia, 1765: Bertoni.	SCHATZ 915
Olimpiade, Milano (1782): Bianchi.	SCHATZ 1004
L'Olimpiade, Firenze, 1785: Borghi.	SCHATZ 1235
L'Olimpiade, Torino, 1737: Brivio.	SCHATZ 1326
L'Olimpiade, Venezia, 1767: Brusa, Pampani, and Guglielmi.	SCHATZ 4316
Olimpiade (n. i., n. d.): Caldara.	ML 50.2.O5C2
L'Olimpiade, Lucca (1784): Cimarosa.	SCHATZ 1960
L'Olimpiade, Vicenza (1794): Cimarosa.	SCHATZ 11686
L'Olimpiade, Torino (1790): Federici.	SCHATZ 3046
L'Olimpiade (Venezia, 1745): Fiorillo.	SCHATZ 3205

L'Olimpiade—Die olympischen spiele, Wolfenbuettel (1749): Fiorillo.   SCHATZ 3202

L'Olimpiade, Siena, 1763: Galuppi.   SCHATZ 3496

Metastasio, Pietro Antonio Domenico Bonaventura—Continued.

L'Olimpiade, Venezia, 1767: P. Guglielmi, Ant. G. Pampani,
and F. Brusa. SCHATZ 4316

Olimpiade—Das olympische spiel, Dresda (1756): Hasse. SCHATZ 4549

L'Olimpiade, Torino (1765): Hasse. SCHATZ 4550

L'Olimpiade—Die olympische spiele, Stutgard, 1761: Jommelli. SCHATZ 4867

L'Olimpiade (Lisbona, 1774): Jommelli. SCHATZ 4885

L'Olimpiade (Venezia, 1752): Latilla. SCHATZ 5449

L'Olimpiade, Venezia, 1767: Pampani, Brusa, and Guglielmi. SCHATZ 4316

L'Olimpiade, Venezia, 1738: Pergolesi. SCHATZ 7904

L'Olimpiade, Berlino, 1791: Reichardt. SCHATZ 8649

Olimpiade, Milano (1778): Rossetti. SCHATZ 8885

L'Olimpiade, Venezia, 1786: pasticcio by Sacchini and
others. SCHATZ 9238

L'Olimpiade, Venezia, 1760: Sciroli. SCHATZ 9783

L'Olimpiade, Venezia, 1747: Scolari. SCHATZ 9797

Olimpiade, Verona (1758): Traetta. SCHATZ 10404

Olimpiade (Firenze, 1767): Traetta. SCHATZ 10396

L'Olimpiade, Venezia, 1734: Vivaldi. SCHATZ 10774

L'Olympiade—Die olympischen spiel, Monaco (1764): Bernasconi. SCHATZ 859

Die Olympiade. Tr. of his L'Olimpiade, Berlino, 1791:
Reichardt. SCHATZ 8649

L'Olympiade ou Le trionphe de l'amitié, Paris, 1777. French
version of his L'Olimpiade: Sacchini. SCHATZ 9239

Das olympische spiel. Tr. of his Olimpiade, Dresda (1756):
Hasse. SCHATZ 4549

Die olympische spiele. Tr. of his L'Olimpiade, Stutgard,
1761: Jommelli. SCHATZ 4867

Die olympischen spiel. Tr. of his L'Olympiade, Monaco
(1764): Bernasconi. SCHATZ 859

Die olympischen spiele. Tr. of his L'Olimpiade, Wolfenbuettel (1749): Fiorillo. SCHATZ 3202

Opernverwalter von den Canarischen inseln. A. T. of his
Der impresarius: Leo.

Gli orti Esperidi (Opere drammatiche, Venezia, 1733–37,
v. 3). ML 49.A2M4

— Gli orti Esperidi (Poesie, Parigi, vedova Quillau, 1755,
t. ix). ML 49.A2M42

— Gli orti Esperidi (Opere, Parigi, 1780–82, t. x). ML 49.A2M44

Gli orti Esperidi (Lisbona, 1779): de Lima. SCHATZ 5620

Gli orti Esperidi, Lisbona (1764): Santos. SCHATZ 9396

La pace fra la virtù e la bellezza (Poesie, Parigi, vedova
Quillau, 1755, t. vii). ML 49.A2M42

La pace fra la virtù e la bellezza (Opere, Parigi, 1780–82, t. iii). ML 49.A2M44

La pace fra le tre dee (Opere, Parigi, 1780–82, t. xi). ML 49.A2M44

Il palladio conservato (Opere drammatiche, Venezia, 1733–37,
v. 4). ML 49.A2M4

— Il palladio conservato (Poesie, Parigi, vedova Quillau,
1755, t. vii). ML 49.A2M42

— Il palladio conservato (Opere, Parigi, 1780–82, t. v). ML 49.A2M44

Il palladio conservato, Lisbona (1771): Santos SCHATZ 9397

Metastasio, Pietro Antonio Domenico Bonaventura—Continued.

Il Parnaso accusato e difeso (Poesie, Parigi, vedova Quillau,
1755, t. vii).   ML 49.A2M42

Il Parnaso accusato e difeso (Opere, Parigi, 1780–82, t. v).   ML 49.A2M44

Il Parnaso confuso (Opere, Parigi, 1780–82, t. viii).   ML 49.A2M44

Il Parnaso confuso, Milano, 1765: Gluck.   Schatz 3936

Partenope (Opere, Parigi, 1780–82, t. ix).   ML 49.A2M44

Partenope (Vienna, 1757): Hasse.   Schatz 4551

Partenope—Parthenope, Berlino, 1775: Hasse.   Schatz 4552

Partenope, Napoli, 1782 (with alterations): Martin y Soler.   Schatz 6013

Parthenope.   Tr. of Metastasio's Partenope, Berlino, 1775:
Hasse.   Schatz 4552

Poro, Torino (1745): Gluck. (Based on his Alessandro nell'
Indie.)   Schatz 3933

[Poro rè d'Italia]—Porus, Londra, 1736: Händel. (Based on
M.'s Alessandro nell' Indie.)   Schatz 4486

Il rè pastore (Poesie, Parigi, vedova Quillau, 1755, t. v).   ML 49.A2M42

Il re pastore (Opere, Parigi, 1780–82, t. vii).   ML 49.A2M44

Il re pastore, Lucca (1765): pasticcio.   ML 50.2.R29

Il rè pastore, Venezia, 1769: Galuppi.   Schatz 3468

Il rè pastore, Venezia, 1767: P. Guglielmi.   Schatz 4302

Il re pastore, Dresda (1755): Hasse.   Schatz 4556

Il re pastore—Der im schaefer verborgene koenig, Berlino,
1770: Hasse.   Schatz 4557

Il re pastore, Venezia, 1753: Sarti.   Schatz 9466

Regulus (Tragedies-opera, Vienne, 1751, t. v).   Tr. of his
Attilio Regolo.   ML 49.A2M47

La rispettosa tenerezza (Opere, Parigi, 1780–82, t. xi).   ML 49.A2M44

La retrosia disarmata (Opere, Parigi, 1780–82, t. xi).   ML 49.A2M44

Romolo ed Ersilia (Opere, Parigi, 1780–82, t. ix).   ML 49.A2M44

Romolo ed Ersilia, Roma, 1765: Hasse.   Schatz 4589

The royal shepherd, London, 2d ed. (176–): Rush. Text
based on "Il rè pastore."   Longe 37

The royal shepherd, London, 3d ed. (176–): Rush.   Longe 192

Il Ruggiero o vero L'eroica gratitudine (Opere, Parigi, 1780–
82, t. ix).   ML 49.A2M4

Il Ruggiero o vero L'eroica gratitudine, Milano, 1771: Hasse.   Schatz 4558

Semiramide (Poesie, Parigi, vedova Quillau, 1755, t. v)
("Nella forma in cui sono stati ridotti dall' autore." *See*
note on p. 169 of vi).   ML 49.A2M42

— Same, t. vii ("Come . . . nell' altre edizioni." Same note).

Semiramide (Opere, Parigi, 1780–82, t. vii).   ML 49.A2M44

Semiramide, Lucca, 1751: unknown.   Schatz 11362

Semiramide—Semiramis, Monaco, 1765 (the licenza by
Giunti): Bernasconi.   Schatz 860

Semiramide, Padova, 1759: Fischietti.   Schatz 3243

Semiramide—Semiramis (Stutgard) 1762. L. T. of his Semiramide riconosciuta: Jommelli.   Schatz 4870

Semiramide, Lisbona (1771): Jommelli.   Schatz 4892

Semiramide—Semiramis (Munich, 1782): Salieri.   ML 50.2.S48S2

Semiramide—Semiramis, Kiøbenhavn (1762): Sarti.   Schatz 9463

Semiramide, Venezia, 1768: Sarti.   Schatz 9476

Semiramide, Venezia, 1765: Traetta.   Schatz 10413

Metastasio, Pietro Antonio Domenico Bonaventura—Continued.

La Semiramide riconosciuta (Opere drammatiche, Venezia, 1733–37, v. 2).   ML 49.A2M4

Semiramide riconosciuta, Venezia (1756): F. Brusa.   Schatz 1377

Semiramide riconosciuta, Venezia, 1753: Cocchi.   Schatz 2045

La Semiramide riconosciuta, Milano, 1749: Galuppi.   Schatz 3469

Semiramide riconosciuta (Venezia, 1745): Hasse.   Schatz 4559

La Semiramide riconosciuta—Die entdeckte Semiramis (Dresda, 1747): Hasse.   Schatz 4560

La Semiramide riconosciuta—Semiramis (Varsavia, 1760): Hasse.   Schatz 4572

Semiramide riconosciuta. O. T. of his Semiramide: Jommelli.

Semiramide riconosciuta, Roma (1741): Lampugnani.   Schatz 5389

La Semiramide riconosciuta, Napoli, 1751: G. de Majo.   Schatz 5864

La Semiramide riconosciuta—A Semiramis reconhecida, Lisbona (1765): Perez.   Schatz 7875

Semiramide riconosciuta, Venezia (1729): Porpora.   Schatz 8361

Semiramide riconosciuta, Roma (1729): Vinci.   Schatz 10752

Semiramis. Tr. of his La Semiramide riconosciuta (Varsavia, 1760): Hasse.   Schatz 4572

Semiramis. Tr. of his Semiramide (Stutgard) 1762: Jommelli.   Schatz 4870

A Semiramis reconhecida. See his La Semiramide riconosciuta: Perez.

Semiramis. Tr. of his Semiramide (Munich, 1782): Salieri.   ML 50.2.S48S2

Semiramis. Tr. of his Semiramide, Kiøbenhavn, 1762: Sarti.   Schatz 9463

Der sieg der Clelia. Tr. of his Il trionfo di Clelia, Monaco (1776): Michl.   Schatz 6489

Siface, Venezia, 1748 [!instead of 1761]: Fischietti.   Schatz 3242

Siface, Bologna (1744): Maggiore.   Schatz 5834

Siface, Venezia, 1726: Porpora.   Schatz 8362

Il Siroe (Opere drammatiche, Venezia, 1733–37, v. 2).   ML 49.A2M4

— Siroe (Poesie, Parigi, vedova Quillau, 1755, t. iii).   ML 49.A2M42

— Siroe (Opere, Parigi, 1780–82, t. iii).   ML 49.A2M44

Il Siroe—Der Siroes (Bronsevigo, 1767): pasticcio from Vinci, Händel, Wagenseil, etc.   Schatz 11365

Siroe, Venezia (1771): Borghi.   Schatz 1237

Siroe, Venezia (1750): Cocchi.   Schatz 2041

(Siroe)—Siroes, king of Persia, London, 1736 (much of the text not by Metastasio): Hasse (and probably others).   Schatz 4587

Siroe, Dresda, 1763: Hasse.   Schatz 4562

Siroe, Padova, 1753: Latilla.   Schatz 5451

Siroe (Venezia, 1743): Manna.   Schatz 5902

Siroe, Torino (1780): Sarti.   Schatz 9464

Siroe, Torino (1750): Scarlatti, Gius.   Schatz 9557

Siroe—Siroes, Monaco (1767): Traetta.   ML 50.2.S6T8

Siroe, rè di Persia, Torino (1730): Fiorè.   Schatz 3193

Siroe, rè di Persia, Roma (1727): Porpora.   ML 50.2.S64P6

Siroe, rè di Persia, Napoli, 1727: Sarro.   Schatz 9420

Siroe, rè di Persia, Venetia (1731): Vinci.   Schatz 10749

Siroe, rè di Persia, Reggio, 1727: Vivaldi.   Schatz 10780

Siroes (Tragédies opéra, Vienne, 1751, t. iii). Tr. of his Siroe.   ML 49.A2M47

Metastasio, Pietro Antonio Domenico Bonaventura—Continued.

Siroës—Siroes, Varsovia (1763). French and German Tr. of
his Siroe: Hasse.   SCHATZ 4592

Siroes, king of Persia, London, 1736 (much of the text not by
Metastasio): Hasse (and probably others).   SCHATZ 4587

Siroes. Tr. of his Siroe, Monaco (1767): Traetta.   ML 50.2.S6T8

La Sofonisba, Milano, 1744 (recitatives by Francesco Silvani,
the lyrics selected from the above): Gluck.   SCHATZ 3932

Il sogno (Opere, Parigi, 1780–82, t. iv).   ML 49.A2M44

Il sogno, Pisa (1757): Reutter.   SCHATZ 8696

Il sogno di Scipione (Poesie, Parigi, vedova Quillau, 1755,
t. ii).   ML 49.A2M42

Il sogno di Scipione (Opere, Parigi, 1780–82, t. i).   ML 49.A2M44

Il sogno di Scipione—Der traum des Scipio, Berlin, 1746:
Nichelmann.   SCHATZ 7103

Der streit der kindlichen pflicht und der liebe oder Die flucht
des Aeneas nach Latien (Hamburg) 1731. Tr. of his
Didone abbandonata: Porpora (recitatives by Telemann).   SCHATZ 8365

Syphax (Hamburg, 1727). Tr. of his Siface: Porpora.   SCHATZ 8363

Il Temistocle (Opere drammatiche, Venezia, 1733–37, v. 4).   ML 49.A2M4

— Temistocle (Poesie, Parigi, vedova Quillau, 1755, t. iv).   ML 49.A2M42

— Temistocle (Opere, Parigi, 1780–82, t. v).   ML 49.A2M44

Temistocle, Firenze, 1793: pasticcio.   ML 48.A5 v.16

Temistocle (Venezia, 1744): Bernasconi.   SCHATZ 861

Il Temistocle, Vienna d'Austria (1736): Caldara.   SCHATZ 1488

Themistocles, Mannheim, 1772 (Tr. of his Temistocle with
Verazi's additions): Bach.   SCHATZ 531

Temistokles, Muenchen (1754). Tr. and Italian text of his
Temistocle: Bernasconi.   SCHATZ 862

Il tempio dell' eternità (Poesie, Parigi, vedova Quillau, 1755,
t. vi).   ML 49.A2M42

Il tempio dell' eternità (Opere, Parigi, 1780–82, t. iv).   ML 49.A2M44

Tito Vespasiano ovvero La clemenza di Tito. O. T. of his
La clemenza di Tito: Hasse.

Titus (Tragedies opera, Vienne, 1751, v. 2). Tr. of his La
clemenza di Tito.   ML 49.A2M47

Titus, Cassel, 1797: Mozart. Tr. of their La clemenza di Tito.   ML 50.2.C58M77

Der traum des Scipio. Tr. of his Il sogno di Scipione, Berlin,
1746: Nichelmann.   SCHATZ 7103

Tributo di rispetto e d'amore (Opere, Parigi, 1780–82, t. xi).   ML 49.A2M44

Le triomphe de l'amitié. A. T. of his L'Olympiade: Sacchini.

Il trionfo d'amore (Opere, Parigi, 1780–82, t. ix).   ML 49.A2M44

Il trionfo d'amore, Milano (1765): Gassmann.   SCHATZ 3628

Il trionfo d'amore. A. T. of his L'Endimione: Jommelli.

Il trionfo di Clelia (Opere, Parigi, 1780–82, t. ix).   ML 49.A2M44

Il trionfo di Clelia, Bologna (1763): Gluck.   ML 48.M2E

Il trionfo di Clelia (Vienna, 1762): Hasse.   SCHATZ 4566

Il trionfo di Clelia, (Lisbona, 1774): Jommelli.   SCHATZ 4883

Il trionfo di Clelia—Der sieg der Clelia, Monaco (1776): Michl.   SCHATZ 6489

Il trionfo di Clelia, Torino (1768): Misliweczek.   SCHATZ 6531

Il trionfo di Clelia, Torino (1787): Tarchi.   SCHATZ 10222

Die triumphirende Claelia (Wien, 1762). Tr. of his Il trionfo
di Clelia: Hasse.   SCHATZ 4567

Metastasio, Pietro Antonio Domenico Bonaventura—Continued.

Den ubeboede øe. Tr. of his L'isola disabitata, Kiøbenhavn,
1772: Traetta. SCHATZ 10395

Die unbewohnte insel. Tr. of his L'isola disabitata (Stutgart,
1761): Jommelli. SCHATZ 4863

Die verlassene Dido. Tr. of his La Didone abbandonata,
Bronsevigo (1751): Fiorillo. SCHATZ 3200

Die verlassene Dido. Tr. of his La Didone abbandonata,
Dresden, 1742: Hasse. SCHATZ 4535

Die verlassene Dido. Tr. of his La Didone abbandonata,
Berlino, 1769: Hasse. SCHATZ 4536

Die verlassene Dido. Tr. of his La Didone abbandonata,
Stutgart, 1751: Jommelli. SCHATZ 4854

Il vero omaggio (Poesie, Parigi, vedova Quillau, 1755, t. vii). ML 49.A2M42

Il vero omaggio (Opere, Parigi, 1780–82, t. ii). ML 49.A2M44

Viriate, Venezia, 1762: Galuppi. ("Siface" text as altered,
according to Schatz, by Domenico Lalli.) SCHATZ 3511

Viriate, Venezia, 1739: Hasse. ("Siface" text altered, according to Schatz, by Domenico Lalli.) SCHATZ 4581

Der wiedererkannte Cyrus. Tr. of his Il Ciro riconosciuto,
Braunschweig (1746): Verocai. SCHATZ 10718

Die wueste insel, Leipzig, 1778. Tr. of his L'isola disabitata:
Schuster. SCHATZ 9758

Zenobia (Poesie, Parigi, vedova Quillau, 1755, t. v). ML 49.A2M42

Zenobia (Opere, Parigi, 1780–82, t. vi). ML 49.A2M44

Zenobia, Venezia, 1746: Micheli. SCHATZ 6481

Zenobia (Lisbona, 1765): Perez. ML 50.2.Z37P3

Zenobia, Venezia (1740): Sbacci. SCHATZ 9512

Zenobia, Monaco (1773): Tozzi. SCHATZ 10384

Zenobia, Roma, 1762: Traetta. SCHATZ 10398

Zenobia—Zenobia, Kiøbenhavn, 1770: Uttini. SCHATZ 10551

Zenobie (Tragédies-opéra, Vienne, 1751, t. i). Tr. of his
Zenobia. ML 49.A2M47

Meyer, Friedrich Ludwig Wilhelm.

Alter schützt für thorheit nicht, Hamburg, 1781: André. SCHATZ 179

Das redende gemaehlde, Mannheim, 1771. Tr. of Grétry's Le
tableau parlant (Anseaume). SCHATZ 4189

Die reue vor der hochzeit, Berlin, 1782: unknown. ML 50.2.R44

Die samnitische vermaehlungsfeyer, Berlin, 1780 (with Joh.
André). Tr. of Grétry's Les marriages Samnites (Rozoy). SCHATZ 4171

Der soldat als zauberer, Mannheim, 1772. Tr. of Philidor's
Le soldat magicien (Anseaume). SCHATZ 8025

Der tempel der wahrheit (Annalen des theaters, Berlin, 1788,
erstes heft): F. W. H. Benda. SCHATZ 767

Meyer, Wilhelm Christian Dietrich.

Das blendwerk, Gotha, 1781. Tr. of Grétry's La fausse magie
(Marmontel). SCHATZ 4155

Die weinlese, Mannheim, 1783: von Becke. SCHATZ 679

Michaelis, Johann Benjamin.

Amors gukkasten, Leipzig, 1772: Neefe. SCHATZ 7069

Der einspruch, Leipzig, 1772: Neefe. SCHATZ 7071

Herkules auf dem Oeta, n. i., n. d.: Gräfe. SCHATZ 4061

Herkules auf dem Oeta, Leipzig, 1772: Schmittbauer. SCHATZ 9656

Michaelis, Johann Benjamin—Continued.

Man kann es ja probieren.   A. T. of his Walmir und Gertraud:
   Schweitzer.

Walmir und Gertraud oder Man kann es ja probieren, n. d.
   (Apparently detached from an ed. of his collected works):
   Schweitzer.   SCHATZ 9776

Michieli, Pietro.

Argiope, Venetia, 1649 (supposed joint author with Fusconi):
   Rovetta and Leardini (?).   SCHATZ 9106

Migliavacca, Giannambrogio.

Armida (Venezia, 1777): Astaritta.   SCHATZ 367

Armida, Milano (1780): Misliweczek. (Text a free translation from Quinault).   ML 48.A5 v.9

Armida, Vienna, 1760: Traetta.   SCHATZ 11382

Armida, Venezia, 1767: Traetta.   SCHATZ 10407

Artemisia—Artemisia, Dresda (1755): Hasse.   SCHATZ 4514

Die burg Hymens. Tr. of his La reggia d'Imenèo, Dresda,
   1787: Naumann.   SCHATZ 7056

La reggia d'Imenèo—Die burg Hymens, Dresda, 1787: Naumann.   SCHATZ 7056

Solimano, Venezia, 1755: Fischietti.   SCHATZ 3240

Solimano, Dresda (1753): Hasse.   SCHATZ 4563

Solimano—Soliman, Dresda (1754): Hasse.   SCHATZ 4564

Solimano, Torino (1756): M. A. Valentini.   SCHATZ 10587

Tetide, Vienna, 1760: Gluck.   SCHATZ 3937

Miles, William Augustus.

The artifice, London, 1780: M. Arne.   LONGE 239

Summer amusement or An adventure at Margate, London,
   1781 (with Andrews): Arnold.   LONGE 91

Mililotti, Giuseppe Maria.

La Francese di spirito, Napoli, 1781: Tritto.   SCHATZ 10471

I sdegni per amore, Napoli, 1776: Cimarosa (with, on p. 29–51,
   his I matrimoni in ballo, text by Pasquale Mililotti). SCHATZ 1993

Mililotti, Pasquale.

L'Arabo cortese, Napoli, 1776: Paisiello (with arias by
   Cimarosa).   SCHATZ 7665

La baronessa Stramba, Napoli, 1786. (L. T. of his I matrimoni in ballo): Cimarosa. See Cimarosa's Il credulo. SCHATZ 1985

Commedianti fortunati, Napoli, 1779: Amicone.   SCHATZ 174

La finta semplice o sia Il tutore (Lisbona, 1773): Insanguine. SCHATZ 4837

La francese brillante. O. T. of his I Francesi brillanti.

La Francese brillante, Lucca, 1767: P. Guglielmi.   SCHATZ 4284

I Francesi brillanti, Lisbona (1765): Paisiello.   SCHATZ 7687

La Frascatana nobile, Napoli, 1776: Cimarosa.   SCHATZ 1995

I matrimoni in ballo. O. T. of his libretto La baronessa
   Stramba.

I matrimoni in ballo, n. i., n. d.: Cimarosa.   Detached copy.
   See below.   SCHATZ 1984

I matrimoni in ballo: Cimarosa (p. 24–51 of their I sdegni per
   amore, Napoli, 1776).   SCHATZ 1993

Le mbroglie de le bajasse.   O. T. of his La serva fatta padrona:
   Paisiello.

Il rè alla caccia, Napoli, 1780: Tarchi.   SCHATZ 10224

Mililotti, Pasquale—Continued.

La serva fatta padrona, Napoli, 1769: Paisiello.   Schatz 7671
I sposi perseguitati, Napoli, 1782: Piccinni.   Schatz 8140
Le stravaganze del conte, Napoli, 1772: Cimarosa.   Schatz 1986
Il trionfo de' pupilli oppressi, Napoli, 1782: Rispoli.   Schatz 8813
Il tutore burlato.   A. T. of his La finta semplice: Insanguine.
Il vagabondo fortunato, Napoli, 1773: Piccinni.   Schatz 8142
I viaggiatori, Napoli, 1776: Piccinni.   Schatz 8134
I viluppi amorosi, Napoli, 1778: Tarchi.   Schatz 10227

Miller, James.

The coffee-house, London, 1737: Burgess and Carey.   Longe 59
An hospital for fools, London, 1739: Arne.   ML 50.2.H7

Milon, L. J.

Héro et Léandre, Paris, an VIII (1799): unknown.   ML 52.2.H3

Milton, John.

Comus, London, 1738, 2d ed. (with Dalton's alterations):
     Arne.   ML 48.M2E
Comus, London, 1738, 3d ed.: Arne.   Longe 40
Comus (J. Bell, British theatre, London, 1791–97, v. 2).
     (Dalton's version.): Arne.   PR 1241.B4
Comus (Collection of the most esteemed farces, Edinburgh,
     1792, t. iv).   (Colman's abridged version): Arne.   Schatz 11753D

Minato, *conte* **Niccolò.**

Antioco, Venetia, 1658: Cavalli.   Schatz 1717
Aristomene Messenio, Vienna (1670): Sances.   Schatz 9367
Artemisia, Venetia, 1656: Cavalli.   Schatz 1730
La caduta di Elio Seiano, Venetia, 1667: Sartorio.   Schatz 9492
Chilonida, Vienna d'Austria (1710): M. A. Ziani.   Schatz 11204
La conquista dell vello d'oro, Reggio, 1717: M. A. Bononcini. Schatz 1207
Creso, Vienna (1678): Draghi.   ML 50.2.C8D7
Dalisa, Venezia (1730): Hasse.   (Text altered by Lalli.)   Schatz 4577
Die durch die tugend gestuerzte wueterey, Wienn (1697).
     Tr. of his La tirannide abbattuta dalla virtù: Draghi.   Schatz 2804
Elena, Venetia, 1659: Cavalli.   Schatz 1746
Il fuoco eterno custodito dalle Vestali, Vienna d'Austria,
     1674: Draghi.   ML 50.2.F89D7
Der gedultige Socrates, Hamburg (1721): Telemann.   (A Tr.
     of the above's "La patienza di Socrate con due moglie.")   Schatz 10261
Das gelaechter des Democritus.   Tr. of his Le risa di Demo-
     crito, Wien (1737).   Schatz 8200
La gemma Ceraunia d'Ulissipone hora Lisbona, Heydelberga,
     1687: Moratelli.   ML 50.2.G25
La generosità di Tiberio, Venezia, 1729: Lapis and Cordans.   Schatz 5431
L'Iffide greca, Venezia, 1722: Scarpari.   Schatz 9561
Iphide Greca.   O. T. of his Iphis auss Gricchen-Land:
     Draghi.
L'Iffide greca, Venezia, 1722: Scarpari.   Schatz 9561
Kriegs-liste dess Bias, Wienn, 1682.   Tr. of his Gli strata-
     gemi di Biante: Draghi.   Schatz 2802
La lanterna di Diogene, Vienna (1674): Draghi.   Schatz 2798
Leonida in Tegea, Venetia, 1676: Draghi (retouched by M. A.
     Ziani).   Schatz 2799
Leonida zu Tegea, Wienn, 1670: Draghi.   Tr. of the above.   Schatz 2800

Minato, *conte* **Niccolò**—Continued.

Mutio Scevola, Venetia, 1665: Cavalli.	Schatz 1739
Il Muzio Scevola, Napoli, 1698: A. Scarlatti(?)	Schatz 9528
L'Orimonte, Venetia, 1650: Cavalli.	Schatz 1723
Il Pompeo, Genova, 1691: Perti.	Schatz 7958
Il Pompeo, Ravenna, 1685: probably Scarlatti.	ML 48.A5 v.3
Pompeo Magno, Venetia, 1666: Cavalli.	Schatz 1732
La prosperità di Elio Seiano, Venetia, 1667: Sartorio.	Schatz 9486
Il ratto delle Sabine, Vienna d'Austria (1724): Draghi.	ML 50.2.R28D7
Le risa di Democrito—Das gelaechter des Democritus, Wien, 1737: Pistocchi.	Schatz 8200
Scipione Africano, Venetia, 1664: Cavalli.	Schatz 1741
Scipione Africano, Venetia, 1678: Cavalli and Viviani.	Schatz 1754
Scipione Affricano, Roma, 1671: A. Scarlatti.	Schatz 9537
Seleuco, Venetia, 1668: Sartorio.	Schatz 9487
Gli stratagemi di Biante: Draghi. O. T. of their Kriegs-liste dess Bias.	
Sulpitia, Vienna d'Austria (1697): Draghi.	Schatz 2803
La tirannide abbattuta dalla virtù: Draghi. O. T. of their Die durch die tugend gestuerzte wueterey.	
Xerse, Venetia, 1654: Cavalli.	Schatz 1743
Il Xerse, Palermo, 1658: Cavalli.	ML 50.2.X3C2

Minelli, Andrea.

La forza vinta dall' onore, Venezia, 1703: Le Mixte.	Schatz 5486

Missoli, Marc Antonio.

Il compimento di quattro desideri, ballet. *See* Anfossi's Ezio.
L'origine degli amori di Marc Antonio nell' arrivo di Cleopatra in Tarso, ballet. *See* Anfossi's Ezio.

Mitchell, Joseph.

The highland fair or Union of the clans, London, 1731: ballad opera.	ML 50.5.H43

Moeller, Heinrich Ferdinand.

Die zigeuner, n. i., 1778: Kaffka.	Schatz 4988

Moissy, N. Moulier de.

La nouvelle école de femmes, Paris, 1770: Philidor.	Schatz 8021

Molière. Poquelin, Jean Baptiste, *known as*

Le carnaval (Recueil général des opéra, t. i, Paris, 1703) (with Quinault and Lully): Lully.	Schatz 5765
Les festes de l'Amour et de Bacchus (Recueil général des opéra, t. i, Paris, 1703) (supposed joint-author with Quinault): Lully.	Schatz 5766
The mock doctor or The dumb lady cur'd, 4th éd., London, 1753. Tr. of his Le medecin malgré lui by Fielding: ballad opera.	ML 50.5.M58
The mock doctor or The dumb lady cur'd, London, 1761.	ML 50.5.M6
The mock doctor or The dumb lady cur'd (Collection of The most esteemed farces, Edinburgh, 1792, t. i).	Schatz 11753A

Moline, Pierre Louis.

Ariane dans l'isle de Naxos, Paris, 1792: Edelmann.	ML 50.2.A74E3
Le duel comique, Paris, 1776: Paisiello. French version of the latter's Il duello.	ML 50.2.D8P19
Le duel comique (Paris) 1777. Tr. of Paisiello's Il duello (Lorenzi) with add. music by Méreaux.	ML 50.2.D8P2

Moline, Pierre Louis—Continued.

L'inconnue persécutée, Paris, 1776. French version of Anfossi's L'incognita perseguitata (Petrosellini).   ML 50.2.I55A6

Orphée et Euridice, Paris, 1775 (Tr. of Calsabigi's Orfeo e Euridice): Gluck.   ML 50.2.O7G45

Orphée et Euridice, Paris, 1782: Gluck.   ML 48.M2H

Roger-Bontems et Javotte, Paris, 1775 (with d'Orvigny). Parody of Gluck's Orphée et Euridice.   SCHATZ 11510

Monari, Vincenzio.

Il giardiniere convinto da Amore, ballet. *See* Galuppi's L'amante di tutte.

Il quadro movibile, ballet. *See* Galuppi's L'amante di tutte.

Il Svizzero ingannato, ballet. *See* Zannetti's Le cognate in contesa.

Il Tartaro generoso, ballet. *See* Zannetti's Le cognate in contesa.

Moncrif, François Augustin Paradis de.

L'empire de l'amour (Recueil général des opéra, Paris, 1739, t. xv): Brassac.   SCHATZ 1308

Erosine (Paris) 1765 (Journal des spectacles, t. ii, 1766): P. Berton.   ML 48.J7

Erosine: P. Berton. Entrée in Les fêtes liriques, Paris, 1766.   ML 52.2.F46

Ismène, n. i. (1759): Rebel and Francoeur.   ML 50.2.I7R22

Ismène (Paris) 1769: Rebel and Francoeur.   ML 50.2.I7R24

La sibille (Paris) 1770: Dauvergne.   ML 50.2.S59D2

Mondonville, Jean Joseph Cassanea de.

L'Amour et Psyché (printed together with Bacchus et Érigone, n. i., n. d.; text also attributed to Voisenon): author.   ML 52.2.B105M6

Daphnis et Alcimaduro, Paris, 1778: author.   ML 50.2.D25M6

Mondorge, Antoine Gaultier de.

Les fêtes d'Hébé ou Les talens lyriques (Paris) 1739: Rameau.   ML 52.2.F4R1

Les fêtes d'Hébé ou Les talens lyriques, Paris, 1756: Rameau.   ML 52.2.F4R2

Moniglia, Giovanni Andrea.

Delle poesie dramatiche di Giovann' Andrea Moniglia . . . parte prima.

Firenze, Vincenzio Vangelisti, 1689. xiv, 629 p. 25 pl. 24 cm.   ML 49.A2M7

— parte seconda.

Firenze, Cesare e Francesco Bindi, 1690. 1 p. l., ii, [2], 504, [1] p. 24 cm.   ML 49.A2M7

The third part (1690) is not in our set, but the majority of the texts appear to be in our collection in detached form. They are: La serva nobile, p. 185–298; La vedova, p. 299–403; Tacere ed amare, p. 405–504; Il conte di Cutro, p. 509–616.

L'amor di figlia, Venezia, 1718 (with alterations by Domenico Lalli. O. T. La pietà di Sabina): Porta.   SCHATZ 8395

Il conte di Cutro, n. i., n. d. (detached copy): Cattani.   SCHATZ 1712

Enea in Italia (Poesie drammatiche, parte prima, Firenze, 1689): Melani.   ML 49.A2M7

L'Ercole in Tebe, Venetia, 1671 (partly rewritten by Aureli): Boretti.   SCHATZ 1222

Ercole in Tebe, Fiorenza, 1661 (with "Descrizione," 23 cm): Melani.   ML 50.2.E6M2

Ercole in Tebe, Fiorenza, 1661 (without "Descrizione," 16½ cm): Melani.   SCHATZ 6290

Moniglia, Giovanni Andrea—Continued.

Ercole in Tebe (Poesie drammatiche, parte prima, Firenze, 1689): Melani.   ML 49.A2M7

L'Ercole trionfante, Parma, 1688 (his "Ercole in Tebe" revised by Aurelio Aureli): Sabadini (with, it seems, a few arias by Antonio Boretti from the earlier version).   Schatz 9196

Il Germanico al Reno (Poesie drammatiche, seconda parte, Firenze, 1690): unknown.   ML 49.A2M7

La Giocasta (Poesie drammatiche, seconda parte, Firenze, 1690): Cesti.   ML 49.A2M7

Giocasta, regina d'Armenia, Venetia, 1677 (altered by unknown author, additions by Giacomo Castoreo): Grossi.   Schatz 4217

Giocasta—Giocasta, Dusseldorf, 1696 (with alterations): Wilderer and Krafft.   Schatz 11014

Gneo Marzio Coriolano (Poesie drammatiche, parte prima, Firenze, 1689): Cattani.   ML 49.A2M7

L'Hipermestra, Firenze, 1658: Cavalli.   ML 50.2.H38C2

Ifianassa e Melampo (Poesie drammatiche, parte prima, Firenze, 1689): Legrenzi.   ML 49.A2M7

L'Ipermestra (Poesie drammatiche, parte prima, Firenze, 1689): Cavalli. L. T. of their L'Hipermestra.   ML 49.A2M7

Il mondo festeggiante (Poesie drammatiche, parte prima, Firenze, 1689): Anglesi.   ML 49.A2M7

Il pellegrino (Poesie drammatiche, seconda parte, Firenze, 1690): Cattani.   ML 49.A2M7

La pietà di Sabina (Poesie drammatiche, seconda parte, Firenze, 1690): Cattani.   ML 49.A2M7

La pietà di Sabina. O. T. of his and Domenico Lalli's L'amor di figlia: Porta.

Quinto Lucrezio proscritto, Firenze, 1681: Cattani.   Schatz 1713

Quinto Lucrezio proscritto (Poesie drammatiche, prima parte, Firenze, 1689): Cattani.   ML 49.A2M7

Il ritorno d'Ulisse (Poesie drammatiche, prima parte, Firenze, 1689): Melani.   ML 49.A2M7

La schiava fortunata, Venetia, 1674 ("ritoccata" by Corradi): Cesti and M. A. Ziani.   Schatz 1782

La Semiramide (Poesie drammatiche, seconda parte, Firenze, 1690): Cesti.   ML 49.A2M7

La Semiramide, Venetia (with alterations) 1671: P. A. Ziani. Schatz 11223

La serva nobile, n. i., n. d. (detached copy): Anglesi.   Schatz 288

Tacere ed amare, n. i., n. d. (detached copy): Melani.   Schatz 6288

Il Teseo (Poesie drammatiche, seconda parte, Firenze, 1690): unknown (Bontempi?).   ML 49.A2M7

Il tiranno di Colco, Firenze, 1688: Pagliardi.   Schatz 7585

Il tiranno di Colco (Poesie drammatiche, seconda parte, Firenze, 1690): Pagliardi.   ML 49.A2M7

La vedova, n. i., n. d. (detached copy): Melani.   Schatz 6289

Montecatini, Giambattista.

Roma liberata dalla signoria de' re, Lucca, 1760: Puccini.
See M. Curzio in Title catalogue.

Monteiro, Jozé Procopio.

O amor conjugal, Lisboa: Portugal.   Schatz 8434

Monticini, Giovanni.

Abduramel, ballet: Nucci. *See* Nasolini's Melinda.

La fata Urgella, ballet. *See* Gnecco's Lo sposo di tre.

L'infausto matrimonio, ballet: Nucci. *See* Portugal's La pazza giornata.

Li pastori d'Arcadia, ballet: *See* Gnecco's Lo sposo di tre.

La Pescatrice in Jassa, ballet: Trento. *See* Gardi's Il contra-voeleno.

Progne e Filomene osia Tereo, tiranno di Nasora, ballet: *See* Nasolini's Timoleone.

Il trionfo di Gustavo rè di Svezia, ballet. *See* Paër's Il nuovo Figaro.

Il trionfo di Gustavo rè di Svezia, ballet. *See* Rugali's Il doppio equivoco.

La vendetta d'amore, ballet: Trento. *See* Paër's La testa riscaldata.

Monvel. Boutet, Jacques Marie, *better known as*

Alexis et Justine, Toulouse, 1785: Dezède.	ML 50.2.A53D3
Ambroise ou Voilà ma journée, Paris, an VII [1798–1799]: Dalayrac.	Schatz 2328
Blaise et Babet ou La suite des Trois fermiers, Paris, 1784: Dezède.	Schatz 2514
Blaise et Babet ou La suite des Trois fermiers, Paris, 1784: Dezède.	Schatz 11689
Die drei pächter, Wien, 1785. Tr. of his Les trois fermiers: Dezède.	Schatz 2524
L'élève de l'amour. A. T. of his Sargines: Dalayrac.	
L'erreur d'un moment, ou La suite de Julie, Paris, 1773 (63 p.): Dezède.	Yudin PQ
L'erreur d'un moment, ou La suite de Julie, Paris, 1773 (39 p.): Dezède.	Schatz 2517
Julie, Paris, 1773: Dezède.	Schatz 2520
Julie, Paris, 1775: Dezede.	Yudin PQ
Julie, Frankfurt am Mayn, 1774. Tr. of this.	Schatz 2521
Der kurze irrthum, n. i., 1790. Tr. of his L'erreur d'un moment: Dezède.	Schatz 2518
Philipp und Georgette, Hamburg, 1798. Tr. of his Philippe et Georgette: Dalayrac.	Schatz 2372
Raollo, signore di Crequi, Lisbona, 1795. Tr. of his Raoul, sire de Créqui: Dalayrac.	Schatz 2376
Raoul, sire de Créqui, Paris, 1790: Dalayrac.	ML 50.2.R24D3
Die reue vor der that, Frankfurt und Leipzig, 1783. Tr. of his L'erreur d'un moment: Dezède.	Schatz 2519
Rudolph von Creki, Riga, 1792. Tr. of his Raoul, sire de Créqui: Dalayrac.	Schatz 2374
Sargines ou L'élève de l'amour, Paris, 1789: Dalayrac.	Schatz 2380
La suite de Julie. A. T. of his L'erreur d'un moment: Dezède.	
Töffel und Dortchen, Hamburg, 1788. Tr. of his Blaise et Babet: Dezède.	Schatz 2515
Les trois fermiers, Paris, 1777: Dezède.	ML 50.2.T83D2
Les trois fermiers, Nouv. éd., Paris, 1781: Dezède.	ML 50.2.T83D3
Les trois fermiers, Paris, 1782: Dezède.	Schatz 2523

Monvel. Boutet, Jacques Marie, *better known as*—Continued.
Voilà ma journée.   A. T. of his Ambroise: Dalayrac.
Was einem recht, ist dem andern billig, Frankfurt und Leip-
zig, 1783.   Tr. of his Julie: Dezède.   SCHATZ 2522

Morani, Lorenzo.
Farnace, Venezia, 1703: Caldara   SCHATZ 1493

Morbilli, *duca* **di Sant Angelo a Frosolone.**
La disfatta di Dario, Alessandria (1779) (reduced by Giuseppe
Casali): Ferrero.   SCHATZ 3081
La disfatta di Dario, Torino (1774): Masi.   SCHATZ 6062
La disfatta di Dario, Firenze, 1776: Paisiello.   SCHATZ 7664
La disfatta di Dario, Genova (1782): Paisiello.   SCHATZ 7664a
La disfatta di Dario, Venezia, 1778: Traetta.   SCHATZ 10409

Morel de Chefdeville, Etienne.
Alexandre aux Indes, Paris, 1783: Méreaux.   SCHATZ 6310
La caravana del Cairo, Milano (1795).   Tr. of his and the comte
de Provence's La caravane du Caire: Grétry.   SCHATZ 4200
La caravane du Caire (Paris) 1783 (together with the comte de
Provence, later Louis XVIII): Grétry.   SCHATZ 4141
Panurge dans l'isle des lanternes (Paris) 1785 (with the comte
de Provence): Grétry.   ML 50.2.P25G7
Thémistocle (Paris), 1785: Philidor.   ML 50.2.T4P3
Thésée.   *See* Quinault.

Moretti, Ferdinando.
Ademira, Napoli, 1789: P. Guglielmi.   SCHATZ 4231
Antioco, Milano (1788): Tarchi.   SCHATZ 10234
Alsinda, Milano (1785): Zingarelli.   SCHATZ 11264
Ariarate, Torino (1789): G. Giordani.   SCHATZ 3842
Ariarate, Palermo (1787): Tarchi.   SCHATZ 10213
L'Arminio, Mantova (1785): Tarchi.   SCHATZ 10230
Il conte di Saldagna, Milano (1787): Tarchi.   SCHATZ 10216
Il conte di Saldagna, Venezia, 1795: Zingarelli.   SCHATZ 11242
Idalide, Torino (1786): Rispoli.   SCHATZ 8814
L'Idalide o sia La vergine del sole, Firenze, 1788: Sarti.   SCHATZ 9444
Ifigenia in Aulide, Torino (1788): Cherubini.   SCHATZ 1838
Ifigenia in Aulide, Milano (1788): Cherubini.   SCHATZ 11684
Ifigenia in Aulide, Milano (1787): Zingarelli.   SCHATZ 11250
Ifigenia in Aulide, Barcellona (1799): Zingarelli.   ML 48.A5 v.16
La vendetta di Nino, Napoli, 1790: Bianchi.   SCHATZ 985
La vergine del sole.   A. T. of his L'Idalide: Sarti.

Morgan, Mac Namara.
Florizel and Perdita or The sheep-shearing (Collection of the
most esteemed farces, Edinburgh, 1792): Arne. *See* The
sheep-shearing.   SCHATZ 11753A
The sheep-shearing or Florizel and Perdita, Dublin, 1755:
Arne.   LONGE 201

Morosini, Marco.
Il Don Chissiot della Mancia, Venetia, 1680: Sajon.   SCHATZ 9264
L'Ermelinda, Venetia, 1679: Sajon.   SCHATZ 9263

Morselli, Adriano.
Amulio e Numitore, Venetia, 1689: Tosi.   SCHATZ 10375
Apio Claudio, Venetia, 1683: Martini, G. M.   SCHATZ 6033

Morselli, Adriano—Continued.

Candaule rè di Lidia, Napoli, 1706: Sarro.	SCHATZ 9417
Candaule, Venetia, 1680: P. A. Ziani.	SCHATZ 11219
Carlo il Grande, Venetia, 1688: Gabrieli.	SCHATZ 3397
Dario, Venetia, 1685. L. T. of his L'incoronazione di Dario: Freschi.	SCHATZ 3357
Etio. A. T. of his L'innocenza risorta: P. A. Ziani.	
Falaride, tiranno d'Agrigento, Venetia, 1684: Bassani.	SCHATZ 634
La forza dell' amicizia (Mantova, 1700): unknown. L. T. of his Pirro e Demetrio.	SCHATZ 11334
Il Gordiano, Venetia, 1688: Gabrieli.	SCHATZ 3404
L'Ibraim sultano, Venetia, 1692: C. F. Pollaroli.	SCHATZ 8296
L'incoronazione di Dario, Venetia, 1684: Freschi.	SCHATZ 3350
L'incoronazione di Đario, Venezia, 1717: Vivaldi.	SCHATZ 10771
L'incoronazione di Serse, Venetia, 1691: Tosi.	SCHATZ 10376
L'innocenza risorta overo Etio, Venetia, 1683: P. A. Ziani.	SCHATZ 11224
Il Mauritio, Venetia, 1687: Gabrieli.	SCHATZ 3399
Il Maurizio, Bergamo, 1689: Gabrieli.	ML 50.2.M47G2
La pace fra Tolomeo e Seleuco, Venetia, 1691: C. F. Pollaroli.	SCHATZ 8308
Pirro e Demetrio, Venetia, 1690: Tosi.	SCHATZ 10378
Pyrrhus and Demetrius, London, 1709. Tr. of his Pirro e Demetrio with additions by McSwiney: Scarlatti and Haym.	ML 50.2.P95
Il Seleuco, Roma, 1693: C. F. Pollaroli. L. T. of their La pace fra Tolomeo e Seleuco.	SCHATZ 8309
Temistocle in bando, Venetia, 1683: Zannettini.	SCHATZ 11147
Teodora Augusta, Venetia, 1686: Gabrieli.	SCHATZ 3401
I tre difensori della patria, Venezia, 1729: Pescetti. L. T. of his Tullo Ostilio.	SCHATZ 7961
Tullo Ostilio, Roma, 1694 (much altered by Stampiglia): G. B. Bononcini.	SCHATZ 1201
Tullo Ostilio, Venezia, 1740: Pescetti.	SCHATZ 7962
Tullo Ostilio, Venezia, 1685: M. A. Ziani.	SCHATZ 11195

Morton, Thomas.

The children in the wood, London, 1794: Arnold.	LONGE 233
The children in the wood, New York, 1795: Arnold (additions by Carr).	PR 1241.D7 vol.4)
Columbus or A world discovered, London, 1792.	E 120.M88
Columbus or The discovery of America, Boston, 1794: Reinagle.	E 120.M885
Zorinski, London, 1795: Arnold.	LONGE 232

Moscardini, Paolo.

La Didone, Bologna, 1656: Mattioli.	SCHATZ 6102

Moscheni, Bernardo.

L'amore della patria, Lucca, 1675. *See* M. Curzio in Title catalogue.

Moscheni, Bernardino.

Il Catone, Lucca, 1690. *See* M. Curzio in Title catalogue.	
La Doralba, Lucca, 1683: unknown.	ML 50.2.D618
Il Fetonte, Lucca, 1675. *See* M. Curzio in Title catalogue.	

Motteux, Peter Anthony.

Arsinoe, queen of Cyprus, London, 1705: Clayton. (Supposed Tr. of Stanzani's L'Arsinoe text.)   ML 50.2.A78

Arsinoe, queen of Cyprus, London, 1707: Clayton.   Longe 106 and 177

Hercules (3d act of "The novelty," London, 1697): Eccles.   Longe 127

The island princess or The generous Portuguese, London, 1724: D. Purcell, J. Clarke, and R. Leveridge.   Longe 75

The loves of Mars and Venus, London, 1722: Finger and Eccles.   Longe 205

Thomyris queen of Scythia, London, 1719: pasticcio from A. Scarlatti, G. B. Bononcini, Pepusch, etc.   Longe 200

Mottley, John.

Penelope, London, 1728 (with Cooke, Th.): ballad opera.   Longe 152

Moultrie, *Rev*. George.

False and true, London, 1798: Arnold.   Longe 249

Muazzo, Francesco.

Paride, Venezia, 1720: Orlandini.   Schatz 7345

Muechler, Friedrich Karl.

Psyche, Berlin, 1789: Wessely.   Schatz 10990

Müller, Johann Samuel.

Don Quixotte in dem Mohrengebuerge, Hamburg, 1722. Tr. of Conti's Don Chisciotte in Sierra Morena (Zeno and Pariati).   Schatz 2195

Mistevojus (Hamburg, 1726): mainly Keiser.   Schatz 5103

Pharao und Joseph (Hamburg, 1728. Free Tr. of Zeno's Gianguir): Caldara.   Schatz 1483

Polidorus (Hamburg) 1735 (Tr. of Piovene's Polidoro): Graun.   Schatz 4110

Musaeus, Carl August.

Das gaertner-maedchen, Weimar, 1771: Wolf.   Schatz 11079

Muzzarelli, Antonio.

Adelasia riconosciuta, ballet. *See* Cherubini's Mesenzio rè d'Etruria.

L'amante del studio, ballet. *See* Bianchi's L'orfano cinese.

Gli amori di Clodio e Pompea, ballet: Trento. *See* Bianchi's Alonso e Cora.

Gli amori d'Igor primo Czar di Moscovia, ballet. *See* Cimarosa's L'impresario in angustie (Milano, 1789).

Gli amori d'Igor, primo Zar di Moscovia, ballet: Trento. *See* Tarchi's Ifigenia in Tauride.

Assedio e liberazione di Vienna, ballet. *See* Rust's Artaserse.

Le avventure d'Ircana, ballet: Stabingher. *See* Salieri's La fiera di Venezia.

Le baruffe chiozzote, ballet. *See* Robuschi's Castrini, padre e figlio.

Il Beverlei o sia Il giouocatore inglese, ballet: Dutillieu. *See* Gardi's Il nuovo convitato di pietra.

Il capitano Cook all' isola Ottaiti, ballet. *See* Cimarosa's L'impresario in angustie (Milano, 1789).

La cappriciosa umiliata, ballet. *See* Anfossi's Le gelosie fortunate.

Il Gonzalvo, ballet. *See* Anfossi's Le gelosie fortunate.

Muzzarelli, Antonio—Continued.

La guerra del MDCLXXXIII fra i Turchi e gli Austriaci, ballet. *See* Rust's Artaserse.

L'impostore punito, ballet: Capuzzi. *See* Robuschi's Castrini, padre e figlio.

Ines de Castro, ballet. *See* Zingarelli's Antigono.

La letteraria fanatica, ballet. *See* Cimarosa's L'impresario in angustie (Milano, 1789).

La liberazione di Castruccio Castracane, ballet. *See* Cimarosa's L'Olimpiade.

La locandiera vivace, ballet. *See* Gardi's Il nuovo convitato di pietra.

La sconfitta delle Amazoni, ballet: Stabingher. *See* Salieri's La fiera di Venezia.

Lo spazzacamino principe, ballet. *See* Bernardini's La donna di spirito.

Ulisse al Monte Etna, ballet. *See* Bianchi's L'orfano cinese.

Nabbes, Thomas.

The springs glory, a maske, London, 1639: unknown.   ML 52.2.S76

Naigeon.

Les Chinois. *See* Favart.

Napoli, Pietro di.

La furba burlata, Napoli, 1762: Piccinni, Logroscino and Insanguine.   SCHATZ 8159

I furbi burlati, Napoli, 1773: Piccinni. (Text=La furba burlata.)   SCHATZ 8127

Natta d'Alfiano, *marchese,* **Giacomo.**

L'Orode, Milano, 1675: Forni.   SCHATZ 3301

Neefe, Christian Gottlob.

Der baum der Diana. Tr. of Martin y Soler's L'arbore di Diana (Da Ponte).   SCHATZ 6003

Die liebe unter den handwerksleuten, Hamburg, 1782. Tr. of Gassmann's L'amore artigiano (Goldoni).   SCHATZ 3612

Melide oder Der schiffer, Frankfurt, 1778 (with Grossmann). Tr. of Philidor's Mélide ou Le navigateur (Fenouillot de Falbaire de Quingey).   SCHATZ 8034

Der schiffer. A. T. of his and Grossmann's Melide: Philidor.

Trofons zauberhoele, Riga, 1794. Tr. of Salieri's La grotta di Trofonio (Casti).   SCHATZ 9299

Das urtheil des Midas, Mitau, 1783. Tr. of Grétry's Le jugement de Midas (d'Hèle).   SCHATZ 4164

Neri, Giovanni Battista.

Amar vendetta, Venezia, 1702. L. T. of his La Clotilde: Ruggeri.   SCHATZ 9135

Gl'amici rivali, Venezia, (1714): C. F. Pollaroli. L. T. of their L'enigma disciolto.   SCHATZ 8283

Amor indovino, Venezia, 1726: Cortona.   SCHATZ 2263

Basilio rè Doriente [!], Venetia, 1696: Navara.   SCHATZ 7065

La Clotilde, Venetia, 1696: Ruggeri.   SCHATZ 9135

L'enigma disciolto, Brescia (1708): C. F. Pollaroli.   SCHATZ 8282

L'Erifile, Venezia, 1697: Ariosti.   SCHATZ 319

Il Gige in Lidia, Bologna, 1683: Gabrieli.   SCHATZ 3398

Nesselrode zu Hugenboet, F. G., *freiherr,* **von.**
    Julie oder Die dankbare tochter, Regensburg, 1780: Kuer-
        zinger.   Schatz 5339
    Minervens ankunft bey den Musen (Regensburg, 1780): Kuer-
        zinger.   Schatz 5340

Neumann, Johann Leopold.
    Amphion, Leipzig, n. d.: Naumann.   Schatz 7038
    Cora, Leipzig, 1781: Naumann.   Schatz 7042
    Cora, Dresden, 1781: Naumann.   Schatz 7042a
    Cora, Danzig, n. d.: Naumann. (These are free translations
        of Adlerbeth's "Cora och Alonzo.")   Schatz 7042b

Neusinger, Caj.
    Demophon. Tr. of Jommelli's Demofoonte, Stutgart, 1764
        (Metastasio).   Schatz 4852

Neville, Edward.
    Plymouth in an uproar, London, 3d éd., 1779: Dibdin.   Longe 153

Newcastle, William, *duke of.*
    The varietie, London, 1649.   PR2729.N5

Nidastio Pegeate, P. A.
    Giunone placata, Roma, 1762: Aurisicchio.   ML50.2.G44A8

Niemeyer, August Hermann.
    Abraham auf Moria, n. i., 1779: Rolle.   Schatz 11392

Nieri, Vincenzio.
    Lucinda, Parma, 1713: unknown.   ML50.2.L83

Nivildo Amarinzio. *Arcadian name of* Gioacchino Pizzi.

Noble.
    The two harlequins, London, 1718. Tr. of the elder Ricco-
        boni's text Les deux arlequins.   Longe 262

Nolfi, Vincenzo.
    Il Bellerofonte, Venetia, 1642: Sacrati.   Schatz 9252

Noris, Matteo.
    Alfonso Primo, Venetia, 1694: C. F. Pollaroli.   Schatz 8268
    L'amore figlio del merito, Venetia, 1694: M. A. Ziani.   Schatz 11179
    Amore inamorato, Venetia, 1686: Pallavicino.   Schatz 7718
    L'amore verso la patria, Die liebe gegen das vaterland oder
        Der sterbende Cato, Hamburg (1715): Keiser. Tr. of his
        text Catone Uticense.   Schatz 5075
    Astiage, Venetia, 1677. (Modernized Apolloni's text):
        Viviani: Schatz 10783
    Attila, Venetia, 1672: P. A. Ziani.   Schatz 11213
    Bassiano, overo Il maggior impossibile, Venetia, 1682: Palla-
        vicino.   Schatz 7720
    Bassiano overo Il maggior impossibile, Napoli, 1694: A. Scar-
        latti.   Schatz 9533
    Berengario rè d'Italia, Venezia, 1709: Polani.   Schatz 8248
    Carlo re d'Italia, Venetia, 1682: Pallavicino.   Schatz 7733
    Carlo re d'I alia, Venetia, 1682: Pallavicino.   Schatz 7733
    Catone Uticense, Venetia, 1701: C. F. Pollaroli.   Schatz 8276
    Il cieco d'acuta vista. A. T. of his Il Licurgo: C. F. Pollaroli.
    Il colore fà la regina, Venetia, 1700: C. F. Pollaroli.   Schatz 8277
    Il delirio comune, per la incostanza de' genii, Venezia, 1701:
        C. F. Pollaroli.   Schatz 8280

Noris, Matteo—Continued.

Il demone amante, overo Giugurta, Venetia, 1686: C. F. Pollaroli.　Schatz 8281

Diocletiano, Venetia, 1685: Pallavicino.　Schatz 7721

Dionisio overo La virtù trionfante del vizio, Venetia, 1681: Franceschini and Partenio.　Schatz 3319

Domitiano, Venezia, 1673: Boretti.　ML 48.M2 O

Domitiano, Venetia, 1673 (Seconda impressione): Boretti.　Schatz 1218

I duo [!] tiranni al soglio, Venetia, 1679: Sartorio.　Schatz 9481

La finta pazzia d'Ulisse, Venetia, 1696: M. A. Ziani.　Schatz 11186

Flavio Cuniberto, Venetia, 1682: Partenio.　Schatz 7778

Flavio Cuniberto, Firenze, 1702: Partenio.　ML 50.2.F6P2

Il furio Camillo, Bologna, 1693: Perti.　Schatz 7950

Il furio Camillo, Mantova (1700): Perti.　ML 50.2.F9P3

Galieno, Venetia, 1676: Pallavicino.　Schatz 7724

Il giorno di notte, Venezia, 1704: C. F. Pollaroli.　Schatz 8295

Giugurta.　A. T. of his Il demone amante: C. F. Pollaroli.

Il Greco in Troia, Firenze, 1688: unknown.　Schatz 11339

L'inganno trionfante in amore (partly rewritten by Ruggeri): Vivaldi.　Schatz 10772

Laodicea e Berenice, Venetia, 1695: Perti.　Schatz 7951

Licinio imperatore, Venetia, 1684: Pallavicino.　Schatz 7726

Il Licurgo, overo Il cieco d'acuta vista, Venetia, 1686: C. F. Pollaroli.　Schatz 8300

Lotario.　See also Judith, gemahlin Kayser Ludewigs des Frommen oder Die siegende unschuld.

Il maggior impossibile.　A. T. of his Bassiano: Pallavicino.

Il maggior impossibile.　A. T. of his Bassiano: A. Scarlatti.

Marcello in Siracusa, Venetia, 1670: Boretti.　Schatz 1220

Marzio Coriolano, Venetia, 1698: C. F. Pollaroli.　Schatz 8303

Nerone fatto Cesare, Venetia, 1693: Perti.　Schatz 7952

Numa Pompilio, Venetia, 1674: Pagliardi.　Schatz 7584

L'odio e l'amore, Napoli, 1704: Aldrovandini.　Schatz 136

L'odio e l'amor, Venezia, 1703: C. F. Pollaroli.　Schatz 8304

Le passioni per troppo amore, Venezia, 1713: Heinichen.　Schatz 4703

Penelope la casta, Venezia, 1716: Chelleri.　Schatz 1813

Penelope la casta, Venetia, 1685: Pallavicino.　Schatz 7730

Il rè infante, Venetia, 1683: Pallavicino.　Schatz 7734

Il rè infante, Bologna (1694): Perti.　Schatz 7953

I regii equivoci, Venezia, 1697: C. F. Pollaroli.　Schatz 8314

La regina creduta rè, Venetia, 1706: M. A. Bononcini.　Schatz 1205

Ricimero, rè de Vandali, Venetia, 1684: Pallavicino.　Schatz 7731

Il ripudio d'Ottavia, Venezia, 1699: C. F. Pollaroli.　Schatz 8315

Tito Manlio, (Venezia, 1746) (modernized by Sanvitale): Jommelli.　Schatz 4900

Tito Manlio, Firenze, 1696: C. F. Pollaroli.　Schatz 8321

Tito Manlio, Firenze, 1720: Predieri.　ML 48.A 5v.18

Totila, Venetia, 1677: Legrenzi.　Schatz 5547

Traiano, Venetia, 1684: Tosi.　Schatz 10380

Virginio consolo, Venetia, 1704: Zannettini.　Schatz 11145

La virtù trionfante del vizio.　A. T. of his Dionisio: Franceschini and Partenio.

La Zenobia, Venetia, 1666: Boretti.　Schatz 1221

North, Francis, *4th earl of Guilford.*

The Kentish barons, London, 1791.   Longe 216

Nothnagel.

Der siegende Phaeton, Hamburg, 1702: Keiser.   Schatz 5110

Der siegreiche koenig der Gothen Alaricus, Hamburg (1702):
Schieferdecker.   Schatz 9603

Le nouveau théatre italien, ou Recueil general des comédies
représentées par les Comédiens italiens ordinaires du roi.
Nouv. éd., cor. & très-augm., & à laquelle on a joint les airs
gravês des vaudevilles à la fin de chaque volume . . .
Paris, Briasson, 1753. 10 v. plates. 19½ cm.

<small>Added t.-p., engr. Each commedy has special t.-p. and separate paging.</small>
<small>No entry made except for comedies that call conspicuously for more music
than the regular " Divertisement" and final "Vaudeville."</small>

PQ 1231.15N6

Novello de Bonis.

Fausta restituita all' impero, Roma, 1697: Perti.   Schatz 7959

Noverre, Jean George.

The works of Monsieur Noverre, tr. from the French.
*London, G. Robinson [etc., etc.] 1783. 3 v. front. (port.)
21½ cm.*

<small>Contents.—v. 1-2. An essay on the art of dancing.—v. 3. The Danaides.
Rinaldo and Armida. Adela of Ponthieu. The Graces. The Horatii
and Curiatii. Agamemnon revenged. Apelles and Campaspe. The
amours of Venus. Alceste.</small>
<small>Vol. 1 has no date on t. p. but dedication is dated April 27, 1782.</small>

GV 1787.N8

Adele di Ponthieu, ballet. *See* Borghi's Artaserse.

Admeto et Alceste, ballet. *See* Jommelli's L'Olimpiade.

Agamemnon vengé (Vienne, 1771), ballet: Starzer.   ML 52.2.A2

Amore e Psiche—Amor und Psyche, ballet: Rudolph. *See*
Jommelli's Semiramide.

Amore vincitore dell' indifferenza, ballet: Rudolph or Deller.
See Jommelli's L'isola disabitata.

Annette and Lubin, pantomime. *See* The fable of the pantomime dances.

Atalanta ed Ippomene—Atalante et Hippomène. *See* Jommelli's Demofoonte.

I capricci di Galatea, ballet. *See* Jommelli's L'Olimpiade.

Le feste persiane, ballet. *See* Jommelli's Semiramide.

Giasone e Medea, ballet. *See* Giordani's Osmane.

Les Horaces et les Curiaces, ballet. *See* P. Guglielmi's Vologeso.

Les incidents, ballet. *See* P. Guglielmi's Vologeso.

Ipermestra—Hipermenestre, ballet: Rudolph. *See* Jommelli's Demofoonte.

Medea e Giasone—Medée et Jason, ballet: Rudolph. *See* Jommelli's La Didone abbandonata.

La morte d'Ercole—Der tod des Hercules, ballet: Rudolph.
See Jommelli's Semiramide.

La morte di Licomede—La mort de Licomède, ballet: Deller.
See Jommelli's Demofoonte.

Orfeo ed Euridice—Orphée et Euridice, ballet: Deller. *See*
Jommelli's La Didone abbandonata.

Il riconoscimento inaspettato, ballet: Rudolph or Deller. *See*
Jommelli's L'isola disabitata.

Odell, Thomas.

The patron or The statesman's opera, London (1729): ballad
    opera.   Longe 262

Odingsells, Gabriel.

Bay's opera, London, 1730: ballad opera.   ML 50.5.B19

Ogelwight, Hendrik.

De schulden, Amsterdam, 1791.   Tr. of Champein's Les dettes
    (Forgeot).   Schatz 1795

De visitandines, Amsterdam, 1796.   Tr. of Devienne's Les
    visitandines (Picard).   Schatz 2563

O'Hara, Kane.

April-day, London, 1777: Arnold.   Longe 126

The golden pippin, London, 1773: partly ballad opera, partly
    music by Arne, Galuppi, Giordani and others.   Longe 26

The golden pippin (Collection of the most esteemed farces,
    Edinburgh, 1792, t. iii).   Schatz 11753C

Midas, London, 1764: ballad opera.   ML 50.2.M65

Midas, London, 1766.   Longe 46

Midas (Collection of the most esteemed farces, Edinburgh,
    1792, t. ii).   Schatz 11753B

The two misers, London, 1775: Dibdin.   Longe 32

O'Keeffe, John.

The agreeable surprise, London, 1781: Arnold.   ML 50.2.A4A7

The agreeable surprise, London, 1782: Arnold.   Longe 91

The agreeable surprise, Dublin, 1786: Arnold.   Longe 149

The agreeable surprise (Dublin, 1791): Arnold.   PR 1269.V6

The banditti or, Love's labyrinth, London, 1781: Arnold.
    O. T. of their The castle of Andalusia.   ML 50.2.B33A7

The birth-day, or, The prince of Arragon, London, 1783:
    mostly Arnold.   Longe 164

Blunders at Brighton.   A. T. of his Irish mimic: Shield.

The castle of Andalusia, London, 1783: Arnold.   L. T. of their
    The banditti, or, Love's labyrinth.   Longe 91

The castle of Andalusia, Dublin, 1783 (with additional songs
    by Tenducci): Arnold.   Longe 148

The Czar, London, 1790: Shield.   (First called The Czar
    Peter and finally The fugitive.)   Longe 204

The dead alive, Dublin, 1783: Arnold.   Longe 148

The dead alive, or The double funeral, New York, 1789:
    Arnold.   ML 50.6.D3

The double funeral.   A. T. of his The dead alive, New York,
    1789: Arnold.

The farmer, Dublin, 1788: Shield.   Longe 149

The farmer, 7th ed., London, 1789: Shield.   ML 50.2.F18S3

The farmer, London, 1791: Shield.   Schatz 7672

The farmer, Dublin, 1792: Shield.   Schatz 9866

A flight from Lapland.   A. T. of his Lord Mayor's day.

Fontainebleau or Our way in France, Dublin, 1787: Shield.   Longe 148

The fugitive.   *See* his The czar.

Harlequin forrester.   A. T. of his Merry Sherwood.

The highland reel, London, 1789 (5th ed.): Shield.   PR 1241.D7

The highland reel, Dublin, 1790: Shield.   Schatz 9869

O'Keeffe, John—Continued.

The Irish mimic or Blunders at Brighton, London, 1795: Shield.   Longe 229

Lord Mayor's day or A flight from Lapland, London, 1783: Shield.   ML 52.2.L6

Love's labyrinth. A. T. of his The banditti: Arnold.

Merry Sherwood or Harlequin forrester, London, 1795: Reeve.   Longe 254

Patrick in Prussia or Love in a camp, Dublin, 1786. L. T. of his Love in a camp or Patrick in Prussia: Shield.   Longe 148

Peeping Tom of Coventry, Dublin, 1786: Arnold.   Longe 149

Peeping Tom of Coventry (Dublin) 1787: Arnold.   Schatz 338

The poor soldier, Dublin, 1785: ballad opera, arranged and partly composed by Shield.   Longe 168

The poor soldier, Dublin, 1791.   PR 1269.V6

The prince of Arragon. A. T. of his The birth-day.

The secret enlarged. *See his* The agreeable surprise.

The Shamrock or Revels on St. Patrick's Day. O. T. of his The poor soldier: Shield.

The shamrock or The anniversary of St. Patrick. Earlier T. of his The poor soldier: Shield.

The son-in-law, Dublin, 1788: Arnold.   Longe 223

Sprigs of laurel, London, 1793: Shield.   Longe 225

Sprigs of laurel, London, 1794.   ML 50.2.S74S3

Oldmixon, *Sir* John.

Apollo turn'd stroller; or, Thereby hangs a tale, London, 1787: pasticcio from Händel and others.   Longe 102

The grove or Love's paradice, London, 1700: D. Purcell.   Longe 79

Oliveri (Olivieri), Cesare.

Atalanta, Torino (1792): G. Giordani.   Schatz 3834

Bacco ed Arianna, Torino (1784): Tarchi.   Schatz 10226

Cleopatra, Torino (1776): Monza.   Schatz 6613

Sicotencal, Pavia (1776): Colla.   Schatz 2110

Sicotencal, Torino (1776): G. M. Rutini.   Schatz 9191

Il trionfo della pace, Torino (1782): Bianchi.   Schatz 991

Il trionfo della pace, Mantova (1783): Sarti.   Schatz 9478

Zulima, Firenze (1777): G. M. Rutini.   Schatz 9189

Olivieri, Luigi.

Chi l'avrebbe mai creduto, ballet. *See* Cimarosa's Il duello per complimento.

Ernesta e Daon, ballet. *See* Cimarosa's Il duello per complimento.

Ollefen, W. van.

De minnaer standbeeld, Amsterdam, 1794. Tr. of Dalayrac's L'amant statue (Desfontaines).   Schatz 2388

Onorati, Giacomo.

L'eroe castigliano o sia Rodrigo Ecimene, ballet. *See* Zingarelli's Apelle.

Orcomeno, Cerilo, P. A. (Real name unknown.)

Amor per oro, Venezia, 1782: Gazzaniga.   Schatz 3690

Orengo, Giuseppe Maria (d').

Enea in Cartagine, Torino (1770): Colla.   Schatz 2109

Enea in Cartagine, Alessandria (1784): Monza.   Schatz 6618

Il trionfo della costanza, Torino (1769): Franchi.   Schatz 3329

Orlandi, Luigi.

 Alarico il Baltha, cioè l'Audace, rè de Gothi, Monaco (1687):
  Steffani.   Schatz 10036

 Cesare trionfante, Bologna (1694). L. T. of the next. ML 50.2.637

 Giulio Cesare trionfante, Venetia, 1682: Freschi.   Schatz 3349

 Niobe, koenigin in Thebe (Muenchen, 1688). Tr. of his
  Niobe, regina di Thebe: Steffani.   Schatz 10033

Orlandini, Andrea.

 Il sospetto senza fondamento, Firenze, 1691: unknown. Schatz 11366

Orneval, d'.

 Achmet et Almanzine. *See* Le Sage.

 L'amour marin. *See* Le Sage.

 Les amours de Nanterre (Le théâtre de la Foire, Paris, 1737,
  t. iii) (with Le Sage): Gillier.   ML 48.L2 III

 Les amours de Protée. *See* Le Sage.

 Arlequin Endymion. *See* Le Sage.

 Arlequin Hulla, ou La femme repudiée. *See* Le Sage.

 Arlequin traitant (Le théâtre de la foire, Paris, 1737, t. ii):
  Gillier.   ML 48.L2 II

 Les arrests de l'amour (Le théâtre de la foire, Paris, 1737,
  t. ii): Aubert.   ML 48.L2 I

 Les comediens corsaires. *See* Le Sage.

 Le corsaire de Salé. *See* Le Sage.

 Les couplets en procès. *See* Le Sage.

 Les desesperés. *See* Le Sage.

 L'enchanteur Mirliton. *See* Le Sage.

 Les enragez. *See* Le Sage.

 L'esperance. *See* Le Sage.

 La forêt de Dodone. *See* Le Sage.

 Les funerailles de la Foire. *See* Le Sage.

 La grand-mère amoureuse. *See* Fuzelier.

 L'indifférence. *See* Le Sage.

 L'industrie. *See* Le Sage.

 L'isle des Amazones. *See* Le Sage.

 Le jeune vieillard. *See* Le Sage.

 Le jugement de Paris (Le théâtre de la foire, Paris, 1737, t. iii):
  Gillier.   ML 48.L2 III

 Le monde renversé. *See* Le Sage.

 L'ombre du cocher poète. *See* Le Sage.

 L'opera-comique assiegé. *See* Le Sage.

 Les pelerins de la Mecque. *See* Le Sage.

 La Penelope moderne. *See* Le Sage.

 Pierrot Romulus ou Le ravisseur poli. *See* Le Sage.

 La princesse de la Chine. *See* Le Sage.

 Le rappel de la Foire à la vie. *See* Le Sage.

 Le ravisseur poli. A. T. of his Pierrot Romulus.

 Le régiment de la Calotte. *See* Le Sage.

 La reine du Barostan. *See* Le Sage.

 Le remouleur d'amour. *See* Le Sage.

 Roger de Sicile. *See* Le Sage.

 Les routes du monde. *See* Le Sage.

 La sauvagesse. *See* Le Sage.

 Sophie et Sigismond. *See* Le Sage.

 Les spectacles malades. *See* Le Sage.

Orneval, d'.—Continued.

La statue merveilleuse. *See* Le Sage.

Le temple de mémoire. *See* Le Sage.

Les trois comères. *See* Le Sage.

Zemine et Almanzor. *See* Le Sage.

Ortanio. *Arcadian name of* Lalli, Domenico (*pseud. of* Biancardi, Sebastiano).

Orvigny, d'.

Roger—Bontems et Javotte, Paris, 1775 (with Moline). Parody of Gluck's Orphée et Euridice. SCHATZ 11510

Osiander.

Berenice e Lucilla overo L'amar per virtù—Berenice und Lucilla, oder Das tugendhaffte lieben, Darmstadt (1710): Graupner. SCHATZ 4119

Oswald, John (*real name of* Sylvester Otway).

The humours of John Bull, n. i., n. d. (detached copy, 1789). LONGE 323

Ottoboni, Pietro, *cardinal.*

Il Colombo, overo L'India scoperta, Roma, 1690: author. SCHATZ 7371

Carlo Magno, Roma, 1729: Costanzi. SCHATZ 2277

La Statira, Roma, 1690: A. Scarlatti. SCHATZ 9536

Ottolini, Alessandro.

Lucca liberata, Lucca, 1787. *See* M. Curzio in Title catalogue.

Otway, Sylvester. *See* James Oswald.

P. F., *abbate, P. A.*

Il D. Tifone, Roma, 1751: Quagliattini. ML 50.2.D595Q2

Paganicesa, Carlo.

La caduta di Leone, imperator d'Oriente, Venezia, 1732: Paganelli. SCHATZ 7571

L'Egeste, Venezia (1727): Cortona. SCHATZ 2265

Nel perdono la vendetta, Venezia, 1728: Porta. SCHATZ 8384

Romilda, Venezia (1731): Cordans. SCHATZ 2229

Paganicesa, Giovanni Carlo.

La pastorella al soglio (Venezia, 1751): Latilla. SCHATZ 5465

Paglia, Francesco Maria.

Il prigioniero fortunato, Napoli, 1698: A. Scarlatti. SCHATZ 9529

Il prigioniero fortunato (Mantova, 1699): A. Scarlatti. ML 50.2.P65S2

Pagliuca, Giuseppe.

Creso in Media (Livorno, 1780): Schuster. SCHATZ 9744

Pain, Marie Joseph.

Le naufrage au port, Paris, an III [1794–95]. ML 48.M2H

Palazzi, Giovanni.

Armida al campo d'Egitto, Venetia, 1718: Vivaldi. SCHATZ 10759

Medea e Giasone, Venezia, 1726: G. F. Brusa. SCHATZ 1374

Rosilena ed Oronta, Venezia, 1728: Vivaldi. SCHATZ 10778

Il vello d'oro, Venezia, 1749: Scolari. SCHATZ 9800

La verità in cimento, Venezia, 1720: Vivaldi. SCHATZ 10782

Pallavicini, Stefano Benedetto.

Alfonso (Dresda, 1738): Hasse.	SCHATZ 4510
Alfonso—Alfonso (Dresda, 1738): Hasse.	SCHATZ 4511
Arianna, Dresda (1736): Ristori.	SCHATZ 8816
Asteria (Dresda, 1737): Hasse.	SCHATZ 4516
Le fate, Dresda (1736): Ristori.	SCHATZ 8817
Irene—Irene (Dresda, 1738): Hasse.	SCHATZ 4544
Numa—Numa (Dresda, 1743): Hasse.	SCHATZ 4548
Otto (Hamburg, 1726). Tr. of his and Haym's Ottone: Händel.	SCHATZ 4482
Pimpinella e Marcantonio—Pimpernelle und Marcantonius. Intermezzi in his Numa (Dresda, 1743): Hasse.	SCHATZ 4548
Senocrita (Dresda, 1737): Hasse.	SCHATZ 4561
Teofane—Theophane, Dresda, 1719: Lotti.	SCHATZ 5723

Pallavicino, Giovanni Domenico.

Tiberio imperadore d'Oriente. O. T. of his Le vicende d'amor e di fortuna: unknown.	
Tiberio imperatore d'Oriente, Venetia (1702): Gasparini.	SCHATZ 3586
Le vicende d'amor e di fortuna, Venetia (1709): unknown. O. T. was Tiberio imperadore d'Oriente.	SCHATZ 11378

Palemone Licurio. *Arcadian name of* Silvio Stampiglia.

Palma, Carlo de.

Stratonica, Napoli (1727) (altered Salvi's text): pasticcio.	ML 50.2.S75

Palomba, Antonio.

L'amore in maschera, Napoli, 1748: Jommelli.	SCHATZ 4875
Il ciarlone, Vienna (1770): d'Avossa. L. T. of their La pupilla.	SCHATZ 512
Il chimico, Napoli, 1742: Palella.	SCHATZ 7711
Il curioso del suo proprio danno, Napoli, 1756: Piccinni.	SCHATZ 8141
Don Saverio, Venezia, 1744: d'Avossa.	SCHATZ 513
La donna di tutti i caratteri, Napoli, 1763: P. Guglielmi.	SCHATZ 4289
La donna vana, Napoli, 1764: Piccinni.	SCHATZ 8123
Le donne dispettose, Napoli, 1754: Piccinni.	SCHATZ 8124
L'Elisa, Napoli (1744): Cocchi.	SCHATZ 2038
La Gismonda, Napoli, 1750: Cocchi.	SCHATZ 2039
Il giuco de' matti, Napoli, 1755: Latilla.	SCHATZ 5453
Madama Arrighetta, Bologna, 1760: Piccinni.	SCHATZ 8150
La maestra, Venezia, 1754: Cocchi.	SCHATZ 2033
La maestra di buon gusto. A. T. of his La scuola moderna: Cocchi.	
La maestra di scuola—Die schulmeisterin, Berlino, 1763: Cocchi.	SCHATZ 2034
Il maestro di cappella (Vienna, 1771): Deller. L. T. of their Orazio.	SCHATZ 2496
Il marchese Sgrana, Napoli, 1738: Auletta.	SCHATZ 499
Monsieur Petitone. O. T. of his Madama Arrighetta: Piccinni.	
Myndlingen og Sladdreren. Tr. of his La pupilla ed il ciarlone, Kiøbenhavn, 1769: d' Avossa.	SCHATZ 511
L'Olindo, Napoli, 1753: N. Conti and Capranica.	SCHATZ 2208
Orazio. O. T. of his Il maestro di cappella: Deller.	
Orazio, Venezia, 1748: Auletta.	SCHATZ 500

Palomba, Antonio—Continued.

Orazio, Venezia, 1743: Latilla and Pergolesi (an extended version of the latter's Il maestro di musica).   SCHATZ 5466

Origille, Venezia, 1744: Palella and others.   SCHATZ 7713

La pupilla: d'Avossa.   O. T. of their La pupilla ed il ciarlone.

La pupilla ed il ciarlone—Myndlingen og Sladdreren, København, 1769: d'Avossa.   (L. T. of their La pupilla.)   SCHATZ 511

La scaltra letterata, Lisbona (1772): Piccinni.   SCHATZ 8139

La scaltra spiritosa, Torino (1761): Piccinni.   SCHATZ 8148

Die schulmeisterin.   Tr. of his La maestra di scuola, Berlino, 1763: Cocchi.   SCHATZ 2034

La scuola moderna o sia La maestra di buon gusto, Venezia, 1748 (his La maestra, retouched by Goldoni): Cocchi.   SCHATZ 2048

La serva bacchettona, Napoli, 1749: Cocchi.   SCHATZ 2040

Lo sposo di trè e marito di nessuna (Vienna, 1768): Anfossi, Guglielmi, and Gassmann.   SCHATZ 284

Lo sposo di trè e marito di nessuna, Napoli, 1781: Anfossi, Guglielmi, and Giordano.   SCHATZ 285

Lo sposo di trè, e marito di nessuna, Milano (1793): Gnecco.   SCHATZ 3965

Palomba, Giuseppe.

Admeto, Napoli, 1794: P. Guglielmi.   SCHATZ 4286

L'amalato per amore.   A. T. of his Il medico parigino: Astaritta.

L'amante combattuto dalle donne di punto, Napoli, 1781: Cimarosa.   SCHATZ 1994

L'amor contrastato, Venezia, 1788: Paisiello.   SCHATZ 7590a

L'amor contrastato—Die streitig gemachte liebschaft, Dresda, 1790: Paisiello.   SCHATZ 7591

Amor non ha riguardi, Napoli, 1787: Platone.   SCHATZ 8218

Amor tra le vendemme, Napoli, 1792: P. Guglielmi.   SCHATZ 4287

L'astuta in amore, Milano (1796): Fioravanti.   ML 48.A5 v.2

L'astuzie villane, Napoli, 1786: P. Guglielmi.   SCHATZ 4235

La ballerina amante—Die verliebte taenzerin, Dresda, 1786: Cimarosa.   SCHATZ 1912

Il barone in angustie, Napoli, 1797: Tritto.   SCHATZ 10459

Die beyden barone von Rocca Azura.   Tr. of his I due baroni di Rocca Azura, Dresda, 1790: Cimarosa.   SCHATZ 1919

Die beyden fluechtlinge, Hamburg, 1791.   Tr. of his Le gare generose: Paisiello.   SCHATZ 7628

La bizarra contadina, Napoli, 1790: Marinelli.   SCHATZ 5959

La cantatrici villane, Napoli, 1798: Fioravanti.   SCHATZ 3122

Chi dell' altrui si veste, presto si spoglia, Napoli, 1783: Cimarosa.   ML 50.2.C42C3

Chi dell' altrui si veste, presto si spoglia, Napoli, 1787: Cimarosa.   SCHATZ 1913

Le convulsioni: Curcio.   See p. 26–48 of P.'s Amor non ha riguardi e Le convulsioni, Napoli, 1787.   SCHATZ 2299

Il corsaro algerino, Napoli, 1765: Astaritta.   (Modernized version of libretto by unknown author.)   SCHATZ 377

La dama avventuriera, Napoli, 1780: P. Guglielmi.   SCHATZ 4240

La donna amante di tutti, e fedele a nessuno, Napoli, 1783: P. Guglielmi.   SCHATZ 4288

La donna sempre al suo peggior s'appiglia, Napoli, 1785: Cimarosa.   SCHATZ 1981

Palomba, Giuseppe—Continued.

Le donne dispettose, Napoli, 1793: Prota.	SCHATZ 8473
Le donne vendicate, Napoli, 1796: Monti and others.	SCHATZ 6601
I due baroni, Napoli, 1793: Cimarosa. L. T. of their I due baroni di Rocca Azurra.	SCHATZ 1978
I due baroni di Rocca Azzurra, Sinigaglia, 1787: Cimarosa.	ML 50.2.D75C3
Li due baroni di Rocca Azurra (Lisboa, 1791): Cimarosa.	SCHATZ 1918
I due baroni di Rocca Azura—Die beyden barone von Rocca Azura, Dresda, 1790: Cimarosa.	SCHATZ 1919
Le due gemelle, Lucca, 1790. L. T. of his L'inganno amoroso: P. Guglielmi. Also A. T. of his L'equivoco amoroso, which is but a L. T. of the same opera.	SCHATZ 4249
Der edle wettstreit. Tr. of his Le gare generose, Dresda, 1793: Paisiello.	SCHATZ 7627
L'equivoco amoroso ossia Le due gemelle, Parma, 1792. L. T. of his L'inganno amoroso: P. Guglielmi.	SCHATZ 4311
L'equivoco curioso, Napoli (1790): Cercià.	SCHATZ 1774
Il falegname, Mantova (1782): Cimarosa.	ML 50.2.F147C4
Il falegname, Venezia, 1784: Cimarosa.	SCHATZ 1922
Il falegname—Der tischler, Dresda, 1787: Cimarosa.	SCHATZ 1923
Le false apparenze, Napoli, 1791: P. Guglielmi.	SCHATZ 4244
Le false magie per amore, Napoli, 1791: Cercià.	SCHATZ 1775
Il fanatico per gli antichi Romani, Napoli, 1777: Cimarosa.	SCHATZ 1982
Le furberie deluse, Napoli, 1793: Prota.	SCHATZ 8474
Il furbo malaccorto, Venezia (1797). L. T. of his L'astuta in amore: Fioravanti. Also used as alternative title.	SCHATZ 3131
Le gare generose, Napoli, 1786: Paisiello.	SCHATZ 7679
Le gare generose ossia Gli schiavi per amore, Parma (1796): Paisiello.	SCHATZ 7626
Le gare generose—Der edle wettstreit, Dresda, 1793: Paisiello.	SCHATZ 7627
La grotta di Trofonio, Napoli, 1785: Paisiello.	SCHATZ 7680
L'indolente (Parma, 1797): Gnecco.	SCHATZ 3962
Gl'inganni delusi, Napoli, 1789: P. Guglielmi.	SCHATZ 4290
L'inganno amoroso, Napoli, 1786: P. Guglielmi.	SCHATZ 4248
L'intrigo delle mogli, Napoli, 1783: Gazzaniga.	SCHATZ 3679
I ladri di spirito, Napoli, 1769: Curcio.	SCHATZ 2310
La lanterna di Diogene, Napoli, 1794: P. Guglielmi. (According to Piovano, the author was Angelo Anelli, whose text Palomba merely retouched.)	SCHATZ 4250
La lanterna di Diogene—Die laterne des Diogenes, Dresda, 1796: P. Guglielmi.	SCHATZ 4251
Il maritato fra le disgrazie, Napoli, 1774: Latilla.	SCHATZ 5464
I matrimonii per inganno, Napoli, 1779: Curcio.	SCHATZ 2302
Il matrimonio in commedia, Milano (1782) (much altered version of his Le nozze in commedia): Caruso.	SCHATZ 1646
Il matrimonio in contrasto, Napoli, 1776: P. Guglielmi.	SCHATZ 4252
Il medico parigino o sia L'ammalato per amore, Venezia, 1791: Astaritta. (Text same as Le nozze in commedia.)	SCHATZ 374
Il molaforbici, Napoli, 1782: Monti.	SCHATZ 6602
La molinara o sia L'amor contrastato—Die müllerin oder Die streitig gemachte liebe, Berlino (n. d.). L. T. of his L'amor contrastato: Paisiello.	SCHATZ 7593

Palomba, Giuseppe—Continued.

Die muellerin, Hamburg (1793?) Tr. of his L'amor contras-
tato: Paisiello.   SCHATZ 7595
Die müllerin oder Die streitiggemachte liebe. Tr. of his La
molinara o sia L'amor contrastato, Berlino, n. d.: Pai-
siello.   SCHATZ 7593
Le nozze a dispetto, Napoli, 1797: Curcio.   SCHATZ 2303
Le nozze in commedia. O. T. of his Il matrimonio in com-
media.
Le nozze in commedia. O. T. of his Il medico parigino.
Le nozze in commedia, Napoli, 1781: P. Guglielmi.   SCHATZ 4254
La pianella persa, Verona, 1798: Gardi.   ML 50.2.P38G2
La pruova reciproca, Napoli, 1789: Tritto.   SCHATZ 10474
Puntigli, e gelosie tra moglie e marito, Napoli, 1784: Caruso.   SCHATZ 1650
La quakera spiritosa, Napoli, 1783: P. Guglielmi.   SCHATZ 4258
Le quattro stagioni, Napoli, 1784: Caruso.   SCHATZ 1651
Il raggiratore di poca fortuna, Napoli, 1779: P. Guglielmi.   SCHATZ 4259
Il ravvedimento del figliuol prodigo, Napoli (1790): Coppola.   SCHATZ 2211
La scaltra avventuriera, Napoli, 1788: Tritto.   SCHATZ 10477
Gli schiavi per amore, Torino (1791) L. T. of his Le gare
generose: Paisiello.   SCHATZ 7700
Gli schiavi per amore. A. T. of his Le gare amorose: Paisiello.
Die schoene muellerin, Berlin (1793?) Tr. of his L'amor
contrastato: Paisiello.   SCHATZ 7594
La scuola degli amanti, Napoli, 1783: Tritto.   SCHATZ 10478
La semplice ad arte, Napoli, 1782: P. Guglielmi.   SCHATZ 4266
La serva innamorata, Lisbona, 1794: P. Guglielmi.   SCHATZ 4294
Li sposi in commedia, Venezia, 1786. L. T. of his Il matri-
monio in commedia: Caruso.   SCHATZ 1647
Die streitig gemachte liebe. A. T. of his Die müllerin: Pai-
siello.
Die streitig gemachte liebschaft. Tr. of his L'amor con-
trastato: Paisiello.
I studenti, Napoli, 1796: Prota.   SCHATZ 8472
Der tischler. Tr. of his Il falegname, Dresda, 1787: Cimarosa. SCHATZ 1923
I Traci amanti, Torino, 1794: Cimarosa.   ML 50.2.T73C2
Le trame spiritose, Genova (1793): Tritto.   SCHATZ 10475
Le tre fanatiche, Napoli, 1785: Andreozzi.   SCHATZ 204
Die Trofonius-hoehle (Wien, 1787?). Tr. of his La grotta di
Trofonio: Paisiello.   SCHATZ 7704
Gli Turchi amanti, Lisbona, 1796: Cimarosa. L. T. of their
I Traci amanti.   SCHATZ 1999
La villana riconosciuta, Napoli, 1791: Cimarosa.   SCHATZ 1987
L'uomo indolente, Napoli, 1795: Farinelli.   SCHATZ 3017
I vecchi burlati, Venezia, 1795. L. T. of his I vecchi delusi:
Marinelli.   SCHATZ 5966
I vecchi delusi, Napoli, 1793: Marinelli.   SCHATZ 5960
La vedova capricciosa, Napoli, 1765: Insanguine and De
Franchi.   SCHATZ 4840
Die verliebte taenzerin. Tr. of his La ballerina amante,
Dresda, 1786: Cimarosa.   SCHATZ 1912

Panard, Charles François. *See* Pannard, Charles François.

Pancieri, Giulio.

L'Almerinda, Venetia, 1691: Boniventi.   SCHATZ 1187

L'Almira, Venetia, 1691: Boniventi.   SCHATZ 1188

Floridea, Venetia, 1688: unknown.   SCHATZ 11333

Il gran Macedone, Venetia, 1690: Boniventi.   SCHATZ 1191

Der in krohnen erlangte glueckswechsel oder Almira, koenigin von Castilien (Hamburg, 1704).   Tr. of his L'Almira: Händel.   SCHATZ 4479

Der in cronen erlangte glueckswechsel oder Almira, Koenigin von Castilien (Hamburg) 1732.   L. ed. of the above.   SCHATZ 4500

Panellenio, Eaco. *Arcadian name* of *conte* Jacopo Antonio Sanvitale.

Panicelli.

La forza d'amore, Venezia (1745): Galuppi.   SCHATZ 3478

Pannard, Charles François.

Théâtre et oeuvres diverses de M. Pannard . . . Pieces représentées sur les Théatres des Comédies françoise & italienne. Divertissements executés sur les mêmes Théâtres. Vaudevilles, avec la musique.

Paris, Duchesne, 1763. 4 v. 17 cm.

Vol. 4 wanting in L. of C. set. The "Théâtre" contains the following librettos in vols. 1–3: v. 1. Roland, parodie.—v. 2. L'Académie bourgeoise, Les deux suivantes, Le magazin des modernes, La mere embarrassée, Le nouvelliste dupé, Les petits comédiens, Pigmalion ou La statue animée, La répétition interrompue.—v. 3. La critique l'Opera-comique, Les époux réunis, Le fossé du scrupule, La piece a deux acteurs, Le rêve.

    PQ 2019.P3

L'impromptu du Pont-Neuf (Le Théâtre de la foire, Paris, 1731, t. vii): Gillier.   ML 48.L2 VII

Supplément de la Soirée des boulevards.   *See* Favart.

Zéphire et Fleurette.   *See* Favart.

Panzieri, Lorenzo.

Cha-Gian in Dely, ballet.   *See* Cimarosa's Gli Orazi e i Curiazi.

Kildar, ballet: Trento.   *See* Zingarelli's Il ratto delle Sabine.

La Lodoiska, ballet.   *See* Mayr's Telemaco.

I morti fatti sposi, ballet.   *See* Cimarosa's Gli Orazi e i Curiazi.

Odervik, ballet: Trento.   *See* Marinelli's Issipile.

I riti della Baja Dreshy, ballet.   *See* Bianchi's Cappricciosa ravveduta.

Il sotteraneo ossia Catterina di Coluga, ballet: Cavos.   *See* Nasolini's Le feste d'Iside.

Papi, *conte* Antonio.

Alessandro in Armenia, Venezia, 1768: Borghi.   SCHATZ 1226

Eurione, Pavia (1775): Bianchi.   ML 48.A5 v.12

Eurione, Venezia, 1754: Pampani.   SCHATZ 7760

Papis, Giuseppe.

L'ambizione depressa, Venezia (1733) L. T. of his L'amor generoso: Galuppi.   SCHATZ 3477

Pariati, Pietro.

For his texts written in collaboration with Apostolo Zeno, *see* the latter's "Poesie drammatiche," Venezia, 1744, vols. 9–10, and Orleans, 1785–86, vols. 9–11.

Alba Cornelia (Bresslau, 1726) (also attributed to Stampiglia): Fr. Conti.   SCHATZ 2203

Pariati, Pietro—Continued.

    Alessandro in Sidone. *See* Zeno.

    Alexander in Sidon. *See* Zeno.

    Ambleto. *See* Zeno.

    Anfitrione, Venezia, 1707: Gasparini.   SCHATZ 3559

    Amphytrion (Hamburg, 1725) Tr. of the above: Gasparini
        and v. Wich.   SCHATZ 3560

    Antioco. *See* Zeno.

    Arianna, Torino, 1728: Feo.   SCHATZ 3061

    Arianna e Teseo, Venezia, 1769: Galuppi.   SCHATZ 3441

    Arianna e Teseo, Torino (1764): Pasque.   SCHATZ 7781

    Arianna e Teseo, Venezia, 1727: Porpora.   SCHATZ 8369

    Arianna e Teseo. A. T. of his I sacrifizi di Creta: Winter.

    Artaserse, Napoli, 1708: Orlandini and Mancini. *See*
        Agosti, G.

    Artaserse. *See* Zeno.

    Astarto. *See* Zeno.

    L'astrologo, Venezia, 1731: Gasparini. L. T. of their Par-
        pagnacco.   SCHATZ 3590

    Ciro, Venezia (1709): Albinoni.   SCHATZ 115

    Cloris und Tirsis—Clori e Tirsi (Hamburg, 1719). Tr. and
        L. T. of his I satiri in Arcadia: Conti.   SCHATZ 2196

    Costantino. *See* Zeno.

    Costanza e fortezza, Vienna d'Austria (1723): Fux.   SCHATZ 3391

    Don Chisciotte in corte della duchessa. *See* Zeno.

    Don Chisciotte in Sierra Morena. *See* Zeno.

    Elisa regina di Tiro. *See* Zeno.

    Engelberta. *See* Zeno.

    Engelberta o sia La forza dell' innocenza. *See* Zeno.

    Le feste d'Iside. *See* Zeno.

    Il finto Policare, Vienna (1716): Conti.   SCHATZ 2200

    Flavio Anicio Olibrio. *See* Zeno.

    La forza dell' innocenza. A. T. of his Engelberta.

    Il Giustino, Bologna (1711) (modernized version of Beregani's
        text): Albinoni.   SCHATZ 129

    Grilletta e Pimpinone: Conti. Intermezzi in their Sesostri
        rè di Egitto, Vienna, 1717.   SCHATZ 2198

    Massimiano. *See* Zeno.

    Parpagnacco, Venezia, 1708: Gasparini.   SCHATZ 3575

    Penelope, Wien (1724): Conti. Tr. of their Penelope.   SCHATZ 2202

    Pimpinone, Venezia, 1708: Albinoni. (At end of his Astarto,
        1708.)   SCHATZ 111

    Pollastrella & Parpagnocco: Gasparini. *In* Broschi's Adriano
        in Siria, Stuccardo, 1737.   SCHATZ 1338

    Le regine di Macedonia. *See* Zeno.

    Ricimero re de' Goti. *See* Zeno.

    I sacrifizi di Creta o sia Arianna e Teseo, Firenze, 1793: Winter. SCHATZ 11051

    I satiri in Arcadia. O. T. of his Cloris und Tirsis.

    Seleuco. *See* Zeno.

    Sesostri. *See* Zeno.

    Sesostri rè d'Egitto. *See* Zeno.

    Sesostri, rè di Egitto, Vienna d'Austria (1717): Conti. (Zeno
        not mentioned as joint author.)   SCHATZ 2197

Pariati, Pietro—Continued.

Sidonio, Venezia, 1706: Lotti. Schatz 5722

Statira. *See* Zeno.

La Ssanvita, Milano (1708): Fiorè. (Text appears in Zeno's
collected works as by Zeno.) Schatz 3195

La tirannide debellata. *See* Zeno.

Il trionfo di Flavio Olibrio, Venezia, 1726 (with Zeno): Porta. Schatz 8382

Die ungleiche heyrath zwischen Vespetta und Pimpinone
(Hamburg, 1725): Telemann. Tr. of his "Vespetta e
Pimpinone." Schatz 10273

Der verstellte Policare (Breslau, 1726): Conti. Tr. of their
Il finto Policare. Schatz 2201

Vespetta e Pimpinone (Monaco, 1722): Albinoni. L. T. of
their Pimpinone. Schatz 100

Parini, Giuseppe.

Ascanio in Alba (Lisbona, 1785) (modernization of Stampa's
text): Moreira. Schatz 6633

Parmentier.

Les jeunes mariés, La Haye, 1751. (Font and Schatz attribute
text to Favart.) Schatz 11715

Les jeunes mariés, Paris, 1767. Schatz 11495

Le plaisir et l'innocence, Paris, 1753: Laruette. ML 50.2.P47L2

Parodi, Innocente (Parrodi, Innocenzo).

Accampamento di Micheletti, ballet. *See* Bosi's La figlia
obbediente.

Le gelosie d'Annetta e Fiorillo, ballet. *See* Bosi's La figlia
obbediente.

La presa de Marochini, ballet. *See* Della Maria's Chi vuol
non puole.

Le reclute per inganno, ballet. *See* Della Maria's Chi vuol
non puole.

Les **parodies du Nouveau theatre italien,** ov Recueil des
parodies représentées sur le théâtre de l'Hôtel de Bour-
gogne, par les Comediens italiens ordinaires du roy.
Avec les airs gravés. Nouv. ed., rev., cor. & augm. de
plusieurs parodies . . .

Paris, Briasson, 1738 4 v. front., plates. 17cm. ML 48.P3

Added t.-p., engr., in v. 2-4.
"Discours a l'occasion d'un discours de M. D. L. M. sur les parodies. Nouvelle édition augmentée . . .": v. 1, p. xix–xxxv.

Parvi.

Thesée. *See* Favart.

Pasqualigo, Benedetto.

Antigona, Venezia, 1718: Orlandini. Schatz 7327

Berenice, Venezia (1725): Orlandini. Schatz 7329

Cimene, Venezia, 1721: Bassani and Zucchini. Schatz 637

La fedeltà coronata, Bologna, 1727: Orlandini. L. T. of their
Antigona. ML 50.2.A718O7

Giul. Flavio Crispo, Venezia, 1722: Capello. Schatz 1591

Ifigenia in Tauride, Milano (1784): Monza. Schatz 6610

Ifigenia in Tauride, Venezia, 1719: Orlandini. Schatz 7335

Ifigenia in Tauride, Venezia, 1786: Tarchi. Schatz 10221

Ifigenia in Tauride, Venezia (1725): Vinci. Schatz 10750

Pasqualigo, Benedetto—Continued.

Mitridate rè di Ponto vincitor di sè stesso, Venezia, 1723:
Capello.   SCHATZ 1592

Il pastor fido, Padoa, 1721 (originally by Guarini): Pietragrua.   SCHATZ 8164

Pasquini, Giovanni Claudio.

Archidamia.   A. T. of his La Spartana generosa: Hasse.

Archidamia, Vienna d'Austria (1727): Reutter.   SCHATZ 8695

Don Chisciotte in corte della duchessa, Vienna d'Austria
(1727): Caldara.   SCHATZ 1502

Don Chisciotte in corte della duchessa, n. i., n. d. (detached):
Caldara.   SCHATZ 1481

Die grossmuethige Spartanerin oder Archidamia.   Tr. of his
La Spartana generosa ovvero Archidamia (Dresda, 1747):
Hasse.   SCHATZ 4565

Leucippo—Leucippus (Dresda, 1747): Hasse.   SCHATZ 4545

Leucippo, Venetia, 1749: Hasse.   SCHATZ 4591

Leucippus.   Tr. of his Leucippo (Dresda, 1747): Hasse.   SCHATZ 4545

Meride, Mannheim (1742): Pietragrua.   SCHATZ 8167

Spartaco, Vienna (1726): Porsile.   SCHATZ 8377

La Spartana generosa ovvero Archidamia—Die grossmuethige
Spartanerin oder Archidamia (Dresda, 1747): Hasse.   SCHATZ 4565

Zenobia, Vienna d'Austria (1732): Reutter.   ML 48.M2C

Passarini, Francesco.

Amore di sangue, Venezia (1729): Porta.   L. T. of their
Amore e fortuna.   SCHATZ 8386

Amore e fortuna, Venezia, 1727: Porta.   SCHATZ 8385

Bertoldo, Venezia, 1717: G. Bassani.   SCHATZ 635

Chi la fà, l'aspetta, Venezia, 1717: Polani.   SCHATZ 8249

Clotilde, Venezia, 1748: Galuppi.   SCHATZ 3516

La costanza nell' Honore.   O. T. of his La vendetta disarmata
dall' amore: Polani.

Le pazzie degl' amanti, Venezia, 1712: C. F. Pollaroli.   SCHATZ 8311

Li sponsali d'Enea, Venezia, 1731: Fini.   SCHATZ 3104

Li stratagemi amorosi, Venezia, 1730: Albinoni.   SCHATZ 131

La vendetta disarmata dall' amore, Venezia, 1704 (L. T. of
his La costanza nell' Honore): Polani.   SCHATZ 8253

La vittoria nella costanza, Venetia (1702): Boniventi.   SCHATZ 1194

Patrat (Patras), Joseph.

Les deux morts ou La ruse de carnaval, Paris, 1781: unknown.   ML 50.2.D487

Toberne ou Le pêcheur suédois, Paris, cinquième année
[1796–97]: Bruni.   SCHATZ 1370

Paulme, *marquis* de.

Le prix de Cythere, Paris, 1761 (Theatre de M. Favart, Paris,
Duchesne, 1763–77, t. vi) (with Favart).   ML 49.A2F1

Pavieri, Bartolomeo (Bortolamio).

L'amore per forza, Venezia, 1721: G. Bassani and Lucchini.   SCHATZ 636

L'inganno fortunato, Venezia, 1721 (based on material furnished by Giov. Batt. Sara): Boniventi.   SCHATZ 1192

Pavoni, Antonio.

Il bravo burlato, Gubbio (1757): Rinaldo di Capua.   SCHATZ 8801

Pazzini, Ranieri.

La pastorella rapita da' corsari, ballet. *See* Paisiello's Il rè Teodoro in Venezia.

Vindemmia, ballet. *See* Salieri's La partenza inaspettata.

Pearce, William.

Arrived at Portsmouth, London, 1794: Shield.   LONGE 228

Hartford-Bridge or The skirts of the camp, London, 1793: Shield.   LONGE 222

The marriage of Peleus and Thetis. *See* his Windsor castle.

The midnight wanderers, London, 1793: Shield.   LONGE 221

Netley Abbey, London, 1794: Shield.   LONGE 229

Windsor castle or The fair maid of Kent, London, 1795: Salomon and Spofforth (includes the masque "The marriage of Peleus and Thetis").   LONGE 231

Pedoni, Bartolomeo.

La Rosílda, Venezia, 1707: Polani.   SCHATZ 8251

Vindice la pazzia della vendetta, Venezia, 1707: Polani.   SCHATZ 8254

La virtù trionfante d'amore vendicativo, Venezia, 1708: Polani.   SCHATZ 8256

Pellegrin, Simon Joseph (de).

Les festes de l'été (Recueil général des opéra, Paris, 1734, t. xii) (with Marie Anne Barbier): Montéclair.   SCHATZ 6589

Hipolyte et Aricie (Recueil général des opéra, t. xv, Paris, 1739): Rameau.   SCHATZ 8587

Hippolyte et Aricie (Paris) 1733: Rameau.   ML 50.2.H4R2

Hippolyte et Aricie, Lyon, 1743: Rameau.   SCHATZ 8587a

Jephté, Paris, 1738: Montéclair.   ML 50.2.J3M6

Jephté (Recueil général des opéra, Paris, 1739, t. xv): Montéclair.   SCHATZ 6590

Le jugement de Paris (Recueil général des opéra, Paris, 1734, t. xii) (with Barbier): Bertin de la Doué.   SCHATZ 880

Medée et Jason: Salomon. (According to Schatz he was joint-author with A. de La Roque.)

Orion (Recueil général des opéra, t. xiv, Paris, 1734) (with de Lafont): La Coste.   SCHATZ 5355

Les plaisirs de la campagne (Recueil général des opéra, Paris, 1734, t. xii) (with Barbier): Bertin de la Doué.   SCHATZ 881

La princesse d'Elide (Recueil général des opéra, t. xiv, Paris, 1734): Villeneuve.   SCHATZ 10738

Renaud (Recueil général des opéra, t. xiii, Paris, 1734): Desmarets.   SCHATZ 2533

Télégone (Recueil général des opéra, t. xiii, Paris, 1734): La Coste.   SCHATZ 5357

Télémaque (Recueil général des opéra, t. xi, Paris, 1720): Destouches.   SCHATZ 2552

Théonoé (Recueil des opéra, t. xi, Paris, 1720): Salomon. (The above was the author according to Schatz, the libretto gives Antoine de La Roque.)   SCHATZ 9344

Pepoli, *conte* **Alessandro.**

Belisa ossia La fedeltà riconosciuta, Milano (1795): Winter.   SCHATZ 11020

Il chinese in Italia, Venezia, 1793: Bianchi.   SCHATZ 977

La fedeltà riconosciuta. A. T. of his Belisa: Winter.

Pepoli, *conte* **Alessandro**—Continued.

I giuochi d'Agrigento, Venezia, 1792: Paisiello.   Schatz 7629

Giuochi d'Agrigento, Lisbona, 1799: Paisiello.   ML 50.2.G45P2

Tancredi, Venezia, 1795: Gardi.   Schatz 3542

Virginia, Venezia, 1793: Alessandri.   Schatz 156

Perelli, Domenico, *duca di* **Monestarace.**

La Circe, Milano (1783): Cimarosa.   Schatz 2005

Circe, Venezia, 1786: Gazzaniga.   Schatz 3659

Circe, Venezia, 1792: Paër.   Schatz 7487

Perinet, Joachim.

Der fagottist, oder Die zauberzither, Wien, 1791: W. Müller.   Schatz 6920

Der fuerst und sein hofnarr. A. T. of his Orion: Seyfried.

Die heyrath auf gewisse art. A. T. of his Liebe macht kurzen prozess: pasticcio.

Kaspars zoegling oder Der sieg der bescheidenheit, Wien, 1791: Kauer.   Schatz 5035

Der kopf ohne mann, Wien, 1798: Woelfl.   Schatz 11106

Liebe macht kurzen prozess oder Die heyrath auf gewisse art (Leipzig, 1799): pasticcio: Henneberg, Woelfl, Stegmayer, and others.   Schatz 4633

Das neusonntagskind, Wien, 1794: W. Müller.   Schatz 6947

Das neue sonntags-kind, n. i., n. d.: W. Müller.   Schatz 6949

Orion oder Der fuerst und sein hofnarr, Wien, 1798: von Seyfried.   Schatz 9858

Pizichi oder Die fortsetzung des Fagottisten, Wien, 1793: W. Müller.   Schatz 6956

Die schwestern von Prag, Wien, 1794: W. Müller.   Schatz 6963

Der sieg der bescheidenheit auf der insel des vergnuegens. A. T. of his Kaspars zoegling: Kauer.

Das sonntagskind, Hamburg, 1798. L. T. of his Das neusonntagskind: W. Müller.   Schatz 6948

Die zauberzither. A. T. of his Der fagottist: W. Müller.

Die zauberzither (Wien), 1795. L. T. of Der fagottist: W. Müller.   Schatz 6921

Die zauberzither oder Der fagottist, Rostock, 1796. L. T. of Der fagottist: W. Müller.   Schatz 6922

Die zauberzither, Prag, 1796: L. T. of Der fagottist: W. Müller.   Schatz 11714

Die zween Savoyarden, Wien, 1792. Tr. of Dalayrac's Les deux petits Savoyards (Marsollier).   Schatz 2340

Perrin, Pierre.

Pastorale mise en musique (Les oeuvres de poesie, Paris, 1661): Cambert.   PQ 1879.P3

Pomone (Recueil général des opéra, Paris, 1703, t. iv: Cambert.   Schatz 1519

Persiani, Orazio.

Gli amori di Giasone e d'Isifile, Venetia, 1642: Marazzoli.   Schatz 5923

Narciso et Ecco immortalati, Venetia, 1642: Cavalli.   Schatz 1747

Le nozze di Teti e di Peleo, Venetia, 1639: Cavalli.   Schatz 1748

Peterson, Joseph.

The raree show or The fox trap't, Chester, 1740: ballad opera.   Longe 271

Petris, Carlo de.

L'humanità nelle fere, Napoli (1708): A. Scarlatti and G. Vignola.   Schatz 9538

Petrosellini, Giuseppe.

Li amanti comici o sia La famiglia in scompiglio, **Torino**
(1797): Cimarosa. — SCHATZ 2003

L'amore in villa, Roma, anno VI (1797): P. Guglielmi. — SCHATZ 4308

L'astratto ovvero Il giocator fortunato, Venezia, 1772: Piccinni. — SCHATZ 8066

L'astratto ovvero Il giuocatore fortunato, Pisa, 1773: Piccinni. SCHATZ 8066a

Il barbiere di Siviglia, Pietroburgo (1782): Paisiello. — ML 50.2.B25P2

Il barone burlato, Napoli, 1784. L. T. of his Il pittore parigino: Cimarosa with new music by Cipolla. — SCHATZ 1979

Il barone di Rocca Antica—Der baron von Alten Felss, Dresda, 1772: Franchi and Anfossi (second act). — SCHATZ 3330

Il barone di Rocca Antica, Lisboa, 1773: Franchi. — SCHATZ 3327

Bondehovmod eller kiøbmanden som adelsmand, og bondepigen som frøken. Tr. of his Il fumo villano, Kiøbenhavn, 1769: Piccinni. — SCHATZ 8082

Der cavalier durch die liebe. Tr. of his Il cavaliere per amore, Dresda, 1766: Piccinni. — SCHATZ 8081

Il cavalier per amore e la contadina dama. A. T. of his Il fumo villano: Piccinni.

Il cavaliere per amore, Vienna (1766): Piccinni. — SCHATZ 8080

Il cavaliere per amore—Der cavalier durch die liebe, Dresda, 1766: Piccinni. — SCHATZ 8081

La cifra, Milano (1790): Salieri. (Text altered by Da Ponte.) SCHATZ 9281

Le contadine bizzarre, Vienna (1767): Piccinni. — SCHATZ 8086

La dama pastorella: Salieri. O. T. of their La cifra.

Le due contesse, Roma, 1776: Paisiello. — ML 50.2.D76P2

Le due contesse, Parma (1777): Paisiello. — SCHATZ 7613

Le due contesse—Die zwey comtessinnen, Dresda, 1781: Paisiello. — SCHATZ 7614

Le due finte gemelle, Venezia, 1783. L. T. of his Le finte gemelle: Piccinni. — SCHATZ 8157

Die entzifferung (n. i.), 1795. Tr. of his La cifra: Salieri. SCHATZ 9283

La famiglia in scompiglio. A. T. of his Li amanti comici: Cimarosa.

Le finte gemelle, Firenze, 1771: Piccinni. — SCHATZ 8094

Le finte gemelle, Lisbona, 1773: Piccinni. — SCHATZ 8093

Il fumo villano o sia Il cavalier per amore e la contadina dama—Bondehovmod eller kiøbmanden som adelsmand, og bondepigen som frøken, Kiøbenhavn, 1769. L. T. and Tr. of his Il cavaliere per amore: Piccinni. — SCHATZ 8082

Il fumo villano, Venezia, 1766. L. T. of his Il cavaliere per amore: Piccinni and Ortani. — SCHATZ 8156

La Giannetta o sia L'incognita perseguitata—Jeannette eller Den fortraengte ubekiendte, Kiøbenhavn, 1775: Anfossi. L. T. of their L'incognita perseguitata. — SCHATZ 240

Il giocator fortunato. A. T. of his L'astratto: Piccinni.

Il giuocatore fortunato. A. T. of his L'astratto: Piccinni.

Der glueckswechsel oder Mutter Natur in ihren kindern (Komische opern der Italiener, Leipzig, 1782). Tr. of his Le vicende della sorte: Piccinni. — SCHATZ 8120

L'incognita perseguitata, Milano (1773): Anfossi. — SCHATZ 238

L'incognita perseguitata, Venezia, 1764: Piccinni. — SCHATZ 8097

L'incognita perseguitata, Lisboa (1766): Piccinni. — ML 48.C6I

Petrosellini, Giuseppe—Continued.

L'incognita perseguitata—Die verfolgte unbekannte, Dresda,
1768: Piccinni.   SCHATZ 8098

L'inconnue persécutée, Paris, 1776.   French version of his
L'incognita perseguitata: Anfossi.   ML 50.2.I55A6

Gl'intrighi amorosi, Venezia, 1772: Galuppi.   SCHATZ 3504

L'inutile precauzione, Venezia, 1787.   L. T. of his Il barbiere
di Seviglia: Paisiello.   SCHATZ 7602

Jeannette eller Den fortraengte ubekiendte.   Tr. of his La
Giannetta o sia L'incognita perseguitata, Kiøbenhavn,
1775: Anfossi.   SCHATZ 240

Das kaestchen mit der chiffer, Berlin, 1793.   Tr. of his La
cifra: Salieri.   SCHATZ 9282

Kiøbmanden som adelsmand, og bondepigen som frøken.
A. T. of his Bondehovmod: Piccinni.

Metilda ritrovata, Vienna, 1773: Anfossi.   L. T. of their L'incognita perseguitata.   SCHATZ 239

Mutter Natur in ihren kindern.   A. T. of his Der glueckswechsel: Piccinni.

La nuova Gianetta, Parma, 1787: Robuschi.   SCHATZ 8841

Der onkel aus Amsterdam, Riga und Mitau, 1796.   Tr. of his
Il pittore parigino: Cimarosa.   SCHATZ 1970

Der Pariser mahler.   Tr. of his Il pittor parigino, Dresda,
1782: Cimarosa.   SCHATZ 1969

La partenza inaspettata, Roma, 1779: Salieri.   ML 50.2.P28S2

La partenza inaspettata, Milano (1781): Salieri.   SCHATZ 9310

La partenza inaspettata—Die unerwartete abreise, Dresda,
1781: Salieri.   SCHATZ 9311

Il pittor parigino—Der Pariser mahler, Dresda, 1782: Cimarosa.   SCHATZ 1969

Il pittor parigino, Lisbona, 1794: Cimarosa.   ML 50.2.P46C3

Il pittore parigino.   O. T. of the above.

Il regno delle Amazoni, Firenze, 1784: Accorimboni.   SCHATZ 14

La sciocchezza in amore, Venezia, 1764.   L. T. of his Le contadine bizzare: Piccinni.   SCHATZ 8087

Die unerwartete abreise.   Tr. of his La partenza inaspettata,
Dresda, 1781: Salieri.   SCHATZ 9311

Die verfolgte unbekanntè.   Tr. of his L'incognita perseguitata,
Dresda, 1768: Piccinni.   SCHATZ 8098

Le vicende della sorte, Torino, 1764: Piccinni.   SCHATZ 8154

Le vicende della sorte, Lisbona (1766): Piccinni.   SCHATZ 8143

Die zwey comtessinnen.   Tr. of his Le due contesse, Dresda,
1781: Paisiello.   SCHATZ 7614

Pfeffel, Conrad Gottlieb.

Der koenig und der pachter, Frankfurt und Leipzig, 1766.
Tr. of Monsigny's Le roi et le fermier (Sedaine).   SCHATZ 6581

Phillips, Edward.

Britons, strike home: or, The sailor's rehearsal, London, 1739:
ballad opera.   LONGE 321

Britons strike home: or, The sailor's rehearsal, Glasgow, 1761.   LONGE 118

The chamber-maid, London, 1730: ballad opera.   ML 50.5.C3

The livery rake and country lass, London, 1733: ballad opera.   ML 50.5.L49

The mock lawyer, London (1733): ballad opera.   LONGE 73

Piazza, Antonio.
    L'amore rammingo, Venezia, 1777: Salari.   Schatz 9266
    La prepotenza delusa, Venezia, 1777: Cavi.   Schatz 1757
    L'isola della luna, Venezia, 1780: Valentini.   Schatz 10585

Piazza, Vincenzo, *conte* **di S. Stefano.**
    L'Eudamia, Roma & Parma, 1718: Capello.   Schatz 1589

Piazzon, Giovanni.
    Antigono tutore di Filippo rè della Macedonia, Venezia, 1724:
        Porta and Albinoni.   Schatz 133

Pic, Jean, *abbé.*
    Aricie (Recueil général des opéra, t. vi, Paris 1703): La Coste.   Schatz 5351
    Ballet des saisons, Amsterdam, 1696: Colasse-Lully.   ML 52.2.B115
    Ballet des saisons (Recueil général des opéra, t. v, Paris, 1703):
        Colasse and (probably the elder) Lully.   Schatz 5782
    La naissance de Vénus (Recueil général des opéra, Paris, t. v,
        1703): Colasse.   Schatz 2101

Picard, Louis Benoît.
    Les comédiens ambulans, Paris, an VII (1798–99): Devienne.   ML 50.2.C62D2
    Liebe wagt alles, Hamburg, 1798.   Tr. of his Les visitandines:
        Devienne.   Schatz 2556
    Les vísitandines, Paris, 1792: Devienne.   ML 50.2.V63D3
    De visitandines, Amsteldam, 1796.   Tr. of his Les visitan-
        dines: Devienne.   Schatz 2563

Piccinni, Domenico.
    Gli amanti riuniti.   A. T. of his La donna sensibile: Tritto.   Schatz 10469
    Chi la dura, la vince, Napoli, 1798: P. C. Guglielmi.   Schatz 4337
    La donna sensibile o sia Gli amanti riuniti, Napoli, 1798:
        Tritto.   Schatz 10469
    La finta matta, Napoli, 1789: di Palma.   Schatz 7741
    Nicaboro in Jucatan, Napoli, 1799: Tritto.   Schatz 10463

Piccinni, Giuseppe Maria.
    Le faux lord, Paris, 1783: Piccinni.   Schatz 8092

Piccioli, Francesco Maria.
    Le Amazoni nell' Isole fortunate, Padova (1679): Pallavicino.   Schatz 7717
    La costanza fortunata in amore, Venezia, 1710: unknown.   Schatz 11317
    Messalina, Venetia, 1680: Pallavicino.   Schatz 7728

Piccoli, Francesco.   (*Same as* Piccioli ?)
    L'incostanza trionfante overo Il Theseo, Venetia, 1658 (with
        others who are not mentioned): P. A. Ziani.   Schatz 11222

Pigault de l'Epinay, Charles Antoine Guillaume, *known as*
        Pigault-Lebrun.
    Le major Palme, Paris, an V [1797]: Bruni.   ML 50.2.M32B7
    Le petit matelot-ou Le mariage im-promptu, Paris, 1796:
        Gaveaux (46 p.).   ML 50.2.P34G2
    Le petit matelot ou Le mariage im-promptu, Paris, 1796:
        Gaveaux (40 p.)   Schatz 3641
    Le petit matelot ou Le mariage impromptu, Avignon, an V
        [1796–97]: Gaveaux.   ML 50.2.P34G22

Pignatta, Pietro Romolo.
    L'Asmiro rè di Corinto, Venetia, 1696: author.   Schatz 8168
    La costanza vince il destino, Venetia, 1695: author.   Schatz 8169

Piguenit, D. J.
   Don Quixote, London, 1774: Arnold.   Longe 291

Piis, Pierre Antoine Auguste, *chevalier* de.
   Les amours d'été, Paris, 1784 (with Barré): unknown.   Schatz 11480
   Aristote amoureux ou Le philosophe bridé, Paris, 1780 (with
      Barré): unknown.   ML 50.2.A746
   La matinée et la veillée villageoisie ou Le sabot perdu, Paris,
      1784 (with Barré): unknown.   Schatz 11499
   L'opéra en province, Paris, 1778 (with Barré): parody of
      Gluck's Armide.   ML 50.2.A76G5
   Le printemps, Paris, 1784 (with Barré): Prot.   Schatz 8471
   La vallée de Montmorency ou Jean Jacques Rousseau dans son
      hermitage, pasticcio.   *See* Title catalogue.
   Les vendangeurs ou Les deux baillis, Paris, 1781 (with Barré):
      unknown.   Schatz 11521

Pillet, Fabien.
   Wenzel ou Le magistrat du peuple, Paris, Seconde année
      (1794): Ladurner.   Schatz 5375

Pilon, Frederick.
   The fair American, London, 1785: Carter.   ML 50.2.F13C2
   The siege of Gibraltar, London, 1780: Shield.   Longe 95

Pinamonte Bonacossi, *conte* **Ercole.**
   La filli di Tracia, Ferrara (1664): Mattioli.   Schatz 6105

Pioli, Alessandro.
   L'amante ridicolo deluso, Lisbona (1763): Piccinni.   Schatz 8063

Pioli, Giovanni Domenico.
   La Dorisbe overo L'amor volubile e tiranno, Roma, 1711: A.
      Scarlatti.   Schatz 9531

Piovene, *conte* **Agostino.**
   Baiazet (Venezia, 1742) (L. T. of his Tamerlano): Bernasconi.   Schatz 868
   Il Bajazet, Reggio, 1719: Gasparini.   Schatz 3562
   Bajazet, Torino (1754): Jommelli.   Schatz 4878
   Bajazet, Verona (1765): Scarlatti, Gius.   Schatz 9558
   Cunegonda, Venezia, 1726: Vivaldi.   Schatz 10764
   Il Gran Tamerlano, Milano (1772): Misliweczek.   Schatz 6530
   Il gran Tamerlano—Den store Tamerlan, Kiøbenhavn (1764):
      Sarti.   Schatz 9445
   Marsia deluso, Venezia (1714): C. F. Pollaroli.   Schatz 8302
   Nero (Hamburg, 1729): Tr. of: Schatz 7344
   Nerone, Venezia, 1721: Orlandini.   Schatz 7343
   Polidoro, Venezia (1714): Lotti.   Schatz 5708
   Polidorus (Hamburg) 1735.   Tr. of his Polidoro: Graun.   Schatz 4110
   Porsenna, Napoli, 1713: Lotti ("musica . . . accomodata
      . . . dal Sig. Alessandro Scarlatti").   Schatz 5711
   La principessa fedele, Venetia (1709): Gasparini.   Schatz 3578
   Publio Cornelio Scipione, Venetia (1712): C. F. Pollaroli.   Schatz 8313
   Scipione nelle Spagne, Venezia, 1746 (later version of his
      Publio Cornelio Scipione): Galuppi.   Schatz 3493
   Spurio Postumio, Venezia (1712): C. F. Pollaroli.   Schatz 8320
   Den store Tamerlan.   Tr. of his Il gran Tamerlano, Kiøben-
      havn (1764): Sarti.   Schatz 9445
   Tamerlan (Hamburg, 1725).   Tr. of his and Haym's Tamer-
      lano: Händel (interpolated intermezzo by Telemann).   Schatz 4492

Piovene, *conte* **Agostino**—Continued.

Tamerlano, Venezia (1754): Cocchi, first act; Pescetti, second; both the third.   SCHATZ 2054

Tamerlano, Venezia (1710): Gasparini.   SCHATZ 3585

Il Tamerlano, Venezia, 1765: P. Guglielmi.   SCHATZ 4306

Tamerlano—Tamerlane, London, 1724 (altered by Haym): Händel.   ML 50.2.T23

Tamerlano, Torino (1730): Porpora.   SCHATZ 8375

Pirker, Franz Joseph.

[Alexander in Indien] Presburgo, 1741. Tr. of Hasse's Alessandro nell' Indie (Metastasio).   SCHATZ 4509

Piron, Alexis.

Œuvres complettes d'Alexis Piron, pub. par Rigoley de Juvigny.

Liege, C. Plomteux, 1776. 7 v. 17½ cm.

Contains the following librettos:

t. 3. Arlequin-Deucalion; L'antre de Trophonius; L'endriague; Le Claperman; Le caprice, L'âne d'or, d'Apulée; La rose.—t. 4. Le facheux veuvage; Les chimeres; La robe de dissention, ou Le faux-prodige; Tirésias.—t. 5. Le mariage de Momus, ou La gigantomachie; Columbine-Nitétis (parodie); Crédit est mort; L'enrolement d'Arlequin; Les huit Mariannes (parodie); Atis (parodie); Philomèle (parodie).

     PQ 2019.P6

Le mariage du caprice et de la folie (Le Théâtre de la foire, Paris, 1731, t. viii): Gillier. (In Piron's Oeuvres complettes the title is simply "Le caprice.")   ML 48.L2 VIII

La rose ou Les jardins de l'Hymen. O. T. of the next entry.

La roze ou Les festes de l'Hymen, Paris, 1754.   ML 50.2.R87

Pitra, Louis Guillaume.

Andromaque, Paris, 1780: Grétry.   SCHATZ 4138

Pitrot, Antonio.

Adelasia, ballet. *See* Zingarelli's Il mercato di Monfregoso.

Alcina e Leone, ballet: Piombanti. *See* Rust's Alessandro nell' Indie.

Don Chisciotte, ballet. *See* Zingarelli's Il mercato di Monfregoso.

Egle e Dafni, ballet: Le Messier. *See* Misliweczek's Il trionfo di Clelia.

Enea e Lavinia, ballet: Piombanti. *See* Caruso's L'Artaserse.

Sansone, ballet. *See* Cimarosa's I tre amanti.

Piudemonte, *marchese* **Giovanni.**

Telemaco ed Eurice nell' isola di Calipso, Venezia, 1777: Bertoni.   SCHATZ 933

Pizzi, (Giuseppe) Giovacchino.

Il Cidde (Lisbona) 1773: Sacchini.   SCHATZ 9223

Creso, Torino (1768): Cafaro.   SCHATZ 1452

Creso, London, 1767: Sacchini.   SCHATZ 9216

Creso, Venezia, 1770: Sacchini.   SCHATZ 9215

Creso, Venezia, 1788: Terziani.   SCHATZ 10289

Creso rè di Lidia, Firenze, 1777: **Borghi.**   SCHATZ 1228

Eumene, Roma (1754): Aurisicchio.   SCHATZ 503

Il Gran Cidde, Torino (1769): Franchi.   SCHATZ 3328

Planterre, Barthélemi Ambroise.
La famille indigente, Paris, 1797, an V.: Gaveaux.   ML 50.2.F172G2

Pleinchêne (Pleinchesne), Roger Timothée Regnard de.
Der gaertner von Sidon, Frankfurt am Mayn, 1773.   Tr. of his
    Le jardinier de Sidon: Philidor.   Schatz 8016
Le jardinier de Sidon, Paris, 1768: Philidor.   Schatz 8015
Le jardinier de Sidon, Paris, 1770: Philidor.   Schatz 11739

Pleissner, Heinrich Christian.
Die Italienerin zu London, Frankfurt am Mayn, 1783.   Tr. of
    Cimarosa's L'Italiana in Londra.   Schatz 1941
Die liebe in der Ukräne oder Hier geben die maedchen auf die
    freierei aus, Frankfurt am Main, 1786: Spindler.   Schatz 9976

Plotwell, Joan.
See The ragged uproar in the Title catalogue.

Pô, Andrêa del.
Artaserse, Napoli, 1708.   *See* this under Agosti, Giulio.   Schatz 7328

Pocobelli, Angelo.
Briseide, Napoli, 1791: Robuschi.   Schatz 8839

Poggi, Domenico.
Die gastwirthinn.   Tr. of his La locandiera, Dresda, 1776:
    Salieri.   Schatz 9301
La locandiera—Die gastwirthinn, Dresda, 1776: Salieri.   Schatz 9301
Il trionfo della costanza, Bronsvic, 1790: Schwanberg.   Schatz 9767

Poggio, Francesco di.
La Psiche, Lucca, 1654: Breni.   Schatz 1315

Poggio, Michele di.
La libertà ramminga, Lucca, 1678.   *See* M. Curzio in Title
    catalogue.

Poinsinet, Antoine Alexandre Henri.
Le cercle ou La soirée à la mode, Paris, 1764.   ML 48.M2N
Ernelinde, Paris, 1767: Philidor.   ML 50.2.E65P3
Gilles, garçon peintre z'amoureux-t-et rival, Paris, 1758: La
    Borde.   Schatz 5348
Sancho Pança dans son isle, Avignon, 1768: Philidor.   ML 50.2.S2P4
Sancho Pança dans son isle, Paris, 1771: Philidor.   Schatz 8022
Sanko Panssa, Halberstadt, 1776.   Tr. of his Sancho Pança
    dans son isle: Philidor.   Schatz 8023
Le sorcier, Copenhague, 1767: Philidor.   Yudin PQ
Le sorcier, Paris, 1770: Philidor.   Schatz 8027
Tom Jones, Paris, 1766: Philidor.   Schatz 11742
Tom Jones, Paris, 1769: Philidor.   ML 48.M2N
Tom Jones, Florence, 1776: Philidor.   ML 48.M2F
Tom Jones, Paris, 1778: Philidor.   Schatz 8029
Tom Jones, Frankfurt am Mayn, 1773: Philidor.   Tr. of this   Schatz 8030
Tom Jones, Hamburg (1779): Philidor.   Another Tr.   Schatz 8031
Tom Jones, Oels, n. d.: Philidor.   Another Tr.   Schatz 8032
Der zauberer, Regensburg, 1781: Croes.   Tr. of Le sorcier.   Schatz 2294
Der zauberer, Frankfurt am Mayn, 1772.   Tr. of Le sorcier:
    Philidor.   Schatz 8028

Poisson, Jean.
Mirtil, Dresden, 1721: André. ML 50.2.M67A5
Les quatre saisons, Dresde, (1719): Schmidt. Schatz 9641
Le triomphe de l'amour, Dresde (1725): André. ML 50.2.T7

Pontau, Claude Florimond Boizard de.
Arlequin Atys (Les parodies du Nouveau théâtre italien, Paris,
 1738, t. iii). ML 48.P3

Porta, Nunzio.
L'Americana in Olanda, Venezia, 1778: Anfossi. Schatz 264
I contrattempi, Milano (1781): Sarti. Schatz 9429
I contratempi—Die zwischenfaelle, Dresda, 1781: Sarti. Schatz 9430
Gli equivoci svelati, Padova, 1786. L. T. of his I contra-
 tempi: Sarti. Schatz 9431
Orlando Paladino—Ritter Roland, Dresda, 1792: Haydn. Schatz 4612
Ritter Roland. Tr. of his Orlando Paladino, Dresda, 1792:
 Haydn. Schatz 4612
Die zwischenfaelle. Tr. of his I contratempi, Dresda, 1781:
 Sarti. Schatz 9430

Postel, Christian Heinrich.
Die betrogene und nachmals vergoetterte Ariadne, Hamburg
 (1722): Keiser. (O. T. of the text was Die schöne und
 getreue Ariadne.) Schatz 5079
Die bey dem allgemeinen weltfriede von dem Grossen Au-
 gustus geschlossene tempel des Janus, Hamburg (1698):
 Keiser. Schatz 5120
Der bey dem allgemeinen weltfrieden . . . [same title],
 (Hamburg, 1729): Keiser. Schatz 5078
Der grosse könig der afrikanischen Wenden Gensericus als
 Roms und Karthagos ueberwinder. O. T. of his Der sieg
 der schoenheit: Conradi.
Iphigenia, Hamburg (1731) (altered from his "Die wunder-
 bahr errettete Iphigenia" by Georg Caspar Schürmann):
 Graun. Schatz 4103
Der koenigliche printz aus Pohlen, Sigismundus, oder Das
 menschliche leben wie ein traum (Hamburg, 1693):
 Conradi. Schatz 2179
Das menschliche leben wie ein traum. A. T. of his Der
 koenigliche printz aus Pohlen, Sigismundus: Conradi.
Sieg der schoenheit, Hamburg, 1722. (His "Der grosse könig
 der afrikanischen Wenden Gensericus als Roms und Kar-
 thagos ueberwinder," rewritten by Weichmann and
 further altered by Telemann, who also composed the
 alterations): Conradi. Schatz 2180
Die verbindung des grossen Hercules mit der schoenen Hebe
 (Hamburg) 1699: Keiser. Schatz 5114
Die wunderbahr-errettete Iphigenia, Hamburg, 1699: Keiser. Schatz 5132
Die wunderschoene Psyche (Hamburg, 1701): Keiser. Schatz 5116

Pottinger, Israel.
The duenna, London, 1776. A parody of Sheridan's Duenna. Longe 310
The duenna. A new ed., London, n. d. ML 50.2.D852

Powell, George.

     Brutus of Alba: or, Augusta's triumph, London, 1697 (with
         John Verbruggen): D. Purcell.   ML 50.2.B85

     Imposture defeated or A trick to cheat the devil, London,
         1698. (Contains the masque Endimion, the man in the
         moon.)   LONGE 195

Praetorius, Johann Philipp.

     Amphytrion (Hamburg, 1725) (Tr. of Anfitrione): Gasparini
         with additional music by v. Wich.   SCHATZ 3560

     Bretislaus oder Die siegende bestaendigkeit, Hamburg (1725):
         mainly by Keiser.   SCHATZ 5133

     Calypso oder Sieg der weissheit ueber die liebe (Hamburg,
         1727): Telemann.   SCHATZ 10257

     La capricciosa e il credulo—Die geliebte eigensinnige und der
         leicht-glaeubige liebhaber (Hamburg, 1725): Telemann.
         (The author of the Italian original unknown.)   SCHATZ 10271

     Circe (Hamburg) 1734: Keiser. (Text really Tr. from Johann
         Mauricius' drama. Music partly consisted of Italian
         arias.)   SCHATZ 5081

     Der Hamburger jahr-marckt oder Der glueckliche betrug
         (Hamburg, 1725): Keiser.   SCHATZ 5095

     Der laecherliche printz Jodelet (Hamburg, 1726): Keiser.   SCHATZ 5100

     Syphax (Hamburg, 1727). Tr. of Metastasio's Siface: Por-
         pora.   SCHATZ 8363

     Tamerlan (Hamburg, 1725). Tr. of Händel's Tamerlano with
         interpolated intermezzo by Telemann.   SCHATZ 4492

     Die ungleiche heyrath zwischen Vespetta und Pimpinone
         (Hamburg, 1725): Telemann. (Tr. of Pariati's Vespetta
         e Pimpinone text.)   SCHATZ 10273

     Die verkehrte welt (Hamburg, 1728): Telemann. (Tr. of Le
         Sage's Le monde renversé.)   SCHATZ 10267

Pram, Christian Henriksen.

     Serenaden eller De sorte naeser, Kiøbenhavn, 1795: Wedel.   SCHATZ 10919

Predamosche, Verdacchio (*pseud.*).

     Il gran Tamerlano vincitore di Bajazet, Venezia, 1746: Barba. SCHATZ 598

Pretis, Carlo.

     La fede tradita e vendicata, Venezia, 1704 (altered version of
         Silvani's text): Gasparini and Vignola.   SCHATZ 3566

     Le regine di Macedonia, Napoli (1708) (his version of Zeno and
         Pariati's Statira): Gasparini and Vignola   SCHATZ 3583

Prévôt-d'Iray.

     Le quart-d'heure de Rabélais, Paris, an. VII, 1798–99 (with
         Dieu-la-Foy).   ML 48.M2K

Prokoff, Anton.

     Achilles in Scyro, Wien, 1735: Caldara. Tr. of his Achille in
         Sciro (Metastasio).   SCHATZ 1477

Prosindio, Ensildo. *Arcadian name of* Giuseppe Petrosellini.

Provence, Louis Stanislas Xavier, *comte* de (*later* Louis XVIII,
    King of France).

La caravana del Cairo, Milano (1795). Tr. of the next entry. Schatz 4200

La caravane du Caire (Paris) 1783 (with Morel de Chefde-
    ville): Grétry. Schatz 4141

Panurge dans l'isle des lanternes (Paris) 1785 (with Morel de
    Chefdeville): Grétry. ML 50.2.P25G7

Provenzali, Carlo.

Il Castruccio, Lucca, 1781: Quilici, Puccini and Finucci.
    See M. Curzio in Title catalogue.

Prunetti, Michelangelo.

La fedeltà nelle selve, Venetia, 1792: Tritto. Schatz 10484

La fedeltà tra le selve, Napoli, 1796: Tritto. L. T. of the
    above. Schatz 10470

L'ombra di Nino ossia L'impostore scoverto, Palermo (1796):
    Ruggi. Schatz 9145

Puttini, Francesco.

La pescatrice fedele (Venezia, 1776): Anfossi. L. T. of their
    La vera costanza. Schatz 248

Den sande bestandighed. Tr. of his La vera costanza, Kiø-
    benhavn, 1778: Anfossi. Schatz 250

La vera costanza, Roma, 1776: Anfossi. O. T. of their La
    pescatrice fedele. ML 50.2.V33A5

La vera costanza, Firenze, 1777: Anfossi. Schatz 249

La vera costanza—Den sande bestandighed, Kiøbenhavn,
    1778: Anfossi. Schatz 250

La vera costanza—Die wahre beständigkeit, Bronsvic, 1783:
    Anfossi. Schatz 251

La vera costanza (Lisbona, 1789): de Lima. Schatz 5617

Die wahre beständigkeit. Tr. of his La vera costanza, Brons-
    vic, 1783: Anfossi. Schatz 251

Pypers, Pieter.

De twee standbeelden, Amsteldam, 1798: Ruloffs. Schatz 9150

Quétant, Antoine François.

Der fassbinder, Berlin, 1796. Tr. of his and Audinot's Le
    tonnelier: Audinot and Gossec. Schatz 489

Der fassbinder, Frankfurt am Mayn, 1773. Faber's Tr. Schatz 488

Les femmes et le secret, Avignon, 1768: Vachon. ML 50.2.F25V22

Les femmes et le secret, Paris, 1770: Vachon. Schatz 10570

Les femmes et le secret, Paris, 1779: Vachon. Schatz 11750

Der hufschmied, Frankfurth und Leipzig, 1772, and Schatz 8019

Der hufschmied, Riga, 1785. Both Tr. of his Le maréchal
    ferrant: Philidor. Schatz 8020

Le marechal ferrant, Seconde éd., Paris, 1761: Philidor. Yudin PQ

Le maréchal ferrant, Paris, 1765: Philidor. Schatz 8018

Le maréchal ferrant, Paris, 1785: Philidor. Schatz 11741

Der schlosser, Frankfurt am Mayn, 1772. Tr. of his Le serru-
    rier: Kohault. Schatz 5206

Le serrurier, Paris, 1765: Kohault. Schatz 5205

Quétant, Antoine François—Continued.

Le serrurier, Paris, 1766: Kohault.	SCHATZ 11716
Le serrurier, Paris, 1771: Kohault.	SCHATZ 11717
Le tonnelier, Paris, 1765 (partly rewrote Audinot's text): Audinot and Gossec.	ML 50.2.T68
Le tonnelier, Nouv. éd. augm., Paris, 1767 (partly rewrote Audinot's text): Audinot and Gossec.	SCHATZ 487

Quinault, Philippe.

Le théatre de Monsieur Quinault, contenant ses tragedies, comedies, et operas. Nouv. ed., enrichie de figures en taille-douce . . .

Paris, Par la Compagnie des libraires, 1739. 5 v. 17 cm.
Added t.-p., engr., v. 1–2 (v. 1 with imprint: Paris, Chez P. Ribault)
Some of the works have special t.-p., engr.

	PQ 1881.A1 1739
Alceste ou Le triomphe d'Alcide (Amsterdam) 1688: Lully.	ML 50.2.A49L9
Alceste ou Le triomphe d'Alcide (Théâtre, Paris, 1739, t. iv).	PQ 1881.A1 1739
Alceste ou Le triomphe d'Alcide (Recueil général des opéra, t. i, Paris, 1703): Lully.	SCHATZ 5758
Amadi, Venezia, 1793. Sertor's Tr. of his Amadis.	SCHATZ 11666
Amadis (Amsterdam) 1687: Lully.	ML 50.2.A59L9
Amadis (Recueil général des opéra, Paris, 1703, t. ii).	SCHATZ 5759
Amadis (Théâtre, Paris, 1739, t. v).	PQ 1881.A1 1739
Armida, Roma, 1690. Tr. of his Armide.	SCHATZ 5779
Armida, Milano (1780): Misliweczek. (A free Tr. by Migliavacca.)	ML 48.A5v.9
Armida, Vienna, 1760 (modified Italian version of his Armide by Migliavacca): Traetta.	SCHATZ 11382
Armide, Paris, 1777: Gluck.	SCHATZ 3893
Armide, Koeln, 1786: Gluck.	SCHATZ 3894
Armide (Amsterdam, 1686): Lully.	ML 50.2.A76L9
Armide (Recueil général des opéra, t. iii, Paris, 1703): Lully.	SCHATZ 5760
Armide (Théâtre, Paris, 1739, t. v): Lully.	PQ 1881.A1 1739
Armide, Lyon, 1742: Lully.	SCHATZ 5760a
Atys (Amsterdam) 1687: Lully.	ML 50.2.A9L9
Atys (Recueil général des opéra, t. i, Paris, 1703): Lully.	SCHATZ 5761
Atys (Paris) 1738: Lully.	ML 50.2.A9L93
Atys (Théâtre, Paris, 1739, t. iv): Lully.	PQ 1881.A1 1739
Atys, Lyon, 1743: Lully.	SCHATZ 5761a
Atys: Piccinni. *See* Marmontel.	
Cadmus et Hermoine, Paris, 1674: Lully.	ML 50.2.C22L9
Cadmus et Hermoine (Amsterdam) 1687: Lully.	ML 50.2.C22L92
Cadmus et Hermoine (Recueil général des opéra, t. i, Paris, 1703): Lully.	SCHATZ 5763
Cadmus et Hermoine (Théâtre, Paris, 1739, t. iv): Lully.	PQ 1881.A1 1739
Le carnaval (Recueil général des opéra, t. i, Paris, 1703) (with Molière and Lully): Lully.	SCHATZ 5765
L'eglogue de Versailles (Recueil général des opéra, t. iii, Paris, 1703): Lully.	SCHATZ 5776a
Les festes de l'Amour et de Bacchus (Amsterdam), 1686: Lully.	ML 50.2.F3L9
Les festes de l'Amour et de Bacchus (Recueil général des opéra, t. i, 1703): Lully.	SCHATZ 5766

Quinault, Philippe—Continued.

Les festes de l'Amour et de Bacchus (Théâtre, Paris, 1739, t. iv): Lully.	PQ 1881.A1 1739
Isis (Amsterdam) 1682: Lully.	ML 50.2.I69L9
Isis (Amsterdam) 1686: Lully.	ML 49.A2L9
Isis (Recueil général des opera, Paris, 1703, t. ii): Lully.	Schatz 5768
Isis (Théâtre, Paris, 1739, t. iv): Lully.	PQ 1881.A1 1739
Persée (Amsterdam) 1685: Lully.	ML 50.2.P33L9
Persée (Recueil général des opéra, t. ii, Paris, 1703): Lully.	Schatz 5769
Persée (Théâtre, Paris, 1739, t. v): Lully.	PQ 1881.A1 1739
Phaëton (Amsterdam) 1683: Lully.	ML 50.2.P347L9
Phaëton (Amsterdam) 1686: Lully.	ML 50.2.P347L92
Phaeton (Recueil général des opéra, t. ii, Paris, 1703): Lully.	Schatz 5777
Phaëton (Théâtre, Paris, 1739, t. v): Lully.	PQ 1881.A1 1739
Proserpine, Paris, 1680: Lully.	ML 50.2.B35L9
Proserpine (Amsterdam) 1688: Lully.	ML 50.2.P7L9
Proserpine (Recueil général des opéra, Paris, 1703, t. ii): Lully.	Schatz 5770
Proserpine (Théâtre, Paris, 1739, t. v): Lully.	PQ 1881.A1 1739
Proserpine, Paris, 1758: Lully.	ML 50.2.P72L9
Roland (Amsterdam) 1685: Lully.	ML 50.2.R65L9
Roland (Recueil général des opéra, t. iii, Paris, 1703): Lully.	Schatz 5778
Roland (Théâtre, Paris, 1739, t. v): Lully.	PQ 1881.A1 1739
Roland, Paris, 1743: Lully.	Schatz 5780
Roland, Paris, 1778: Piccinni.	ML 50.2.R65P3
Le temple de la paix (Amsterdam) 1686, ballet: Lully.	ML 49.A2L9
Le temple de la paix (Recueil des opéra, Paris, 1703, t. iii): Lully.	Schatz 5772
Le temple de la paix (Théâtre, Paris, 1739, t. v).	PQ 1881.A1 1739
Le temple de la paix, ballet (Recueil général des opéra, t. iii, Paris, 1703): Lully.	Schatz 5772
Thésée, Paris, 1782 (retouched by Morel de Chefdeville): Gossec.	Schatz 4012
Thesée, Paris (Anvers) 1687: Lully.	Schatz 11722
Thesée (Amsterdam) 1688: Lully.	ML 50.2.T45L92
Thesée (Recueil général des opéra, t. i, Paris, 1703): Lully.	Schatz 5773
Thesée (Quinault, Théâtre, 1739, t. iv): Lully.	PQ 1881.A1 1739
Thesée (Paris) 1765 (Journal des spectacles, Paris, 1766, t. ii): Mondonville.	ML 48.J7
Le triomphe d'Alcide. A. T. of his Alceste: Lully.	
Le triomphe de l'amour (Amsterdam) 1686: Lully.	ML 49.A2L9
Le triomphe de l'amour (Recueil général des opéra, Paris, 1703, t. ii): Lully.	Schatz 5774
Le triomphe de l'amour, ballet (Théâtre, Paris, 1739, t. v): Lully.	PQ 1881.A1 1739

Quolfinger, F. G., *ritter* **von Steinberg.**

Hanns Klachl, oder Das rendezvous in der neuen alee, n. pl., 1797: Tuczek.	Schatz 10500
Hanns Klachls zweyter theil, n. pl., 1797: Tuczek.	Schatz 10501

Racine, Jean.

Athalia, Kiel, n. d. Tr. of his Athalie: Schulz.	Schatz 9719
Athalia, Kiøbenhavn, 1790: Schulz.	Schatz 9720

Racine, Jean—Continued.
    Athaliah, London, 1746. Tr. of his Athalie.   Longe 70
    L'idylle sur la paix (Recueil général des opéra, t. iii, Paris,
       1703): Lully.   Schatz 5776

Radet, Jean Baptiste.
    La fête de l'égalité, Paris, an III (1794–95) (with Desfontaines). ML 48.M2L
    Le noble roturier, Paris, an II (1793–94).   ML 48.M2K
    Reinald, Hamburg, 1790. Tr. of his and Barré's Renaud
       d'Ast: Dalayrac.   Schatz 2378
    Renaud d'Ast, Paris, Prault, 1788 (with Barré): Dalayrac. ML 50.2.R39D21
    Renaud d'Ast, Paris, Brunet, 1788 (with Barré): Dalayrac. ML 50.2.R39D22
    Renaud d'Ast (Copenhague, 1793). Tr. of his and Barré's
       text of same title: Dalayrac.   Schatz 2379
    La soirée orageuse, Paris, 1791: Dalayrac.   ML 50.2.S67D2
    La vallée de Montmorency ou Jean Jacques Rousseau dans
       son hermitage, pasticcio. *See* Title catalogue.

Ralph, James.
    The fashionable lady; or, Harlequin's opera, London, 1730:
       ballad opera.   Longe 276

Ramler, Carl Wilhelm.
    Cephalus und Prokris (Theater-Journal fuer Deutschland,
       Gotha, 1778): Reichardt.   Schatz 11754
    Der krieg. *See* this under Weisse.
    Das opfer der Nymphen, Berlin (1774): Schulz.   Schatz 9725
    Procris et Cephale, Berlin, 1777. Tr. of his Cephalus und
       Prokris: Reichardt.   Schatz 8639

Ramsay, Allan.
    The gentle shepherd, London, 1763: ballad opera.   Longe 69
    The gentle shepherd, London, 1796 (Bell, British theatre,
       v. 25).   PR 1241.B4

Raparini, Giorgio Maria.
    I giochi olimpici overo Che fingendo si prova un vero affetto
       (Düsseldorf, 1694): Moratelli.   Schatz 6628

Rasetti, Francesco.
    L'incostanza del militare in amore, ballet. *See* Borghi's La
       donna instabile.

Rau, Johann Christian.
    Narciso. Tr. of Zeno's Il Narciso, Anspach (1697): Pistocchi. Schatz 8197

Rautenstrauch, Johann.
    Der haushahn, Wien, 1783: Hoffmeister.   Schatz 4749

Raymond, B. Louis.
    L'amateur de musique, Paris, 1785: author.   Schatz 8617

Rebel, François.
    Amour pour amour, intermèdes (Journal des spectacles, Paris,
       1766, t. i): author.   ML 48.J7

Recueil general des opera representez par l'Academie royale
de musique, depuis son etablissement . . .
Paris, C. Ballard, 1703–45. 16 v. plates. 15 cm.

Vol. 11–16: De l'imprimerie de J. B. C. Ballard.

Vol. 11: Nouv. éd., 1738.

Edited by J. N. de Francini, H. de Gaureault, sieur de Dumont, Guyenet,
and L. A. E. de Thuret.

Contents.—t. 1. Pomone.—Les peines & les plaisirs de
l'amour.—Les festes de l'Amour & de Bachus.—Cadmus.—Alceste.—Thesée.—Le carnaval.—Atys. t. 2.
Isis.—Psyché.—Bellerophon.—Proserpine.—Le triomphe
de l'Amour.—Persée.—Phaeton.—Amadis. t. 3. Roland.—L'idyle sur la paix & L'eglogue de Versailles.—Le
temple de la paix.—Armide.—Acis & Galatée.—Achille.—
Zephire & Flore.—Thetis & Pelée. t. 4. Orphée.—Enée
& Lavinie.—Coronis.—Astrée.—Ballet, dansé a Villeneuve Saint Georges.—Alcide.—Didon.—Medée.—Cephale & Procris. t. 5. Circé.—Theagene & Cariclée.—
Les amours de Momus.—Les saisons.—Jason, ou La toison
d'or.—Ariadne & Bachus.—La naissance de Venus.—
Meduse. t. 6. Venus & Adonis.—Aricie.—L'Europe galante.—Issé.—Les festes galantes.—Le carneval de Venise.—Amadis de Grece.—Marthésie. t. 7. Le triomphe
des arts.—Canente.—Hesione.—Arethuse. — Scylla. —
Omphale.—Medus.—Fragments de Mr. de Lully. t. 8.
Tancrede.—Ulysse.—Les muses.—Amarillis.—Le carnaval & la folie.—Iphigenie.—Telemaque.—Alcine.—La
Venitienne. t. 9. Philomele. — Alcione. — Cassandre. —
Polixene & Pirrhus. — Bradamante. — Hippodamie. —
Issé.—Semelé. t. 10. Méléagre.—Diomede.—Les festes
venitiennes.—Manto.—Idomenée.—Créuse.—Les amours
de Venus.—Callirhoé.—Medée et Jason. t. 11. Les
amours déguisez.—Arion.—Telephe.—Les festes de Thalie.—La Provencale.—Telemaque.—Les plaisirs de la
paix.—Theonoé.—Ajax. t. 12. Les festes de l'eté.—Hypermnestre.—Ariane.—Camille.—Le jugement de Paris.—
Le ballet des ages.—Semiramis.—Les plaisirs de la campagne. t. 13. Polidor.—Les amours de Protée.—Renaud.—Pirithous.—Les festes grecques et romaines.—La
reine des Péris.—Les elemens.—Telegone. t. 14. Les
stratagesmes de l'amour.—Pyrame et Thisbé.—Les amours
des dieux.—Orion.—La princesse d'Elide.—Tarsis et
Zelie.—Les amours des déesses.—Pirrhus. t. 15. Endimion.—Jephté.—Le ballet des sens.—Biblis.—L'empire
de l'amour.—Hippolyte et Aricie.—Les festes nouvelles.—
Achilles et Deidamie. t. 16. Les graces.—Les Indes
galantes.—Scanderbeg.—Les voyages de l'amour.—Les
romans.—Les genies.—Le triomphe de l'harmonie.—
Castor et Pollux. **ML 48. R4**

The Schatz collection contains another copy of this collection, but the single
librettos were detached by Mr. Schatz and distributed through his collection under composers.

*All these detached copies, and they only, have been entered in the main (title)
catalogue,* whereas the contents of the ML 48.R4 set have not been so
treated, in order to avoid needless duplication and waste of space. An
exception has been made whenever the Schatz collection was found to
lack librettos that form part of the "Recueil général" and which Mr.
Schatz either did not detach or which have disappeared.

Reed, Joseph.

Tom Jones, London, 1769: pasticcio from Arnold, Arne, Joh.
Chr. Bach, and others.   ML 50.2.T71

Tom Jones, London, 1769, second ed: pasticcio from Arnold,
Arne, Joh. Chr. Bach, and others.   LONGE 25

Regali, Matteo.

Il trionfo del ben pubblico, Lucca, 1678: Roncaglia. *See* M.
Curzio in Title catalogue.

Regina.

L'Espagnol genereux—Der grossmuethige Spanier, ballet.
See Tozzi's Zenobia.

Il francese in Londra, ballet. *See* Anfossi's Le gelosie villane.

Le serenate noturne, ballet. *See* Anfossi's Le gelosie villane.

Reichard, Heinrich August Ottokar.

Das fest der Thalie (Gotha, 1775): Schweitzer.   SCHATZ 9773

Das fest der Thalie. (Litteratur und Theater Zeitung, Berlin, 1783.)   SCHATZ 4772

Der hufschmied, Riga, 1785. Tr. of Philidor's Le maréchal
ferrant (Quétant).   SCHATZ 8020

Das redende gemaehlde, Hamburg, 1780. Tr. of Grétry's Le
tableau parlant.   SCHATZ 4190

Zemire und Azor, Mitau, 1782. Tr. of Grétry's Zémire et
Azor (Marmontel).   SCHATZ 4194

Reichert, Ignaz.

Emma und Edgar, Menmmingen[!] 1788: Lacher.   SCHATZ 5362

Reinhard, Bernhard Heinrich Carl.

Heinrich der Loewe, herzog von Braunschweig, Braunschweig, 1793: unknown.   SCHATZ 11618

Reinwald, Wilhelm Friedrich Hermann.

Milton und Elmire, Augsburg, 1780 (alteration of count Spaur's
text): Michl.   SCHATZ 6487

Remena, Marc' Antonio.

Gl' amori tra' gl'odii o sia Il Ramiro in Norvegia, Venetia,
1699: M. A. Ziani.   SCHATZ 11199

Renard, François.

Le carnaval de Venise, Amsterdam, 1699: Campra.   ML 52.2.C23C3

Le carnaval de Venise (Recueil général des opéra, Paris, 1703,
t. vi): Campra.   SCHATZ 1547

Reuling, Carl Ludwig.

Der verliebte eigensinn oder Nannerl bei Hofe, Pressburg,
1778. Tr. of Favart's parody Le caprice amoureux.   SCHATZ 1878

Rezzonico, *conte* **Gastone della Torredi.**

Alessandro e Timoteo, Parma (1782): Sarti.   SCHATZ 9424

Ricci, Francesco.

La sposa persiana, ballet. *See* Anfossi's Il curioso indiscreto.

Ricciardi, *fratelli.*

La morte di Arrigo Sesto rè d'Inghilterra, ballet: Stabingher.
See G. Giordani's Elpinice.

Ricciardi, Domenico.

Alonzo e Cora. A. T. of his ballet La vergine del Sole.

Alonso e Cora, ballet: Capuzzi. *See* Bianchi's Piramo e Tisbe.

Il barbier di Siviglia, ballet. *See* Il Demetrio, Livorno, 1785.

Le congiure del duca di Guisa, ballet. *See* Bianchi's Demetrio.

Il convito di Cesare, ballet. *See* Bianchi's La morte di Cesare.

Cresfonte, rè di Scizia, ballet: Capuzzi. *See* Bianchi's Pizzarro.

Cristiano II, rè di Danimarca, ballet: Martini. *See* Sarti's Attalo rè di Bitinia.

Giasone e Medea, ballet: Horban. *See* Andreozzi's L'Arbace.

Giasone e Medea, ballet: Horban. *See* Borghi's Olimpiade.

L'inaspettata consolazione nelle sventure, ballet: Canavasso. *See* Bianchi's Il trionfo della pace.

L'italiano maritato a Parigi, ballet. *See* Bianchi's Pizzarro.

La liberazione di Lilla, ballet: Canavasso. *See* Bertoni's Medonte.

Il marito ravveduto, ballet. *See* Bianchi's Piramo e Tisbe.

La morte di Pirro, ballet: Trento. *See* Bertoni's Nitteti.

Orfeo, ballet: Schuster. *See* Paisiello's La disfatta di Dario.

Il ratto delle Sabine, ballet. *See* Bertoni's Narbale.

Rinaldo nel giardino incantato d'Armida, ballet: Canavasso. *See* Bianchi's Il trionfo della pace.

Timugino, gran Kan de' Tartari, ballet. *See* Bianchi's Morte di Cesare.

Il trionfo di Alessandro o sia La prigionia di Dario, ballet: Stabingher. *See* Piticchio's Il militare amante.

Il trionfo di Alessandro o sia La prigionia di Dario, ballet: Stabingher. *See* Zanetti's La Didone abbandonata.

La vergine del sole o sia Alonzo e Cora, ballet: Capuzzi. *See* Prati's L'Ifigenia in Aulide.

Ricciardi, Giacomo.

Dorcis e Cleobisa, ballet. *See* G. Giordani's Caio Ostilio.

Gli sposi per inganno, ballet. *See* G. Giordani's Caio Ostilio.

Riccoboni, Francesco, *the younger, sometimes called* Lelio *fils.*

Les catastrophes, Paris, 1732. Third act of his and Romagnesi's "Les amusemens à la mode."   ML 52.2.C25

Medée et Jason. *See* Dominique.

Pirame et Thisbé. *See* Dominique.

Le prétendu, Paris, 1760: Gaviniés.   ML 50.2.P63G2

Riccoboni, Luigi.

The two harlequins, London, 1718. Tr. of his Les deux arlequins.   Longe 262

Riccoboni, Mme**. (Marie Jeanne Laboras de Mezières).**

Sophie ou Le mariage caché, Paris, 1771: Kohault.   Schatz 5207

Richelet, César Pierre.

Tragedies-opera, de l'abbé Metastasio—Traduites en françois. *Vienne, 1751, 5 v.*   ML 49.A2M47

Contains: Aetius (t. i), Cyrus (t. i), Démophon (t. iv), Les Graces vengées (t. iv), Hypsipile (t. v), Regulus (t. v), Siroes (t. iii), Titus (t. ii), Zenobie (t. i).

Rigaud, *Mrs.*

    Artaserse, London, 1779. English Tr. of Bertoni's Artaserse
        (Metastasio).   Schatz 906

    L'avaro deluso, London, 1778. English Tr. of Sacchini's
        opera.   Schatz 9209

Rigauld-Lebrun. *See* Pigault-Lebrun.

Rigo, Antonio (*called by anagram* **Gori** *or* **Goanto Rinio**).

    Il Cajetto, Venezia, 1746: Bertoni.   Schatz 908

    L'isola d'amore, Venezia, 1752: Latilla.   Schatz 5461

    Le metamorfosi odiamorose in birba trionfale nelle gare delle
        terre amanti, Venezia, 1732: Apolloni.   Schatz 301

Rincorato, Academico Olympico. *Academic name of* Pietro
    Paolo Bissari.

Rinio, Goanto. *Anagram of* Rigo, Antonio.

Rinuccini, Ottavio.

    L'Arianna, Mantova, 1608: Monteverdi.   Schatz 6595

    L'Arianna, Venetia, 1640: Monteverdi.   Schatz 6592

    La Dafne, Firenze, 1600: Corsi; Peri; Caccini; Marco di
        Gagliano. *See* Title catalogue.   Schatz 7918

    L'Euridice, Fiorenza, 1600: Peri; Caccini.   Schatz 7919

Riva, Gian Antonio.

    La colonia, Parma, 1775: unknown.   Schatz 11314

Riva, Pietro.

    L'Ifigenia, Venezia, 1707 (with alterations by Aureli): Colletti. Schatz 2112

Rivarota, Ardio. *Anagram of* Dario Varotari.

Riviera, Guido.

    L'Agrippina, moglie di Tiberio, Milano, 1743: Sammartini.   ML 48.A5 v.18

Rizzi, Urbano.

    Achille placato, Venezia, 1707: Lotti.   Schatz 5713

    Creusa, Venezia, 1739: Cardena.   Schatz 1622

    Taican rè della Cina, Venezia, 1707: Gasparini.   Schatz 3584

Roberti, *conte* **Girolamo Frigimelica.**

    Alessandro in Susa, Venezia, 1708: Manza.   Schatz 5916

    Il Dafni, Venezia, 1705: C. F. Pollaroli.   Schatz 8279

    Ercole in cielo, Venetia, 1696: C. F. Pollaroli.   Schatz 8284

    La fortuna per dote, Venezia, 1704: C. F. Pollaroli.   Schatz 8291

    Irene, Venetia, 1695: C. F. Pollaroli.   Schatz 8299

    L'Irene, Napoli, 1704 (with interpolations by N. Barbapic-
        cola): G. B. Pullaroli and D. Scarlatti.   Schatz 9539

    Il Mitridate Eupatore, Venezia, 1707: A. Scarlatti.   Schatz 9524

    Ottone, Venetia, 1694: C. F. Pollaroli.   Schatz 8307

    Il pastore d'Anfriso, Venetia, 1695: C. F. Pollaroli.   Schatz 8310

    Rosimonda, Venetia, 1696: C. F. Pollaroli.   Schatz 8316

    Il selvaggio eroe, Venezia (1707): Caldara.   Schatz 1497

    Il trionfo della libertà, Venezia, 1707: A. Scarlatti.   Schatz 9525

Robineau, Alexandre Louis Bertrand, (*known also as* Mme
    de Beaunoir).

    Le mariage d'Antonio, Paris, 1787: Lucile Grétry.   ML 50.2.M4G7

Roccaforte, Gaetano.

Alcibiade, (Venezia, 1746): Carcano. Schatz 1621

Antigona, Torino, 1752: Casali. Schatz 1678

Antigona, Roma (1751): Galuppi. ML 50.2.A718G3

Antigona, Venezia, 1754: Galuppi. Schatz 3437

Antigona, Mannheim (1752) (German Tr.): Galuppi. Schatz 3438

Antigona, Roma, 1768: G. F. de Majo. Schatz 5862

Antigona, Venezia, 1776: Mortellari. Schatz 6679

Cajo Mario, Venezia (1770): Anfossi. Schatz 231

Il Cajo Mario, Venezia, 1781: Bertoni. Schatz 909

Cajo Mario, Napoli, 1784: Bianchi. Schatz 995

Cajo Mario, Genova (1782): Cimarosa. Schatz 1991

Cajo Mario, Venezia, 1764: Galuppi. Schatz 3502

Cajo Mario, Milano (1791): G. Giordani. Schatz 3835

Cajo Mario, Verona, 1761: Jommelli. Schatz 4896

Cajo Mario, Venezia, 1777: Monza. Schatz 6617

Cajo Mario, Milano, 1765: Scolari. Schatz 9788

Pelopida, Torino (1763): Scarlatti, Gius. Schatz 9551

Talestri, Roma (1727): Jommelli. ML 50.2.T13J6

Tito Manlio, Torino, (1743): Jommelli. Schatz 4881

Rochon de la Valette.

L'école des auteurs, Paris, 1754: unknown. ML 50.2.E23

Rodier.

Ganimede, ballet. *See* Bernabei's L'Ermione.

Rodoteo, Giovanni Battista.

L'Adelaide regia principessa di Susa, Venetia, 1670: Riva. Schatz 8833

Roemer, Georg Christian.

Die lustigen weiber, (Mannheim?), 1792: Ritter. Schatz 8825

Rogatis, Francesco Saverio.

Armida abbandonata, (Lisbona, 1773): Jommelli. Schatz 4901

Armida abbandonata, Napoli, 1780: Jommelli. Schatz 4842

Rolli, Paolo Antonio.

Componimenti poetici in vario genere di Paolo Rolli . . .
Nuova edizione di molte cose inedite, e divisa in quattro
tomi . . .

*Verona, Giannalberto Tumermani, 1744. 1 p. l., xii, [2],
460 p. 17cm.* ML 49.A2R7

On the p. l. a "manifesto dello stampatore" in which he says that the second
to fourth volumes would be issued at intervals of three months after
the first, but as Fassini in the Riv. Mus. It., 1912, p. 37 has pointed out,
only this the first volume was actually published. On p. iii-v a list of
contents of the four volumes as planned for publication. The third and
fourth contained no opera librettos. Those in the first volume are
listed below. The second volume was to contain the following: Merode
e Selinunte, Olimpia in Ebuda, Busiri, Deidamia, Alfonso, Rosane,
Procri, Aristodemo, Rosalinda, Penelope, Fernando.

On p. vii-xii an editorial preface, which Fassini quoted in part in his essay
(*loco cit.*) "Il melodramma italiano a Londra al tempo del Rolli."
The composers of the texts are not mentioned.

Alessandro (Componimenti poetici, Nuova ed., Verona, 1744):
Händel. ML 49.A2R7

Arianna in Naxo (Componimenti poetici, Nuova ed., Verona,
1744): Porpora. ML 49.A2R7

Rolli, Paolo Antonio—Continued.

L'Astarto—Astartus (Hamburg, 1721) (Rev. ed. of Zeno and
　　Pariati's text): G. B. Bononcini.　　　　　　　　　　　Schatz 1202

Crispo, Roma, 1721: G. B. Bononcini.　　　　　　　　　Schatz 1200

Enea nel Lazio (Componimenti poetici, Nuova ed., Verona,
　　1744): Porpora.　　　　　　　　　　　　　　　　　　ML 49.A2R7

Floridante (Componimenti poetici, Nuova ed., Verona, 1744):
　　Händel.　　　　　　　　　　　　　　　　　　　　　ML 49.A2R7

Griselda (Componimenti poetici, Nuova ed., Verona, 1744):
　　G. B. Bononcini.　　　　　　　　　　　　　　　　　ML 49.A2R7

Die heldenmuethige schaefer Romulus und Remus (Hamburg,
　　1724): Porta and Kuntze.　Tr. of Rolli and Porta's Numi-
　　tore, also known as Rhea Sylvia.　　　　　　　　　　Schatz 8381

Der hochmuethige Alexander, Hamburg (1726).　Tr. of his
　　Alessandro: Händel.　　　　　　　　　　　　　　　Schatz 4473

Ifigenia in Aulide (Componimenti poetici, Nuova ed., Verona,
　　1744): Porpora.　　　　　　　　　　　　　　　　　　ML 49.A2R7

Der misslungene braut-wechsel, oder Richardus I, Koenig
　　von England, (Hamburg), 1729.　Tr. of his Riccardo I, rè
　　d'Inghilterra: Händel and partly by the transl. Wend,
　　whose German arias were composed by Telemann.　　Schatz 4488

Muzio Scevola—Mutius Scaevola, Hamburg (1723): Mattei
　　(act I), G. B. Bononcini (act II), Händel (act III).　　Schatz 168

Muzio Scevola (Componimenti poetici, Nuova ed., Verona,
　　1744): Händel, Bononcini, Mattei.　　　　　　　　　ML 49.A2R7

Numitore (Componimenti poetici, Nuova ed., Verona, 1744):
　　Porta.　　　　　　　　　　　　　　　　　　　　　ML 49.A2R7

Orfeo (Componimenti poetici, Nuova ed., Verona, 1744):
　　pasticcio from Hasse, Vinci, Araja, Porpora.　　　　ML 49.A2R7

Il Polifemo (Madrid) 1748: Corselli, Corradini, and Mele.　Schatz 2253

Polifemo (Componimenti poetici, Nuova ed., Verona, 1744):
　　Porpora.　　　　　　　　　　　　　　　　　　　　ML 49.A2R7

Sabrina (Componimenti poetici, Nuova ed., Verona, 1744):
　　Pescetti and others.　　　　　　　　　　　　　　　ML 49.A2R7

Sabrina, London, 1737: Pescetti and others.　　　　　Schatz 8859

Scipione (Componimenti poetici, Nuova ed., Verona, 1744):
　　Händel.　　　　　　　　　　　　　　　　　　　　ML 49.A2R7

Der thrazische printz Floridantes, Hamburg, 1723.　Tr. of his
　　Floridante: Händel.　　　　　　　　　　　　　　　Schatz 4477

Rolt, Richard.

Almena, London, 1764: Arne, M., and Battishill.　　　Longe 37

Amintas, London, 1769: Rush, Guglielmi, etc.　Altered ver-
　　sion of The royal shepherd.　　　　　　　　　　　Longe 37

Amintas (Collection of the most esteemed farces, Edinburgh,
　　1792, t. vi).　　　　　　　　　　　　　　　　　　Schatz 11753F

Eliza (London) 1754: Arne.　　　　　　　　　　　　Longe 116

Eliza (London) 1757: Arne.　　　　　　　　　　　　Longe 183

The royal shepherd, London, 2d ed. (176–): Rush.　Text
　　based on Metastasio's "Il rè pastore."　　　　　　　Longe 37

The royal shepherd, London, 3d ed. (176–): Rush.　　Longe 192

Romagnesi, Giovanni Antonio (Jean Antoine).

Alceste.　*See* Dominique.

Arlequin Bellérophon.　*See* Dominique.

Romagnesi, Giovanni Antonio (Jean Antoine)—Continued.

Arlequin Phaëton. *See* Dominique.

Arlequin Roland. *See* Dominique.

Arlequin Tancrede. *See* Dominique.

La bonne femme. *See* Dominique.

Les catastrophes. *See* Riccoboni.

Don Micco e Lesbina. *See* Dominique.

Hesione. *See* Dominique.

Le joueur. *See* Dominique.

Medée et Jason. *See* Dominique.

Pirame et Thisbé. *See* Dominique.

Romanelli, Luigi.

Il ritratto, Milano (1799): Zingarelli.   SCHATZ 11257

Il trionfo del bel sesso, Milano, 1799: Nicolini.   SCHATZ 7138

Romoli, Giacomo.

Venere e Adoue, ballet. *See* Anfossi's La contadina incivilita.

Ronzi, Gaspare.

Amor vince tutto, ballet. *See* P. Guglielmi's La morte di Cleopatra.

Astarbea, ballet. *See* Zingarelli's Giulietta e Romeo.

La Didone, ballet. *See* Tritto's Apelle e Campaspe.

Enea e Lavinia, ballet. *See* P. Guglielmi's La morte di Cleopatra.

L'equivoco, ballet: Trento. *See* Paër's Cinna.

Ergasto ed Eurilla vinti dall' amore, ballet. *See* Mayr's Lodoiska.

La fanciulla mal custodita, ballet. *See* Anfossi's Gli artigiani.

La fanciulla mal custodita, ballet. *See* Sarti's Fra i due litiganti il terzo gode, Milano, 1795.

Il geloso sincerato. A. T. of his ballet Giannina e Bernadone.

La ghinghetta, ballet. *See* Tarchi's L'impostura poco dura.

Giannina e Bernadone ossia Il geloso sincerato, ballet. *See* Cimarosa's Artemisia.

Ginevra di Scozia, ballet. *See* Mayr's Lodoiska.

Giulietta e Romeo, ballet. *See* Tritto's Nicaboro in Jucatan.

L'ircana in Julfa, ballet. *See* Calegari's Le due sorelle incognite.

Lausa e Lidia, ballet. *See* Tarchi's L'impostura poco dura.

Lauso e Lidia o sia Il trionfo dell' amicizia, ballet. *See* Nasolini's Teseo a Stige.

La morte di Calisto, ballet. *See* Paër's Cinna.

Le nozze di Peleo e Teti, ballet. *See* Cimarosa's Artemisia.

Odervik, ballet. *See* Zingarelli's Il ritratto.

Ottocaro, ballet. *See* Nicolini's Il trionfo del bel sesso.

Il re pastore, ballet. *See* Anfossi's Gli artigiani.

Il rè pastore, ballet. *See* Sarti's Fra i due litiganti il terzo gode, Milano, 1795.

Le reclute d'amore, ballet. *See* Tritto's Apelle e Campaspe.

Il segreto, ballet. *See* Nicolini's Il trionfo del bel sesso.

Li Zingani in fiera, ballet. *See* Tritto's Nicaboro in Jucatan.

Rordorf, Ernst Friedrich.

Hass und aussoehnung oder Die verfolgte und triumphirende liebe, Glatz, 1797: Grueger.   SCHATZ 4223

Rose, Johann Wilhelm.

Pocahontas, Jamestown [Ansbach] 1784: unknown. Schatz 11641

Rose, John.

Caernarvon Castle, or The birth of the Prince of Wales, London, 1793: Attwood. Longe 239

The prisoner (London, 1792): Attwood. Longe 236

Rospigliosi, Giulio, *cardinal.*

Chi soffre speri, Roma, 1639: V. Mazzocchi and M. Marazzoli. Schatz 6223

Ross, Anna.

The cottagers, London, 1788: Shield(?). Longe 119

Rossi, Domenico.

Alessandro nell' Indie, ballet. *See* Cimarosa's La Circe.

Chi la fà l'aspetta, ballet. *See* Tarchi's Ifigenia in Aulide.

La contadina in corte, ballet. *See* Sacchini's Armida.

Il disertore francese, ballet. *See* Jommelli's Armida abbandonata.

Il giardino delle Tuillerie in Parigi, ballet. *See* Cimarosa's Circe.

Il primo giorno dell' anno nella China, ballet: Marescalchi. *See* Tarchi's Ifigenia in Aulide.

Il servo di due padroni, ballet. *See* Martin y Soler's Ifigenia in Aulide.

La vittoria di Tamerlano contro Bajazette ossia La Rossana, ballet. *See* Sacchini's Armida.

Rossi, Francesco.

La caduta di Gelone, Venezia, 1719: Buini. Schatz 1390

La Nicopoli, Venetia, 1700: Borgognini. Schatz 1241

Il Paolo Emilio, Venetia (1699): Pignatta. Schatz 8170

Rossi, Gaetano.

Antigona, Venezia, 1799: Basili. Schatz 630

Carolina e Mexicow, Venezia (1798): Zingarelli. Schatz 11268

Le feste d'Iside, Venezia, 1799 (Retouched version of Zeno and Pariati's Sesostri rè d'Egitto): Nasolini. Schatz 7002

Labino e Carlotta (Venezia, 1799): Mayr. Schatz 6155

Lodoiska, Venezia (1796): Mayr. (Text really by Francesco Gonella.) Schatz 6158

Lodoiska, Venezia (1799–1800): Mayr. Schatz 6159

Il matrimonio di Figaro. A. T. of his La pazza giornata: Portugal.

La pazza giornata, ossia Il matrimonio di Figaro, Venezia, 1799: Portugal. Schatz 8439

Il ratto delle Sabine, Venezia, 1799: Zingarelli. Schatz 11256

Gli Sciti, Milano (1799): Nicolini. Schatz 7133

Rossi, Giacomo.

Rinaldo, Hamburg (1715). Tr. of his and Hill's Rinaldo: Händel. Schatz 4489

Rinaldo (Hamburg, 1723). L. ed. of the above. Schatz 4501

Rinaldo, Napoli, 1718: Händel, added arias by Leo. Schatz 4495

Rinaldo (A. Hill, Dramatic works, London, 1760, t. I) (plan by Hill, Italian text by the above, English Tr. by Hill): Händel. Longe 325

Rossi, Carlo Giuseppe Lanfranchi-

L'accorta cameriera, Torino (1783): Martin y Soler. L. T. of
 his In amor ci vuol destrezza.   Schatz 6031
L'amante per bisogno, Venezia, 1781: Gazzaniga.   Schatz 3689
Gli amanti canuti, Venezia, 1781: Anfossi.   Schatz 223
Gli amanti canuti—Die liebenden greise (Dresda, 1783):
 Anfossi.   Schatz 224
Le cognate in contesa, Venezia (1780): Zannetti.   Schatz 11137
In amor ci vuol destrezza, Venezia, 1782: Martin y Soler.   Schatz 6010
Die liebenden greise. Tr. of his Gli amanti canuti (Dresda,
 1783): Anfossi.   Schatz 224
Il Muzio Scevola, Padova, 1762: Galuppi.   Schatz 3464
La sposa bizzarra, Venezia (1781): Santi.   Schatz 9394
Telemaco nell' isola di Calipso, Firenze, 1773: Meucci.   Schatz 6400
Il trionfo d'Arianna, Venezia (1781): Anfossi.   Schatz 271
La vergine del sole, Napoli, 1786: Tritto.   Schatz 10464

Rossi, Vinceslao de.

Diana e Endimione, ballet. *See* Bertoni's L'anello incantato.
Diana ed Endimione, ballet. *See* P. Guglielmi's Il disertore.
Le due sultane rivali, ballet. *See* Sarti's La giardiniera
 brillante.

Rossini, Andrea.

Il Dioclete, Venetia, 1687: Orgiani.   Schatz 7297
Irene e Costantino, Venetia, 1681: Zannettini.   Schatz 11142
Silla, Venetia, 1683: Freschi.   Schatz 3355

Rossy, Domenico, *or* **Giuseppe Domenico de** (*same as* **Rossi, Domenico?**).

Alfonso di Castiglia, ballet. *See* Paër's Tegene e Laodicea.
L'equivoco delli due amanti molinari, ballet. *See* Nasolini's
 Gl'Indiani.
L'equivoco dei due mulinari, ballet. *See* Paër's Tegene e
 Laodicea.
Mysis ed Eufrasia ossia I due gemelli, ballet. *See* Trento's
 Bianca de' Rossi.

Rost, Johann Christoph.

Rodelinde, königinn der Longobarden. Tr. of Rodelinda,
 regina de' Longobardi (Berlino) 1741: Graun (Bottarelli). Schatz 4111
———— Same title, Berlino, 1778: Graun.   Schatz 4117

Rothammer, Wilhelm.

Johann, der muntere scifensieder, Wien, 1791: unknown.   Schatz 11626

Rothmann.

Das urtheil des Midas, Muenster, 1781. Tr. of Grétry's Le
 jugement de Midas (d'Hèle).   Schatz 4162

Rousseau, Jean Baptiste.

Jason ou La toison d'or (Recueil général des opéra, Paris, 1703,
 t. v): Colasse.   Schatz 2100
Venus et Adonis (Amsterdam) 1699: Desmarets.   ML 50.2.V3D2
Venus et Adonis (Recueil général des opéra, t. vi, Paris, 1703):
 Desmarets.   Schatz 2535
Venus und Adonis (Hamburg, 1725). Tr. of the above.   Schatz 2536

Rousseau, Jean Jacques.

The cunning man, London, 1766. Tr. of his Le devin du vil-
    lage: author.   Longe 257

The cunning man, London, 1766 (2d ed.).   Longe 26

The cunning man (Collection of the most esteemed farces,
    Edinburgh, 1792, t. ii).   Schatz 11753B

Le devin du village, Geneve, 1760: author.   ML 50.2.D515R6

Le devin du village, Geneve, 1796: author.   ML 50.2.D515R7

Pigmalion, n. i., 1772: Coignet and Rousseau.   ML 50.2.P41R7

Pygmalion, Genève (Lyon) 1786: Coignet and Rousseau.   Schatz 2095

Pygmalion, Mannheim, 1778. Tr. of the above.   Schatz 2096

Pygmalion (Melodramen, Pilsen und Klattau, 1791): Benda.
    Tr. of his monodrame.   Schatz 775

Rousseau, Pierre.

La coquette sans le sçavoir. *See* Favart.

Rowson, Susanna.

Slaves in Algiers or A struggle for freedom, Philadelphia, 1794:
    Reinagle.   PR 1241.D7   **v.9**

Roy, Pierre Charles.

Ariane, Paris, 1717 (with La Grange): Mouret.   ML 50.2.A739M6

Ariane (Recuei général des opéra, t. xii, Paris, 1734 (with
    Lagrange): Mouret.   Schatz 6694.

Les Augustales, Paris, 1744: Rebel and Francoeur.   Schatz 8621

Le ballet des sens (Recueil général des opéra, t. xv, Paris,
    1739): Mouret. (Also called Le triomphe des sens).   Schatz 6744

Bradamante (Recueil général des opéra, t. ix, Paris, 1710): La
    Coste.   Schatz 5353

Callirhoé (Recueil général des opéra, t. x, Paris, 1714): Des-
    touches.   Schatz 2544

Créuse l'Athénienne (Recueil général des opéra, t. x, Paris,
    1714): La Coste.   Schatz 5354

Les élémens, n. i., n. d.: Lalande and Destouches.   ML 52.2.E4

Les élémens (Recueil général des opéra, t. xiii, Paris, 1734):
    Lalande and Destouches.   Schatz 5379

Les Graces (Recueil général des opéra, Paris, 1745, t. xvi):
    Mouret.   ML 48.R4

Hippodamie (Recueil général des opéra, Paris, 1710, t. ix):
    Campra.   Schatz 1556

Philomele, Amsterdam, 1706: La Coste.   ML 50.2.P36L2

Philomèle (Recueil général des opéra, t. ix, Paris, 1710): La
    Coste.   Schatz 5356

Philomèle, Lyon, 1742: La Coste.   Schatz 5356a

Sémiramis (Recueil général des opéra, t. xii, Paris, 1734):
    Destouches.   Schatz 2550

Les stratagèmes de l'amour (Recueil général des opera, t. xiv,
    Paris, 1734): Destouches.   Schatz 2551

Rozoy, Barnabé Farmain de.

Henri IV, Paris, 1775: Martini.   Schatz 6039

Les mariages Samnites, Paris, 1776: Grétry (with music).   Schatz 4169

Les mariages Samnites, Nouv. éd., Paris, 1776 (without music):
    Grétry.   Yudin PQ

Les mariages Samnites, Paris, 1782: Grétry.   Schatz 4170

Die samnitische vermaehlungsfeyer, Berlin, 1780. Tr. of his
    Les marriages Samnites: Grétry.   Schatz 4171

Ruberti, Oratio Francesco.

L'inganno trionfato overo La disperata speranza ravvivata
ne' successi di Giacopo Quinto di Scozia e Maddalena di
Francia, Parma (1673): Bazzani.   Schatz 670

Ruggeri, Giovanni Maria.

L'inganno trionfante in amore, Venezia, 1725. (Merely rewrote Noris's text): Vivaldi.   Schatz 10772

Rulant, Godfrid.

Giocasta. Tr. of Wilderer and Krafft's Giocasta, Dusseldorf
(1696) (Moniglia).   Schatz 11014

Ruloffs, Bartholomeus

Pandolfus en Zerbina of De meid meesteres, Amsteldam, 1793.
Tr. of Pergolesi's La serva padrona (Federico).   Schatz 7896

De shoone Arsène, Amsteldam, 1789. Tr. of Monsigny's La
belle Arsène (Favart).   Schatz 6586

De visschers, Amsterdam, 1793. Tr. of Gossec's Les pêcheurs
(de La Salle).   Schatz 4015

Ruprecht, Stephan.

Das wuetende heer oder Das maedchen im thurme (Wien,
1787) (revision of Bretzner's text): Ruprecht.   Schatz 9162

Ryves, Eliza.

The prude, n. i. (1777): ballad opera (detached from her
"Poems on several occasions").   Longe 197

S., G. (Sertor, Gaetano?).

Il conte Policronio o sia Le bugie hanno le gambe corte,
Firenze, 1791: Moneta.   Schatz 6551

Sacco, Antonio.

Inca il tiranno, ballet. *See* Bertoni's Andromaca.
Pane e Siringa, ballet. *See* Piccinni's La pescatrice.
La pietà inaspettata, ballet. *See* Bertoni's Andromaca.
La sposa gronlandese, ballet: *See* Piccinni's La pescatrice.

Saddumene, Bernardo.

Il capitan Galoppo, Venezia, 1741: Hasse. O. T. was La
Fantesca.   Schatz 4588

La fantesca. O. T. of his Il capitan Galoppo, Venezia, 1741:
Hasse.

Sainctonge (Saintonge), Louise Geneviéve Gillot, Mme de.

Circe, Amsterdam, 1695: Desmarets.   ML 50.2.C51D2
Circe (Recueil général des opéra, t. v, Paris, 1703): Desmarets. Schatz 2530
Didon (Recueil général des opéra, t. iv, Paris, 1703): Des-
marets.   Schatz 2531

Saint-Cyr, Jacques Antoine, *baron* de Révéroni.

Le délire ou Les suites d'une erreur, Paris, an VIII (1799):
Berton.   ML 50.2.D35B2
Elisa ou Le voyage au Mont-Bernard, Paris (1794): Cherubini. ML 50.2.E3C3

Saint-Jean.

Ariane et Bachus, Amsterdam, 1699: Marais.   ML 50.2.A742M2
Ariadne et Bacchus (Recueil général des opéra, t. v, Paris,
1703): Marais.   Schatz 5920

St. John, John.
The island of St. Marguerite, London, 1789: Shaw.   Longe 203

Saint-Just, Claude Godard d'Aucour de.
La famille suisse, Paris (1797): Boieldieu.   ML 50.2.F176B6
Zoraime et Zulnar, Paris, an VI (1798): Boieldieu.   ML 50.2.Z65B6

Salfi, Francesco.
La congiura Pisoniana, Milano (1797): Tarchi.   Schatz 10215

Salomoni, Francesco.
I cacciatori burlati, ballet: Le Messier. *See* Hasse's L'Olim
piade.

Salomoni (Salamoni), Giuseppe.
Arianna, ballet: Sighizzelli. *See* Colla's Sicotencal.
La clemenza di Tito, ballet: Le Messier. *See* Galuppi's La
clemenza di Tito.
La isola incantata di Circe la maga, ballet. *See* Pampani's
Demofoonte.
Il matematico, ballet: unknown. *See* Pampani's Demofoonte.

Salvadori, Andrea.
Il Medoro, Fiorenza, 1623: Marco da Gagliano (and Peri).   ML 48.M2F
La regina Sant[!] Orsola, Fiorenza, 1625: Marco da Gagliano
(14½^{cm}).   Schatz 3410
La regina Sant' Orsola, Fiorenza, 1625: Marco da Gagliano
(23½^{cm}).   ML 50.2.R34

Salvi, Antonio.
Adelaide, Roma, 1743: Cocchi.   Schatz 2052
Adelaide-Adelheid, Hamburg (1744): Finazzi, Scalabrini,
etc.   Schatz 3101
Adelaide, Venezia, 1729: Orlandini.   Schatz 7326
Adelaide, Mantova (1731): Orlandini.   ML 50.2.A31O7
Adelaide, Roma, Bernabò, 1723: Porpora.   Schatz 8376
Adelaide, Roma, Ferri, 1723: Porpora.   ML 50.2.A31P6
Amore e maestà, Bologna, 1721: Buini.   Schatz 1384
Andromaca, Venezia (1772): Bertoni.   Schatz 904
L'Andromaca, Napoli (1742): Leo.   Schatz 5556
Andromaca, Torino (1781): Martin y Soler.   Schatz 6027
Andromaca, Venezia, 1790: Nasolini.   Schatz 6999
Ariodante, Venezia, 1716: C. F. Pollaroli.   Schatz 8272
Ariodante (Venezia, 1745): G. C. Wagenseil.   Schatz 10816
Arminio, Firenze, 1725: pasticcio.   ML 48.A5 v.16
L'Arminio (Venezia) 1747: Galuppi.   Schatz 3482
Arminio, Milano, 1730: Hasse.   Schatz 4575
Arminio—Arminio (Dresden, 1745): Hasse.   Schatz 4512
L'Arminio, Venezia, 1722: C. F. Pollaroli.   Schatz 8273
Arminio, London, 1760 (with interpolations from Metastasio):
pasticcio from Perez and others.   ML 50.2.A77
Arminio, Roma, 1722: A. Scarlatti.   ML 50.2.A77S2
Arsace, Venezia, 1768: Franchi.   Schatz 3326
Arsace, Venezia, 1718: M. A. Gasparini.   Schatz 3599
L'Arsace, Venezia (1737): Giacomelli.   Schatz 3810
Arsace, Firenze (1732): Orlandini.   ML 48.A5 v.18
Arsace, Napoli, 1754: Sabatini.   Schatz 9201

Salvi, Antonio—Continued.

Arsace, Napoli, 1718: Sarro.	Schatz 9414
L'artigiano gentiluomo. O. T. of his Il bottegaro gentiluomo.	
L'artigiano gentiluomo: Hasse. O. T.: Larinda e Vanesio.	
Astianatte, (Monaco, 1717): M. A. Bononcini.	Schatz 1204
Astianatte, Venezia, 1755: Pampani.	Schatz 7755
Attalo rè di Bitinia, Roma (1790): Caruso.	Schatz 1661
Attalo rè di Bitinia (Lisboa, 1791): Robuschi.	Schatz 8842
Attalo rè di Bitinia, Venezia, 1783: Sarti.	Schatz 9472
L'avaro, Venezia, 1720: Gasparini.	Schatz 3594
Barillotto, Venezia, 1712: Sarro.	Schatz 9421
Barilotto e Slapina. L. T. of his Barillotto. *See* Gasparini's Lucio Papirio.	ML 50.2.L85G2
Berenice. O. T. of his Le gare di politica e d'amore.	
Berenice, Venezia, 1734: Araya.	Schatz 305
Il Bertarido, rè de Longobardi, Venezia, 1727: Boniventi. (L. T. of S.'s Rodelinda regina de' Longobardi.)	Schatz 1185
Il bottegaro gentiluomo, Venezia: Orlandini(?). L. T. of Salvi's "L'artigiano gentiluomo," known also as "Larinda e Vanesio."	Schatz 7350
Dionisio re di Portogallo, Firenze, 1707: Perti.	ML 50.2.D57P3
Dionisio Siracusano, Parma (1689): Perti.	Schatz 7955
Gl'equivoci d'amore, e d'innocenza, Venezia, 1723: Gasparini.	Schatz 3565
Eumene, Venezia (1717): Albinoni.	Schatz 92
Eumene, Monaco (1720): Torri.	Schatz 10364
The gamester—(Il giocatore), London, 1736: Orlandini. Tr. and L. T. of Salvi's Il marito giogatore e la moglie bacchettona.	Schatz 7339
Le gare di politica e d'amore, Venezia, 1711: Ruggeri.	Schatz 9137
Ginevra, Venezia (1753): Bertoni.	Schatz 913
Ginevra, Venezia (1733): Sellitti.	Schatz 9826
Il giocatore. *See his* The gamester.	
Il giocatore—Le joueur, Paris, 1752: Orlandini and others. L. T. of his Il marito giogatore e la moglie bacchettona.	ML 50.2.G4O7
Der handwercks-mann ein edelmann (Dresden, 1734). Tr. of his L'artigiano gentiluomo: Hasse.	Schatz 4523
Ipermestra, Venezia, 1724: Giacomelli.	
Ipermestra, Milano, 1727: Brivio and others.	Schatz 1327
Le joueur. Tr. of his Il giocatore, Paris, 1752: Orlandini and others.	ML 50.2.G4O7
Larinda e Vanesio. *See also* for L. T. *his* Il bottegaro gentiluomo, Venice, 1739 (Schatz 7350).	
Larinda e Vanesio. O. T. of his L'artigiano gentiluomo: Hasse.	
Lucio Papirio—Lucius Papirius (Breslavia, 1732): Bioni.	Schatz 1044
Lucio Papirio, Roma, 1714: Gasparini.	ML 50.2.L85G2
Lucio Papirio, Mantova (1718): Orlandini.	Schatz 7352
Lucio Papirio, Venezia, 1737: Porpora.	Schatz 8371
Lucio Papirio, Venezia, 1715: Predieri.	Schatz 8457
Lucius Papirius. Tr. of his Lucio Papirio (Breslavia, 1732): Bioni.	Schatz 104
Il marito giocatore e la moglie bacchettona, Venezia, 1719: Orlandini or Vinci.	Schatz 7337
Ottone, Venezia, 1740: G. d'Alessandri.	Schatz 157
Publio Cornelio Scipione, Torino (1726): Giai	Schatz 3817

Salvi, Antonio—Continued.

La Rodelinda, Venezia, 1731: Cordans. SCHATZ 2227

Rodelinda, koenigin in der Lombardey (Hamburg, 1734). Tr.
of his and Haym's Rodelinda: Händel. SCHATZ 4490

Serpilla e Bacocco (Monaco, 1722): Orlandini? L. T. of
Salvi's Il marito giogatore e la moglie bacchettona. SCHATZ 7338

Stratonica, Napoli (1727) (altered by de Palma): pasticcio. ML 50.2.S75

Teodorico, Bologna (1728): Buini and others. SCHATZ 1383

Teodorico, Venezia, 1720: Porta. SCHATZ 8393

Salvioli, *conte* de.

Aristo e Temira e Orfeo ed Euridice, Venezia, 1776: Bertoni.
(Text of Orfeo by Calsabigi.) SCHATZ 934

Aristo e Temira, Bologna, 1771: Monza. SCHATZ 3934

Temira e Aristo, Venezia, 1795: Mayr. (Originally De S.'s
title was "Aristo e Temira.") SCHATZ 6203

Salvioni, *abbate.*

Fedra, Napoli, 1788: Paisiello. (Merely a modification of
Frugoni's "Ippolito ed Aricia" libretto.) SCHATZ 7668

Salvoni, Luigi Bernardo.

Le gare degli amanti, Parma (1773): Fortunati. SCHATZ 3310

Saminiati, Amadeo.

La città felice, Lucca, 1669. *See* M. Curzio in Title catalogue.

Il consiglio fedele, Lucca, 1672. *See* M. Curzio in Title catalogue.

San Stefano, *conte* di. *See* Piazza.

Sanctis, Luigi De.

Ines de Castro, Venezia, 1795: Bianchi, Nasolini, Gerace,
Cervellini. SCHATZ 1012

Sander, Johann Daniel.

Alfsol (Cramer's Musik, 1789). ML 4.M3

Sanseverino, Carlo.

Romeo e Giulia, Seconda ed.—Romeo et Julie, Berlino—
Berlin, 1776. ML 50.2.R67

Romeo e Giulia—Romeo und Julie, Brunsviga, 1778: Schwanberg. SCHATZ 9766

Romeo e Giulia—Romeo und Julie (Berlino, 1780): Schwanberg. SCHATZ 9766a

Santerre, Jean Baptiste Lourdet de.

Annette et Lubin. *See* Mad. Favart.

Colinette à la cour. A. T. of his La double épreuve: Grétry.

La double épreuve, ou Colinette à la cour, Paris, 1784: Grétry. SCHATZ 4147

L'embarras de richesses, Paris, 1782: Grétry. SCHATZ 4148

La fille mal gardée, ou Le pédant amoureux. *See* Mad.
Favart.

Le savetier et le financier (Paris, 1778): Rigel. ML 50.2.S3R3

Santucci, Leone.

Martio Coriolano, Lucca, 1669. *See* M. Curzio in Title catalogue

San Vitale, *conte* **Jacopo Antonio.**

Il Bajazette, Parma (1765): Bertoni.   SCHATZ 936

Enea e Lavinia (Firenze, 1768): Traetta.   SCHATZ 10399

Tito Manlio (Venezia, 1746) (modernization of Matteo Noris'
text): Jommelli.   SCHATZ 4900

Uranio e Erasitea, Parma (1773): Colla.   SCHATZ 2108

Sara, Giovanni Battista.

L'inganno fortunato, Venezia, 1721 (finished by Pavieri):
Boniventi.   SCHATZ 1192

Sarcone, Michele.

Cerere placata (Napoli, 1772): Jommelli.   SCHATZ 4876

Sarker.

Axur, koenig von Ormus, Wien, 1788. Tr. of Salieri's Axur,
rè d'Ormus (Da Ponte).   SCHATZ 9327

Il Satirico. *See* Verdacchio Predamosche.

Saunier, Vincenzo.

Cadmo ed Ino, ballet: Le Messier. *See* Piccinni's Tigrane.

Cerere e Trittolemo, ballet: Gioanetti. *See* Calderara's Ricimero.

Cittadini di Sinope festeggianti le nozze di Mitridate, ballet:
Le Messier. *See* Piccinni's Tigrane.

Giudicio di Paride, ballet: Gioanetti. *See* Calderara's Ricimero.

La morte ed il rinascimento del pastore Adone, ballet: Le
Messier. *See* Bach's Artaserse.

Sacrifizio detto Taurobolio pella elezione ed inaugurazione di
un re di Norvegia, ballet: Gioanetti. *See* Calderara's
Ricimero.

Telemaco nell' isola di Calipso, ballet: Le Messier. *See* Piccinni's Tigrane.

Sauveterre, Francesco.

La statua animata, ballet. *See* Piccinni's La scaltra litterata.

Li vendemmiatori, ballet. *See* Piccinni's La scaltra letterata

Sauvigny, Edme Billardon de.

Péronne sauvée, Paris, 1783: Dezède.   SCHATZ 2526

Sbarra, Francesco.

Alessandro il vincitor di se stesso, Lucca, 1654 (3d impression):
Cesti and Bigongiari.   SCHATZ 1786

Alessandro vincitor di se stesso, Venetia, 1651: Cavalli.   SCHATZ 1715

Alessandro vincitor di se stesso, Bologna, 1655: Cavalli.   SCHATZ 11681

L'amor della patria, superiore ad og'altro, Venetia, 1668: unknown.   SCHATZ 11301

La corte, n. i., n. d. apparently detached from collected works:
Bigongiari.   SCHATZ 1036

Il disinganno. *See his* La verità raminga, Venetia, 1664.

La nave d'Argo, Lucca, 1654: Roncaglia. *See* M. Curzio in
Title catalogue.

La tirannide dell' interesse, Lucca, 1653: Bigongiari.   ML 50.2.T55

La tirannide dell' interesse, Venetia, 1658: Bigongiari.   SCHATZ 1035

La verità raminga, e'l Disinganno, Venetia, 1664: unknown.   ML 50.2.V35

Scalesi, Giuseppe.

Le donne invidiose ossia L'onestà trionfante, ballet: Trento. *See* Bianchi's La sposa in equivoco.

Enrichetta, ballet: Trento. *See* Bianchi's La sposa in equivoco.

Gelosia per gelosia, ballet. *See* Paisiello's Il rè Teodoro in Venezia.

Scawen, John.

New Spain or Love in Mexico, London, 1790: Arnold.   ML 50.2.N43

Schacht, Theodor, *freiherr* **von.**

Die insel der liebe, Regensburg, 1781. Tr. and expansion of Sacchini's "L'isola d'amore," with additional music by the above.   Schatz 9231

Schiebeler, Daniel.

Basilio und Quiteria, n. i., n. d.: Telemann.   Schatz 10256

Die frage und die antwort. A. T. of his Lisuart und Dariolette: Joh. Ad. Hiller.

Lisuart und Dariolette oder Die frage und die antwort (Wien) 1766: Joh. Ad. Hiller.   Schatz 4726

Lisuart und Dariolette, Riga, 1773: Joh. Ad. Hiller.   Schatz 4734

Lisuart und Dariolette (Nuernberg, 1780): Joh. Ad. Hiller.   Schatz 4727

Schietti, *conte* **Angelo.**

Arianna abbandonata, Venezia, 1719: Boniventi.   Schatz 1189

Il giuramento alla vendetta, Venezia, 1744 (L. T. of his La pace per amore): Micheli.   Schatz 6482

Laodice, Venezia (1724): Albinoni.   Schatz 130

Il nemico amante, Venezia (1724): Buini and Chelleri. L. T. of their La pace per amore.   Schatz 1401

La pace per amore. O. T. of his Il giuramento alla vendetta.

La pace per amore, Venezia, 1719: Buini and Chelleri.   Schatz 1400

Schikaneder, Johann Emanuel.

Anton der dumme gaertner oder Der name thut nichts zur sache. O. T. of his Die beiden Antone oder Der name thut nichts zur sache and Der dumme gaertner: Schack.

Die beiden Antone oder Der name thut nichts zur sache, Leipzig, 1797: Schack. (Altered version of their Anton der dumme gaertner oder Der name thut nichts zur sache.)   Schatz 9566

Die drey ringe oder Kaspar der mundkoch (Regensburg) 1796: Schack.   Schatz 9568

Der dumme gaertner, Augsburg, 1793. L. T. of his Anton der dumme gaertner: Schack.   Schatz 9567

Der fall ist noch viel seltener. O. T. of his Die geplagten ehemaenner: Schack.

Il flauto magico (Dresda) 1794. Tr. of his Die zauberflöte: Mozart.   Schatz 6850

Die geplagten ehemaenner, Hamburg, 1792: Schack. (Originally the A. T. of their Der fall ist noch viel seltener.)   Schatz 9569

Der koenigsohn aus Ithaka, Wien, 1797: Hoffmeister.   Schatz 4750

Der name thut nichts zur sache. A. T. of his Anton der dumme gaertner und Die beiden Antone: Schack.

Die neuen Arkadier, Weimar, 1796. L. T. of his Der spiegel von Arkadien (altered by Vulpius): Süssmayer.   Schatz 10184

Schikaneder, Johann Emanuel—Continued.

Der spiegel von Arkadien (Vienna) 1796: Süssmayer.   Schatz 10183

Der spiegel von Arkadien—Die neuen Arkadier, Weimar, 1796 (rev. by Vulpius): Süssmayer.   Schatz 10184

Der stein der weisen, oder Die zauberinsel, Frankfurt am Main, 1796: Schack.   Schatz 9570

Telemach, Hamburg (1797) (much-altered version of his Der koenigsohn aus Ithaka): Hoffmeister.   Schatz 4751

Telemach, koenigssohn aus Ithaka, Frankfurt a/M., 1798. Another version of this opera.   Schatz 4753

Telemach, prinz von Ithaka, Weimar, 1797 (Vulpius's version of the above): Hoffmeister.   Schatz 4752

Der wohlthaetige derwisch oder Die schellenkappe. O. T. of his Die zaubertrommel oder Der wohlthaetige derwisch: Schack.

Die waldmaenner, Hamburg, 1797: Henneberg.   Schatz 4631

Die zauberflöte, n. i., 1794 (text partly planned by Gieseke): Mozart.   ML 50.2.Z25M7

Die zauberflöte, Leipzig (1794) (text partly planned by Gieseke, in this version altered by Vulpius): Mozart.   Schatz 6849

Die zauberinsel. A. T. of his Der stein der weisen.

Die zaubertrommel oder Der wohlthaetige derwisch, Augsburg, 1793. L. T. of his Der wohlthaetige derwisch oder Die schellenkappe: Schack.   Schatz 9571

Schink, Johann Friedrich.

Adelstan und Roeschen (Güstrow, 1792): Friedr. Adam Hiller.   Schatz 4714

Doktor Faust (Theater Journal fuer Deutschland, Gotha, 1778).   Schatz 11754

Im trueben ist gut fischen, Hamburg (1785). Tr. of Sarti's Fra i due litiganti il terzo gode (Goldoni).   Schatz 9459

Rosalia, Gotha, 1777: Schubert.   Schatz 9704

Schizza. *See real name*, Graziolli, Giovanni.

Schlenkert, Friedrich Christian.

Agaton und Psiche, Leipzig, 1780: unknown.   Schatz 11598

Schlicht, Friedrich Gustav.

Das Hallorenfest, Magdeburg, 1783: unknown.   ML 50.2.H16

Schmidel, F. L.

Die betrogne arglist, Wien, 1783. Unauthorized one-act version of his Das unnuetze bestreben: Weigl.   Schatz 10959

Das unnuetze bestreben (Theatralische Werke, Wien & Leipzig, 1785): Weigl.   Schatz 10958

Schmidt, Johann Friedrich.

Diesmal hat der mann den willen!, Wien, 1778: Ordonez.   Schatz 7291

La Frascatana, n. i., 1782. Practically same text as: ML 50.2.F84P2

La Frascatana oder Das maedchen von Fraskati, n. i., 1782. Tr. of Paisiello's La Frascatana (Livigni).   Schatz 7624

Das maedchen von Fraskati, Luebeck, 1785. Tr. of Paisiello's La Frascatana (Livigni).   Schatz 7625

Schmieder, Heinrich Gottlieb.

Axur, koenig von Ormus, Hamburg und Altona, 1799. Tr. of Beaumarchais's Tarare: Salieri. (*See also* Schmieder's Tarar.)   Schatz 9332

Schmieder, Heinrich Gottlieb—Continued.

Axur, koenig von Ormus, n. i., n. d. (after 1800?) Tr. of
Salieri's Axur, rè d'Ormus (Da Ponte).   SCHATZ 9334

Die beyden fluechtlinge, Hamburg, 1791. Tr. of Paisiello's
Le gare generose (Palomba).   SCHATZ 7628

Die beyden kleinen Savoyarden, Leipzig, 1795. Tr. of Dalayrac's Les deux petits Savoyards (Marsollier).   SCHATZ 2338

Doktor Faust, Bremen (1797): Walter.   SCHATZ 10859

Don Juan, Frankfurt, 1789. Tr. of Mozart's Il dissoluto
punito (Da Ponte).   SCHATZ 6789

Die entzifferung (n. i.) 1795. Tr. of Salieri's La cifra (Petrosellini).   SCHATZ 9283

Graf Albert, Berlin, 1798. Tr. of Grétry's Le comte d'Albert
(Sedaine).   SCHATZ 4142

Heinrich der Löwe (Mainz) 1792: Stegmann.   SCHATZ 10039

Liebe wagt alles, Hamburg, 1798. Tr. of Devienne's Les
visitandines (Picard).   SCHATZ 2556

Nina oder Wahnsinn aus liebe, Mainz, 1787. Tr. of Dalayrac's
Nina ou La folle par amour (Marsollier).   SCHATZ 2368

Oberon oder Koenig der elfen, Hamburg, 1792. Additional
arias for Wranitzky's opera, text by Friederike Sophie
Seyler.   SCHATZ 11112

Reinald, Hamburg, 1790. Tr. of Radet and Barre's Renaud
d'Ast: Dalayrac.   SCHATZ 2378

Rudolph von Creki, Riga, 1792. Tr. of Dalayrac's Raoul, sire
de Créqui (Monvel).   SCHATZ 2374

Der talisman oder Die zigeuner, n. i., 1790. Tr. of Salieri's
Il talismano (Goldoni, altered by Da Ponte).   SCHATZ 9323

Tarar, Hamburg, 1791. Tr. of Salieri's Tarare (resp. Axur, rè
d'Ormus).   SCHATZ 9330

Die wilden, Frankfurt am Main, 1791. Tr. of Dalayrac's
Azémia (de la Chabeaussière).   SCHATZ 2371

Die zigeuner. A. T. of his Der talisman: Salieri.

Schoepfel, Johann Wilhelm August.

Palaemon, Frankfurt und Leipzig, 1774: unknown.   ML 50.2.P16

Die fruehlingsnacht, Frankfurt und Leipzig, 1773.   SCHATZ 11612

Die puzmacherin, Baireuth, 1790: Preu.   SCHATZ 8465

Schomberg, Ralph.

The judgment of Paris, London, 1768: Barthélémon.   LONGE 52

Schreiber, Aloys Wilhelm.

Die harfe, Offenbach und Brede, 1793: Walter. O. T. of
their: SCHATZ 10861

Die zauberharfe, Offenbach, 1798.   SCHATZ 11664

Schröder, Friedrich Ludwig.

Orpheus der zweite, Hamburg, 1788. Altered version of Die
liebe im narrenhause: Dittersdorf (Stephanie d. jung.).   SCHATZ 2600

Schubert, Karl Emil.

Deukalion und Pyrrha, Breslau und Leipzig, 1779: Holly.   SCHATZ 4769

Das opfer der treue, Breslau u. Leipzig, 1779: Holly.   SCHATZ 4771

Der tempel des schicksals (Litteratur u. Theater Zeitung, Berlin, 1779, Bd. II, th. I): Holly.   SCHATZ 4772

Schubert, Karl Emil—Continued.

Zemire und Azor, Breslau, 1775. Only the lyrics for Baumgarten's opera. Schatz 658

Zemire und Azor, Breslau u. Leipzig, 1779. Tr. of Grétry's Zémire et Azor (Marmontel). Schatz 4193

Schueller, Johann Nepomuck.

Julius Sabinus, Pressburg, 1785. Tr. of Sarti's Giulio Sabino (Giovannini). Schatz 9442

Schulz, C.

Die neuen Amazonen (Theater Journal fuer Deutschland, Gotha, 1778, 5tes St.): Schweitzer. Schatz 11754

Schwaldopler, Johann.

Die koenigin von den Schwarzen inseln, n. i., 1797: Süssmayr. ML 50.2.K7S9

Schwan, Christian Friedrich.

Azakia, Mannheim, 1778: C. Cannabich. Schatz 1573

Der kaufmann von Smirna, Hamburg, 1792: Stegmann. Schatz 10040

Der kaufmann von Smyrna, Frankfurt und Leipzig, 1774: Holly. Schatz 4770

Der kaufmann von Smyrna, Mannheim, 1771: G. J. Vogler. Schatz 10797

Das milchmaedchen und die beiden jaeger, Frankfurt am Mayn, 1772. Tr. of Duni's Les deux chasseurs et la laitière (Anseaume). Schatz 2839

Der sclavenhaendler, Mannheim, 1790: Ritter. Schatz 8830

Schwemmschu.

Il capitano: Telemann. (Forms third act of the pasticcio Der beschluss des carnevals, Hamburg, 1724.) Schatz 1564

Il capitano (Hamburg, 1726): Telemann. Schatz 10270

Schwick, Dr.

Der rabe, Hamburg, 1794: A. Romberg. Schatz 8870

Scolopio, Orazio Gherardi.

L'esilio di M. T. Cicerone, Lucca, 1768: Puccini and di Poggio. See M. Curzio in Title catalogue.

Scriblerus Secundus. Pseud. of Fielding, Henry.

Scriblerus Tertius. Pseud. of Cooke, Thomas.

Secinuntino, Lereno. See Lereno Secinuntino.

Sedaine, Jean Michel.

Aline, dronning i Golconda, Kiøbenhavn, 1789. Tr. of his Aline reine de Golconde: Schulz. Schatz 9717

Aline, königinn von Golconda (Cramer's Musik, 1789). Tr. of his Aline, reine de Golconde. ML4.M3

Aline, reine de Golconde. O. T. of his La reine de Golconde: Monsigny.

L'anneau perdu et retrouvé, Paris, 1764: La Borde. Schatz 5350

Aucassin et Nicolette ou Les moeurs du bon vieux tems, Paris, 1782: Grétry. ML 50.2.A92G7

Aucassin et Nicolette, ou Les moeurs du bon vieux temps, Paris, 1784: Grétry. Schatz 4139

Blaise le savetier, Paris, 1759: Philidor. ML 50.2.B39P4

Sedaine, Jean Michel—Continued.

Blaise le savetier, Paris, 1769: Philidor.	Schatz 8007
Blaise le savetier, Paris, 1771: Philidor.	Schatz 11736
Le comte d'Albert, Paris, 1787: Grétry.	ML50.2.C64G7
Le comte d'Albert, Amsterdam, 1788: Grétry.	ML50.2.C64G8
The deserter, London, 1773. Tr. of his Le déserteur: Monsigny (with additional music by Dibdin and Philidor).	Longe 13
The deserter (Collection of the most esteemed farces, Edinburgh, 1792, t. iv).	Schatz 11753D
The deserter, New York, 1787: Monsigny-Dibdin-Philidor. Tr. of Le déserteur.	ML50.6.D36
Le déserteur, Paris, 1769: Monsigny.	Schatz 6569
Le deserteur, Paris, 1770: Monsigny.	ML50.2.D45
Der deserteur, Frankfurt am Mayn (1773): Monsigny. Tr. of their Le déserteur.	Schatz 6570
Le diable a quatre ou La double métamorphose, La Haye, 1757: arr. by Philidor.	ML 50.2.D52P4
Le diable à quatre ou La double métamorphose, Paris, 1762: arr. by Philidor.	Schatz 11490
Le diable à quatre ou La double métamorphose, Paris, 1770: arr. by Philidor.	Schatz 11691
Der dorfbalbier, Leipzig, 1772: Joh. Ad. Hiller. ("Nachahmung," by Weisse, of his Blaise le savatier.)	Schatz 4719
La double métamorphose. A. T. of his Le diable à quatre.	
L'enfant trouvé. A. T. of his Felix: Monsigny.	
Le faucon, Paris, Herissant, 1772 (47 p.): Monsigny.	Schatz 6573
Le faucon, Paris, Herissant, 1772 (32 p.): Monsigny.	Schatz 11726
Les feintes infidélités. A. T. of his Les femmes vengées: Philidor.	
Félix ou L'enfant trouvé, Paris, 1777: Monsigny.	ML 50.2.F25M7
Félix ou L'enfant trouvé, Paris, 1784: Monsigny.	Schatz 6574
Felix oder Der findling, Riga, 1790. Tr. of his Félix ou L'enfant trouvé: Monsigny.	Schatz 6575
Les femmes vengées, ou Les feintes infidélités, Paris, 1775: Philidor.	Schatz 8014
Les femmes vengées, ou Les feintes infidélités, Paris, 1782: Philidor.	Schatz 11738
Ferdinand und Nicolette, oder Liebe erhaelt den sieg, Hamburg, 1787. Tr. of his Aucassin et Nicolette: Grétry.	Schatz 4140
Der findling. A. T. of his Felix: Monsigny.	
Den forstilte tvistighed (Kiøbenhavn, 1777). Tr. of his Rose et Colas: Monsigny.	Schatz 6585
Graf Albert, Berlin, 1798. Tr. of his Le comte d'Albert: Grétry.	Schatz 4142
Hanns der schuhflicker, Frankfurt am Mayn, 1772. Tr. of his Blaise le savetier: Philidor.	Schatz 8008
L'huitre et les plaideurs ou Le tribunal de la chicane, Paris, 1761: Philidor.	Schatz 8036
Le jardinier et son seigneur, Paris, 1769: Philidor.	Schatz 11740
Le jardinier et son seigneur, Paris, 1785: Philidor.	Schatz 8017
Der koenig und der pachter, Frankfurt und Leipzig, 1766. Tr. of his Le roi et le fermier: Monsigny.	Schatz 6581
Der koenig und der paechter, Frankfurt am Mayn, 1773. Another Tr.	Schatz 6582

Sedaine, Jean Michel—Continued.

Liebe erhaelt den sieg. A. T. of his Ferdinand und Nicolette: Grétry.

Le magnifique, Paris, Herissant, 1773: Grétry (52 p.)   ML50.2.M2G7

Le magnifique, Paris, Herissant, 1773: Grétry (56 p.)   Schatz 4167

Le magnifique, Paris, 1782: Grétry.   Schatz 11708

Man sieht niemals alles voraus, Frankfurt am Mayn, 1772. Tr. of his On ne s'avise jamais de tout: Monsigny.   Schatz 6579

Les moeurs du bon vieux temps. A. T. of his Aucassin et Nicolette: Grétry.

On ne s'avise jamais de tout, Avignon, 1764: Monsigny   Schatz 6578

On ne s'avise jamais de tout (Dresde, 1766): Monsigny.   Schatz 11729

On ne s'avise jamais de tout, Paris, 1775: Monsigny.   Schatz 11728

Petrine. *See* Favart.

Der praechtige freygebige, Frankfurt am Mayn, 1774. Tr. of his Le magnifique: Grétry.   Schatz 4168

Raoul, Barbe Bleue, Amsterdam, 1791: Grétry.   ML50.2.R22G72

Raoul Barbe Bleue, Bruxelles, 1791: Grétry.   ML50.2.R22G73

La reine de Golconde, Paris, 1772: Monsigny. L. T. of their Aline, reine de Golconde.   Schatz 6587

Riccardo cor di Leone, Milano (1787). Tr. of his Richard, Coeur de Lion: Grétry.   Schatz 4201

Riccardo cor di Leone, Venezia, 1789. (Tr. of his Richard Coeur de Lion): Robuschi.   Schatz 8844

Richard Coeur de Lion, Paris, 1786: Grétry.   ML48.M2H

Richard, Coeur de Lion, Paris, 1787: Grétry.   Schatz 4177

Richard Coeur de Lion, London, 1786. English Tr. of this, music adapted by Linley.   Longe 98

Richard Löwenherz, Berlin, n. d. Tr. of his Richard Coeur de Lion: Grétry.   Schatz 4179

Le roi et le fermier, Bruxelles, 1765: Monsigny.   ML 50.2.R7M7

Le roi et le fermier (Dresde, 1766): Monsigny.   Schatz 11732

Le roi et le fermier, Paris, 1768: Monsigny.   Schatz 11730

Le roi et le fermier, Paris, 1779: Monsigny.   Schatz 6580

Roschen und Colas, Frankfurt am Mayn, 1772. Tr. of his Rose et Colas: Monsigny.   Schatz 6584

Rose et Colas, Paris, 1764: Monsigny.   ML 50.2.R74M6

Rose et Colas, Paris, 1770: Monsigny.   Schatz 6583

Rose et Colas, Paris, 1779: Monsigny.   Schatz 11733

Les sabots, Paris, 1769 (with Cazotte): Duni.   ML 50.2.S2D9

Les sabots, Paris, 1770: Duni.   Schatz 2855

Les sabots, Paris, 1777: Duni.   Schatz 11698

Thalie au nouveau théatre, Paris, 1783: Grétry.   ML 50.2.T395G7

Thémire, Paris, 1771: Duni.   Schatz 2856

Le tribunal de la chicane. A. T. of his L'huitre et les plaideurs: Philidor.

Seidel, Carl August (*recte* Gottlieb)

Karoline oder Die parforcejagd, n. i., 1781: unknown.   ML 50.2.K2

Semplici, Luigi.

Apollo in Tessaglia, Firenze, 1769: Felici.   Schatz 3052

Seguineau, N.

Pirithous (Recueil général des opéra, t. xiii, Paris, 1734 (with
de La Serre): Mouret. Schatz 6743

Ségur, Joseph Alexandre Pierre, *vicomte* **de.**

L'opéra comique, Paris, an VI [1797–98] (with Dupaty): Della
Maria. ML 50.2.O6D2

L'opéra comique, Toulouse, an VII [1798–99]. ML 50.2.O6D22

Roméo et Juliette, Paris, an II [1793]: Steibelt. ML 50.2.R68S8

Roméo et Juliette, Paris, an III, 2d ed. [1794–95]. ML 50.2.R68S82

Sellini, Pietro, *misprint for* **Petrosellini Giuseppe.**

Serafini, *abate.*

Cesare nella Brettagna, Lucca, 1779. *See* M. Curzio in Title
catalogue.

Seriman(n), *conte* **Zaccaria.**

Caio Marzio Coriolano, Venezia, 1747: Pulli. Schatz 8513

Telemaco—Telemach, Monaco, 1780: Grua. Schatz 4222

Serino, Nicola.

Il Gran Mogol, Napoli, 1713 (buffo scenes and some arias only,
mainly by Lalli): Mancini. Schatz 5879

Lesbina e Nesso (in Händel's Rinaldo, Napoli, 1718): Leo. Schatz 4495

Rinaldo, Napoli, 1718 (supposed author of additions to Hill
and Rossi's text of Händel's opera). Schatz 4495

Serio, Luigi.

Ifigenia in Aulide, Napoli, 1779: Martin y Soler. Schatz 6028

L'Ifigenia in Aulide, Firenze, 1784: Prati. Schatz 8451

Ifigenia in Aulide, Genova (1784): Lorenzo Rossi. Schatz 8918

Oreste, Napoli, 1783: Cimarosa. Schatz 1966

Sernicola, Carlo.

Amelia ed Ottiero (Trieste, 1797): Andreozzi. Schatz 201

Arsinoe e Breno, Siena (1790). Secularization of his Debora e
Sisara: P. Guglielmi. Schatz 4315

Debora e Sisara, Napoli, 1788: P. Guglielmi. Schatz 4241

Olindo e Sofronia, Venezia, 1798: Andreozzi. L. T. of their
Sofronia ed Olindo. Schatz 220

Sofronia ed Olindo, Napoli, 1793: Andreozzi. Schatz 200

Serré de Rieux, Jean.

Nouvelle chasse du cerf (*in his* Les dons des enfans de Latone,
Paris, 1734): Händel and others. ML 63.S36

Sertor, Gaetano.

Angelica e Medoro, Firenze, 1792: Andreozzi. Schatz 194

L'Arbace, Firenze, 1785: Andreozzi. Schatz 214

Amadi, Venezia, 1793. Tr. of Quinault's text Amadis. Schatz 11666

Arbace, Venezia, 1782: Borghi. Schatz 1239

Armida abbandonata—Die verlassene Armide (Monaco, 1785):
Prati. Schatz 8450

Aspard, Roma (1784): Bianchi. ML 50.2.A82B3

Il conte Policronio o sia Le bugie hanno le gambe corte,
Firenze, 1791: Moneta. (Authorship hypothetical; the
libretto mentions as author "sig. G. S."). Schatz 6551

Le Danaidi, Milano (1795): Tarchi. Schatz 10217

Sertor, Gaetano—Continued.

Il divorzio sepra matrimonio ossia La donna che non parla.
O. T. of his:

La donna ne sa più del diavolo ovvero Il matrimonio non è per
i vecchi, Lisbona, 1797: Longarini.   SCHATZ 5683

Enea e Lavinia, Napoli, 1785: P. Guglielmi. (According to
Piovano, the text is by Vincenzo de Stefano.)   SCHATZ 4285

Enea e Lavinia, Genova (1796): P. Guglielmi.   SCHATZ 11711

Giulio Cesare, Trieste (1790): Bianchi. L. T. of their La
morte di Cesare.   SCHATZ 1006

La morte di Cesare, Venezia, 1788: Bianchi.   SCHATZ 1005

La morte di Cesare, Milano (1791): Zingarelli.   SCHATZ 11263

Nettuno ed Egle (Lisboa) 1785: Carvalho.   SCHATZ 1671

Nettuno ed Egle, Venezia, 1783: Pio.   SCHATZ 8188

Osmane, Venezia, 1784: G. Giordani.   SCHATZ 3848

Piramo e Tisbe, Venezia, 1783: Bianchi.   SCHATZ 980

Protesilao—Protesilaus, Berlin (1793): Naumann.   SCHATZ 7055

Protesilao—Protesilaus, Berlino (1789): Reichardt and Naumann.   SCHATZ 8654

Tarara o sia La virtù premiata, Venezia, 1792: Bianchi.   SCHATZ 984

Die verlassene Armide. Tr. of his Armida abbandonata
(Monaco, 1785): Prati.   SCHATZ 8450

La virtù premiata. A. T. of his Tarara: Bianchi.

Zemira, Venezia, 1782: Anfossi.   SCHATZ 272

Zemira, Padova (1786): Bianchi.   SCHATZ 1001

Zenobia in Palmira (Livorno, 1796): Anfossi.   SCHATZ 257

Sertori, *abbate*.

Il conclave del MDCCLXXIV—Das conclave von
MDCCLXXIV, Roma (1775). (Satire, with names of
Metastasio and Piccinni as fictitious author, resp. com-
poser.)   SCHATZ 8084

Das conclave von MDCCLXXIV, Rom (1775). Separate ed.
of the above.   SCHATZ 8085

Il conclave del 1774, Venezia (1797). L. ed. of the above.   SCHATZ 8132

Servandoni.

La forest enchantée (Paris) 1754: Geminiani.   ML 52.2.F6G3

Settle, Elkanah.

The world in the moon, London, 1697: Clarke and D. Purcell.   LONGE 180

Sewrin, Charles Augustin.

La ruse villageoise, Paris, 1794: unknown.   SCHATZ 11511

Seyler, Friederike Sophie.

Oberon oder Koenig der elfen, Hamburg, 1792 (arias added by
Schmieder, composed by Stegmann): Wranitzky.   SCHATZ 11112

Shapter, Thomas.

The fugitive or Happy recess, London (1790): Moulds.   LONGE 207

Sheridan, Richard Brinsley.

The camp, London, 1795: Linley.   LONGE 233

The duenna, or, The double elopement, London, 1775: Linley,
father and son.   ML 50.2.D85

The duenna, or, The double elopement (Dublin, 1791).   PR 1269.V6

Sheridan, Richard Brinsley—Continued.

The governess, Dublin, 1777. Pirated version of his The
duenna: Linley, father and son. LONGE 148

St. Patrick's day or The scheming lieutenant (Dublin) 1788:
unknown. LONGE 223

Selima & Azor, London, 1784. Alterations in Collier's English
version of Marmontel's Zémire et Azor: Linley, utilizing
Grétry. LONGE 95

Shirley, James.

The triumph of peace, London, 1633: Lawes and Ives. LONGE 188

Shirley, William.

King Pepin's campaign, London, 1755 [! instead of 1745]: Th.
A. Arne. LONGE 59

Shirrefs, Andrew.

Jamie and Bess or The laird in disguise (Poems, Edinburgh,
1790). LONGE 283

Siddons, Henry.

The Sicilian romance or The apparition of the cliffs, London,
1794: Reeve. LONGE 239

Signoretti, Francesco Antonio.

L'impresario burlato, Napoli, 1797: Mosca. ML 50.2.I49M6

La sposa tra le imposture, Napoli, 1798: Mosca. SCHATZ 6725

Silvani, Francesco.

Ama più chi men si crede, Venezia, 1709: Lotti. SCHATZ 5715

Amore e sdegno, Venezia, 1726: Tavelli. (Text is his La
moglie nemica, as rewritten by Boccardi). SCHATZ 10253

Gl'amori ministri della fortuna, Milano (1694): M. A. Ziani. SCHATZ 11208

Armida abbandonata, Venezia (1723): Buini. SCHATZ 1388

Armida abbandonata, Venezia, 1707: Ruggeri. SCHATZ 9133

Armida abbandonata, Mantova (1711): Ruggeri. ML 48.A5　v.3

Armida al campo, Venezia, 1707: Boniventi. SCHATZ 1184

Armida al campo, Napoli, 1718: Sarro. SCHATZ 9413

Arrenione, Venezia, 1708: Ruggeri. SCHATZ 9131

Arrenione, Mantova (1711): Ruggeri. ML 50.2.A775R9

Artaserse rè di Persia, Napoli, 1713 (his Il tradimento traditore
di se stesso with introduction of buffo scenes): Lotti and
Mancini. SCHATZ 5712

L'arte in garra con l'arte, Venezia (1702): Albinoni. SCHATZ 88

Atalo, Venezia, 1742: Chinzer. SCHATZ 1866

Attalo rè di Bitinia, Napoli, 1752: G. Conti. L. T. of S.'s text
La verità nell' inganno. SCHATZ 2206

Attalo rè di Bitinia, Ferrara (1739): Hasse. L. T. of S.'s text
La verità nell' inganno. SCHATZ 4517

Barsina, Venezia, 1742: Paganelli. SCHATZ 7573

Candace, Venezia (1740) (his "I veri amici" as altered by
Lalli): Lampugnani. SCHATZ 5392

La Candace o'siano Li veri amici, Mantova (1720): Vivaldi. ML 50.2.C26V3

Il comando non inteso, et ubbidito, Venezia, 1709: Lotti. SCHATZ 5716

La costanza combattuta in amore, Venezia, 1716: Porta. SCHATZ 8390

La costanza in trionfo, Venezia, 1697: M. A. Ziani. SCHATZ 11180

Il duello d'amore e di vendetta. O. T. of his text Li sdegni
cangiati in amore.

Silvani, Francesco—Continued.

Il duello d'amore e di vendetta, Venezia, 1700: M. A. Ziani.   Schatz 11183

Ernelinda, Venezia, 1750: Galuppi and others(?). L. T. of
    his La fede tradita e vendicata.   Schatz 3522

Evergete, Venezia, 1748 (with Domenico Lalli): Gibelli.   Schatz 3828

La fede tra gl'inganni, Venezia, 1707: Albinoni.   Schatz 119

La fede tradita e vendicata, Venezia, 1704: Gasparini.   Schatz 3566

La fede tradita e vendicata, Napoli, 1707: Gasparini, addi-
    tional music by Vignola.   Schatz 3567

La fede tradita e vendicata, Venezia, 1726: Vivaldi.   Schatz 10767

Feraspe, Venezia, 1739 (partly rewritten by Vitturi): Vivaldi.   Schatz 10768

La fortezza al cimento, Venetia (1699): Aldrovandini.   Schatz 134

La forza del sanguine. O. T. of his libretto Zoe.

La forza del sangue, Venezia, 1711: Lotti.   Schatz 5718

I fratelli riconosciuti, Parma, 1726. (L. T. of his libretto La
    verità nell' inganno, alterations by Frugoni): Capello.   Schatz 1590

La Fredegonda, Venezia, 1705: Gasparini.   Schatz 3569

Gl'imenei stabiliti dal caso, Venezia, 1703: Gasparini.   Schatz 3570

L'infedeltà punita, Venezia, 1712: C. F. Pollaroli and A.
    Lotti.   Schatz 8326

L'inganno innocente, Venezia, 1701: Albinoni.   Schatz 121

L'inganno scoperto per vendetta, Venetia, 1691: Perti.   Schatz 7956

L'ingratitudine gastigata, Venezia, 1698: Albinoni.   Schatz 96

L'innocenza difesa. L. T. of his L'innocenza giustificata.

L'innocenza difesa, Roma, 1720: Orlandini.   Schatz 7336

L'innocenza difesa, Venezia, 1722: Chelleri. L. T. of their
    L'innocenza giustificata.   Schatz 1814

L'innocenza difesa. *See also* Judith, gemahlin Kayser Lude-
    wigs des Frommen oder Die siegende unschuld.

L'innocenza giustificata. O. T. of his L'innocenza difesa.

L'innocenza giustificata, Venezia, 1699: Vinacese.   Schatz 10740

L'innocenza giustificata, Mantova (1700): Vinacese.   ML 50.2.I58

Irene augusta, Venezia, 1713: Lotti.   Schatz 5720

Lisetta ed Astrobolo: Caldara. Intermezzi in their La verità
    nell' inganno, Vienna, 1717.

Martio Coriolano, Venetia, 1683: Perti.   Schatz 7957

La maschera levata al vitio, Venetia, 1704: Gasparini.   Schatz 3571

Il miglior d'ogni amore per il peggiore d'ogni odio, Venezia,
    1703: Gasparini.   Schatz 3572

La moglie nemica. O. T. of his Amore e sdegno, as partly re-
    written by Boccardi di Mazzera.

La moglie nemica, Venetia, 1694: M. A. Ziani.   Schatz 11203

L'odio placato, Venezia, 1730: Galuppi.   Schatz 3490

L'oracolo in sogno, Venezia, 1700: unknown.   Schatz 11353

Ottone il Grande, Venetia, 1683: Biego.   Schatz 1015

La pace generosa, Venetia, 1700: M. A. Ziani.   Schatz 11192

Il più fedel frà i vassalli, Venezia, 1703: Gasparini.   Schatz 3579

Il più fedel trà vassalli, Venezia, 1716: Gasparini.   ML 48.M2 O

Il più fedel tra' gl'amici, Venezia, 1724: M. A. Gasparini.   Schatz 3602

Il più fedel tra vasalli, Napoli, 1705 (substitute arias by Convò
    and one scene by Stampiglia): Aldrovandini.   Schatz 138

Il principato custodito dalla frode, Venezia, 1705: Gasparini.   Schatz 3577

Il principe selvaggio, Venezia, 1695: Gasparini.   Schatz 3603

Ricimero, Venezia, 1773: Borghi.   Schatz 1236

Silvani, Francesco—Continued.

Ricimero, Verona (1778): Borghi.   ML 50.2.R47B6

Ricimero: Galuppi. L. T. of S.'s La fede tradita e vendicata.

Ricimero, Napoli, 1789: Siri. (L. T. of S.'s La fede tradita
    e vendicata.   Schatz 9896

Li sdegni cangiati in amore, Veneza (1725). (His "Il duello
    d'amore e di vendetta" as altered by the composer):
    Buini.   Schatz 1394

Semiramide (Venezia, 1743): Jommelli.   Schatz 4880

Semiramide, Venezia, 1714: C. F. Pollaroli.   Schatz 8318

Sofonisba, Venezia, 1708: Caldara.   Schatz 1500

La Sofonisba, Milano, 1744 (recitatives by Silvani, lyrics by
    Metastasio): Gluck.   Schatz 3932

Sofonisba, Napoli, 1718: Leo.   Schatz 5555

Statira (Venezia, 1742): Porpora.   Schatz 8364

Il Tigrane, Brescia (1743): Gluck. (The text is a moderniza-
    tion with final revisions (1741) by Goldoni of S.'s La virtù
    trionfante dell' amore e dell' odio.)   ML 50.2.T56G3

Tigrane, Napoli (1745): Hasse and Palella. (See above.)   Schatz 4584

Tigrane, Venezia, 1747: Lampugnani. (See above.)   Schatz 5390

Tigrane, Torino (1761): Piccinni. (See above.)   Schatz 8118

Tigrane, Venezia, 1762: Tozzi. (See above.)   Schatz 10387

Il tradimento tradito, Venetia, 1709: Albinoni.   Schatz 103

Il tradimento traditore di se stesso, Venezia, 1711: Lotti.
    (Same text as La Statira and Artaserse rè di Persia.   Schatz 5710

I veri amici. O. T. of his Candace (alterations by Lalli).

I veri amici, Monaco (1722) (with Lalli): Albinoni.   Schatz 99

I veri amici, Venezia, 1713 (with Lalli): Paulati.   Schatz 7786

La verità nell' inganno, Vienna d'Austria (1717): Caldara.   Schatz 1490

La verità nell' inganno. O. T. of his Attalo rè di Bitinia.

La verità nell' inganno, Venezia, 1713: Gasparini.   Schatz 3587

La virtù trionfante dell' amore e dell' odio, Venetia, 1681:
    M. A. Ziani.   Schatz 11207

Zoe, Venezia, 1756 (L. T. of his La forza del sanguine): Cocchi. Schatz 2047

La Zoe, Venezia, 1736: Predieri.   Schatz 8459

Sinibaldi, Giacomo.

Lisimaco riamato da Alessandro, Venetia, 1682 (partly rewrit-
    ten by Aureli): Legrenzi.   Schatz 5545

La libertà sempre stabile nelle vicende del principato, Lucca,
    1693: unknown. See M. Curzio in Title catalogue.

Smith, Charles.

A day at Rome, London, 1798: Attwood.   Longe 254

Smith, James.

The cottage, Tewkesbury, n. d.: unknown.   Longe 237

Smith, John Christopher.

The fairies, London, 1755 (authorship doubtful): J. C. Smith. ML 50.2.F14

The fairies, 2d ed., London, 1755 (authorship doubtful):
    J. C. Smith.   ML 50.2.F142

The tempest, London, 1756 (compiled from Shakespeare):
    J. C. Smith.   Longe 198

Smoke, Timothy (*pseud?*)

The commodity excis'd or The women in an uproar, London, 1733: ballad opera. LONGE 191

Smollett, Tobias George.

The reprisal or The tars of Old England (Collection of farces, Edinburgh, 1792, t. ii): unknown. SCHATZ 11753B

Soden von Sassanfart, Friedrich Julius Heinrich, *freiherr* **von.**

Arkadien (Schauspiele, Berlin, 1788). L. T. of his Lindor und Ismene: Schmittbauer. SCHATZ 9659

Don Quixotte (Schauspiele, Berlin, 1788, v. i): von Becke. SCHATZ 678

Ein grab in Arkadien, Leipzig, 1779. L. T. of his Lindor und Ismene: Schmittbauer. SCHATZ 9658

Laura, n. i., n. d. SCHATZ 11459

Lindor und Ismene (Anspach, 1773?): Mühle. SCHATZ 6873

Lindor und Ismene (n. i., 1771): Schmittbauer. SCHATZ 9657

Mit dem glockenschlag zwoelf, Anspach, 1781: Mühle. SCHATZ 6871

Soelberg, Rasmus.

Alcines oe. Tr. of Gazzaniga's L'isola d'Alcina, Kiøbenhavn, 1777 (Bertati). SCHATZ 3667

Astrea tilfredsstillet eller Jordens lyksalighed, Copenhagen, 1760. Tr. of Sarti's Astrea placata ovvero La felicità della terra (Metastasio). SCHATZ 9426

Bønderfolks elskov. Tr. of Lampugnani's L'amor contadino, Kiøbenhavn (1763) (Goldoni). SCHATZ 5387

Den flanevurne kone. Tr. of Bald. Galuppi's La moglie bizzarra, Kiøbenhavn (1763) (Ant. Galuppi). SCHATZ 3434

Den fortraengte ubekiendte. Tr. of Anfossi's La Giannetta o sia L'incognita perseguitata, Kiøbenhavn, 1775 (Petrosellini). SCHATZ 240

Den giaerrige. Tr. of Anfossi's L'avaro, Kiobenhavn, 1776 (Bertati). SCHATZ 229

Julius Caesar i Aegypten. Tr. of Sarti's Cesare in Egitto, Kiøbenhavn (1763) (Metastasio). SCHATZ 9427

Lands bye-pigen fra Frascati. Tr. of Paisiello's La Frascatana, Kiøbenhavn, 1776 (Livigni). SCHATZ 7623

Markedet i Venedig. Tr. of Salieri's La fiera di Venezia, Kiøbenhavn (1777) (Boccherini). SCHATZ 9295

Skibbruddet ved Cypren. Tr. of Sarti's Il naufragio di Cipro, Kiøbenhavn (1764) (Zani). SCHATZ 9451

Den store Tamerlan. Tr. of Sarti's Il gran Tamerlano, Kiøbenhavn (1764) (Piovene). SCHATZ 9445

Sografi, Antonio Simone.

Alceste, Venezia (1799): Portugal. SCHATZ 8396

L'amante servitore, Venezia, 1796: Paër. SCHATZ 7478

Apelle (Venezia, 1793): Zingarelli. SCHATZ 11266

Apelle e Campaspe, Milano (1796): Tritto. SCHATZ 10452

Apelle e Campaspe, Bologna, 1795. L. T. of Zingarelli's Apelle. SCHATZ 11267

Gli Argonauti in Colco, o sia La conquista del vello d'oro, Venezia, 1789: Gazzaniga. SCHATZ 3657

I bagni d'Abano o sia La forza delle prime impressioni, Venezia, 1793: Capuzzi. SCHATZ 1597

Sografi, Antonio Simone—Continued.

Cleopatra, regina d'Egitto, Genova (1795). (L. T. of his La
morte di Cleopatra): Nasolini.　　　　　　　　SCHATZ 7023

La conquista del vello d'oro. A. T. of his Gli argonauti in
Colco: Gazzaniga.

Il contravveleno. A. T. of his La principessa filosofa: Andreozzi.

La forza delle prime impressioni. A. T. of his I bagni
d'Abano: Capuzzi.

Gerusalemme distrutta, Firenze, 1794: Zingarelli.　　　SCHATZ 11244

Giovanna d'Arco o sia La pucella d'Orleans, Venezia, 1797:
Andreozzi.　　　　　　　　　　　　　　　　SCHATZ 196

La morte di Cleopatra. O. T. of his Cleopatra, regina d'Egitto.

La morte di Cleopatra, Napoli, 1798: P. Guglielmi.　　　SCHATZ 4253

La morte di Mitridate, Venezia (1797): Zingarelli.　　　SCHATZ 11269

La morte di Semiramide, Milano (1791): Borghi.　　　SCHATZ 1234

La morte di Semiramide ossia La vendetta di Nino, Lisbona,
1799: Borghi.　　　　　　　　　　　　　　SCHATZ 1240

Gli Orazi e i Curiazi, Venezia (1797): Cimarosa.　　　SCHATZ 1961

Gli Orazi e I Curiazi, Venezia (1798): Portugal.　　　SCHATZ 8442

Pietro il Grande ossia Il trionfo dell' innocenza, Venezia
(1793): Giuseppe Rossi.　　　　　　　　　　SCHATZ 8893

Pimmalione, Venezia, 1790: Cimador.　　　　　　　SCHATZ 1903

La principessa filosofa ossia Il contravveleno, Venezia (1794):
Andreozzi.　　　　　　　　　　　　　　　　SCHATZ 198

La pulcella d'Orleans. A. T. of his Giovanna d'Arco: Andreozzi.

I riti d'Apollo Leucadio. A. T. of his Saffo: Mayr.

Saffo o sia I riti d'Apollo Leucadio, Venezia (1794): Mayr.　　SCHATZ 6171

Telemaco in Sicilia, Padova, 1792: Calegari.　　　SCHATZ 1508

Telemaco nell' isola di Calipso, Venezia (1797): Mayr.　　SCHATZ 6175

Timoleone, Reggio (1798): Nasolini.　　　　　　　SCHATZ 7026

Il trionfo dell' innocenza. A. T. of his Pietro il Grande:
Gius. Rossi.

Il trionfo di Clelia, Milano (1799): Nasolini.　　　SCHATZ 7028

La vendetta di Nino. A. T. of his La morte di Semiramide:
Borghi.

Soliva, Antonio (*supposed real name of* Filostrato Lucàno Cinnèo.)

La Rosilla, Napoli, 1733: Orefici and Leo.　　　　SCHATZ 7293

Sommer, Henry.

Orpheus and Eurydice, London, 1740: Lampe.　　　LONGE 199

Sonié.

Il Giudizio di Paride,

I molinari francesi,

Venere ed Adone,

　　Ballets, composers unknown. *See* Monza's Sesostri.

Soralli, Marco.

Der nachlaessige, n. i., n. d. Tr. of Ciampi's Il negligente
(Goldoni).　　　　　　　　　　　　　　　　SCHATZ 1889

La serva padrona (Frankfurt a/M., 1755). An altered version
of Pergolesi's La serva padrona (Federico).　　　SCHATZ 7902

Sorentino, Giulio Cesare.
Il Ciro, Venetia, 1654 (altered by unknown author): Cavalli
    (only the new matter).   Schatz 1736
Ciro, Venetia, 1665: Cavalli and Mattioli.   Schatz 1753

Sorietti, Angelo.
Il più infedele trà gli amanti, Venezia, 1731: Albinoni.   Schatz 123

Spaur, H., *graf* **von.**
Fremore und Meline, Frankfurt a. M., 1778: Michl   Schatz 6484
Milton und Elmire, Frankfurt und Leipzig, 1775: Michl.   Schatz 6486
Milton und Elmire, Augsburg, 1780: Michl.   Schatz 6487
Milton und Elmire, n. pl., 1782.   Schatz 6487a
Der schiffbruch, Frankfurt am Mayn, 1778: von Kerpen.   Schatz 5142

Spiess, Christian Heinrich.
Fuenf und zwanzig tausend gulden.   A. T. of Im dunkeln ist
    nicht gut munkeln: Walter.
Im dunkeln ist nicht gut munkeln oder Fuenf und zwanzig
    tausend gulden (n. i., n. d.): Walter.   Schatz 10862

Sporon, Frederik Gottlob.
Entrepreneuren i knibe, Kjøbenhavn, 1795.   Tr. of Cima-
    rosa's L'impresario in angustie (Diodati).   Schatz 1933

Spriekmann, Anton Matthias.
Die wilddiebe.   *See* this under Stühle, Wilh.

Squallini (*pseud.*).
The man of the mill, London, 1765.   Parody of The maid of
    the mill.   Longe 125

Stampa, *conte* **Claudio Nicola** (**Niccolò**).
Aldiso, Venezia, 1726: Porta.   Schatz 8383
L'Arpippo, Milano, 1722 (originally by Domenico Lalli):
    Fiorè.   Schatz 3191
Ascanio in Alba (Lisbona, 1785) (altered by Parini): Moreira.   Schatz 6633
Eurene.   O. T. of his Rosbale.
Eurene, Milano, 1729: Predieri.   ML 48.A5   v.3
L'Oronta, Napoli, 1728: Mancini.   ML 50.2.O7M2
Rosbale, Venezia (1737): Porpora.   Schatz 8360
Venere placata, Venezia, 1731: Courcelle.   Schatz 2284

Stampiglia, Silvio.
Alba Cornelia (Breslau, 1726) (also attributed to Pariati): Fr.
    Conti.   Schatz 2203
La caduta de Decemviri, Milano, 1723: Porta.   Schatz 8389
La caduta de' Decemviri, Napoli, 1697: A. Scarlatti.   Schatz 9523
La caduta de' decemviri, Napoli, 1727: Vinci.   ML 50.2.C23V4
Caio Gracco, Vienna d'Austria, 1710: G. B. Bononcini.   Schatz 1203
Camilla, regina de' Volsci, Venezia, 1749: pasticcio.   Schatz 11312
Camilla, London, 1706: M. A. Bononcini.   Tr. of their Il
    trionfo di Camilla.   Longe 132
Camilla, regina de' Volsci, Venetia, 1698: M. A. Bononcini.
    L. T. of their Il trionfo di Camilla, regina de' Volsci.   Schatz 1208
Cirene, Venezia, 1742: P. Pellegrini.   Schatz 7860
Imeneo in Atene, Venezia, 1726: Porpora.   Schatz 8359
Imeneo in Atene, Venezia (1750): Terradellas.   Schatz 10284
La Partenope, Venezia (1707): Caldara.   Schatz 1495

Stampiglia, Silvio—Continued.

Partenope—Parthenope, Londra, 1730: Händel.   SCHATZ 4483

Partenope—Parthenope, n. i. (Salzthal, 1731): Händel.   SCHATZ 4484

Partenope, Torino (1749): Scarlatti, Gius.   SCHATZ 9556

Parthenope. Tr. of his Partenope, Londra, 1730: Händel.   SCHATZ 4483

Parthenope. Tr. of his Partenope, n. i. (Salzthal, 1731): Händel.   SCHATZ 4484

Parthenope (Hamburg) 1733. Tr. of his Partenope: Händel, recitatives by Keiser.   SCHATZ 4485

Il più fedel tra vasalli, Napoli, 1705 (one scene only. Mainly by Silvani): Aldrovandini.   SCHATZ 138

Rosmira, Venezia, 1738: Vivaldi.   SCHATZ 10779

La Rosmira fedele, Venezia (1753): Cocchi.   SCHATZ 2044

La Rosmira fedele, Venezia (1725): Vinci.   SCHATZ 10751

Il trionfo di Camilla, regina de' Volsci. (Title page supplied in ms. with wrong date, Napoli, 1696): M. A. Bononcini.   SCHATZ 1206

Il trionfo di Camilla regina de' Volsci, Livorno, 1701: M. A. Bononcini.   ML 50.2.T82B9

Tullo Ostilio, Roma, 1694 (alterations in Morselli's text): G. B. Bononcini.   SCHATZ 1201

Turno Aricino, Genova, 1702: Aldrovandini.   SCHATZ 140

Vespetta e Milo, Dresda, 1717 (Intermezzi in Lotti's Giove in Argo): I–II by A. Scarlatti (text by the above); III by Conti (text by baron Francesco Ballerini).   SCHATZ 5719

Vespetta e Milo, Dresde, 1717 (with baron Ballerini): A. Scarlatti and F. B. Conti.   SCHATZ 9522

Stanzani, Tomaso.

L'anarchia dell' imperio, Venetia, 1684: Legrenzi.   SCHATZ 5541

Apollo in Tessaglia, Bologna (1679): Franceschini.   SCHATZ 3316

Arsinoe (Insprugg, 1686): Franceschini.   ML 50.2.A779F7

L'Arsinoe, Bologna (1677): Franceschini.   SCHATZ 3317

Arsinoe, queen of Cyprus, London, 1705: Clayton. (Tr. of his L'Arsinoe.)   ML 50.2.A78

Arsinoe, queen of Cyprus, London, 1707: Clayton.   LONGE 106 and 177

Atide, Bologna (1679): Tosi (act I), Pietro degli Antoni (act II), and G. A. Perti (act III).   SCHATZ 10381

L'Oronta di Menfi, Bologna (1676): Franceschini.   SCHATZ 3318

Rodoaldo rè d'Italia, Venetia, 1685: Gabrieli.   SCHATZ 3400

Stapleton (Stapylton), *Sir* Robert.

Diana's mask—Apollo's mask. *In his* The stepmother, London, 1664.   LONGE 122

Stefano, Vincenzo di.

Lo scroprimento inaspettato, Napoli, 1787: P. Guglielmi.   SCHATZ 4265

Enea e Lavinia, Napoli, 1785. P. Guglielmi. (The text is also attributed to Gaetano Sertor.)   SCHATZ 4285

Stegmayer, Matthäus.

Die brueder als nebenbuhler, Frankfurt am Main, 1798. Tr. of P. v. Winter's I fratelli rivali (unknown).   SCHATZ 11034

Steinel.

Poltis oder Das gerettete Troja. *See* this under Brunner.

Stephanie, Gottlieb (*called* der juengere).

Die abgeredite zauberey, Wien, 1778. Tr. of Grétry's La
fausse magie (Marmontel).   SCHATZ 4154

De apothecar en de doctor, Amsteldam, 1796: Dittersdorf.
Tr. of their Der apotheker und der doktor.   SCHATZ 2611

Der apotheker and der doctor, n. i., 1788: Dittersdorf.   SCHATZ 2585

Belmonte und Konstanze, Berlin, 1788. L. T. of his Die entfuehrung aus dem serail: Mozart.   ML 50.2.E5M8

Belmonte und Konstanze, Berlin, 1798: Mozart.   SCHATZ 6812

Da ist nicht gut zu rathen, Wien, 1778: Barta.   SCHATZ 615

The doctor and the apothecary, London, 1788. Tr. of his Der
apotheker und der doctor: Dittersdorf—Storace.   SCHATZ 2586

Der eifersuechtige liebhaber, Wien, 1780. Tr. of Grétry's Les
fausses apparences (d'Hèle).   SCHATZ 4158

Die eingebildeten philosophen (Wien), 1781. Tr. of Paisiello's
I filosofi imaginari (Bertati).   SCHATZ 7617

Die entfuehrung aus dem serail, Wien, 1782 (retouched version of Bretzner's text): Mozart.   SCHATZ 6811

Die entführung aus dem serail, Warschau (1783): Mozart.   SCHATZ 6856

Der glueckliche zufall. A. T. of his List und ungefaehr:
Lange.

Die gluecklichen jaeger (Singspiele, Liegnitz, 1792): Umlauf.   SCHATZ 10525

Die liebe im narrenhause, n. i., n. d. (Detached from his
Singspiele, 1792?): Dittersdorf.   SCHATZ 2599

Der liebhaber von funfzehn jahren, Wien, 1778. Tr. of Martini's L'amoureux de quinze aus (Laujon).   SCHATZ 6035

List und ungefaehr oder Der glueckliche zufall, Riga, 1793:
Lange.   SCHATZ 5415

Orpheus der zweite, Hamburg, 1788. L. T. of his Die liebe
im narrenhause, as altered by Schröder: Dittersdorf.   SCHATZ 2600

Die philosophen (n. i., n. d.). Same as his Die eingebildeten philosophen.   SCHATZ 7618

Die puecefarbnen schuhe oder Die schoene schusterinn, Wien,
1779: Umlauf.   SCHATZ 10529

Rose oder Pflicht und liebe im streit, Wien, 1783: Mederitsch.   ML 50.2.R74M3

Der schauspieldirektor, Liegnitz, 1792 (detached from his
Singspiele, with special title page): Mozart.   SCHATZ 6840

Die schoene schusterinn (Singspiele, Liegnitz, 1792). L. T.
of his Die puecefarbnen schuhe oder Die schoene schusterinn: Umlauf.   SCHATZ 10530

Die schoene schusterinn oder Die schuhe à la Marlborough,
lin, 1794: Umlauf. Still L. T. of the same.   SCHATZ 10531

Die schuhe à la Marlborough. A. T. of Umlauf's Die schoene
schusterinn.

Die sklavinn und der grossmuethige seefahrer, Wien, 1781.
Tr. of Piccinni's La schiava riconosciuta (unknown).   SCHATZ 8116

Die Trofonius-hoehle (Wien, 1787?). Tr. of Paisiello's La
grotta di Trofonio (Palomba).   SCHATZ 7704

Die unvermutheten zufaelle, Wien, 1781. Tr. of Grétry's Les
événements imprévues (d'Hèle).   SCHATZ 4152

Der verstellte narr aus liebe, Wien, 1779. Tr. of Sacchini's Il
soldato per forza impazzito per amore (Mariani).   SCHATZ 9222

Stevens, George Alexander.
The court of Alexander, London (1770): J. A. Fisher.   LONGE 37
The trip to Portsmouth, London (1773): Dibdin.   LONGE 40

Streek, C. van.
Camille. *See* Brinkman.

Strombeck, Friedrich Karl von.
Diana und Endymion, Braunschweig, 1795: unknown.   SCHATZ 11604

Strozzi, Giulio.
La Delia o sia La sera sposa del sole, Venetia, 1639: Sacrati.   SCHATZ 9256
La finta pazza, Venetia, 1641: Sacrati.   SCHATZ 9253
La finta Savia, Venetia, 1643: Laurenzi, Crivelli, Merula and
    Ferrari.   SCHATZ 5474
Il Romolo e'l Remo, Venetia, 1645: Cavalli.   SCHATZ 1727

Stuart, Charles.
The cobler of Castlebury, London, n. d.: Shield.   LONGE 125
Gretna Green (Dublin, 178–): Arnold.   LONGE 233

Stühle, Wilhelm.
Die wilddiebe, Muenster, 1774 (with A. M. Sprickmann):
    Nicolai, J. G.   SCHATZ 7114

Suarez, Pietro Maria.
Leucippe e Teonoe, Venezia, 1719: A. Pollaroli.   SCHATZ 8262

Tagliazucchi, Giampietro?
Aetius: Graun. Tr. of:
Ezio-Aetius, Berlino, 1755: Graun.   SCHATZ 4096
I fratelli nemici—Die uneinigen brueder, Berlino (1756)
    (based on a French text by Frederick the Great): Graun.   SCHATZ 4100
I fratelli nemici—Les frères ennemis, Berlino (1756): Graun.   SCHATZ 4101
Merope—Merope, Berlino, 1756 (after a French text by Fred-
    erick the Great): Graun.   SCHATZ 4105
Montezuma—Montezuma, Berlino, 1771 (after a French prose
    text by Frederick the Great): Graun.   SCHATZ 4108
La pastorella illustre—Die vornehme schaeferin (Stuttgardt,
    1763): Jommelli.   SCHATZ 4868
La pastorella illustre, Lisbona (1773): Jommelli.   SCHATZ 4886
Semiramide—Semiramis, Berlino, 1754: Graun.   SCHATZ 4112
Silla—Silla, Berlino, 1753 (based on French prose text by
    Frederick the Great): Graun.   SCHATZ 4116
Sylla, London, 1753: Graun. Tr. of their Silla.   LONGE 262
Il trionfo d'amore—Der triumph des Amors (Stuttgart, 1763):
    Jommelli.   SCHATZ 4872
Die uneinigen brueder. Tr. of his I fratelli nemici, Berlino
    (1756): Graun.   SCHATZ 4100
Die vornehme schaeferin. Tr. of his La pastorella illustre
    (Stuttgardt, 1763): Jommelli.   SCHATZ 4868

Taglioni, Carlo.
Li due sindaci ossia La vendemmia, ballet. *See* P. Guglielmi's
    Le due gemelle.
La pazza per amore. *See* Nasolini's La Calliroe.
La scuola olandese ossia L'amante in statua, ballet. *See* Por-
    tugal's La donna di genio volubile.

Taglioni, Carlo—Continued.

La sposa rapita, ballet. *See* Portugal's La donna di genio
volubile.

Li sposi contenti, ballet: Cappucci. *See* Martin y Soler's
L'isola piacevole.

La vendemmia. A. T. of his ballet Li due sindaci.

Talassi, Angelo.

Armida, Lisboa, 1798: unknown.	ML 50.2.A75
—Second copy.	SCHATZ 9247

Tarducci, Filippo.

Fernando nel Messico, Roma, 1787 (with interpolation of verses by Metastasio): G. Giordani.	SCHATZ 3838
Fernando nel Messico, Venezia, 1798: Portugal.	SCHATZ 8409

Tassi (Tassis), Niccolò.

L'amante che spende. O. T. of his libretto Il cavalier magnifico.

L'amante che spende, Venezia, 1770: P. Guglielmi.	SCHATZ 4309
L'amor per rigiro, Venezia (1781): Gagni.	SCHATZ 3411
L'amore soldato, Venezia, 1769: Felici.	SCHATZ 3054
L'amore soldato ou L'amour soldat, Paris, 1779: Sacchini.	ML 50.2.A697S2
Il cavalier magnifico, Venezia, 1789 [! *recte* 1779]. (L. T. of his L'amante che spende): Caruso.	SCHATZ 1657
Le nozze della Bita, Firenze, 1778: Ottani.	SCHATZ 7362
L'Olandese in Italia, Lisbona (1766): G. M. Rutini.	SCHATZ 9190

Telemann, Georg Philipp.

Flavius Bertaridus, koenig der Longobarden (Hamburg, 1729). (Tr. by the above and Wendt of Ghigi's Flavio Bertarido, rè de' Longobardi and composed by the above).	SCHATZ 10260
Omphale (Hamburg, 1724): Telemann. (His Tr. of La Motte's Omphale.)	SCHATZ 10265
Sieg der schoenheit, Hamburg (1722) (only alterations in Pos- tel's text, the alterations composed by himself): Conradi.	SCHATZ 2180

Tenducci, Giuseppe Ferdinando.

Amintas, London, 1769. Alteration of Rolt's The royal shep- herd text: Rush, Guglielmi, etc.	LONGE 37
Amintas (Collection of the most esteemed farces, Edinburgh, t. vi, 1792).	SCHATZ 11753

Teofilo (*pseud?*).

Achille riconosciuto, Vienna, 1668: Draghi (ballet airs by Schmelzer).	ML 50.2.A29D7

Terrades, Antonio.

Apelle e Campaspe, ballet. *See* Schuster's L'amor artigiano.

L'ospedale de' pazzi, ballet. *See* G. Giordani's Don Mirtillo
contrastato.

Terrades, Federico.

Il barbiere di Siviglia, ballet. *See* Bianchi's La villanella
rapita.

Eschila e Timoleone ossia La caduta di Timofane, ballet. *See*
Cimarosa's I Traci amanti.

La forza delle donne, ballet. *See* Stabingher's L'astuzie di
Bettina.

Terrades, Federico—Continued.
La pastorella fedele, ballet: Stabingher. *See* Bianchi's La villanella rapita.
La superbia umiliata ossia L'egualità d'amore, ballet. *See* Cimarosa's I Traci amanti.
Il veglione, ballet. *See* Stabingher's L'astuzie di Bettina.

Terzago, Ventura.
La Dori, Monaco, 1680 (alterations of Apolloni's text and new prologue, music by Bernabei): Cesti.   Schatz 1779
Enea in Italia, Monaco (1679): Bernabei.   Schatz 825
L'Ermione, Monaco (1680): Bernabei.   Schatz 826

Testi, *conte* Fulvio.
L'isola d'Alcina, Bologna, 1648: Sacrati.   Schatz 9250

Thaarup, Thomas.
Aline, dronning i Golconda, Kiøbenhavn, 1789: Schulz. Tr. of the original French version Aline, reine de Golconde (Sedaine).   Schatz 9717
Das erndte-fest, Altona, 1795. Tr. of his Høst-gildet: Schulz.   Schatz 9722
Høst-gildet, Kiøbenhavn, 1790: Schulz.   Schatz 9721
Peters Bryllup, Kiøbenhavn, 1793: Schulz.   Schatz 9726

Theobald, Lewis.
Decius and Paulina, masque. *See his* The lady's triumph.
The happy captive, London, 1741.   Longe 191
The lady's triumph, London, 1718 (with the masque Decius and Paulina): Galliard.   Longe 59
Orestes, London, 1731.   Longe 191
The rape of Proserpine, London, 1727: Galliard.   ML 50.2.R24

Thompson, *captain* Edward.
The syrens, London, 1776: Fisher.   Longe 200

Thompson, James.
Alfred, London, 1740 (with Mallet): Arne.   AC 901.M5 v.596
Alfred, London, 1773 (altered, supposedly by Garrick): Arne.   Longe 36

Thoroup, Adam Gottlob.
Hemmeligheden, Kiøbenhavn, 1796: Kunzen.   Schatz 5320
Den skiønne Arsene, n. i., n. d. (Copenhagen, 1781). Tr. of Monsigny's La belle Arsene (Favart).   Schatz 6566
Veddemaalet eller Elskernes skole, Kiøbenhavn, 1798. Tr. of Mozart's Così fan tutte (Da Ponte).   Schatz 6768

Timido. *Arcadian name of* unknown author.
Le vicende amorose, Venezia, 1760: Bertoni.   Schatz 928

Tirabosco, Marc' Antonio.
L'Alcate, Venetia, 1642: Manelli.   Schatz 5890

Törring zu Seefeld, Anton, *graf*.
Telemach. Tr. of Grua's Telemaco, Monaco, 1780 (conte Serimann).   Schatz 4222

Toms, Edward.
The accomplish'd maid, London, 1767. Tr. of Piccinni's La buona figliuola (Goldoni).   Longe 32

Tonioli, Girolamo.

Il Begliar-Bey di Caramania—Der Begjlerbey in Caramanien,
Dresden (1780): Amendola. SCHATZ 173

Il geloso (Lisbona, 1775): da Silva. SCHATZ 9880

Torcigliani, Silvestro.

La visione, Lucca, 1651. *See* M. Curzio in Title-catalogue.

Traffieri (Trafieri), Giuseppe.

L'Americana in Scozia, ballet. *See* Nasolini's Eugenia.

Adone e Venere, ballet: Canavasso. *See* Pugnani's Demofoonte.

Amore premiato, ballet. *See* Paisiello's Il tamburo notturno.

L'avaro, ballet. *See* Curcio's Emira e Zopiro.

Bianca de' Rossi, ballet: Trento. *See* P. Guglielmi's La pupilla scaltra.

Bianca de' Rossi, ballet: Trento. *See* Tarchi's Dorval e Virginia.

Il cambio felice o sia Pulcinella sposo deluso, ballet. *See* Curcio's La Nitteti.

La contadina impertinente. A. T. of his ballet La vendemia.

Le Danaidi, ballet. *See* Borghi's La morte di Semiramide.

Didone abbandonata, ballet: Cimarosa. *See* Cherubini's Ifigenia in Aulide.

Edipo, ballet. *See* Zingarelli's La morte di Cesare.

Fallaride, tiranno d'Agricento, ballet: Trento. *See* Andreozzi's La principessa filosofa.

Il fido amante, ballet: Giuliani. *See* Sarti's Medonte.

Giulio Villenvelt, osia L'assassino di Scozia, ballet. *See* G. Giordani's Aspasia.

Mercato fiammengo, ballet: Canavasso. *See* Cherubini's Ifigenia in Aulide.

Le nemiche degli nomini, ballet. *See* Tarchi's Dorval e Virginia.

La nuova della pace, ballet: Canavasso. *See* Cherubini's Ifigenia in Aulide.

Odoacre, ballet: Trento. *See* Piccinni's Il servo padrone.

Il rapitore punito, ballet. *See* Winter's I sacrifizi di Crèta.

Il ratto delle castellane fatto dai Triestini, ballet: Trento. *See* Andreozzi's La principessa filosofa.

Rinaldo d'Asti, ballet. *See* Borghi's La morte di Semiramide.

Rosa e Nicola, ballet. *See* P. Guglielmi's La pupilla scaltra.

Lo sposalizio de' Morlacchi, ballet. *See* Caruso's Oro non compra amore.

La vendemmia ossia La contadina impertinente, ballet. *See* Anfossi's Il curioso indiscreto.

La vendemia ossia La contadina impertinente, ballet: Giordani. *See* Insanguine's Calipso.

La vendetta di Nino, ballet. *See* pasticcio Elena e Paride.

La vendetta di Nino, ballet. *See* Curcio's Emira e Zopiro.

I viaggiatori areostatici, ballet: Canavasso. *See* Pugnani's Demofoonte.

Traiteur, Karl Theodor.

Albert der Dritte von Bayern (Stuttgart, 1781): G. J. Vogler. SCHATZ 10791

Trancart (Trancard), Antonio.

Ajace e Cassandra, ballet. *See* Borghi's Ricimero.

Le feste o Le gelosie del seraglio, ballet. *See* Borghi's Ricimero.

Les fêtes ou Jalousies du sérail—Das festin oder Die eifersucht
der frauenzimmer des tuerkischen kaisers, ballet. *See*
Bernasconi's Demetrio.

Medée et Jason—Medea und Jason, ballet. *See* Bernasconi's
Demetrio.

Il ratto di Proserpina, ballet. *See* Naumann's Ipermestra.

Télémaque dans l'isle de Calypso.

Vénus et Adonis.

For both these ballets *see* Michl's Il trionfo di Clelia.

Trenta, Pier Angelo.

La confederazione de i Sabini con Roma, Lucca, 1765: Puccini. *See* M. Curzio in Title catalogue.

Trinchera, Pietro.

L'abate Collarone. O. T. of his Le chiajese cantarine.

Le chiajese cantarine, Nuapole (1754): Logroscino, Maraucci
and Fischietti.   ML 50.2.C45

Don Paduano, Napoli, 1745: Logroscino.   Schatz 5672

L'Elmira generosa, Napoli, 1753: Logroscino and Barbella.   Schatz 5675

Le fenzeune abbentorate, Napoli (1745): Gomes.   ML 50.2.F26G6

L'incanti per amore, Napoli, 1741: Palella.   Schatz 7712

Li nnamorate correvate, Napoli, 1752: Sciroli and others.   Schatz 9785

Tronsarelli, Ottavio

Drammi musicali di Ottavio Tronsarelli.

Roma, Francesco Corbelletti, 1632. 452, [3] p. 15½ cm.

Contains: "Narciso," p. 9–55; "Fetonte," p. 71–103; "La danza di Diana,"
p. 105–141; "Il ritorno d'Angelica nell' India," p. 143–154; "La crea-
tione del mondo," p. 171–204; "Marsia," p. 217–242; "L'età dell' oro,"
p. 259–286; "Il ballo de' segni celesti," p. 317–326: and a variety of
cantatas, prologues, dramatic scenes. The volume does not contain
the texts of "La catena d'Adone" and "Il martirio de' Santi Abondio
prete, Abundantio diacono . . . "

La catena d' Adone (Roma), 1626: Mazzocchi.   Schatz 6222

Trotti, *marchese.*

La preziosa ridicola, Venezia, 1719: Orlandini.   Schatz 7346

Tschudi, Ludwig Theodor, *baron* **von.**

Les Danaides, Paris, 1784 (with Du Roullet): Salieri.   Schatz 9285

Tullio, Francesco Antonio (*real name of* **Filostrato Lucàno
Cinnèo**).

La Rosilla, Napoli, 1733: Orefici and Leo.   Schatz 7293

Le viecchie coffejate, Nuenezia, 1710: unknown.   Schatz 11381

Lo viecchio avaro, Napole, 1727: Gius. de Majo.   ML 50.2.V41M2

Turchi, Francesco.

Orfeo ed Euridice, ballet. *See* Il Bellerofonte, by Misliweczek.

Ulbrich, Maximilian.

Der blaue schmetterling, oder Der sieg der natur ueber die
schwaermerey, Wien, 1782: author.   Schatz 10522

Vaccina, *abbate.*

    Amore in tarantola, Venezia, 1750: Latilla.   Schatz 5444

Vadé, Jean Joseph.

    Oeuvres de M. Vadé, ou Recueil des opera-comiques, & paro-
        dies qu'il a donnés depuis quelques années. Avec les air,
        rondes, & vaudevilles notés; & autres ouvrages du même
        auteur . . .

    La Haye, P. Gosse, 1759–60. 4 v. 16ᶜᵐ.

    Vol. 1–2 dated 1760.

    Contains the following librettos: t. I—La fileuse, Le poirier, Le bouquet du
        roi, Le suffisant; t. II—Les troqueurs, Le rien, Le trompeur trompé,
        Il étoit temps, La nouvelle Bastienne, La fontaine de Jouvence; t.
        III—Les Troyennes en Champagne, Jerosme et Fanchonnette, Le
        confident heureux, Folette, Compliment de la clôture de la Foire S.
        Laurent; t. IV — Nicaise, L'impromptu du coeur, Le mauvais
        plaisant.

                                        ML 49.A2V2

    — Œuvres complettes de Vadé, ou, Recueil des opéra-com-
        iques, parodies & pieces fugitives de cet auteur. Avec
        les airs, rondes & vaudevilles. Nouv. éd.

    Troyes, F. Mallet, an vi [1798] 6 v. in 3. 15½ᶜᵐ

    Contains the same librettos (distributed slightly differently) with the
        addtion of (v. 3) "Les racoleurs" and (v. 4) "La veuve indécise."

                                      PQ 2068.V2 1798

    Bertholde à la ville. *See* title catalogue.

    Le bouquet du roi, Paris, 1766.   Schatz 11485

    Le confident heureux, Paris, 1766.   Schatz 11486

    Le drole de corps. A. T. of his Le mauvais plaisant.

    L'enfant gâté ou Folette et Roger-Bontems, Nouv. éd., Paris,
        1758: F. Krafft? Parody of Destouches's Le carnaval et
        la folie.   ML 50.2.E45

    La fileuse, Paris, 1766. Parody of Destouches's Omphale.   Schatz 11492

    La fontaine de jouvence. *See his* La nouvelle Bastienne.

    Jerosme et Fanchonette, Nouv. éd., Paris, 1757: unknown.   ML 50.2.J4

    Le mauvais plaisant ou Le drole de corps, Paris, 1757: un-
        known.   ML 50.2.M48

    Le mauvais plaisant ou Le drole de corps, Paris, 1766: unknown. Schatz 11500

    Nicaise, Paris, 1756: Bambini.   ML 50.2.N3

    Nicaise, Paris, 1766: Bambini.   Schatz 11501

    La nouvelle Bastienne, Paris, 1766: unknown.   Schatz 11503

    Le poirier, Paris, 1752: unknown.   ML 50.2.P53S2

    Les racoleurs, Paris, 1756: unknown.   ML 50.2.R15

    La rencontre imprévue. A. T. of Le trompeur trompé.

    Le rien, Paris, 1753 (parody of Mondonville's Titon et L'Au-
        rore). *See also* Les troqueurs.   ML 48.P2

    Le suffisant, Paris, 1753: unknown.   ML 50.2.S9

    Le trompeur trompé ou La rencontre imprévue, Paris, 1754:
        unknown.   ML 50.2.T835

    Les troqueurs, n. i., n. d.: Dauvergne.   ML 50.2.T84D3

    La veuve indécise, Paris, 1767: Duni.   Schatz 2858

Valbray, de.

    L'heureuse nouvelle, Liège, 1782: unknown.   Schatz 11494

Valeriani, Belisario.
La caccia in Etolia.　O. T. of his Gl'inganni fortunati.
　La caccia in Etolia, Terræra, 1715: Chelleri.　　　　Schatz 1817
　Gl'inganni fortunati, Venezia, 1720: Buini.　　　　Schatz 1393
　Ircano inamorato, Venezia, 1729: Chelleri.　　　　Schatz 1816

Valli, Antonio.
　L'amante statua, Venezia, 1794: L. Piccirni.　　　　Schatz 8062
　Le fallaci apparenze, Venezia, 1793 (modernization of Lorenzi's
　　text Gelosia per gelosia): Astaritta.　　　　Schatz 386

Valli, Antonio Pasquale (presumably the same as Antonio).
　I pastori delle Alpe, Gorizia (1780): Moneta.　　　　Schatz 6557

Vallier, François Charles de, *comte* **du Sauflay.**
　Églé (Journal des spectacles, Paris, 1766, t. II): Dauvergne.　　ML 48.J7
　Le triomphe de Flore (Journal des spectacles, Paris, 1766,
　　t. II): Dauvergne.　　　　ML 48.J7

Valsini, Frencasco.　*Anagram of* Silvani, Francesco.

Vanneschi, Francesco.
　L'Enrico, Firenze, 1732: unknown.　　　　ML 48.A5　v.18

Vanni, Domenico.
　La pace, Lucca, 1657: Roncaglia.　*See* M. Curzio in Title
　　catalogue.

Vanstryp, Filippo.
　Adone rè di Cipro, Roma (1731): Caballone.　　　　Schatz 1446
　Annibale, Venezia, 1731: Porpora.　　　　Schatz 8368
　Mitridate, Roma (1730): Porpora.　　　　Schatz 8373

Varesco, Giovanni Battista.
　Idomeneo—Idomeneus, Monaco (1781): Mozart.　　　　Schatz 6818

Varotari, Dario.
　Il Cesare amante, Venetia, 1651: Cesti.　　　　Schatz 1783

Vasini, Carlo Antonio.
　Li tre Cicisbei ridicoli, Venezia, 1748: Resta.　　　　Schatz 8692

Vaux, de.　*See his real name,* Lemonnier, Guillaume Antoine.

Vedoa, Carlo.
　Angelica, Venezia, 1738: Lampugnani.　　　　Schatz 5391

Vendramino, Paolo.
　L'Adone, Venetia, 1640: Monteverdi.　　　　Schatz 6594

Verazi, Mattia.
　Adriano in Siria, Mannheim (1769): Holzbauer.　(V. wrote
　　the licenza only.)　　　　Schatz 4778
　Apollo placato: Salieri and de Baillou.　(Forms part of
　　Salieri's Europa riconosciuta, Milano, 1778.)　　　　Schatz 9288
　Cajus Fabricius, Mannheim (1760): Jommelli and Colla.　Tr.
　　of V.'s text Cajo Fabricio.　　　　Schatz 4846
　Calliroe, Milano (1779): Alessandri.　　　　Schatz 142
　La Calliroe, Firenze, 1792: Nasolini.　　　　ML 48.A5　v.22
　Calliroe, Venezia (1776): ·Rust.　　　　Schatz 9173
　Calliroe—Calliroe (French transl.) Stuttgart, 1770: Sacchini.　Schatz 9210
　Cleopatra, Milano (1779): Anfossi.　　　　Schatz 278

Verazi, Mattia—Continued.

Enea nel Lazio, Lisbona (1767): Jommelli.	SCHATZ 4893
Europa riconosciuta, Milano (1778): Salieri.	SCHATZ 9288
Fetonte—Phaeton (Stutgart), 1768: Jommelli.	SCHATZ 4860
Fetonte, Lisbona (1769): Jommelli.	SCHATZ 4859
L'Ifigenia—Iphigenia, Cassel, 1766: Jommelli. Same as L'Ifigenia in Aulide.	SCHATZ 4862
Ifigenia in Aulide, Napoli (1753): Jommelli and Traetta. L. T. of V.'s L'Ifigenia.	SCHATZ 4861
Ifigenia in Tauride (Lisbona, 1776): Jommelli.	SCHATZ 4890
Ifigenia in Tauride, Mannheim (1764): G. F. de Majo.	SCHATZ 5856
Iphigenia. Tr. of his L'Ifigenia, Cassel, 1766: Jommelli.	SCHATZ 4862
Iphigenia in Tauris, Mannheim (1764). Tr. of his Ifigenia in Tauride: G. F. de Majo.	SCHATZ 5857
Lucio Silla (altered version of Gamerra's text): Bach.	SCHATZ 529
Lucius Silla, Mannheim, 1774. Tr. of the above.	SCHATZ 530
Oreste, Torino (1766): Monza.	SCHATZ 6611
Pelope—Pelops, Stutgart, 1755: Jommelli.	SCHATZ 4869
Phaeton. Tr. of his Fetonte (Stutgart), 1768: Jommelli.	SCHATZ 4860
Sofonisba, Venezia, 1764: Boroni.	SCHATZ 1251
Sofonisba, Torino (1764): Galuppi.	SCHATZ 3470
Themistocles, Mannheim, 1772. (Only additions to Metastasio's Temistocle, music by Bach.)	SCHATZ 531
Troja distrutta, Milano (1778): Mortellari.	SCHATZ 6687
Zemira e Azore, London, 1779. Tr. of Grétry's Zémire et Azor (Marmontel).	SCHATZ 4196

Verbruggen, John.

Brutus of Alba: or, Augusta's triumph, London, 1697 (with George Powell): D. Purcell. — ML 50.2.B85

Vestri, Gaetano.

Coronazione d'Apollo e Dafne, ballet: Gioanetti. *See* Bertoni's Sesostri.

Vial, Jean Baptiste Charles.

Clémentine ou La belle-mère, Paris, an VIII (1799–1800): Fay. SCHATZ 3037

Viganò, Giuseppe Maria.

L'Andromaca, Milano (1757): Scolari. SCHATZ 9803

Viganò, Onorato.

Adelaide, ballet. *See* Portugal's Fernando nel Messico.
Le Amazzoni: Holler. *See* Zingarelli's Il conte di Saldagna.
Amore e magia, ballet. *See* Portugal's Fernando nel Messico.
Amore trionfator della magia, ballet. *See* Mareschalchi's Il tutore ingannato.
Andromaca in Epiro, ballet: Marescalchi. *See* Gazzaniga's Tullo Ostilio.
Andromaca in Epiro, ballet: Canobbio. *See* Sarti's Farnace.
Andromeda e Perseo, ballet. *See* Bernardini's Achille in Sciro.
Andromeda e Perseo, ballet. *See* Mortellari's Le astuzie amorose.
Arianna abbandonata da Teseo e soccorsa da Bacco, ballet. *See* Rust's L'idolo cinese.
Armida e Rinaldo, ballet. *See* Cimarosa's Ginnio Bruto.

Viganò, Onorato—Continued.

Le avventure di Milord Wilver e di Miledi sua sposa, ballet.
See Giordani's Ines de Castro.

I bacchanali, ballet: Nucci.   See Farinelli's Seldano.

La capanna incantata, ballet.   See Gazzaniga's Amor per oro.

Cefalo e Procri, ballet: Boccherini.   See Sarti's Scipione.

Cefalo e Procri, ballet: Salvatore Viganò.   See Tritto's L'Arminio.

Il convitato di pietra, ballet.   See Gazzaniga's Tullo Ostilio.

Diana al bagno, ballet.   See Gazzaniga's Amor per oro.

Diana sorpresa, ballet.   See Marescalchi's Il tutore ingannato.

La dolce vendetta, ballet: Marescalchi.   See Cherubini's
Quinto Fabio.

La donna di spirito, ballet.   See Tritto's L'Arminio.

La donna difficile, ballet.   See Rust's L'idolo cinese.

Enrico IV, ballet.   See Mugnes' Fernando Cortes.

La figlia dell' aria o sia L'innalzamento di Semiramide, ballet:
G. and S. Viganò.   See Righini's Armida.

La follia e la saggiezza, ballet.   See Bianchi's Alessandro nell'
Indie.

Le furie d'Oreste.   A. T. of his La morte d'Egisto.

Gelosia per gelosia, ballet: Marescalchi.   See Giordani's Fernando nel Messico.

Il giocatore, ballet.   See Anfossi's Il curioso indiscreto.

Il giocatore, ballet.   See Mortellari's Le astuzie amorose.

Giulio Sabino, ballet.   See Bianchi's Alessandro nell' Indie.

L'innalzamento di Semiramide.   A. T. of his ballet La figlia
dell' aria.

Il Meleagro, ballet: Marescalchi.   See Sarti's Mitridate a
Sinope.

Minosse rè di Creta osia La fuga d'Arianna e di Fedra, ballet:
Marescalchi.   See Martin y Soler's In amor ci vuol destrezza.

Il misantropo o sia Il poter delle donne, ballet.   See Cimarosa's
Giunio Bruto.

La morte d'Egisto ossia Le furie d'Oreste, ballet: Marescalchi.
See Caruso's Antigono.

La morte d'Ettore, ballet: La Motte.   See Nasolini's Gl'Indiani.

La morte di Clitennestra.   A. T. of his ballet Oreste.

La morte di Geta, ballet: Gianella.   See Portugal's Alceste.

Ninias tiranno di Babilonia punito de Zoroastro o sia Piramo
e Tisbe, ballet.   See Anfossi's Gli amanti canuti.

Oreste o sia La morte di Clitennestra, ballet: Marescalchi.
See Giordani's Fernando nel Messico.

Oreste o sia La morte di Clitennestra, ballet.   See Rust's Il
baron di Terra Asciuta.

La pastorella impertinente, ballet.   See Anfossi's Il curioso
indiscreto.

Il poter delle donne.   A. T. of his ballet Il misantropo.

Il rè de' ciarlatani, ballet: Marescalchi.   See Cherubini's
Quinto Fabio.

Il Rinaldo, ballet.   See Marescalchi's L'Alessandro nell' Indie.

Viganò, Onorato—Continued.

Li sposi ridicoli burlati, ballet: Marescalchi. *See* Anfossi's Gli amanti canuti.

Il trionfo d'Arianna o sia Arianna abbandonata da Teseo, e soccorsa da Bacco, ballet. *See* Alessandri's I puntigli gelosi.

Viganò, Salvatore.

Giorgio principe della Servia, ballet: V. Trento. *See* Portugal's Gli Orazi e I Curiazi.

Raul, signore di Crechi o sia La tirannide represa—Raoul, herr von Crequi oder Die verhinderte grausamkeit, ballet: author. *See* Himmel's Semiramide.

Riccardo Cuor di Lione, ballet: Weigl. *See* Andreozzi's Olindo e Sofronia.

Villafranchi, Giovanni Cosimo.

L'ipocondriaco, Firenze, 1695: unknown, but not Buini.	Schatz 1395
La serva favorita, Firenze (1741): Chinzer.	Schatz 1864

Villano, Antonio, *called by anagram* **Liviano Lantino.**

L'equivoco, Napoli, 1764: Piccinni.	Schatz 8125
Il pazzo glorioso, Venezia, 1753 (altered by Goldoni from his Lo stravagante): Cocchi.	Schatz 2053
Il pazzo glorioso, Monaco, 1758: Cocchi.	Schatz 2037
Lo stravagante. O. T. of his libretto (as altered by Goldoni) Il pazzo glorioso.	
Lo stravagante, Napoli, 1764: Piccinni.	Schatz 8130

Villati, Leopoldo de.

(Angelica e Medoro)—Angelica und Medorus, Berlin, 1749: Graun.	Schatz 4088
Armida—Armida, Berlino, 1751: Graun.	Schatz 4089
Britannico—Britannicus, Berlino (1751): Graun.	Schatz 4091
Ciro, Muenchen (1733): Ferrandini.	Schatz 3064
Coriolano—Coriolanus, Berlino, 1782 (after sketches by Frederick the Great): Graun.	Schatz 4093
L'Europa galante—Das galante Europa, Berlino, 1748: Graun.	Schatz 4095
Le feste galanti—Die galanten feste, Berlino, 1747: Graun.	Schatz 4114
Le feste galanti—Die galanten feste, Berlino, 1767: Graun.	Schatz 4097
Fetonte—Phaeton, Berlino, 1770 (assisted by Algarotti): Graun.	Schatz 4098
Das galante Europa. Tr. of his L'Europa galante, Berlino, 1748: Graun.	Schatz 4095
Die galanten feste. Tr. of his Le feste galanti, Berlino, 1747 and 1767: Graun.	Schatz 4114 and 4097
Galatea ed Acide—Galathee und Alcides, Posdamo, 1748: Hasse (pasticcio from his works).	Schatz 4541
Il giudicio di Paride—Das urtheil des Paris, Berlino, 1752 (assisted by Frederick the Great and Algarotti): Graun.	Schatz 4099
Iphigenia in Aulis—Ifigenia in Aulide, Berlino, 1768 (perhaps in collaboration with Frederick the Great): Graun.	
Mitridate, Berlino, 1751. A French version of the following:	Schatz 4107
Mitridates—Mithridates, Berlino, 1750: Graun.	Schatz 4106
Orfeo—Orpheus, Berlino, 1752: Graun.	Schatz 4115

Villati, Leopoldo de—Continued.

 Orfeo—Orpheus, Hamburg, 1764: Graun.   Schatz 4109

 Phaeton. Tr. of his Fetonte, Berlino, 1770: Graun.   Schatz 4098

 Das urtheil des Paris. Tr. of his Il giudicio di Paride, Berlino,
  1752: Graun.   Schatz 4099

Vimina, Alberto.

 La gara, Vienna, 1652: unknown.   ML 50.2.G2

Vitturi, Bartolomeo.

 L'Ardelinda, Venezia (1732): Albinoni.   Schatz 106

 Armida, Venezia, 1747: Bertoni.   Schatz 925

 Artamene, Venezia (1740): Albinoni.   Schatz 87

 Berenice, Venezia, 1759: Perillo.   Schatz 7925

 Candalide, Venezia, 1734: Albinoni.   Schatz 114

 Candaspe, regina de Sciti, Venezia, 1740: Casali.   Schatz 1677

 Chi tutto abbraccia nulla stringe, Venezia, 1753: Scolari.   Schatz 9791

 Cleonice, Venezia, 1740: Hasse. (Partly based on his first
  setting of Demetrio, text by Metastasio.)   Schatz 4578

 Ergilda, Venezia, 1736: Galuppi.   Schatz 3486

 Feraspe, Venezia, 1739. Alterations in the text of Vivaldi's
  opera (Silvani).   Schatz 10768

 La gara per la gloria, Venezia, 1744: Latilla.   Schatz 5459

 Mandame [!], Venezia, 1736: Fiorillo.   Schatz 3203

 Nicoraste rè di Tracia, Venezia, 1745: Pattoni.   Schatz 7785

 Nicoraste, Venezia, 1769: Sacchini.   Schatz 9233

 L'odio vinto dalla costanza, Venezia, 1731. Only the alterations in this opera by Vivaldi (Marchi).   Schatz 10763

 Pompeo in Armenia, Venezia, 1747: Scarlatti, Gius.   Schatz 9552

 I rigiri delle cantarine, Venezia, 1745: Maggiore.   Schatz 5833

 Tamiri, Venezia (1734): Galuppi.   Schatz 3495

 Tigrane, Venezia (1733): Paganelli.   Schatz 7370

 Trionfo della costanza in Statira vedova d'Alessandro, Venezia (1731): Galeazzi.   Schatz 3418

Vogler, Georg Joseph.

 Castore e Polluce (Monaco), 1788. Reduced Frugoni's Tr. of
  Bernard's Castor et Pollux from five to three acts and in
  this form composed it.   Schatz 10800

Voisenon, Claude Henri Fusée de.

 L'amant déguisé ou Le jardinier supposé, Paris, 1769 (Theatre
  de M. Favart, Paris, Duchesne, 1763–77, t. x) (with Favart): Philidor.   ML 49.A2F1

 L'amant déguisé, ou Le jardinier supposé, Paris, 1772 (with
  Favart): Philidor.   Schatz 8005

 L'amant déguisé ou Le jardinier supposé, Paris, 1785 (with
  Favart): Philidor.   Schatz 11735

 L'Amour et Psyché (printed together with Bacchus et Erigone, n. i., n. d.; text also claimed by the composer):
  Mondonville.   ML 52.2.B105M6

 Annette et Lubin. See Title catalogue.

 La fée Urgele. See Favart.

 Fleur d'épine, Paris, 1777: Louis.   Schatz 11721

Voisenon, Claude Henri Fusée de—Continued.

Le jardinier supposé. A. T. of his and Favart's L'amant déguisé: Philidor.

Der verkleidete liebhaber oder Der verstellte gaertner, Frankfurt am Mayn, 1774. Tr. of his and Favart's L'amant déguisé ou Le jardinier supposé: Philidor.   Schatz 8006

Der verstellte gaertner. A. T. of his and Favart's Der verkleidete liebhaber: Philidor.

Voltaire, François Marie Arouet de.

La princesse de Navarre (Paris, 1745): Rameau.   ML 52.2.P7

Le temple de la gloire (Paris), 1745: Rameau.   ML 50.2.T38R2

Vovi, Montebaldo.

La fama dell' onore, della 'virtù, dell' innocenza in carro trionfante, Venezia, 1727: Apolloni.   Schatz 300

Vulpius, Christian August.

Bella und Fernando, oder Die satire (Operetten, Baireuth, 1790): Preu.   Schatz 8463

Der betrogene geizige, oder Wer das glueck hat, Leipzig, 1794. Tr. of Paisiello's La discordia fortunata (unknown).   Schatz 7610

Elisinde (Operetten, Baireuth & Leipzig, 1790): Dieter.   Schatz 2577

Das gaukelspiel. A. T. of his Hokus Pokus: Dittersdorf.

Hieronimus Kniker, Passau, 1793. Altered version of Dittersdorf's Hieronimus Knicker.   Schatz 2593

Hieronimus Knicker, n. i., 1793: Dittersdorf.   Schatz 2594

Die hochzeit des Figaro, Leipzig, 1794. Tr. of Mozart's Le nozze di Figaro (Da Ponte).   Schatz 6829

Hokus Pokus, Leipzig, 1794: Dittersdorf. (According to Schatz, Vulpius's text is not the original text).   Schatz 2597

Hokus Pokus oder Das gaukelspiel, n. i., 1795. Slightly different from the above.   Schatz 2598

Das kaestchen mit der chiffer, Berlin, 1793. Tr. of Salieri's La cifra (Petrosellini).   Schatz 9282

Myrrha und Elvira, oder Das opferfest, Hamburg, 1797. His version of Winter's Das unterbrochene opferfest (Huber).   Schatz 11060

Die neuen Arkadier, Weimar, 1796. (Revised version of Schikaneder's Der spiegel von Arkadien): Süssmayer.   Schatz 10184

Das opferfest. A. T. of his Myrrha und Elvira, which is but his version of P. v. Winter's Das unterbrochene opferfest (Huber).

Das opferfest, Hamburg (1798). The same version with this as main title.   Schatz 11062

Das rothe kaeppchen, Weimar, 1792. Altered version of Dittersdorf's text for his comic opera.   Schatz 2604

Die satire. A. T. of his Bella und Fernando: Preu.

Der schleyer, Hamburg, 1788: Wolf.   Schatz 11084

Der schleier (Opern, Baireuth & Leipzig, 1790): Wolf.   Schatz 11084a

Was thut die liebe nicht, Leipzig, 1793. Tr. of Naumann's La dama soldato (Mazzolà).   Schatz 7044

Wer das glueck hat. A. T. of his Der betrogene geizige.

Die zauberflöte, Leipzig, 1794 (revision of Schikaneder's text): Mozart.   Schatz 6849

Wagenseil, Christian Jacob.

Die belohnte rechtschaffenheit (Kaufbeuren, 1785): author.   Schatz 10814

Der beschaemte geizhals, Kaufbeuren, 1787: author.   Schatz 10815

Ehrlichkeit und liebe, Kaufbeuren, 1781: Wolf.   Schatz 11078

Die liebe fuer den kaiser, Kaufbeuren, 1790: Steudle.   Schatz 10062

Walker, Thomas.

The quaker's opera, London, 1728: ballad opera.   ML 50.5.Q91

Wandall, Peter Topp.

Det uventede møde (Kiøbenhavn, 1776?). Tr. of Gluck's La rencontre imprévue (Dancourt).   Schatz 3922

Ward, Henry.

The happy lovers or The beau metamorphos'd (London, 1736?): ballad opera.   Longe 159

Watelet, Claude Henri.

Phaon (Paris) 1778: Piccinni.   Schatz 8158

Weaver, John.

Perseus and Andromeda, with The rape of Columbine or The flying lovers, London, 1728: Pepusch.   Longe 191

Perseus and Andromeda, 4th ed., London, 1730: Pepusch.   Longe 40

Weber, von, *obrist.*

Titania oder Liebe durch zauberei, Cassel, 1792: Grossheim.   Schatz 4215

Weichmann.

Sieg der schoenheit, Hamburg, 1722 (only alterations in Postel's text): Conradi.   Schatz 2180

Weidmann, Joseph.

Der dorfbarbier, Hamburg, 1799 (with Paul Weidmann): Schenck.   Schatz 9592

Weidmann, Paul.

Die bergknappen, Regensburg, 1773: Kuerzinger.   Schatz 5337

Die bergknappen, Wien, 1778: Umlauf.   Schatz 10524

Der bettelstudent oder Das donnerwetter (n. i.), 1789, Winter. Schatz 11023

Das donnerwetter. A. T. of his Der bettelstudent: Winter.

Der dorfbarbier, Hamburg, 1799 (with Joseph Weidmann): Schenck.   Schatz 9592

Der glueckliche schatzgraeber, Wien, 1773.   Schatz 11455

Ein gutes herz ziert jeden stand. A. T. of his Der lumpensammler: Weigl.

Der lumpensammler oder Ein gutes herz ziert jeden stand (Wien, 1792): Weigl.   Schatz 10940

Weidemann.

Le bon vivant oder Die Leipziger messe, Hamburg (1710).   Schatz 5121

Weinwich, N. H.

Claudine af Villa bella, Kiøbenhavn (1787): Schall. Tr. of Goethe's Claudine von Villa Bella.   Schatz 9584

Weisse, Christian Felix.

Komische opern von C. F. Weisse . . .

• *Carlsruhe, C. G. Schmieder, 1778.   3 v. in 1.   18½ cm.*

    Added t-p.: Sammlung der besten deutschen prosaischen schriftsteller und dichter, 73–75. th.   Added t.-p. wanting (?) in v. 1.

           ML 49.A2W2

Weisse, Christian Felix—Continued.

Der aerndtekranz, Leipzig, 1771: Joh. Ad. Hiller.   SCHATZ 4718

Der aerntekranz (Komische opern, Carlsruhe, 1778): Hiller.   ML 49.A2W2

Der dorfbalbier, Leipzig, 1772: Joh. Ad. Hiller.   SCHATZ 4719

Der dorfbalbier (Komische opern, Carlsruhe, 1778, t. ii): Joh. Ad. Hiller.   ML 49.A2W2

Die jagd, Leipzig, 1770: Joh. Ad. Hiller.   SCHATZ 4721

Die jagd (Komische opern, Carlsruhe, 1778, t. iii): Hiller.   ML 49.A2W2

Die jubelhochzeit, Leipzig, 1773: Joh. Ad. Hiller.   SCHATZ 4722

Die kleine aehrenleserin, Luebeck, 1785: Wittrock.   SCHATZ 11068

Der krieg, Leipzig, 1773: Joh. Ad. Hiller. (W. really only contributed songs and "intermezzi" for operatic purposes to Ramler's revision of Schal's translation of Goldoni's "La guerra.")   SCHATZ 4723

Die liebe auf dem lande, Leipzig, 1776: Joh. Ad. Hiller. (Text after Madame Favart's Annette et Lubin and Anseaume's La clochette.)   SCHATZ 4724

Die liebe auf dem Lande (Komische opern, Carlsruhe, 1778, t. i): Joh. Ad. Hiller.   ML 49.A2W2

Lottchen am hofe, Leipzig, 1776: Joh. Ad. Hiller. (Text after Favart's Le caprice amoureux ou Ninette à la cour.)   SCHATZ 4728

Lottchen, oder Das bauernmaegdchen am hofe, Altona, 1770: Joh. Ad. Hiller. L. T. of the above.   SCHATZ 4729

Lottchen am hofe (Komische opern, Carlsruhe, 1778, t. i): Joh. Ad. Hiller.   ML 49.A2W2

Der lustige schuster oder Der zweyte theil vom Teufel ist los, n. i., n. d. (detached copy): Standfuss and Hiller. (Text after Coffey's Merry cobbler.)   SCHATZ 4733

Der lustige schuster (Komische opern, Carlsruhe, 1778, t. ii): Standfuss und Hiller.   ML 49.A2W2

Die schadenfreude (Der kinderfreund, Tuebingen, 1778): Weimar.   SCHATZ 10963

Der teufel ist los oder Die verwandelten weiber. O. T. of his Die verwandelten weiber oder Der teufel ist los: Standfuss and Hiller.

Die verwandelten weiber, oder Der teufel ist los, Leipzig, 1772: Standfuss, revised and added to by Hiller. (Text after Coffey's "Devil to pay or The wives metamorphosed.")   SCHATZ 4732

———— [same title] Riga, 1794: Standfuss and Hiller.   SCHATZ 4732a

Die verwandelten weiber oder Der teufel ist los (Komische opern, Carlsruhe, 1778, t. ii): Standfuss and Hiller.   ML 49.A2W2

Weissflog, Christian Gotthilf.

Das fruehstueck auf der jagd, oder Der neue richter, Sorau und Leipzig, 1785: author.   SCHATZ 10983

Wellander, Johan.

Thetis och Pelee, Stockholm, 1773: Uttini.   SCHATZ 10550

Wendt (Wend), Christian Gottlieb.

Admetus, koenig in Thessalien (Hamburg, 1730). Tr. of Händel's Admeto (Aureli).   SCHATZ 4470

Admetus, koenig in Thessalien (Hamburg, 1731). L. ed. of the above.   SCHATZ 11713

Wendt, (Wend) Christian Gottlieb—Continued.

Die aus der einsamkeit in die welt zurueckgekehrte opera
(Hamburg, 1729): Telemann. SCHATZ 10269

Emma und Eginhard. A. T. of his Die last-tragende liebe:
Telemann.

Flavius Bertaridus, koenig der Longobarden (Hamburg, 1729):
Telemann. (The text is a Tr. of Ghigi's Flavio Bertarido,
rè de' Longobardi, by the above and the composer.) SCHATZ 10260

Die last-tragende liebe, oder Emma und Eginhard (Hamburg,
1728): Telemann. SCHATZ 10261

Der misslungene braut-wechsel oder Richardus I, koenig von
England (Hamburg) 1729. Tr. of Händel's Riccardo I rè
d'Inghilterra (Rolli) with additional matter. (The German arias were composed by Telemann.) SCHATZ 4488

Rodelinda, koenigin in der Lombardey (Hamburg, 1734). Tr.
of Händel's Rodelinda (Salvi and Haym). SCHATZ 4490

Triumph der grossmuth und treue oder Cleofida, koenigin
von Indien, Hamburg (1732). Tr. of Händel's Poro rè
d'Italia. SCHATZ 4487

Weppen, Johann August.

Das freyschiessen oder Das gluekliche bauernmaedchen, Goettingen, 1786: Dieter. SCHATZ 2575

Wezel, Johann Carl.

Der kluge Jakob, Leipzig, 1787: von Kospoth. SCHATZ 5219

Wieland, Christoph Martin.

Alceste (Weimar) 1773: Schweitzer. SCHATZ 9768

Alceste, n. d. (Wielands Sämmtl. werke, xxvi bd.). (Detached copy.) SCHATZ 9768a

Rosamund, Mannheim, 1778: Schweitzer. SCHATZ 9774

Die wahl des Herkules, n. d. (Detached from a probably
19th cent. ed. of his works): Schweitzer. SCHATZ 9775

Woodward, Henry.

The druids, London, 1775 (2d ed.): Fisher. ML 52.2.D72

Harlequin's jubilee, London, 1770: Dibdin (?). LONGE 32

Worsdale, James.

A cure for a scold, London (1735): ballad farce. LONGE 275

Wrighten, J.

The fairy Favour, or Harlequin animated, London (1790). LONGE 207

Xaintonge. *See* Sainctonge.

Ximenez, Ottavio, *cavaliere.*

Chi più sà, manco l'intende overo Gli amori di Clodio e
Pompea, Vienna, 1669: Draghi. SCHATZ 2805

Yarrow, Joseph.

Love at first sight or The wit of a woman, York, 1742. LONGE 321

Zabuesnig, Johann Christoph von.

Philemon und Baucis oder Gastfreiheit und Armuth, Augsburg, 1792: Kaffka. SCHATZ 4985

Zaguri, Pietro Angelo.

Gl'avvenimenti d'Orinda, Venetia, 1659: Castrovillari. SCHATZ 1096

Zanelli, Ippolito.

Nino, Venezia (1732) (revised by Cassani): Courcelle. Schatz 2283

Zanetti, Antonio.

Li birbi, Venezia, 1732: Fini. Schatz 3105

Li birbi—Die schelmen, Braunschweig (1749): Fiorillo. Schatz 3199

Sofonisba (Venezia, 1746) (with Girolamo Zanetti): Jommelli. Schatz 4871

Zanetti, Girolamo.

Eurimedonte e Timocleone ovvero I rivali delusi, Venezia,
1746: Hasse. Schatz 4579

Sofonisba (Venezia, 1746) (with Antonio Zanetti): Jommelli. Schatz 4871

Zani, Pietro Antonio.

Il naufragio di Cipro—Skibbruddet ved Cypren, København
(1764): Sarti. Schatz 9451

Zaniboni, _conte_ Antonio.

L'Anagilda, Venezia, 1735: Pampino. Schatz 7756

L'Arsacide, Venezia, 1721: Chelleri. Schatz 1810

Cleofile, Venezia, 1721: Buini. Schatz 1381

Le gare generose, Venezia (1702) [! instead of 1712]: Albinoni. Schatz 94

Il vincitor di se stesso, Venezia, 1741: Fiorillo. Schatz 3204

Zehnmark, Ludwig.

Die schule der eifersucht oder Liebe hasst allen zwang, Koeln
am Rhein, 1787. Tr. of Salieri's La scuola de' gelosi
(Mazzolà). Schatz 9316

Unter zwey streitenden zieht der dritte den nutzen, Salzburg,
1787. Tr. of Sarti's Fra i due litiganti il terzo gode (Goldoni). Schatz 9461

Was erhält die männer treu?, Wien, 1780: Ruprecht. Schatz 9161

Zeno, Apostolo.

Poesie drammatiche di Apostolo Zeno . . . [vignette]

Venezia, G. B. Pasquali, 1744. 10 v. front. 19 cm.

In v. 1, in the preliminary matter of "Ifigenia in Aulide," the publisher
says:

"Dopo un lunghissimo tempo, che le presenti poesie drammatiche del Signor Apostolo Zeno andarano in molti libretti
sparse, ed alterate da varie penne, per diverse rappresen-
tazioni, che d'esse furono fatte ne' teatri; ora finalmente
vengono in luce. Correvano già pericolo di rimanere
raminghe, e disperse per sempre; o d'essere anche alla
fine un dì, da chì avesse voluto, pubblicate; ma certa-
mente non sarebbero, nè intere nè quelle che uschirono
della penna del loro scrittore. Questi dopo grandi, e calde
instanze, fattegli da molti, acciocchè si contentasse di las-
ciarle uscire; finalmente cedè alle domande reiterate del
Signor Gasparo conte Gozzi, e tutte le diede a lui, acciocchè
il suo piacere ne facesse . . ."

No composer is mentioned.

In v. 4 Gasparo conte Gozzi, the editor, in his preface (xiv p.), comments
on the necessity for an edition like this in view of the custom of alter-
ing librettos to suit local conditions and personal whims. He says:

Zeno, Apostolo—Continued.

"... Sempre fu un costume, e oggidì è cresciuto, bontà de
tempi, che mettendosi più volte i Drammi d'un autore ne'
Teatri, per fare qualche varietà, accomodare i maestri di
musica, ed altre persone, che in que' luoghi o dipingono, o
altri lavori fanno, ed hanno capricci, e fantasie un mare,
s'è preso uno spediente, di porre le mani ne' lavori del
poeta, e quelli allungare, accorciare, cambiarvi person-
aggi, aggiungerne, levarne via, far nuove canzonette, intere, per metà, e chi sa, e chi non sa rappiastra, e malmena
come può, o come gli è conceduto di poter fare dalla natura
medesima della cosa: poichè posto, che colui, il quale
questi ritoccamenti, o rappezzamenti fa, fosse persona di
giudizio, e di dottrina quanto si vuole eccellente, non
potrebbe far sì, che il buono originale non peggiorasse ..."

"E perciò il far l'uovo nell' altrui nido, come si dice, non può
mai produrre altro, che in qualche parte ingiuria al primo
scrittore, poichè, quantunque per un certo rispetto, se ne
levi il nome di lui dalla fronte del libro; con tuttociò
rimane sempre la memoria, e il vestigio di chi dettò prima;
sicchè con l'andare degli anni, molte di queste copie
ritoccate, e lacerate, vanno in cambio d'originali per le
mani di molti, e a poco a poco l'autore ne mette del
suo ..."

A prefatory note in vol. ix reads:

"I drammi che compongono il presente volume, e quelli che
formeranno l'ultimo ... non sono intera fatica del Signor
Apostolo Zeno; ma alternativamente v'impiegò una parte
di suo studio il Signor dottore Pietro Pariate da Reggio
di Lombardia, auch' egli Poeta Cesareo.

"Facitura del primo è la tessitura e l'ordinazione di ciascun
soggetto; al versaggiare applicarono vicendevolmente
l'uno e l'altro."

Vols. ix-x contain the following dramas: Alessandro in Sidone, Ambleto,
Antioco, Artaserse, Astarto, Costantino, D. Chisciotte in corte della
duchessa, Flavio Anicio Olibrio, Sesostri re Egitto, Statira.

Since exactly the same dramas are printed in the Orleans (1785-86) ed. as
written jointly by Zeno and Pariati, this would appear to be a complete list of the librettos written in collaboration by them. *This collaboration was not always noted in the early editions of individual librettos.*
Occasionally a jointly written text is found issued as either by Zeno
or by Pariati only. In such cases the data contained in the collected
works should be accepted as final and corrective.

Vol. iii of the Venice ed. contains seventeen "azioni sacre," which have
not been entered here, though Zeno, commenting, in the preface, on
his efforts to abolish the abuses that had crept into such texts, says:
"procurai finalmente di ordinarli in guisa, e di stenderli, che fossero
non solamente cantabili, ma rappresentabili ancora; sicchè ...
eglino sacre musicali tragedie ragionevolmente nomar si potes-
sero ..." Such texts ("Sisara," "Tobia," "David umiliato")
will be entered in the catalogue of oratorio texts.

At the end of the tenth volume (p. 477-480) is a "Catalogo de' drammi con-
tenuti in questi dieci volumi; con la dichiarazione de' luoghi, e de'
tempi in cui l'autore stesso gli ha pubblicati." The editor says at the
end of this list: "oltre a' quali [drami] l'autore in veruna maniera non
ne riconosce altri per suoi."

ML 49.A2Z3

— Poesie drammatiche di Apostolo Zeno ...

Zeno, Apostolo—Continued.

Orleans, Da' torchj di L. P. Couret de Villeneuve, 1785–86.
   11 v.   21 cm.

(*Half-title:* Bibliotheque des meilleurs poëtes italiens . . . 12.–27.
   v. . . .)

Vol. 8 has title: Poesie sacro-drammatiche . . . v. 9–11: Poesie drammatiche di Apostolo Zeno, composte insieme con Pietro Pariati.

Conte Gozzi's edition. His comments, printed in the fourth vol. of the Venice (1744) ed., here precede the first volume. The contents of this
   edition are arranged in chronological order. The titles in each volume
   (with date and place of first issue) are followed in our copy by ms.
   records of place and date of first performance, with name of the composer.

   ML 49.A2Z4

Alessandro in Sidone (Poesie drammatiche, Venezia, 1744,
   t. ix) (with Pariati).   ML 49.A2Z3

— — (Poesie drammatiche, Orleans, 1785–86, t. xi).   ML 49.A2Z4

Alessandro in Sidone, Vienna d'Austria (1721) (with Pariati):
   Fr. Conti.   Schatz 2192

Alessandro in Sidone—Alexander in Sidon, Wolffenbüttel
   (1726): Fr. Conti.   Schatz 2193

Alessandro Severo (Poesie drammatiche, Venezia, 1744, t. vi).   ML 49.A2Z3

— — (Poesie drammatiche, Orleans, 1785–86, t. iv).   ML 49.A2Z4

Alessandro Severo, Venezia, 1738: Bernasconi.   Schatz 867

Alessandro Severo, Venezia, 1717: Lotti.   Schatz 5714

Alessandro Severo, Venezia, 1763: Sacchini.   Schatz 9241

Alessandro Severo, Napoli, 1719: Sarro.   Schatz 9412

Alexander in Sidon. Tr. of his and Pariati's Alessandro in
   Sidone: Fr. Conti.   Schatz 2193

L'Alvilda, Venezia, 1737 (his "L'amor generoso" retouched
   by Lalli): Galuppi.   Schatz 3480

Ambleto (Poesie drammatiche, Venezia, 1744, t. ix) (with
   Pariati).   ML 49.A2Z3

— — (Poesie drammatiche, Orleans, 1785–86, t. ix).   ML 49.A2Z4

Ambleto, Venezia, 1742 (with Pariati): Carcano.   Schatz 1620

Ambleto, Venezia, 1705 (with Pariati): Gasparini.   Schatz 3556

Aminta (Poesie drammatiche, Venezia, 1744, t. vi).   ML 49.A2Z3

— — (Poesie drammatiche, Orleans, 1785–86, t. ii).   ML 49.A2Z4

L'Amor generoso (Poesie drammatiche, Venezia, 1744, t. vi).
   (O. T. of L'Alvilda.)   ML 49.A2Z3

— — (Poesie drammatiche, Orleans, 1785–86, t. iii).   ML 49.A2Z4

L'amor generoso, Roma (1727): Costanzi.   Schatz 2276

L'amor generoso, Venezia (1707): Gasparini.   Schatz 3557

Andromaca (Poesie drammatiche, Venezia, 1744, t. ii).   ML 49.A2Z3

Andromaca (Poesie drammatiche, Orleans, 1785–86, t. vi). ML 49.A2Z4

Andromaca, Roma, 1730: Feo.   Schatz 3062

Antioco (Poesie drammatiche, Venezia, 1744, t. x) (with
   Pariati).   ML 49.A2Z3

Antioco (Poesie drammatiche, Orleans, 1785–86, t. ix).   ML 49.A2Z4

Antioco, Venezia, 1705 (with Pariati): Gasparini.   Schatz 3561

Artaserse (Poesie drammatiche, Venezia, 1744, t. x) (with
   Pariati).   ML 49.A2Z3

Artaserse (Poesie drammatiche, Orleans, 1785–86, t. ix). ML 49.A2Z4

Artaserse, Livorno, 1706 (with Pariati): unknown.   Schatz 11383

Artaserse, Napoli, 1708: Orlandini and Mancini. *See* this
   under Giulio Agosti.

Zeno, Apostolo—Continued.

Artaserse, Venezia, 1705 (with Pariati): Zannettini.	SCHATZ 11141
Astarto (Poesie drammatiche, Venezia, 1744, t. x) (with Pariati).	ML 49.A2Z3
Astarto (Poesie drammatiche, Orleans, 1785–86, t. x).	ML 49.A2Z4
Astarto, Venezia, 1708 (with Pariati): Albinoni.	SCHATZ 110
L'Astarto, Mantova (1714) (with Pariati): Albinoni.	ML 50.2.A83A4
L'Astarto—Astartus (Hamburg, 1721) (with Pariati and partly rewritten by Rolli): G. B. Bononcini.	SCHATZ 1202
Atenaide (Poesie drammatiche, Venezia, 1744, t. i).	ML 49.A2Z3
Atenaide (Poesie drammatiche, Orleans, 1785–86, t. iv).	ML 49.A2Z4
La Berenice, Verona, 1762. (Altered version of his Lucio Vero): Perez.	SCHATZ 7879
C. Fabbrizio (Poesie drammatiche, Venezia, 1744, t. i).	ML 49.A2Z3
C. Fabbrizio (Poesie drammatiche, Orleans, 1785–86, t. vii).	ML 49.A2Z4
Cajo Fabricio, Venezia, 1735: Hasse.	SCHATZ 4522a
Cajo Fabricio, Salisburgo, 1737: Hasse.	SCHATZ 4522
Cajo Fabricio—Cajus Fabricius, Berlino, 1766: Hasse.	SCHATZ 4523
Cajo Fabricio, Roma (1755): Scolari.	SCHATZ 9804
Cajus Fabritius, Dresden, 1734. Tr. of his Cajo Fabricio: Hasse.	SCHATZ 4523
Cajus Fabricius. Tr. of his Cajo Fabricio, Berlino, 1766: Hasse.	SCHATZ 4524
Cosroe, Roma, 1723. (Later T. of his Ormisda): A. Pollaroli.	SCHATZ 8267
Costantino (Poesie drammatiche, Venezia, 1744, t. ix) (with Pariati).	ML 49.A2Z3
Costantino (Poesie drammatiche, Orleans, 1785–86, t. xi) (with Pariati).	ML 49.A2Z4
Costantino, Venezia, 1711 (with Pariati): Gasparini.	SCHATZ 3589
Costantino (with Pariati). For the L. V., as retouched by Boldoni, see Massimiano: Orlandini.	
Don Chisciotte in corte della duchessa (Poesie drammatiche, Venezia, 1744, t. ix) (with Pariati).	ML 49.A2Z3
Don Chisciotte in corte della duchessa (Poesie drammatiche, Orleans, 1785–86, t. xi).	ML 49.A2Z4
Don Chisciotte in Sierra Morena, Vienna (1719) (with Pariati): Conti. O. T. of the above.	SCHATZ 2194
Don Quixotte in dem Mohrengebuerge, Hamburg, 1722. Tr. of the above.	SCHATZ 2195
I due dittatori (Poesie drammatiche, Venezia, 1744, t. ii).	ML 49.A2Z3
I due dittatori (Poesie drammatiche, Orleans, 1785–86, t. vi).	ML 49.A2Z4
Elisa regina di Tiro, Venezia, 1736. (Altered version of his and Pariati's Astarto): Galuppi.	SCHATZ 3485
Engelberta (Poesie drammatiche, Venezia, 1744, t. iv).	ML 49.A2Z3
Engelberta (Poesie drammatiche, Venezia, Orleans, 1785–86, t. iii).	ML 49A2Z4
Engelberta, Venezia, 1708: Gasparini.	SCHATZ 3564
Engelberta, Venezia, 1743: Paganelli.	SCHATZ 7354
Engelberta o sia La forza dell' innocenza, Bologna (1709): unknown.	SCHATZ 11323
L'Engelberta o sia La forza dell' innocenza, Napoli (1709): Orefici and Mancini.	SCHATZ 7294
Enone (Poesie drammatiche, Venezia, 1744, t. iii).	ML 49.A2Z3
Enone (Poesie drammatiche, Orleans, 1785–86, t. vii).	ML 49.A2Z4

Zeno, Apostolo—Continued.

Eumene (Poesie drammatiche, Venezia, 1744, t. v).	ML 49.A2Z3
Eumene (Poesie drammatiche, Orleans, 1785–86, t. i).	ML 49.A2Z4
Eumene, Venezia, 1723: Albinoni.	Schatz 118
Eumene, Venezia, 1784: Bertoni.	Schatz 938
Eumene, Venezia, 1778: Borghi.	Schatz 1233
Eumene (Lisboa, 1773): Carvalho.	Schatz 1668
Eumene, Torino (1778): Insanguine.	Schatz 4838
Eumene, Roma, 1721: Porpora.	Schatz 8366
Eumene, Roma, 1765: Sacchini.	ML 50.2E85S2
Eumene, Venetia, 1697: M. A. Ziani.	Schatz 11201
Euristeo (Poesie drammatiche, Venezia, 1744, t. v).	ML 49.A2Z3
Euristeo (Poesie drammatiche, Orleans, 1785–86, t. vi).	ML 49.A2Z4
Euristeo, Venezia, 1732: Hasse. (Text altered by Lalli.)	Schatz 4580
Faramondo (Poesie drammatiche, Venezia, 1744, t. vi).	ML 49.A2Z3
Faramondo (Poesie drammatiche, Orleans, 1785–86, t. I).	ML 49.A2Z4
Faramondo, Venetia, 1699: C. F. Pollaroli.	Schatz 8286
Faramondo, Firenze, 1699: C. F. Pollaroli.	Schatz 8325
La fede in cimento, Venezia, 1730: Gasparini and Lapis. L. T. of his L'amor generoso as originally composed by F. Gasparini alone.	Schatz 3596
Le feste d'Iside, Venezia, 1799. (L. T. of his and Pariati's "Sesostri rè d'Egitto," as retouched by Gaetano Rossi): Nasolini.	Schatz 7002
Flavio Anicio Olibrio (Poesie drammatiche, Venezia, 1744, t. x) (with Pariati).	ML 49.A2Z3
Flavio Anicio Olibrio (Poesie drammatiche, Orleans, 1785–86, t. x).	ML 49.A2Z4
Flavio Anicio Olibrio, Firenze (1723) (with Pariati): Gasparini.	Schatz 3568
La forza dell' innocenza. A. T. of his Engelberta.	
Il fratricida innocente (O. T. of his Venceslao), Bologna, 1708: Perti.	Schatz 7949
Gianguir (Poesie drammatiche, Venezia, 1744, t. ii).	ML 49.A2Z3
Gianguir (Poesie drammatiche, Orleans, 1785–86, t. vi).	ML 49.A2Z4
Gianguir—Janguir, Kiøbenhavn (1755): pasticcio.	Schatz 11337
Gianguir. O. T. of Pharao und Joseph: Caldara.	
Gianguir, Venezia, 1760: Ciampi.	Schatz 1881
Gianguir, Venezia (1729): Giacomelli.	Schatz 3812
Gianguir, Venezia (1738): Giai.	Schatz 3814
Griselda (Poesie drammatiche, Venezia, 1744, t. iii).	ML 49.A2Z3
Griselda (Poesie drammatiche, Orleans, 1785–86, t. ii).	ML 49.A2Z4
Griselda, Venezia, 1708 [! instead of 1728]: Albinoni.	Schatz 120
Griselda (Venezia, 1751): Latilla.	Schatz 5460
Griselda, Venezia, 1720: Orlandini.	Schatz 7330
Griselda, Venezia, 1701: A. Pollaroli.	Schatz 8266
Griselda, Monaco (1735): Torri.	Schatz 10365
Griselda, Venezia, 1735: Vivaldi.	Schatz 10770
Ifigenia in Aulide (Poesie drammatiche, Venezia, 1744, t. i).	ML 49.A2Z3
Ifigenia in Aulide (Poesie drammatiche, Orleans, 1785–86, t. i. v).	ML 49.A2Z4
Ifigenia in Aulide, Venezia (1718): Caldara.	Schatz 1484
Ifigenia in Aulide, Firenze (1732): Orlandini.	Schatz 7334
Ifigenia in Aulide, Monaco (1738): Porta.	Schatz 8380
Gl'inganni felici (Poesie drammatiche, Venezia, 1744, t. vii).	ML 49.A2Z3

Zeno, Apostolo—Continued.

Gl'inganni felici (Poesie drammatiche, Orleans, 1785–86, t. i).   ML 49.A2Z4

Gl'inganni felici, Venezia, 1722: Buini.   Schatz 1392

Gl'inganni felici, Venezia, 1696: C. F. Pollaroli.   Schatz 8297

L'inganno vinto dalla ragione, Napoli, 1708.   (Altered version
of his Teuzzone): Lotti and Vignola.   Schatz 5727

Imeneo (Poesie drammatiche, Venezia, 1744, t. iv).   ML 49.A2Z3

Imeneo (Poesie drammatiche, Orleans, 1785–86, t. vii).   ML 49.A2Z4

Janguir.   Tr. of his Gianguir, Kiøbenhavn, 1755: pasticcio.   Schatz 11337

Lucio Papirio (Poesie drammatiche, Venezia, 1744, t. i).   ML 49.A2Z3

Lucio Papirio (Poesie drammatiche, Orleans, 1785–86, t. v).   ML 49.A2Z4

Lucio Papirio—Lucius Papirius, Copenhagen, 1756: pasticcio.   Schatz 11346

Lucio Papirio, Torino, 1753: Balbi.   Schatz 557

Lucio Papirio—Lucius Papirius, Berlino, 1745: Graun.   Schatz 4104

Lucio Papirio—Lucius Papirius, Berlino, 1784: Hasse.   Schatz 4546

Lucio Papirio dittatore, Venezia, 1720: Caldara.   Schatz 1499

Lucio Papirio dittatore, Parma, 1729 (retouched by Carlo Innocente Frugoni): Giacomelli.   Schatz 3809

Lucio Papirio dittatore (Lisboa, 1775): Paisiello.   Schatz 7674

Lucio Papirio dittatore, Venezia, 1721: A. Pollaroli.   Schatz 8259

Lucio Vero (Poesie drammatiche, Venezia, 1744, t. iii).   ML 49.A2Z3

Lucio Vero (Poesie drammatiche, Orleans, 1785–86, t. ii).   ML 49.A2Z4

Lucio Vero—Lucius Verus (Bronsevico, 1756): unknown.   Schatz 11347

Lucio Vero, Venezia (1735): Araja.   Schatz 306

Lucio Vero, Verona (1754): Perez.   Schatz 7873

Lucio Vero, Venezia, 1700: C. F. Pollaroli.   Schatz 8301

Lucio Vero, Napoli, 1785: Sacchini.   Schatz 9242

Lucio Vero, Monaco (1720): Torri.   Schatz 10366

Lucius Papirius.   Tr. of his Lucio Papirio, Copenhagen, 1756:
pasticcio.   Schatz 11346

Lucius Papirius.   Tr. of his Lucio Papirio, Berlino, 1745:
Graun.   Schatz 4104

Lucius Papirius.   Tr. of his Lucio Papirio, Berlino, 1784:
Hasse.   Schatz 4546

Lucius Verus.   Tr. of his Lucio Vero (Bronsevico, 1756).   Schatz 11347

Massimiano, Venetia (1731) (his and Pariati's "Costantino"
retouched by Giovanni Boldoni): Orlandini.   Schatz 7351

Meride e Selinunte (Poesie drammatiche, Venezia, 1744,
t. iii).   ML 49.A2Z3

Meride e Selinunte (Poesie drammatiche, Orleans, 1785–86,
t. v).   ML 49.A2Z4

Meride e Selinunte (Venezia, 1744): Chiarini.   Schatz 1851

Meride e Selinunte, Venezia, 1726: Porpora.   Schatz 8372

Merope (Poesie drammatiche, Venezia, 1744, t. i).   ML 49.A2Z3

Merope (Poesie drammatiche, Orleans, 1785–86, t. iv).   ML 49.A2Z4

Merope, Napoli, 1716: unknown.   ML 50.2.M6

La Merope (much altered), Verona, 1763: pasticcio.   ML 50.2.M62

Merope, London, 1736: Broschi.   Schatz 1341

Merope, Napoli, 1748: Cocchi.   Schatz 2049

Merope, Venezia, 1711: Gasparini.   Schatz 3573

Merope, Venezia, 1757: Gassmann.   Schatz 3619

Merope, Venezia, 1734: Giacomelli.   Schatz 3807

Merope, Venezia, 1773: Insanguine.   Schatz 4834

Merope (Venezia, 1742): Jommelli.   Schatz 4865

Zeno, Apostolo—Continued.

Merope, Wien (1749). German Tr. of Jommelli's second version. SCHATZ 4866

La Merope, Bologna (1727): Orlandini. SCHATZ 7348

Merope, Venezia (1750): Perez. SCHATZ 7874

La Merope, Milano (1776): Traetta. SCHATZ 10412

Mitridate (Poesie drammatiche, Venezia, 1744, t. v). ML 49.A2Z3

Mitridate (Poesie drammatiche, Orleans, 1785–86, t. vii). ML 49.A2Z4

Mitridate, Vienna d'Austria (1728): Caldara. SCHATZ 1494

Mitridate, Venezia (1730): Giai. SCHATZ 3815

Il Narciso (Poesie drammatiche, Venezia, 1744, t. vii): Pistocchi. ML 49.A2Z3

Il Narciso (Poesie drammatiche, Orleans, 1785–86, t. i). ML 49.A2Z4

Il Narciso, Anspach (1697): Pistocchi. SCHATZ 8197

Il Narciso—Narcissus, Kiøbenhavn (1763): Sarti. SCHATZ 9450

Narcissus. Tr. of his Il Narciso, Kiøbenhavn (1763): Sarti. SCHATZ 9450

Nitocri (Poesie drammatiche, Venezia, 1744, t. iii). ML 49.A2Z3

Nitocri (Poesie drammatiche, Orleans, 1785–86, t. v). ML 49.A2Z4

Nitocri, Torino, 1751: Cocchi. SCHATZ 2050

Nitocri, Venezia (1733): Sellitti. SCHATZ 9827

Nitocri, koenigin in Egypten, Wienn (1722): Caldara. Tr. of their Nitocri. SCHATZ 1486

Odoardo, Venezia, 1698 (not in Zeno's collected works): M. A. Ziani. SCHATZ 11191

L'oracolo in Messenia, Venezia (1738). (L. T. of his Merope): Vivaldi. SCHATZ 10775

Ormisda (Poesie drammatiche, Venezia, 1744, t. iv). ML 49.A2Z3

Ormisda (Poesie drammatiche, Orleans, 1785–86, t. v). ML 49.A2Z4

Ormisda, Vienna d'Austria (1721): Caldara. SCHATZ 1501

Ormisda, Venezia, 1728: Cordans. SCHATZ 2226

Ornospade (Poesie drammatiche, Venezia, 1744, t. ii). ML 49.A2Z3

Ornospade (Poesie drammatiche, Orleans, 1785–86, t. vii). ML 49.A2Z4

Ornospade, Vienna d'Austria (1727): Caldara. SCHATZ 1503

Pharamundus, Wolffenbuettel (1746): principally by Hasse. (Tr. of Zeno's Faramondo.) SCHATZ 4553

Pirro (Poesie drammatiche, Venezia, 1744, t. vii). ML 49.A2Z3

Pirro (Poesie drammatiche, Orleans, 1785–86, t. iii). ML 49.A2Z4

Pirro, Venezia, 1704: Aldrovandini. SCHATZ 137

Psiche (Poesie drammatiche, Venezia, 1744, t. vii). ML 49.A2Z3

Psiche (Poesie drammatiche, Orleans, 1785–86, t. xi). ML 49.A2Z4

Quinto Fabio, Padova, 1778. (L. T. of his Lucio Papirio): Bertoni. SCHATZ 932

Quinto Fabio, Roma, 1783. (L. T. of his Lucio Papirio): Cherubini. SCHATZ 1847

Quinto Fabio (Livorno, 1794): Zingarelli. (A modernization of Zeno's Lucio Papirio.) SCHATZ 11255

Le regime di Macedonia, Napoli (1708). L. T. of his and Pariati's Statira (as altered by Carlo de Pretis): Gasparini and Vignola. SCHATZ 3585

Ricimero rè de' Goti, Roma (1740) (*rifacimento* of his and Pariati's Flavio Anicio Olibrio): Jommelli. ML 50.2.R48J6

I rivali generosi (Poesie drammatiche, Venezia, 1744, t. v). ML 49.A2Z3

I rivali generosi (Poesie drammatiche, Orleans, 1785–86, t. i). ML 49.A2Z4

I rivali generosi, Messina, 1712: Facco. SCHATZ 2979

Zeno, Apostolo—Continued.

I rivali generosi, Venezia, 1726: Vignati.	SCHATZ 10724
I rivali generosi, Venetia, 1697: M. A. Ziani.	SCHATZ 11206
Salustia, Venezia (1753): Bernasconi. L. T. of their Alessandro Severo.	SCHATZ 866
Scipione nelle Spagna (Poesie drammatiche, Venetia, 1744, t. iv).	ML 49.A2Z3
Scipione nelle Spagne (Poesie drammatiche, Orleans, 1785–86, t. iv).	ML 49.A2Z4
Scipione nelle Spagne, Venesia, 1724: Albinoni.	SCHATZ 125
Seleuco, Venezia (1725) (L. T. of his and Pariati's Antioco): Zuccari.	SCHATZ 11286
Semiramide (Poesie drammatiche, Orléans, 1785–86, t. vi).	ML 49.A2Z4
Semiramide in Ascalona (Poesie drammatiche, Venezia, 1744, t. ii).	ML 49.A2Z3
Sesostri (Poesie drammatiche, Orleans, 1785–86, t. x) (with Pariati. Same as Sesostri rè di Egitto).	ML 49.A2Z4
Sesostri, Torino (1755): Bertoni.	SCHATZ 918
Sesostri, Venezia, 1757 (with Pariati): Galuppi.	SCHATZ 3494
Sesostri, rè di Egitto (Poesie drammatiche, Venezia, 1744, t. ix) (with Pariati).	ML 49.A2Z3
Sesostri rè d'Egitto—Sesostris, König in Egypten, Praga (1766) (with Pariati): Bertoni. L. T. of B.'s Sesostri.	SCHATZ 919
Sesostri rè d'Egitto, Napoli, 1752 (with Pariati): Cocchi.	SCHATZ 2046
Sesostri re d'Egitto, Venezia, 1756 (with Pariati): Cocchi.	SCHATZ 11687
Sesostri rè d'Egitto, Torino, 1717 (with Pariati): Fiorè.	SCHATZ 3192
Sesostri rè di Egitto, Venezia (1709) (with Pariati): Gasparini.	SCHATZ 3581
Sesostri rè d'Egitto, Milano, 1759 (with Pariati): Monza.	SCHATZ 6612
Sesostri rè d'Egitto, Roma (1751) (with Pariati): Terradellas.	ML 50.2.S55T2
Sesostris, König in Egypten. Tr. of his Sesostri, rè d'Egitto, Praga (1766): Bertoni.	SCHATZ 919
Sirita (Poesie drammatiche, Venezia, 1744, t. vi).	ML 49.A2Z3
Sirita (Poesie drammatiche, Orleans, 1785–86, t. v).	ML 49.A2Z4
Sirita, Vienna d'Austria, 1719: Caldara.	SCHATZ 1487
Statira (Poesie drammatiche, Venezia, 1744, t. x) (with Pariati).	ML 49.A2Z3
Statira (Poesie drammatiche, Orleans, 1785–86, t. ix) (with Pariati).	ML 49.A2Z4
Statira, Roma (1726) (with Pariati): Albinoni.	SCHATZ 98
Statira, Venezia, 1705 (with Pariati): Gasparini.	SCHATZ 3582
La Svanvita (Poesie drammatiche, Venezia, 1744, t. vii).	ML 49.A2Z3
Svanvita (Poesie drammatiche, Orleans, 1785–1786, t. iii).	ML 49.A2Z4
La Svanvita, Milano (1708): Fiorè. (The title page attributes this libretto to Pariati.)	SCHATZ 3195
Temistocle (Poesie drammatiche, Venezia, 1744, t. i).	ML 49.A2Z3
Temistocle (Poesie drammatiche, Orléans, 1785–86, t. ii).	ML 49.A2Z4
Temistocle, Padova, 1721: Chelleri.	SCHATZ 1815
Teuzzone (Poesie drammatiche, Venezia, 1744, t. iv).	ML 49.A2Z3
Teuzzone (Poesie drammatiche, Orléans, 1785–86, t. iii).	ML 49.A2Z4
Teuzzone, Torino, 1716: Casanova and Fiorè.	SCHATZ 1682
Teuzzone, Venezia (1707): Lotti.	SCHATZ 5709
La tirannide debellata, Milano, 1736. (L. T. of his and Pariati's Flavio Anicio Olibrio): Duni.	SCHATZ 2857

Zeno, Apostolo—Continued.

Il Tirsi, Venezia (1696) (not in Zeno's collected works): Lotti,
Caldara and Ariosti. SCHATZ 5728

Il trionfo di Flavio Olibrio, Venezia, 1726. (L. T. of his and
Pariati's Flavio Anicio Olibrio): Porta. SCHATZ 8382

Venceslao (Poesie drammatiche, Venezia, 1744, t. v). ML 49.A2Z3

Venceslao (Poesie drammatiche, Orleans, 1785–86, t. ii). ML 49.A2Z4

Venceslao, Torino, 1721: Boniventi. SCHATZ 1195

Venceslao, Vienna d'Austria (1725): Caldara. SCHATZ 1489

Venceslao (Venezia, 1752): Pampani. SCHATZ 7759

Venceslao, Venezia, 1703: C. F. Pollaroli. SCHATZ 8322

Venceslao—Wenceslaus, Hamburg, 1744: Scalabrini and
others. SCHATZ 9518

Venceslao (Muenchen, 1725): Torri. SCHATZ 10367

La virtù nel cimento, Mantova (1717): Orlandini. L. T. of
their Griselda. SCHATZ 7331

Vologeso, Venezia, 1770 (L. T. of his Lucio Vero): Colla. SCHATZ 2111

Vologeso, Venezia, 1796 (L. T. of his Lucio Vero): Gerace. SCHATZ 3780

Vologeso, Milano (1776) (L. T. of his Lucio Vero): P.
Guglielmi. SCHATZ 4307

Il Vologeso, Lisbona (1769) (L. T. of his Lucio Vero): Jommelli. SCHATZ 4877

Vologeso, Torino (1763) (L. T. of his Lucio Vero): Martin y
Soler. SCHATZ 6024

Vologeso, Venezia (1765) (L. T. of his Lucio Vero): Sarti. SCHATZ 9465

Vologeso, Venezia, 1769 (L. T. of his Lucio Vero): Sarti. ML 50.2.V7S3

Il Vologeso (Lipsia, 1753) (L. T. of his Lucio Vero): Zoppis. SCHATZ 11284

Vologeso rè de' Parti, Torino (1744). (L. T. of his Lucio Vero):
Leo. SCHATZ 5562

Wenceslaus. Tr. of his Venceslao, Hamburg, 1744: Scalabrini and others. SCHATZ 9518

Zenobia in Palmira (with Pariati). *See* Title catalogue.

Zimdar, Carl Friedrich.

Die totale mondfinsterniss, Stuttgart, 1786: C. G. Weber. SCHATZ 10915

Zini, Saverio.

Gli accidenti della villa, Napoli, 1797: Dutillieu. SCHATZ 2877

L'amante confuso, Napoli, 1772: Anfossi. SCHATZ 258

Gli amanti della dote, Cremona (1794): di Palma. SCHATZ 7747

La bella pescatrice, Napoli, 1789: P. Guglielmi. SCHATZ 4237

La bella pescatrice—Das schoene fischermaedchen, Dresda,
1791: P. Guglielmi. SCHATZ 4238

Chi la dura la vince, ossia La finta cantatrice, Cremona (1791).
L. T. of his La virtuosa in Mergellina: P. Guglielmi. SCHATZ 4299

Il fanatico burlato, Napoli (1787): Cimarosa. SCHATZ 1924

Dal finto il vero, Napoli, 1776: Paisiello. SCHATZ 7604

Dal finto il vero—Das ist er ja selbst, Dresda, 1782: Paisiello. SCHATZ 7605

Das ist er ja selbst. Tr. of his Dal finto il vero, Dresda, 1782:
Paisiello. SCHATZ 7605

La finta cantatrice. A. T. of his Chi la dura la vince: P.
Guglielmi.

Das fischermaedchen, Frankfurt am Main, 1794. Tr. of P.
Guglielmi's La bella pescatrice. SCHATZ 4239

Li fratelli Pappamosca (Lisboa, 1786). L. T. of his La villanella ingentilita: P. Guglielmi. SCHATZ 4283

Zini, Saverio—Continued.

L'impegno, Napoli, 1783: Furno.	Schatz 3389
L'inganno poco dura, Napoli, 1796: Portugal.	Schatz 8426
Liretta e Giannino, Napoli, 1795: Fioravanti.	Schatz 3158
Mietitori, Napoli, 1781: P. Guglielmi.	Schatz 4291
La molinara spiritosa, Napoli, 1787: Tritto.	Schatz 10476
La pastorella nobile, Napoli, 1788: P. Guglielmi.	Schatz 4255
La pastorella nobile—Die adliche schaeferin, Dresda, 1791: P. Guglielmi.	Schatz 4256
La pastorella nobile, Brescia (1792): P. Guglielmi.	ML 48.A5 v.12
La pescatrice, Napoli, 1790. L. T. of his La bella pescatrice: P. Guglielmi.	Schatz 4281
Il poeta di campagna, Napoli, 1792: P. Guglielmi.	Schatz 4263
Il ritratto, Napoli (1791): Bianchi.	Schatz 981
Das schoene fischermaedchen. Tr. of his La bella pescatrice, Dresda, 1791: P. Guglielmi.	Schatz 4238
Lo sciocco poeta di campagna, Milano (1793): P. Guglielmi.	Schatz 4264
Lo sciocco poeta di campagna, Lisbona, 1794: P. Guglielmi.	ML 50.2.S38G9
La sposa contrastata, Napoli (1791): P. Guglielmi.	Schatz 4269
Lo studente, Napoli, 1783: Monti.	Schatz 6604
L'ultima che si perde è la speranza, Napoli, 1790: Bernardini.	Schatz 841
L'ultima che si perde è la speranza, Venezia, 1792: Bernardini.	Schatz 836
La villanella ingentilita, Napoli, 1779: P. Guglielmi.	Schatz 4292
La virtuosa bizzara, Venezia, 1791. L. T. of his La virtuosa in Mergellina: P. Guglielmi.	Schatz 4280
La virtuosa in Mergellina (Livorno, 1793): P. Guglielmi.	Schatz 4279

Zorzisto, Luigi. *See real name,* Bisaccioni, *conte* Maiolino.

Zschiedrich, Karl August.

Der schorsteinfeger Peter oder Das spiel des ohngefaehrs, Pirna, 1799. Tr. of Portugal's Lo spazzacamino principe (Foppa).	Schatz 8419

COMPOSER LIST

COMPOSER LIST

[As a rule, doubtful or only approximate dates of birth or death have not been given.]

Ab(b)os, Girolamo, *d.* 1786.
    Arianna e Teseo, Venezia (1751).   SCHATZ 9
    Erifile, Roma (1752).   ML 50.2.E63A2
    Maid of the mill, pasticcio. *See* Title catalogue.
    Love in a village, pasticcio. *See* Title catalogue.
    Medo, Torino, 1753.   SCHATZ 10

Abbos, Giuseppe. *See* Avossa, Giuseppe d'.

Abel, Karl Friedrich, 1725–1787.
    Love in a village, pasticcio. *See* Title catalogue.
    Tom Jones, pasticcio. *See* Title catalogue.

Acciajuoli, Filippo, *d.* 1700.
    Chi e cagion del suo mal, pianga se stesso, Roma, 1682.   ML 50.2.C43A2

Accorimboni, Agostino, *d.* 1818.
    L'amore artigiano, Roma, 1788.   SCHATZ 16
    Il finto cavaliere. O. T. of his Das herbstabentheuer oder Wer
        wagt, gewinnt.
    Il governatore dell' isole Canarie, Roma (1785).   ML 50.2.G6A2
    Das herbstabentheuer oder Wer wagt, gewinnt, n. i., 1790.
        Tr. of his Il finto cavaliere.   SCHATZ 11678
    Das herbstabentheuer oder Wer wagt, gewinnt (Komische
        Opern der Italiener, th. ii, no. 3).   SCHATZ 15
    Il marchese di Castel Verde, Roma, 1779.   SCHATZ 13
    Il podestà di Tufo antico o sia Il tutore burlato, Roma (1786). SCHATZ 17
    Il regno delle Amazoni, Firenze, 1784.   SCHATZ 14
    Le virtuose bizzarre, Roma, 1778.   ML 50.2.V6A2
    Wer wagt, gewinnt. A. T. of his Das herbstabentheuer.

Adam, Johann August.
    Zoroastro, Dresda (1752) (overture and first chorus from Ra-
        meau's Zoroastre).   SCHATZ 55

Adolfati, Andrea.
    Didone abbandonata, Venezia, 1747.   SCHATZ 57

Agnesi, Maria Teresia, 1724–*ca.* 1780.
    Ciro in Armenia, Milano, 1753.   SCHATZ 61

Agostini, Pietro Simone.
    Il ratto delle Sabine, Venetia, 1680.   SCHATZ 65

Agus, Joseph.
    Love in a village, pasticcio. *See* Title catalogue.

Agricola, Johann Friedrich, 1720–1774.
    Achille in Sciro—Achilles in Scirus, Berlino, 1765.   SCHATZ 66
    Cleofide, Berlino (1754).   SCHATZ 67
    I Greci in Tauride—Die Griechen in Taurica, Berlino, 1772.
        (Rev. version of his Oreste e Pilade).   SCHATZ 68

Agthe, Carl Christian, 1762–1797.
    Martin Velten, n. i., n. d.   Schatz 62

Åhlström, Olof, 1756–1835.
    Frigga, Stockholm, 1787.   Schatz 69

Akeroyd(e), Samuel.
    The comical history of Don Quixote, London, 1729. *See* Title
       catalogue.   Longe 68

Albergati, *conte* **Pirro Capacelli,** 1663–1735.
    Gli amici, Bologna (1699).   Schatz 77

Albertini, Gioacchino, *d.* 1811.
    Virginia, Roma (1786).   Schatz 86

Albinoni, Tommaso, 1674–1745.
    Alcina delusa da Rugero, Venezia, 1725.   Schatz 113
    Aminta. *See* Zeno's Poesie drammatiche.
    L'amor di figlio non conosciuto, Venezia, 1715.   Schatz 102
    Antigono tutore di Filippo rè della Macedonia, Venezia, 1724
       (with G. Porta).   Schatz 133
    L'Ardelinda, Venezia (1732).   Schatz 106
    Artamene, Venezia (1740).   Schatz 87
    L'arte in garra con l'arte, Venezia (1702).   Schatz 88
    Astarto, Venezia, 1708.   Schatz 110
    L'Astarto, Mantova (1714).   ML 50.2.A83A4
    Candalide, Venezia, 1734.   Schatz 114
    Ciro, Venezia (1709).   Schatz 115
    Cleomene, Venezia, 1718.   Schatz 128
    Dido (Bresslau, 1726). Tr. of: Schatz 90
    Didone abbandonata, Venezia (1775).   Schatz 89
    Diomede punito da Alcide, Venezia, 1701.   Schatz 107
    Le due rivali in amore, Venezia (1728).   Schatz 108
    Gl'eccessi della gelosia, Venezia, 1722.   Schatz 116
    L'Elenia, Venezia, 1730.   Schatz 105
    L'Ermengarda, Venezia (1723).   Schatz 91
    Eumene, Venezia (1717). (Text by Salvi.)   Schatz 92
    Eumene, Venezia, 1723. (Text by Zeno.)   Schatz 118
    Gl'evenimenti di Rugero, Venezia, 1732. L. T. of his Alcina
       delusa da Rugero.   Schatz 113
    La fede tra gl'inganni, Venezia, 1707.   Schatz 119
    Filandro, Venezia (1729). "Edizione seconda" of his L'in-
       costanza schernita.   Schatz 109
    Le gare generose, Venezia (1702) [! instead of 1712].   Schatz 94
    Il Giustino, Bologna (1711).   Schatz 129
    Griselda, Venezia, 1708 [! instead of 1728].   Schatz 120
    L'incostanza schernita, Venezia, 1727.   Schatz 95
    L'inganno innocente, Venezia, 1701.   Schatz 121
    L'ingratitudine gastigata, Venezia, 1698.   Schatz 96
    Laodice, Venezia (1724).   Schatz 130
    La Mariane, Venezia (1724). (Four arias from his Gl'eccessi
       della gelosia. Mainly by Giov. Porta.)   Schatz 117
    La Mariane, Firenze (1726). (Partly by Porta and others.)   ML 48.A5   v.18
    Meleagro, Venezia, 1718.   Schatz 122
    Pimpinone, Venezia, 1708. (At end of his Astarto, 1708.)   Schatz 111
    Il più infedele trà gli amanti, Venezia, 1731.   Schatz 123

Albinoni, Tommaso, 1674-1745—Continued.

Primislao, primo rè di Boemia, Venetia, 1697.	Schatz 124
Il prodigio dell' innocenza, Venetia, 1695.	Schatz 104
Radamisto, Venetia, 1698.	Schatz 97
Scipione nelle Spagne, Venezia, 1724.	Schatz 125
Statira, Roma (1726).	Schatz 98
Li stratagemi amorosi, Venezia, 1730.	Schatz 131
Thomyris, queen of Scythia, pasticcio. _See_ Title catalogue.	
Il Tigrane rè d'Armenia, Venezia, 1697.	Schatz 126
Il tiranno eroe, Venezia, 1710.	Schatz 127
Il tradimento tradito, Venetia, 1709.	Schatz 103
Il trionfo d'Armida, Venezia (1726).	Schatz 132
I veri amici, Monaco (1722).	Schatz 99
Vespetta e Pimpinone (Monaco, 1722). L. T. of his Pimpinone.	Schatz 100
Zenobia, regina de Palmireni, Venetia, 1694.	Schatz 112
Zenone, imperator d'Oriente, Venetia, 1696.	Schatz 101

Aldrovandini, Giuseppe Antonio Vincenzo, 1665–1707.

Dafni, Bologna (1696).	ML 50.2.D2
La fortezza al cimento, Venetia (1699).	Schatz 134
Gl'inganni amorosi scoperti in villa, Bologna (1696).	Schatz 135
Mitridate in Sebastia, Firenze (1704).	Schatz 139
L'odio e l'amore, Napoli, 1704.	Schatz 136
Pirro, Venezia, 1704.	Schatz 137
Il più fedel tra vasalli, Napoli, 1705.	Schatz 138
Turno Aricino, Genova, 1702.	Schatz 140

Alessandri, Felice, 1747–1798.

Adriano in Siria, Venezia, 1780.	Schatz 153
Alcina e Ruggero, Torino (1775).	Schatz 141
Calliroe, Milano (1779).	Schatz 142
La cameriera per amore (Lisbona, 1776).	Schatz 152
La compagnia d'opera a Nanchino—Die operisten in Nanking, Berlino, 1790.	Schatz 143
Dario—Darius, Berlino (1791).	Schatz 144
Li due fratelli ridicoli. A. T. of his La finta baronessa.	
L'enlèvement des Sabines, ballet heroique. _See_ Ferrero's La disfatta di Dario.	
Ezio, Lucca (1782).	Schatz 145
La finta baronessa o Li due fratelli ridicoli, Lisbona, 1795. L. T. of next entry.	Schatz 150
La finta principessa, Genova (1783).	Schatz 146
Il marito geloso, Livorno (1784).	Schatz 147
Il matrimonio per concorso (Lisbona, 1773).	Schatz 148
Die operisten in Nanking. Tr. of his La compagnia d'opera a Nanchino, Berlino, 1790.	Schatz 143
I puntigli gelosi, Venezia, 1783.	Schatz 154
Il ritorno di Ulisse a Penelope—Ulysses rückkunft zur Penelope, Berlino (1790).	Schatz 149
Ulysses rückkunft zur Penelope. Tr. of his Il ritorno di Ulisse a Penelope, Berlino (1790).	Schatz 149
Vasco di Gama, pasticcio. _See_ Title catalogue.	
Il vecchio geloso, Torino (1782).	Schatz 151
Virginia, Venezia, 1793.	Schatz 156

Alessandri (Alessandro), Gennaro d'.
    Ottone, Venezia, 1740.   Schatz 157

Alexandre, Charles Guillaume.
    Georgét et Georgette, Avignon, 1768.   Yudin PQ
    Le petit maître en province, Paris, 1765.   ML 50.2.P337A4
    Le petit-maître en province, Paris, 1771.   Schatz 159

Algisi (Alghisi), Francesco Paris, 1666–1733.
    L'amor di Curzio per la patria, Venetia, 1690.   Schatz 160
    Il trionfo della continenza, Venetia, 1691.   Schatz 161

Amadei, Filippo, b. ca. 1683.[1]
    Der ehrsuechtige Arsaces (Hamburg, 1722) (partly by Or-
        landini).   Schatz 7354
    Muzio Scevola. *See* Mattei, Filippo.
    Teodosio il giovane, Roma (1711).   Schatz 167

Amendola, Giuseppe.
    Il Begliar-Bey di Caramania—Der Begjlerbey in Caramanien,
        Dresden (1780).   Schatz 173

Amicone (Amiconi), Antonio.
    Commedianti fortunati, Napoli, 1779.   Schatz 174
    La grotta del mago Merlino, Roma, 1786.   Schatz 175

André Johann, 1741–1799.
    Der alchymist. A. T. of his (?) Der liebesteufel.
    Der alchymist (Berlin) 1778.   Schatz 177
    Der alte freyer, Frankfurt am Mayn, 1775.   Schatz 178
    Alter schützt für thorheit nicht, Hamburg, 1781.   Schatz 179
    Der authomat, Hamburg, 1783.   Schatz 180
    Das automat, Lübeck, 1784. L. T. of this.   Schatz 181
    Der barbier von Sevilien oder Die unnütze vorsicht, Offen-
        bach am Mayn, 1776.   Schatz 182
    Belmont und Constanze oder Die entfuehrung aus dem serail,
        Leipzig, 1781.   Schatz 183
    Die bezauberten, Berlin, 1777.   Schatz 184
    Elmine, Nürnberg, 1781.   Schatz 185
    Die entfuehrung aus dem serail. A. T. of his Belmont und
        Constanze.
    Die Grazien (Theater-Journal fuer Deutschland, Gotha, 1778). Schatz 11754
    Laura Rosetti, Leipzig, 1777.   Schatz 188
    Der liebesteufel oder Der alchymist (Meissner, Operetten,
        Leipzig, 1778) (doubtful).   ML 49.A2M3
    Mehr als grossmuth, Berlin, 1782.   Schatz 189
    Das tartarische gesez, Leipzig, 1779.   Schatz 190
    Der töpfer, Frankfurt und Leipzig, 1774.   Schatz 191
    Die unnütze vorsicht. A. T. of his Der barbier von Sevilien.

André, Louis, d. 1739.
    Mirtil, Dresden, 1721.   ML 50.2.M67A5
    Le triomphe de l'amour, Dresde (1725).   ML 50.2.T7

Andreozzi, Gaetano, 1763–1826.
    See also Catalogue of 19th century librettos.
    Agesilao, Venezia, 1787.   Schatz 221

---

[1] Schatz claims that this is the real name of Filippo Mattei.

Andreozzi, Gaetano—Continued.

L'Agesilao, Verona (1792).	ML 50.2.A38A5
Gli amanti in Tempe, Firenze, 1792.	SCHATZ 216
Amelia ed Ottiero (Trieste, 1797).	SCHATZ 201
Amleto, Padova (1792).	SCHATZ 212
Angelica e Medoro, Firenze, 1792.	SCHATZ 194
L'Arbace, Firenze, 1785.	SCHATZ 214
Argea, Torino (1799).	SCHATZ 215
Arsinoe, Napoli, 1795.	SCHATZ 206
Catone in Utica, Livorno (1789).	SCHATZ 195
Il disprezzo vinto dal disprezzo, Napoli, 1795.	SCHATZ 207
Giovanna d'Arco o sia La pulcella d'Orleans, Venezia (1797).	SCHATZ 196
Ines de Castro, Firenze, 1793.	SCHATZ 213
Lodoiska, London (1794). (Pasticcio by the above, Storace, Cherubini, and Kreutzer.)	LONGE 228
Le nozze inaspettate, Napoli, 1793.	SCHATZ 208
Olindo e Sofronia, Venezia, 1798. L. T. of his Sofronia ed Olindo.	SCHATZ 220
Partenope sul lido etrusco, Lucca, 1785.	SCHATZ 197
I pazzi per disimpegno, Venezia (1782).	SCHATZ 222
La principessa filosofa ossia Il contravveleno, Venezia (1794).	SCHATZ 198
La pulcella d'Orleans. A. T. of his Giovanna d'Arco.	
Quello che può accadere, Venezia (1784).	SCHATZ 218
Sofronia ed Olindo, Napoli, 1793.	SCHATZ 200
Teodelinda. Torino (1789).	SCHATZ 211
Le tre fanatiche, Napoli, 1785.	SCHATZ 204
La vergine del sole, Livorno (1799).	SCHATZ 203

Anfossi, Pasquale, 1727–1797.

Alessandro nell' Indie, Roma (1772).	SCHATZ 282
L'amante confuso, Napoli, 1772.	SCHATZ 258
Gli amanti canuti, Venezia, 1781.	SCHATZ 223
Gli amanti canuti—Die liebenden greise, Dresda, 1783.	SCHATZ 224
Amanti canuti. (Second act forms part also of his Il disprezzo, Venezia, 1782 libretto.)	
L'Americana in Olanda, Venezia, 1778.	SCHATZ 264
Antigono, Venezia, 1773.	SCHATZ 225
Antigono, Milano (1781) (largely by Gatti).	SCHATZ 283
Armida, Torino (1770).	SCHATZ 226
Gli artigiani, Milano (1795).	SCHATZ 227
L'avaro, Firenze (1777).	SCHATZ 228
L'avaro—Den giaerrige, Kiobenhavn, 1776.	SCHATZ 229
L'avaro—Der geizige (Dresden, 1780).	SCHATZ 230
Azor rè di Kibinga, Venezia (1779).	SCHATZ 265
Il barone di Rocca Antica—Der baron von Alten Fels, Dresden (1772) (acts II–III; act I by Franchi).	SCHATZ 3330
Die beständigkeit in der liebe. A. T. of his Isabella und Rodrigo.	
Cajo Mario, Venezia (1770).	SCHATZ 231
Der civilisirte bauer. Tr. of his Il zotico incivilito, Dresda, 1792.	SCHATZ 253
La clemenza di Tito, Napoli, 1772.	SCHATZ 273
Cleopatra, Milano (1779).	SCHATZ 278

Anfossi, Pasquale—Continued.

La contadina incivilita, Venezia, 1775.	Schatz 266
La costanza in amore. A. T. of his Isabella e Rodrigo.	
Il curioso indiscreto, Roma (1777).	ML 50.2.C9A6
Il curioso indiscreto, Firenze, 1777.	Schatz 232
Il curioso indiscreto, Lucca, n. d.	Schatz 11670
Demofoonte, Genova (1774) (A. and others).	Schatz 274
Didone abbandonata, Lucca, 1775.	Schatz 233
Il disprezzo, Venezia, 1782 (one act, after that second act of his Amanti canuti).	Schatz 279
Die eifersucht auf der probe, Gera, 1791. Tr. of his Il geloso in cimento.	Schatz 237
Ezio, Venezia (1778).	Schatz 275
La finta Cingara per amore, Venetia, 1780 (act II; act I by Franchi).	Schatz 3331
La finta giardiniera, Firenze, 1775.	Schatz 234
La finta giardiniera—Die verstellte gaertnerin, Dresda, 1775.	Schatz 235
Den fortraengte ubekiendte. A. T. of his Jeannette.	
La forza delle donne (Venezia, 1778).	Schatz 267
Der geizige. Tr. of his L'avaro (Dresden, 1780).	Schatz 230
Le gelosie fortunate, Venezia, 1786.	Schatz 269
Le gelosie villane, Casale (1779).	Schatz 280
Il geloso in cimento, Venezia, 1774.	Schatz 236
Gengis-Kan, Torino, 1777.	Schatz 260
Den giaerrige. Tr. of his L'avaro, Kiobenhavn, 1776.	Schatz 229
La Giannetta o sia L'incognita perseguitata—Jeannette eller Den fortraengte ubekiendte, Kiøbenhavn, 1775. L. T. and Tr. of his L'incognita perseguitata.	Schatz 240
Die gluecklichen reisenden. Tr. of his I viaggiatori felici, Dresda, 1781.	Schatz 255
Die gluecklichen reisenden. Tr. of his I viaggiatori felici (Vienna, 1783).	Schatz 256
Die heyrath durch betrug. Tr. of his Il matrimonio per inganno, Brunsevic, 1782.	Schatz 245
L'incognita perseguitata, Milano (1773).	Schatz 238
L'inconnue persecutée, Paris, 1776. Rochefort's version of his L'incognita perseguitata.	ML 50.2.I55A6
Isabella e Rodrigo o sia La costanza in amore, Venezia, 1776.	Schatz 241
Isabella e Rodrigo o sia La costanza in amore—Isabella und Rodrigo oder Die beständigkeit in der liebe, Dresda, 1784.	Schatz 242
Jeannette eller Den fortraengte ubekiendte. Tr. of his La Giannetta o sia L'incognita perseguitata, Kiøbenhavn, 1775.	Schatz 240
Die liebenden greise. Tr. of his Gli amanti canuti (Dresda, 1783).	Schatz 224
Lucio Silla, Venezia (1774).	Schatz 243
La maga Circe, Roma (1788). (Printed together with Basili's La bella incognita.)	ML 50.2.B28B2
La maga Circe, Siena, 1792.	Schatz 262
La maga Circe, Lisbona, 1797.	Schatz 263
I matrimonj per fanatisimo, Napoli, 1788.	Schatz 259
Il matrimonio per inganno, Vicenza (1780).	Schatz 244
Il matrimonio per inganno—Die heyrath durch betrug, Brunsevic, 1782.	Schatz 245

Anfossi, Pasquale—Continued.

Metilda ritrovata, Vienna, 1773. L. T. of his L'incognita
perseguitata.   Schatz 239

Die narrheiten der eifersucht. Tr. of his Le pazzie de' gelosi,
Dresda, 1788.   Schatz 247

La Nitteti, Venezia (1780).   Schatz 276

L'Olimpiade, Venezia, 1774.   Schatz 246

L'orfanella americana, Venezia (1787).   Schatz 270

Orpheus and Eurydice, London, 1785. A pasticcio from
(principally) Gluck, Bach, Händel, and the above.   Schatz 3926

Le pazzie de'gelosi, Roma, 1787.   ML 50.2.P3A5

Le pazzie de'gelosi—Die narrheiten der eifersucht, Dresda,
1788.   Schatz 247

La pescatrice fedele (Venezia, 1776). L. T. of his La vera
costanza.   Schatz 248

Robin Hood, pasticcio. *See* Title catalogue.

Den sande bestandighed. Tr. of his La vera costanza, Kiøbenhavn, 1778.   Schatz 250

Lo sposo di trè e marito di nessuna (Vienna, 1768) (partly by
P. Guglielmi and Gassmann).   Schatz 284

Lo sposo di trè e marito di nessuna, Napoli, 1781 (partly by P.
Guglielmi and Giordano).   Schatz 285

Lo sposo disperato (Venezia, 1777).   Schatz 252

Lo sposo per equivoco, Venezia (1783).   Schatz 277

Sprigs of laurel. *See* Title catalogue.

Il trionfo d'Arianna, Venezia (1781).   Schatz 271

Il valore delle donne, Casale (1783).   Schatz 268

La vedova bizzarra, Napoli, 1788.   Schatz 261

La vera costanza, Roma, 1776. O. T. of his La pescatrice
fedele.   ML 50.2.V33A5

La vera costanza, Firenze, 1777.   Schatz 249

La vera costanza—Den sande bestandighed, Kiøbenhavn,
1778.   Schatz 250

La vera costanza—Die wahre beständigkeit, Bronsvic, 1783.   Schatz 251

Die verstellte gaertnerin. Tr. of his La finta giardiniera,
Dresda, 1775.   Schatz 235

I viaggiatori felici—Die gluecklichen reisenden, Dresda, 1781.   Schatz 255

I viaggiatori felici, London, 1782.   Schatz 254

I viaggiatori felici—Die gluecklichen reisenden (Vienna,
1783).   Schatz 256

Die wahre beständigkeit. Tr. of his La vera costanza, Bronsvic, 1783.   Schatz 251

Zemira, Venezia, 1782.   Schatz 272

Zenobia in Palmira (Livorno, 1796).   Schatz 257

Il zotico incivilito—Der civilisirte bauer, Dresda, 1792. L. T.
of his Lo sposo disperato.   Schatz 253

Angiolini, Gaspero (Gasparo).

L'amore e l'azzardo, ballet. *See* Rust's Gli antiquari in
Palmira.

Amore e Psiche, ballet. *See* Bianchi's Nitteti.

Attila, ballet. *See* Gatti and Anfossi's Antigono.

Il castigo de'Bonzi, ballet. *See* Gatti and Anfossi's Antigono.

Il diavolo a quattro ossia La doppia metamorfosi, ballet. *See*
Calegari's Artemisia.

Angiolini, Gaspero (Gasparo)—Continued.

Il diavolo a quattro, ballet. *See* Calvi's Ezio.

Il diavolo a quattro ossia La doppia metamorfosi, ballet. *See* Caruso's Il matrimonio in commedia.

Il diavolo a quattro ossia La doppia metamorfosi, ballet. *See* Gassmann's L'amore artigiano.

Il disertore francese, ballet. *See* Anfossi's Antigono.

La doppia metamorfosi. A. T. of his ballet Il diavolo a quattro.

Dorina e l'uomo selvatico, ballet. *See* G. Giordani's La disfatta di Dario.

Fedra, ballet. *See* Campobasso's Antigona.

I geni riuniti, ballet. *See* Caruso's Il matrimonio in commedia.

I geni riuniti. *See* Gassmann's L'amore artigiano.

La Lauretta, ballet. *See* Caruso's Il matrimonio in commedia.

La Lauretta, ballet. *See* Gassmann's L'amore artigiano.

Lorezzo, ballet. *See* Campobasso's Antigona.

Lorezzo, ballet. *See* V. Federici's L'Olimpiade.

La morte di Cleopatra, ballet. *See* Rust's Gli anti quari in Palmira.

Le nozze de' Sanniti, ballet. *See* G. Giordani's La disfatta di Dario.

L'orfano, ballet. *See* Tarchi's Giulio Sabino.

La partenza di Berenice. A. T. of his ballet Tito.

Il rè alla caccia, ballet. *See* Naumann's Solimano.

Il rè alla caccia, ballet. *See* Tarchi's Giulio Sabino.

Sargine, ballet. *See* V. Federici's L'Olimpiade.

Semiramide. *See* Anfossi's Antigono.

Il Solimano secondo, ballet. *See* Caruso's Il matrimonio in commedia.

Il Solimano, secondo, ballet. *See* Gassmann's L'amore artigiano.

Solimano II, ballet. *See* P. Guglielmi's Le pazzie di Orlando.

Il suffi e lo schiavo, ballet. *See* G. Calegari's Artemisia.

Tito o La partenza di Berenice, ballet. *See* Tarchi's L'apoteosi d'Ercole.

Il tuture sorpreso, ballet. *See* Tarchi's Giulio Sabino.

I vincitori de' giuochi olimpici, ballet. *See* V. Federici's L'Olimpiade.

Anglesi, Domenico.

Il mondo festeggiante (G. A. Moniglia, Poesie drammatiche, parte prima, Firenze, 1689).　　ML 49.A2M7

La serva nobile, n. i. n. d. (detached from same work).　　Schatz 288

Anglois, d' (Giorgio?).

Il trionfo d'Arbace, ballet. *See* Nasolini's La morte di Semiramide.

Antonelli Torre, Francesco.

Catone in Utica, Napoli, 1784.　　Schatz 289

Antoni, Pietro degli.

Atide, Bologna (1679). (Second act only; act I by G. F. Tosi; act III by G. A. Perti.)　　Schatz 10381

Apell, David Philipp von, 1754–1833.
L'amour peintre ou Le jaloux dupé, Cassel, 1794.   Schatz 292

Apolloni, Salvatore.
La fama dell' onore, della virtù, dell' innocenza in carro trion-
　fante, Venezia (1727).   Schatz 300
Le metamorfosi odiamorose in birba trionfale nelle gare delle
　terre amanti, Venezia, 1732.   Schatz 301

Araya, Francesco, d. ca. 1770.
Alessandro nell' Indie, St. Pietroburgo, 1759.   Schatz 304
Bellerophon, St. Petersburg, 1757. Tr. of his Bellerofonte. ML 50.2.B35A7
Berenice, Venezia, 1734.   Schatz 305
Il Cleomene, Roma (1731).   ML 50.2.C59A7
Lucio Vero, Venezia (1735).   Schatz 306
Orfeo, pasticcio. See Title catalogue.

Ardespin (Dardespin, Ardespine), Melchior d', ca. 1643–1717.
Alarico il Baltha. Incidental ballet music for this opera by
　Steffani.
L'Ascanio, Monaco (1686). Only the ballet music for Ber-
　nabei's opera.   Schatz 824

Arefice, Antonio.   See Orefici, Ant

Arena, Giuseppe.
Artaserse, Torino (1741).   Schatz 308
La clemenza di Tito, Torino (1739).   Schatz 309

Aresti, Floriano.
La costanza in cimento con la crudeltà, Venetia, 1712.   Schatz 313
Crisippo, Ferrara (1710).   ML 50.2.C85A7
Il trionfo di Pallade in Arcadia, Bologna, 1715.   Schatz 312

Ariosti, Attilio, 1666–ca. 1740.
Il Danubio consolato (P. A. Bernardoni, Poemi drammatici,
　terza parte, Vienna, 1707).   ML 49.A2B4
L'Erifile, Venezia, 1697.   Schatz 319
Muzio Scevola. See Title catalogue.
Il Tirsi, Venezia (1696) (with Lotti and Caldara).   Schatz 5728

Arne, Michael, 1740 or 1741–1786.
Almena, London, 1764 (with Battishill).   Longe 37
The choice of Harlequin or The Indian chief, London, 1782. Longe 102
The choice of Harlequin, n. i., n. d.   ML 52.2.C3
Cymon, London, 1767.   Longe 46
Cymon (Collection of the most esteemed farces, Edinburgh,
　1792, t. iii).   Schatz 11753C
Cymon (J. Bell, British theatre, 1791–97, v. 29).   PR 1241.B4
Edgar and Emmeline (Collection of the most esteemed farces,
　Edinburgh, 1792, t. iv).   Schatz 11753D
A fairy tale, London, 1777 (with Dibdin and others).   Longe 243
The Indian chief. A. T. of his The choice of Harlequin.

Arne, Thomas Augustine, 1710–1778.
See also Catalogue of 19th cent. librettos.
Achilles in petticoats, London, 1774.   Longe 26
Alfred, London, 1740.   AC 901.M5   v.596
Alfred, London, 1773.   Longe 36
Artaxerxes, London, n. d.   Longe 308

Arne, Thomas Augustine—Continued.

Artaxerxes, London, 1763.	ML.50.2.A81A7
Artaxerxes, London, 1792.	Longe 218
The blind beggar of Bethnal Green, London, 1741.	Longe 124
The British worthy. A. T. of his King Arthur.	
Caractacus, London, 1759.	Longe 42
Caractacus, York, 1777.	PR 3548.M2A65
Caractacus, London, 1796 (Bell's British theatre, 1791–97, v. 34).	PR 1241.B4
The castle of Andalusia, pasticcio. *See* Title catalogue.	
Comus, London, 1738, 2d ed.	ML 48.M2E
Comus, London, 1738, 3d ed.	Longe 40
Comus (J. Bell's British theatre, London, 1791–97, v. 2).	PR 1241.B4
These three in Dalton's version of Milton's masque; the next, Colman's abridged version:	
Comus (Collection of farces, Edinburgh, 1792, t. iv).	Schatz 11753D
The cooper (Collection of the most esteemed farces, Edinburgh, 1792, t. vi).	Schatz 11753F
Dido. *See* Title catalogue.	
Don Saverio, London, 1750.	Longe 241
Elfrida, London, 1796 (J. Bell, British theatre, London, 1791–97, v. 35).	PR 1241.B4
Eliza (London) 1754.	Longe 116
Eliza (London) 1757.	Longe 183
The fairy prince, London, 1771.	Longe 52
The fall of Phaeton, London, 1736.	ML 50.2.F15A7
Florizel and Perdita or The sheep-shearing (Collection of the most esteemed farces, Edinburgh, 1792, t. i).	Schatz 11753A
Florizel and Perdita. A. T. of his The sheep-shearing.	
Fontainebleau. *See* Title catalogue.	
The golden pippin, London, 1773 (and others. *See* Title catalogue).	Longe 26
The golden pippin (Collection of the most esteemed farces, Edinburgh, 1792, t. iii).	Schatz 11753C
The guardian out-witted, London, 1764.	Longe 36
An hospital for fools, London, 1739.	ML 50.2.H7
The jovial crew. *See* Title catalogue.	
King Arthur or The British worthy, London, 1781. (Altered from Purcell.)	Longe 251
King Pepin's campaign, London, 1755 [! instead of 1745].	Longe 59
Lionel and Clarissa, pasticcio. *See* Title catalogue.	
The little gipsy. A. T. of his May-day.	
Love in a village, London, 1763 (partly pasticcio. *See* Title catalogue).	Longe 42
Love in a village, London, 1781.	Longe 322
Love in a village (J. Bell, British theatre, London, 1791–97, v. 1).	PR 1241.B4
Love in a village, Philadelphia, 1794.	ML 50.6.L72
May-day or The little gipsy, London, 1775.	Longe 78
May-day, or The little gipsy (Collection of the most esteemed farces, Edinburgh, 1792, t. vi).	Schatz 11753F
Poor Vulcan. *See* Title catalogue.	
The prophetess or The history of Dioclesian, 1759 (alterations and new music only).	Longe 72

Arne, Thomas Augustine—Continued.

The rose, London, 1773.	LONGE 37
The sailor's return. A. T. of his Thomas and Sally.	
The school for fathers, pasticcio. *See* Lionel and Clarissa in Title catalogue.	
The sheep-shearing or Florizel and Perdita, Dublin, 1755.	LONGE 201
The sot, London, 1775.	LONGE 274
Squire Badger. *See his* The sot.	
Squire Savage. *See his* The sot.	
Summer amusement. *See* Title catalogue.	
The summer's tale, pasticcio. *See* Title catalogue.	
The temple of dullness, with the humour of Signor Capocchio and Signora Dorinna, London, 1745.	ML 50.2.T39A7
Thomas and Sally or The sailor's return, London, n. d.	LONGE 37
Thomas and Sally or The sailor's return, New ed., Dublin, 1773.	AC 901.T5
Thomas and Sally (Collection of the most esteemed farces, Edinburgh, 1792, v. 2).	SCHATZ 11753B
Tom Jones, pasticcio. *See* Title catalogue.	
The triumph of peace, London, 1749.	AC 901.M5 v.519

Arnold, Samuel, 1740–1802.

See also Catalogue of 19th cent. librettos.

The agreeable surprise, London, 1781.	ML 50.2.A4A7
The agreeable surprise, London, 1782.	LONGE 91
The agreeable surprise, Dublin, 1786.	LONGE 149
The agreeable surprise (Dublin, 1791).	PR 1269.V6
Amelia, pasticcio. *See* Title catalogue.	
April-day, London, 1777.	LONGE 126
Auld Robin Gray, London, 1794.	LONGE 239
An adventure at Margate. A. T. of his Summer amusement.	
The banditti or Love's labyrinth, London, 1781. O. T. of his The castle of Andalusia.	ML 50.2.B23A7
Bannian day, London, 1796.	LONGE 234
The baron Kinkvervankotsdorsprakingatchdern, London, 1781.	LONGE 196
The battle of Hexham, Dublin, 1790.	LONGE 233
The birth-day, or, The prince of Arragon, London, 1783 (two arias by Piccinni).	LONGE 164
Britain's glory, or, A trip to Portsmouth, London (1794).	LONGE 246
Caleb Quotem and his wife. *See his* Throw physick to the dogs!	
Cambro-Britons, London, 1798.	LONGE 248
The castle of Andalusia, London, 1783. L. T. of his The banditti.	LONGE 91
The castle of Andalusia, Dublin, 1783 (with additional songs by Tenducci).	LONGE 148
The children in the wood, London, 1794.	LONGE 233
The children in the wood, New York, 1795 (additions by Carr).	PR 1241.D7(vol.4)
The dead alive, Dublin, 1783.	LONGE 148
The dead alive or The double funeral, New York, 1789.	ML 50.6.D3
Don Quixote, London, 1774.	LONGE 291
The double funeral. A. T. of his The dead alive, New York, 1789.	
The fair Caledonian. A. T. of his Love and money.	
False and true, London, 1798.	LONGE 249

Arnold, Samuel—Continued.

Fire and water, London, 1780.   Longe 135

The giant's causeway. A. T. of his Harlequin Teague.

The gipsies, London, 1778.   Longe 102

Gretna Green (Dublin, 178–).   Longe 233

Harlequin Teague or The giant's causeway, London, 1782.   ML 52.2.H2A7

Hunt the slipper (Dublin) 1792.   Longe 223

Inkle and Yarico, London, n. d.   Longe 99

Love and money or The fair Caledonian, London (1795).   Longe 246

Love in Mexico. A. T. of his New Spain.

Love's labyrinth. A. T. of his The banditti.

The maid of the mill, London, 1765 (pasticcio, only partly
    composed by Arnold).   Longe 46

Mother Shipton, 2d ed., London, 1771.   ML 52.2.M6

The mountaineers, London, 1793.   Longe 227

The mountaineers, London, 1795.   Longe 231

New Spain or Love in Mexico, London, 1790.   ML 50.2.N43

Peeping Tom of Coventry, Dublin, 1786.   Longe 149

Peeping Tom of Coventry (Dublin) 1787.   Schatz 338

Polly. *See* Title catalogue.

Poor Vulcan. *See* Title catalogue.

The portrait, London, MCCCLXX [! instead of 1770]   ML 50.2.P59A5

The portrait, London, MCCCLXX [!]   Longe 26

The prince of Arragon. A. T. of his The birth-day.

Rosamond, London, 1767.   ML 50.2.R73A7

The revenge, London, 1795.   Longe 296

The royal garland, London, 1768.   Longe 36

The seraglio, London, 1776 (mainly by Dibdin).   Longe 124

The seraglio, airs, chorusses, London, 1776.   ML 50.2.S48

The son-in-law, Dublin, 1788.   Longe 223

The Spanish barber, London, 1783.   Longe 91

Summer amusement or An adventure at Margate, London,
    1781.   Longe 91

The summer's tale, pasticcio. *See* Title catalogue.

The surrender of Calais, Dublin, 1792.   Longe 233

Throw physick to the dogs, London, 1798 (also known as
    "Caleb Quotem and his wife").   ML 50.2.T52

Tom Jones, pasticcio. *See* Title catalogue.

A trip to Portsmouth. A. T. of his Britain's glory.

Two to one, Dublin, 1785.   PR

Zorinski, London, 1795.   Longe 232

Asioli, Bonefazio, 1769–1832.

See also Catalogue of 19th cent. librettos.

Cinna, Milano (1793).   Schatz 348

Aspelmayer, Franz, *ca.* 1721–1786.

Die kinder der natur, Wien, 1778.   Schatz 364

Astaritta, Gennaro.

L'amalato per amore. A. T. of his Il medico parigino.

Armida (Venezia, 1777).   Schatz 367

L'avaro, Ferrara (1776).   Schatz 381

I capricci in amore, Venezia, 1791.   Schatz 384

La contessa di Bimbinpoli (Lisbona, 1773).   Schatz 368

Il corsaro algerino, Napoli, 1765.   Schatz 377

Astaritta, Gennaro—Continued.

La critica teatrale, Venezia, 1775.   SCHATZ 378

Il curioso accidente, Venezia, 1789.   SCHATZ 385

La dama immaginaria (Venezia, 1777).   SCHATZ 370

Il divertimento in campagna—Der zeitvertreib auf dem lande, Dresda, 1783. (L. T. of his La contessa di Bimbinpoli.)   SCHATZ 369

Le fallaci apparenze, Venezia, 1793.   SCHATZ 386

I filosofi immaginarj (Lisbona, 1775). L. T. of his I visionari.   SCHATZ 379

Il francese bizzarro, Venezia, 1779.   SCHATZ 371

Il francese bizzarro—Der wunderliche Franzos, Dresda, 1786.   SCHATZ 372

L'inganno del ritratto, Frenze, 1791.   ML 48A5 v. 15

Ipermestra, Venezia, 1789.   SCHATZ 387

L'isola di Bengodi (Venezia, 1777).   SCHATZ 382

Die lächerlichen gelehrten. Tr. of his I visionari, Dresda, 1774.   SCHATZ 376

Il marito che non ha moglie, Venezia, 1774.   SCHATZ 373

Il medico parigino o sia L'amalato per amore, Venezia, 1791.   SCHATZ 374

Il mondo della luna, Venezia, 1775.   SCHATZ 383

L'Olimpiade, ballet. *See* Meucci's Telemaco.

I visionarj, Venezia, 1772.   SCHATZ 375

I visionari—Die lächerlichen gelehrten, Dresda, 1774.   SCHATZ 376

Der wunderliche Franzos. Tr. of his Il francese bizzarro.   SCHATZ 372

Der zeitvertreib auf dem lande. Tr. of his Il divertimento in campagna.   SCHATZ 369

Attwood, Thomas, 1765–1838.

See also Catalogue of 19th cent. librettos.

The adopted child, London, 1795.   LONGE 230

The birth of the Prince of Wales. A. T. of his Caernarvon castle.

Caernarvon castle, or, The birth of the Prince of Wales, London, 1793.   LONGE 239

The castle of Sorrento, London, 1799. English adaptation of Della Maria's Le prisonnier, with new music.   LONGE 256

A day at Rome, London, 1798.   LONGE 254

The glorious first of August. A. T. of his The mouth of the Nile.

The mariners, London, 1793.   LONGE 227

The mouth of the Nile or The glorious first of August, London, 1798 (2d ed.).   LONGE 254

The prisoner (London, 1792).   LONGE 236

The smugglers, London, 1796.   LONGE 238

Aubert, Jacques, 1678–1753.

Arlequin Hulla, ou La femme repudiée (Le Théâtre de la foire, Paris, 1737, t. ii).   ML 48.L2 II

Les arrests de l'amour (Le Théâtre de la foire, Paris, 1737, t. ii).   ML 48.L2 I

Le ballet des XXIV heures, Paris, 1723.   ML 52.2.B11

Le régiment de la Calotte. *See* Title catalogue.

La reine des Péris (Recueil général des opéra, Paris, 1734, t. xiii).   SCHATZ 486

Audinot, Nicolas Médard, *b.* 1730.

Der fassbinder, Berlin, 1796. Tr. of his and Gossec's Le tonnelier.   SCHATZ 489

Audinot, Nicolas Médard—Continued.

Der fassbinder, Frankfurt am Mayn, 1773. Another Tr.	SCHATZ 488
Le tonnelier, Paris, 1765. Rev. and music partly new by Gossec.	ML 50.2.T68
Le tonnelier, Paris, Nouv. éd. augm., 1767.	SCHATZ 487
Le tonnelier, Paris, 1768.	SCHATZ 11672
Le tonnelier, Paris, 1768. "Nouv. éd." of the above.	SCHATZ 11674
Le tonnelier, Paris, 1770. "Nouv. éd. augmentée" of the above.	SCHATZ 11673

Augustini, Pietro Simone. *See* Agostini, Pietro Simone.

Auletta, Pietro.

Il conte immaginario, Venezia, 1748.	SCHATZ 501
Ezio, Roma (1729).	SCHATZ 498
Il maestro di musica. *See* Title catalogue.	
Il marchese di Spartivento ovvero Il cabalista ne sa' men del caso, Roma, 1747 (some arias by Micheli).	ML 50.2.M37A9
Il marchese Sgrana, Napoli, 1738.	SCHATZ 499
Orazio, Venezia, 1748.	SCHATZ 500

Aurisicchio, Antonio.

Eumene, Roma (1754).	SCHATZ 503
Giunone placata, Roma, 1762.	ML 50.2.G44A8

Avondano, Pietro Antonio.

Il mondo della luna, Lisbona (1765).	SCHATZ 510

Avossa, Giuseppe d' (*same as* Giuseppe Abbos).

Il ciarlone, Vienna (1770). L. T. of his La pupilla ed il ciarlone.	SCHATZ 512
Don Saverio, Venezia, 1744.	SCHATZ 513
La pupilla ed il ciarlone—Myndlingen og sladdreren, Kiøbenhavn, 1769.	SCHATZ 511

Bacelli, Domenico.

Le nouveau marié ou Les importuns, Paris, 1771.	SCHATZ 520

Bach, Johann Christian, 1735–1782.

Amelia, pasticcio. *See* Title catalogue.	
Artaserse, Torino (1761).	SCHATZ 532
Il Catone in Utica, Pavia (1763).	SCHATZ 526
Il Catone in Utica—Cato in Utika (Bronsevigo, 1768).	SCHATZ 527
La clemenza di Scipione, London, 1778.	SCHATZ 528
Ezio, London, 1764–5 (pasticcio from B. and Pescetti, Galuppi, etc.).	ML 48.M2N
Lucio Silla, Mannheim (1773).	SCHATZ 529
Lucius Silla, Mannheim, 1774. Tr. of the above.	SCHATZ 530
The maid of the mill, pasticcio. *See* Title catalogue.	
Orpheus and Eurydice, London, 1785 (a pasticcio from (principally) Gluck, Bach, Händel, Anfossi).	SCHATZ 3926
The summer's tale, pasticcio. *See* Title catalogue.	
Themistocles (Temistocle) Mannheim, 1772.	SCHATZ 531
Tom Jones, pasticcio. *See* Title catalogue.	
Zophilette. *See* Title catalogue.	

Bachmann, Gottlob, 1763–1840.

Der tod des Orpheus (J. G. Jacobi, Theater schriften, Leipzig, 1792).	SCHATZ 537

Badia, Carlo Agostino, 1672–1738.

Gli amori di Circe con Ulisse—Les amours d'Ulisse & de Circe
(Dresden, 1709).   Schatz 543

La concordia della virtù e della fortuna (P. A. Bernardoni,
Poemi drammatici, terza parte, Vienna, 1707).   ML 49.A2B4

La costanza d'Ulisse, Vienna (1700).   Schatz 544

— — Second copy, with two folded plates, lacking in the
other.   ML 50.2.C69B2

La Psiche (P. A. Bernardoni, Poemi drammatici, terza parte,
Vienna, 1707).   ML 49.A2B4

La Rosaura overo Amore figlio della gratitudine, Insprugg
(1692).   Schatz 542

Baildon, Joseph, d. 1774.

Love in a village, pasticcio. *See* Title catalogue.

Tom Jones, pasticcio. *See* Title catalogue.

Baillou, Luigi de.

Apollo placato, ballet (with Salieri). *See* the latter's Europa
riconosciuta.

Baini, Lorenzo.

Il finto Parigino, Venezia (1784).   Schatz 552

Il Pariggino in Italia, Venezia, 1784.   Schatz 553

Balbi, Ignazio.

Lucio Papirio, Torino, 1753.   Schatz 557

Ballarotti, Francesco.

L'Alciade overo La violenza d'amore (originally L'eroico
amore) Milano, 1709.   Schatz 3597

L'amante impazzito, Venetia (1714). L. T. of his L'Alciade. Schatz 3598

Esione, Torino (1699).   Schatz 592

La violenza d'amore. A. T. of his L'Alciade.

Bambini, Felice.

Nicaise, Paris, 1756.   ML 50.2.N3

Nicaise (Vadé, Œuvres, La Haye, 1759, t. 4)   ML 49.A2V2

Nicaise, Paris, 1766.   Schatz 11501

Banister, John, 1630–1679.

Circe, London, 1703.   Longe 128

Bannister, *Miss.*

The mariners, pasticcio. *See* Title catalogue.

Barba, Daniel.

Il gran Tamerlano vincitore di Bajazet, Venezia, 1746.   Schatz 598

Barbella, Manuele.

L'Elmira generosa, Napoli, 1753 (partly by Logroscino).   Schatz 5675

Barta, Joseph, 1744–1804.

Da ist nicht gut zu rathen, Wien, 1778.   Schatz 615

Barthélémon, François Hippolyte, 1741–1808.

Belphegor, or, The wishes (Dublin) 1788.   Longe 223

The judgment of Paris, London, 1768.   Longe 52

Love in the city, pasticcio. *See* Title catalogue.

The maid of the oaks, London, 1774 (partly selected from
Rousseau, Philidor, and La Borde).   Longe 48

Barthélémon, Francois, Hippolyte—Continued.

The noble pedlar or The fortune hunter, 2d ed., London, 1771. LONGE 213

Oithóna, London, 1768. LONGE 163

Orpheus (a musical burletta in A peep behind the curtain or The new rehearsal, London, 1767). ML 50.2.P31

A peep behind the curtain or The new rehearsal, New ed., London, 1772. LONGE 27

Beseggio, Lorenzo.

Laomedonte, Venezia, 1715. SCHATZ 619

Basili, Francesco, 1766–1850.

See also Catalogue of 19th cent. librettos.

Antigona, Venezia, 1799. SCHATZ 630

La bella incognita e La maga Circe [this by Anfossi], Roma (1788). ML 50.2.B28B2

Il ritorno d'Ulisse, Firenze, 1798. SCHATZ 629

Bassani, Giovanni Battista, *ca.* 1657–1716.

L'Alarico, Bologna (1716). SCHATZ 633

Falaride, tiranno d'Agrigento, Venetia, 1684. SCHATZ 634

La Ginevra infanta di Scozia, Ferrara (1690). SCHATZ 632

Bassani, Girolamo.

L'amore per forza, Venezia, 1721 (first act; M. Lucchini the two others). SCHATZ 636

Bertoldo, Venezia, 1717. SCHATZ 635

Cimene, Venezia, 1721 (with Zucchini). SCHATZ 637

Bates, William.

Flora or Hob in the well, 7th ed., London, 1768. LONGE 73

The golden pippin. *See* Title catalogue.

Pharnaces, London, 1765. LONGE 50

The theatrical candidates, London, 1775 (printed together with "May-day"). LONGE 78

The theatrical candidates (Collection of the most esteemed farces, Edinburgh, 1792, t. vi). SCHATZ 11753

The theatrical candidates, n. i., n. d. (detached). LONGE 239

Bati, Luca, *d.* 1608.

Il rapimento di Cefalo, Firenze, 1600 (mainly by Caccini, with some music by the above, Venturi del Nibbio, and Strozzi). SCHATZ 1449

Battishill, Jonathan, 1738–1801.

Almena, London, 1764 (with M. Arne). LONGE 37

Baumgarten, C. F.

Netley Abbey. *See* Title catalogue.

Robin Hood, pasticcio. *See* Title catalogue.

Baumgarten, Gotthilf von, 1741–1813.

Zemire und Azor, Breslau, 1775. SCHATZ 658

Bazzani, Francesco Maria.

L'inganno trionfato overo La disperata speranza ravvivata ne' successi di Giacopo Quinto di Scozia e Maddalena di Francia, Parma (1673). SCHATZ 670

Becke (Beecke), Ignaz von, *ca.* 1730–1803.

Claudine von Villa Bella, Wien, 1780.   SCHATZ 677

Don Quixote (J. von Soden, Schauspiele, Berlin, 1788, v. 1).   SCHATZ 678

Die weinlese, Mannheim, 1783.   SCHATZ 679

Beckmann, Johann Friedrich Gottlieb, 1737–1792.

Lukas und Hannchen, Braunschweig, 1768.   SCHATZ 685

Beffroy de Reigny, Louis Abel (*called* Cousin Jacques), 1757–1811.

Le club des bons-gens ou La reconciliation, Marseille, cinquième année [1796–97].   SCHATZ 704

Les deux charbonniers ou Les contrastes, Paris, an VIII [1799–1800].   SCHATZ 705

Magdelon, Paris, an VIII [1799–1800].   SCHATZ 706

Nicodème dans la lune ou La révolution pacifique, Paris, 1791.   SCHATZ 707

La petite Nannette, Paris, an V—1797.   SCHATZ 703

Benda, Friedrich Ludwig, 1746–1793.

Der barbier von Seville oder Die vergebliche vorsicht, Leipzig, 1784.   SCHATZ 764

Louise, Riga, 1794.   SCHATZ 765

Benda, Friedrich Wilhelm Heinrich, 1745–1814.

Orpheus, n. i., 1785.   SCHATZ 766

Der tempel der wahrheit (Annalen des theaters, Berlin, 1788, erstes heft).   SCHATZ 767

Benda, Georg, 1722–1795.

See also Catalogue of 19th cent. librettos.

Ariadne auf Naxos, Gotha, 1775.   SCHATZ 768

Ariadne auf Naxos, Leipzig, 1790.   ML 50.2.A737

Der dorfjahrmarkt, n. i., 1790. L. T. of his Der jahrmarkt.   SCHATZ 773

Die drey wuensche. A. T. of his Der holzhauer.

Der holzhauer oder Die drey wuensche, Berlin, 1772.   SCHATZ 770a

Der holzhauer, Riga (1785).   SCHATZ 770b

Der jahrmarkt, Leipzig, 1778 (with Engel's additions to the text as composed by Joh. Adam Hiller).   ML 50.2.J2B2

Julie und Romeo, Berlin, 1796. L. T. of his Romeo und Julie.   SCHATZ 777

Der kluge mann oder Die drey wuensche. *See* Der holzhauer in the Title catalogue.

Lukas (Lucas) und Bärbchen. L. T. of his Der jahrmarkt.

Medea, Hamburg, 1776.   SCHATZ 774

Medea (Melodramen, Pilsen und Klattau, Joseph Johann Morgensaeuler, 1791, iii).   SCHATZ 774a

Pygmalion (Melodramen, Pilsen und Klattau, Joseph Johann Morgensaeuler, 1791, I).   SCHATZ 775

Romeo und Julie, Leipzig, 1779.   SCHATZ 776

Walder, Gotha, 1778.   SCHATZ 778

Bernabei, Giuseppe Antonio, 1659–1732.

L'Ascanio, Monaco (1686).   SCHATZ 824

La Dori, Monaco, 1680 (new prologue for Cesti's opera).   SCHATZ 1779

Enea in Italia, Monaco (1679).   SCHATZ 825

L'Ermione, Monaco (1680).   SCHATZ 826

Bernard.

Love in a village, pasticcio. *See* Title catalogue.

Bernardini, Marcello (*known also as* Marcello di (da) Capua).
  See also Catalogue of 19th cent. librettos.

Achille in Sciro, Venezia, 1794.	SCHATZ 829
Amore e musica, Roma (1773).	ML 50.2.A68B3
L'allegria della campagna, Napoli (1791).	SCHATZ 839
Amore per incanto, Napoli (1791).	SCHATZ 838
L'antiquario fanatico. A. T. of his Le donne bisbetiche.	
Il barone a forza o sia Il trionfo di Bacco, Roma (1786).	ML 50.2.B29B2
Il barone a forza o sia Il trionfo di Bacco, Bologna (1788).	SCHATZ 845
Il bassa generoso—Der grossmuethige bassa, Dresda, 1782.	SCHATZ 830
Li cinque pretendenti, Trieste (1794). L. T. of his La donna di spirito.	SCHATZ 849
Il conte di bell' umore, Roma (1783).	SCHATZ 844
Il conte di bell' umore—Der graf bey guter laune (Praga, 1783).	SCHATZ 831
Il conte di bell' umore—O conde de bello humor, Lisbona, 1791.	SCHATZ 843
La contessina, Roma (1773).	ML 50.2.C665B3
La donna bizarra, Napoli, 1791. *See his* La donna di spirito.	SCHATZ 832
La donna di spirito, Milano (1791).	SCHATZ 842
Le donne bisbetiche o sia L'antiquario fanatico, Orvieto (1791). (L. T. of his La finta Galatea o sia L'antiquario fanatico).	ML 50.2.D61B2
La finta sposa olandese, Roma, 1776.	SCHATZ 846
Il fonte d'acqua gialla o sia Il trionfo della pazzia, Roma (1786).	ML 50.2.F7B2
Furberia e puntiglio, Venezia, 1798.	SCHATZ 834
Der graf bey guter laune. Tr. of his Il conte di beli' umore (Praga, 1783).	SCHATZ 831
Der grossmuethige bassa. Tr. of his Il bassa generoso, Dresda, 1782.	SCHATZ 830
Gl'incontri stravaganti, Napoli, 1790.	SCHATZ 840
Maid of the mill, pasticcio. *See* the Title catalogue.	
Il muto per astuzia (Venezia, 1799).	SCHATZ 851
Il pazzo glorioso, Casalmaggiore (1790).	SCHATZ 850
Le quattro nazioni, Firenze, 1793. L. T. of his La donna di spirito.	SCHATZ 833
La schiava astuta, Roma (1765).	ML 50.2.S42B3
La scola di musica. A. T. of his Le tre orfanelle.	
La sposa polacca, Venezia (1799).	SCHATZ 852
La statua per puntiglio, Venezia, 1791.	SCHATZ 835
Le tre orfanelle o sia La scola di musica, Venezia, 1798.	SCHATZ 847
Li tre Orfei, Venezia (1787).	SCHATZ 848
Il trionfo della pazzia. A. T. of his Il fonte d'acqua gialla.	
Il trionfo di Bacco. A. T. of his Il barone a forza.	
L'ultima che si perde è la speranza, Napoli, 1790.	SCHATZ 841
L'ultima che si perde è la speranza, Venezia, 1792.	SCHATZ 836

Bernasconi, Andrea, 1706–1784.

Adriano in Siria—Adrian in Syrien, Monaco (1755).	SCHATZ 854
Alessandro Severo, Venezia, 1738.	SCHATZ 867
Baiazet (Venezia, 1742).	SCHATZ 868
La clemenza di Tito—Die guetigkeit des Titus, Monaco (1768).	SCHATZ 856
Demetrio—Demetrius, Monaco (1772).	SCHATZ 857
Demofoonte—Demophoon, Monaco (1766).	SCHATZ 864
La Didone abbandonata, Monaco (1760).	SCHATZ 858

Bernasconi, Andrea—Continued.

Endimione, Venezia (1742).   SCHATZ 869

Germanico, Torino (1744).   SCHATZ 865

Die guetigkeit des Titus. Tr. of his La clemenza di Tito,
    Monaco (1768).   SCHATZ 856

L'Olympiade—Die olympischen spiel, Monaco (1764).   SCHATZ 859

Salustia, Venezia (1753). L. T. of his Alessandro Severo.   SCHATZ 866

Semiramide—Semiramis, Monaco, 1765.   SCHATZ 860

Temistocle (Venezia, 1744).   SCHATZ 861

Temistokles, Muenchen (1754). Tr. of the above.   SCHATZ 862

Bertali, Antonio, *d.* 1669.

L'inganno d'amore—Liebs betrug (Regensburg, 1653).   SCHATZ 874

Theti—Niobe, Mantova, 1652.   SCHATZ 872–873

Bertin de la Doué, T., *ca.* 1680–1745.

Ajax (Recueil général des opéra, t. xi, Paris, 1720).   SCHATZ 878

Ajax, Lyon, 1742.   SCHATZ 11668

Cassandre, Amsterdam, 1707 (with Bouvard)   ML.50.2.C28B6

Cassandre (Recueil général des opéra, Paris, 1710, t. ix) (with
    Bouvard).   SCHATZ 1275

Diomède (Recueil général des opéra, Paris, 1714, t. x).   SCHATZ 879

Le jugement de Paris (Recueil général des opéra, Paris, 1734,
    t. xii).   SCHATZ 880

Les plaisirs de la campagne (Recueil général des opéra, Paris,
    1734, t. xii).   SCHATZ 881

Bertoja, Valentino.

Il trionfo di Alessandro ossia La prigionia di Dario, ballet.
    See Paisiello's Elfrida.

Berton, Henri Montan, 1767–1844.

See also Catalogue of 19th cent. librettos.

Le délire ou Les suites d'une erreur, Paris, an VIII (1799).   ML 50.2.D35B2

Le nouveau d'Assas, Paris, 1790.   ML 50.2.N6B2

Ponce de Léon, Paris, 1797.   SCHATZ 896

Les promesses de mariages, Paris, 1788.   SCHATZ 902

Les rigueurs du cloitre, Paris, 1793.   SCHATZ 898

Les suites d'une erreur. A. T. of his Le délire.

Berton, Pierre Montan, 1727–1780.

Erosine (Paris) 1765 (Journal des spectacles, 1766, t. ii).   ML 48.J7

Erosine. Entrée in Les fêtes liriques, Paris, 1766.   ML 52.2.F46

Issé (Paris) 1773 (alterations only in Destouches' opera).   ML 50.2.I75D2

Silvie (Paris) 1765 (Journal des spectacles, t. ii, 1766) (with
    Trial).   ML 48.J7

Bertoni, Ferdinando Giuseppe, 1725–1813.

Achille in Sciro, Venezia, 1764.   SCHATZ 903

Andromaca, Venezia (1772).   SCHATZ 904

L'anello incantato (Lisbona, 1772).   SCHATZ 929

Aristo e Temira e Orfeo ed Euridice, Venezia, 1776.   SCHATZ 934–935

Armida, Venezia, 1747.   SCHATZ 925

Armida abbandonata, Genova (1786).   SCHATZ 931

Artaserse, Milano (1777).   SCHATZ 905

Artaserse, London (1779).   SCHATZ 906

Artaserse, Genova (1788).   SCHATZ 907

I bagni d'Abano, Venezia, 1753 (partly by Galuppi).   SCHATZ 3519

Bertoni, Ferdinando Giuseppe—Continued.

Il Bajazette, Parma (1765).	SCHATZ 936
The banquet. Tr. of his Il convito, London, 1782.	SCHATZ 910
La bella Girometta, Venezia, 1761.	SCHATZ 937
Il Cajetto, Venezia, 1746.	SCHATZ 908
Il Cajo Mario, Venezia, 1781.	SCHATZ 909
The castle of Andalusia, pasticcio. *See* Title catalogue.	
Cleonice regina di Siria—Cleonice, queen of Syria, London, 1763, pasticcio. *See* Title catalogue.	ML 50.2.C5
Il convito or The banquet, London, 1782.	SCHATZ 910
Demofoonte, London, 1778.	SCHATZ 911
Il duca d'Atene, London, 1780.	ML 48.M2K
Eumene, Venezia, 1784.	SCHATZ 938
Ezio, Venezia, 1767.	SCHATZ 912
Ginevra, Venezia (1753).	SCHATZ 913
Der fuerst und sein volk, Leipzig (1791). (Pasticcio made up from his, Dittersdorf's, and Pitterlin's music.)	SCHATZ 8204
Der fuerst und sein volk, n. i., 1794.	SCHATZ 11613
Ifigenia in Aulide, Torino (1762).	SCHATZ 914
L'ingannatore ingannato, Venezia, 1764.	SCHATZ 939
Ipermestra (Venezia, 1748).	SCHATZ 926
Medonte, Torino (1778).	SCHATZ 923
La moda, Venezia, 1754.	SCHATZ 922
Narbale, Venezia, 1774.	SCHATZ 940
Nitteti, Venezia, 1789.	SCHATZ 941
L'Olimpiade, Venezia, 1765.	SCHATZ 915
Orazio Curiazo (Venezia, 1746).	SCHATZ 924
Orfeo ed Euridice. For original ed. *see his* Aristo e Temira e Orfeo ed Euridice, Venezia, 1776.	SCHATZ 934–935
Orfeo—Orpheus, Berlin (1788) (additions by Reichardt). L. T. of:	SCHATZ 917
Orfeo ed Euridice, Venezia, 1776.	SCHATZ 916
Orfeo ed Euridice. On p. [29]–51 of Joh. Simon Mayr's cantata Temira e Aristo, Venezia, 1795.	SCHATZ 6203
Le pescatrici, Venezia, 1752.	SCHATZ 921
Quinto Fabio, Padova, 1778.	SCHATZ 932
Robin Hood, pasticcio. *See* Title catalogue.	
Sesostri, Torino (1755).	SCHATZ 918
Sesostri, rè d'Egitto—Sesostris, könig in Egypten, Praga (1766). L. T. of the above.	SCHATZ 919
The summer's tale, pasticcio. *See* Title catalogue.	
Tancredi, Torino (1767).	SCHATZ 930
Telemaco ed Eurice nell' isola di Calipso, Venezia, 1777.	SCHATZ 933
La vedova accorta, Venezia, 1746.	SCHATZ 927
Le vicende amorose, Venezia, 1760.	SCHATZ 928

Bianchi, Antonio, *b.* 1758.

Die insel der Alcina, Berlin, 1794.	SCHATZ 972

Bianchi, Francesco, 1752–1810.

See also Catalogue of 19th cent. librettos.

Aci e Galatea, Venezia, 1792.	SCHATZ 993
Alessandro nell' Indie, Bologna (1787).	ML 50.2.A517B25
Alessandro nell' Indie, Venezia, 1792.	SCHATZ 974
Alonso e Cora, Venezia, 1786.	SCHATZ 994

Bianchi, Francesco—Continued.

Aspard, Roma (1784).	ML 50.2.A82B3
Briseide, Torino (1784).	Schatz 1002
Cajo Mario, Napoli, 1784.	Schatz 995
Calto, Venezia, 1788.	Schatz 996
La cappricciosa ravveduta, Venezia, 1794.	Schatz 976
Il chinese in Italia, Venezia, 1793.	Schatz 977
Daliso e Delmita, Padova (1789).	Schatz 997
Il Demetrio, Venezia, 1780.	Schatz 1008
Il disertore, Venezia, 1784.	Schatz 978
Das entfuehrte bauernmaedchen. Tr. of his La villanella rapita, Dresden, 1785.	Schatz 987
Erifile, Modena (1781).	Schatz 989
Eurione, Pavia (1775).	ML 48.A5 v.12
La fedeltà tra le selve, Roma (1789). (Four arias by V. Fioravanti.) L. T. of his La villanella rapita.	Schatz 992
Il finto astrologo (Lisbona, 1792).	Schatz 998
Le gelosie di Pippo. A. T. of his La villanella rapita, Lisbona, 1796.	
Giulio Cesare, Trieste (1790). L. T. of his La morte di Cesare.	Schatz 1006
Ines de Castro, Venezia, 1795 (with Nasolini, Gerace, and Cervellini).	Schatz 1012
La morte di Cesare, Venezia, 1788.	Schatz 1005
Nitteti, Milano (1789).	Schatz 1003
Olimpiade, Milano (1782).	Schatz 1004
L'orfano cinese, Venezia, 1787.	Schatz 979
Piramo e Tisbe, Venezia, 1783.	Schatz 980
Pizzarro, Venezia, 1787.	Schatz 999
Il ritratto, Napoli (1791).	Schatz 981
La secchia rapita, Venezia, 1794.	Schatz 982
Seleuco, rè di Siria, Venezia, 1791.	Schatz 1000
La sposa in equivoco, Venezia, 1791.	Schatz 1007
Li sposi in commedia, Venezia, 1786. See Title catalogue.	Schatz 1647
Lo stravagante, Bronsvic, 1788.	Schatz 983
Tarara o sia La virtù premiata, Venezia, 1792.	Schatz 984
Il trionfo della pace, Torino (1782).	Schatz 991
Vasco di Gama, pasticcio. See Title catalogue.	
La vendetta di Nino, Napoli, 1790.	Schatz 985
La villanella rapita, Venezia, 1783.	Schatz 986
La villanella rapita—Das entfuehrte bauernmaedchen, Dresden, 1785.	Schatz 987
La villanella rapita, Milano (1785).	ML 48.A5 v.12
La villanella rapita, London, 1790.	ML 48.M2N
La villanella rapita, o sia Le gelosie di Pippo, Lisbona, 1796.	Schatz 990
Le villanelle astute, Venezia, 1786.	Schatz 1010
La virtù premiata. A. T. of his Tarara.	
Zemira, Padova (1786).	Schatz 1001

Biego, Paolo.

La fortuna tra le disgratie, Venetia, 1688.	Schatz 1014
Ottone il Grande, Venetia, 1683.	Schatz 1015
Il pertinace, Venetia, 1689.	Schatz 1016

Bierey, Gottlob Benedict, 1772–1840.

See also Catalogue of 19th cent. librettos.

Der schlaftrunk, Breslau (179–?).   Schatz 1028

Der zauber-hain, oder Das land der liebe, n. i., 1799.   Schatz 1032

Bigongiari, Marco, 1637–1686.

Alessandro il vincitor di se stesso, Lucca, 1654 (mainly by
Cesti).   Schatz 1786

La corte, n. i., n. d. (detached from Sbarra's works?).   Schatz 1036

La libertà trionfante, Lucca, 1654. *See* M. Curzio in Title
catalogue.

La tirannide dell' interesse, Lucca, 1653.   ML 50.2.T55

La tirannide dell' interesse, Venetia, 1658.   Schatz 1035

Bihler, Franz Peter Gregorius, 1760–1824.

Die falschen verdachte (Botzen, 1796).   Schatz 1037

Bioni, Antonio, *b.* 1698.

Endimion (Endimione) (Breslau, 1727).   Schatz 1043

Lucio Papirio—Lucius Papirius (Breslava, 1732).   Schatz 104

Il Siroe (Bronsevigo, 1767) pasticcio. *See* Title catalogue.

Bisoni, Antonio, *detto il Rossetto.*

L'assedio di Belgrado, ballet. *See* Bianchi's Aspard.

Bizzarri, Pietro.

L'arrivo d'Enea nel Lazio. *See* Galuppi's opera of this title.

Blaise, Adolphe, *d.* 1772.

Annette et Lubin, Paris, 1763.   Schatz 1063

Annette et Lubin, Paris, Duchesne, 1763 (Theatre de M.
Favart, Paris, Duchesne, 1763–77, t. v).   ML 49.A2F1

Annette et Lubin, Paris, 1770.   Schatz 11675

Annette et Lubin, Avignon, 1774.   ML 48.M2M

[Annette et Lubin] (imperfect copy).   Schatz 11676

Die erdichtete luft-geister. A. T. of his Isabella und Gertraude.

Das fest der weiblichen tugend. A. T. of his Das rosenmaedchen (with Philidor and Duni).

Isabelle et Gertrude ou Les sylphes supposés, Paris, 1765.   Schatz 1064

Isabelle et Gertrude ou Les sylphes supposés—Isabella und
Gertraude oder Die erdichtete luft-geister, Mannheim,
1765.   Schatz 1065

Isabelle et Gertrude ou Les sylphes supposés, n. i., n. d.
(Theatre de M. Favart, Paris, Duchesne, 1763–77, t. ix.)   ML 49.A2F1

Isabelle et Gertrude ou Les sylphes supposés, Paris, 1784.   Schatz 11677

Das rosenmaedchen, oder, Das fest der weiblichen tugend,
1772 (with Philidor, Duni, etc.). Tr. of their La rose de
Salenci.   Schatz 2860

La rosiere de Salenci, Paris, veuve Duchesne, 1770 (Theatre
de M. Favart, Paris, Duchesne, 1763–77, t. x) (with Duni
Philidor, etc.).   ML 49.A2F1

Les sylphes supposés. A. T. of his Isabelle et Gertrude.

Blasis, Francesco Antonio De, 1765–1851.

L'isola di Bellamarina, Napoli, 1792.   Schatz 2420

Blumhofer, Max.
Die luftschiffer oder Der strafplanet der erde, Leipzig und
    Koeln, 1787.   ML 50.2.L9B4

Boccherini, Luigi, 1743–1805.
Cefalo e Procri, ballet. *See* Sarti's Scipione.
La confederazione de i Sabini con Roma, Lucca, 1765. *See*
    M. Curzio in Title catalogue.

**Boecklin (Boeklin), von Boecklinsau, Franz Friedrich-
Siegismund August, von,** *reichsfreiherr zu Rust,* 1745–
1813.
Phaedon und Naide oder Der redende baum (J. G. Jacobi,
    Theatralische schriften. Nachtrag zu seinen saemtlichen
    werken, Leipzig, 1792.)   Schatz 1113

Böhm, Johann.
Maegera, n. i., 1774.   Schatz 1115

Boieldieu, François Adrien, 1775–1834.
See also Catalogue of 19th cent. librettos.
La dot de Suzette, Paris, an VI (1798).   ML 50.2.D64B6
La famille suisse, Paris (1797).   ML 50.2.F176B6
Zoraime et Zulnar, Paris, an VI (1798).   ML 50.2.Z65B6

Boini. *Misprint for* Buini.

Boismortier, Joseph Bodin de, *ca.* 1691–1765.
Don Quichote chez la duchesse, Paris, 1760 (Theatre de M.
    Favart, Paris, Duchesne, 1763–77, t. vi).   ML 49.A2F1
Les voyages de l'amour (Recueil général des opéra, Paris,
    1745, t. xvi).   ML 48.R4

Bonazzi, Antonio, *d.* 1802.
Enea nel Lazio, ballet. *See* Sarti's Il trionfo della pace.
Il pellegrinaggio o sia La vindemmia fiamminga, ballet. *See*
    Sarti's Il trionfo della pace.

Bondineri, Michele (*called* Neri Bondi).

Boni, Gaetano.
Il figlio delle selve, Modona [!] (1701).   Schatz 1181

Boniventi, Giuseppe.
L'Almerinda, Venetia, 1691.   Schatz 1187
L'Almira, Venetia, 1691.   Schatz 1188
Arianna abbandonata, Venezia, 1719.   Schatz 1189
Armida al campo, Venezia, 1707.   Schatz 1184
Il Bertarido, rè de Longobardi, Venezia, 1727.   Schatz 1185
Circe delusa, Venetia, 1711.   Schatz 1186
L'Endimione, Venetia, 1709.   Schatz 1190
Filippo rè di Macedonia, Venezia, 1721. (Third act by
    Vivaldi.)   Schatz 1196
Il gran Macedone, Venetia, 1690.   Schatz 1191
L'inganno fortunato, Venezia, 1721.   Schatz 1192
Venceslao, Torino, 1721.   Schatz 1195
La virtù tra' nemici, Venezia, 1718.   Schatz 1193
La vittoria nella costanza, Venetia (1702).   Schatz 1194

Bonno, Giuseppe Baptista (Josephus Johannes), 1710–1788.
L'Atenaide o vero Gli affetti generosi.   *See* Metastasio's Opere.
Der chinesische held, Wienn, 1755.   Tr. of his L'eroe cinese.   SCHATZ 1197
La danza.   *See* Metastasio's Opere.
L'eroe cinese.   *See* Metastasio's Opere.
L'isola disabitata.   *See* Metastasio's Opere.
Il natal di Giove.   *See* Metastasio's Opere.
Il rè pastore.   *See* Metastasio's Opere.
Il vero omaggio.   *See* Metastasio's Opere.

Bononcini, Giovanni Battista, ca. 1660–1750.
Gli affetti più grandi vinti dal più giusto, Vienna d'Austria
      (1701).   SCHATZ 1199
L'Astarto—Astartus (Hamburg, 1721).   SCHATZ 1202
Caio Gracco, Vienna d'Austria (1710).   SCHATZ 1203
Crispo, Roma, 1721.   SCHATZ 1200
Griselda (Rolli, Componimenti poetici, Nuova ed., Verona,
      1744)   ML 49.A2R7
Intermedi [Mirena e Floro] Dresde, 1718.   SCHATZ 5707
Muzio Scevola—Mutius Scaevola, Hamburg (1723) (act II
      only; act I by Mattei; act III by Händel).   SCHATZ 168
Proteo sul Reno (P. A. Bernardoni, Poemi drammatici, terza
      parte, Vienna, 1707).   ML 49.A2B4
Thomyris, queen of Scythia, pasticcio.   *See* Title catalogue.
Tullo Ostilio, Roma, 1694.   SCHATZ 1201

Bononcini, Marc' Antonio, 1675–1726.
Astianatte (Monaco, 1717).   SCHATZ 1204
Camilla, regina de' Volsci, Venetia, 1698.   L. T. of his Il
      trionfo di Camilla, regina de' Volsci.   SCHATZ 1208
Camilla, London, 1706.   Tr. of his Il trionfo di Camilla.   LONGE 132
La conquista del vello d'oro, Reggio, 1717.   SCHATZ 1207
La regina creduta rè, Venetia, 1706.   SCHATZ 1205
Il trionfo di Camilla, regina de' Volsci (Napoli, the incor-
      rect date 1696 on t.-p. supplied in ms.).   SCHATZ 1206
Il trionfo di Camilla regina de' Volsci, Livorno, 1701.   ML 50.2.T82B39

Bontempi, Giovanni Andrea Angelini, 1624–1705.
Il Paride—Paris, Dresda, 1662.   SCHATZ 1209

Boretti, Giovanni Antonio, ca. 1640–1673.
L'Alessandro amante, Venetia, 1667.   SCHATZ 1215
Claudio Cesare, Venezia, 1672.   SCHATZ 1216
Dario in Babilonia, Venetia, 1671.   SCHATZ 1217
Domitiano, Seconda impr., Venetia, 1673.   SCHATZ 1218
Domitiano, Venezia, 1673.   ML 48.M2O
Eliogabalo, Venetia, 1668.   SCHATZ 1219
L'Ercole in Tebe, Venetia, 1671.   SCHATZ 1222
L'Ercole trionfante, Parma, 1688 (only a few arias retained
      from his "L'Ercole in Tebe," the original title of this text
      by Moniglia before its revision under the above title by
      Aureli; practically composed anew by Sabadini). SCHATZ 9196
Marcello in Siracusa, Venetia, 1670.   SCHATZ 1220
La Zenobia, Venetia, 1666.   SCHATZ 1221

Borghi, Giovanni Battista, *ca.* 1740–1799.

Alessandro in Armenia, Venezia, 1768.	SCHATZ 1226
Arbace, Venezia, 1782.	SCHATZ 1239
Artaserse, Venezia, 1776.	SCHATZ 1227
Creso rè di Lidia, Firenze, 1777.	SCHATZ 1228
La donna instabile, Venezia (1776).	SCHATZ 1229
Egilina, Milano (1793).	SCHATZ 1231
Eumene, Venezia, 1778.	SCHATZ 1233
Il filosofo amante (Lisbona, 1776).	SCHATZ 1232
La morte di Semiramide, Milano (1791).	SCHATZ 1234
La morte di Semiramide ossia La vendetta di Nino, Lisbona, 1799.	SCHATZ 1240
L'Olimpiade, Firenze, 1785.	SCHATZ 1235
Ricimero, Venezia, 1773.	SCHATZ 1236
Ricimero, Verona (1778).	ML 50.2.R47B6
La schiava amorosa, Roma (1770).	ML 50.2.S41B6
Siroe, Venezia (1771).	SCHATZ 1237
Gli tre pretendenti, Bologna (1777).	SCHATZ 1230
La vendetta di Nino. A. T. of his La morte di Semiramide.	
Le villanelle innamorate—Die verliebten bauernmaedchen, Dresda (1778).	SCHATZ 1238

Borgognini, Bernardo.

La Nicopoli, Venetia, 1700.	SCHATZ 1241

Boroni, Antonio, *ca.* 1738–1792.

L'amore in musica, Venezia (1763).	SCHATZ 1244
L'amore in musica—L'amour en musique (Stuttgart) 1770.	SCHATZ 1245
L'amore in musica (t.-p. wanting).	ML 50.2.A69B6
Artaserse, Verona (1770).	SCHATZ 1250
Le contadine furlane, Venezia, 1771.	SCHATZ 1252
Die critische nacht. Tr. of his La notte critica, Dresda, 1768.	SCHATZ 1247
La moda, Venezia, 1769.	SCHATZ 1249
La notte critica, Venezia, 1766.	SCHATZ 1246
La notte critica—Die critische nacht, Dresda, 1768.	SCHATZ 1247
Le orfane svizzere, Venezia, 1770.	SCHATZ 1248
La pupilla rapita, Venezia (1763) (mostly by Laurenti).	SCHATZ 5473
Sofonisba, Venezia, 1764.	SCHATZ 1251
Le villeggiatrici ridicole, Venezia, 1765.	SCHATZ 1253

Bortio (Borzio), Carlo.

Il Narciso, Lodi (1676).	SCHATZ 1254

Bortniansky, Dimitrij Stefanovich, 1752–1825.

Creonte, Venezia, 1776.	SCHATZ 1255

Bosi, Carlo.

La figlia obbediente, Milano (1780).	SCHATZ 1256

Bourgeois, Louis Thomas, 1676–1750.

Les amours déguisez (Recueil général des opéra, Paris, 1720, t. xi).	SCHATZ 1272
Les plaisirs de la paix (Recueil général des opéra, Paris, 1720, t. xi).	SCHATZ 1273

Bouvard, François.
 Cassandre, Amsterdam, 1707 (with Bertin de la Doué)   ML 50.2.C28B6
 Cassandre (Recueil général des opéra, Paris, 1710, t. ix) (with
  Bertin de la Doué).   SCHATZ 1275
 Medus, roy des Mèdes (Recueil général des opéra, Paris, 1703,
  t. vii).   SCHATZ 1274

Boyce, William, 1710–1779.
 The chaplet, London, 1750.   AC 901.M5   v.519
 The chaplet, London, 1767.   LONGE 73
 The chaplet (Collection of the most esteemed farces, Edin-
  burgh, 1792, v. 1).   SCHATZ 11753A
 Love in a village, pasticcio. *See* Title catalogue.
 The rehearsal or Bays in petticoats, London, 1753.   LONGE 270
 The shepherds lottery, London, 1751.   LONGE 54
 The summer's tale, pasticcio. *See* Title catalogue.
 Tom Jones, pasticcio. *See* Title catalogue.

Boyer (Pascal?)
 Les étrennes de l'amour, Paris, 1769   ML 50.2.E75

Brassac, Réné de Béarn, *marquis* de.
 L'empire de l'amour (Recueil général des opéra, Paris, 1739,
  t. xv).   SCHATZ 1308

Breni, Tommaso, *ca.* 1603–1650.
 La Psiche, Lucca, 1654.   SCHATZ 1315

Brivio, Giuseppe Ferdinando, *ca.* 1700–1758.
 Artaserse, Padova, 1738.   SCHATZ 1325
 Ipermestra, Milano, 1727 (with others?).   SCHATZ 1327
 L'Olimpiade, Torino, 1737.   SCHATZ 1326

Bronner, Georg, 1666–1724.
 Berenice (Hamburg) 1702.   SCHATZ 1332
 Echo und Narcissus (Hamburg, 1694).   SCHATZ 1334
 Procris und Cephalus, Hamburg, 1701.   SCHATZ 1333
 Victor, hertzog der Normannen (Hamburg, 1702). (Only
  third act; first by J. Chr. Schieferdecker; second by Joh.
  Mattheson.)   SCHATZ 9605

Broschi, Riccardo, *ca.* 1700–1756.
 Adriano in Siria—Der in Syrien triumphirende kayser Had-
  rianus (Stuggarda, 1737).   SCHATZ 1338
 Bradamante nell' isola d'Alcina, Parma, 1729. L. T. of his
  L'isola d'Alcina.   SCHATZ 1342
 Ezio, Torino (1731).   SCHATZ 1340
 Idaspe, Venezia (1730).   SCHATZ 1339
 Merope, London, 1736.   SCHATZ 1341

Brunetti, Antonio.
 Il Bertoldo, Firenze (1788).   SCHATZ 1363
 Bertoldo e Bertoldino, Genova (1791). L. T. of the above.   SCHATZ 1364
Brunetti, Giovanni Gualberto.
 Il trionfo dell' Arno (Pisa, 1766).   SCHATZ 1366

Bruni, Antoine Bartélémy, 1759–1823.
 See also Catalogue of 19th cent. opera librettos.
 L'auteur dans son ménage, Paris, an VII [1799].   ML 50.2.A93B8

Bruni, Antoine Bartélémy—Continued.

Claudine ou Le petit commissionnaire, Paris, an II (1794).   ML 50.2.C57B7
Le major Palme, Paris, an V [1797].   ML 50.2.M32B7
Le petit commissionnaire.   A. T. of Claudine.
Toberne ou Le pêcheur suédois, Paris, cinquième année [1796–
97].   Schatz 1370

Brusa, Francesco.

Adriano in Siria, Venezia, 1757.   Schatz 1376
L'Olimpiade, Venezia, 1767 (with P. Guglielmi and A. G.
Pampani).   Schatz 4316
Semiramide riconosciuta, Venezia (1756).   Schatz 1377
Le statue, Venezia, 1757.   Schatz 1378

Brusa, Giovanni Francesco.

L'amore eroico, Venezia, 1725.   Schatz 1373
Medea e Giasone, Venezia, 1726.   Schatz 1374
Il trionfo della virtù, Venezia (1724).   Schatz 1375

Bryan, Joseph.

The golden pippin.   See Title catalogue.

Buini, Giuseppe Maria.

Albumazar, Venezia, 1727.   Schatz 1387
Amore e maestà, Bologna, 1721.   Schatz 1384
Apollo geloso, Bologna (1720).   ML 50.2.B727A9
Armida abbandonata, Venezia (1723).   Schatz 1388
Armida delusa, Venezia, 1720.   Schatz 1389
Artanagamenone, Venezia (1731).   L. T. of his Malmosor.   Schatz 1397
La caduta di Gelone, Venezia, 1719.   Schatz 1390
Chi non fà, non falla, Venezia (1732).   Schatz 1391
Cleofide, Venezia, 1721.   Schatz 1381
La fede ne' tradimenti, Faenza (1723).   ML 48.A5   v.4
Fidarsi è bene, ma non fidarsi è meglio, Venezia (1731).   Schatz 1396
Il Filindo, Venezia, 1720.   Schatz 1382
Le frenesie d'amore, Venezia, 1726.   L. T. of his Il savio
delirante.   Schatz 1386
Gl'inganni felici, Venezia, 1722.   Schatz 1392
Il giocatore, pasticcio.   See Il marito giogatore.
Gl'inganni fortunati, Venezia, 1720.   Schatz 1393
Malmosor.   O. T. of his Artanaganamenone.
Il nemico amante, Venezia (1724) (with Chelleri).   L. T. of
their La pace per amore.   Schatz 1401
La pace per amore, Venezia, 1719 (with Chelleri).   Schatz 1400
Il protettore alla moda, Venezia, 1749 (but largèly by Galuppi).   Schatz 3520
Il savio delirante, Bologna (1726).   Schatz 1385
Li sdegni cangiati in amore, Venezia (1725).   Schatz 1394
Teodorico, Bologna (1728) (one of several composers).   Schatz 1383
La Zanina maga per amore, Bologna (1737).   Schatz 1398
Zanina maga per amore, Bologna (1745).   Schatz 1399

Burgess, Henry.

The coffee-house, London, 1737 (partly by Carey).   Longe 59

Buri, Ernst Karl Ludwig Ysenburg von.

Das gespenst, Neuwied, 1789.   Schatz 1421
Der kohlenbrenner, Neuwied, 1789.   Schatz 1422
Die matrosen, n. i., n. d.   Schatz 1423

Burney, Charles, 1726–1814.
　A fairy tale, London, 1777 (with M. Arne (principally) and
　　others).　　　　　　　　　　　　　　　　　　　　　Longe 243
　Robin Hood, London, 1751 (doubtful. According to t.-p.,
　　"compos'd by the Society of the Temple of Apollo," of
　　which B. was a member).　　　　　　　　　　　AC 901.M5　v.519

Bury, Bernard de, *b.* 1720.
　Palmire, Paris, 1765 (Journal des spectacles, t. ii, Paris, 1766). ML 48.J7
　La vengeance de l'amour, ou Diane et Endimion (with his
　　Palmire, Journal des spectacles, Paris, t. ii, 1766).

Butler, Thomas Hamly, 1762–1823.
　Calypso, London, 1779.　　　　　　　　　　　　　　Longe 102

Caballone (Gabellone), Michele.
　Adone rè di Cipro, Roma (1731).　　　　　　　　　Schatz 1446
　La cantarina, Napole, 1728 (1st act only; acts 2–3 by Ro-
　　berto).　　　　　　　　　　　　　　　　　ML 50.2.C265C2

Caccini, Giulio, [1558]–1618.
　La Dafne, Firenze, 1600.　　　　　　　　　　　　Schatz 7918
　L'Euridice, Fiorenza, 1600.　　　　　　　　　　　Schatz 7919
　Il rapimento di Cefalo, Firenze, 1600 (partly by Venturi del
　　Nibbio, Bati and Strozzi).　　　　　　　　　　Schatz 1449

Cafaro, Pasquale, 1706–1787.
　Creso, Torino (1768).　　　　　　　　　　　　　Schatz 1452
　Il natal d'Apollo, Napoli, 1775.　　　　　　　　　ML 48. M2G

Cajani, Giuseppi, *ca.* 1774–1821.
　See also Catalogue of 19th cent. librettos.
　Armida e Rinaldo, ballet.　*See* Cimarosa's Il pittor parigino.
　Berilowitz in Tartaria, ballo eroico pantomimo.　*See* Fiora-
　　vanti's L'amor per interesse.
　Caterina e Blech, ballet.　*See* Bernardini's Furberia e pun-
　　tiglio.
　Elisabetta e Blech, ballet.　*See* Curcio's Le nozze a dispetto.

Calandra, Nicola (*called* Frascia).
　I tre matrimoni, Venezia, 1756.　　　　　　　　　Schatz 1474

Caldara, Antonio, *ca.* 1670–1736.
　Achille in Sciro, Vienna d'Austria (1736).　　　　　Schatz 1476
　Achilles in Scyro, Wien, 1735.　Tr. of the above.　　Schatz 1477
　Adriano in Siria, Vienna d'Austria (1732).　　　　Schatz 1478
　L'Anagilda, Roma (1711).　　　　　　　　　　　Schatz 1491
　Andromaca.　*See* Zeno's Poesie drammatiche.
　L'Argene, Venetia, 1689.　　　　　　　　　　　Schatz 1492
　L'asilio d'Amore.　*See* Metastasio's Opere.
　Atamo huomo vecchio e Palancha giovine.　**Intermezzi in his**
　　L'inganno tradito dall' amore.
　Atenaide.　*See* Zeno's Poesie drammatiche.
　Un ballo cinese.　*See* Le Cinesi in Title catalogue.
　Cajo Fabrizio.　*See* Zeno's Poesie drammatiche.
　Camaide, imperatore della China o vero Li figliuoli rivali del
　　padre, Salisburgo (1722).　　　　　　　　　　Schatz 1479
　Le Cinesi.　*See* Title catalogue.
　Ciro riconosciuto (Vienna, 1736).　*See* Metastasio's Opere.

Caldara, Antonio—Continued.

Ciro riconosciuto, Venice, 1737. (Galuppi, perhaps partly by
    Caldara.)   SCHATZ 3517

La clemenza di Tito, Vienna d'Austria (1734).   SCHATZ 1498

Il Demetrio rè della Siria, Wolfenbuettel (1734).   SCHATZ 1480

Demofoonte. *See* Metastasio's Opere.

Don Chisciotte in corte della duchessa, Vienna d'Austria
    (1727).   SCHATZ 1502

Don Chisciotte in corte della duchessa, n. i., n. d. (detached). SCHATZ 1481

Dorina e Grullo, intermezzi. *In his* L'Anagilda, Rome (1711). SCHATZ 1491

I due dittatori. *See* Zeno's Poesie drammatiche.

Enone. *See* Zeno's Poesie drammatiche.

Gli equivoci del sembiante, Milano (1703).   ML 48.A5 v.12

Euristeo. *See* Zeno's Poesie drammatiche.

Farnace, Venezia, 1703.   SCHATZ 1493

Li figliuoli rivali del padre. A. T. of his Camaide, imperatore
    della China.

Il Germanico Marte, Salisburgo, n. d.   SCHATZ 1482

Gianguir. *See* Zeno's Poesie drammatiche.

Grespilla e Fanfarone. Intermezzi in his Il Germanico
    Marte.

Le Grazie vendicate. *See* Metastasio's Opere.

Ifigenia in Aulide. *See* Zeno's Poesie drammatiche.

Ifigenia in Aulide, Venezia (1718).   SCHATZ 1484

Imeneo. *See* Zeno's Poesie drammatiche.

L'inganno tradito dall' amore, Salisburgo (172–?).   SCHATZ 1485

Lisetta ed Astrobolo. Intermezzi in his La verità nell' in-
    ganno.

Lucio Papirio. *See* Zeno's Poesie drammatiche.

Lucio Papirio dittatore, Venezia, 1720.   SCHATZ 1499

La marchesina di Nanchin ed il conte di Pelusio. Intermezzi
    in his Camaide, imperatore della China.

Mitridate, Vienna d'Austria (1728).   SCHATZ 1494

Nitocri, koenigin in Egypten, Wienn (1722). Tr. of his
    Nitocri.   SCHATZ 1486

Olimpiade (n. i., n. d.). *See also* Metastasio's Opere.   ML 50.2.O5C2

Ormisda, Vienna d'Austria (1721).   SCHATZ 1501

Ornospade, Vienna d'Austria (1727).   SCHATZ 1503

La Partenope, Venezia (1707).   SCHATZ 1495

Pharao und Joseph (Hamburg, 1728). (Arias from his Gian-
    guir).   SCHATZ 1483

La promessa serbato al primo, Venetia, 1697.   SCHATZ 1496

Psiche (with Fux). *See* Zeno's Poesie drammatiche.

Scipione nelle Spagne. *See* Zeno's Poesie drammatiche.

Il selvaggio eroe, Venezia (1707).   SCHATZ 1497

Semiramide in Ascalona. *See* Zeno's Poesie drammatiche.

Sirita, Vienna d'Austria, 1719.   SCHATZ 1487

Sofonisba, Venezia, 1708.   SCHATZ 1500

Il Temistocle, Vienna d'Austria (1736).   SCHATZ 1488

Venceslao, Vienna d'Austria (1725).   SCHATZ 1489

Teodosio—Theodosius, Hamburg (1718). (Partly by Fux
    and Gasparini.)   SCHATZ 3392

Il Tirsi, Venezia (1696) (with Lotti and Ariosti).   SCHATZ 5728

La verità nell' inganno, Vienna d'Austria (1717).   SCHATZ 1490

Calderara, Giacinto.
Ricimero, Torino (1756).   SCHATZ 1507

Calegari, Antonio, 1757–1828.
Le due sorelle incognite, Venezia (1783).   SCHATZ 1509
Telemaco in Sicilià, Padova, 1792.   SCHATZ 1508

Callcott, John Wall, 1766–1821.
The naval pillar. *See* Title catalogue.

Callegari, Giuseppe.
Artemisia, Venezia, 1782.   SCHATZ 1510
Il convitato di pietra, Venezia, 1777.   SCHATZ 1511

Calvi, Giovanni Battista.
Ezio, Pavia (1784).   SCHATZ 1518

Cambefort, Jean de, *d.* 1661.
Le ballet du temps. *See* Title catalogue.

Cambert, Robert, 1628–1677.
Pastorale mise en musique (Perrin, Les oeuvres de poesie,
    Paris, 1661).   PQ 1879.P3
Les peines et les plaisirs de l'amour (Recueil général des
    opéra, Paris, 1703, t. i).   SCHATZ 1520
Pomone (Recueil général des opéra, Paris, 1703, t. i).   SCHATZ 1519

Camerlocher, Joseph Anton, *d.* 1743.
La clemenza di Tito—Die guetigkeit des Titus, Monaco (1747). SCHATZ 1523

Campelli, Carlo.
Amore fra gl' Impossibili, Roma & Siena, 1693.   SCHATZ 1532

Campion (Campioni), Carlo Antonio.
Venere placata, Livorno (1760).   SCHATZ 1536

Campion, Thomas, 1575–1619.
A relation of the late royall entertainment . . . whereunto is
    annexed . . . The Lords maske, London, 1613 (but com-
    poser doubtful).   ML 52.2.R38

Campobasso d'Alessandro, Vincenzo.
Antigona, Milano (1789).   SCHATZ 1538

Campra, André, 1660–1744.
Achille et Deidamie (Recueil général des opéra, t. xv, Paris,
    1739).   SCHATZ 1539
Achille et Deidamie (Danchet, Théâtre, Paris, 1751, t. iii). PQ 1972.D2
Les ages, ballet (Recueil général des opéra, 1734, t. xii). SCHATZ 1540
Alcine, Amsterdam, 1707.   ML 50.2.A512C2
Alcine (Recueil général des opéra, t. viii, Paris, 1706).   SCHATZ 1541
Alcine (Danchet, Théâtre, t. ii, Paris, 1751).   PQ 1972.D2
Amarillis (Recueil général des opéra, Paris, 1706, t. viii). *See*
    his Les Muses.   SCHATZ 1542
Amarillis (Danchet, Théâtre, Paris, 1751, t. ii). Substitute
    pastorale in his Les Muses.   PQ 1972.D2
Les amours de Mars et de Venus, ballet (Recueil des général
    opera, Paris, 1714, t. x).   SCHATZ 1543
Les amours de Vénus (Danchet, Théâtre, Paris, 1751, t. iii).
    L. T. of his Les amours de Mars et Vénus.   PQ 1972.D2
Arethuse (Recueil général des opéra, Paris, 1703, t. vii).   SCHATZ 1544

Campra, Andre—Continued.

Arethuse (Danchet, Théâtre, Paris, 1751, t. ii).   PQ 1972.D2

Le bal interrompu.   *See his* Trois nouvelles entrées.

Ballet des ages.   *See his* Les ages.

Der beschluss des carnevals (Hamburg, 1724) (partly based on
his L'Europe galante, partly composed by Telemann).   Schatz 1564

Camille, reine des Volsques, Paris, 1717.   ML 50.2.C253C2

Camille reine des Volsques (Recueil général des opéra, Paris,
1734, t. xii).   Schatz 1546

Camille, reine des Volsques (Danchet, Théâtre, Paris, 1751,
t. iii).   PQ 1972.D2

Le carnaval de Venise, Amsterdam, 1699.   ML 52.2.C23C3

Le carnaval de Venise (Recueil général des opéra, Paris, 1703,
t. vi).

Diane (Danchet, Théâtre, Paris, 1751, t. iii). (Same as
"Diane & Endimion" entrée in their condensed version
of Lully's Le triomphe de l'amour.)   PQ 1972.D2

L'Europe galante (Recueil général des opéra, Paris, 1703,
t. vi).   Schatz 1548

Les festes venitiennes (Recueil général des opéra, Paris, 1714,
t. x).   Schatz 1549

Les fêtes vénitiennes (Danchet, Théâtre, Paris, 1751, t. iii).   PQ 1972.D2

Hesione (Recueil général des opéra, Paris, 1703, t. vii).   Schatz 1555

Hesione (Danchet, Théâtre, Paris, 1751, t. ii).   PQ 1972.D2

Hippodamie (Recueil général des opéra, Paris, 1710, t. ix).   Schatz 1556

Idomenée (Recueil général des opéra, Paris, 1714, t. x).   Schatz 1557

Idoménée (Danchet, Théâtre, Paris, 1751, t. iii).   PQ 1972.D2

Iphigénie en Tauride, 1706. *See* this under Desmarests and
Campra.

Les Muses (Recueil général des opéra, Paris, 1706, t. viii).   Schatz 1558

Les Muses (Danchet, Théâtre, t. ii, Paris, 1751).   PQ 1972.D2

Orfeo ne'll inferi—Orphée aux enfers. *See his* Le carnaval de
Venise.

La sérénade vénitienne. *See his* Trois nouvelles entrées.

Tancrede (Recueil général des opéra, Paris, 1706, t. viii).   Schatz 1560

Tancrede (Danchet, Théâtre, Paris, 1751, t. ii).   PQ 1972.D2

Télémaque, Amsterdam, 1705 (partly composed, partly selected the music)   ML 50.2.T34C3

Télémaque (Recueil général des opéra, Paris, 1706, t. viii)
(partly composed, partly selected the music).   Schatz 1561

Telephe (Recueil général des opéra, Paris, 1720, t. xi).   Schatz 1562

Telephe (Danchet, Théâtre, Paris, 1751, t. iii).   PQ 1972.D2

Le triomphe de Vénus. *See his* Trois nouvelles entrées.

Trois nouvelles entrées ajoutées (Recueil général des opéra,
Paris, 1703, t. vii). *See* Fragments de Mr. de Lully.   Schatz 1563

Canavasso, Vittorio Amedeo.

Aci e Galatea, ballet.   *See* Curcio's Solimano.

Adone e Venere, ballet.   *See* Pugnani's Demofoonte.

Annibale in Torino, ballet.   *See* Tarchi's Bacco ed Arianna.

Le avventure del carnovale, ballet.   *See* Rispoli's Idalide.

Bacco ed Arianna, ballet.   *See* Insanguine's Motezuma.

I barbari sacrifizi distrutti, ballet.   *See* Rispoli's Idalide.

Il Beiram, o sia Il carnovale, ballet.   *See* Curcio's Solimano.

Canavasso, Vittorio Amedeo——Continued.

La bella Arsena, and Il teatro italiano alla China, ballets. *See* Martin y Soler's Andromaca.

La caduta di Troia, ballet. *See* Monza's Erifile.

Calipso. Ballets for this opera by Ottani.

Chi ne fa ne aspetta, ballet. *See* Cimarosa's Volodomiro.

La contadina nel palazzo signorile. A.T.of his ballet Ninetta.

La costanza coniugale, ballet. *See* Andreozzi's Teodelinda.

La costanza guerriera, ballet. *See* Ottani's Fatima.

Didone abbandonata, ballet. *See* Cherubini's Ifigenia in Aulide.

Il disertore francese, ballet. *See* G. Giordani's Ariarate.

La disfatta di Vario. A. T. of his ballet La Tusnelda.

Li due avari, ballet. *See* Anfossi's Gengis-Kan.

Enea e Turno, ballet. *See* Bianchi's Briseide.

Eumene. Composed the ballets performed with this opera by Insanguine, Turin, 1778.

La favola d'Apollo e Dafne, ballet. *See* Rispoli's Nitteti.

La fiera di Batavia, ballet. *See* Curcio's Solimano.

La fiera di Sinigaglia, ballet. *See* Andreozzi's Teodelinda.

La Galzeuca ossia Golconda liberata dalla tirannide di Scour-Malou, ballet. *See* Pugnani's Achille in Sciro.

Il Gastaldo burlato, ballet. *See* Andreozzi's Teodelinda.

Gioconda, ballet. *See* Cimarosa's Artaserse.

Golconda liberata dalla tirannide di Scour-Malou. A. T. of his ballet La Galzeuca.

Di Greci festeggianti la riconciliazione d'Achille e d'Agamennone, ballet. *See* Bianchi's Briseide.

Il guerrier generoso, ballet. *See* Insanguine's Motezuma.

L'inaspettata consolazione nelle sventure, ballet. *See* Bianchi's Trionfo della pace.

L'incoronazione di Siroe, ballet. *See* Sarti's Siroe.

Lauso e Lidia, ballet. *See* Rust's Adriano in Siria.

La liberazione di Lilla, ballet. *See* Bertoni's Medonte.

Lucio Silla. Ballets for Mortellari's opera.

Ludovico Sforza, detto il Moro, ballet. *See* Cimarosa's Volodomiro.

Il macchinista ossia La susta matematica, ballet. *See* Martin y Soler's Vologeso.

Il manescalco, ballet. *See* Rust's Adriano in Siria.

Il matrimonio cinese, ballet. *See* Anfossi's Gengis-Kan.

Il matrimonio de' Groelandesi, ballet. *See* Rispoli's Nitteti.

Il matrimonio per concorso, ballet. *See* Pugnani's Achille in Sciro.

Mercato fiammengo, ballet. *See* Cherubini's Ifigenia in Aulide.

Li montanari nel Perù, ballet. *See* Rispoli's Idalide.

Ninetta o sia La contadina nel palazzo signorile, ballet. *See* Sarti's Siroe.

La nuova della pace, ballet. *See* Cherubini's Ifigenia in Aulide.

Il rè pastore, ballet. *See* Anfossi's Gengis-Kan.

Il riconoscimento di Teseo ossia Teseo e Medea, ballet. *See* G. Giordani's Ariarate.

Canavasso, Vittorio Amedeo—Continued.

Rinaldo nel giardino incantato d'Armida, ballet. *See* Bianchi's Trionfo della pace.

Rinaldo nella Silva incantata, ballet. *See* Sarti's Siroe.

Il signore benefico, ballet. *See* Tarchi's Il trionfo di Clelia.

La sposa peruviana, ballet. *See* Martin y Soler's Vologeso.

Gli sposi delusi dalle astuzie di Crespino, ballet. *See* Cimarosa's Artaserse.

Il tempio della pazzia, ballet. *See* Insanguine's Motezuma.

Il trionfo improvviso, ballet. *See* Pugnani's Demetrio a Rodi.

La Tusnelda o sia La disfatta di Vario, ballet. *See* Cimarosa's Artaserse.

La vanità corretta dal disprezzo, ballet. *See* Monza's Erifile.

I viaggiatori aerostatici, ballet. *See* Pugnani's Demofoonte.

La viaggiatrice o sia Le circostanze imbarazzanti, ballet. *See* Bianchi's Briseide.

Il volubile assodato, ballet. *See* Ottani's Arminio.

Candeille, Julie, 1767–1834 (*later,* Mme Simons; *still later,* Mme Périé).

Catherine ou La belle fermière, Paris, 1793.   ML 50.2.C31C2

Cannabich, Christian, 1731–1798.

Achilles und Ulysses auf der insel Scyros, ballet. *See* Bach's Lucius Silla.

Azakia, Mannheim, 1778.   Schatz 1573

Cephal und Procris, ballet. (The libretto mentions as composers of this and "Reinald und Armide": "Cannabich und Toeschi.") *See* Holzbauer's Hadrian in Syrien.

Elektra, Mannheim, 1780.   Schatz 1574

Die hoellenfarth des Herkules um Alcesten zurueck zu holen, ballet. *See* Schweitzer's Rosamund.

Ippolito ed Aricia. Ballet music for Holzbauer's opera.

Medea und Jason, ballet. *See* Bach's Temistocle.

Reinald und Armide, ballet. (The libretto mentions as composers of this and "Cephal und Procris": "Cannabich und Toeschi.") *See* Holzbauer's Hadrian in Syrien.

Canobio (Canobbio), Carlo.

Alceste ed Admeto. A. T. of his ballet La discesa d'Ercole all' inferno.

Andromaca in Epiro, ballet. *See* Sarti's Farnace.

Cupido trionfatore o sia Apollo e Dafne, ballet. *See* Pio's Nettuno ed Egle.

La discesa d'Ercole all' inferno o sia Alceste ed Admeto, ballet. *See* Antonelli's Catone in Utica.

La maggior impresa d'Ercole o sia Admeto ed Alceste. *See* Pio's Nettuno ed Egle.

Canuti, Giovanni Antonio, *d.* 1739.

Lucio Giunio Bruto primo consolo di Roma, Lucca, 1735. *See* M. Curzio in Title catalogue.

Capello, Giovanni Maria.

L'Eudamia, Roma & Parma, 1718.   Schatz 1589

I fratelli riconosciuti, Parma, 1726.   Schatz 1590

Giul. Flavio Crispo, Venezia, 1722.   Schatz 1591

Mitridate rè di Ponto vincitor di sè stesso, Venezia, 1723.   Schatz 1592

Cappucci, Antonio (*same as* Capuzzi?).
Li sposi contenti, ballet. *See* Martin y Soler's L'isola piacevole.

Capranica, Matteo.
L'Olindo, Napoli, 1753 (partly by N. Conti).   SCHATZ 2208

Caproli, Carlo, *del Violino.*
The nuptials of Peleus and Thetis, London, 1654. Tr. of his
Le nozze di Peleo e di Theti.   LONGE 241

Capuzzi, Giuseppe Antonio, 1753–1818. (*Same as* Capucci?)
See also Catalogue of 19th cent. librettos.
Alonzo e Cora, ballet. *See* Bianchi's Aspard.
Alonso e Cora, ballet. *See* Bianchi's Piramo e Tisbe.
Alonzo e Cora. A. T. of his ballet La vergine del sole.
Annetta e Fierillo, ballet. *See* Millico's La Zelinda.
I bagni d'Abano o sia La forza delle prime impressioni, Venezia, 1793.   SCHATZ 1597
Cresfonte, rè di Scizia, ballet. *See* Bianchi's Pizzarro.
L'impostore punito, ballet. *See* Robuschi's Castrini, padre e figlio.
La vergine del sole o sia Alonzo e Cora, ballet. *See* Prati's
L'Ifigenia in Aulide.

Caramanica, Pietro.
Il viaggiatore ridicolo, Brescia (1771).   SCHATZ 1619

Carcano, Giuseppe.
Alcibiade (Venezia, 1746).   SCHATZ 1621
Ambleto, Venezia, 1742.   SCHATZ 1620

Cardena, Pietro Lione.
Creusa, Venezia, 1739.   SCHATZ 1622

Carey, Henry, *ca.* 1690–1743.
Britannia and Batavia, London, 1740.   ML 52.2.B86
The coffee-house, London, 1737 (partly by H. Burgess).   LONGE 59
The contrivances (*his* Dramatick works, London, 1743).   ML 49.A2C2
The contrivances, London, 1765.   LONGE 69
The contrivances (Collection of the most esteemed farces,
Edinburgh, 1792, t. iv).   SCHATZ 11753D
The generous Free-mason or The constant lady. *See* Title
catalogue.
The honest Yorkshire-man, London, 1736 (partly ballad opera,
O. T. of which was: The Wonder! An honest Yorkshireman).   ML 50.5.H65
The honest Yorkshire-man (*his* Dramatick works, London,
1743).   ML 49.A2C2
The honest Yorkshire-man, London, 1763.   LONGE 73
Love in a village, pasticcio. *See* Title catalogue.
Midas. *See* Title catalogue.
Nancy or The parting lovers (*his* Dramatick works, London,
1743).   ML 49.A2C2

Carr, Benjamin, 1769–1831.
The archers or Mountaineers of Switzerland, New York, 1796.   ML 50.6.A72
The children in the wood, New York, 1795 (additions to Arnold's music).   PR 1241.D7   v.4

Carter, Thomas, 1734–1804.

The constant maid, or, Poll of Plympton, London, 1787.	Longe 102
The fair American, London, 1785.	ML 50.2.F13C2
Just in time, London (1792).	Longe 220
The Milesian, London, 1777.	Longe 86
The rival candidates, London, 1775.	Longe 32
The rival candidates (Collection of the most esteemed farces, Edinburgh, 1792, t. iv).	Schatz 11753D

Caruso, Carlo, *recte* **Luigi.**

Caruso, Luigi, 1754–1821.

See also Catalogue of 19th cent. librettos.

L'albergatrice vivace, Parma (1781).	Schatz 1655
L'amante imprudente. A. T. of his La sposa volubile.	
Gli amanti dispettosi, Napoli, 1787. L. T. of his Gli amanti alla prova.	Schatz 1653 .
L'amore volubile, Bologna (1779).	Schatz 1666
Antigono, Venezia, 1794.	Schatz 1659
L'arrivo del Burchello da Padova in Venezia, Venezia, 1779.	Schatz 1660
L'Artaserse (Firenze, 1780).	Schatz 1656
Attalo rè di Bitinia, Roma (1790).	Schatz 1661
Il barone di Moscabianca. A. T. of his Oro non compra amore.	
I campi Elisi ossia Le spose ricuperate, Milano (1788).	Schatz 1662
Il cavalier magnifico, Venezia, 1789 (*recte* 1779).	Schatz 1657
Li due amanti rivali, Venezia, 1779. L. T. of his La virtuosa alla moda.	Schatz 1663
Il fanatico per la musica, Bologna (1782) (with Spontoni).	Schatz 1667
L'inganno, Napoli, 1782.	Schatz 1652
Il marito geloso, Venezia (1781).	Schatz 1645
Il matrimonio in commedia, Milano (1782).	Schatz 1646
Oro non compra amore o sia Il barone di Moscabianca, Venezia, 1794.	Schatz 1649
Il poeta di villa, Roma (1786).	Schatz 1658
Il poeta melodrammatica in Parnaso, Verona, 1786.	ML 50.2.P48C2
Puntigli e gelosie tra moglie e marito, Napoli, 1784.	Schatz 1650
Le quattro stagioni, Napoli, 1784.	Schatz 1651
Le spose ricuperate. A. T. of his I campi Elisi.	
Li sposi in commedia, Venezia, 1786. (L. T. of his Il matrimonio in commedia.)	Schatz 1647
La sposa volubile ossia L'amante imprudente, Lisbona, 1795.	Schatz 1654
Il vecchio burlato, Venezia (1783).	Schatz 1664
La virtuosa alla moda, Siena, 1777.	Schatz 1648

Carvalho, João de Sousa.

Adrasto rè degli Argivi (Lisboa, 1784).	Schatz 1670
Alcione (Lisboa, 1787).	Schatz 1674
L'Angelica (Lisbona, 1778).	ML 50.2.A71C2
Eumene (Lisboa, 1773).	Schatz 1668
Nettuno ed Egle (Lisboa, 1785).	Schatz 1671
Numa Pompilio II rè de Romani (Lisbona, 1789).	Schatz 1672
Penelope nella partenza da Sparta (Lisbona) 1782.	Schatz 1673
Testoride Argonauta (Lisboa, 1780).	Schatz 1669
Tomiri (Lisbona, 1783).	Schatz 1675

Casali, Giovanni Battista, *d.* 1792.

Antigona, Torino, 1752.	SCHATZ 1678
Candaspe, regina de Sciti, Venezia, 1740.	SCHATZ 1677
La finta Tedesca, Roma, 1753.	ML 50.2.F44C2
L'impazzito, Roma, 1748.	ML 50.2.I45C2
La lavandarina, Roma, 1746.	ML 48.A5 v.3

Casanova, Girolamo.

Teuzzone, Torino, 1716 (with Fiorè).	SCHATZ 1682

Castrovillari, Daniele.

Gl' avvenimenti d'Orinda, Venetia, 1659.	SCHATZ 1690
La Cleopatra, Venetia, 1662.	SCHATZ 1691
La Pasife o vero L'impossibile fatto possibile, Venetia, 1661.	SCHATZ 1689

Cattani, Lorenzo.

Il conte di Cutro, n. i., n. d. (detached copy).	SCHATZ 1712
Gneo Marzio Coriolano (G. A. Moniglia, Poesie drammatiche, prima parte, Firenze, 1689).	ML 49.A2M7
Il pellegrino (G. A. Moniglia, Poesie drammatiche, seconda parte, Firenze, 1690).	ML 49.A2M7
La pietà di Sabina (G. A. Moniglia, Poesie drammatiche, seconda parte, Firenze, 1690).	ML 49.A2M7
Quinto Lucrezio proscritto, Firenze, 1681.	SCHATZ 1713
Quinto Lucrezio proscritto (G. A. Moniglia, Poesie drammatiche, parte prima, Firenze, 1689).	ML 49.A2M7

Cavalli, Pietro Francesco, 1602–1676 (*real name* Pier Francesco Caletti-Bruni).

Alessandro vincitor di se stesso, Venetia, 1651.	SCHATZ 1715
Alessandro vincitor di se stesso, Bologna, 1655.	SCHATZ 11681
Amore innamorato, Venetia, 1642.	SCHATZ 1734
Gli amori d'Apollo e di Dafne, Venetia, 1656 [! instead of 1640].	SCHATZ 1716
Antioco, Venetia, 1658.	SCHATZ 1717
Artemisia, Venetia, 1656.	SCHATZ 1730
La Bradamante, Venetia, 1650.	SCHATZ 1731
La Calisto, Venetia, 1651.	SCHATZ 1744
Il Ciro, Venetia, 1654.	SCHATZ 1736
Ciro, Venetia, 1665 (with substitute arias by Mattioli).	SCHATZ 1753
La Deidamia, Venetia, 1644.	SCHATZ 1745
La Didone, 1656.	SCHATZ 1718
La Doriclea, Venetia, 1645.	SCHATZ 1737
L'Egisto, Venezia, 1643.	SCHATZ 1719
L'Egisto, Firenze, 1646.	SCHATZ 1719a
Elena, Venetia, 1659.	SCHATZ 1746
L'Erismena, Venetia, 1655.	SCHATZ 1720
L'Eritrea, Venetia, 1652.	SCHATZ 1721
L'Euripo, Venetia, 1649.	SCHATZ 1738
Giasone, Venetia, 1649.	SCHATZ 1751
Il Giasone, Venetia, 1664.	SCHATZ 1722
Il Giasone, Venetia, 1666.	ML 50.2.G36C1
Il Giasone, Milan, n. d.	ML 50.2.G36C2
L'Helena rapita da Theseo, Venetia, 1653.	SCHATZ 1735
L'Hipermestra, Firenze, 1658. O. T. of:	ML 50.2.H38C2
L'Ipermestra (G. A. Moniglia, Poesie drammatiche, parte prima, Firenze, 1689).	ML 49.A2M7
Mutio Scevola, Venetia, 1665.	SCHATZ 1739

Cavalli, Pietro Francesco—Continued.

Narciso et Ecco immortalati, Venetia, 1642.	SCHATZ 1747
Il novello Giasone, Roma, 1671. (*See* his Giasone.)	SCHATZ 1750
Le nozze di Teti e di Peleo, Venetia, 1639.	SCHATZ 1748
L'Orimonte, Venetia, 1650.	SCHATZ 1723
L'Orione, Venetia, 1653.	SCHATZ 1740
L'Oristeo, Venetia, 1651.	SCHATZ 1752
L'Oristeo travestito, Bologna, 1656 (L'Oristeo with many alterations).	SCHATZ 1724
L'Ormindo, Venetia, 1644.	SCHATZ 1725
Pompeo Magno, Venetia, 1666.	SCHATZ 1732
La prosperità infelice di Giulio Cesare dittatore, Venetia, 1656.	SCHATZ 1726
Il Romolo e'l Remo, Venetia, 1645.	SCHATZ 1727
Scipione, Africano, Venetia, 1664.	SCHATZ 1741
Scipione Africano, Venetia, 1678 (partly by Bonaventura Viviani).	SCHATZ 1754
La Statira, principessa di Persia, Venetia, 1655.	SCHATZ 1728
La Statira, principessa di Persia, Venetia, 1656.	SCHATZ 11682
Il Titone, Venetia, 1645.	SCHATZ 1749
La Torilda, Venetia, 1648.	SCHATZ 1733
Veremonda l'Amazzone di Aragona, Venetia, 1652.	SCHATZ 1742
La virtù de' strali d'amore, Venetia, 1642.	SCHATZ 1729
Xerse, Venetia, 1654.	SCHATZ 1743
Il Xerse, Palermo, 1658.	ML 50.2.X3C2

Cavi, Giovanni Battista, *d.* 1820.

La prepotenza delusa, Venezia, 1777.	SCHATZ 1757

Cavos, Catterino, *ca.* 1775–1840.

Il sotteraneo ossia Catterina di Coluga, ballet. *See* Nasolini's
Le feste d'Iside.

Celoniat, Ignazio.

Il caffè di campagna, Torino (1762).	SCHATZ 1772
Ecuba, Torino (1769).	SCHATZ 1771

Cercià, Domenico.

L'equivoco curioso, Napoli, 1790.	SCHATZ 1774
Le false magie per amore, Napoli, 1791.	SCHATZ 1775

Ceruso, Luigi. (*Misprint for* Caruso.)

Cervellini, Giuseppe.

Ines de Castro, Venezia, 1795 (with Bianchi, Nasolini, and Gerace).	SCHATZ 1012

Cesti, Marc' Antonio, 1620–1669.

Alessandro il vincitòr di se stesso, Lucca, 1654 (partly by Bigongiari).	SCHATZ 1786
L'Argia, Insprugg, 1655.	SCHATZ 1777
L'Argia, Venetia, 1669.	SCHATZ 1777a
Il Cesare amante, Venetia, 1651.	SCHATZ 1783
La Dori, Venetia, 1663.	SCHATZ 1778
La Dori, Venetia, 1666.	SCHATZ 11683
La Dori ovvero Lo schiavo reggio, Venetia, 1667.	SCHATZ 1785
La Dori, Monaco, 1680 (new prologue by Bernabei).	SCHATZ 1779
Il Genserico, Venetia, 1669.	SCHATZ 1780

Cesti, Marc' Antonio—Continued.

La Giocasta (G. A. Moniglia, Poesie drammatiche, seconda
parte, Firenze, 1690).   ML 49.A2M7

Orontea, Torino, 1662.   Schatz 1781

Orontea, regina d'Egitto, Venetia, n. publ., n. d.   ML 50.2.O73C2

Il regio schiavo o sia La Dori, Mantova, 1672.   ML 50.2.D62C3

La schiava fedele. A. T. of his La Dori.

La schiava fortunata, Venetia, 1674 (partly by M. A. Ziani).   Schatz 1782

Lo schiavo reggio. A. T. of his La Dori.

La Semiramide (G. A. Moniglia, Poesie drammatiche, seconda
parte, Firenze, 1690).   ML 49.A2M7

Il Tito, Venetia, 1666.   Schatz 1784

Champein, Stanislas, 1753–1830.

See also Catalogue of 19th century librettos.

Les dettes, Paris, 1787.   Schatz 1794

La mélomanie, Nouv. éd., Toulon, 1787.   ML 50.2.M52C4

Le nouveau Don-Quichotte, Nantes (Bruxelles) 1792.   ML 50.2.N62C3

Le poète supposé ou Les préparatifs de fête, 2d éd., Paris
(1782).   ML 50.2.P5C3

De schulden, Amsterdam, 1791. Tr. of his Les dettes.   Schatz 1795

Chapelle, Pierre David Augustin, 1756–1821.

La famille réunie, Paris, 1790.   ML 50.2.F174C3

La vieillesse d'Annette et Lubin, Paris, 1790.   ML 50.2.V45C3

Chardiny, Louis Claude Armand, *d.* 1793.

La ruse d'amour ou L'épreuve, Paris, 1786.   ML 50.2.R9C3

Charke, Richard.

The generous Free-mason. *See* Title catalogue.

The lovers opera, ballad opera. *See* Title catalogue.

Charpentier, Marc' Antoine, 1634–1704.

Medée, Amsterdam, 1695.   ML 50.2.M5C2

Medée (Recueil général des opéra, Paris, 1703, t. iv).   Schatz 1801

Telemaque, pasticcio. *See* Title catalogue.

Chelleri, Fortunato, *b.* 1686.

Alessandro fra le Amazoni, Venezia, 1715.   Schatz 1812

Amalasunta, Venezia, 1719.   Schatz 1811

L'amor tirannico, Venezia, 1722 (third act by G. Porta).   Schatz 1819

L'Arsacide, Venezia, 1721.   Schatz 1810

La caccia in Etolia, Ferrara, 1715.   Schatz 1817

L'innocenza difesa. *See also his* Judith, gemahlin kayser
Ludewigs des Frommen.

L'innocenza difesa, Venezia, 1722. L. T. of his L'innocenza
giustificata.   Schatz 1814

Ircano inamorato, Venezia, 1729.   Schatz 1816

Judith, gemahlin kayser Ludewigs des Frommen oder Die
siegende unschuld, Hamburg (1732). Pasticcio, arias
from his L'innocenza difesa, Händel's Lotario, recitatives
by Telemann.   Schatz 4481

Il nemico amante, Venezia (1724) (with Buini). L. T. of
their La pace per amore.   Schatz 1401

La pace per amore, Venezia, 1719 (with Buini).   Schatz 1400

Penelope la casta, Venezia, 1716.   Schatz 1813

Chelleri, Fortunato—Continued.
    Temistocle, Padova, 1721.   Schatz 1815
    Die siegende unschuld.   A. T. of his Judith, gemahlin kayser
        Ludewigs des Frommen.
    Zenobia in Palmira, Milano (1710).   Schatz 1818

Cherubini, Maria Luigi Zenobio Carlo Salvatore, 1760–1842.
    See also Catalogue of 19th cent. librettos.
    Elisa ou Le voyage au Mont-Bernard, Paris (1794).   ML 50.2.E3C3
    Le génie Asouf, ou Les deux coffrets, Paris, an VIII [1799]
        (pasticcio, partly music by the above).   Schatz 10591
    Ifigenia in Aulide, Milano (1788).   Schatz 11684
    Ifigenia in Aulide, Torino (1788).   Schatz 1838
    Lodoiska, London (1794) (pasticcio from the above, Storace,
        Kreutzer and Andreozzi).   Longe 228
    Médée, Paris, an V, 1797.   ML 50.2.M5C3
    Mesenzio rè d'Etruria, Firenze, 1782.   Schatz 1846
    Quinto Fabio, Roma, 1783.   Schatz 1847
    Lo sposo di tre e marito di nessuno, Venezia (1783).   Schatz 1848
    Le voyage au Mont-Bernard.   A. T. of his Elisa.

Chiarini, Pietro.
    Achille in Sciro, Venezia, 1739.   Schatz 1852
    Argenide, Venezia, 1738.   Schatz 1853
    Artaserse, Verona (1741).   Schatz 1854
    La donna dottoressa, Cremona, 1754.   Schatz 1855
    Meride e Selinunte (Venezia, 1744).   •   Schatz 1851
    Statira.   *See* Goldoni's Opere teatrali.

Chierici, Sebastiano.
    Amor piaga ogni core, Ferrara, 1690.   ML 50.2.A65C3

Chinzer (Chintzer, Ghinzer), Giovanni.
    Atalo, Venezia, 1742.   Schatz 1866
    La serva favorita, Firenze (1741).   Schatz 1864
    La vanità delusa, Firenze, 1731.   Schatz 1865

Chiocchetti, Pier Vincenzo, *d.* 1753.
    Solone, Lucca, 1741.   *See* M. Curzio in Title catalogue.

Chudy, Joseph.
    Der docktor, Pressburg (1779).   Schatz 1872

Ciampi, Francesco, *b.* 1704.
    Onorio, Venezia (1729).   Schatz 1874

Ciampi, Legrenzio Vincenzo, *b.* 1719.
    L'Adriano (Venice, 1748).   Schatz 1875
    Amore in caricatura, Venezia, 1761.   Schatz 1888
    L'Arcadia in Brenta.   *See* Goldoni's Opere teatrali.
    Bertholde à la ville, Paris, 1766.   Parody of his Bertoldo, Ber-
        toldino e Cacasenno.   Schatz 1883
    Bertoldo, Argentina, 1751.   L. T. of his Bertoldo, Bertoldino
        e Cacasenno.   Schatz 1876
    Bertoldo, Bertoldino e Cacasenno, Venezia, 1749.   Schatz 1882
    Bertoldo, Bertoldino e Cacasenno—Bertoldus, Bertoldinus
        und Cacasennus (Bronsevico, 1750).   Schatz 1879
    Bertoldo in corte, Ferrara (1755).   L. T. of the above.   Schatz 1887

Ciampi, Legrenzio Vincenzo—Continued.

Bondepigen ved hoffet, Kjøbenhavn, 1776. Tr. of Le caprice amoureux ou Ninette à la cour. SCHATZ 2852

Le caprice amoureux, ou Ninette à la cour. Parody by Favart of his "Bertoldo, Bertoldino e Cacasenno." *See* Title catalogue.

The captive, pasticcio. *See* Title catalogue.

Catone in Utica, Venezia, 1757. SCHATZ 1884

Il chimico, Venezia, 1757. SCHATZ 1885

La clemenza di Tito, Reggio (1759). SCHATZ 1880

La favola de' tre gobbi. *See* Goldoni's Opere teatrali.

Gianguir, Venezia, 1760. SCHATZ 1881

Lionel and Clarissa, pasticcio. *See* Title catalogue.

Maid of the mill, pasticcio. *See* Title catalogue.

Il negligente, Venezia, 1749. SCHATZ 1886

Il negligente—Der nachlaessige, n. i., n. d. SCHATZ 1889

Ninette à la cour. A. T. Le caprice amoureux.

The school for fathers, pasticcio. *See* Lionel and Clarissa in Title catalogue.

The summer's tale, pasticcio. *See* Title catalogue.

Cifolelli, Giovanni.

L'Indienne, Paris, 1771. SCHATZ 1897

Cignani.

Il ritorno d'Angelica nell' Indie (Ottavio Tronsarelli, Drammi musicali, Roma, Francesco Corbelletti, 1632). ML 49.A2T7

Cimador, Giovanni Battista, 1761–1808.

Pimmalione, Venezia, 1790. SCHATZ 1903

Il ratto di Proserpina, Venezia (1791). SCHATZ 1902

Cimarosa, Domenico Nicola, 1749–1801.

See also Catalogue of 19th cent. librettos.

L'amante combattuto dalle donne di punto, Napoli, 1781. SCHATZ 1994

Li amanti comici o sia La famiglia in scompiglio, Torino (1797). SCHATZ 2003

L'amor costante (Lisboa, 1785). SCHATZ 1927

L'apparenza inganna o sia La villeggiatura, Napoli, 1784. SCHATZ 1980

L'apprensivo raggirato, Napoli, 1798. SCHATZ 1904

L'Arabo cortese, Napoli, 1776 (opera by Paisiello with arias by Cimarosa). SCHATZ 7665

Artaserse, Torino (1785). SCHATZ 1905

Artemisia regina di Caria, Napoli, 1797. SCHATZ 1990

La ballerina amante—Die verliebte taenzerin, Dresda, 1786. SCHATZ 1912

Il barone burlato, Napoli, 1784. Altered version of his Il pittore parigino with new music by Cipolla. SCHATZ 1979

La baronessa Stramba. *See his* Il credulo, Napoli, 1786 (Schatz 1977). SCHATZ 1985

Die bestrafte eifersucht, Berlin, 1794. Tr. of his Il marito disperato. SCHATZ 1943

Die beyden barons von Rocca Azura. Tr. of his I due baroni di Rocca Azura, Dresda, 1790. SCHATZ 1919

Cajo Mario, Genova (1782). SCHATZ 1991

Chi dell' altrui si veste, presto si spoglia, Napoli, 1783. ML 50.2.C42C3

Chi dell' altrui si veste, presto si spoglia, Napoli, 1787. SCHATZ 1913

La Circe, Milano (1783). SCHATZ 2005

Il convito—Das gastmahl, Dresda, 1783. SCHATZ 1915

Cimarosa, Domenico Nicola—Continued.

Il convito, Lisbona, 1796.	Schatz 1914
Il credulo con farsa La baronessa Stramba, Napoli, 1786.	Schatz 1977 and 1985
Il credulo con farsa L'impresario in angustie, Napoli, 1786.	Schatz 1916 and 1929
Le directeur dans l'embarras. Tr. of his L'impresario in angustie, Paris (Bruxelles) 1792.	ML 50.2.I5C3
La donna sempre al suo peggior s'appiglia, Napoli, 1785.	Schatz 1981
Le donne rivali, Roma, 1780.	ML 50.2.D616C3
Le donne rivali, Venezia (1780).	Schatz 2004
Die drey liebhaber. Tr. of his I tre amanti, Dresda, 1781.	Schatz 1976
I due baroni, Napoli, 1793. L. T. of the next entry.	Schatz 1978
I due baroni di Rocca Azzurra, Sinigaglia, 1787.	ML 50.2.D75C3
Li due baroni di Rocca Azurra (Lisbona, 1791).	Schatz 1918
I due baròni di Rocca Azura—Die beyden barons von Rocca Azura, Dresda, 1790.	Schatz 1919
I due supposti conti ossia Lo sposo senza moglie, Milano (1784)	Schatz 1920
I due supposti conti ossia Lo sposo senza moglie—Die vorgebildeten grafen oder Der braeutigam ohne braut, Dresda, 1787.	Schatz 1921
Il duello per complimento. A. T. of his I nemici generosi.	
Il duello per complimento, Venezia, Anno primo [1797]. L. T. of his I nemici generosi.	Schatz 2002
Entrepreneuren i knibe, Kjøbenhavn, 1795. Tr. of his L'impresario in angustie.	Schatz 1933
Il falegname, Mantova (1782)	ML 50.2.F147C4
Il falegname, Venezia, 1784.	Schatz 1922
Il falegname—Der tischler, Dresda, 1787.	Schatz 1923
La famiglia in scompiglio. A. T. of his Li amanti comici.	
Il fanatico burlato, Napoli, 1787.	Schatz 1924
Il fanatico per gli antichi Romani, Napoli, 1777.	Schatz 1982
La finta amalata, Lisbona, 1796.	ML 48.C6 iii
La Frascatana nobile, Napoli, 1776.	Schatz 1995
Das gastmahl. Tr. of his Il convito, Dresda, 1783.	Schatz 1915
Giannina e Bernardone—Hannchen und Bernardon, Dresda, 1785.	Schatz 1926
Giannina e Bernadone, Napoli, 1795.	ML 50.2.G33C3
Giulietta ed Armidoro—Julie und Armidor, Dresda, 1790. L. T. of his L'amor costante.	Schatz 1928
Giunio Bruto, Genova (1782).	Schatz 1992
Die grossmuethigen feinde. Tr. of his I nemici generosi, Dresda, 1797.	Schatz 1958
Hannchen und Bernardon. Tr. of his Giannina e Bernardone, Dresda, 1785.	Schatz 1926
Die heimlich geschlossene ehe. Tr. of his Il matrimonio segreto, Dresda, 1792.	Schatz 1948
L'impegno superato, Napoli, 1795.	Schatz 1996
L'impresario in angustie. See his Il credulo, Napoli, 1786 (Schatz 1916).	Schatz 1929
L'impresario in angustie—Der schauspiel direktor in der klemme, Dresda, 1794.	Schatz 1930
L'impresario in angustie ed Il convitato di pietra, Milano (1789).	Schatz 11755

Cimarosa, Domenico Nicola—Continued.

L'impresario in angustie, Lisbona, 1792.	ML 48.C6 II
L'impresario in angustie con farsa Il convitato di pietra, Napoli, 1793. (The second by Tritto.)	Schatz 10466
L'impresario in angustie ou Le directeur dans l'embarras, Paris (Bruxelles) 1792.	ML 50.2.I5C3
L'infedeltà fedele, Napoli, 1779.	Schatz 1936
L'infedeltà fedele—Treu in der untreue, Dresda, 1782.	Schatz 1937
L'Italiana in Londra, Roma, 1779.	ML 50.2.I8C2
L'Italiana in Londra—Die Italienerin zu London, Brunsvic, 1781.	Schatz 1939
L'Italiana in Londra, Napoli, 1794.	Schatz 1938
Die Italienerin zu London, Brunsvic, 1781. Tr. of his L'Italiana in Londra.	Schatz 1939
Die Italienerin zu London, Frankfurt am Mayn, 1783. Another Tr.	Schatz 1941
Die Italienerin zu London, Hamburg, 1789. Another Tr.	Schatz 1940
Julie und Armidor. Tr. of his Giuletta ed Armidoro, Dresda, 1790.	Schatz 1928
Il marito disperato, Napoli, 1785.	Schatz 1942
I matrimoni in ballo. See p. 29–51 of his I sdegni per amore, Napoli, 1776.	Schatz 1993
I matrimoni in ballo. A detached copy.	Schatz 1984
Il matrimonio segreto—Die heimlich geschlossene ehe, Dresda, 1792.	Schatz 1948
I nemici generosi o sia Il duello per complimento, Firenze, 1797.	Schatz 1957
I nemici generosi—Die grossmuethigen feinde, Dresda, 1797.	Schatz 1958
L'Olimpiade, Lucca (1784).	Schatz 1960
L'Olimpiade, Vicenza, 1794.	Schatz 11686
Der onkel aus Amsterdam, Riga und Mitau, 1796. Tr. of his Il pittore parigino.	Schatz 1970
Gli Orazi e i Curiazi, Venezia (1797).	Schatz 1961
Oreste, Napoli, 1783.	Schatz 1966
Der Pariser mahler. Tr. of Cimarosa's Il pittor parigino, Dresda, 1782.	Schatz 1969
Penelope (Livorno, 1795).	Schatz 1967
Il pittor parigino—Der Pariser mahler, Dresda, 1782.	Schatz 1969
Il pittor parigino, Lisbona, 1794.	ML 50.2.P46C3
Il ritorno di D. Calandrino, Roma, 1778.	ML 50.2.R5C3
Der schauspieldirektor in der klemme. Tr. of his L'impresario in angustie, Dresda, 1794.	Schatz 1930
I sdegni per amore, Napoli, 1776.	Schatz 1993
Lo sposo senza moglie. A. T. of his I due supposti conti.	
Lo sposo senza moglie, Treviso, 1792. L. T. of his I due supposti conti.	Schatz 2006
Le stravaganze del conte, Napoli, 1772.	Schatz 1986
Der tischler. Tr. of his Il falegname, Dresda, 1787.	Schatz 1923
I Traci amanti, Torino, 1794.	ML 50.2.T73C2
Le trame deluse, Vienna (1787).	Schatz 1972
Le trame deluse—Die vereitelten raenke, Dresda, 1788.	Schatz 1973
I tre amanti, Firenze, 1777.	Schatz 1975
I tre amanti—Die drey liebhaber, Dresda, 1781.	Schatz 1976
Treu in der untreue. Tr. of his L'infideltà fedele, Dresda, 1782.	Schatz 1937

Cimarosa, Domenico Nicola—Continued.

Gli Turchi amanti, Lisbona, 1796. L. T. of his I Traci amanti. Schatz 1999

Die vereitelten raenke. Tr. of his Le trame deluse, Dresda,
1788. Schatz 1973

Die verliebte taenzerin. Tr. of his La ballerina amante,
Dresda, 1786. Schatz 1912

La villana riconosciuta, Napoli, 1791. Schatz 1987

La villeggiatura. A. T. of his L'apparenza inganna.

Die vorgeblichen grafen. Tr. of his I due supposti conti,
Dresda, 1787. Schatz 1921

Volodomiro, Torino (1787). Schatz 2000

Cingoni, Giovanni.

La donna giudice e parte, Venezia, 1746. Schatz 2009

La scolara fatta maestra—Die zur meisterin gewordene schue-
lerin, Potsdam, 1749. Schatz 2010

Ciochetti, Pietro Vincenzo.

La clemenza di Tito, Genova, 1736. Schatz 2011

Cipolla, Francesco.

Il barone burlato, Napoli, 1784. New music for this altered
version of Cimarosa's Il pittore parigino. Schatz 1979

Il Polifemo, Napoli, 1786. Schatz 2013

Telemaco nella isola di Calipso, Napoli, 1785. Schatz 2012

Clarke, Jeremiah, *d.* 1707.

The four seasons or Love in every age. Interlude in The island
princess, London, 1724. Longe 75

The world in the moon, London, 1697 (with D. Purcell). Longe 180

Clayton, Thomas, *ca.* 1670–1730.

Arsinoe, queen of Cyprus, London, 1705. ML 50.2.A78

Arsinoe, queen of Cyprus, London, 1707. Longe 106 and
177

Clerico, Francesco.

Lo sposo burlato, ballet. *See* Caruso's Il vecchio burlato.

Zemira e Azor, ballet. *See* Andreozzi's Giovanna d'Arco.

Zemira e Azor, ballet. *See* Caruso's Il vecchio burlato.

Zorei e Ozai, ballet. *See* G. Giordani's Erifile.

Cocchi, Gioacchino, 1720–1804.

Adelaide, Roma, 1743. Schatz 2052

Amelia, pasticcio. *See* Title catalogue.

Andromeda, Torino (1755). Schatz 2051

Bertholde à la ville. *See* Title catalogue.

Le caprice amoureux ou Ninette à la cour. *See* Title catalogue.

The captive, pasticcio. *See* Title catalogue.

Les Chinois. *See* Title catalogue.

Daphne and Amintor, pasticcio. *See* Title catalogue.

Demofonte, Venezia, 1754. Schatz 2042

Le donne vindicate, Venezia, 1751. Schatz 2043

L'Elisa, Napoli (1744). Schatz 2038

Emira, Venezia, 1756. Schatz 2032

Farsetta per musica, Roma, 1751. ML 50.2.F22C7

Farsetta per musica, Spoleti (1758) (same text). ML 50.2.F22C72

La Gismonda, Napoli, 1750. Schatz 2039

L'ipocondrico risanato, Roma, 1746. ML 50.2.I67C6

Cocchi, Gioacchino—Continued.

Love in the city, pasticcio. *See* Title catalogue.

La maestra, Venezia, 1754.   SCHATZ 2033

La maestra di buon gusto. A. T. of his La scuola moderna.

La maestra di scuola—Die schulmeisterin, Berlino, 1763.
     L. T. of his La maestra.   SCHATZ 2034

Maid of the mill, pasticcio. *See* the Title catalogue.

La mascherata, Venezia, 1751. *See* this under Galuppi.   SCHATZ 3487

Li matti per amore, Venezia, 1754.   SCHATZ 2035

Li matti per amore—Die narren für liebe, Berlino, 1764.   SCHATZ 2036

Merope, Napoli, 1748.   SCHATZ 2049

Die narren für liebe. Tr. of his Li matti per amore, Berlino,
     1764.   SCHATZ 2036

Nitocri, Torino, 1751.   SCHATZ 2050

Le nozze di Monsù Fagotto, Roma, 1754.   ML 50.2.N7C6

Il pazzo glorioso, Venezia, 1753.   SCHATZ 2053

Il pazzo glorioso, Monaco (1758).   SCHATZ 2037

La Rosmira fedele, Venezia (1753).   SCHATZ 2044

La scaltra governatrice. L. T. of his La maestra.

Die schulmeisterin. Tr. of his La maestra di scuola, Berlino,
     1763.   SCHATZ 2034

La scuola moderna o sia La maestra di buon gusto, Venezia,
     1748. L. T. of his La maestra.   SCHATZ 2048

Semiramide riconosciuta, Venezia, 1753.   SCHATZ 2045

La serva bacchettona, Napoli, 1749.   SCHATZ 2040

Sesostri rè d'Egitto, Napoli, 1752.   SCHATZ 2046

Sesostri re d'Egitto, Venezia, 1756.   SCHATZ 11687

Siroe, Venezia (1750).   SCHATZ 2041

The summer's tale, pasticcio. *See* Title catalogue.

Tamerlano, Venezia (1754) (first act only; second act by
     Pescetti; third act by both).   SCHATZ 2054

Zoe, Venezia (1756).   SCHATZ 2047

Coignet, Horace, 1736–1821.

Pigmalion, n. i., 1772 (in part by Rousseau).   ML 50.2.P41R7

Pygmalion, Genève (Lyon) 1786 (in part by Rousseau).   SCHATZ 2095

Pygmalion, Mannheim, 1778. Tr. of the above.   SCHATZ 2096

Colasse, Pascal, 1649–1709.

Achille et Polixene (Amsterdam) 1687 (1st act by Lully).   ML 49.A2L9

— same, Amsterdam, 1701.   ML 50.2.A25L9

Achille et Polixene (Recueil général des opéra, t. iii, Paris,
     1703) (first act by Lully).   SCHATZ 5781

Astrée (Amsterdam) 1692.   ML 50.2.A86C6

Astrée (Recueil général des opéra, Paris, 1703, t. iv.)   SCHATZ 2097

Ballet dansé a Ville-Neuve-Saint-George (Recueil général des
     opéra, Paris, 1703, t. iv).   SCHATZ 2104

Ballet des saisons, Amsterdam, 1696 (with Lully)   ML 52.2.B115

Ballet des saisons (Recueil général des opéra, t. v., Paris,
     1703) (with music by Lully).   SCHATZ 5782

Canente (Recueil général des opéra, Paris, 1703, t. vii).   SCHATZ 2098

Enée et Lavinie (Amsterdam) 1696.   ML 50.2.E4C6

Enée et Lavinie (Recueil général des opéra, Paris, 1703,
     t. iv).   SCHATZ 2099

Jason ou La toison d'or (Recueil général des opéra, Paris, 1703,
     t. v).   SCHATZ 2100

Colasse, Pascal—Continued.
La naissance de Vénus (Recueil général des opéra, Paris, t. v,
    1703).   Schatz 2101
Polixène et Pirrhus (Recueil général des opéra, Paris, t. ix,
    1710).   Schatz 2102
Telemaque, pasticcio.   *See* Title catalogue.
Thetis et Pelée, Paris, 1699 [!].   ML 50.2.T48C6
Thetis et Pelée (Amsterdam) 1689.   ML 50.2.T48C62
Thetis et Pelée (Recueil général des opéra, Paris, 1703, t. iii).   Schatz 2103
La toison d'or.   A. T. of his Jason.

Coleman, Charles, *d.* 1664.
The siege of Rhodes, London, 1663 (with H. Lawes, Cook,
    Locke, and Hudson).   ML 50.2.S62

Colin de Blamont, François, 1690–1760.
Endymion (Recueil général des opéra, Paris, 1739, t. xv).   Schatz 1066
Les festes grecques et romaines (Recueil général des opéra,
    Paris, 1734, t. xiii).   Schatz 1067

Colla, Giuseppe, *ca.* 1730–1806.
Andromeda, Torino (1772).   Schatz 2106
Cajus Fabricius, Mannheim (1760).   Interpolated arias in
    Jommelli's Cajo Fabricio.   Schatz 4846
Didone, Torino (1773).   Schatz 2107
Enea in Cartagine, Torino (1770).   Schatz 2109
Sicotencal, Pavia (1776).   Schatz 2110
Uranio e Erasitea, Parma (1773).   Schatz 2108
Vologeso, Venezia, 1770.   Schatz 2111

Colletti, Agostino Bonaventura, 1683–1752.
L'Ifigenia, Venezia, 1707.   Schatz 2112
Prassitele in Gnido, Venezia, 1700.   Schatz 2113
Paride in Ida, Venezia, 1706 (with Carlo Manza).   Schatz 5917

Colli, Antonio.
La finta contessina, Roma, 1751.   ML 50.2.F433C7

Colombo, Antonio.
Cesare in Egitto (Venezia, 1744).   Schatz 2115

Colonna, Giovanni Paolo, *d.* 1695.
Le contese di Pallade e Venere sopra il bando d'Amore, Bo-
    logna [16—].   ML 50.2.C66C6

Conforto, Niccolò.
Adriano in Siria—Adriano en Syria, Madrid (1757).   Schatz 2121
Nitteti.   *See* Metastasio's Opere.

Conradi, Johann Melchior.
Freud- und Liesbes-streitt, Oettingen, 1699.   Schatz 2181
Der koenigliche printz aus Pohlen, Sigismundus, oder Das
    menschliche leben wie ein traum (Hamburg, 1693).   Schatz 2179
Sieg der schoenheit, Hamburg (1722).   L. T. (with some new
    music by Telemann) of his Der grosse koenig der afri-
    kanischen Wenden Gensericus als Roms und Karthagos
    ueberwinder.   Schatz 2180

Conti, Francesco Bartolomeo, 1681–1732.

Alba Cornelia (Bresslau, 1726). SCHATZ 2203

Alessandro in Sidone, Vienna d'Austria (1721). SCHATZ 2192

Alessandro in Sidone—Alexander in Sidon, Wolffenbüttel (1726). SCHATZ 2193

L'ammalato immaginario, Perugia (1727). SCHATZ 2204

Cloris und Tirsis—Clori e Tirsi (Hamburg, 1719). Tr. and L. T. of his I satiri in Arcadia. SCHATZ 2196

Don Chisciotte in Sierra Morena, Vienna d'Austria (1719). SCHATZ 2194

Don Quixotte in dem Mohrengebuerge, Hamburg, 1722. Tr. of his Don Chisciotte in Sierra Morena. SCHATZ 2195

Il finto Policare, Vienna d'Austria (1716). SCHATZ 2200

Grilletta e Pimpinone. *See* p. 69–80 of his Sesostri, rè di Egitto, Vienna (1717). SCHATZ 2198

L'Issipile, Vienna d'Austria (1732). SCHATZ 2205

Penelope, Wien (1724). SCHATZ 2202

Sesostri, rè di Egitto, Vienna d'Austria (1717). SCHATZ 2197

I satiri in Arcadia. O. T. of his Cloris und Tirsis—Clori e Tirsi.

Il trionfo dell' amore & della costanza—Der triumph der liebe und bestaendigkeit, Hamburg (1718). SCHATZ 2199

Der verstellte Policare (Bresslau, 1726). Tr. of his Il finto Policare. SCHATZ 2201

Vespetta e Milo, Dresde, 1717. (The first two of the three intermezzi by Al. Scarlatti.) SCHATZ 9522

Vespetta e Milo, Dresde, 1717. Same, but 19 cm., unpaged, forming part of libretto of Antonio Lotti's Giove in Argo. SCHATZ 5719

Conti, Giuseppe.

Attalo rè di Bitinia, Napoli, 1752. SCHATZ 2206

Conti, Niccolò.

L'Ippolita, Napoli (1733). SCHATZ 2207

L'Olindo, Napoli, 1753 (partly by Capranica). SCHATZ 2208

Cook(e), Henry, *d.* 1672.

The siege of Rhodes, London, 1663 (with H. Lawes, Cook, Locke, Coleman, and Hudson). ML 50.2.S62

Cooke, Benjamin, 1734–1793.

The noble peasant. *See* Title catalogue.

Coperario, Giovanni. *Italianized name of* John Cooper, d. 1627.

The Lords maske. *See* A relation of the late royall entertainment.

Coppola, Giuseppe.

L'amor vendicativo, Napoli (1783). SCHATZ 2212

Il ravvedimento del figliuol prodigo, Napoli (1798). SCHATZ 2211

Cordans (Cornans), Bartolomeo (Bortolamio), *d.* 1757.

La generosità di Tiberio, Venezia, 1729 (acts I–II by Lapis). SCHATZ 5431

Ormisda, Venezia, 1728. SCHATZ 2226

La Rodelinda, Venezia (1731). SCHATZ 2227

Romilda, Venezia (1731). SCHATZ 2229

La Silvia, Venezia (1730). SCHATZ 2228

Cordicelli, Giovanni.

La felicità di Partenope, Roma, 1747. ML 48.M2A

Corelli, Arcangelo, 1653–1713.
The princess of Tarento, pasticcio. *See* Title catalogue.
Tom Jones, pasticcio. *See* Title catalogue.

Corradini, Francesco.
Il Polifemo (Madrid, 1748) (second act; first by Corselli,
third by Mele). Schatz 2253

Corrette, Michel.
Les audiences de Thalie (Le théâtre de la foire, Paris, 1737,
t. ix, 2). ML 48.L2X
L'isle du mariage (Le théâtre de la foire, Paris, 1737). ML 48.L48X
Le père rival (Le théâtre de la foire, Paris, 1737, t. ix, 2). ML 48.L2X
Le retour de l'opéra comique au faubourg S. Germain (Le
théâtre de la foire, Paris, 1737, t. ix, 2). ML 48.L2X

Corri, Domenico, 1746–1825.
Fontainebleau. *See* Title catalogue.

Corselli, Francesco.
Il Polifemo (Madrid, 1748) (first act; second by Corradini,
third by Mele). Schatz 2253

Corsi, Jacopo, *d.* 1604.
La Dafne, Firenze, 1600. Schatz 7918

Corteccia, Francesco.
Descrizione dell' apparato . . . [Psiche ed Amore, inter-
medii], Fiorenza, 1566 (with Striggio). ML 52.2.D3
Descrizione de gl'intermedii . . . [Psiche ed Amore], Firenze, 1593 (with Striggio). PQ

Cortona, Antonio.
Amor indovino, Venezia, 1726. Schatz 2263
L'Egeste, Venezia (1727). Schatz 2265
Ezio, Verona (1740) (partly by others). Schatz 2264
Farnace, Brusselle (1729). ML 50.2.F21C6

Costanzi, Giovanni.
L'amor generoso, Roma (1727). Schatz 2276
Carlo Magno, Roma, 1729. Schatz 2277

Courcelle, Francesco.
Nino, Venezia (1732). Schatz 2283
Venere placata, Venezia, 1731. Schatz 2284

Courteville, Raphael.
The comical history of Don Quixote, London, 1729. *See* Title
catalogue.

Cousin Jacques. *See* Beffroy de Reigny, Louis Abel.

Cousser. *See* Kusser.

Crippa, Luigi.
Le confusioni per la somiglianza, Milano (1792). Schatz 2290

Cristiani, Stefano.
L'amante democratico, Torino (1799). Schatz 2293
La città nuova, Milano (1798). Schatz 2292
La clemenza di Tito, Camerino (1757). Schatz 2291

Crivelli (Crivello), Arcangelo.
La finta Savia, Venetia, 1643 (only partly by him, Merula and
Ferrari, mostly by Laurenzi).   Schatz 5474

Croes, Henri de, 1758–1842.
Der zauberer, Regensburg, 1781.   Schatz 2294

Croscino, Niccolò, *same as* Logroscino, Nicola.

Curcio (Curci), Giuseppe Maria.
See also Catalogue of 19th cent. librettos.
Amore e Psiche, ballet. *See* Robuschi's Briseide.
La conquista di Granata, Firenze, 1796. L. T. of his La presa
di Granata.   Schatz 2306
Le convulsioni. *See* p. 26–48 of G. Palomba's librettos
Amor non ha riguardi e La convulsioni, Napoli, 1787. Schatz 2299
Emira e Zopiro, Firenze, 1795.   Schatz 2308
I ladri di spirito, Napoli, 1769.   Schatz 2310
I matrimonii per inganno, Napoli, 1779.   Schatz 2302
La Nitteti, Napoli, 1783.   Schatz 2300
Le nozze a dispetto, Napoli, 1797.   Schatz 2303
La presa di Granata (Livorno, 1795).   Schatz 2305
Solimano, Torino (1782).   Schatz 2301
Il trionfo di Scipione in Cartagine, Firenze, 1795.   Schatz 2307

Cziak. *Better known as* Schack.

Dalayrac, Nicolas, 1753–1809.
See also Catalogue of 19th cent. librettos.
—Adolphe et Clara ou Les deux prisonniers, Paris, an VII (1799). ML 50.2.A33D2
—Alexis, ou L'erreur d'un bon père, Paris, 1798.   ML 50.2.A52D2
—L'amant statue, Paris, 1786.   ML 50.2.A64D2
—Ambroise ou Voilà ma journée, Paris, an VII [1798–99].   Schatz 2328
Azémia, ou Les sauvages, Paris, 1787.   ML 50.2.A98D2
Azémia, ou Les sauvages, Toulouse, 1787.   ML 50.2.A98D22
Azémia, ou Les sauvages, Paris, 1788.   ML 48.M2L
Die beyden kleinen Savoyarden, Leipzig, 1795. Tr. of his
Les deux petits Savoyards.   Schatz 2338
Camilla ossia La sepolta viva, Lisbona, 1799. Tr. of his Ca-
mille ou Le souterrain.   Schatz 2332
Camille of Het onderaardsch gewelf, Amsterdam, 1796. Tr. of
his Camille ou Le souterrain.   Schatz 2392
—Camille ou Le souterrain, Paris, 1791.   ML 50.2.C25D2
Camille ou Le souterrain, Paris, 1793.   ML 50.2.C25D22
Le château de Montenero. A. T. of his Léon.
—Les deux petits Savoyards, Hambourg, 1795.   ML 50.2.D49D2
Les deux petits Savoyards, Hamburg (179–).   Schatz 11688
Les deux prisonniers. A. T. of his Adolphe et Clara.
—Les deux tuteurs, Paris, 1784.   ML 50.2.D51D2
Les deux tuteurs, Paris, 1785.   ML 50.2.D51D22
Os dois rapazes Saboyanos, Lisboa, 1796. Tr. of his Les deux
petits Savoyards.   Schatz 2339
—La dot, Paris, 1784.   ML 50.2.D63D2
La dot, Paris, 1786.   ML 50.2.D63D22
—L'éclipse totale, Paris, 1782.   Schatz 2342
L'élève de l'amour. A. T. of his Sargines.

Dalayrac, Nicolas—Continued.

—L'enfance de Jean Jacques Rousseau, Paris, Seconde année
(1794).   Schatz 2343

L'erreur d'un bon père. A. T. of his Alexis.

—La famille américaine, Blois, an IV (1796).   ML 50.2.F17D2

La folle par amour. A. T. of his Nina.

—La leçon ou La tasse de glaces, Paris, an V (1797).   ML 50.2.L23D2

—Léon ou Le château de Montenero, Paris, an 7 (1798).   ML 50.2.L26D2

The love distracted maid. Tr. A. T. of his Nina.

—La maison isolée ou Le vieillard des Vosges, Paris, an cinquième (1797).   Schatz 2363

—Marianne, Paris (1796).   ML 50.2.M45D2

Marianne, Paris (? 1796).   ML 50.2.M45D21

De minnaer standbeeld, Amsterdam, 1794. Tr. of his L'amant
statue.   Schatz 2388

—Nina ou La folle par amour, Paris, 1788.   ML 50.2.N4D2

Nina or The love distracted maid, London, 1787. Tr. of
above.   Longe 99

Nina oder Wahnsinn aus liebe, Hamburg, 1787. d'Arien's Tr.   Schatz 2367

— Same title, Mainz, 1787. Schmieder's Tr.   Schatz 2368

— Same title, Berlin, 1790. André's Tr.   Schatz 2369

Nina oder Was vermag die liebe nicht, Berlin, 1789. Another Tr.   Schatz 2370

Het onderaardsch gewelf. A. T. of his Camille.

—La pauvre femme, Paris, An V [1796–97]   ML 50.2.P295D2

—Philipp und Georgette, Hamburg, 1798. Tr. of his Philippe
et Georgette.   Schatz 2372

Raollo, signore di Crequi, Lisbona, 1795. Tr. of his Raoul,
sire de Créqui.   Schatz 2376

—Raoul, sire de Créqui, Paris, 1790.   ML 50.2.R24D3

Reinald, Hamburg, 1790. Tr. of his Renaud d'Ast.   Schatz 2378

—Renaud d'Ast, Paris, Prault, 1788.   ML 50.2.R29D21

Renaud d'Ast, Paris, Brunet, 1788.   ML 50.2R39D22

Renaud d'Ast (Copenhague, 1793). Tr. of the above.   Schatz 2379

Rudolph von Creki, Riga, 1792. Tr. of his Raoul, sire de
Créqui.   Schatz 2374

—Sargines, ou L'élève de l'amour, Paris, 1789.   Schatz 2380

Les sauvages. A. T. of his Azémia.

La sepolta viva. A. T. of his Camilla.

—La soirée orageuse, Paris, 1791.   ML 50.2.S67D2

Le souterrain. A. T. of his Camille.

La tasse de glaces. A. T. of his La leçon.

Le vieillard des Vosges. A. T. of his La maison isolée.

Voilà ma journée. A. T. of his Ambroise.

Die wilden, Frankfurt am Main, 1791. Tr. of his Azémia.   Schatz 2371

Die zween Savoyarden, Wien, 1792. Tr. of his Les deux
petits Savoyards.   Schatz 2340

Die zwey vormuender, Hamburg, 1788. Tr. of his Les deux
tuteurs.   Schatz 2341

Dalindo Stinfalido, *Accademico Filarmonico.*

Chi è cagion del suo mal, pianga se stesso, Firenze, 1785.   Schatz 11313

Danzi, Franz, 1763–1826.

See also Catalogue of 19th cent. librettos.

Der quasi-mann, Muenchen, 1789.   Schatz 2410

Darcis (D'Arcis), François Joseph.
　Le bal masqué, Nouv. éd., Paris, 1773.　　　　　　　ML 50.2.B21G7
　La fausse peur, Paris, 1775.　　　　　　　　　　　SCHATZ 2411

Dardespin, Melchior.　*See* Ardespin.

Dauvergne, Antoine, 1713–1797.
　L'amour enjoué.　*See* Fragments, composés . . . de l'acte
　　de . . .
　La coquette trompée, n. i., n. d. (Theatre de M. Favart, Paris,
　　1763–77, t. i).　　　　　　　　　　　　　　　　ML 49.A2F1
　Eglé (Journal des spectacles, Paris, t. ii, 1766).　　　ML 48.J7
　Enée et Lavinie, Paris, 1758.　　　　　　　　　　　ML 50.2.E4D2
　La sibille (Paris) 1770.　　　　　　　　　　　　　ML 50.2.S59D2
　Le triomphe de Flore (Journal des spectacles, Paris, 1766,
　　t. ii).　　　　　　　　　　　　　　　　　　　ML 48.J7
　Les troqueurs, n. i., n. d.　　　　　　　　　　　　ML 50.2.T84
　Les troqueurs (Vadé, Oeuvres, A la Haye, 1760, t. ii).　ML 49.A2V2

De Franchi.　*See* Franchi, Carlo.

Della Maria, Pierre Antoine Dominique, 1769–1800.
　See also Catalogue of 19th cent. librettos.
　Der arrestant, Frankfurt am Main, 1799.　Tr. of his Le prison-
　　nier.　　　　　　　　　　　　　　　　　　　SCHATZ 2486
　The castle of Sorrento, London, 1799.　English adaptation
　　with new music by Attwood of his Le prisonnier.　LONGE 256
　Chi vuol non puole, Vicenza (1795).　　　　　　　SCHATZ 2493
　La guerra aperta.　A. T. of his Il matrimonio per scomessa.
　Il matrimonio per scomessa ossia La guerra aperta, Venezia,
　　1795.　　　　　　　　　　　　　　　　　　　SCHATZ 2494
　L'opéra comique, Paris, an vi (1797–98).　　　　　ML 50.2.O6D2
　L'opéra comique, Toulouse, an vii (1798–99).　　　ML 50.2.O6D22
　The prisoner or The resemblance, London, 1799.　Tr. of his
　　Le prisonnier ou La ressemblance.　　　　　　　LONGE 254
　Le prisonnier ou La ressemblance, Amsterdam, 1798.　SCHATZ 2485
　La rencontre.　A. T. of his Le vieux château.
　Le vieux château ou La rencontre, Paris, an vi (1798).　ML 50.2.V49D2

Deller, Florian Johann, *ca.* 1730–1774.
　Amore vincitore dell' indifferenza, ballet.　(If not by him,
　　then composed by Rudolph.)　*See* Jommelli's L'isola dis-
　　abitata.
　Eigensinn und launen der liebe, Frankfurt und Leipzig, 1783.
　　Tr. of his Le contese per amore.　　　　　　　SCHATZ 2495
　Il maestro di cappella (Vienna, 1771).　L. T. of his Orazio.　SCHATZ 2496
　La morte di Licomede—La mort de Licomède, ballet.　*See*
　　Jommelli's Demofoonte.
　Orfeo ed Euridice—Orpheé et Euridice, ballet.　*See* Jom-
　　melli's La Didone abbandonata.
　Il riconoscimento inaspettato, ballet.　(If not by him, then
　　composed by Rudolph.)　*See* Jommelli's L'isola disabi-
　　tata.

Dem(m)ler, Johann Michael,
　Dasius ein junger blutzeug Jesu Christi (Augsburg, 1784)　SCHATZ 2504
　Der entsatz Bethuliens.　*See* his Judith, 1797.
　Ganymed in Vulkans schmiede, Augsburg (1797).　SCHATZ 2505

Dem(m)ler, Johann Michael—Continued.

Jakob und Benjamin, Augsburg (1784).   Schatz 2506

Judith oder Der entsatz Bethuliens (Augsburg, 1780).   Schatz 2507

Nilus, der grossmuetige veraechter der welt (Augsburg, 1785).   Schatz 2508

Desaugiers, Marc' Antoine, 1742–1793

Les deux sylphes, Paris, 1781.   ML 50.2.D5D2

Desbrosses, Robert, *ca.* 1719–1799.

Les deux cousines ou La bonne amie, Bruxelles, 1764.   Schatz 2528

Les deux sœurs rivales, Paris, 1762.   ML 50.2.D495D2

Deshayes, Prosper Didier.

Zelia, Paris, 1793.   ML 50.2.Z33D2

Desmarets, Henri, 1662–1741.

Ballet des Amours de Momus, Amsterdam, 1696.   ML 52.2.A4D2

Les amours de Momus (Recueil général des opera, t. v, Paris,
    1703).   Schatz 2529

Circe, Amsterdam, 1695.   ML 50.2.C5D2

Circé (Recueil général des opera, t. v, Paris, 1703).   Schatz 2530

Didon, *ibidem*, t. iv, 1703.   Schatz 2531

Les festes galantes, *ibidem*, t. vi, 1703.   Schatz 2532

Iphigénie en Tauride, *ibidem*, t. viii, 1706 (partly by Campra).   Schatz 2537

Renaud, *ibidem*, t. xiii, 1734.   Schatz 2533

Téagene et Cariclée, Amsterdam, 1695.   ML 50.2.T3D3

Téagène et Cariclée (Recueil général des opéra, t. v, Paris,
    1703).   Schatz 2534

Telemaque, pasticcio.   *See* Title catalogue.

Venus et Adonis (Amsterdam) 1699.   ML 50.2.V3D2

Vénus et Adonis (Recueil général des opera, t. vi, Paris, 1703).   Schatz 2535

Venus et Adonis—Venus und Adonis (Hamburg, 1725).   Schatz 2536

Desormery, Leopold Bastien, *ca.* 1740–1810.

Myrtil et Lycoris (Paris) 1778.   ML 50.2.M92D2

Destouches, André Cardinal, 1672–1749.

Amadis de Grèce, Amsterdam, 1699.   ML 50.2.A595D2

—— (Recueil général des opéra, t. vi, Paris, 1703).   Schatz 2543

Amadis de Grèce, Lyon, 1742.   Schatz 2543A

Callirhoé (Recueil général des opera, t. x, Paris, 1714).   Schatz 2544

Le carnival et la folie, *ibidem*, t. viii, 1706.   Schatz 2545

Les élémens, n. i., n. d. (with Lalande).   ML 52.2.E4

Les élémens (Recueil général des opéra, t. xiii, Paris, 1734)
    (with Lalande).   Schatz 5379

Issé, *ibidem*, t. vi, 1703.   Schatz 2546

Issé, *ibidem*, t. ix, 1710.   Schatz 2547

Issé, Lyon, 1749.   Schatz 2547A

Issé (Paris) 1773 (with alterations by Berton).   ML 50.2.I75D2

Marthesie première reine des Amazones (Recueil général des
    opera, t. vi, Paris, 1703).   Schatz 2548

Omphale, *ibidem*, t. vii, 1703.   Schatz 2549

Omphale, Paris, 1752.   Schatz 2549A

Sémiramis (Recueil général des opera, t. xii, Paris, 1734).   Schatz 2550

Les stratagêmes de l'amour, *ibidem*, t. xiv, 1734.   Schatz 2551

Télémaque, *ibidem*, t. xi, Paris, 1720.   Schatz 2252

Devienne, François, 1759–1803.

   See also Catalogue of 19th cent. librettos.

     Les comédiens ambulans, Paris, an vii (1798–99).   ML 50.2.C62D2

     Liebe wagt alles, Hamburg, 1798. Tr. of his Les visitan-
       dines.   SCHATZ 2556

     Les visitandines, Paris, 1792.   ML 50.2.V63D3

     De visitandines, Amsteldam, 1796. Tr. of Les visitandines.   SCHATZ 2563

Dezède, Nicolas, 1740?–1792. (*Sometimes called* Desaides, Des
   Aides, etc.).

     Alexis et Justine, Toulouse, 1785.   ML 50.2.A53D3

     Auguste et Théodore, ou, Le deux pages, Paris, 1790.   SCHATZ 2525

     Blaise et Babet ou La suite des Trois fermiers, Paris, 1784.   SCHATZ 2514

     Cécile, Paris, 1781.   SCHATZ 2516

     Les deux pages. A. T. of his Auguste et Théodore.

     Die drey paechter, Wien, 1785. Tr. of his Les trois fermiers. SCHATZ 2524

     L'erreur d'un moment ou La suite de Julie, Paris, 1773 (63 p.). YUDIN PQ

     L'erreur d'un moment ou La suite de Julie, Paris, 1773 (39 p.). SCHATZ 2517

     La fête de la cinquantaine, Paris, 1796.   SCHATZ 2527

     Julie, Paris, 1773.   SCHATZ 2520

     Julie, Frankfurt am Mayn, 1774. Tr. of the above.   SCHATZ 2521

     Julie, Paris, 1775.   YUDIN PQ

     Der kurze irrthum, n. i., 1790. Tr. of his L'erreur d'un mo-
       ment.   SCHATZ 2518

     Péronne sauvée, Paris, 1783.   SCHATZ 2526

     Die reue vor der that, Frankfurt und Leipzig, 1783. Tr. of his
       L'erreur d'un moment.   SCHATZ 2519

     La suite de Julie. *See his* L'erreur d'un moment.

     La suite des trois fermiers. *See his* Blaise et Babet.

     Toeffel und Dortchen, Hamburg, 1788. Tr. of his Blaise et
       Babet.   SCHATZ 2515

     Les trois fermiers, Paris, 1777.   ML 50.2.T83D2

     Les trois fermiers, Nouv. éd., Paris, 1781.   ML 50.2.T83D3

     Les trois fermiers, Paris, 1782.   SCHATZ 2523

     Was einem recht, ist dem andern billig, Frankfurt und Leip-
       zig, 1783. Tr. of his Julie.   SCHATZ 2522

Dibdin, Charles, 1745–1814.

   See also Catalogue of 19th cent. librettos.

     Amelia, London, 1771 (altered from The summer's tale)
       (pasticcio, other composers: Piccinni, Potenza, Cocchi,
       etc.).   LONGE 298

     Annette and Lubin, London, 1778.   LONGE 102

     The captive, London, 1769 (and others, a pasticcio).   LONGE 37

     The Chelsea prisoner, London, 1779.   LONGE 164

     A Christmas tale, London, 1774.   LONGE 16

     The cobler or A wife of ten thousand, London, 1774 (partly
       ballad opera).   LONGE 32

     Damon and Phillida, London, 1768.   LONGE 322

     The deserter, London, 1773. Additional music for his Tr. of
       Monsigny's Le déserteur.   LONGE 13

     The deserter (Collection of the most esteemed farces, Edin-
       burgh, 1792, t. iv).   SCHATZ 11753D

     The deserter, New York, 1787.   ML 50.6.D36

     The deserter of Naples. *See* Title catalogue.

Dibdin, Charles—Continued.

The Ephesian matron, London, 1769.	Longe 306
The Ephesian matron (Collection of the most esteemed farces, Edinburgh, 1792, t. vi).	Schatz 11753F
A fairy tale, London, 1777 (with M. Arne, Burney, and others).	Longe 243
Favourite songs . . . London (ca. 1790).	Longe 214
The first of August. A. T. of his The waterman.	
The frolics of fancy. A. T. of his A match for a widow.	
The Graces, London, 1782.	Longe 256
Harlequin everywhere. A. T. of his The mirror.	
Harlequin traveller. A. T. of his The touchstone.	
Harvest-home, London, 1787.	Longe 99
He wou'd if he cou'd or An old fool worse than any, London, 1771.	Longe 251
He would if he cou'd or An old fool worse than any (Collection of the most esteemed farces, Edinburgh, 1792, t. v).	Schatz 11753E
Liberty-hall or A test of good fellowship, London, 1785.	Longe 95
Lionel and Clarissa, London, 1768 (partly by other composers. See Title catalogue).	Longe 14
Love in the city, 2d ed., London, 1767 (largely selected). Became better known as The romp.	Longe 32
The marriage act, London, 1781 (reduced version of his The islanders).	Longe 91
A match for a widow or The frolics of fancy, London, 1788.	Longe 110
The metamorphoses, London, 1776.	Longe 214
The mirror or Harlequin everywhere, London, 1779.	Longe 102
An old fool worse than any. A. T. of his He wou'd if he cou'd.	
The padlock, London (1768).	Longe 46
The padlock (Collection of the most esteemed farces, Edinburgh, 1792, t. iii).	Schatz 11753
Plymouth in an uproar, 3d ed., London, 1779.	Longe 153
Poor Vulcan, London, 1778.	Longe 87
The quaker, London, 1777.	Longe 87
The recruiting serjeant, London, 1770.	Longe 37
The recruiting serjeant (Collection of the most esteemed farces, Edinburgh, 1792).	Schatz 11753F
The romp, London, 1786.	Longe 97
The romp (Collection of the most esteemed farces, Edinburgh, 1792, t. vi).	Schatz 11753F
Rose and Colin, London, 1778.	Longe 87
The school for fathers or Lionel and Clarissa, London, 1791 (J. Bell, British theatre, London, 1791–97, t. 1). Rev. version of his (and others') Lionel and Clarissa. See this in Title catalogue.	PR 1241.B4
The seraglio, London, 1776 (partly by Arnold).	Longe 124
The seraglio, airs, chorusses, London, 1776.	ML 50.2.S48
The shepherd's artifice, London, 1765.	Longe 52
The shepherdess of the Alps, London, 1780.	Longe 126
Summer amusement. See Title catalogue.	
A test of good fellowship. A. T. of his Liberty-hall.	
The touchstone or Harlequin traveller, London, 1779.	Longe 102
The trip to Portsmouth, London (1773).	Longe 40
A trip to the Nore. See Title catalogue.	

Dibdin, Charles—Continued.

The two misers, London, 1775.   Longe 32

The waterman or The first of August, London, 1783.   Longe 121

The waterman or The first of August (Collection of the most esteemed farces, Edinburgh, 1792, t. vi).   Schatz 11753F

The wedding ring, London, 1773.   Longe 28

A wife of ten thousand. A. T. of his The cobler.

The wives revenged, London, 1778.   Longe 87

Dieter, Christian Ludwig, 1757–1822.

See also Catalogue of 19th cent. librettos.

Belmont und Constanze, oder, Die entfuehrung aus dem serail, Stuttgart, 1784.   Schatz 2574

Elisinde (Vulpius, Operetten, Bayreuth & Leipzig, 1790).   Schatz 2577

Endlich fand er sie. A. T. of his Der Irrwisch.

Die entfuehrung aus dem serail. A. T. of his Belmonte und Constanze.

Die familien-heirath oder Der rekrutenaushub, Weimar, 1780.   Schatz 2578

Das freyschiessen oder Das gluekliche bauernmaedchen, Goettingen, 1786.   Schatz 2575

Das gluekliche bauernmaedchen. *See his* Das freyschiessen.

Der irrwisch, oder Endlich fand er sie, Stuttgart, 1782.   Schatz 2579

Der schulze im dorfe, oder Der verliebte herr doctor, Weimar, 1779.   Schatz 2580

Dittersdorf, Carl Ditters von, 1739–1799.

See also Catalogue of 19th cent. librettos.

De apothecar en de doctor, Amsteldam, 1796. Tr. of next entry.   Schatz 2611

Der apotheker und der doctor, n. pl., 1788.   Schatz 2585

Betrug durch aberglauben, Wien (1787).   Schatz 2587

Democrit der zweyte, Hamburg, 1791. Tr. of his Democrito corretto.   Schatz 2588

The doctor and the apothecary, London, 1788. Tr. of his Der apotheker und der doctor, with additions by Storace.   Schatz 2586

Don Quixotte der zweite, Oels (1795).   Schatz 2589

Der eiserne mann. A. T. of his Gott Mars.

Der fuerst und sein volk, Leipzig (1791) (pasticcio made up from his, Bertoni's, and Pitterlin's music).   Schatz 8204

Der fuerst und sein volk, n. i., 1794. Mainly by Pitterlin.   Schatz 11613

Der gedemuethigte stolz. A. T. of his Terno secco.

Der gefoppte braeutigam, Hall am Kocher, n. d. Tr. of his Lo sposo burlato.   Schatz 2590

Der gefoppte braeutigam, n. i., n. d.   Schatz 2590A

Das gespenst mit der trommel, Oels (1794).   Schatz 2591

Gott Mars oder Der eiserne mann, Oels (1795).   Schatz 2592

Der Gutsherr. A. T. of his Der schiffspatron.

Hieronimus Knicker, Hamburg, 1792.   ML 50.2.H35D4

Hieronymus Kniker [!] Passau, 1793.   Schatz 2593

Hieronimus Knicker, n. i., 1793.   Schatz 2594

Hilft's nicht, so schadt's nicht. A. T. of his Das rothe Kaeppchen.

Die hochzeit des Figaro, Bruenn, 1789.   Schatz 2596

Hokus Pokus, Leipzig, 1794.   Schatz 2597

Hokus Pokus oder Das gaukenspiel, n. i., 1795.   Schatz 2598

Dittersdorf, Carl Ditters von—Continued.

Die liebe im narrenhause, n. i., n. d. (detached from Stephanie's Singspiele, 1792?). Schatz 2599

Der maedchenmarkt (Herklots, Operetten, Berlin, 1793). Schatz 2601

Der neue gutsherr. A. T. of his Der schiffspatron.

The mariners, pasticcio. *See* Title catalogue.

Orpheus der zweyte, Hamburg, 1788. (An altered version of
his Die liebe im narrenhause.) Schatz 2600

Das rothekaeppchen, oder Hilft's nicht, so schadt's nicht,
Koeln am Rheine, 1791. Schatz 2603

Das rothe kaeppchen, Weimar, 1792. Schatz 2604

Der schiffspatron oder Der gutsherr, Hamburg, 1794. Schatz 2608

Der schiffspatron oder Der neue gutsherr, Leipzig, 1793. Schatz 2607

Lo sposo burlato. O. T. of his Der gefoppte braeutigam.

Terno secco, oder Der gedemuethigte stolz, Oels (1797). Schatz 2609

Draghi, Antonio, 1635–1700.

Achille riconosciuto, Vienna, 1688 (ballet airs by Schmelzer). ML 50.2.A29D7

L'amar per virtù, Venetia, 1699. Schatz 2806

Gli amori di Clodio e Pompea. A. T. of the following.

Chi più sà manco, overo Gli amori di Clodio, Vienna, 1669. Schatz 2805

Cidippe, Venetia, 1683. Schatz 2807

Creso, Vienna (1678). ML 50.2.C8D7

Die durch die Tugend gesteurzte wueterey, Wienn (1697).
Tr. of his La tirannide abbattuta dalla virtù. Schatz 2804

La finta cecità di Antioco il Grande, Vienna d'Austria (1695). Schatz 2797

Il fuoco eterno custodito dalle Vestali, Vienna d'Austria, 1674. ML 50.2.F89D7

Iphis auss Griechen-Land, Wienn, 1670. Tr. of his Iphide
Greca. Schatz 2801

Kriegs-liste des Bias, Wienn, 1682. Tr. of his Gli stratagemi
di Biante. Schatz 2802

La lanterna di Diogene, Vienna d'Austria (1674). Schatz 2798

Leonida in Tegea, Venetia, 1676 (with M. A. Ziani). Schatz 2799

Leonida zu Tegea, Wienn, 1670. Tr. of the original version of
the above. Schatz 2800

Il ratto delle Sabine, Vienna d'Austria (1674). ML 50.2.R28D7

Sulpitia, Vienna d'Austria, 1697. Schatz 2803

Drexel, Johann Evangelist, *d.* 1801.

Cyrillus, der Kappadozier, ein junger martyrer (Augsburg,
1785). Schatz 2816

Joseph, der unterkoenig in Aegypten, von seinen brüdern
erkannt (Augsburg, 1786). Schatz 2817

Die kleinen wagehaelse (Augsburg, 1785). Schatz 2818

Pythias und Damon, Augsburg (1781). Schatz 2819

Duni, Egidio Romualdo, 1709–1775.

Le Barnevelt françois. A. T. of his L'école de la jeunesse. Schatz 2841

La buona figliuola, Torino, 1758. Schatz 2834

Il Catone in Utica, Lucca, 1749. Schatz 2835

The captive, pasticcio. *See* Title catalogue.

Ce qui plait aux dames. A. T. of his La fée Urgèle.

La chercheuse d'esprit. *See* Title catalogue.

La clochette, Paris, 1766. Schatz 2836

La clochette, Paris, 1771. Schatz 11692

La clochette, Paris, 1782. Schatz 11693

Duni, Egidio Romualdo—Continued.

Demophontes, king of Thrace, London, 1737. (Tr. and Italian
　　text of his Demofoonte.) 　　　　　　　　　　　Schatz 2837

Les deux chasseurs et la laitière, Paris, 1771. 　　　　Schatz 2838

Les deux chasseurs et la laitière, Paris, 1780. 　　　　Schatz 11694

Le docteur Sangrado, Paris, 1758 (with La Ruette). 　　Schatz 2859

L'école de la jeunesse ou Le Barnevelt françois, Paris, 1765. 　ML 50.2.E2D9

L'école de la jeunesse, ou Le Barnevelt françois, Paris, 1770. 　Schatz 2841

The Englishman. A. T. of his The reapers.

La fée Urgele ou Ce qui plait aux dames, Paris, veuve Du-
　　chesne, 1765 (Theatre de M. Favart, Paris, Duchesne,
　　1763–77, t. ix). 　　　　　　　　　　　　　　ML 49.A2F1

La fée Urgele (Paris) 1765 (Journal des spectacles, 1766, t. ii). 　ML 48.J7

La fée Urgèle, ou Ce qui plait aux dames, Paris, 1768. 　Schatz 2843

La fée Urgele ou Ce qui plait aux dames, Copenhague, 1770. 　Yudin PQ

La fée Urgèle ou Ce qui plaît aux dames, Paris, 1781. 　Schatz 11695

Die fee Urgele oder Was den damen gefaellt, Frankfurt am
　　Mayn (1776). 　　　　　　　　　　　　　　　Schatz 2844

Das fest der weiblichen tugend. A. T. of Das rosenmaed-
　　chen.

La fête du château. *See* Title catalogue.

La fille mal guardée ou Le pédant amoureux, Paris, 1759. 　Schatz 2845

La fille mal gardée ou Le pedant amoureux, Paris, 1758
　　(Theatre de M. Favart, Paris, Duchesne, 1763–77, t. v). 　ML 49.A2F1

The golden pippin. *See* Title catalogue.

L'isle des foux, Paris, 1762. 　　　　　　　　　　　Schatz 2846

Die laecherliche werbung. A. T. of Der militz.

Maid of the mill, pasticcio. *See* Title catalogue.

Mazet, Bruxelles, 1763. 　　　　　　　　　　　　ML 50.2.M48D9

Mazet, Paris, 1769. 　　　　　　　　　　　　　　Schatz 2847

Mazet, Paris, 1771. 　　　　　　　　　　　　　　Schatz 11696

Das milchmaedchen und die beiden jaeger, Frankfurt am
　　Mayn, 1772. Tr. of his Les deux chasseurs et la laitière. 　Schatz 2839

Das milchmaedgen und die zween jaeger, n. i., n. d. Another
　　Tr. 　　　　　　　　　　　　　　　　　　　Schatz 2840

Le milicien, Bruxelles, 1763. 　　　　　　　　　　Schatz 2848

Le milicien, Paris, 1774. 　　　　　　　　　　　　Schatz 11697

Der militz oder Die laecherliche werbung, Frankfurt am
　　Mayn, 1775. 　　　　　　　　　　　　　　　Schatz 2849

Les moissonneurs, Paris, 1768. 　　　　　　　　　Schatz 2850

Les moissonneurs, Paris, veuve Duchesne, 1768 (91, [4] p.)
　　(Theatre de M. Favart, Paris, Duchesne, 1763–77, t. x). 　ML 49.A2F1

The noble peasant. *See* Title catalogue.

Le pédant amoureux. A. T. of his La fille mal gardée.

Le peintre amoureux de son modèle, Paris, 1757. 　　ML 50.2.P32D9

Le peintre amoureux de son modèle, Nouv. ed., Paris, 1767. 　Schatz 2853

The reapers or The Englishman out of Paris, London, 1770.
　　Tr. of his Les moissonneurs. 　　　　　　　　　Longe 204

Das rosenmaedchen oder Das fest der weiblichen tugend,
　　Frankfurt am Mayn, 1772. Tr. of La rosière de Salenci. 　Schatz 2860

La rosiere de Salenci, Paris, veuve Duchesne, 1770 (Theatre
　　de M. Favart, Paris, Duchesne, 1763–77, t. x) (with Blaise
　　and Philidor). 　　　　　　　　　　　　　　ML 49.A2F1

Les sabots, Paris, 1769. 　　　　　　　　　　　　ML 50.2.S2D9

Duni, Egidio Romualdo—Continued.

Les sabots, Paris, 1770. SCHATZ 2855

Les sabots, Paris, 1777. SCHATZ 11698

Die schnitter, Frankfurt am Mayn (1769) Tr. of his Les
moissonneurs (Favart) ML 50 2.M75D94

Die schnitter, Frankfurt am Mayn, 1772. Tr. of his Les
moissonneurs. SCHATZ 2851

Die schule der jugend, Frankfurt am Mayn, 1774. Tr. of
his L'école de la jeunesse, 1774. SCHATZ 2842

The summer's tale, pasticcio. *See* Title catalogue.

Thémire, Paris, 1771. SCHATZ 2856

La tirannida debellata, Milano, 1736. SCHATZ 2857

Der verliebte maler, Frankfurt am Mayn, 1773. Tr. of his
Le peintre amoureux de son modèle. SCHATZ 2854

La veuve indécise, Paris, 1767. SCHATZ 2854

La veuve indécise (Vadé, Oeuvres complettes, Nouv. éd.,
Troyes, an VI [1798]). PQ 2068.V2

Was den damen gefaellt. A. T. of his Die fee Urgele.

Duplessis, le jeune.

Les festes nouvelles (Recueil général des opera, t. xv, Paris,
1739). SCHATZ 2861

Dussek, Johann Ladislaus, 1761–1812.

The captive of Spilburg, London, 1799. LONGE 249

Dutillieu, Pierre (Pietro), *d.* 1798.

Gli accidenti della villa, Napoli, 1797. SCHATZ 2877

Astarbea ossia Pimmalione vendicato, ballet. *See* Anfossi's
I matrimonj per fanatisimo.

Il Beverlei o sia Il giouocatore inglese, ballet. *See* Gardi's
Il nuovo convitato di pietra.

Magia contro magia, ballet. *See* Bernardini's L'ultima che
si perde è la speranza.

Magia contra magia, ballet. *See* P. Guglielmi's L'azzardo.

Orbecch, ballet. *See* Fioravanti's Gl'inganni fortunati.

La superba corretta, Vienna (1795). SCHATZ 2876

Telemaco nell' isola di Calipso, ballet. *See* P. Guglielmi's
Alessandro nelle Indie.

Il trionfo de' Spagnoli o sia La disfatta de' Marrocchini, ballet.
See Bernardini's Amore per incanto.

Il trionfo de' Spagnoli o sia La disfatta de' Marocchini, ballet.
See Bernardini's La donna bizarra.

Duval, *Mlle*.

Les genies (Paris) 1736. ML 52.2.G3

Les génies (Recueil général des opéra, Paris, 1745, t. xvi). ML 48.R4

Eberl, Anton, 1766–1807.

See also Catalogue of 19th cent. librettos.

Pyramus und Thisbe, Wien, 1795. SCHATZ 2889

Ebers, Carl Friedrich, 1770–1836.

See also Catalogue of 19th cent. librettos.

Inkle und Yariko, oder: Er war nicht ganz barbar, Cassel,
1798. SCHATZ 2891

Eccles, John, *d.* 1735.

The comical history of Don Quixote, London, 1729. *See* Title
   catalogue.

Hercules (forms 3d act of The novelty, London, 1697).   Longe 127

The loves of Mars and Venus, London, 1722 (prologue and
   third act by Finger).   Longe 205

Wonders in the sun. *See* Title catalogue.

Edelmann, Johann Friedrich, 1749–1794.

Ariane dans l'isle de Naxos, Paris, 1792.   ML 50.2.A74E3

Eler, André, *ca.* 1764–1821.

See also Catalogue of 19th cent. librettos.

Apelle et Campaspe, Paris, an VI [1798].   Schatz 2912

Elia, Giuseppe.

La pupilla astuta, Padova (1794).   Schatz 2913

Elmer, Johann Conrad.

Der tempel des gedächtnisses, Frankfurt und Leipzig, 1770.   Schatz 2917

Engelmann.

See Kaffka, Johann Christoph.

Ercolani (Ercolano), Giuseppe.

La fata benefica, ballet (music partly by Paisiello). *See* Cimarosa's I nemici generosi.

Gl'Inglesi in America, ballet. *See* Bianchi's Il ritratto.

Il moro di corpo bianco o sia Lo schiavo del proprio onore,
   ballet. *See* P. Guglielmi's La sposa contrastata.

La morte di Meleagro, ballet. *See* Tritto's L'equivoco.

Orlina ossia La famiglia riunita, ballet. *See* Zingarelli's Carolina e Mexicow.

Gli sventurati amori di Cleide ed Almindo o sia Il trionfo de'
   Goti, ballet. *See* Bianchi's La vendetta di Nino.

Il trionfo de' Goti. A. T. of his ballet Gli sventurati amori
   di Cleide ed Almindo.

Ermelinda Talèa, *Arcadian name of* Maria Antonia Walpurgis,
princess of Saxony.

Eule, Card David, *ca.* 1776–1827.

See also Catalogue of 19th cent. librettos.

Der verliebte werber, Hamburg, 1799.   Schatz 2961

Fabbrini, Giuseppe.

Il Coriolano, Siena, 1706.   ML 48.A5   v.46

L'Eudossia, Siena (1696).   ML 48.A5   v.46

La fede ne' tradimenti, Siena, 1689 (5 p. l., 49 p.).   Schatz 2962

La fede ne' tradimenti, Siena, 1689 (3 p. l., 48 p.)   ML 50.2.F24F2

La forza d'amore, Siena (ca. 1690).   ML 48.A5   v.46

La forza del sangue e della pietà, Siena, 1686.   Schatz 2963

La Geneviefa, Siena (1685).   ML 50.2.G29

Lodovico Pio, Siena, 1687.   ML 50.2.L4F2

Fabrizj, Vincenzo.

L'amore per interesse, Parma, 1787.   Schatz 2971

Li castellani burlati—Die betrogenen kastellane, Dresda, 1788.   Schatz 2967

Chi la fa, l'aspetta, Milano (1788).   Schatz 2968

La contessa di Novaluna, Venezia (1786).   Schatz 2975

Fabrizj, Vincenzo—Continued.

Don Giovanni Tenorio, ossia Il convitato di pietra, Bologna (1791). SCHATZ 2973

Il convitato di pietra (p. 69–167 of La finta amalata, Lisboa, 1796). ML 48.C6 III

Li due castellani burlati, Lisbona, 1797. L. T. of his I castellani burlati. ML 50.2.D7F2

La necessità non ha legge, Bologna (1784). SCHATZ 2976

La necessità non ha legge—Noth hat kein gesetz, Dresda, 1786. SCHATZ 2969

La sposa invisibile—Die unsichtbare braut, Dresda, 1788. SCHATZ 2970

I tre gobbi rivali, Napoli, 1783. SCHATZ 2972

Die unsichtbare braut. Tr. of his La sposa invisibile, Dresda, 1788. SCHATZ 2970

Facco, Michele.

I rivali generosi, Messina, 1712. SCHATZ 2979

Fago, Nicolò, 1674–1730.

La Cassandra indovina, Napoli, 1713. SCHATZ 2980

Il Radamisto, Venetia, 1707. SCHATZ 2981

Farinelli, Giuseppe, 1769–1837.

See also Catalogue of 18th cent. librettos.

Il nuovo savio della Grecia, Napoli, 1796. SCHATZ 3019

Seldano, duce degli Svedesi, Venezia (1797). SCHATZ 3030

L'uomo indolente, Napoli, 1795. SCHATZ 3017

Fascetti, Giovanni Lorenzo.

Teramene, Lucca, 1744. See M. Curzio in Title catalogue.

Favart, Charles Simon, 1710–1792.

La ressource des théâtres, Paris, 1760 (only the final vaudeville). SCHATZ 11509

Fay, Etienne, ca. 1770–1845.

Clémentine ou La belle-mère, Paris, an VIII (1799–1800). SCHATZ 3037

Fedele, Teofilo. Italianisation of Treu, Daniel Gottlieb.

Fedeli, Ruggiero, d. 1722.

Silvia—Silvia, Ratisbona, 1690. SCHATZ 3038

Federici, Vincenzo, ca. 1764–1827.

See also Catalogue of 19th cent. librettos.

L'Olimpiade, Torino (1790). SCHATZ 3046

Felici, Alessandro.

L'Amante contrastata, Venezia, 1768. SCHATZ 3053

L'amore soldato, Venezia, 1769. SCHATZ 3054

Apollo in Tessaglia, Firenze, 1769. SCHATZ 3052

Feo, Francesco, 1689–1750.

Andromaca, Roma (1730). SCHATZ 3062

Arianna, Torino (1728). (The libretto mentions as composer Leonardo Leo.) SCHATZ 3061

Ferradini, Antonio.

Demofoonte, Milano (1759). SCHATZ 3063

Il festino. See Goldoni's Opere teatrali.

Ferrandini, Giovanni, *d.* 1793.
    Ciro, Muenchen (1733).   Schatz 3064
    Zophilette.   *See* Title catalogue.

Ferrari, Benedetto, 1597–1681.
    L'Armida, Venezia (1639).   Schatz 3065
    L'Armida (Poesie drammatiche, Milano, 1644).   Schatz 11699 .
    La finta Savia, Venetia, 1643 (only partly by him, Crivelli,
        and Merula, mostly by Laurenzi).   Schatz 5474
    La Gara degli elementi, Parma, 1660.   Schatz 3070
    La Ninfa avara (Poesie drammatiche, Milano, 1644).   Schatz 3066
    Il pastor regio, Venetia, 1640.   Schatz 3067
    Il pastor regio (Poesie drammatiche, Milano, 1644).   Schatz 11700
    Il prencipe giardiniero (Poesie drammatiche, Milano, 1644).   Schatz 3068
    Proserpina rapita (Poesie drammatiche, Milano, 1644).   Schatz 3069

Ferrari, (Domenico *or* Jacopo Goffredo?).
    The mariners, pasticcio.   *See* Title catalogue.

Ferrari, Francesco.
    L'amorosa libertà, Macerata, 1647.   Schatz 3076

Ferrero, Giuseppe.
    La disfatta di Dario, Alessandria (1779).   Schatz 3081

Festing, Michael Christian, *d.* 1752.
    Love in a village, pasticcio.   *See* Title catalogue.

Finazzi, Filippo, *d.* 1776.
    Adelaide–Adelheid, Hamburg (1744) (with Scalabrini and
        others).   Schatz 3101

Finger, Godfrey.
    The loves of Mars and Venus, London, 1722 (only prologue
        and third act, acts 1–2 by Eccles).   Longe 205

Fini, Michele.
    Li Birbi, Venezia, 1732.   Schatz 3105
    Li sponsali d'Enea, Venezia, 1731.   Schatz 3104
    I trionfi di Goffredo in Gerusalemme, Pisa, 1739.   Schatz 3106

Finucci, Giuseppe, 1755–1784.
    Il Castruccio, Lucca, 1781.   *See* M. Curzio in Title catalogue.
    Cesare nella Brettagna, Lucca, 1779.   *See* M. Curzio in Title
        catalogue.
    Leonida rè di Sparta, Lucca, 1783.   *See* M. Curzio in Title
        catalogue.

Fioravanti, Valentino, 1764–1837.
    See also Catalogue of 19th century librettos.
    L'amor per interesse, Napoli, 1797.   Schatz 3112
    L'Amore immaginario, Napoli, 1794.   Schatz 3114
    L'astuta in amore, Milano (1796).   ML 48.A5 v.2
    L'audacia fortunata, Napoli, 1793.   Schatz 3117
    L'audacia fortunata, Lisboa (1796).   Schatz 3173
    Le cantatrici villane, Napoli, 1798.   Schatz 3122
    La fedeltà tra le selve, Roma (1789). (Only four arias for
        Bianchi's opera.)   Schatz 992
    Il furbo contro al furbo, Venezia (1797).   Schatz 3131

Fioravanti, Valentino—Continued.

Il furbo malaccorto, Lisboa (1797). L. T. of his L'astuta in
amore. SCHATZ 3161

Gl'inganni fortunati, Napoli, 1788. SCHATZ 3157

Liretta e Giannino, Napoli, 1795. SCHATZ 3158

I matrimoni per magia, Napoli, 1797. SCHATZ 3135

La schiava fortunata, Napoli, 1796. SCHATZ 3130

Fiorè, Stefano Andrea.

L'Argippo, Milano, 1722. SCHATZ 3191

Atenaide. *See* Zeno's Poesie drammatiche.

Il pentimento generoso, 1719. SCHATZ 3194

Sesostri, rè d'Egitto, Torino, 1717. SCHATZ 3192

Siroe, rè di Persia, Torino (1730). SCHATZ 3193

La Svanvita, Milano (1708). SCHATZ 3195

Teuzzone, Torino, 1716 (with Casanova). SCHATZ 1682

Fiorillo, Ignazio, 1715–1787.

Alessandro nell' Indie—Alexander in Indien, Bronsevigo,
1752. SCHATZ 3198

Li birbi—Die schelmen, Bronsevigo (1749). SCHATZ 3199

Didone abbandonata—Die verlassene Didone, Bronsevigo,
1751. SCHATZ 3200

Ipermestra—Hypermenestra (Bronsevico, 1759). SCHATZ 3201

Mandame [!] Venezia, 1736. SCHATZ 3203

L'Olimpiade (Venezia, 1745). SCHATZ 3205

L'Olimpiade—Die olympischen spiele, Wolfenbuettel (1749). SCHATZ 3202

Die schelmen. *See his* Li birbi.

Die verlassene Didone. *See his* Didone abbandonata.

Il vincitor di se stesso, Venezia, 1741. SCHATZ 3204

Fioriti, Giovanni Antonio.

Il contrasto de fiumi Serchio di Lucca; Tebro di Roma; Ronco
di Ravenna, Bologna, 1674. ML 48.A5 v.5

Fioroni, Giovanni Andrea, *d.* 1778.

La Didone abbandonata, Milano, 1755. SCHATZ 3206

Fischer, Anton Joseph.

See also Catalogue of 19th cent. librettos.

Die ruinen von Portici, Breslau, 1798. SCHATZ 3216

Fischer, Matthäus.

See also Catalogue of 19th cent. librettos.

Der faschingschmaus ([Augsburg] 1797). SCHATZ 3220

Koenig Saul (Augsburg, 1798). SCHATZ 3222

Matthatia, der eiferer fuer Gottesehre (Augsburg, 1797). SCHATZ 3223

Der wahre menschenfreund (Augsburg, 1790). SCHATZ 3226

Der wohlthätige (Augsburg, 1799). SCHATZ 3228

Fischietti, Domenico.

Der apotheker. Tr. of his and Pallavicini's Lo speziale
(Dresden, 1755). SCHATZ 7715

Il bottanico novellista, Venezia, 1770. L. T. of his Lo speziale. SCHATZ 3241

Le chiajese cantarine, Nnapole (1754) (with Logroscino and
Maraucci) ML.50.2.C45

La donna di governo. *See* Goldoni's Opere teatrali.

Fischietti, Domenico—Continued.

La fiera di Sinigaglia, Rome, 1760.   SCHATZ 3239

The golden pippin. *See* Title catalogue.

Der herr doctor. Tr. of his Il signor dottore Dresda, 1768.   SCHATZ 3237

Der jahrmarkt zu Magerndorf. Der jahrmarkt zu Malmantile. Both Tr. of the following:

Il mercato di Malmantile, Venezia, 1758.   SCHATZ 3231

Il mercato di Malmantile—Der jahrmarkt von Magerndorf (Dresda, 1766).   SCHATZ 3232

Il mercato di Malmantile—Der jahrmarkt zu Malmantile (Hannover, 1770).   SCHATZ 3238

La molinara, Venezia, 1778.   SCHATZ 3233

La ritornata di Londra, Venezia (1756).   SCHATZ 3234

La ritornata di Londra—Die zurueckkunft aus Londen (Dresden, 1756).   SCHATZ 3235

Semiramide, Padova, 1759.   SCHATZ 3243

Siface, Venezia, 1748 [!instead of 1761].   SCHATZ 3242

Il signor dottore (Monaco, 1760).   SCHATZ 3236

Il signor dottore—Der herr doctor, Dresda, 1768.   SCHATZ 3237

Solimano, Venezia, 1755.   SCHATZ 3240

Lo speziale, Venezia, 1755 (with Vincenzo Pallavicini).   SCHATZ 7714

Lo speziale—Der apotheker (Dresden, 1755).   SCHATZ 7715

Die zurueckkunft aus Londen. Tr. of his La ritornata di Londra (Dresda, 1756).   SCHATZ 3235

Fisher, John Abraham, 1744–1806.

The court of Alexander, London (1770).   LONGE 37

The druids, London, 1775.   ML 52.2.D72

The golden pippin. *See* Title catalogue.

The Norwood gypsies, London, 1777.   LONGE 124

The seraglio. *See* Title catalogue.

The syrens, London, 1776.   LONGE 200

Fliess, Bernhard, *b. ca.* 1770.

Die regata zu Venedig, Berlin, 1798.   SCHATZ 3247

Floquet, Etienne Joseph, 1750–1785.

Le seigneur bienfaisant, Paris, 1782.   SCHATZ 3249

L'union de l'amour et des arts (Paris) 1774.   ML 52.2.U5

Fontei, Niccolò.

Sidonio e Dorisbe, Venetia (1642).   SCHATZ 3290

Forni, Pietro Paolo.

L'Orode, Milano (1675).   SCHATZ 3301

Fortunati, Gian-Francesco, 1746–1821.

Le gare degli amanti, Parma (1773).   SCHATZ 3310

Fraja, Bernardo di, 1763–1814.

I sposi in Rissa, Napoli, 1791.   SCHATZ 3314

Francheschini, Petronio, *d.* 1680.

Apollo in Tessaglia, Bologna (1679).   SCHATZ 3316

L'Arsinoe, Bologna (1677).   SCHATZ 3317

Arsinoe (Insprugg, 1686)   ML 50.2.A779F7

Dionisio overo La virtù trionfante del vizio, Venetia, 1681 (act I only; acts II–III by Partenio).   SCHATZ 3319

L'Oronte di Menfi, Bologna (1676).   SCHATZ 3318

Franchi, Carlo (*sometimes called* De Franchi), *d.* 1772.

Arsace, Venezia, 1768.	SCHATZ 3326
Il barone di Rocca Antica—Der baron von Alten Fels, Dresden (1772) (act II by Anfossi).	SCHATZ 3330
Il barone di Rocca Antica, Lisboa (1773) (Franchi alone).	SCHATZ 3327
La finta Cingara per amore, Venezia, 1780 (act II by Anfossi).	SCHATZ 3331
Il gran Cidde, Torino (1769).	SCHATZ 3328
Ifigenia, Roma (1766).	ML 50.2.I4F7
Il trionfo della costanza, Torino (1769).	SCHATZ 3329
La vedova capricciosa, Napoli, 1765 (with Giacomo Insanguine).	SCHATZ 4840

Franck, Johann Wolfgang, *b.* 1641.

Hannibal in Capua, Hamburg (1735).	SCHATZ 3335

Francoeur, François, 1698–1787.

Les Augustales, Paris, 1744 (with Rebel).	SCHATZ 8621
Ismène, n. i. (1759) (with Rebel).	ML 50.2.I7R22
Ismène (Paris) 1769 (with Rebel).	ML 50.2.I7R24
Pirame et Thisbé (Recueil général des opéra, t. xiv) Paris, 1734 (with Rebel).	SCHATZ 3336
Pirame et Thisbé (Lyon) 1741 (with Rebel).	ML 50.2.P43R2
Scanderberg (Recueil général des opéra, Paris, 1745, t. xvi) (with Rebel).	ML 48.R4
Scanderberg (Paris) 1763 (with Rebel).	ML 50.2S34R2
Tarsis et Zélie (Recueil général des opéra, t. xiv, Paris, 1734) (with Rebel).	SCHATZ 3337

Francoeur, Louis Joseph, 1738–1804.

Lindor et Ismene. His Entrée in Les fêtes liriques, Paris, Paris, 1766.	ML 52.2.F46

Frascia. *See* Calandra.

Frederick the Great, *king of Prussia,* 1712–1786.
See Graun's Demofoonte, rè di Tracia.

Freschi, Giovanni Domenico, 1640–1690.

Cesare trionfante, Bologna (1694) L. T. of his Giulio Cesare trionfante	ML 50.2.C27
La Circe, Venetia, 1679.	SCHATZ 3347
Dario, Venezia, 1685. L. T. of his L'incoronazione di Dario.	SCHATZ 3357
Elena rapita da Paride (with Francesco Navarra), Venezia, 1687. L. T. of his Helena rapita da Paride.	SCHATZ 3358
Giulio Cesare trionfante, Venetia, 1678.	SCHATZ 3349
Helena rapita da Paride, Venetia, 1677.	SCHATZ 3351
L'incoronazione di Dario, Venetia, 1684.	SCHATZ 3350
Iphide Greca, Venetia, 1671 (first act by G. D. Partenio, third by G. Sartorio).	SCHATZ 7779
Olimpia placata (with Sabadini), Parma, 1687. L. T. of his:	SCHATZ 3359
Olimpia vendicata, Venetia, 1682.	SCHATZ 3352
Pompeo Magno in Cilicia, Venetia, 1681.	SCHATZ 3353
Sardanapalo, Venetia, 1679.	SCHATZ 3354
Silla, Venetia, 1683.	SCHATZ 3355
Teseo tra le rivali, Venetia, 1685.	SCHATZ 3348
Tullia Superba, Venetia, 1678.	SCHATZ 3356

Fridzeri. Frixer, Alexandre Marie Antoine, 1741–1825, *called.*

    Die beiden militzen, Frankfurt a/M, 1773.   Tr. of: Schatz 3371

    Les deux miliciens ou L'orpheline villageoise, Paris, 1772.   Schatz 3370

    Les souliers mors-dorés, ou La cordonnière allemande, Paris,
      1776.   Schatz 3372

Frischmuth, Johann Christian, 1741–1790.

    Das monden-reich (Berlin, 1769).   Schatz 3373

Frixer, Alexandre Marie Antoine. *See* Fridzeri.

Furno, Giovanni, 1748–1837.

    L'impegno, Napoli, 1783.   Schatz 3389

Fux, Johann Joseph, 1660–1741.

    Costanza e fortezza, Vienna (1723)   Schatz 3391

    Enea negli Elisi ovvero Il tempio dell'eternità (Metastasio,
      Opere drammatiche, 1733–37, v. 2)   O. T. of the A. T.

    Psiche (with Caldara).   *See* Zeno's Poesie drammatiche.

    Il tempio dell' eternità.   *See* Enea negli Elisi.

    Teodosio—Theodosius, Hamburg (1718) (partly by Gasparini
      and Caldara).   Schatz 3392

Gabellone, Michele. *See* Caballone.

Gabrie(l)li, Domenico, 1659–1690.

    Carlo il Grande, Venezia, 1688.   Schatz 3397

    Clearco in Negroponte, Venezia, 1685.   Schatz 3402

    Le generose gare tra Cesare e Pompeo, Venezia, 1686.   Schatz 3403

    Il Maurizio, Bergamo, 1689.   ML 50.2.M47G2

    Il Gige in Lidia, Bologna, 1683.   Schatz 3398

    Il Gordiano, Venezia, 1688.   Schatz 3404

    Il Mauritio, Venezia, 1687.   Schatz 3399

    Rodoaldo, rè d'Italia, Venetia, 1685.   Schatz 3400

    Teodora Augusta, Venezia, 1686.   Schatz 3401

Gaertner, Johann.

    Ich heisse Theiss, oder Der aepfeldieb, Regensburg, 1778.   Schatz 3553

Gagliano, Marco da, [1575]–1642.

    Il Medoro, Fiorenza, 1623 (partly by Peri).   ML 48.M2F

    La regina Sant [!] Orsola, Fiorenza, 1625 (14½cm.).   Schatz 3410

    La regina Sant' [!] Orsola, Fiorenza, 1625 (23½cm.).   ML 50.2.R34

Gagni, Angelo.

    L'amor per rigiro, Venezia (1781).   Schatz 3411

    I matti gloriosi, Venezia, 1783.   Schatz 3412

    Le nozze alla Mira, Venezia, 1780.   Schatz 3413

Galeazzi, Antonio.

    Belmira in Creta, Venezia, 1729.   Schatz 3419

    L'odio vinto dalla costanza, Venezia, 1731.   New music only
      for Vivaldi's opera.   Schatz 10763

    Il trionfo della costanza in Statira vedova d'Alessandro,
      Venezia, 1731.   Schatz 3418

Galliard, John Ernest, *d.* 1749.

    The lady's triumph, London, 1718 (with the masque Decius
      and Paulina).   Longe 59

    The rape of Proserpina, London, 1727.   ML 50.2.R24

Galuppi, Baldassare, 1706–1784.

Adriano in Siria, Venezia, 1760.	Schatz 3473
Alcimena principessa dell' Isole Fortunate o sia L'amore fortunato ne' suoi disprezzi, Venezia, 1750.	Schatz 3479
Alessandro nell' Indie, Venezia (1755).	Schatz 3430
Alessandro nell' Indie—Alexander in Indien, Monaco (1755).	Schatz 3431
L'Alvilda, Venezia, 1737.	Schatz 3480
L'amante di tutte, Urbino, 1761.	Schatz 3432
L'amante di tutte, Firenze, 1764.	ML 48.A5 v.20
L'amante di tutte—Der liebhaber von allen, Dresda, 1770.	Schatz 3433
L'ambizione depressa, Venezia (1733).	Schatz 3477
Amor lunatico, Venezia, 1770.	Schatz 3436
L'amore fortunato ne' suoi disprezzi. A. T. of his Alcimena . . .	
Antigona, Roma (1751).	ML 50.2.A718G3
Antigona, Venezia, 1754.	Schatz 3437
Antigona, Mannheim (1752).	Schatz 3438
Antigono, Venezia, 1762.	Schatz 3439
L'Arcadia in Brenta, Milano, 1750.	Schatz 3440
L'Arcadia in Brenta, Monaco, 1759.	Schatz 3518
Arcifanfano, rè dei matti, Venezia, 1750.	Schatz 3442
Arcifano, rè dei matti, Torino (1759).	Schatz 3497
Argenide, Venezia, 1733.	Schatz 3481
Arianna e Teseo, Venezia, 1769.	Schatz 3441
L'Arminio (Venezia) 1747.	Schatz 3482
L'arrivo d'Enea nel Lazio, Firenze, 1765.	Schatz 3443
L'Artaserse (Vienna, 1749).	Schatz 3444
Die artigen zufaelle zwischen liebe und eifersucht (Leipzig, 1756). Tr. of his Li vaghi accidenti fra amore e gelosia.	Schatz 3450
I bagni d'Abano, Venezia, 1753 (partly by Bertoni).	Schatz 3519
Berenice, Venezia (1741).	Schatz 3483
Bertoldo in corte. See Title catalogue.	
Il caffè di campagna, Venezia, 1761.	Schatz 3501
Cajo Mario, Venezia, 1764.	Schatz 3502
La calamita de' cuori, Venezia, 1753.	Schatz 3476
The captive, pasticcio. See Title catalogue.	
Ciro riconosciuto, Venezia, 1737 (partly by Caldara?).	Schatz 3517
Ciro riconosciuto, Milan (1746).	ML 50.2.C53G3
Ciro riconosciuto, Roma (1759).	Schatz 3445
La clemenza di Tito, Torino (1760).	Schatz 3498
Cleonice regina di Siria—Cleonice, queen of Syria, London, 1763, pasticcio. See Title catalogue.	ML 50.2.C5
Clotilde, Venezia, 1748.	Schatz 3516
Il conte Caramella, Vicenza, 1759.	Schatz 3446
Il conte Caramella—Der graf Caramella (Dresden, 1755).	Schatz 3447
Le contese domestiche, Siena (1769).	Schatz 3448
Il Demofoonte, Padova, 1758.	Schatz 3484
La diavolessa, Venezia, 1755.	Schatz 3449
Didone abbandonata, Venezia (1764).	Schatz 3503
La donna di governo, Venezia, 1764.	Schatz 3451
Le donne che comandano. A. T. of his Il mondo alla roversa.	
Dorinda, Venezia (1729). With Pescetti.	Schatz 7967
Elisa regina di Tiro, Venezia, 1736.	Schatz 3485
Ergilda, Venezia, 1736.	Schatz 3486

Galuppi, Baldassare—Continued.

Ernelinda, Venezia, 1750 (probably a pasticcio).   SCHATZ 3522

Ezio, London, 1764–5 (pasticcio from above and Pescetti, Bach, etc.).   ML 48.M2N

La fede tradita e vendicata. *See his* Ernelinda, 1750, in Title catalogue.

Il filosofo di campagna, Venezia, 1754.   SCHATZ 3452

Il filosofo di campagna—Der landmann ein philosoph (Dresden, 1755).   SCHATZ 3453

Il filosofo in campagna. A. T. of his La serva astuta.

La finta cameriera—Das verstellte kammermaedgen (Bronsevigo, 1751).   SCHATZ 3454

Den flanevurne kone. Tr. of his La moglie bizzarra, Kiøbenhavn (1763).   SCHATZ 3434

La forza d'amore, Venezia (1745).   SCHATZ 3478

The golden pippin. *See* Title catalogue.

Der graf Caramella (Dresden, 1755). Tr. of his Il conte Caramella.   SCHATZ 3447

Gustavo Primo, rè di Svezia, Venezia (1740).   SCHATZ 3474

Idomeneo, Roma (1756).   ML 50.2.I3G2

L'inimico delle donne, Venezia (1771).   SCHATZ 3455

Gl'intrighi amorosi, Venezia, 1772.   SCHATZ 3504

L'Ipermestra, Venezia, 1761.   SCHATZ 3457

Issipile, Torino, 1738.   SCHATZ 3499

Issipile, Parma (1756).   SCHATZ 3514

Der landmann ein philosoph. Tr. of his Il filosofo di campagna (Dresden, 1755).   SCHATZ 3453

La lavandara, Torino (1770). L. T. of his Il marchese villano.   SCHATZ 3515

La lavandara astuta, Mantova (1771). Another version of this.   SCHATZ 3505

Der liebhaber von allen, Mannheim (1770). Tr. of his L'amante di tutte.   SCHATZ 3435

Lionel and Clarissa. *See* Title catalogue.

Love in a village, pasticcio. *See* Title catalogue.

Love in the city, pasticcio. *See* Title catalogue.

The maid of the mill, pasticcio. *See* Title catalogue.

Il marchese villano, Vienna (1767).   SCHATZ 3458

La mascherata, Venezia, 1751 (also attributed to Cocchi).   SCHATZ 3487

Il matrimonio per inganno, Venezia, 1771. L. T. of his Il marchese villano.   SCHATZ 3506

La moglie bizzarra—Den flanevurne kone, Kiøbenhavn (1763). L. T. of his L'amante di tutte.   SCHATZ 3434

Il mondo alla roversa, o sia Le donne che comandono, Venezia, 1753.   SCHATZ 3459

Il mondo alla roverscia (Dresda, 1768).   SCHATZ 3460

Il mondo della luna, Venezia, 1750.   SCHATZ 3461

Il mondo nella luna, London, 1760 (pasticcio, chiefly from Galuppi).   ML 48.M2H

Motezuma, Venezia, 1772.   SCHATZ 3463

Il Muzio Scevola, Padova, 1762.   SCHATZ 3464

Il nemico delle donne (Vienna, 1775). L. T. of his L'inimico delle donne.   SCHATZ 3456

La ninfa Apollo, Venezia, 1734.   SCHATZ 3488

Galuppi, Baldassare—Continued.

Le nozze, Venezia, 1757.	Schatz 3465
Le nozze di Paride, Venezia, 1756.	Schatz 3489
Gl'odj delusi dal sangue, Venezia, 1728.	Schatz 3521
L'odio placato, Venezia, 1730.	Schatz 3490
L'Olimpiade, Siena, 1763.	Schatz 3496
Oronte rè de' Sciti. *See* Goldoni's Opere teatrali.	
Il paese della Cuccagna, Venezia, 1750.	Schatz 3492
La partenza e il ritorno de' marinari, Venezia, 1765.	Schatz 3466
Il povero superbo, Venezia, 1755.	Schatz 3467
Il protettore alla moda, Venezia, 1749 (partly by Buini).	Schatz 3520
Il puntiglio amoroso, Venezia, 1763.	Schatz 3507
Il rè alla caccia, Venezia, 1763.	Schatz 3475
Il rè pastore, Venezia, 1769.	Schatz 3468
Il regno delle donne. *See his* Il mondo alla roversa.	
Ricimero. *See his* Ernelinda, 1750.	
The school for fathers, pasticcio. *See* Lionel and Clarissa in Title catalogue.	
Scipione nelle Spagne, Venezia, 1746.	Schatz 3493
La Semiramide riconosciuta, Milano, 1749.	Schatz 3469
La serva astuta o sia Il filosofo in campagna, Venezia (1761).	Schatz 3513
La serva per amore, Venezia, 1773.	Schatz 3508
Sesostri, Venezia, 1757.	Schatz 3494
Sofonisba, Torino (1764).	Schatz 3470
Tamiri, Venezia (1734).	Schatz 3495
Tom Jones, pasticcio. *See* Title catalogue.	
Li tre amanti ridicoli, Gubbio (1765).	Schatz 3471
L'uomo femmina, Venezia (1762).	Schatz 3509
Li vaghi accidenti fra amore e gelosia (Leipzig, 1756).	Schatz 3450
Il vecchio geloso (Vienna, 1767). L. T. of his L'amante di tutte.	Schatz 3510
Die verkehrte welt. Tr. of his Il mondo alla roverscia (Dresda, 1768).	Schatz 3460
Das verstellte kammermaedgen. Tr. of his La finta cameriera (Bronsevigo, 1751).	Schatz 3454
Il villano geloso, Venezia, 1769.	Schatz 3472
Viriate, Venezia, 1762.	Schatz 3511
Le virtuose ridicole, Venezia, 1752.	Schatz 3512
La vittoria d'Imeneo, Torino (1750).	Schatz 3500
Die welt im monde, Oels (17—). Tr. of his Il mondo della luna.	Schatz 3462
Zophilette. *See* Title catalogue.	

Garcia (Garzia), Francesco Saverio (*called* Spagnoletto), ca. 1731–1809.

Die pfleg-tochter, Mannheim (1758), Tr. of his:	Schatz 3555
La pupilla, Roma, 1755.	ML 50.2.P9G2

Gardi, Francesco.

See also Catalogue of 19th century librettos.

Amor l'astuzia insegna, Venezia, 1797.	Schatz 3536
La bella Lauretta, Venezia, 1795.	Schatz 3537
Il contraveleno, Venezia, 1799.	Schatz 3547
La fata capricciosa, Venezia, 1789.	Schatz 3548
Il finto Stregone, Venezia, 1798.	Schatz 3549

Gardi, Francesco—Continued.

Il nuovo convitato di pietra, Venezia, 1787.	Schatz 3540
La pianella persa, Verona, 1798.	ML 50.2.P38G2
La semplice ovvero La virtù premiata, Venezia, 1798.	Schatz 3541
Tancredi, Venezia, 1795.	Schatz 3542
La virtù premiata. A. T. of his La semplice.	

Garzia, Francesco Saverio.   *See* Garcia.

Gasparini, Carlo Francesco, 1668–1727.

L'Alciade overo La violenza d'amore, Milano, 1709 (with Polaroli and Ballarotti).	Schatz 3597
L'amante impazzito, Venetia (1714). Later version of the above.	Schatz 3598
Ambleto, Venezia, 1705.	Schatz 3556
L'amor generoso, Venezia (1707).	Schatz 3557
L'amor tirannico, Venezia, 1710.	Schatz 3558
Amphytrion [Hamburg, 1725]. Tr. (with additional music by Joh. v. Wich) of:	Schatz 3560
Anfitrione, Venezia, 1707.	Schatz 3559
Antioco, Venezia, 1705.	Schatz 3561
L'Astrologo, Venezia, 1731. L. T. of his Parpagnacco.	Schatz 3590
Atenaide. *See* Zeno's Poesie drammatiche.	
L'avaro, Venezia, 1720.	Schatz 3594
Il Bajazet, Reggio, 1719. L. T. of his Tamerlano.	Schatz 3562
Costantino, Venezia, 1711.	Schatz 3589
Democrito, Torino, 1718.	Schatz 3563
La Dorinda, Roma, 1723.	Schatz 3592
Engelberta, Venezia, 1708.	Schatz 3564
Gl'equivoci d'amore, e d'innocenza, Venezia, 1723.	Schatz 3565
Ernelinda, 1750. *See* this under Galuppi.	
L'eroico amore. A. T. of his and Ballarotti's L'Alciade.	
Il Faramondo, Roma, 1720.	ML 50.2.F2G3
La fede in cimento, Venezia, 1730 (his L'amor generoso, with additional music by Santo Lapis).	Schatz 3596
La fede tradita e vendicata, Venezia, 1704.	Schatz 3566
La fede tradita e vendicata, Napoli, 1707 (with new music by Vignola).	Schatz 3567
Flavio Anicio Olibrio, Firenze (1723).	Schatz 3568
La Fredegonda, Venezia, 1705.	Schatz 3569
Gerone tiranno di Siracusa, Genova (1700).	Schatz 3588
Gli Imenei stabiliti dal caso, Venezia, 1703.	Schatz 3570
Intermezzi in derisione della setta Maomettana, Napoli (1717).	ML 50.2.I59G2
Lisetta ed Astrobolo, Vienna, 1717. (*In* Caldara's La verità nell' inganno.)	Schatz 1490
Lucio Papirio, Roma, 1714.	ML 50.2.L85G2
La maschera levata al vitio, Venetia, 1704.	Schatz 3571
Merope, Venezia, 1711.	Schatz 3573
Il miglior d'ogni amore per il peggiore d'ogni odio, Venezia, 1703.	Schatz 3572
Mirena e Floro. (*In* Lotti's Gl'odi delusi dal sangue, Dresda, 1718. Together with Bononcini.)	Schatz 5707
La ninfa Apollo, Venezia, 1709.	Schatz 3574
Parpagnacco, Venezia, 1708.	Schatz 3575
Il più fedel fra i vassalli, Venezia, 1703.	Schatz 3579

Gasparini, Carlo Francesco—Continued.

Il più fedel fra i vassalli, Venezia, 1716.   ML 48.M2O

Pollastrella & Parpagnacco. (*In* R. Broschi's Adriano in Siria, Stuccarda, 1737.)   Schatz 1338

Il principato custodito dalla frode, Venezia, 1705.   Schatz 3577

La principessa fedele, Venezia (1709).   Schatz 3578

Le regine di Macedonia, Napoli (1708). L. T. with new music by Vignola of his Statira.   Schatz 3583

Il Roderico, Roma, 1694.   Schatz 3580

Sesostri rè di Egitto, Venezia (1709).   Schatz 3581

Statira, Venezia, 1705.   Schatz 3582

Taican rè della Cina, Venezia, 1707.   Schatz 3584

Tamerlano, Venezia (1710).   Schatz 3585

Teodosio—Theodosius, Hamburg (1718) (with Fux and Caldara).   Schatz 3392

Thomyris, queen of Scythia, pasticcio. *See* Title catalogue.

Tiberio imperatore d'Oriente, Venetia (1702).   Schatz 3586

Il Trace in catena, Roma, 1717 ("e di dui suoi allievi")   ML 50.2.T73G2

La verità nell' inganno, Venezia, 1713.   Schatz 3587

La violenza d'amore. A. T. of his Polaroli and Ballarotti's L'Alciade.

Zamberlucco e Palandrana, Ferrara (1721).   Schatz 3591

Gasparini, Michel Angelo, 1672–1732.

Arsace, Venezia, 1718.   Schatz 3599

Il Lamano, Venezia, 1719.   Schatz 3600

Il più fedel tra' gl'amici, Venezia, 1724.   Schatz 3602

Il principe selvaggio, Venezia, 1695.   Schatz 3603

Rodomonte sdegnato, Venezia, 1714.   Schatz 3601

Gasparini, Quirino, *d.* 1778.

Mitridate rè di Ponto, Torino (1767).   Schatz 3604

Gassmann, Florian Leopold, 1723–1774.

Achille in Sciro, Venezia, 1766.   Schatz 3607

L'amore artigiano—Die liebe unter den handwerksleuten, Dresda, 1770.   Schatz 3609

L'amore artigiano, Firenze, 1770.   Schatz 3608*

L'amore artigiano, Milano (1782).   Schatz 3608

L'amor artigiano—Die liebe bey den handwerkern, Regensburg (178–?).   Schatz 3610

Amore e Psiche, Vienna, 1767.   Schatz 3626

Catone in Utica, Venezia, 1761.   Schatz 3625

La contessina, Brescia (1774) (pasticcio).   Schatz 3613

La contessina—Den unge grevinde, Kiobenhavn, 1778.   Schatz 3614

Don Quischott von Mancia, Wien (1771). (Acts 1–2 by Paisiello; act 3 and several arias in the first two acts by the above.)   Schatz 7612

Filosofia ed amore, Venezia, 1760.   Schatz 3615

L'Issipile, Venezia, 1758.   Schatz 3622

Die liebe bey den handwerkern. Tr. of his L'amore artigiano, Regensburg (178–?).   Schatz 3610

Die liebe unter den handwerksleuten. Tr. of his L'amore artigiano, Dresda (1770).   Schatz 3609

Gassmann, Florian Leopold—Continued.

Die liebe unter den handwerksleuten, Mannheim (1772).   SCHATZ 3620
Die liebe unter den handwerksleuten, Wien, 1779.   SCHATZ 3611
Die liebe unter den handwerksleuten, Hamburg, 1782.   SCHATZ 3612
Merope, Venezia, 1757.   SCHATZ 3619
La notte critica.   O. T. of his Die unruhige nacht.
L'opera seria (Firenze, 1772).   SCHATZ 3623
Un pazzo ne fa cento, Venezia (1762).   SCHATZ 3624
Lo sposo di trè e marito di nessuna (Vienna, 1768) (with
     Guglielmi and (mainly) Anfossi).   SCHATZ 284
Il superbo deluso (Lisboa, 1774).   L. T. of his La contes-
     sina.   SCHATZ 3621
Il trionfo d'amore, Milano (1765).   SCHATZ 3628
Li uccellatori, Venezia, 1759.   SCHATZ 3617
Gl'uccellatori, Vienna (1768).   SCHATZ 3627
Den unge grevinde.   Tr. of his La contessina, Kiobenhavn,
     1778.   SCHATZ 3614
Die unruhige nacht, Wien, 1783.   Tr. of his La notte critica.   SCHATZ 3616
Il viaggiator ridicolo (Vienna, 1766).   SCHATZ 3618
La Zingara, Vienna, 1769 (additional music for Vento's opera).   SCHATZ 10611
La Zingara (Firenze, 1771).   The same as the above.   SCHATZ 10612

Gatti, Luigi, 1740–1817.
Antigono, Milano (1781) (partly by Anfossi).   SCHATZ 283
Germanico in Germania, ballet.   See Rossetti's Olimpiade.

Gatti, Teobaldo di (*called* Théobald), [1650]–1727.
Coronis (Amsterdam) 1692.   ML 50.2.C67G2
Coronis (Recueil général des opéra, Paris, 1703, t. iv).   SCHATZ 3632
Scylla (Recueil général des opéra, t. vii, Paris, 1703).   SCHATZ 3633

Gaudio, Antonio del (dal).
L'Almerico in Cipro, Venetia, 1675.   SCHATZ 3635
L'Ulisse in Feaccia, Venetia, 1681.   SCHATZ 3634

Gaveaux, Pierre, 1761–1825.
See also Catalogue of 19th cent. librettos.
L'amour conjugal.   A. T. of his Léonore.
L'amour filial, Paris, an second [1793–94].   ML 50.2.A7G2
La famille indigente, Paris, 1797, an V.   ML 50.2.F172G2
L'intrigue portugaise.   A. T. of his Sophie et Moncars.
Lise et Colin ou La surveillance inutile, Paris, an 4 (1796).   ML 50.2.L4G2
Kindliche liebe, Frankfurt a/M., 1798.   Tr. of his L'amour
     filial.   SCHATZ 3637
Léonore ou L'amour conjugal, Paris (1798).   SCHATZ 3649
Le mariage impromptu.   A. T. of his Le petit matelot.
Le petit matelot ou Le mariage im-promptu, Paris, 1796 (46 p.).   ML 50.2.P34G2
Le petit matelot ou Le mariage impromptu, Paris, 1796 (40 p.).   SCHATZ 3641
Le petit matelot ou Le mariage impromptu, Avignon, an V
     (1796–97).   ML 50.2.P34G22
Sophie et Moncars ou L'intrigue portugaise, Paris, an VI
     (1797).   ML 50.2.S7G2
La surveillance inutile.   A. T. of his Lise et Colin.
Le traité nul, Paris, an V (1797).   ML 50.2.T77G2
Le traité nul, Paris, an VII (1799).   ML 50.2.T77G22
Het vernietigd verdrag, Amsterdam, 1799.   Tr. of his Le traité
     nui.   SCHATZ 3644

Gaviniès, Pierre, 1726–1800.
    Le prétendu, Paris, 1760.   ML 50.2.P63G2

Gazzaniga, Giuseppe, 1743–1818 *or* 1819.
  See also Catalogue of 19th cent. librettos.
    Alcines øe. Tr. of his L'isola d'Alcina, Kiøbenhavn, 1777.   Schatz 3667
    L'amante per bisogno, Venezia, 1781.   Schatz 3689
    Amor per oro, Venezia, 1782.   Schatz 3690
    L'amore costante, Venezia (1787).   Schatz 3683
    Gli argonauti in Colco o sia La conquista del vello d'oro,
      Venezia, 1789.   Schatz 3657
    Armida, Roma (1773).   ML 50.2.A75G2
    La bizzarria degli umori, Roma, 1777.   Schatz 3684
    Calandrano, Venezia (1771).   Schatz 3658
    Circe, Venezia, 1786.   Schatz 3659
    La conquista del vello d'oro. A. T. of his Gli argonauti in
      Colco.
    O convidado de pedra. A. T. of his Dom Joco.
    Il convitato di pietra. A. T. of his Il Don Giovanni.
    La costanza in amor rende felice, Trieste (1787). L. T. of his
      L'amore costante.   Schatz 3686
    La creduta infedele, Napoli, 1783.   Schatz 3677
    La dama soldato, Venezia, 1792.   Schatz 3660
    Il disertor francese, Lisbona, 1796.   Schatz 3681
    La disfatta de' Mori, Torino (1791).   Schatz 3662
    Dom João, ou O convidado de pedra, Lisbona, 1792. Tr. of
      the following.   Schatz 3682
    Don Giovanni o sia Il convitato di pietra. (Forms second act
      of Bertati's text Il cappriccio drammatico, Venezia, 1787;
      first act composed by Valentini and others.)   Schatz 10580
    Il Don Giovanni, ossia Il convitato di pietra, Lisbonna, 1792.   Schatz 3682
    La donna astuta, Venezia, 1793.   Schatz 3691
    Die eigensinnige ehefrau. Tr. of his La moglie capricciosa,
      Dresda, 1786.   Schatz 3672
    Ezio, Venezia, 1772.   Schatz 3687
    Die insel der Alcina. Tr. of his L'isola d'Alcina, Dresda,
      1773.   Schatz 3666
    L'intrigo delle moglie, Napoli (1783).   Schatz 3679
    L'isola d'Alcina—Alcines øe, Kiøbenhavn, 1777.   Schatz 3667
    L'isola d'Alcina, Bologna (1779).   ML 48.A5 v.30
    L'isola di Alcina, Venezia, 1772.   Schatz 3665
    L'isola di Alcina—Die insel der Alcina, Dresda, 1773.   Schatz 3666
    La locanda, Venezia, 1771.   Schatz 3668
    La moglie capricciosa—Die eigensinnige ehefrau, Dresda, 1786. Schatz 3672
    La moglie capricciosa, Firenze, 1791.   ML 48.A5 v.24
    La moglie capricciosa, Pisa, 1795.   Schatz 3671
    A mulher caprichosa, Lisboa, 1791. Tr. of the above.   Schatz 3678
    Il palazzo d'Osmano, Lisbona, 1795. L. T. of the following: Schatz 3680
    Il seraglio di Osmano, Venezia (1785).   Schatz 3676
    La tomba di Merlino, Venezia, 1772.   Schatz 3673
    Tullo Ostilio, Roma, 1784.   Schatz 3685
    La vendemmia, Vienna (1779)   ML 50.2.V28G3
    La vendemmia—Die weinlese, Dresda, 1783.   Schatz 3675
    La vendemmia, Lisbona, 1794.   Schatz 3674
    Zon-Zon principe di Kibin-Kin-Ka, Milano (1773).   Schatz 3688

Gebhard, Paolo.　*See* Ghebhard.

Gehot, Jean.
　　The cobler of Castleburg, London, n. d.　(A few airs only,
　　　　otherwise by Shield.)　　　　　　　　　　　　　　　LONGE 125

Geminiani Francesco, 1680–1762.
　　La forest enchantée (Paris) 1754.　　　　　　　　　　ML 52.2.F6G3
　　Love in a village, pasticcio.　*See* Title catalogue.

Gerace, Ignazio.
　See also Catalogue of 19th cent. librettos.
　　Ines de Castro, Venezia, 1795 (with Bianchi. Nasolini, and
　　　　Cervellini).　　　　　　　　　　　　　　　　　SCHATZ 1012
　　Vologeso, Venezia, 1796.　　　　　　　　　　　　　SCHATZ 3780

Gerl, Franz.
　　Der bestrafte hochmuth, oder, Liebe macht alle stände gleich,
　　　　Hamburg, 1798.　L. T. of his Graf Balberone oder Die
　　　　maskerade.　　　　　　　　　　　　　　　　　　SCHATZ 3785

Gervais, Charles Hubert, 1671–1744.
　　Les amours de Protée (Recueil général des opéra, t. xiii, Paris,
　　　　1734).　　　　　　　　　　　　　　　　　　　SCHATZ 3790a
　　Les amours de Protée, Lyon, 1742.　　　　　　　　　SCHATZ 3790b
　　Hypermnestre (Recueil général des opéra, t. xii, Paris, 1734).　SCHATZ 3791a
　　Hypermnestre, Lyon, 1742.　　　　　　　　　　　　SCHATZ 3791b
　　Méduse (Recueil général des opera, t. v, Paris, 1703).　　SCHATZ 3792

Gestewitz, Friedrich Christopher, 1753–1805.
　　L'orfanella americana—Die verwaiste Amerikanerin, Dresda,
　　　　1790.　　　　　　　　　　　　　　　　　　　　SCHATZ 3796

Ghebhard, Paolo (*also* Ghebart, *probably originally* Gebhard or
　　　　Gebhardt, Paul).
　　Alcina e Ruggero, ballet music.　*See* Alessandri.
　　Ecuba.　Ballet music in Celoniat's opera.
　　Il gran Cidde.　Ballet airs together with Le Messier for
　　　　Franchi's opera.
　　I panduri accampati, ballet.　*See* Pugnani's Tamas Kouli-
　　　　Kan nell' India.
　　Piramo e Tisbe, ballet.　*See* Colla's Didone.

Gherardesca, Filippo.
　　L'astuzia fedele, Venezia, 1767.　　　　　　　　　　SCHATZ 3800
　　La notte critica, Pisa, 1769.　　　　　　　　　　　SCHATZ 3801

Ghinassi, Stefano.
　　Il governatore dell' isole Canarie—Der gouverneur der cana-
　　　　rischen inseln, Dresda, 1785.　　　　　　　　　SCHATZ 3802
　　Il seraglio di Osmano—Osmanns serail, Dresden, 1787.　SCHATZ 3805

Ghinzer, Giovanni.　*See* Chinzer.

Giacobbi, Girolamo, *d.* 1630.
　　L'Aurora ingannata (intermedii in the favola pastorale, Filar-
　　　　mindo, Venezia, 1628).　　　　　　　　　　　　PQ
　　Proserpina rapita, Bologna, 1613 (doubtful).　　　　ML 50.2.P68
　　Il Reno sacrificante, Bologna, 1617.　　　　　　　　SCHATZ 3804

Giacomelli, Geminiano, *ca.* 1686–1743.

Achille in Aulide, Roma (1739).	ML 50.2.A26G3
Adriano in Siria, Venezia, 1733.	SCHATZ 3805
Arsace, Venezia (1737).	SCHATZ 3810
Cesare in Egitto, Milano (1735).	SCHATZ 3806
Epaminonda, Venezia (1732).	SCHATZ 3811
Gianguir, Venezia (1729).	SCHATZ 3812
Golpone e Birina. *See his* Achille in Aulide.	
Ipermestra, Venezia, 1724.	SCHATZ 3813
Lucio Papirio dittatore, Parma, 1729.	SCHATZ 3809
Merope, Venezia, 1734.	SCHATZ 3807
Scipione in Carthagine nuova, Parma (1730).	SCHATZ 3808

Giai, Giovanni Antonio, *d.* 1764.

Adriano in Siria, Venezia, 1740.	SCHATZ 3819
Demetrio (Roma, 1732).	SCHATZ 3816
Fetonte sulle rive del Po, Torino, 1750.	SCHATZ 3818
Gianguir, Venezia (1738).	SCHATZ 3814
Mitridate, Venezia (1730).	SCHATZ 3815
Publio Cornelio Scipione, Torino (1726).	SCHATZ 3817

Gianella, Luigi.

La morte di Geta, ballet. *See* Portugal's Alceste.

Giannettini. *See* Zannettini.

Giardini, Felice, 1716–1796.

The castle of Andalusia, pasticcio. *See* Title catalogue.
Cleonice regina di Siria—Cleonice, queen of Syria, London,
    1763, pasticcio. *See* Title catalogue.   ML 50.2.C5
Love in a village, pasticcio. *See* Title catalogue.
Maid of the mill, pasticcio. *See* Title catalogue.
The princess of Tarento, pasticcio. *See* Title catalogue.
The summer's tale, pasticcio. *See* Title catalogue.
The two misers. *See* Title catalogue.

Gibelli, Lorenzo, 1719–1812.

Evergete, Venezia, 1748.	SCHATZ 3828

Gibert, Paul César, 1717–1787.

La fortune au village, Paris, 1761 (Theatre de M. Favart,
    Paris, Duchesne, 1763–77, t. v).   ML 49.A2F1
Soliman Second, Paris, 1762 (Theatre de M. Favart, Paris,
    Duchesne, 1763–77, t. iv).   ML 49.A2F1
Soliman second, ou Les trois sultanes, Nouv. éd., Paris, 1772. ML 48.M2N

Giles, Thomas.

The Lords Maske. *See* A relation of the late royall entertain-
    ment.

Gillier (Gilliers), Jean Claude, *d.* 1737.

Le Théâtre de la foire, Paris, 1724–37.   ML 48.L2
    He arranged and partly composed the music (especially
the final vaudevilles) in his capacity as "compositeur"
of the theatre for most of the plays there performed. For
this reason he may have furnished the music for the plays
listed below in addition to the next entry:
Les deux suivantes, Pannard, Théâtre, Paris, 1763, v. 2).   PQ 2019.P3
Achmet et Almanzine, t. vi.

Gillier (Gilliers), Jean Claude—Continued.

L'allure, t. ix, 2.
L'amour marin, t. viii.
Les amours de Nanterre, t. iii.
Les amours de Protée, t. vii.
Les amours déguisez, t. vi.
Les animaux raisonnables, t. iii.
Arlequin défenseur, d'Homère, t. ii.
Arlequin Endymion, t. iv.
Arlequin invisible (chez le roi de Chine).
Arlequin Mahomet, t. i.
Arlequin, roy de Serendib.
Arlequin, sultane favorite.
Arlequin Thétis.
Arlequin traitant, t. ii.
La ceinture de Venus, t. i.
Colombine Arlequin, t. ii.
Les comediens corsaires, t. vi.
Le corsaire de Salé, t. vii.
Les couplets en procès, t. vii.
Les desesperés, t. ix.
Les eaux de Merlin, t. ii.
L'école des amans, t. ii.
L'enchanteur Mirliton, t. vi.
Les enragez, t. vi.
L'esperance, t. viii.
Les funerailles de la Foire, t. iii.
La forêt de Dodone, t. iv.
La grand-mère amoureuse, t. viii.
L'impromptu du Pont-neuf, t. vii.
L'indifférence, t. viii.
L'industrie, t. viii.
L'isle des Amazones, t. iii.
Le jugement de Paris, t. iii.
La lanterne véridique, t. ix, 2.
Le mari préferé, t. ix.
Le mariage du caprice et de la folie, **t. viii.**
Les mariages de Canada, t. ix.
La mère jalouse, t. vi, 2.
Le monde renversé, t. iii.
L'obstacle favorable, t. vi.
L'ombre du cocher poète, t. v.
L'Opéra-comique assiegé, t. vii.
Le parterre merveilleux, t. ix, 2.
Les pelerins de la Mecque, t. vi.
La Penelope moderne, t. vii.
Le Pharaon, t. ii.
Pierrot Romulus ou Le ravisseur poli, **t. v.**
La premiere représentation, t. ix.
La princesse de Carizme, t. iii.
La princesse de la Chine, t. vii.
La querelle des théâtres, t. iii.
Le rappel de la Foire à la vie, t. iii.
Le régiment de la Calotte, t. iv.

Gillier (Gilliers), Jean Claude—Continued.
 La reine du Barostan, t. vii.
 Le remouleur d'amour, t. v.
 Le reveil de l'opéra-comique, t. ix, 2.
 Roger de Sicile, surnommé Le roi sans chagrin, **t. ix.**
 Le rival de lui-même, ix, 2.
 Les routes du monde, t. viii.
 La sauvagesse, t. ix.
 Sophie et Sigismond, t. ix.
 Les spectacles malades, t. vii.
 La statue merveilleuse, t. iv.
 Le tableau du mariage, t. ii.
 Télémaque, parodie, t. i.
 Le temple de l'ennuy, t. ii.
 Le temple de mémoire, t. vi.
 Le temple du destin, t. i.
 Le tombeau de Nostradamus, **t. i.**
 Les trois comères, t. ix.
 Zemine et Almanzor, t. viii.

Gioannetti, Rocco.
 Andromeda. Composed the incidental ballet music for Cocchi's opera.
 Ballets called "Di selvaggi," "Del Bezestan o Mercato di schiavi," and "Di Marte, Venere e la Gloria." *See* M. A. Valentini's Solimano.
 Cerere e Trittolemo, ballet. *See* Calderara's Ricimero.
 Coronazione d'Apollo e Dafne, ballet. *See* Bertoni's Serostri.
 Demofoonte. Composed the dances in this opera by Gennaro Manna.
 Giudicio di Paride, ballet. *See* Calderara's Ricimero.
 Lucio Papirio, Torino, 1753. Ballet music for Balbi's opera.
 Le pescatrici (Torino, 1754).   Schatz 3831
 Sacrifizio detto Taurobolio pella elezione ed inaugurazione di un re di Norvegia, ballet. *See* Calderara's Ricimero.

Giordani (Giordano), Giuseppe (*called* Giordaniello), 1744–1798.
 L'Acomate, Pisa, 1783 (lacks t.-p.).   ML 48.A5 v.7
 L'Acomate, Firenze, 1784.   Schatz 3832
 Ariarate, Torino (1789).   Schatz 3842
 Aspasia, Venezia, 1790.   Schatz 3833
 Atalanta, Torino (1792).   Schatz 3834
 Cajo Mario, Milano (1791).   Schatz 3835
 Caio Ostilio, Firenze, 1794.   Schatz 3850
 Chi la fa l'aspetti. A. T. of his L'impegno.
 Il Corrivo, Napoli, 1787.   Schatz 3839
 La disfatta di Dario, Milano (1789).   Schatz 3836
 La distruzione del Perù. A. T. of his Pizzarro nell' Indie.
 Don Mirtillo contrastato, Venezia, 1791.   Schatz 3837
 Elpinice, Bologna (1783). L. T. of his L'Acomate.   Schatz 3843
 Erifile, Genova (1783).   Schatz 3844
 Fernando nel Messico, Roma, 1787.   Schatz 3838
 L'impegno, o sia Chi la fa, l'aspetti, Roma, 1786.   Schatz 3845
 Ines de Castro, Venezia, 1793.   Schatz 3846
 Nicomede, Genova (1790).   Schatz 3847

Giordani (Giordano), Giuseppe—Continued.

Osmane, Venezia, 1784.　　　　　　　　　　　　　　　　Schatz 3848

Pizzarro nell' Indie o sia La distruzione del Perù, Firenze,
　　1784.　　　　　　　　　　　　　　　　　　　　　　　Schatz 3849

La principessa di Tingi, ballet.　*See* Insanguine's Calipso.

Lo sposo di trè e marito di nessuna, Napoli, 1781 (with Gugli-
　　elmi and (mainly) Anfossi).　　　　　　　　　　　　Schatz 285

Tito Manlio, Genoa (1784).　　　　　　　　　　　　　Schatz 3841

La vendemia ossia La contadina impertinente, ballet.　*See*
　　Insanguine's Calipso.

Giordani, Tommaso, *d.* 1806.

The castle of Andalusia, pasticcio.　*See* Title catalogue.

The golden pippin.　*See* Title catalogue.

Gretna Green.　*See* Title catalogue.

No song no supper, pasticcio.　*See* Title catalogue.

Il padre e il figlio rivali—The father and the son rivals, Lon-
　　don, 1769.　　　　　　　　　　　　　　　　　　　　Schatz 3851

Phillis at court, London, 1767.　　　　　　　　　　　Longe 36

Summer amusement.　*See* Title catalogue.

To arms! or The British recruit, London, 1793 (with Shield).　Longe 221

Giordaniello.　*See* Giordani, Giuseppe.

Giovannini.　*See* St. Germain.

Giovanni, Veneziano.

Patro Tonno d'Isca, Mmenezia, 1714.　　　　　　　　ML 50.2.P29V2

Giuliani, Giovanni Francesco.

See Albertini's Virginia.

Il fido amante, ballet.　*See* Sarti's Medonte.

Il generoso perdono, ballet.　*See* Anfossi's La maga Circe.

Gluck, Christoph Willibald, *ritter von,* 1714–1787.

See also Catalogue of 19th cent. librettos.

Alceste, Vienna, 1767.　　　　　　　　　　　　　　　Schatz 3885

Alceste, Bologna (1778).　　　　　　　　　　　　　　ML 48.A5　v.29

Alceste, Paris, 1779.　　　　　　　　　　　　　　　　Schatz 3888

Alceste, Paris, 1786.　　　　　　　　　　　　　　　　Schatz 3940

Alceste (Mainz?) 1792.　　　　　　　　　　　　　　Schatz 3889

Antigono, Roma (1756).　　　　　　　　　　　　　　ML 50.2.A72G5

Aristeo.　*See* Le feste d'Apollo.

Armide, Paris, 1777.　　　　　　　　　　　　　　　　Schatz 3893

Armide, Koeln, 1786.　Tr. of the above.　　　　　　Schatz 3894

Bauci e Filemone.　*See his* Le feste d'Apollo.

Le cadi dupé, Vienne, 1768.　　　　　　　　　　　　Schatz 3929

Il convitato di pietra, ballet.　(Same as his Don Juan?)　*See*
　　Calvi's Ezio.

La corona.　*See* Metastasio's Opere.

La Cythère assiégée.　*See* Title Catalogue.

Demetrio, Venezia (1742).　　　　　　　　　　　　　Schatz 3929

Le feste d'Apollo, Parma (1769).　　　　　　　　　　Schatz 3897

L'Ifigenia in Tauride, Vienna, 1783.　Tr. of his Iphigénic en　Schatz 3905
　　Tauride.

Ipermestra (Venezia) 1744.　　　　　　　　　　　　Schatz 3930

Iphigénie en Aulide, Paris, 1774.　　　　　　　　　Schatz 3898

Iphigénie en Aulide, Nouv. éd., Bordeaux, 1783.　　ML 48.M2L

Gluck, Christoph Willibald—Continued.

Iphigénie en Tauride, Paris, 1779.	Schatz 3903
Iphigenia in Tauris, Wien, 1781. Tr. of the above.	Schatz 3904
L'Ipolito [!], Milano, 1745.	Schatz 3931
Der letzte rausch, Mannheim, 1780. Tr. of his L'ivrogne corrigé ou Le mariage du diable.	Schatz 3909
No song no supper, pasticcio. *See* Title catalogue.	
Orfeo. *See* third act of Le feste d'Apollo, Parma (1769).	
Orfeo ed Euridice, ballet. *See* Gazzaniga's La disfatta d' Mori.	
Orfeo ed Euridice, Vienna (1762).	ML 50.2.O7G4
Orfeo ed Euridice, Bologna (1771).	Schatz 3934
Orphée et Euridice, Paris, 1775. Tr. of his Orfeo e Euridice.	ML 50.2.O7G45
Orphée et Euridice, Paris, 1782.	ML 48.M2H
Orpheus and Eurydice, London, 1785.	Schatz 3926
Orpheus und Euridice, 1785 (Cramer's Magazin der musik).	Schatz 3912
Paride ed Elena, Napoli, 1777.	ML 50.2.P27G5
Il Parnaso confuso, Milano, 1765.	Schatz 3936
Die pilgrime von Mecca. A. T. of his Die unvermuthete zusammenkunft.	
Poro, Torino (1745).	Schatz 3933
The princess of Tarento, pasticcio. *See* Title catalogue.	
La rencontre imprévue, Paris, 1776.	Schatz 3919
La Sofonisba, Milano, 1744.	Schatz 3932
Tetide, Vienna, 1760.	Schatz 3937
Il Tigrane, Brescia (1743).	ML 50.2.G56T3
Il trionfo di Clelia, Bologna (1763).	ML 48.M2E
Die unvermuthete zusammenkunft oder Die pilgrime von Mecca, Frankfurt a/M, 1772. Tr. of his La rencontre imprévue.	Schatz 3920
Det uventede møde (Kjobenhavn, 1776). Another Tr. of the above.	Schatz 3922
Zophilette. *See* Title catalogue.	

Gnecco, Francesco, 1769–1810.

See also Catalogue of 19th cent. librettos.

Auretta e Masullo ossia Il contratempo, Genova (1792).	Schatz 3958
L'indolente, Parma (1797).	Schatz 3962
Lo sposo di tre e marito di nessuna, Milano (1793).	Schatz 3965

Gomes, Pietro.

Le fenzeune abbentorate, Napoli (1745).	ML 50.2.F26G6
Il nuovo D. Chisciotte, Napoli, 1748. Altered version of Leo's Il fantastico.	ML 50.2.F178L3

Gossec, François Joseph, 1734–1829.

Anton und Antonette (Mannheim, 1778). Tr. of his Toinon et Toinette.	Schatz 4014
Der fassbinder, Frankfurt am Mayn, 1773. Tr. of his and Audinot's Le tonnelier.	Schatz 488
Der fassbinder, Berlin, 1796. Another Tr.	Schatz 489
Les pêcheurs, Avignon, 1766.	ML 50.2.P305G7
Les pêcheurs, Paris, 1767.	Schatz 4010
Les pêcheurs, Paris, 1771.	Schatz 11702
Les pêcheurs, Paris, 1782.	Schatz 11701
Sabinus, Paris, 1773.	Schatz 4011

Gossec, François Joseph—Continued.

Thésée, Paris, 1782.	SCHATZ 4012
Toinon et Toinette, Paris, 1768.	SCHATZ 4013
Toinon et Toinette, Paris, 1781.	SCHATZ 11703
Le tonnelier, Paris, 1765. Rev. of Audinot's score and music partly new.	ML 50.2.T68
Le tonnelier, Nouv. éd. augm., Paris, 1767.	SCHATZ 487
Le tonnelier, Paris, 1768.	SCHATZ 11672
Le tonnelier, Paris, 1768. "Nouv. éd." of the above.	SCHATZ 11674
Le tonnelier, Paris, 1770. "Nouv. éd. augmentée" of the above.	SCHATZ 11673
De visschers, Amsterdam, 1793. Tr. of his Les pêcheurs.	SCHATZ 4015

Grabut, Louis (Grabu, Lewis, *also* Grebus).

Albion and Albanius, London, 1685.	ML 50.2.A43
Albion and Albanius, London, 1691.	SCHATZ 4060

Gräfe, Johann Friedrich, 1711–1787.

Herkules auf dem Oeta, n. i., n. d.	SCHATZ 4061

Granom, Lewis Christian Austin.

The summer's tale, pasticcio. *See* Title catalogue.

Tom Jones, pasticcio. *See* Title catalogue.

Graun, Carl Heinrich, 1701–1759.

Aetius. Tr. of his Ezio, Berlino, 1755.	SCHATZ 4096
Alessandro e Poro—Alexander und Porus, Berlino, 1744.	SCHATZ 4087
(Angelica e Medoro)—Angelica und Medorus, Berlin, 1749.	SCHATZ 4088
Armida, Berlino, 1751.	SCHATZ 4089
Artaserse—Artaxerxes, Stutgart (1751).	SCHATZ 4090
Britannico—Britannicus, Berlino (1751).	SCHATZ 4091
Catone in Utica—Cato in Utica, Berlino, 1743.	SCHATZ 4092
Coriolano—Coriolanus, Berlino, 1782.	SCHATZ 4093
Demofoonte—Demophontes, Berlino, 1774. L. T. of his Demofoonte ré di Tracia.	SCHATZ 4094
Demofoonte, rè di Tracià—Demophontes, koenig in Thracien, Berlino, 1745. (Two or three arias by Frederick the Great.)	SCHATZ 4113
L'Europa galante—Das galante Europa, Berlino, 1748.	SCHATZ 4095
Ezio—Aetius, Berlino, 1755.	SCHATZ 4096
Le feste galanti—Die galanten feste, Berlino, 1747.	SCHATZ 4114
— Same title, Berlino, 1767.	SCHATZ 4097
Fetonte—Phaeton, Berlino, 1770.	SCHATZ 4098
I fratelli nemici—Die uneinigen brüder, Berlino (1756).	SCHATZ 4100
I fratelli nemici—Les frères ennemis, Berlino (1756).	SCHATZ 4101
Galatea ed Acide, pasticcio. *See* Title catalogue.	
Das galante Europa. *See* L'Europa galante.	
Die galanten feste. *See* Le feste galanti.	
Il giudicio di Paride—Das urtheil des Paris, Berlino, 1752.	SCHATZ 4099
Ifigenia in Aulide—Iphigenia in Aulis, Berlino, 1768.	SCHATZ 4102
Iphigenia (Hamburg, 1731).	SCHATZ 4103
Lucio Papirio—Lucius Papirius, Berlino, 1745.	SCHATZ 4104
Merope—Merope, Berlino, 1756.	SCHATZ 4105
Mitridate—Mithridates, Berlino, 1750.	SCHATZ 4106
Mitridate, Berlin, 1751. French version of the above.	SCHATZ 4107
Montezuma—Montezuma, Berlino, 1771.	SCHATZ 4108
Orfeo—Orpheus, Berlino, 1752.	SCHATZ 4115

Graun, Carl Heinrich—Continued.

Orfeo, Hamburg, 1764 (German and Italian text).   SCHATZ 4109

Phaeton.   Tr. of Fetonte, Berlino, 1770.   SCHATZ 4098

Polidorus (Hamburg) 1735.   SCHATZ 4110

Rodelinda, regina de' Longobardi—Rodelinde, königinn der Longobarden (Berlino) 1741.   SCHATZ 4117

— Same title, Berlino, 1778.   SCHATZ 4111

Semiramide—Semiramis, Berlino, 1754.   SCHATZ 4112

Silla—Silla, Berlino, 1753.   SCHATZ 4116

Sylla, London, 1753.   Tr. of his Silla.   LONGE 262

Die uneinigen brueder.   Tr. of his I fratelli nemici, Berlino (1756).   SCHATZ 4100

Das urtheil des Paris.   Tr. of his Il giudicio di Paride, Berlino, 1752.   SCHATZ 4099

Graupner, Christoph, 1687–1760.

L'amore ammalato—Die kranckende liebe oder Antiochus und Stratonica (Hamburg, 1708).   SCHATZ 4129

L'amore ammalato.   Die kranckende liebe.   Oder: Antiochus und Stratonica (Barth. Feind, Deutsche gedichte, Stade, 1708).   ML 49.A2F2

Bellerophon oder Das in die preussische krone verwandelte wagengestirn (Hamburg, 1708).   SCHATZ 4118

Berenice e Lucilla overo L'amar per virtù—Berenice und Lucilla, oder Das tugendhaffte lieben, Darmstadt (1710).   SCHATZ 4119

La costanza vince l'inganno—Die bestaendigkeit besieget den betrug (Darmstadt, 1719).   SCHATZ 4121

Dido, koenigin von Carthago (Hamburg) 1707.   SCHATZ 4122

Il fido amico, oder Der getreue freund Hercules und Theseus (Hamburg) 1708.   SCHATZ 4123

Greber, Giacomo (Jacob).

The temple of love.   *See* Saggioni, G. F.

Grebus.   *See* Grabut.

Greene, Maurice, 1695–1755.

Phoebe, London, 1748.   LONGE 274

Grenet, François Lupien.

Le triomphe de l'harmonie (Recueil général des opéra, Paris, 1745, t. xvi).   ML 48.R4

Gresnich, Antoine Frédéric, 1752–1799.

Le baiser donné et rendu, Paris, 1796.   ML 50.2.B2G7

Les faux monnoyeurs, ou La vengeance, Paris (1797).   SCHATZ 4131

Grétry, André Ernest Modeste, 1741–1813.

See also Catalogue of 19th cent. librettos.

Aucassin et Nicolette ou Les mœurs du bon vieux tems, Paris, 1782.   ML 50.2.A92G7

L'amant jaloux.   A. T. of his Les fausses apparences.

L'amant jaloux, ou Les fausses apparences, Toulouse, 1780. Inverted T. of his Les fausses apparences.   ML 50.2.F235G7

Die abgeredete zauberey, Wien, 1778.   Tr. of his La fausse magie.   SCHATZ 4154

L'ami de la maison, Paris, Vente, 1772 (52 p.).   YUDIN PQ

L'ami de la maison, Paris, 1772.   SCHATZ 4132

L'ami de la maison, Paris, 1776.   ML 48.M2M

Grétry, André Ernest Modeste—Continued.

L'amitié à l'épreuve, Paris, 1771.	SCHATZ 4134
L'amitié à l'épreuve, Paris, 1777.	ML 48M2M
L'amitié a l'épreuve, Paris, 1776 (Theatre de M. Favart, Paris, Duchesne, 1763–77, t. x). (One-act version.)	ML 49.A2F1
L'amour conjugal. A. T. of his Céphale et Procris.	
L'amour maternel. A. T. of his Elisca.	
Anacréon chez Polycrate, Paris (1797).	SCHATZ 4137
Andromaque, Paris, 1780.	SCHATZ 4138
Aucassin et Nicolette, Paris, 1784.	SCHATZ 4139
Die beiden geizigen, Frankfurt am Mayn, 1772. Tr. of his Les deux avares.	SCHATZ 4146
Das blendwerk, Gotha, 1781. Tr. of his La fausse magie.	SCHATZ 4155
Callias, ou Nature et patrie, Paris (1795).	SCHATZ 4202
La caravana del Cairo, Milano (1795) (with additional airs by Pichl). Tr. of the following:	SCHATZ 4200
La caravane du Caire, Paris, 1783.	SCHATZ 4141
Céphale et Procris, Paris, 1773.	SCHATZ 4198
Colinette à la cour. A. T. of his La double épreuve.	
Le comte d'Albert, Paris, 1787.	ML 50.2.C64G7
Le comte d'Albert, Amsterdam, 1788.	ML 50.2.C64G8
Les deux avares, Paris, 1750.	ML 50.2.D48G7
Les deux avares, Paris, Delalain, 1771.	SCHATZ 11704
Les deux avares, Paris, Ballard, 1771.	SCHATZ 4143
La double épreuve, ou Colinette à la cour, Paris, 1784.	SCHATZ 4147
Der eifersuechtige liebhaber, Wien, 1780. Tr. of his Les fausses apparences.	SCHATZ 4158
Elisca ou L'amour maternel, Paris, an VII (1799).	ML 50.2.E33G7
L'embarras des richesses, Paris, 1782.	SCHATZ 4148
L'épreuve villageoise, Paris, 1784.	ML 50.2.E55G7
L'épreuve villageoise, Paris, 1785.	SCHATZ 4149
Erast und Lucinde, Muenster, 1777. Tr. of his Silvain.	SCHATZ 4187
Les événements imprévues, Paris, 1780.	SCHATZ 4151
La fausse magie, Paris, 1775 (72 p.)	ML 50.2.F23G7
La fausse magie, Paris, 1775 (48 p.)	SCHATZ 4153
Les fausses apparences ou L'amant jaloux, Paris, 1779.	ML 50.2.F235G6
Les fausses apparences, ou L'amant jaloux, Paris, 1780.	SCHATZ 4157
Ferdinand und Nicolette, oder Liebe erhält den sieg, Hamburg, 1787. Tr. of his Aucassin et Nicolette.	SCHATZ 4140
Die freundschaft auf der probe, Frankfurt am Mayn, 1772. Tr. of his L'amitié à l'épreuve.	SCHATZ 4135
— Same title, Wien, 1780.	SCHATZ 4136
Le génie Asouf, ou Les deux coffrets, Paris, an VIII (1799–1800) (pasticcio, music partly by Grétry).	SCHATZ 10591
Das grab des Mufti, oder Die zwey geitzigen, Stettin, 1778. Tr. of his Les deux avares.	SCHATZ 4144
Graf Albert, Berlin, 1798. Tr. of his Le comte d'Albert.	SCHATZ 4142
Der hausffeund, Frankfurt am Mayn, 1774. Tr. of his L'ami de la maison.	SCHATZ 4133
Le Huron, Paris, 1768.	ML 50.2.H8G
Le Huron, Paris, 1770.	SCHATZ 4159
Le Huron, Paris, 1772.	ML 50.2.H8G7
Le Huron, Paris, 1779.	SCHATZ 11705
Le jugement de Midas, Paris, 1778.	ML 50.2.J9G7

Grétry, André Ernest Modeste—Continued.

Le jugement de Midas, Paris, 1779.	SCHATZ 4161
Liebe erhaelt den sieg. A. T. of his Ferdinand und Nicolette.	
Lucile, Paris, Veuve Duchesne, 1769.	ML 50.2.L8G7
Lucile, Paris, Merlin, 1769.	SCHATZ 4165
Lucile, Paris, 1770.	SCHATZ 11706
Lucile, Paris, 1774.	SCHATZ 11707
Lucile, Frankfurt am Mayn, 1772. Tr. of the above.	SCHATZ 4166
Le magnifique, Paris, Herissant, 1773 (52 p.)	ML 50.2.M2G7
Le magnifique, Paris, Herissant, 1773 (56 p.).	SCHATZ 4167
Les mariages Samnites, Paris, 1776 (with music).	SCHATZ 4169
Les mariages Samnites, Nouv. éd., Paris, 1776 (without music).	YUDIN PQ
Les mariages Samnites, Paris, 1782.	
Matroco, Paris, 1778.	ML 50.2.M465G7
The midnight wanderers. *See* Title catalogue.	
Les moeurs du bon vieux temps. A. T. of his Aucassin et Nicolette.	
Nature et patrie. A. T. of his Callias.	SCHATZ 4170
No song no supper, pasticcio. *See* Title catalogue.	
Panurge dans l'isle des lanternes (Paris), 1785.	ML 50.2.P25G7
Le pouvoir de l'amour. A. T. of his Le premier navigateur.	
Der praechtige freygebige, Frankfurt am Mayn, 1774. Tr. of his Le magnifique.	SCHATZ 4168
Le premier navigateur ou Le pouvoir de l'amour, Paris, 1785. Ballet pasticcio from his works.	ML 52.2.P6
Raoul Barbe Bleue, Amsterdam, 1791.	ML 50.2.R22G72
Raoul Barbe Bleue, Bruxelles, 1791.	ML 50.2.R22G73
Das redende gemaehlde, Mannheim, 1771.	SCHATZ 4189
— Same title, Hamburg, 1780. Both Tr. of his Le tableau parlant.	SCHATZ 4190
Riccardo Cor di Leone, Milano (1787). Tr; of the following.	SCHATZ 4201
Richard Coeur de Lion, Paris, 1786.	ML 48.M2H
Richard Coeur de Lion, London, 1786. Tr. of the above, music adapted by Linley.	LONGE 98
Richard Coeur de Lion, Paris, 1787.	SCHATZ 4177
Richard Löwenherz, Berlin (1790).	SCHATZ 4179
Le rival confident, Paris, 1788.	ML 50.2.R58G7
Das rosenfest zu Salenci, Frankfurt am Mayn, 1775. Tr. of:	SCHATZ 4183
La rosière de Salenci, Paris, 1774 (67 p.).	ML 50.2.R8G71
La rosière de Salenci, Paris, 1775.	SCHATZ 4182
La rosière de Salenci, Paris, 1785 (54 p.).	ML 50.2.R8G73
Die samnitische vermaehlungsfeyer, Berlin, 1780. Tr. of his Les mariages Samnites.	SCHATZ 4171
Selima & Azor, London, 1784 (largely by Linley).	LONGE 95
Silvain, Paris, Merlin, 1770 (55 p.).	ML 50.2.S63
Silvain, Paris, Merlin, 1770 (40 p.).	SCHATZ 4184
Silvain, Frankfurt am Mayn, 1772. Tr. of the above.	SCHATZ 4185
Sylvain, Wien, 1778. Another Tr.	SCHATZ 4186
Le tableau parlant, Paris, 1769.	
Thalie au nouveau théâtre, Paris, 1783.	ML 50.2.T395G7
Théodore et Paulin. O. T. of his L'épreuve villageoise.	SCHATZ 4188
Die unvermutheten zufaelle, Wien, 1781. Tr. of his Les événements imprévues.	SCHATZ 4152

Grétry, André Ernest Modeste—Continued.

Das urteil des Midas (Berlin, 1781). Tr. of Grétry's Le jugement de Midas.	SCHATZ 4163
Das urtheil des Midas, Muenster, 1781. Another Tr.	SCHATZ 4162
Das urtheil des Midas, Mitau, 1783. Another Tr.	SCHATZ 4164
Der zauberspiegel (n. i., n. d.). Tr. of his La fausse magie.	SCHATZ 4156
Zemira e Azore, London, 1779. Tr. of the following.	SCHATZ 4196
Zémire et Azor, Paris, 1772.	YUDIN PQ
Zemire et Azor, Berlin, 1773.	SCHATZ 11709
Zémire et Azor, Paris, 1774.	SCHATZ 4191
Zémire et Azor (imperfect copy).	ML 52.2Z45
Zemire und Azor, Frankfurt am Mayn, 1775. Tr. of the above.	SCHATZ 4192
— Same title, Breslau und Leipzig, 1779.	SCHATZ 4193
Zemire und Azor, Mitau, 1782.	SCHATZ 4194
Zemire und Azor, Muenster, 1777.	SCHATZ 4195
Zemire und Azor (n. i., n. d.) (detached copy).	SCHATZ 11710

Grétry, Lucile, 1773–1793.

Le mariage d'Antonio, Paris, 1787.	ML 50.2.M4G7

Gros(s)heim, Georg Christoph, 1764–1847.

Titania oder Liebe durch zauberei, Cassel, 1792.	SCHATZ 4215

Grossi, Carlo.

L'Artaxerse ovvero L'Ormonda costante, Venetia, 1669.	SCHATZ 4216
Giocasta, regina d'Armenia, Venetia, 1677.	SCHATZ 4217
Il Nicomede in Bitinia, Venetia, 1677.	SCHATZ 4218
La Romilda, Vicenza, 1659.	SCHATZ 4219

Grua, Carlo Pietro. *See* Pietragrua, Carlo Luigi.

Grua, Paul, 1754–1833.

Telemaco-Telemach, Monaco, 1780.	SCHATZ 4222

Grueger, Joseph, *d.* 1814.

Hass und aussoehnung oder Die verfolgte und triumphirende liebe, Glatz, 1797.	SCHATZ 4223

Grünewald, Carl Heinrich.

Die errettete unschuld, oder Germanicus, roemischer general (Hamburg, 1706).	SCHATZ 4226

Gürrlich, Joseph Augustin, 1761–1817.

See also Catalogue of 19th cent. librettos.

Das inkognito (Herklots operetten, Berlin, 1793).	SCHATZ 4372a

Guglielmi, Pietro (Pier Alessandro), 1727–1804.

See also Catalogue of 19th cent. librettos.

Ademira, Napoli, 1789.	SCHATZ 4231
Die adliche schaeferin. Tr. of his La pastorella nobile, Dresda, 1791.	SCHATZ 4256
Admeto, Napoli, 1794.	SCHATZ 4286
Adriano in Siria, Venezia (1766).	SCHATZ 4232
Alceste, Milano, 1768.	SCHATZ 4233
Alessandro nell' Indie, Napoli, 1789.	SCHATZ 4234
L'amante che spende, Venezia, 1770.	SCHATZ 4309
Gli amanti della dote, Lisbona, 1794.	SCHATZ 4293
Amintas, pasticcio. *See* Title catalogue under The royal shepherd.	
Amor tra le vendemmie, Napoli, 1792.	SCHATZ 4287

Guglielmi, Pietro (Pier Alessandro)—Continued.

L'amore in villa, Roma, anno VI (1797).   Schatz 4308

Arsace, Venezia, 1788.   Schatz 4297

Arsinoe e Breno, Siena (1790).   Secularization of his Debora e
    Sisara.   Schatz 4315

Artaserse, Bologna (1789).   Schatz 4298

L'astuzie villane, Napoli, 1786.   Schatz 4235

L'Azzardo, Napoli (1790).   Schatz 4236

La bella pescatrice, Napoli (1789).   Schatz 4237

La bella pescatrice—Das schoene fischermaedchen, Dresda,
    1791.   Schatz 4238

Chi la dura la vince ossia La finta cantatrice, Cremona (1791).
    L. T. of his La virtuosa in Mergellina.   Schatz 4299

La contadina superba, ossia Il giocatore burlato (Lisbona,
    1776).   Schatz 4295

La dama avventuriera, Napoli, 1780.   Schatz 4240

Debora e Sisara, Napoli, 1788.   Schatz 4241

Il Demetrio, Venezia, 1775.   Schatz 4310

Il disertore—The deserter, London, 1770.   Schatz 4242

Il disertore, Lisbona (1772).   Schatz 4243

La donna amante di tutti e fedele a nessuno, Napoli, 1783.   Schatz 4288

La donna di tutti caratteri, Napoli, 1763.   Schatz 4289

Le due gemelle, Lucca, 1790.   L. T. of his L'inganno amoroso.
    Also A. T. of his L'equivoco amoroso, another L. T. of
    the same opera.   Schatz 4249

Enea e Lavinia, Napoli, 1785.   Schatz 4285

Enea e Lavinia, Genova (1796).   Schatz 11711

L'equivoco amoroso ossia Le due gemelle, Parma (1792).
    L. T. of his L'inganno amoroso.   Schatz 4311

Le false apparenze, Napoli, 1791.   Schatz 4244

La finta cantatrice.   A. T. of his Chi la dura, la vince.

La finta zingana ossia Il solachianello, Napoli, 1791.   L. T.
    of his: Schatz 4245

La finta zingara.   (Forms p. 33–71 of his Le sventurate fortu-
    nate, Napoli, 1785.)   Schatz 4274

I finti amori, Napoli, 1784.   Schatz 4246

I finti amori—Liebe zum schein, Dresda, 1790.   Schatz 4247

Das fischermaedchen, Frankfurt am Main, 1794.   Tr. of his
    La bella pescatrice.   Schatz 4239

De forsonede medbeylere.   Tr. of his I rivali placati, Kiøben-
    havn, 1777.   Schatz 4262

Li fratelli Pappamosca (Lisboa, 1786).   L. T. of his La vil-
    lanella ingentilita.   Schatz 4283

Die getreue braut.   Tr. of his La sposa fedele, Dresda, 1771.   Schatz 4272

Il giocatore burlato.   A. T. of his La contadina superba.

Il giuoco di picchetto.   See Title catalogue.

L'impostore punito, Milano (1785).   L. T. of his I finti amori.   Schatz 4300

L'impresa d'opera, Venezia, 1769.   Schatz 4282

Gl'inganni delusi, Napoli, 1789.   Schatz 4290

L'inganno amoroso, Napoli, 1786.   Schatz 4248

Gl'intrichi di Don Facilone (Lisbona, 1786).   Schatz 4296

La lanterna di Diogene, Napoli, 1794.   Schatz 4250

La lanterna di Diogene—Die laterne des Diogenes, Dresda,
    1796.   Schatz 4251

Guglielmi, Pietro (Pier Alessandro)—Continued.

Liebe zum schein. Tr. of his I finti amori, Dresda, 1790.	SCHATZ 4247
Il matrimonio in contrasto, Napoli, 1776.	SCHATZ 4252
Mietitori, Napoli, 1781.	SCHATZ 4291
La morte di Cleopatra, Napoli, 1798.	SCHATZ 4253
La morte d'Oloferne. O. T. and A. T. of his Il trionfo di Giuditta o sia La morte d'Oloferne.	
La morte d'Oloferne, Napoli (1791).	ML 50.2.M8G92
La morte di Oloferne, Roma, 1791.	ML 50.2.M8G93
Le nozze in commedia, Napoli, 1781.	SCHATZ 4254
L'Olimpiade, Venezia, 1767 (with A. G. Pampani and G. F. Brusa).	SCHATZ 4316
La pastorella nobile, Napoli, 1788.	SCHATZ 4255
La pastorella nobile—Die adliche schaeferin, Dresda, 1791.	SCHATZ 4256
La pastorella nobile, Brescia (1792).	ML 48.A5 v.12
Le pazzie di Orlando, Milano (1773).	SCHATZ 4301
La pescatrice, Napoli, 1790. L. T. of his La bella pescatrice.	SCHATZ 4281
Il poeta di campagna, Napoli, 1792.	SCHATZ 4263
La pupilla scaltra, Venezia, 1795.	SCHATZ 4257
La quakera spiritosa, Napoli, 1783.	SCHATZ 4258
Il raggiratore di poca fortuna, Napoli, 1779.	SCHATZ 4259
Il ratto della sposa, Venezia, 1765.	SCHATZ 4280
Il ratto della sposa, Lisbona (1767).	ML 50.2.R27G9
Il rè pastore, Venezia, 1767.	SCHATZ 4302
La ricca locandiera, Roma (1759).	ML 48.A5 v.3
Rinaldo, Venezia, 1789.	SCHATZ 4303
Li rivali placati, Bonn, 1774.	SCHATZ 4261
I rivali placati—De forsonede medbeylere, Kiøbenhavn, 1777.	SCHATZ 4262
Robert und Kalliste oder Der triumph der treue, Breslau und Leipzig, 1776. Tr. of his La sposa fedele.	SCHATZ 4273
Ruggiero, Venezia, 1769.	SCHATZ 4304
Das schoene fischermaedchen. Tr. of his La bella pescatrice, Dresda, 1791.	SCHATZ 4238
Lo sciocco poeta di campagna, Milano (1793). L. T. of his Il poeta di campagna.	SCHATZ 4264
Lo sciocco poeta di campagna, Lisbona, 1794.	ML 50.2.S38G9
Lo scroprimento inaspettato, Napoli, 1787.	SCHATZ 4265
La semplice ad arte, Napoli, 1782.	SCHATZ 4266
La serva innamorata, Lisbona, 1794.	SCHATZ 4294
Sesostri, London, 1768.	SCHATZ 4267
Il solachianello. A. T. of his La finta zingana.	
Lo spirito di contradizione, Venezia, 1766.	SCHATZ 4305
La sposa contrastata, Napoli (1791).	SCHATZ 4269
La sposa fedele (Lisbona, 1773).	SCHATZ 4270
La sposa fedele—Den troe bruud, Kiøbenhavn, 1768.	SCHATZ 4271
La sposa fedele—Die getreue braut, Dresda, 1771.	SCHATZ 4272
La sposa fedele, Cremona, n. d.	ML 50.2.S72
Lo sposo di trè e marito di nessuna (Vienna, 1768) (with Gassmann and (mainly) Anfossi).	SCHATZ 284
Lo sposo di trè e marito di nessuna, Napoli, 1781 (with Giordano and (mainly) Anfossi).	SCHATZ 285
Le sventurate fortunate, Napoli, 1785.	SCHATZ 4274
Il Tamerlano, Venezia, 1765.	SCHATZ 4306
Tomiri, Venezia, 1795.	SCHATZ 4276

Guglielmi, Pietro (Pier Alessandro)—Continued.

Il trionfo di Giuditta o sia La morte d'Oloferne, Firenze, 1795.	SCHATZ 4277
Il trionfo di Giuditta o sia La morte d'Oloferne (Livorno, 1796).	SCHATZ 11712
Der triumph der treue. A. T. of his Robert und Kalliste.	
Den troe bruud. Tr. of his La sposa fedele, Kiøbenhavn, 1768.	SCHATZ 4271
Le vicende d'amore, Vienna, 1784.	SCHATZ 4278
La villanella ingentilita, Napoli, 1779.	SCHATZ 4292
La virtuosa bizzara, Venezia, 1791. L. T. of his:	SCHATZ 4280
La virtuosa in Mergellina (Livorno, 1793).	SCHATZ 4279
Vologeso, Milano (1776).	SCHATZ 4307

Guglielmi, Pietro Carlo, 1763–1817.

See also Catalogue of 19th cent. librettos.

Chi la dura la vince, Napoli, 1798.	SCHATZ 4337
Dorval e Virginia, Lisbona, 1795.	SCHATZ 4344
La sposa bisbetica, Torino (1798).	SCHATZ 4312
La sposa di stravagante, Venezia, 1798. L. T. of his La sposa bisbetica.	SCHATZ 4313

Gurzia, Francesco Saverio. *See* Garcia.

Händel, Georg Friedrich, 1685–1759.

Acis och Galatea, Stockholm, 1773 (partly by Johnsen and others).	SCHATZ 4494
Admetus, koenig in Thessalien (Hamburg, 1730). Tr. of his Admeto.	SCHATZ 4470
Admetus, koenig in Thessalien (Hamburg, 1731).	SCHATZ 11713
Agrippina, Venezia, 1709.	SCHATZ 4471
Agrippina—Agrippina, Hamburg, 1718.	SCHATZ 4472
Alcina, London, 1736.	SCHATZ 4496
Alessandro (Rolli, Componimenti poetici, Nuova ed., Verona, 1744)	ML 49.A2R7
Almira, koenigin von Castilien. A. T. of his Der in krohnen erlangte glueckswechsel.	
Apollo turn'd stroller, or, Thereby hangs a tale, London, 1787 (pasticcio).	LONGE 102
Der beglueckte Florindo (Hamburg) 1708.	SCHATZ 4476
The castle of Andalusia, pasticcio. *See* Title catalogue.	
Cleofida, koenigin von Indien. A. T. of his Triumph der grossmuth und treue.	
Daphnis and Amaryllis, Exon, 1766: pasticcio.	LONGE 293
Die durch blut und mord erlangete liebe oder Nero (Hamburg, 1705).	SCHATZ 4475
The golden pippin. *See* Title catalogue.	
Floridante (Rolli, Componimenti poetici, Nuova ed., Verona, 1744)	ML 49.A2R7
Hercules, London, 1745. (In title "A musical drama," whereas a secular oratorio.)	LONGE 306
Der hochmuethige Alexander, Hamburg (1726). Tr. of his Alessandro.	SCHATZ 4473
The honest Yorkshire-man. *See* Title catalogue.	
Der in krohnen erlangte glueckswechsel oder Almira, koenigin von Castilien (Hamburg, 1704).	SCHATZ 4479
Der in cronen erlangte glueckswechsel oder Almira, koenigin von Castilien (Hamburg) 1732. L. ed. of the above.	SCHATZ 4500

72251°—VOL 2—14——23

Händel, Georg Friedrich—Continued.

Judith, gemahlin kayser Ludewigs des Frommen oder Die siegende unschuld, Hamburg (1732) (pasticcio, arias from his Lotario and Chelleri's L'innocenza difesa, recitatives by Telemann).　　SCHATZ 4481

Julius Caesar in Aegypten (Hamburg, 1725).　Tr. of his Giulio Cesare in Egitto, German recitatives, etc., by Linike.　　SCHATZ 4478

Julius Caesar in Aegypten (Hamburg, 1733).　L. ed. of above.　SCHATZ 11690

Lotario.　*See also his* Judith, gemahlin kayser Ludewigs des Frommen.

Love in a village, pasticcio.　*See* Title catalogue.

Der misslungene braut-wechsel, oder Richardus I, Koenig von England (Hamburg, 1729).　Tr. of his Riccardo I, rè d'Inghilterra.　(The added German arias by Telemann).　SCHATZ 4488

Das muster rechtschaffener ehelichen liebe.　A. T. of his Zenobia.

Muzio Scevola—Mutius Scaevola, Hamburg (1723).　(Act III only; act I by Mattei; act II by G. B. Bononcini.)　　SCHATZ 168

Muzio Scevola (Rolli, Componimenti poetici, Nuova ed., Verona, 1744)　　ML 49.A2R7

Nero.　A. T. of his Die durch blut und mord erlangete liebe.

Nouvelle chasse du cerf (*in* Serré de Rieux's Les dons des enfans de Latone, Paris, 1734).　(Pasticcio, chiefly from H.)　ML 63.S36

Oriana (Hamburg, 1717).　Tr. of his Amadigi di Gaula.　SCHATZ 4474

Orpheus and Eurydice, London, 1785.　(A pasticcio from (principally) Gluck, Bach, Händel, and Anfossi.)　　SCHATZ 3926

Otto (Hamburg, 1726).　Tr. of his Ottone.　SCHATZ 4482

Parthenope.　Tr. of his Partenope, Londra, 1730.　SCHATZ 4483

Parthenope.　Tr. of his Partenope (Salzthal, 1731).　SCHATZ 4484

Parthenope (Hamburg) 1733.　Tr. of Partenope, recitatives composed by Keiser.　　SCHATZ 4485

[Poro rè d'Italia]—Porus, Londra, 1736.　SCHATZ 4486

The princess of Tarento, pasticcio.　*See* Title catalogue.

Richardus I, koenig von England.　A. T. of his and Telemann's Der misslungene brautwechsel.

Rinaldo (A. Hill, Dramatic works, London, 1760, t. i).　LONGE 325

Rinaldo, Hamburg (1715).　SCHATZ 4489

Rinaldo (Hamburg, 1723).　L. ed. of the above.　SCHATZ 4501

Rinaldo, Napoli, 1718 (added scenes and arias by Leo).　SCHATZ 4495

Rodelinda, koenigin in der Lombardey (Hamburg, 1734). Tr. of his Rodelinda.　　SCHATZ 4490

Scipione (Rolli, Componimenti poetici, Nuova ed., Verona, 1744)　　ML 49.A2R7

Die siegende unschuld.　A. T. of his, Chelleri and Telemann's Judith, gemahlin kayser Ludewigs des Frommen.

Il Siroe (Bronsevigo, 1767) pasticcio.　*See* Title catalogue.

Sprigs of laurel.　*See* Title catalogue.

The Spring, London (1762).　(Selected from his and the music of others.)　　ML 50.2.S743H2

Tamerlan (Hamburg, 1725).　Tr. of his Tamerlano with interpolated intermezzo by Telemann.　　SCHATZ 4492

Tamerlano—Tamerlane, London, 1724.　ML 50.2.T23

Händel, Georg Friedrich—Continued.

Thereby hangs a tale. A. T. of the pasticcio Apollo turn'd stroller.

Der thrazische printz Floridantes, Hamburg, 1723. Tr. of his Floridante.   SCHATZ 4477

Tom Jones, pasticcio. *See* Title catalogue.

Triumph der grossmuth und treue oder Cleofida, koenigin von Indien, Hamburg (1732). Tr. of his Poro rè d'Italia, recitatives by Telemann.   SCHATZ 4487

Die verwandelte Daphne (Hamburg) 1708. Second part of his Der beglueckte Florindo.   SCHATZ 4493

Zenobia oder Das muster rechtschaffener ehelichen liebe (Hamburg, 1726). Tr. of his Radamisto.   SCHATZ 4502

Haibel, Jacob, *ca.* 1761–1826.

Liebe macht kurzen prozess oder Die heyrath auf gewisse art (Leipzig, 1799) (with Henneberg, Woelfl, and others).   SCHATZ 4633

Halter, Wilhelm Ferdinand, *d.* 1806.

Die kantons-revision, Koenigsberg, 1794.   SCHATZ 4449

Harington (Harrington), Henry, 1727–1816.

No song no supper, pasticcio. *See* Title catalogue.

The princess of Tarento, pasticcio. *See* Title catalogue.

Robin Hood, pasticcio. *See* Title catalogue.

Harny de Guerville.

Les ensorcelés, ou Jeannot et Jeannette, Paris, 1757 (selected and arranged the music of this parody ot de Marivaux-Rameau's Les surprises de l'amour).   SCHATZ 4454

— Same title, Paris, 1758 (Theatre de M. Favart, Paris, Duchesne, 1763–77, t. v).   ML 49.A2F1

Hartmann, Johann Ernst, 1726–1793.

See also Catalogue of 19th cent. librettos.

Balders død, n. i., n. d. (*ca.* 1778).   SCHATZ 4463

Balders tod, Kopenhagen, 1785. Tr. of this.   SCHATZ 4464

Fiskerne, n. d., n. i. (*ca.* 1780).   SCHATZ 4465

Hasse, Johann Adolph, 1699–1783.

See also Catalogue of 19th cent. librettos.

Adriano in Siria, Dresda (1752).   SCHATZ 4503

Adriano in Siria—Adrianus in Syrien, Dresda (1752).   SCHATZ 4504

Alcide al bivio (Vienna, 1760).   SCHATZ 4505

Alcide al bivio—Alcides ved te to veie, Kiøbenhavn, 1774.   SCHATZ 4507

Alcides en der doppel-strasse (Wien, 1760). Tr. of his Alcide al bivio.   SCHATZ 4506

Alcides ved te to veie. Tr. of his Alcide al bivio, Kiøbenhavn, 1774.   SCHATZ 4507

L'Alessandro nell' Indie, Venezia, 1736. (Mennicke calls this second version, numbering "Cleofide" of 1731 as first.)   SCHATZ 4508

Alessandro nell' Indie, Presburgo (1741).   SCHATZ 4509

Alessandro nell' Indie (Venezia, 1743).   SCHATZ 4593

Alfonso (Dresda, 1738).   SCHATZ 4510

Alfonso—Alfonso, Dresden, 1738.   SCHATZ 4511

Antigono (Dresda, 1744).   ML 50.2.A72H2

Antigono, Lucca, 1744.   ML 48.M2M

Hasse, Johann Adolph—Continued.

Archidamia. A. T. of his La Spartana generosa.

Arminio, Milano, 1730.	SCHATZ 4575
Arminio—Arminio (Dresda, 1745).	SCHATZ 4512
Artaserse, Venezia, 1730.	SCHATZ 4576
Artaserse—Artaxerxes (Dresda, 1740) (so-called second version).	SCHATZ 4513
Artaserse, Ferrara (1765). (Schatz: third version.)	SCHATZ 4590
Artaxerxes. Tr. of his Artaserse (Dresda, 1740).	SCHATZ 4513
Artemisia—Artemisia, Dresda (1755).	SCHATZ 4514
L'artigiano gentiluomo. L. T. of his intermezzi Larindae Vanesio.	
Asteria (Dresda, 1737).	SCHATZ 4516
Attalo rè di Britinia, Ferrara (1739).	SCHATZ 4517
Attilio Regolo, Friedrichstadt (1750).	SCHATZ 4518
Attilio Regolo—Attilius Regulus, Friedrichstadt (1750).	SCHATZ 4519
Il bevitore—Der saeuffer (Dresda, 1747).	SCHATZ 4520
Cajo Fabricio, Venezia, 1735.	SCHATZ 4522a
Cajo Fabricio, Salisburgo, 1737.	SCHATZ 4522
Cajo Fabricio—Cajus Fabricius, Berlino, 1766.	SCHATZ 4524
Cajus Fabritius, Dresden, 1734. Tr. of his Cajo Fabricio.	SCHATZ 4523
Il capitan Galoppo, Venezia, 1741. L. T. of his La fantesca.	SCHATZ 4588
Catone in Utica, Torino, 1732.	SCHATZ 4586
Der chinesische held. Tr. of his L'eroe cinese, Berlino, 1773.	SCHATZ 4538
Il Ciro riconosciuto—Der erkennte Cyrus, Stutgart (1752).	SCHATZ 4525
La clemenza di Tito, Verona, 1738. L. T. of his Tito Vespasiano ovvero La clemenza di Tito.	SCHATZ 4526
La clemenza di Tito, Hamburg, 1748.	SCHATZ 4528
Cleofide, Berlino, 1777.	SCHATZ 4573
Cleonice, Venezia, 1740. (Mennicke confuses this with Demetrio.)	SCHATZ 4578
La contadina. O. T. of his Don Tabarrano.	
Dalisa, Venezia, 1730.	SCHATZ 4577
Il Demetrio, Venezia (1732).	SCHATZ 4532
Il Demetrio—Demetrius (Dresda, 1740) (socalled second version).	SCHATZ 4533
Demetrio, Torino (1748).	SCHATZ 4585
Demetrius. Tr. of his Il Demetrio (Dresda, 1740).	SCHATZ 4533
Demofoonte—Demophoon (Dresda, 1748).	SCHATZ 4534
Demofoonte, Venezia, 1749.	SCHATZ 4582
Il Demofoonte, Malta (1765) (socalled second version).	SCHATZ 4574
Demophoon. Tr. of his Demofoonte (Dresda, 1748).	SCHATZ 4534
La Didone abbandonata—Die verlassene Dido, Dresda, 1742.	SCHATZ 4535
Didone abbandonata—Die verlassene Dido, Berlino, 1769.	SCHATZ 4536
Don Tabarrano, n. i., n. d. (Dresda, 1737?). L. T. of his La contadina.	SCHATZ 4529
Don Tabarrano—Don Tabarrano (Dresda, 1747).	SCHATZ 4530
Egeria (Vienna, 1764).	SCHATZ 4537
Die entdeckte Semiramis. Tr. of his La Semiramide riconosciuta (Dresda, 1747).	SCHATZ 4560
Der erkennte Cyrus. Tr. of his Ciro riconoscinto, Stutgart (1752).	SCHATZ 4525
L'eroe cinese—Der chinesische held, Berlino, 1773.	SCHATZ 4538
L'eroica gratitudine. A. T. of his Il Ruggiero.	

Hasse, Johann Adolph—Continued.

Eurimedonte e Timocleone, Venezia, 1746.	SCHATZ 4579
Euristeo, Venezia, 1732.	SCHATZ 4580
Ezio, Dresda (1755) (socalled second version).	SCHATZ 4539
La fantesca. O. T. of his Il capitano Galoppo.	
La finta Tedesca—Die verstellte teutsche, Potsdam, 1749.	
L. T. of his Pantaleone e Carlotta.	SCHATZ 4540
Galatea ed Acide—Galathee und Alcides, Posdamo, 1748.	
(Music selected mainly from his works.)	SCHATZ 4541
Gerone tiranno di Siracusa, Napoli, 1727.	ML 50.2.G3H2
Die gnade des Titus. Tr. of his La clemenza di Tito, Hamburg, 1748.	SCHATZ 4528
Die grossmuethige Spartanerin. Tr. of his La Spartana generosa (Dresda, 1747).	SCHATZ 4565
Die guetigkeit des Titus Vespasianus, Wolfenbuettel (1744). Tr. of his La clemenza di Tito.	SCHATZ 4527
Der handwercks-mann ein edel-mann. Intermezzi in his Cajus Fabritius, Dresden, 1734. Tr. 4. of his L'artigano gentiluomo.	SCHATZ 4523
Hypermenestra. Tr. of his Ipermestra (Friedrichstadt, 1751).	SCHATZ 4543
Der im schaefer verborgene koenig. Tr. of his Il rè pastore, Berlino, 1770.	SCHATZ 4557
L'Ipermestra, Vienna (1744). (The licenza by Luca Ant. Predieri.)	SCHATZ 4542
Ipermestra-Hypermenestra (Friedrichstadt, 1751) (socalled second version).	SCHATZ 4543
Irene—Irene (Dresda, 1738).	SCHATZ 4544
Larinda e Vanesio. O. T. of his L'artigiano gentiluomo.	
Leucippo—Leucippus (Dresda, 1747).	SCHATZ 4545
Leucippo, Venetia, 1749.	SCHATZ 4591
Maid of the mill, pasticcio. *See* the Title catalogue.	
Lucio Papirio—Lucius Papirius, Berlino, 1784.	SCHATZ 4546
La Nitteti, Firenze, 1758.	SCHATZ 4547
Numa—Numa (Dresda, 1743).	SCHATZ 4548
Olimpiade—Das olympische spiel, Dresda (1756).	SCHATZ 4549
L'Olimpiade, Torino (1765).	SCHATZ 4550
Das olympische spiel. Tr. of his Olimpiade, Dresda (1756)	SCHATZ 4549
Orfeo, pasticcio. *See* Title catalogue.	
Pandolfo, Venezia, 1739. L. T. of his Il tutore.	SCHATZ 4583
Pantaleone e Carlotta. O. T. of his La finta Tedesca.	
Partenope (Vienna, 1757).	SCHATZ 4551
Partenope—Parthenope, Berlino, 1775.	SCHATZ 4552
Pharamundus, Wolfenbuettel (1746) (mainly by Hasse).	SCHATZ 4553
Pimpinella e Marcantonio—Pimpernelle und Marcantonius. Intermezzi in his Numa (Dresda, 1743).	SCHATZ 4548
Piramo e Tisbe—Piramus und Thisbe, Berlino, 1771.	SCHATZ 4555
Porsugnacco e Grilletta. Intermezzi in his Gerone tiranno di Siracusa, Napoli, 1727.	ML 50.2.G3H2
Il re pastore, Dresda (1755).	SCHATZ 4556
Il re pastore—Der im schaefer verborgene koenig, Berlino, 1770.	SCHATZ 4557
I rivali delusi. A. T. of his Eurimedonte e Timocleone.	
Romolo ed Ersilea, Roma, 1765.	SCHATZ 4589
Il Ruggiero o vero L'eroica gratitudine, Vienna, 1771.	SCHATZ 4558

Hasse, Johann Adolph—Continued.

Der saeuffer. Tr. of his Il bevitore (Dresda, 1747).	SCHATZ 4520
Semiramide riconosciuta (Venezia, 1745).	SCHATZ 4559
La Semiramide riconosciuta—Die entdeckte Semiramis (Dresda, 1747). (Mennicke calls this second version.)	SCHATZ 4560
La Semiramide riconosciuta—Semiramis (Varsavia, 1760).	SCHATZ 4572
Senocrita (Dresda, 1737).	SCHATZ 4561
[Siroe]—Siroes, King of Persia, London, 1736.	SCHATZ 4587
Siroe, Dresda, 1763 (socalled second version).	SCHATZ 4562
Il Siroe (Bronsevigo, 1767), pasticcio. *See* Title catalogue.	
Siroës—Siroes, Varsovie (1763).	SCHATZ 4592
Solimano, Dresda (1753).	SCHATZ 4563
Solimano—Soliman, Dresda (1754).	SCHATZ 4564
La Spartana generosa ovvero Archidamia—Die grossmuethige Spartanerin (Dresda, 1747).	SCHATZ 4565
The summer's tale, pasticcio. *See* Title catalogue.	
Il Tabarano—Der Tarbaran, Braunschweig (1749). L. T. of his Don Tabarrano.	SCHATZ 4531
Tigrane, Napoli (1745) (the overture, some recitatives and some arias by Antonio Palella).	SCHATZ 4584
Tito Vespasiano ovvero La clemenza di Tito. O. T. of his La clemenza di Tito.	
Tom Jones, pasticcio. *See* Title catalogue.	
Il trionfo della fedeltà. *See* Title catalogue.	
Il trionfo di Clelia (Vienna, 1762).	SCHATZ 4566
Die triumphirende Claelia (Wien, 1762). Tr. of the above.	SCHATZ 4567
Il tutore. (Forms part of his Alfonso, Dresda, 1738.)	SCHATZ 4510
Il tutore—Der vormund (Dresda, 1738).	SCHATZ 4569
Il tutore e la pupilla (Vienna, 1747). L. T. of the above.	SCHATZ 4570
Die verlassene Dido. Tr. of his La Didone abbandonata, Dresden, 1742.	SCHATZ 4535
Die verlassene Dido. Tr. of his Didone abbandonata, Berlino, 1769.	SCHATZ 4536
Die verstellte Teutsche. Tr. of his La finta Tedesca, Potsdam, 1749.	SCHATZ 4540
Viriate, Venezia, 1739.	SCHATZ 4581
Der vormund. Tr. of his Il tutore (Dresda, 1738).	SCHATZ 4569

Haydn, Franz Joseph, 1732–1809.

See also Catalogue of 19th cent. librettos.

Asmodeus der krumme teufel, Wien, 1770. O. T. was Der neue krumme teufel.	SCHATZ 4609
Egle e Cloco o siano I satiri puniti, ballet. *See* Tritto's La fedeltà tra le selve.	
Der freybrief, Berlin, 1788. Music selected from Haydn, Mozart, von Weber.	SCHATZ 4610a
Der freybrief (Nürnberg?) 1797. Two-act version.	SCHATZ 4610
Le jugement de Paris, Paris, an VI (1797–98): pasticcio ballet with music by the above, Pleyel, and Méhul.	ML 52.2J9
Mahmoud, pasticcio, London, 1796. *See* Title catalogue.	
Orlando Paladino—Ritter Roland, Dresda, 1792.	SCHATZ 4612

Hayes, Philip, 1738–1797.

The two misers. *See* Title catalogue.

Two to one. *See* Title catalogue.

Haym, Nicolo, *d.* 1729.
 Pyrrhus and Demetrius, London, 1709. Additional music for
  Tr. version of Scarlatti's Pirro e Demetrio. ML 50.2.P95

Hearn, Jeremy.
 The Lords maske. *See* A relation of the late royall entertainment.

Heiberger, Giuseppe.
 Il colonnello, Roma (1727). ML 50.2.C61H3

Heinichen, Johann David, 1683–1729.
 Calfurnia, Venezia, 1713. Schatz 4701
 Die roemische grossmuht oder Calfurnia, Hamburg (1716).
  Tr. of the above. Schatz 4702
 Diana su l'Elba—Diane sur l'Elbe, Dresde (1719). Schatz 4704
 La gara degli dei—L'émulation parmy les divinitez, Dresde
  (1719). Schatz 4705
 Le passioni per troppo amore, Venezia, 1713. Schatz 4703

Henneberg, Johann Baptist, 1768–1822.
 See also Catalogue of 19th cent. librettos.
 Liebe macht kurzen prozess oder Die heyrath auf gewisse art
  (Leipzig, 1799): with Woelfl, Stegmayer, and others. Schatz 4633
 Die waldmaenner, Hamburg, 1797. Schatz 4631

Hensel, Johann Daniel.
 Daphne oder Die fruehlingsfeier in Arkadien, Hirschberg,
  1799. *In his* Singspiele, Erstes baendchen, together
  with his:
 Die geisterbeschwoerung. Schatz 4635
 Die geisterinsel, Hirschberg, 1799. Schatz 4637

Herbain, *chevalier* d', *ca.* 1734–1769.
 Nanette et Lucas ou La paysanne curieuse, Paris, 1754 [*recte*
  1764] ML 50.2.N15H3
 Nanette et Lucas ou La paysanne curieuse, Paris, 1775. Schatz 4644

Hiller, Friedrich Adam, 1766–1812.
 See also Catalogue of 19th cent. librettos.
 Adelstan und Roeschen (Güstrow, 1792). Schatz 4714
 Biondetta (Schwerin, 1790). Schatz 4715

Hiller, Johann Adam, 1728–1804.
 See also Catalogue of 19th cent. librettos.
 Der aerndtekranz, Leipzig, 1771. Schatz 4718
 Der aerntekranz (C. F. Weisse, Komische opern, Carlsruhe,
  1778). ML 49.A2W2
 Das bauernmaegdchen am hofe. A. T. of his Lottchen.
 Der dorfbalbier, Leipzig, 1772. Schatz 4719
 Der dorfbalbier (Weisse, Komische opern, Carlsruhe, 1778,
  t. ii). ML 49.A2W2
 Die frage und die antwort. A. T. of his Lisuart und Dario-
  lette.
 Das gerettete Troja. A. T. of his Poltis.
 Das grab des Mufti, oder Die zwey geizigen, Leipzig, 1776. Schatz 4720
 Das grab des Mufti, oder Die zwey geizigen (Meissner, Oper-
  etten, 1778). ML 49.A2M3
 Die jagd, Leipzig, 1770. Schatz 4721

Hiller, Johann Adam—Continued.

Die jagd (Weisse, Komische opern, Carlsruhe, 1778, t. iii). ML 49.A2W2

Die jubelhochzeit, Leipzig, 1773. Schatz 4722

Der krieg, Leipzig, 1773. Schatz 4723

Die liebe auf dem lande, Leipzig, 1776. Schatz 4724

Die liebe auf dem lande (Weisse, Komische opern, Carlsruhe, 1778, t. i). ML 49.A2W2

Lisuart und Dariolette oder Die frage und die antwort (Wien) 1766. Schatz 4726

Lisuart und Dariolette, Riga, 1773. Schatz 4734

Lisuart und Dariolette (Nuernberg, 1780). Schatz 4727

Lottchen oder Das bauermaegdchen am hofe, Altona, 1770. Schatz 4729

Lottchen am hofe, Leipzig, 1776. Schatz 4728

Lottchen am hofe (Weisse, Komische opern, Carlsruhe, 1778, t. i). ML 49.A2W2

Der lustige schuster oder Der zweyte theil vom Teufel ist los, n. i., n. d. (Detached copy.) Revisions of, additions to, and partly new recomposition of Standfuss's singspiel. Schatz 4733

Der lustige schuster (Weisse, Komische opern, Carlsruhe, 1778, t. ii). ML 49.A2W2

Der neue gutsherr, n. i., n. d. (detached copy). Schatz 4730

Poltis oder Das gerettete Troja, Leipzig, 1773. Schatz 4731

Der teufel ist los. *See his* Die verwandelten weiber, also Der lustige schuster for a "zweiter theil."

Die verwandelten weiber oder Der teufel ist los, Leipzig, 1772. (H.'s revision and partly recomposition of Standfuss's singspiel. For the second part *see* Der lustige schuster). Schatz 4732

Die verwandelten weiber oder Der teufel ist los (Weisse, Komische opern, Carlsruhe, 1778, t. ii). ML 49.A2W2

Die verwandelten weiber oder Der teufel ist los, Riga, 1794. Schatz 4732a

Die zwey geizigen. A. T. of his Das grab des Mufti.

Himmel, Friedrich Heinrich, 1765–1814.

See also Catalogue of 19th cent. librettos.

Alessandro, S. Pietroburgo, 1799. Schatz 4741

Semiramide—Semiramis, Berlino, 1797. Schatz 4738

Hönicke, Johann Friedrich, 1755–1809.

Heyrath aus liebe, Gotha, 1781. Schatz 4787

Hoffer, Johann Jakob, *d.* 1737.

Gli affetti più grandi vinti dal più giusto. Ballet music in Bononcini's opera.

La costanza d'Ulisse, 1700. Ballet music for Badia's opera.

L'Esopo. Ballet music for M. A. Ziani's opera, Vienna, 1703.

La finta cecità di Antioco il Grande, dances. *See* Draghi's opera, 1695.

Il Gordiano Pio. Ballet music for M. A. Ziani's opera, Vienna, 1700.

Il Romolo. Ballet music for M. A. Ziani's opera, Vienna, 1702.

Sulpitia, 1697. Dances for Draghi's opera.

La tirannide abbattuta dalla virtù. Dances for Draghi's opera, 1697.

Hoffmeister, Franz Anton, 1754–1812.

Der haushahn, Wien, 1783.   Schatz 4749

Der koenigssohn aus Ithaka, Wien, 1797.   Schatz 4750

Liebe macht kurzen prozess, oder Die heyrath auf gewisse art (Leipzig, 1799) (with Henneberg, Woelfl, and others).   Schatz 4633

Telemach, Hamburg (1797). L. T. of his Der koenigssohn aus Ithaka.   Schatz 4751

Telemach, koenigssohn aus Ithaka, Frankfurt a Main, 1798. L. T. of his Der koenigssohn aus Ithaka.   Schatz 4753

Telemach, prinz von Ithaka, Weimar, 1797. (Vulpius's version of the same opera.)   Schatz 4752

Hofmann, Melchior, d. 1715.

Rhea Sylvia, Hamburg (1720).   Schatz 4760

Holcombe, Henry.

Tom Jones, pasticcio. *See* Title catalogue.

Holler, Antonio.

Le Amazzoni, ballet. *See* Zingarelli's Il conte di Saldagna.

Holly, Franz Andreas, 1747–1783.

Der bassa von Tunis, Berlin u. Leipzig, 1774.   Schatz 4768

Deukalion und Pyrrha, Breslau und Leipzig, 1779.   Schatz 4769

Der kaufmann von Smyrna, Frankfurth und Leipzig, 1774.   Schatz 4770

Das opfer der treue, Breslau u. Leipzig, 1779.   Schatz 4771

Der tempel des schicksals (Literatur u. Theater Zeitung, Berlin, 1779).   Schatz 4772

Der zaubrer, Prag, 1772.   Schatz 4773

Holzbauer, Ignaz Jacob, 1711–1783.

Adriano in Siria, Mannheim (1769).   Schatz 4778

Die Chineser (Mannheim, 1756). Tr. of his Le Cinesi.   Schatz 4780

Il figlio delle selve, Mannheim (1753).   Schatz 4781

Il filosofo di campagna, Mannheim (1756).   Schatz 4782

Günther von Schwarzburg, Mannheim (1777).   Schatz 4783

Hadrian in Syrien, Mannheim, 1768. Tr. of his Adriano in Siria.   Schatz 4779

Hysipile, Mannheim (1754). Tr. of his Issipile.   Schatz 4785

Ippolito ed Aricia, Mannheim (1759).   Schatz 4784

L'Ipermestra, Vienna (1744). Ballet music for Hasse's opera.

Tancredi—Tankred (München, 1783).   Schatz 4786

Hook, James, 1746–1827.

See also Catalogue of 19th cent. operas.

Cupid's revenge, London, 1772.   Longe 244

Il dilettante, London, 1772.   ML 50.2.D56H6

The divorce, London, 1771.   Longe 184

The double disguise, London, 1784.   Longe 95

A fairy tale, London, 1777, pasticcio. *See* Title catalogue.   Longe 243

The lady of the manor, London, 1778.   Longe 85

Love and innocence, London, 1769.   Longe 40

The Peruvian, London, 1786.   Longe 97

The snuff box or A trip to Bath, London, 1775.   Longe 310

A trip to Bath. A. T. of The snuff box.

Horban, Giuseppe.

Giasone e Medea, ballet. *See* Andreozzi's L'Arbace.
Giasone e Medea, ballet. *See* Borghi's L'Olimpiade.

Howard, Samuel, 1710–1782.

Love in a village, pasticcio. *See* Title catalogue.
Netley Abbey. *See* Title catalogue.
The summer's tale, pasticcio. *See* Title catalogue.

Hudson, George.

The siege of Rhodes, London, 1663 (with H. Lawes, Cook,
  Locke and Coleman).   ML 50.2.S62

Insanguine, Domenico.

La furba burlata, Napoli, 1762.   (Interpolations in Piccinni's
  opera.)   SCHATZ 8159

Insanguine, Giacomo (*known also as* Monopoli), *d.* 1795.

Calipso, Napoli, 1782.   SCHATZ 4839
Eumene, Torino (1778).   SCHATZ 4838
La finta semplice o sia Il tutore burlato (Lisbona, 1773).   SCHATZ 4837
Medonte, Napoli, 1779.   SCHATZ 4836
Merope, Venezia, 1773.   SCHATZ 4834
Motezuma, Torino (1780).   SCHATZ 4835
Il tutore burlato.   A. T. of his La finta semplice.
La vedova capricciosa, Napoli, 1765.   SCHATZ 4840

Isola, Gaetano, *b.* 1754.

La conquista del vello d'oro, Torino (1791).   SCHATZ 4905
Lisandro, Genova (1790).   SCHATZ 4906

Isouard, Niccolò, 1775–1818.

See also Catalogue of 19th cent. librettos.
L'avviso ai maritati—Die schule der ehemaenner, Dresda,
  1795.   SCHATZ 4908
Aviso aos casados, Lisboa, 1796.   Tr. of the above.   SCHATZ 4944

Ives, Simon, 1600–1662.

The triumph of peace, London, 1633 (with W. Lawes).   LONGE 188

Jackson, William, 1730–1803.

See also Catalogue of 19th cent. librettos.
The lord of the manor, London, 1781.   LONGE 91
The lord of the manor, Philadelphia, 1790.   ML 50.6.L62
The lord of the manor, Philadelphia, 1791.   ML 50.6.L63
Lycidas, London, 1767.   LONGE 198

Jadin, Louis Emmanuel, 1768–1853.

See also Catalogue of 19th cent. librettos.
Alisbelle ou Les crimes de la féodalité, Paris, an II (1794).   SCHATZ 4949
Comment faire? ou, Les épreuves de misanthropie et repentir,
  Paris, an VII (1799).   Only a small part of the music by
  him.   ML 48.M2L
La lettre. *See* Title catalogue.

Jast, F. *See* Jost, F.

Johnsen, Henrik Filip, 1717–1779.

Acis och Galatea, Stockholm, 1773 (mainly by Händel and
  others).   SCHATZ 4494
Procris och Cephal, Stockholm, 1778 (only the recitatives and
  one of the choruses, the arias selected and arranged by
  Lalin).   SCHATZ 4967

Johnson, Robert, *d.* 1634.
    The Lords Maske. *See* A relation of the late royall entertainment.

Jommelli, Niccolò, 1714–1774.
    L'accademia di musica e La conversazione (Lisbona, 1775).   SCHATZ 4887
    Aetius. Tr. of his Ezio, Stutgart, 1758.   SCHATZ 4858
    L'Alessandro nell' Indie—Alexander in Indien, Stutgart, 1760.   SCHATZ 4841
    Alessandro nell' Indie (Lisbona, 1776).   SCHATZ 4899
    L'amore in maschera, Napoli (1748).   SCHATZ 4875
    Armida abbandonata (Lisbona, 1773).   SCHATZ 4901
    Armida abbandonata, Napoli, 1780.   SCHATZ 4842
    Artaserse—Artaxerxes, Stutgart, 1756.   SCHATZ 4843
    Attilio Regolo, Roma, 1753.   SCHATZ 4844
    Le avventure di Cleomede, Lisbona (1772).   SCHATZ 4889
    Bajazet, Torino (1754).   SCHATZ 4878
    Il cacciatore deluso, Lisbona (1771).   SCHATZ 4897
    Cajo Mario, Verona, 1761.   SCHATZ 4896
    Cajus Fabricius, Mannheim, 1760 (with interpolated arias by
      Colla). Tr. of his Cajo Fabricio.   SCHATZ 4846
    La cantata e disfida di D. Trastullo, Roma, 1756.   ML 50.2.C266J6
    Le caprice amoureux ou Ninette à la cour. *See* Title catalogue.
    Il Catone in Utica (Venezia, 1747). (Contributed some arias
      to this opera (principally) by Vinci.)   SCHATZ 10754
    Il Catone in Utica—Der Cato in Utica, Stutgart, 1754.   SCHATZ 4847
    Cerere placata (Napoli, 1772).   SCHATZ 4876
    Cesare in Egitto, Argentina, 1751.   SCHATZ 4848
    César en Egipte, Strasbourg, 1751. Tr. of the above.   SCHATZ 4902
    Ciro riconosciuto, Bologna, 1744.   SCHATZ 4879
    La clemenza di Tito—Die mildigkeit des Titus, Stutgart, 1753.   SCHATZ 4849
    La clemenza di Tito, Lisbona (1771).   SCHATZ 4884
    La conversazione. Forms part of his L'accademia di musica,
      Lisbona (1775).   SCHATZ 4887
    La critica. *See* Title catalogue.
    Il Demetrio, Mannheim (1753).   SCHATZ 4850
    Demetrius, Mannheim (1753). Tr. of the above.   SCHATZ 4851
    Demofoonte, Padova (1743).   ML 50.2.D39J5
    Demofoonte, Milano (1753).   ML 50.2.D39J6
    Demofoonte—Demophon, Stutgart, 1764.   SCHATZ 4852
    Demofoonte, Lisbona (1775).   SCHATZ 4853
    La Didone abbandonata—Die verlassene Dido, Stutgart, 1751.   SCHATZ 4854
    La Didone abbandonata—Didon abandonnée, Stutgart, 1763.   SCHATZ 4855
    Il Don Trastullo, Lucca, 1762. L. T. of his La cantata e disfida di Don Trastullo.   SCHATZ 4882
    L'Endimione ovvero Il trionfo d'amore—Endymion oder Der
      triumph des Amors, Stutgart (1759).   SCHATZ 4856
    L'Endimione (Lisbona, 1780).   SCHATZ 4895
    Enea nel Lazio, Lisbona (1767).   SCHATZ 4893
    Ezio, Bologna (1741).   SCHATZ 4857
    Ezio—Aetius, Stutgart (1758).   SCHATZ 4858
    Ezio, Lisbona (1772).   SCHATZ 4894
    Fetonte—Phaeton (Stutgart) 1768.   SCHATZ 4860
    Fetonte, Lisbona (1769).   SCHATZ 4859
    Il giuoco di picchetto, Mannheim (1773).   SCHATZ, 50.2.G47

Jommelli, Niccolò—Continued.

L'Ifigenia. O. T. of his Ifigenia in Aulide.

L'Ifigenia—Iphigenia, Cassel, 1766.   Schatz 4862

Ifigenia in Aulide, Napoli, 1753. (Interpolated arias by
    Traetta.)   Schatz 4861

Ifigenia in Tauride (Lisbona) 1776.   Schatz 4890

Iphigenia. Tr. of his L'Ifigenia, Cassel, 1766.   Schatz 4862

L'isola disabitata—Die unbewohnte insel (Stuttgart, 1761).   Schatz 4863

Love in the city, pasticcio. See Title catalogue.

The maid of the mill, pasticcio. See Title catalogue.

Il matrimonio per concorso, Milano (1768).   Schatz·4864

Il matto Don Narciso (Dresda, 1762). L. T. of his L'uccel-
    latrice.   Schatz 4874

Merope, Venezia, 1742.   Schatz 4865

Merope, Wien (1749).   Schatz 4866

Die mildigkeit des Titus. Tr. of his La clemenza di Tito,
    Stutgart, 1753.   Schatz 4849

La Nitteti, Lisbona (1770).   Schatz 4891

L'Olimpiade—Die olympische spiele, Stutgard, 1761.   Schatz 4867

L'Olimpiade (Lisbona, 1774).   Schatz 4885

La pastorella illustre—Die vornehme schaeferin (Stuttgardt,
    1763).   Schatz 4868

La pastorella illustre, Lisbona (1773).   Schatz 4886

Pelope—Pelops, Stutgart, 1755.   Schatz 4869

Phaeton. Tr. of his Fetonte, Stutgart, 1768.   Schatz 4860

Ricimero re de' Goti, Roma (1740).   ML 50.2.R48J6

I rivali delusi, Roma, 1752.   ML 50.2.R59J6

La schiava liberata, Lisbona (1770).   Schatz 4898

Semiramide (Venezia, 1743) (text by Silvani).   Schatz 4880

Semiramide—Semiramis (Stutgard) 1762 (text by Metastasio).
    L. T. of his Semiramide riconosciuta.   Schatz 4870

Semiramide, Lisbona (1771) (text by Metastasio).   Schatz 4892

Semiramide in bernesco. Same as his Il cacciatore deluso.

Sofonisba (Venezia, 1746).   Schatz 4871

Talestri, Roma (1727).   ML 50.2.T13J6

Tito Manlio, Torino (1743) (text by Roccaforte).   Schatz 4881

Tito Manlio (Venezia, 1746) (text by Noris). (According to
    Schatz, arias by Antonio Zanetti were interpolated.)   Schatz 4900

Il trionfo d'amore. A. T. of his L'Endimione.

Il trionfo d'amore—Der triumph des Amors (Stuttgardt, 1763). Schatz 4872

Der triumph des Amors. A. T. of his Endymion.

Der triumph des Amors. Tr. of his Il trionfo d'Amore (Stutt-
    gardt, 1763).   Schatz 4872

Il trionfo di Clelia (Lisbona, 1774).   Schatz 4883

L'uccellatrice, Venezia (1750).   Schatz 4873

Die unbewohnte insel. Tr. of his L'isola disabitata (Stutgart,
    1761).   Schatz 4863

Die verlassene Dido. Tr. of his La Didone abbandonata,
    Stutgart, 1751.   Schatz 4854

Vasco di Gama, pasticcio. See Title catalogue.

Il Vologeso, Lisbona (1769).   Schatz 4877

Die vornehme schaeferin. Tr. of his La pastorella illustre
    (Stuttgardt, 1763).   Schatz 4868

Zophilette. See Title catalogue.

Jost (Jast), F.
Der aepfeldieb, Wien, 1781.   Schatz 4979

Kaffka, Johann Christoph, 1754–1815 (*real name* Engelmann).
Der aepfeldieb oder Der schatzgraeber (Bretzner, Operetten, Leipzig, 1779).   Schatz 4982
Antonius und Cleopatra (Literatur und Theater Zeitung, Berlin, 1779).   Schatz 4772
Das beste komt zulezt. A. T. of his Der guckkasten.
Bitten und erhoerung (Litteratur und Theater Zeitung, Berlin, 1783).   Schatz 4772
Gastfreiheit und armuth. A. T. of his Philemon und Baucis.
Der guckkasten oder Das beste komt zulezt (Sammlung auserlesener theaterstücke, Breslau, 1784).   Schatz 4984
Philemon und Baucis oder Gastfreiheit und armuth, Augsburg, 1792.   Schatz 4985
Rosemunde (Litteratur und Theater Zeitung, Berlin, 1780).   Schatz 4772
Der schatzgraeber. A. T. of his Der aepfeldieb.
So prellt man alte fuechse (Sammlung auserlesener theaterstücke, Breslau, 1784).   Schatz 4987
Die zigeuner, n. i., 1778.   Schatz 4988

Kalkbrenner, Christian, 1755–1806.
Demokrit, Berlin, 1791.   Schatz 4997
Olimpie, Paris, an VII (1798–99).   Schatz 4998

Kallenbach, Georg Ernst Gottlieb.
Opera buffa (Bretzner, Singspiele, 1796).   Schatz 4999
Schattenspiel an der wand (Bretzner, Singspiele, Leipzig, 1796).   Schatz 5000
Der schlaftrunk, Altona, n. d.   Schatz 5001

Kauer, Ferdinand, 1751–1831.
See also Catalogue of 19th cent. librettos.
Auf dem land kennt man die rache nicht. A. T. of his Der unschuldige betrug.
Das faustrecht in Thueringen, Erster theil, Wien, 1797.   Schatz 5027
— Zweyter theil, Wien, 1797.   Schatz 5028
— Dritter theil, Wien, 1797.   Schatz 5029
Das goldene gefaess. A. T. of his Ritter Willibald.
Gute menschen lieben ihren fuersten oder Die Jakobiner in Deutschland, Wien, 1799.   Schatz 5032
Kaspars zoegling oder Der sieg der bescheidenheit auf der insel des vergnuegens, Wien, 1791.   Schatz 5035
Die loewenritter, Wien, 1799.   ML 50.2.L5K2
Ritter Willibald oder Das goldene gefaess, Wien, 1794.   Schatz 5053
Der sieg der bescheidenheit auf der insel des vergnuegens. A. T. of his Kaspars zoegling.
Der unschuldige betrug, oder Auf dem land kennt man die rache nicht, Wien, 1790.   Schatz 5061
Der waffenschmied, Wien, 1797.   Schatz 5065

Keiser, Reinhard, 1674–1739.
Achilles. *See his* Das zerstoerte Troja.
Almira, koenigin in Castilien. A. T. of his Der durchlauchtige secretarius.

Keiser, Reinhard—Continued.

L'amore verso la patria, Die liebe gegen das vaterland oder
    Der sterbende Cato, Hamburg (1715).   Schatz 5075

Der angenehme betrug oder Der carneval von Venedig (Ham-
    burg, 1707).   Schatz 5076

— Same, Hamburg, 1716.   Schatz 5118

— Same, Hamburg (1723).   Schatz 5119

Ariadne. *See his* Die betrogene . . .

Arsinoe. A. T. of his La grandezza d'animo.

Artemisia, Hamburg (1715).   Schatz 5077

Aurora. A. T. of his Der morgen des europaeischen glueckes.

Der bestuerzte und wieder erhoehte Nebucadnezar, koenig
    zu Babylon (Hamburg, 1704).   Schatz 5092

Die betrogene und nachmals vergoetterte Ariadne (Hamburg,
    1722).   Schatz 5079

Der bey dem allgemeinen weltfriede von dem Grossen Augus-
    tus geschlossene tempel des Janus, Hamburg (1698).   Schatz 5120

— Same (Hamburg, 1729).   Schatz 5078

Die biss in und nach dem todt unerhoerte treue des Orpheus,
    Hamburg (1709) (5-act version of his Orpheus).   Schatz 5105

Die blut-durstige rache oder Heliates und Olympia (Ham-
    burg, 1709).   Schatz 5080

Le bon vivant oder Die Leipziger messe, Hamburg (1710).   Schatz 5121

Bretislaus oder Die siegende bestaendigkeit, Hamburg (1725). Schatz 5133

Der carneval von Venedig. A. T. of his Der angenehme
    betrug.

Carolus V. A. T. of his Die oesterreichische grossmuht.

Circe (Hamburg) 1734.   Schatz 5081

Circe oder Des Ulisses erster theil, Hamburg, 1702.   Schatz 5082

Claudius, roemischer kaeyser (Hamburg, 1726). *See his* Die
    verdammte staat-sucht.   Schatz 5083

La costanza sforzata. Die gezwungene bestaendigkeit oder
    Die listige rache des Sueno (Hamburg, 1706).   Schatz 5084

— Same (Feind, Deutsche gedichte, Stade, 1708).   ML 49.A2F2

Croesus. *See his* Der hochmuethige.

Cupido. *See his* Der sich raechende Cupido.

Desiderius, koenig der Longobarden (Hamburg, 1709).   Schatz 5085

Diana. *See his* Die entdeckte verstellung.

Der durch den fall des grossen Pompejus erhoehete Julius
    Caesar (Hamburg, 1710).   Schatz 5086

Der durch den tod Helenen versoehnte Achilles. A. T. of
    his Das zerstoerte Troja.

Die durch verstellung und grossmuth uber die grausamkeit
    siegende liebe oder Julia, Hamburg (1717).   Schatz 5087

Der durchlauchtige secretarius oder Almira, Koenigin in Cas-
    tilien (Hamburg, 1706).   Schatz 5122

Die edelmuehtige Octavia. A. T. of his Die roemische
    unruhe.

Die entdeckte verstellung oder Die geheime liebe der Diana,
    Hamburg (1712).   Schatz 5088

Die eroberung des gueldenen fluesses. A. T. of his Jason.

La fedeltà coronata oder Die gekroente treue (Hamburg,
    1706).   Schatz 5089

Keiser, Reinhard—Continued.

La forza dell' amore, Die macht der liebe oder Die von Paris
    entfuehrte Helena, Hamburg, 1709.   Schatz 5090

Fredegunda, Hamburg, 1716.   Schatz 5123

Fredegunda, Hamburg (1736).   Schatz 5091

Die gecroente tapferkeit des Heraclius. A. T. of his Die
    wiederhergestellte ruh.

Die geheime liebe der Diana. A. T. of his Die entdeckte
    verstellung.

Die gekroente treue. A. T. of his La fedeltà coronata.

Der gestuerzte und wieder erhoehte Nebucadnezar, koenig
    zu Babylon (Hunold, Theatralische . . . gedichte, Ham-
    burg, 1706).   ML 49.A2H9

Die gezwungene bestaendigkeit oder Die listige rache des
    Sueno. German title of his La costanza sforzata.

Der glueckliche betrug. A. T. of his Der Hamburger jahr-
    marckt.

La grandezza d'animo oder Arsinoe (Hamburg, 1710).   Schatz 5093

Die grossmuethige Tomyris, Hamburg (1717).   Schatz 5094

Der Hamburger jahr-marckt oder Der glueckliche betrug
    (Hamburg, 1725).   Schatz 5095

Helena. *See his* La forza dell' amore.

Heliates und Olympia (Hamburg) 1709.

Heraclius. *See his* Die wiederhergestellte ruh.

Hercules. *See his* Die verbindung des grossen . . .

Der hochmuethige, gestuerzte und wieder erhabne Croesus,
    Hamburg (1711).   Schatz 5124

— Same (Hamburg) 1730.   Schatz 5096

Janus. *See his* Der bey dem allgemeinen welt-friede . . .

Jason oder Die eroberung des gueldenen fluesses (Hamburg,
    1720).   Schatz 5097

Julia. *See his* Die durch verstellung . . . siegende liebe.

Julius Caesar. *See his* Der durch den fall . . . erhoehete.

Die kleinmuethige selbst-moerderin Lucretia oder Die staats-
    thorheit des Brutus (Hamburg, 1705).   Schatz 5099

— Same (B. Feind, Deutsche gedichte, Staden, 1708). ML 49.A2F2

Der laecherliche printz Jodelet (Hamburg, 1726).   Schatz 5100

Die Leipziger messe. A. T. of his Le bon vivant.

Die liebe gegen das vaterland oder Der sterbende Cato, Ham-
    burg (1715). German title of his L'amore verso la patria. Schatz 5075

Die listige rache des Sueno. A. T. of his La costanza sforzata.

Lucius Verus oder Die siegende treue (Hamburg, 1728). Schatz 5101

Lucretia. *See his* Die kleinmuethige . . .

Die macht der liebe oder Die von Paris entfuehrte Helena.
    German title of his La forza dell' amore.

Masagniello furioso oder Die neapolitanische fischer-em-
    poerung (B. Feind, Deutsche gedichte, Stade, 1708). ML 49.A2F2

Masagniello furioso . . . Die neapolitanische fischer-empoe-
    rung, Hamburg (date torn off).   Schatz 5125

Masagniello furioso . . . [port.] Die neapolitanische fischer-
    empoerung, Hamburg, 1714.   Schatz 5126

Masagniello furioso oder Die neapolitanische fischer-empoe-
    rung (Hamburg) 1727.   Schatz 5102

Mistevojus (Hamburg, 1726).   Schatz 5103

Keiser, Reinhard—Continued.

Der morgen des europaeischen glueckes oder Aurora, Hamburg (1710).   Schatz 5104

Die neapolitanische fischer-empoerung. A. T. of his Masagniello furioso.

Nebucadnezar. *See his* Der bestuerzte . . .

Nebucadnezor. *See his* Der gestuerzte und wieder erhoehte

Octavia. *See his* Die roemische unruhe.

Die oesterreichische grossmuht oder Carolus V (Hamburg, 1712).   Schatz 5108

Orpheus, erster theil. *See his* Die sterbende Eurydice.

Orpheus, ander theil (Hamburg, 1702). *See also his* Die biss in und nach dem todt unerhoerte treue des Orpheus.   Schatz 5107

Parthenope (Hamburg) 1733. Recitatives only, arias by Händel.   Schatz 4485

Penelope und Ulysses, ander theil, Hamburg, 1702.   Schatz 5109

Die roemische unruhe oder Die edelmuehtige Octavia (Hamburg) 1705.   Schatz 5128

Die roemische unruhe oder Die edelmuetige Octavia (B. Feind, Deutsche gedichte, Stade, 1708).   ML 49.A2F2

Das roemische April-fest, Hamburg (1716).   Schatz 5127

Salomon. A. T. of his Die ueber die liebe triumphirende weissheit.

Die schöne und getreue Ariadne. O. T. of his Die betrogene . . . Ariadne.

Der sich raechende Cupido, Hamburg (1724). L. T. of his Die endeckte verstellung.   Schatz 5129

Die siegende bestaendigkeit. A. T. of his Bretislaus.

Die siegende liebe. *See his* Die durch verstellung . . .

Der siegende Phaeton, Hamburg, 1702.   Schatz 5110

Die siegende treue. A. T. of his Lucius Verus.

Die staats-thorheit des Brutus. A. T. of his Die kleinmuehtige selbst-moerderin Lucretia.

Die sterbende Eurydice oder Orpheus erster theil (Hamburg, 1702).   Schatz 5106

Stoertebecker und Joedge Michaels, erster theil, Hamburg, 1701.   Schatz 5111

— Same, zweyter theil, Hamburg, 1701.   Schatz 5112

Die triumphirende weissheit. *See* next entry.

Die ueber die liebe triumphirende weissheit oder Salomon (Hamburg) 1703.   Schatz 5113

Die unerhoerte treue des Orpheus. *See his* Die biss in und nach dem todt . . .

Die verbindung des grossen Hercules mit der schoenen Hebe (Hamburg) 1699.   Schatz 5114

Die verdammte staat-sucht oder Der verfuehrte Claudius, Hamburg, 1703.   Schatz 5130

Der verfuehrte Claudius. A. T. of his Die verdammte staatsucht.

Die von Paris entfuehrte Helena. A. T. of his Die macht der liebe.

Die wiederhergestellte ruh oder Die gecroente tapferkeit des Heraclius (Hamburg, 1712).   Schatz 5115

Die wiederkehr der gueldenen zeit (Hamburg) 1699.   Schatz 5131

Keiser, Reinhard—Continued.
Die wunderbahr-errettete Iphigenia, Hamburg, 1699.   Schatz 5132
Die wunderschoene Psyche (Hamburg) 1701.   Schatz 5116
Das zerstoerte Troja oder Der durch den tod Helenen ver-
    soehnte Achilles, Hamburg (1716).   Schatz 5117

Kelly, Michael, 1762–1826.
See also Catalogue of 19th cent. librettos.
Blue-beard, or, Female curiosity, London, 1798.   Longe 246
Feudal times or The banquet-gallery, London (1799).   Longe 249
The siege of Belgrade. *See* Title catalogue.

Kelly, Thomas Alexander Erskine, *earl of,* 1732–1781.
Maid of the mill, pasticcio. *See* Title catalogue.

Kerl, Johann Caspar, 1628–1693.
L'Erinto, Monaco, 1671.   Schatz 5141

Kerpen, Franz Hugo, *freiherr* von.
Der schiffbruch, Frankfurt am Mayn, 1778.   Schatz 5142

Knecht, Justin Heinrich, 1752–1817.
Die entfuehrung aus dem serail, Kaufbeuren (1790).   Schatz 5197
Die treuen koehler, Kaufbeuren (1789).   Schatz 5198

Kohault, Joseph, *ca.* 1736–1793.
La bergère des Alpes, Avignon, 1766.   ML 48.M2I
La bergère des Alpes, Bruxelles, 1770.   Schatz 5204
Der schlosser, Frankfurt am Mayn, 1772. Tr. of his Le
    serrurier.   Schatz 5206
Le serrurier, Paris, 1765.   Schatz 5205
Le serrurier, Paris, 1766.   Schatz 11716
Le serrurier, Paris, 1771.   Schatz 11717
Sophie ou Le mariage caché, Paris, 1771.   Schatz 5207

Kospoth, Otto Carl Erdmann, *freiherr von, d.* 1817.
Adrast und Isidore, n. i., 1787.   Schatz 5217
Den irrwisch, n. i., 1784.   ML 50.2.I68K6
Der irrwisch oder Endlich fand er sie, n. i., 1787.   Schatz 5218
Der kluge Jacob, Leipzig, 1787.   Schatz 5219
Der maedchenmarkt, Hamburg, 1793.   Schatz 5220

Krafft, François, *b.* 1733.
L'enfant gâté, ou Folette et Roger-Bontems, Paris, 1758.
    Parody of Destouches' Le carnaval et la folie.   ML 50.2.E45
Folette ou L'enfant gâté (Vadé, Œuvres, 1759, t. iii). An-
    other Title of this parody.   ML 49.A2V2

Krafft, Georg.
Giocasta-Giocasta, Dusseldorf (1696) (mainly by Wilderer).   Schatz 11014
Il giorno di salute ovvero Demetrio in Athene—Der tag des
    heyls oder Demetrius in Athen, Dusseldorf (1697). (Only
    the incidental ballets for Wilderer's opera.)   Schatz 11015

Kreutzer, Rodolphe, 1766–1831.
See also Catalogue of 19th cent. librettos.
Le Franc Breton ou Le négociant de Nantes, Paris, 1791 (with
    Solié).   ML 50.2.F8K7

Kreutzer, Rodolphe—Continued.

Le génie Asouf, ou Les deux coffrets, Paris, an VIII [1799]
(pasticcio, partly music by the above).   Schatz 10591

Lodoiska, Paris, 1792.   Schatz 5265

Lodoiska, London (1794) (pasticcio from the above, Storace,
Cherubini, and Andreozzi).   Longe 228

La Lodoiska, Lisbona, 1796. Tr. of the above, with additional
music by others.   Schatz 5269

Paul et Virginie, Hambourg, 1796.   Schatz 5266

Krieger, Johann Philipp, 1649–1725.

Hercules unter denen Amazonen, Hamburg (1694).   Schatz 5272

— Hercules. Anderer theil (Hamburg, 1694).   Schatz 5273

Kueffner, Wilhelm Joseph, d. 1798.

La corona d'Imeneo, Wirzburgo, 1772.   Schatz 5283

Kuerzinger, Paul Ignaz.

Die bergknappen, Regensburg, 1773.   Schatz 5337

Die illumination (Wien) 1787.   Schatz 5338

Julie oder Die dankbare tochter, Regensburg, 1780.   Schatz 5339

Minervens ankunft bey den Musen (Regensburg, 1780).   Schatz 5340

Kuntzen (Kunz), Johann Paul, 1696–1757.

Cadmus, Hamburg (1725).   Schatz 5314

Die helden-muethige schaefer Romulus und Remus (Hamburg, 1724). Recitatives and some arias of this Tr. of
Porta's Numitore, alias Rhea Sylvia.   Schatz 8381

Die uber eyffersucht und list triumphirende bestaendige
liebe, Wittenberg (ca. 1720).   Schatz 5315

Kunzen, Friedrich Ludwig Aemilius, 1761–1817.

See also Catalogue of 19th cent. librettos.

Erik Eiegod, Kiøbenhavn, 1798.   Schatz 5316

Das fest der winzer, n. i., n. d., and   Schatz 5332

Das fest der winzer, oder Wer fuehrt die braut nach hause?
Both L. T. of his Die weinlese.   Schatz 5333

Hemmeligheden, Kiøbenhavn, 1796.   Schatz 5320

Holger Danske (Cramer's Musik, 1789). Tr. of his opera of
same title.   ML 4.M3 and Schatz 5321

Naturens røst, Kiøbenhavn, 1799.   Schatz 5327

Die weinlese, Frankfurt am Main, 1793.   Schatz 5331

Wer fuehrt die braut nach hause? A. T. of his Das fest der
winzer.

Kusser (Cousser), Johann Sigismund, 1660–1727.

Der grossmuethige Scipio Africanus (Hamburg, 1694).   Schatz 2285

La Barre, Michel de, d. 1743.

Le triomphe des arts (Recueil général des opéra, t. vii, Paris,
1703).   Schatz 5344

La Venitienne (Recueil général des opéra, t. viii, Paris, 1706).   Schatz 5345

La Borde, Jean Benjamin de, 1734–1794.

Les amours de Gonesse. A. T. of his Le Mitron et la Mitronne.

L'anneau perdu et retrouvé, Paris, 1764.   Schatz 5350

Gilles, garçon peintre z'amoureux-t-et rival, Paris, 1758.   Schatz 5348

Ismene et Ismenias, Paris, 1770.   ML 50.2.I7L2

La Borde, Jean Benjamin de—Continued.

    The maid of the oaks. *See* Title catalogue.

    La meunière de Gentilly, Paris, 1768.   ML 50.2.M63L2

    La meunière de Gentilly, Avignon, 1768.   ML 50.2.M63L22

    La meunière de Gentilly, Paris, 1770.   Schatz 5346

    La meunière de Gentilly, Paris, 1779.   Schatz 11718

    Le Mitron et la Mitronne, ou Les amours de Gonesse, Paris, 1765.   Schatz 5349

    Die muellerin, Frankfurt am Mayn, 1773. Tr. of his La meunière de Gentilly.   Schatz 5347

    Thétis et Pélée (Paris) 1765 (Journal des spectacles, Paris, 1766, t. i).   ML 48.J7

    Zenis et Almasie (Paris) 1765 (Journal des spectacles, t. ii, Paris, 1766).   ML 48.J7

Lacher, Johann Joseph, 1739–1798.

    Emma und Edgar, Menmmingen [!] 1788.   Schatz 5362

    Der schulze im dorfe, oder Der verliebte herr doctor, n. i., 1789.   Schatz 5363

La Coste.

    Aricie (Recueil général des opéra, **t. vi**, Paris, 1703).   Schatz 5351

    Biblis (*ibid.*, t. xv, Paris, 1739).   Schatz 5352

    Bradamante (*ibid.*, t. ix, Paris, 1710).   Schatz 5353

    Créuse l'Athénienne (*ibid.*, t. x, Paris, 1714).   Schatz 5354

    Orion (*ibid.*, t. xiv, Paris, 1734).   Schatz 5355

    Philomele, Amsterdam, 1706.   ML 50.2.P36L2

    Philomèle (Recueil général des opéra, ix, Paris, 1710).   Schatz 5356

    Philomèle, Lyon, 1742.   Schatz 5356a

    Télégone (Recueil général des opéra, t. xiii, Paris, 1734).   Schatz 5357

Ladurner, Ignaz Anton, 1766–1839.

    Wenzel ou Le magistrat du peuple, Paris, Seconde année (1794).   Schatz 5375

Laguerre, Elisabeth Claude Jacquet, Mme Marin de, *d.* 1729.

    Céphale et Procris (Recueil général des opéra, t. iv, Paris, 1703).   Schatz 5376

La Lande, Michel Richard de, 1657–1726.

    Ballet de la Jeunesse (Amsterdam) 1686.   ML 49.A2L9

    Les élémens, n. i., n. d. (with Destouches).   ML 52.2.E4

    Les élémens (Recueil général des opéra, t. xiii, Paris, 1734) (with Destouches).   Schatz 5379

Lalin, Lars Samuel.

    Procris och Cephal, Stockholm, 1778 (selected merely the arias; Johnsen composed the recitatives and one of the choruses).   Schatz 4967

Lambert, Michel.

    Ballet du Dereiglement des passions, de l'interest, de l'amour, & de la gloire (Paris, 1648).   ML 52.2B12

La Motte Foucher, Alessandro.

    La locandiera, Lucca, 1798.   Schatz 5358

    La morte d'Ettore, ballet. *See* Nasolini's Gl'Indiani.

Lampe, Johann (*or* Georg Friedrich), *b.* 1744.

    Das maedchen im Eichthale, Hamburg, 1785.   Schatz 5384

Lampe, John Frederick, 1703–1751.

Amelia, London, 1732.	Longe 105
Amelia (Henry Carey, Dramatick works, London, 1743).	ML 49.A2C2
The dragon of Wantley, London, 1738 (12th ed.).	ML 50.2.D67L2
The dragon of Wantley (Henry Carey, Dramatick works, London, 1743).	ML 49.A2C2
The dragon of Wantley, London, 1770.	ML 50.2.D67L3
The dragon of Wantley, London, n. d.	Longe 69
The dragoness (Henry Carey, Dramatick works, London, 1743). L. T. of their Margery.	ML 49.A2C2
Margery or A worse plague than the dragon, London, 1738. (3d ed.).	Longe 153
Orpheus and Eurydice, London, 1740.	Longe 199
The summer's tale, pasticcio. *See* Title catalogue.	

Lampugnani, Giovanni Battista, *ca.* 1706–1786.

Amor contadino, Venezia, 1760.	Schatz 5386
L'amor contadino—Bønderfolks elskov, Kiøbenhavn (1763).	Schatz 5387
Angelica, Venezia, 1738.	Schatz 5391
Candace, Venezia (1740).	Schatz 5392
Ezio, Venezia (1737).	Schatz 5388
Ezio, Venetia (1743).	Schatz 11719
Semiramide riconosciuta, Roma, 1741.	Schatz 5389
The summer's tale, pasticcio. *See* Title catalogue.	
Tigrane, Venezia, 1747.	Schatz 5390

Lange, Georg Ernst. *Pseud.* of Georg Ernst Lüderwald.

Der freybrief, Berlin, 1788.	Schatz 4610a
List und ungefaehr, oder Der glueckliche zufall, Riga, 1793.	Schatz 5415

Laniere, Nicholas, 1588–1666.

Luminalia or The festivall of light, London, 1737 (doubtful).	ML 52.2.L92

Lapis, Santo.

La fede in cimento, Venezia, 1730. (Same as Gasparini's L'amor generoso, with additions by the above.)	Schatz 3596
La generosità di Tiberio, Venezia, 1729 (act III by Cordans).	Schatz 5431

La Ruette (Laruette), Jean Louis, 1731–1792.

Les amans trompés, Paris, 1756.	ML 50.2.A63
Les amants trompés, Paris, 1756.	Schatz 11478
Cendrillon, Paris, 1759.	Schatz 5436
Le docteur San Grado, 1758 (with Duni).	Schatz 2859
La fausse aventuriere, Paris, 1757.	Schatz 5437
Le Guy de Chesne, ou La feste des Druides, Paris, 1763.	Schatz 5439
Der letzte rausch, Mannheim, 1780. Tr. of his L'yvrogne corrigé, as arranged by Gluck.	Schatz 3909
Le medecin de l'amour, Prais, 1758.	Schatz 5438
Le plaisir et l'innocence, Paris, 1753.	ML 50.2.P47L2
L'yvrogne corrigé, Paris, 1759.	Schatz 5434

Lasalle d'Offemont, Adrien Nicolas, *marquis,* 1734–1818.

Bertholde à la ville, Paris, 1754. Parody of Ciampi's Bertoldo, Bertoldino e Cacasenno.	ML 50.2.B37C31
Bertholde a la ville, La Haye, 1755.	ML 48.A4
Bertholde à la ville, Paris, 1766.	Schatz 1883

Latilla, Gaetano, 1711–1791.

Alessandro nell' Indie, Venezia, 1753 (with others).   Schatz 5455

L'ambizione delusa, Torino (1747). L. T. of his Madama
Ciana.   Schatz 5462

L'amore artigiano, Venezia, 1761.   Schatz 5442

L'amore artigiano—De forelskte haandverksfolk, Kiøbenhavn (1762).   Schatz 5443

Amore in tarantola, Venezia, 1750.   Schatz 5444

L'astuzia felice. *See* Goldoni's Opere teatrali.

Le caprice amoureux ou Ninette à la cour. *See* Title catalogue.

Catone in Utica, Roma, 1747.   Schatz 5456

Ciana, Monaco, 1749. L. T. of his Madama Ciana.   Schatz 5448

La commedia in commedia, Ferrara (1747).   Schatz 5457

Demofoonte, Venezia (1738).   Schatz 5458

La finta cameriera, Venezia, 1743.   Schatz 5445

La finta cameriera. *See also* Galuppi's La finta cameriera,
Brunswick, 1751.

De forelskte haandverksfolk. Tr. of his L'amore artigiano,
Kiøbenhavn (1762).   Schatz 5443

La gara per la gloria, Venezia, 1744.   Schatz 5459

Il giuoco de' matti, Napoli, 1755.   Schatz 5453

Griselda (Venezia, 1751).   Schatz 5460

Gl'impostori, Venezia (1751).   Schatz 5446

Gl'ingannati, Napoli, 1734.   Schatz 5454

L'isola d'amore, Venezia, 1752.   Schatz 5461

Madama Ciana, Venezia (1744).   Schatz 5447

Il maritato fra le disgrazie, Napoli, 1774.   Schatz 5464

L'Olimpiade (Venezia, 1752).   Schatz 5449

L'opera in prova alla moda—La répétition ordinaire de l'opéra
(followed by) Urganostoctor, Amsterdam, 1753.   Schatz 5450

Orazio, Venezia, 1743 (partly by Pergolesi, on whose Il
maestro di musica the text is based).   Schatz 5466

L'Ottavio, Napoli (1733).   Schatz 5452

La pastorella al soglio (Venezia, 1751).   Schatz 5465

Polipodio e Rucchetta (Rome, 1738).   ML 50.2.P54L2

Il protettor del poeta, Roma, 1754.   ML 50.2.P73L2

La répétition ordinaire de l'opéra. Tr. of his L'opera in
prova alla moda, Amsterdam, 1753.   Schatz 5450

Siroe, Padova, 1753.   Schatz 5451

Urganostocor. *See his* L'opera in prova alla moda.

Il vecchio amante, Torino (1747).   Schatz 5463

Laurenti, Saverio.

La pupilla rapita, Venezia (1763) (partly by Boroni).   Schatz 5473

Laurenzi, Filiberto.

L'esiglio di Amore, Ferrara, 1651 (with Andrea Mattioli).   Schatz 6106

La finta Savia, Venetia, 1643 (partly by Crivelli, Merula,
and Ferrari).   Schatz 5474

Lawes, Henry, 1595–1662.

The siege of Rhodes, London, 1663 (with Cook, Locke, Coleman and Hudson).   ML 50.2.S62

Lawes, William, *d.* 1645.

The triumph of peace, London, 1633 (with Ives).   Longe 188

Leardini, Alessandro.

Argiope, Venezia, 1649 (supposedly with G. Rovetta, but it
is doubtful if their joint setting was performed).   SCHATZ 9106

Psiche, Mantova, 1649.   ML 50.2.P78L3

Lebreton.   *See* Berton.

Lebrun, Louis Sébastien, 1764–1829.

Le bon fils, Paris, an quatrième (1795–96)   ML 50.2.B7L3

Leger, F. P. A.

Belle et bonne, Paris, an VI, 1798.   ML 48.M2L

Ziste et Zeste ou Les importuns, Paris, an V (1796) (only
part of the music).   ML 48.M2E

Legrenzi, Giovanni, *ca.* 1625–1690.

L'Achille in Sciro, Venetia, 1663.   SCHATZ 5532

L'Achille in Sciro, Venetia, 1664.   SCHATZ 11720

Adone in Cipro, Venetia, 1676.   SCHATZ 5540

L'anarchia dell' imperio, Venetia, 1684.   SCHATZ 5541

Antioco il Grande, Venetia, 1681.   SCHATZ 5533

Il Creso, Venetia, 1681.   SCHATZ 5542

La divisione del mondo, Venetia, 1675.   SCHATZ 5534

I due Cesari, Venetia, 1683.   SCHATZ 5543

Eteocle e Polinice, Venetia, 1675.   SCHATZ 5535

Germanico sul Reno, Venetia, 1676.   SCHATZ 5536

Giustino, Venetia, 1683.   SCHATZ 5544

Ifianassa e Melampo (G. A. Moniglia, Poesie drammatiche,
parte prima, Firenze, 1689).   ML 49.A2M7

Lisimaco riamato da Alessandro, Venetia, 1682.   SCHATZ 5545

Ottaviano Ces. Augusto, Venetia, 1682.   SCHATZ 5537

Il Pausania, Venetia, 1682.   SCHATZ 5546

Pub. Elio Pertinace, Venetia, 1684.   SCHATZ 5538

Tiridate, Venetia, 1668.   SCHATZ 5539

Totila, Venetia, 1677.   SCHATZ 5547

Le Messier, Giuseppe Antonio.

Accampamento o sia La lotteria militare, ballet. *See* Anfossi's Armida.

Alceste e Admeto, ballet.   *See* Monza's Cleopatra.

Le allegrezze per le vittorie di Scipione, ballet.   *See* Galuppi's
Sofonisba.

L'amante travestita, ballet.   *See* G. M. Rutini's Sicotencal.

Amor corsaro, ballet.   *See* Monza's Oreste.

Amore custode del giardino di Armida, ballet.   *See* Anfossi's
Armida.

Amore e Psiche, ballet.   *See* Bertoni's Tancredi.

L'amore vinto dall' amicizia, ballet.   *See* G. F. de Majo's
Catone in Utica.

L'Arrivo d'Europa nell' isola di Creta, ballet.   *See* Bertoni's
Ifigenia in Aulide.

Berenice.   Ballet music for Ignazio Platania's opera.

Bradamante Ruggero, ballet.   *See* Monza's Oreste.

I cacciatori burlati, ballet.   *See* Hasse's L'Olimpiade, Torino,
1765.

Cadmo ed Ino, ballet.   *See* Piccinni's Tigrane.

Le Messier, Giuseppe Antonio—Continued.

Cittadini di Sinope festeggianti le nozze di Mitridate, ballet.
See Piccinni's Tigrane.

La costanza affricana soccorsa dall' arte magica, ballet. See
Galuppi's Sofonisba.

La contribuzione sforzata, ballet. See Galuppi's Sofonisba.

Il convitato di pietra, ballet. See Bertoni's Tancredi.

Creso. Ballet music in Cafaro's opera.

Demetrio. Ballet music for Ponzo's opera.

La disgrazia opportuna, ballet. See Monza's Cleopatra.

Le dissensioni d'amore nel campo, ballet. See G. M. Rutini's
Sicotencal.

Le donne Ateniesi e i loro compagni, ballet. See Pasque's
Arianna e Teseo.

Ecuba. Ballet music in Celoniat's opera.

Egle e Dafni, ballet. See Misliweczek's Il trionfo di Clelia.

Enea in Cartagine. Ballet music for Colla's opera.

Enea nel Lazio. Ballet music for Traetta's opera.

Feste in onore di Bacco, ballet. See Colla's Andromeda.

Le fontane incantate, ballet. See Pasque's Arianna e Teseo.

Il gran Cidde, ballet music (with Ghebard) for Franchi's opera.

Il guoco dell' arco, ballet. See Pasque's Arianna e Teseo.

Issea. Ballet music for this opera by Pugnani.

La morte d'Orfeo, ballet. See Gius. Scarlatti's Pelopida.

La morte ed il rinascimento del pastore Adone, ballet. See
Bach's Artaserse.

Le nozze americane, ballet. See Colla's Andromeda.

Orfeo e Euridice, ballet. See Galuppi's La clemenza di Tito.

Il rapimento di Proserpina, ballet. See G. F. de Majo's Catone
in Utica.

Il ritorno della primavera, ballet. See Colla's Andromeda.

Lo sbarco de' Spagnuoli nella America, ballet. See G. M.
Rutini's Sicotencal.

I selvatici, ballet. See Gius. Scarlatti's Pelopida.

Telemaco nell' isola di Calipso, ballet. See Piccinni's Tigrane.

Il trionfo di Cesare in Egitto, ballet. See Monza's Cleopatra.

Le Mixte, Niccolò.

La forza vinta dall' onore, Venezia, 1703.   Schatz 5486

Le Moyne (Le Moine). (Jean Baptiste Moyne, *called*), 1751–
1796.

Phèdre, Bordeaux, 1786.   ML 50.2.P35L2

Les pommiers et le moulin, Paris, 1791.   ML 50.2.P56L2

Les prétendus, Paris, 1789.   Schatz 5487

Lenzi, Francesco.

Li tre Eugenj, Napoli, 1778.   Schatz 5551

Leo, Leonardo, 1694–1744.

L'Andromaca, Napoli (1742).   Schatz 5556

Argeno, Venezia, 1728.   Schatz 5552

Bertoldo. See Title catalogue under Bertoldo, Bertoldino e
Cacasenno.

Catone in Utica, Venezia (1729).   Schatz 5557

La clemenza di Tito, Venezia, 1735.   Schatz 5553

Leo, Leonardo—Continued.

Il fantastico. O. T. of his (and Gomes') Il nuovo D. Chisciotte.

Il giramondo, Venezia, 1749.   Schatz 5561

L'impresario dell' isole Canarie, Vienna (1747).   Schatz 5558

L'impresario dell' isole Canarie—Der impresarius oder Opern verwalter von den Canarischen inseln, Potsdam, 1748.   Schatz 5559

Lesbina e Nesso (in Händel's Rinaldo, Napoli, 1718).   Schatz 4495

Die listige wittwe. Tr. of his La vedova ingegnosa (Dresda, 1747).   Schatz 5554

La mogliere fedele, Napoli, 1731. (Aria interpolated in Vinci and Sellitti's opera.)   Schatz 10755

Il nuovo D. Chisciotte, Napoli, 1748 (with Gomes). L. T. of his Il fantastico.   ML 50.2.F178L3

Opernverwalter von den Canarischen inseln. A. T. of his Der impresarius.

Rinaldo, Napoli, 1718 (only the additions to Händel's opera).   Schatz 4495

La Rosilla, Napoli, 1733 (partly composed by Antonio Orefici).   Schatz 7293

Sofonisba, Napoli, 1718.   Schatz 5555

Timocrate, Venezia, 1723.   Schatz 5560

La vedova ingegnosa (Dresde, 1747 (also attributed to Prota and Sellitti). (Italian text only.)   ML 50.2.V25L2

La vedova ingegnosa—Die listige wittwe (Dresda, 1747).   Schatz 5554

Vologeso rè de' Parti, Torino (1744).   Schatz 5562

Leopold I, *Emperor* (b. 1640) 1658–1705.

Apollo deluso, Vienna, 1669 (partly by Sances).   ML 48.M2D

Chi più sà manco l'intende. *See* Draghi's opera.

Cidippe. *See* Draghi's opera.

La lanterna di Diogene. *See* Draghi's opera.

Leonida in Tegea. *See* Draghi's opera.

Gli stratagemi di Biante. *See* Draghi's opera.

Sulpitia. *See* Draghi's opera.

La tirannide abbattuta dalla virtù. *See* Draghi's opera.

Le Petit.

Le combat nocturne ou Les morts vivans, La Haye, 1770.   Schatz 5489

Lesueur (Sueur, Jean Francois, 1760–1837, *called*).

See also Catalogue of 19th cent. librettos.

La caverne, Liège, 1795.   ML 50.2.C34L2

Le génie Asouf ou Les deux coffrets, Paris, an VIII, (1799). (Pasticcio, music partly by the above.)   Schatz 10591

Telemaque dans l'isle de Calypso, Paris, an IV (1796).   ML 50.2.T35L3

Leveridge, Richard, *d.* 1758.

The island princess or the generous Portuguese, London, 1724 (with D. Purcell and J. Clarke).   Longe 75

Pyramus and Thisbe, London, 1716.   Longe 54

Lichtenstein, Carl August, *freiherr* von, 1767–1845.

See also Catalogue of 19th cent. librettos.

Die steinerne braut, Dessau, 1799.   Schatz 5599

Lima, Jeronymo Francisco de, *d.* 1822.

Le nozze d'Ercole e d'Ebe, Lisbona, 1785.   Schatz 5618

Gli Orti Esperidi (Lisbona, 1779).   Schatz 5620

Lima, Jeronymo Francisco de—Continued.
Lo spirito di contradizione, Lisbona (1772).   SCHATZ 5616
Teséo (Lisbona, 1783).   SCHATZ 5619
La vera costanza (Lisbona, 1789).   SCHATZ 5617

Linike, Johann Georg.
Julius Caesar in Aegypten (Hamburg, 1725). German recitatives, etc., in this Tr. of Händel's Giulio Cesare in
Egitto.   SCHATZ 4478
Julius Caesar in Aegypten (Hamburg, 1733). L. ed of above. SCHATZ 11690

Linley, Thomas, 1732–1795.
See also Catalogue of 19th cent. librettos.
The camp, London, 1795.   LONGE 233
The duenna, or, The double elopement, London, 1775 (with
his son Thomas).   ML 50.2.D85
The duenna, or, The double elopement (Dublin, 1791).   PR 1269.V6
The governess, Dublin, 1777 (with his son Thomas). A
pirated ed. of their The Duenna.   LONGE 148
Harlequin's wedding. A. T. of his the triumph of mirth.
The haunted tower. *See* Title catalogue.
Love in the East or Adventures of twelve hours, London, 1788. LONGE 110
The quaker. *See* Title catalogue.
Richard Coeur de Lion, London, 1786. Adaptation of Grétry's
opera.   LONGE 98
The royal merchant, London, 1768.   LONGE 197
Selima & Azor, London, 1784 (utilizing Grétry's Zémire et
Azor).   LONGE 95
The Spanish rivals, London, 1784.   LONGE 95
The strangers at home, London, 1786.   LONGE 96
The triumph of mirth or Harlequin's wedding, London, 1782. ML 52.2.T81

Linley, Thomas, 1756–1778.
The duenna, or, the double elopement, London, 1775 (with
his father).   ML 50.2.D85
The duenna, or, The double elopement (Dublin, 1791).   PR 1269.V6
The governess, Dublin, 1777. Pirated ed. of his and his father's The duenna.   LONGE 148

Locke, Matthew, 1677.
The siege of Rhodes, London, 1663 (with H. Lawes, Cook,
Coleman and Hudson).   ML 50.2.S62

Logroscino, Nicola, *d.* 1763.
Le chiajese cantarine, Nnapole (1754) (with Maraucci and
Fischietti)   ML 50.2.C45
Don Paduano, Napoli, 1745.   SCHATZ 5672
L'Elmira generosa, Napoli, 1753 (partly by Barbella).   SCHATZ 5675
La furba burlata, Napoli, 1762 (interpolations in Piccinni's
opera).   SCHATZ 8159
La gelosia, Venezia, 1765.   SCHATZ 5671
Il governadore, Napoli, 1747.   SCHATZ 5673
La pastorella scaltra, Roma (1753).   ML 50.2.P286L6
Il Riccardo (Napoli, 1743).   SCHATZ 5674

Lombardini, Antonio.
Il trionfo di Amore e di Marte, Venetia, 1689.   SCHATZ 5679

Lonati, Carlo Ambrogio.

Ariberto e Flavio, regi de Longobardi, Venetia, 1684 [!].   SCHATZ 5680

L'Ajace, Napoli, 1697 (partly by Magni).   SCHATZ 5682

Antioco principe della Siria, Genova (1690).   SCHATZ 5681

Longarini, Giovanni Battista.

La donna ne sa più del diavolo ovvero Il matrimonio non è
per i vecchi, Lisbona, 1797.   SCHATZ 5683

Longchamps.

See Comment faire? in Title catalogue.

Lorazi, Girolamo.

Der kapellmeister oder Ist's nicht die eine, so ist's die andre,
n. i. n. d. (Komische opern der Italiener, Leipzig, 1781,
Bd. I). Tr. of his Il maestro di cappella burlato.   SCHATZ 5684

Lotti, Antonio, 1667–1740.

Achille placato, Venezia, 1707.   SCHATZ 5713

Alessandro Severo, Venezia, 1717.   SCHATZ 5714

Ama più chi.men si crede, Venezia, 1709.   SCHATZ 5715

Artaserse rè di Persia, Napoli, 1713 (the buffo scenes and
added arias by Mancini).   SCHATZ 5712

Il comando non inteso, et ubbidito, Venezia, 1709.   SCHATZ 5716

Foca Superbo, Venezia, 1716.   SCHATZ 5717

La forza del sangue, Venezia, 1711.   SCHATZ 5718

Giove in Argo—Jupiter en Argos, Dresda (1717).   SCHATZ 5719

L'infedeltà punita, Venezia, 1712 (with C. F. Pollaroli).   SCHATZ 8326

La haine vaincue par la force du sangue. Tr. of his Gl'odj
delusi dal sangue, Dresda (1718).   SCHATZ 5707

L'inganno vinto dalla ragione, Napoli, 1708 (the buffo scenes
and added arias by Vignola). Altered from his Teuzzone.   SCHATZ 5727

Irene augusta, Venezia, 1713.   SCHATZ 5720

Isacio tiranno, Venezia, 1710.   SCHATZ 5721

Jupiter en Argos. Tr. of his Giove in Argo, Dresda (1717).   SCHATZ 5719

Gl'odj delusi dal sangue—La haine vaincue par la force du
sang, Dresda (1718).   SCHATZ 5707

Polidoro, Venezia (1714).   SCHATZ 5708

Porsenna, Napoli, 1713 ("musica . . . accomodata . . . dal
Sig. Alessandro Scarlatti").   SCHATZ 5711

Li quattro elementi—Carrousel des quatre élémens, Dresda
(1719).   SCHATZ 5725

Sidonio, Venezia, 1706.   SCHATZ 5722

Teofane=Theophane, Dresda, 1719.   SCHATZ 5723

Teuzzone, Venezia (1707). O. T. of his L'inganno vinto dalla
ragione.   SCHATZ 5709

Il Tirsi, Venezia (1696) (with Caldara and Ariosti).   SCHATZ 5728

Il tradimento traditor di se stesso, Venezia, 1711.   SCHATZ 5710

Il trionfo della innocenza, Venetia, 1692.   SCHATZ 5724

Il vincitor generoso, Venezia, 1708.   SCHATZ 5726

Louis, *Mme*, *neé* Bajon.

Fleur d'épine, Paris, 1776.   ML 50.2.F65L7

Fleur d'épine, Paris, 1777.   SCHATZ 11721

Lucchini, Matteo.

L'amore per forza, Venezia, 1721 (first act by G. Bassani).   SCHATZ 636

Luccio (Luzzo), Francesco.
    Gl'amori di Alessandro Magno i di Rossane, Venetia, 1651.   Schatz 5745
    L'Euridamante, Venetia, 1654.   Schatz 5746
    Il Medoro, Venetia, 1658.   Schatz 5744
    Pericle effeminato, Venetia, 1653.   Schatz 5747

Luchesi (Lucchesi), Andrea, *b.* 1741.
    Ademira, Venezia, 1784.   Schatz 5739
    Le donne sempre donne, Venezia, 1767.   Schatz 5741
    L'isola della fortuna, Lisbona (1767).   Schatz 5742
    Il matrimonio per astuzia, Venezia (1771).   Schatz 5740

Lüderwald, Georg Ernst.   *See his pseud.* Lange.

Lully, Jean Baptiste de, 1632–1687.
    Achille et Polixene (Amsterdam) 1687 (act 2–5 by Colasse).   ML 49.A2L9
    — Same, Amsterdam, 1701.   ML 50.2.A25L9
    Achille et Polixene (Recueil général des opéra, t. iii, Paris, 1703).   Schatz 5781
    Acis et Galatée (Amsterdam) 1686.   ML 49.A2L9
    Acis et Galatée (Recueil général des opéra, t. iii, Paris, 1703).   Schatz 5756
    Acis und Galatée, Stuttgart, 1698.   Schatz 5757
    Alceste ou Le triomphe d'Alcide (Amsterdam) 1688.   ML 50.2.A49L9
    Alceste ou Le triomphe d'Alcide (Recueil général des opera, t. i, Paris, 1703).   Schatz 5758
    Alceste ou Le triomphe d'Alcide (Quinault, Théatre, Paris, 1739, t. iv).   PQ 1881.A1
    Amadis (Amsterdam) 1687.   ML 50.2.A59L9
    Amadis (Recueil général des opéra, Paris, 1703, t. ii).   Schatz 5759
    Amadis (Quinault, Théâtre, Paris, 1739, t. v).   PQ 1881.A1
    [L'amour malade, Paris, 1657.]   ML 52.2.B15
    Armida, Roma, 1690.   Tr. of the following.   Schatz 5779
    Armide (Amsterdam) 1686.   ML 50.2.A76L9
    Armide (Recueil général des opéra, t. iii, Paris, 1703).   Schatz 5760
    Armide (Quinault, Théâtre, Paris, t. v, 1739).   PQ 1881.A1
    Armide, Lyon, 1742.   Schatz 5760a
    Atys (Amsterdam) 1687.   ML 50.2.A9L9
    Atys (Recueil général des opéra, t. i, Paris, 1703).   Schatz 5761
    Atys (Paris) 1738.   ML 50.2.A9L93
    Atys (Quinault, Théâtre, Paris, 1739, t. iv).   PQ 1881.A1
    Atys, Lyon, 1743.   Schatz 5761
    Le bal interrompu (Danchet, Théâtre, Paris, 1751, t. ii). Entrée in Fragments de Monsieur Lully.   PQ 1972.D2
    Ballet des Saisons (Recueil général des opera, Paris, 1703) (principally by Colasse).   Schatz 5782
    Ballet du temps, Paris, 1654.   ML 52.2.B17
    Bellerophon, Paris, 1679.   ML 50.2.B35L7
    Bellerophon (Amsterdam) 1679.   ML 50.2.B35L8
    Bellerophon (Amsterdam) 1682.   ML 49.A2L9
    Bellerophon (Recueil général des opéra, Paris, 1703, t. ii).   Schatz 5762
    Cadmus et Hermione, Paris, 1674.   ML 50.2.C22L9
    Cadmus et Hermione (Amsterdam) 1687.   ML 50:2.C22L92
    Cadmus et Hermione (Recueil général des opera, t. i, Paris, 1703).   Schatz 5763
    Cadmus et Hermione (Quinault, Théâtre, Paris, 1739, t. iv).   PQ 1881.A1
    Cariselli.   *See his* Fragments.

Lully, Jean Baptiste de—Continued.

Le carnaval (Recueil général des opéra, t. i, Paris, 1703).	SCHATZ 5765
L'eglogue de Versailles (Recueil général des opéra, t. iii, Paris, 1703). (Forms part of his L'idylle sur la paix).	SCHATZ 5776a
Les festes de l'Amour et de Bacchus (Amsterdam) 1686.	ML 50.2.F3L9
Les festes de l'Amour et de Bacchus (Recueil général des opéra, Paris, 1703, t. i).	SCHATZ 5766
Les festes de l'Amour et de Bacchus (Quinault Théâtre, Paris, 1739, t. iv).	PQ 1881.A1
Fragments de Mr de Lully (Recueil général des opéra, t. vii, Paris, 1703).	SCHATZ 5767
L'idylle sur la paix, et L'eglogue de Versailles (Recueil général des opéra, t. iii, Paris, 1703).	SCHATZ 5776
Isis (Amsterdam) 1682.	ML 50.2.J69L9
Isis (Amsterdam) 1686.	ML 49.A2L9
Isis (Recueil général des opéra, Paris, 1703, t. ii).	SCHATZ 5768
Isis (Quinault, Théâtre, Paris, 1739, t. iv).	PQ 1881.A1
Le jaloux trompé (Danchet, Théâtre, 1751, t. ii). Entrée in Fragments de Monsieur Lully.	PQ 1972.D2
Les nopces de Pelée et de Thetis, Paris, 1654. Part of the music of this ballet accredited to Lully.	ML 52.2.N67
Persée (Amsterdam) 1685.	ML 50.2.P33L9
Persée (Recueil général des opéra, t. ii, Paris, 1703).	SCHATZ 5769
Persée (Quinault, Théâtre, Paris, 1739, t. v).	PQ 1881.A1
Phaëton (Amsterdam) 1683.	ML 50.2.P347L9
Phaëton (Amsterdam) 1686.	ML 50.2.P347L92
Phaeton (Recueil général des opéra, t. ii, Paris, 1703).	SCHATZ 5777
Phaëton (Quinault, Théâtre, Paris, 1739, t. v).	PQ 1881.A1
Proserpine, Paris, 1680.	ML 50.2.B35L9
Proserpine (Amsterdam) 1688.	ML 50.2.P7L9
Proserpine (Recueil général des opéra, Paris, 1703, t. ii).	SCHATZ 5770
Proserpine (Quinault, Théâtre, Paris, 1739, t. v).	PQ 1881.A1
Proserpine, Paris, 1758.	ML 50.2.P72L9
Psyché (Amsterdam) 1688.	ML 50.2.P8L92
Psyché (Recueil général des opera, t. ii, Paris, 1703).	SCHATZ 5771
Roland (Amsterdam) 1685.	ML 50.2.R65L9
Roland (Recueil général des opera, t. iii, Paris, 1703).	SCHATZ 5778
Roland, Paris, 1743.	SCHATZ 5780
Roland (Quinault, Théâtre, Paris, 1739, t. v).	PQ 1881.A1
Le temple de la paix (Amsterdam) 1686.	ML 49.A2L9
Le temple de la paix (Recueil général des opéra, Paris, 1703, t. iii).	SCHATZ 5772
Le temple de la paix (Quinault, Théâtre, 1739, t. v).	PQ 1881.A1
Thesée, Paris (Anvers) 1687.	SCHATZ 11722
Thesée (Amsterdam) 1688.	ML 50.2.T45L92
Thesée (Recueil général des opera, t. i, Paris, 1703).	SCHATZ 5773
Thesée (Quinault, Théâtre, 1739, t. iv).	PQ 1881.A1
Le triomphe d'Alcide. A. T. of his Alceste.	
Le triomphe de l'amour (Amsterdam) 1686.	ML 49.A2L9
Le triomphe de l'amour (Recueil général des opéra, Paris, 1703, t. ii).	SCHATZ 5774
Le triomphe de l'amour (Quinault, Théâtre, Paris, 1739, t. v).	PQ 1881.A1
Wonders in the sun. *See* Title catalogue.	

Lully, Jean Baptiste de, 1665–1701.
Le triomphe de la raison sur l'amour, Amsterdam, 1699.   ML 50.2.T8L9

Lully, Jean Louis de, 1667–1688.
Zephire et Flore (Amsterdam) 1688 (with L. de Lully)   ML 50.2.Z4L9
Zephire et Flore, Paris (Anvers) 1689 (with L. de Lully).   ML 50.2.Z4L9
Zephire et Flore (Recueil général des opéra, t. iii, Paris, 1703).   Schatz 5784

Lully, Louis de, *b.* 1664.
Alcide (Recueil général des opéra, t. iv, Paris, 1703) (with
    Marais).   Schatz 5785
Apollon et Daphné, Amsterdam, 1699.   ML 50.2.A73L9
Apollon et Daphné (Danchet, Théâtre, Paris, 1751, t. ii).   PQ 1972.D2
La mort d'Hercule, Paris, 1705. L. T. of his and Marais'
    Alcide.   ML 50.2.A51L9
Orphée (Amsterdam) 1690.   ML 50.2.O75L9
Orphée (Recueil général des opéra, t. iv, Paris, 1703).   Schatz 5783
Zephire et Flore (Amsterdam) 1688 (with J. L. de Lully)   ML 50.2.Z4L9
Zephire et Flore, Paris (Anvers) 1689 (with his brother Jean
    Louis).   ML 50.2.Z4L9
Zephire et Flore (Recueil général des opera, t. iii, Paris, 1703).   Schatz 5784

Lupo, Thomas.
The Lords Maske. *See* A relation of the late royall entertain-
    ment.

Luzzo, Francesco. *See* Luccio.

Macari (Maccari), Giacomo.
L'Adaloaldo furioso, Venezia (1727).   Schatz 5807
Aristide, Venezia, 1735.   Schatz 5808
La contessina, Venezia (1743).   Schatz 5809
La fondazion di Venezia, Venezia (1736).   Schatz 5810
Lugrezia Romana in Constantinopoli, Venezia, 1737.   Schatz 5811

Maggiore, Francesco.
I rigiri delle cantarine, Venezia, 1745.   Schatz 5833
Siface, Bologna (1744).   Schatz 5834
Statira, Venezia, 1751 (a pasticcio mainly by other, anony-
    mous, composers).   Schatz 5832

Magni, Paolo.
Admeto rè di Tessaglia, Milano, 1702.   Schatz 5839
L'Ajace, Napoli, 1697 (partly by Lonati).   Schatz 5682
Teuzzone. *See* Zeno's Poesie drammatiche.

Maier, J. Ludwig F. C.
Wallrad und Evchen, oder Die parforsjagd, Zweibruecken,
    1782.   Schatz 5844

Majo, Giovanni Francesco de (di), *ca.* 1740–1771.
L'Almeria, Livorno, 1761.   ML 50.2.A54M3
Antigona, Roma (1768).   Schatz 5862
Antigono, Venezia, 1768.   Schatz 5854
Artaserse, Venezia, 1762.   Schatz 5861
Catone in Utica, Torino (1763).   Schatz 5860
Didone abbandonata, Venezia, 1770.   Schatz 5855
Ezio, London, 1764–5 (pasticcio from above and Pescetti,
    Bach, etc.).   ML 48.M2N

Majo, Giovanni Francesco de (di)—Continued.

    The golden pippin. *See* Title catalogue.

    Ifigenia in Tauride, Mannheim (1760).   Schatz 5856

    Iphigenia in Tauris, Mannheim, 1760. Tr. of the above.   Schatz 5857

    Motezuma, Torino (1765).   Schatz 5858

    Ricimero rè de' Goti, Roma (1759).   Schatz 5859

Majo, Giuseppe de, *ca.* 1698–1772.

    La Milorda, Napoli (1728).   Schatz 5863

    La Semiramide riconosciuta, Napoli, 1751.   Schatz 5864

    Lo viecchio avaro, Napole, 1727.   ML 50.2.V41M2

Maldere, Pierre van, 1724–1768.

    La medecin de l'amour, Bruxelles, 1766.   Schatz 5867

    Tom Jones, pasticcio. *See* Title catalogue.

Mancini, Francesco, 1674–1739.

    Artaserse, Napoli, 1708 (partly by Orlandini).   Schatz 7328

    Artaserse rè di Persia, Napoli, 1713 (only the buffo scenes and
        added arias; the opera mainly by Lotti).   Schatz 5712

    L'Engelberta o sia La forza dell' innocenza, Napoli (1709).
        (Partly composed by Antonio Orefici.)   Schatz 7294

    Il Gran Mogol, Napoli, 1713.   Schatz 5879

    Melissa schernita. Intermezzi in his and Orefici's L'Engel-
        berta, Napoli (1709).   Schatz 7294

    L'Oronta, Napoli, 1728.   ML 50.2.O7M2

    Perichitta e Bertone, intermezzi. *See his* L'Oronta, Napoli,
        1728.   ML 50.2.O7M2

Manelli, Francesco, *ca.* 1595–1670.

    L'Alcate, Venetia, 1642.   Schatz 5890

    L'Andromeda, Venetia, 1637.   Schatz 5887

    La Filo ovvero Giunone repacificata, Parma, 1660.   Schatz 5889

    La maga fulminata (Benedetto Ferrari's Poesie drammatiche,
        Milano, 1644).   Schatz 5888

    I sei gigli, Parma, 1660.   Schatz 5891

Manfredini, Vincenzo, 1737–1799.

    Armida, Verona (1771).   Schatz 5893

    Artaserse, Venezia (1772).   Schatz 5892

Manna, Gennaro, 1721–1788.

    Demofoonte, Torino (1754).   Schatz 5903

    Didone abbandonata, Venezia (1751).   Schatz 5901

    Siroe (Venezia, 1743).   Schatz 5902

Manza, Luigi.[1]

    Alessandro in Susa, Venezia, 1708.   Schatz 5916

    Paride in Ida, Venezia, 1706 (with Agostino Bonaventura
        Colletti).   Schatz 5917

Marais, Marin, 1656–1728.

    Alcide (Recueil général des opéra, t. iv, Paris, 1703) (with
        Louis de Lully).   Schatz 5785

    Alcione, Amsterdam, 1707.   ML 50.2.A513M2

    Alcione (Recueil général des opéra, t. ix, Paris, 1710). Schatz 5919

    Alcione. *See also* Parodie de l'opera de Telemaque.

---

[1] Schatz has Carlo Manza, instead of Luigi.

Marais, Marin—Continued.

Ariadne et Bachus, Amsterdam, 1699. ML 50.2.A742M2

Ariadne et Bacchus (Recueil général des opéra, t. v, Paris, 1703). Schatz 5920

La mort d'Hercule, Paris, 1705. L. T. of his and L. de Lully's Alcide. ML 50.2.A51L9

Sémélé (Recueil général des opéra, t. ix, Paris, 1710). Schatz 5921

Telemaque, pasticcio. *See* Title catalogue.

Maraucci, Giacomo.

Le chiajese cantarine, Nnapole (1754) (with Logroscino and Fischietti). ML 50.2.C45

Marazzoli, Marco, 1619–1662.

Gli amori di Giasone e d'Isifile, Venetia, 1642. Schatz 5923

Chi soffre, speri, Roma, 1639 (with Virgilio Mazzocchi). Schatz 6223

Marcello di Capua. *See real name* Bernardini, Marcello.

Marchi, Giovanni Maria.

La clemenza di Tito, Milano, 1738. Schatz 5937

La generosità politica, Venezia, 1736. Schatz 5936

Marescalchi, Luigi.

L'Alessandro nell' Indie, Venezia, 1778. Schatz 5946

Andromaca in Epiro, ballet. *See* Gazzaniga's Tullo Ostilio.

Il convitato di pietra, ballet. *See* Gazzaniga's Tullo Ostilio.

La dolce vendetta, ballet. *See* Cherubini's Quinto Fabio.

Le furie d'Oreste. A. T. of his La morte d'Egisto.

Gelosia per gelosia, ballet. *See* Giordani's Fernando nel Messico.

Il Meleagro, ballet. *See* Sarti's Mitridate a Sinope.

Minosse, rè di Creta o sia La fuga d'Arianna e di Fedra, ballet. *See* Martin y Soler's In amor ci vuol destrezza.

La morte d'Egisto ossia Le furie d'Oreste, ballet. *See* Caruso's Antigono.

Oreste o sia La morte di Clitennestra, ballet. *See* Giordani's Fernando nel Messico.

Il primo giorno dell' anno nella China, ballet. *See* Tarchi's Ifigenia in Aulide.

Il proseguimento del Chiarlone—Proceguimento, ou segunda parte do Falador, Lisbona (1766). Schatz 5947

Il rè de' ciarlatani, ballet. *See* Cherubini's Quinto Fabio.

Li sposi ridicoli burlati, ballet. *See* Anfossi's Gli amanti canuti.

Il tutore ingannato, Venezia, 1774. Schatz 5945

Maria Antonia Walpurgis, *princess of Saxony*, 1724–1780. (Ermelinda Talèa, P. A.)

Talestri, regina delle Amazoni, Monaco, 1760. Schatz 5950

Talestri, regina delle Amazzoni, Dresda, 1770. Schatz 5948

Il trionfo della fedeltà, Dresda, 1754 (partly composed by her teacher, Hasse). Schatz 5949

Maria, Dominico della. *See* Della Maria.

Marinelli, Gaetano, 1760–1820.

See also Catalogue of 19th cent. librettos.

Amore aguzza l'ingegno, Napoli, 1792. Schatz 5958

Marinelli, Gaetano—Continued.

Baldassare punito, Firenze, 1796.	ML 48.A5 v.14
La bizarra contadina, Napoli, 1790.	Schatz 5959
La contadina semplice, Napoli, 1790.	Schatz 5954
La finta principessa, Venezia, 1796.	Schatz 5967
Germanico, Venezia, 1797.	Schatz 5955
L'interesse gabba tutti, Firenze, 1795.	Schatz 5961
Issipile, Venezia (1796).	Schatz 5956
Lucio Papirio, Firenze, 1795.	ML 48.A5 v.16
I vecchi burlati, Venezia, 1795. L. T. of the next.	Schatz 5966
I vecchi delusi, Napoli, 1793.	Schatz 5960

Marino, Settiminio.

Didone, Lisbona, 1799.	Schatz 5968

Martin y Soler (Solar), Atanasio Martin Ignacio Vicente Tadeo Francisco Pelegrin, 1754–1806 (*called also* Martin(i) Vincenzo).

See also Catalogue of 19th cent. librettos.

L'accorta cameriera, Torino (1783).	Schatz 6031
L'amor geloso, Napoli (1782).	Schatz 6026
Andromaca, Torino (1781).	Schatz 6027
L'arbore di Diana, Milano (1788).	Schatz 5999
Der baum der Diana, Wien, 1787. Tr. of his L'arbore di Diana.	Schatz 6000
Der baum der Diana, Wien, 1788.	Schatz 6001
Der baum der Diana, Hamburg, 1792.	Schatz 6002
Der baum der Diana, Oels (1795).	Schatz 6003
Bellezza ed Onestà. A. T. of his Una cosa rara.	
Bellezza ed onestà, Venezia (1788).	Schatz 6030
Il burbero di buon cuore, Venezia, 1789.	Schatz 6005
Il burbero di buon cuore—Der gutherzige polterer, Dresda, 1789.	Schatz 6006
Le burle per amore, Venezia (1784).	Schatz 6007
La capricciosa corretta—So bessert sie sich, Dresda, 1796.	Schatz 6008
Il castello d'Atlante, Brescia (1791).	Schatz 6029
Una cosa rara, o sia Bellezza ed onestà, Vienna, 1787.	Schatz 6015
Una cosa rara osia Bellezza ed onestà—Die seltne sache oder Schoenheit und tugend, Wien, 1787. (Bound with Dittersdorf's Betrug durch aberglauben.)	Schatz 2587
Una cosa rara o sia Bellezza ed onestà—Die seltenheit oder Schönheit und tugend, Dresda, 1787.	Schatz 6017
Una cosa rara o sia Bellezza ed onestà, Firenze, 1791.	ML 48.A5 v.16
La cosa rara, London, 1789.	ML 48.M2M
Cosa rara oder Der seltne fall, n. i., 1797.	Schatz 6019
Cristiano II, rè di Danimarca, ballet. *See* Sarti's Attalo rè di Bitinia.	
Etwas seltsames oder Schoenheit und ehrbarkeit, Wien, 1787. Tr. of his Una cosa rara.	Schatz 6016
Der gutherzige polterer. Tr. of his Il burbero di buon cuore, Dresda, 1789.	Schatz 6006
The haunted tower. *See* Title catalogue.	
Ifigenia in Aulide, Napoli, 1779.	Schatz 6028
In amor ci vuol destrezza, Venezia, 1782.	Schatz 6010
L'isola piacevole, Venezia, 1797.	Schatz 6011

Martin y Soler (Solar), Atanasio Martin Ignacio Vicente Tadeo Francisco Pelegrin—Continued.

L'isola piacevole, Firenze, 1797.	ML 48.A5 v.15
The mariners, pasticcio. *See* Title catalogue.	
Partenope, Napoli, 1782.	SCHATZ 6013
Schoenheit und ehrbarkeit. A. T. of his Etwas seltsames.	
Schoenheit und tugend. A. T. of his Die seltne sache.	
Schoenheit und tugend. A. T. of his Die seltenheit.	
Die seltenheit oder Schoenheit und tugend. Tr. of his Una cosa rara, Dresda, 1787.	SCHATZ 6017
Der seltne fall, n. i., 1797. Tr. of his Una cosa rara.	SCHATZ 6019
Die seltne sache oder Schoenheit und tugend. Tr. of his Una cosa rara osia Bellezza ed onestà, Wien, 1787.	SCHATZ 2587
The siege of Belgrade, London, 1791 (partly selected from his Una cosa rara, partly composed by Storace).	LONGE 207
The siege of Belgrade, Dublin (179–).	LONGE 233
The siege of Belgrade, London (1796).	SCHATZ 6021 and LONGE 263
So bessert sie sich. Tr. of his La capricciosa corretta, Dresda, 1796.	SCHATZ 6008
Vologeso, Torino (1783).	SCHATZ 6024

Martinengo, Antonio Francesco.

L'Arsiade (Mantova, 1700).	ML 50.2.A778 M2
Arsiade, Torino, 1703.	SCHATZ 6032

Martini, Giovanni Marco.

Apio Claudio, Venezia, 1683.	SCHATZ 6033

Martini, Jean Paul Egide, 1741–1816. *Originally* Schwartzendorf, Johann Paul Egidius *and called* Martini il Tedesco.

L'amoureux de quinze ans ou La double fête, Paris, la veuve Duchesne, 1771 (64 p.).	YUDIN PQ
L'amoureux de quinze ans, ou La double fête, Paris, la veuve Duchesne, 1771 (68 p.).	SCHATZ 6034
Le droit du seigneur, Amsterdam, 1784.	SCHATZ 6036
Henri IV, Paris, 1775.	SCHATZ 6039
Das herrnrecht, Hamburg, 1789. Tr. of his Le droit du seigneur.	SCHATZ 6037
Der liebhaber von funfzehn jahren, Wien, 1778. Tr. of his L'amoureux de quinze ans.	SCHATZ 6035
Das recht des lehnsherrn, Oels (1796). Tr. of his Le droit du seigneur.	SCHATZ 6038

Martini, Vincenzo. *See* Martin y Soler.

Masi, Giovanni.

La disfatta di Dario, Torino (1774).	SCHATZ 6062

Masini, Vincenzo.

Cesare al Rubicone, Faenza, 1725.	SCHATZ 6063

Massi, Giovanni.

Il gran conte di Cordanova, Roma, 1754.	ML 50.2.G68M2

Mastini, Giovanni Battista.

L'amor fra gl'impossibili, Ancona, 1727.	SCHATZ 6095

Matho, Jean Baptiste, *ca.* 1660–1746.

Arion (Recueil général des opéra, t. xi, Paris, 1720).	SCHATZ 6097

Mattei, Baldassare Filippo.

Medonte, ballet. *See* Cavi's La prepotenza delusa.

Medonte, ballet. *See* Salari's L'amore rammingo.

Mattei, Filippo (*called* Pippo).[1]

Muzio Scevola—Mutius Scaevola, Hamburg (1723) (act I only,
act II by G. B. Bononcini, act III by Händel). SCHATZ 168

Matteis, Niccola, *d.* 1737.

Achille in Sciro. Ballet music for Caldara's Achille in Sciro,
1736.

Adriano in Siria. Ballet music for Caldara's opera.

La clemenza di Tito. Ballet music for Caldara's opera.

Costanza e fortezza, Vienna (1723). Dances. *See* this under
Joh. Jos. Fux.

Ifigenia in Aulide. Ballet music for Caldara's opera.

Lucio Papirio dittatore. Ballet music for Caldara's opera.

Mitridate. Ballet music for Caldara's opera.

Ormisda. Ballet music for Caldara's opera.

Sirita. Ballet music for Caldara's opera.

Spartaco. Ballet music for Porsile's opera.

Il Temistocle. Ballet music for Caldara's opera.

Venceslao. Ballet music for Caldara's opera.

La verità nell' inganno. Ballet music for Caldara's opera.

Matteo, Frediano.

Marco Manlio Capitolino, Lucca, 1755. *See* M. Curzio in
Title catalogue.

Mattheson, Johann, 1681–1764.

Die geheimen begebenheiten Henrico IV, koenigs von Castilien und Leon; oder Die getheilte liebe, Hamburg (1711). SCHATZ 6100

Die betrogene staats-liebe, oder, Die unglueckselige Cleopatra,
koenigin von Egypten, Hamburg, 1704. SCHATZ 6101

Victor, hertzog der Normannen (Hamburg, 1702). (Only
second act, first act by J. Chr. Schieferdecker, third by
Georg Bronner.) SCHATZ 9605

Mattioli, Andrea, *d.* 1679.

Ciro, Venetia, 1665 (substitute arias in Cavalli's opera). SCHATZ 1753

Didone, Bologne, 1656. SCHATZ 6102

L'esiglio d'amore, Ferrara, 1651 (with Filiberto Laurenzi). SCHATZ 6106

La filli di Tracia, Ferrara (1664). SCHATZ 6105

La palma d'amore, Ferrara, 1650. SCHATZ 6104

Perseo, Venetia, 1665. SCHATZ 6103

Mayr, Johann Simon, 1763–1845.

See also Catalogue of 19th cent. librettos.

Avviso ai maritati, Venezia (1798). SCHATZ 6188

L'intrigo della lettera, Venezia (1797). SCHATZ 6154

L'intrigo della lettera, Lisboa, 1798. ML 50.2.I65M2

Labino e Carlotta (Venezia, 1799). SCHATZ 6155

Lauso e Lidia, Venezia (1798). SCHATZ 6156

La Lodoiska, Venezia (1796). SCHATZ 6158

Lodoiska, Milano (1799). SCHATZ 6159

Un pazzo ne fa cento, Venezia (1796). SCHATZ 6176

---

[1] Schatz claims that his real name was Filippo Amadei.

Mayr, Johann Simon—Continued.
Saffo o sia I riti d'Apollo Leucadio, Venezia (1794).   Schatz 6171
Il secreto. *See* p. 39–64 of Cimarosa's Il duello per compli-
    mento, Venezia (1797).   Schatz 2002
Telemaco nell' isola di Calipso, Venezia (1797).   Schatz 6175
Temira e Aristo, Venezia, 1795.   Schatz 6203

Mazzinghi, Felice.
Il figlio delle selve, Genova (1755) (with others).   Schatz 6217

Mazzinghi, Joseph, 1765–1844.
See also Catalogue of 19th cent. librettos.
The turnpike gate, London, 1799 (with Reeve).   Longe 258

Mazzocchi, Domenico.
La catena d'Adone, Roma, 1626.   Schatz 6222

Mazzocchi, Virgilio, *d.* 1646.
Chi soffre, speri (with M. Marazzoli), Roma, 1639.   Schatz 6223

Mazzoni, Antonio Maria, 1718–1785.
Adriano in Siria, Venezia, 1760.   Schatz 6225
La clemenza di Tito, Lisbona, 1755.   Schatz 6229
L'Inglese in Italia, Bologna (1769).   Schatz 6230
L'Issipile, Macerata, 1748.   Schatz 6226
La Nitteti, Napoli, 1764.   Schatz 6227
Le stravaganze del caso, Venezia, 1761.   Schatz 6228
Il viaggiatore ridicolo. *See* Goldoni's Opere teatrali.

Mederitsch, Johann, *called* **Gallus,** 1755–1835.
Rose oder Pflicht und liebe in streit, Wien, 1783.   ML 50.2.R74M3

Méhul, Etienne Nicolas, 1763–1817.
See also Catalogue of 19th cent. librettos.
Adrien, Paris, An VII (1798–99).   Schatz 6276
Euphrosine et le tyran corrigé, ou Le pouvoir de l'amour,
    Liège, troisième année (1794–95).   Schatz 6242
Eufrosine, Amsteldam, 1798. Tr. of this.   Schatz 6274
Horatius Coclès, n. i., n. d. (before 1800?).   ML 50.2.H63M2
Le jugement de Paris, ballet, Paris, an VI (1797–98): pas-
    ticcio of music by the above, Haydn and Pleyel.   ML 52.2.J9
Mélidore et Phrosine, Paris, an second (1793–94).   Schatz 6277

Melani, Jacopo.
Enea in Italia (G. A. Moniglia, Poesie drammatiche, parte
    prima, Firenze, 1689).   ML 49.A2M7
Ercole in Tebe, Fiorenza, 1661 (with "Descrizione." 23ᶜᵐ).   ML 50.2.E6M2
Ercole in Tebe, Fiorenza, 1661 (without "Descrizione."
    16½ᶜᵐ).   Schatz 6290
Ercole in Tebe (G. A. Moniglia, Poesie drammatiche, parte
    prima, Firenze, 1689).   ML 49.A2M7
Il ritorno d'Ulisse (G. A. Moniglia, Poesie drammatiche, parte
    prima, Firenze, 1689).   ML 49.A2M7
Tacere ed amare, n. i., n. d. (detached from Moniglia's Poesie
    drammatiche, parte terza, Firenze, 1690).   Schatz 6288
La vedova, n. i., n. d. (detached from Moniglia's Poesie dram-
    matiche, parte terza, Firenze, 1690).   Schatz 6289

Mele, Giovanni Battista.
Il Polifemo (Madrid, 1748) (third act; first by Corselli; second
by Corradini).   Schatz 2253

Meli, Carlo Ambrogio.
Farsa per musica [Imene ed Armonia] Firenze, 1762.   ML 48.M2F

Mereaux, Jean Nicolas Amédée Le Froid de, 1745–1797 (*also
known as* Merault).
Alexandre aux Indes, Paris, 1783.   Schatz 6310
Le duel comique (Paris) 1777. Added music to Tr. of Pais-
iello's Il duello.   ML 50.2.D8P2
La ressource comique, Paris, 1772.   ML 50.2.R42M2
Le retour de tendresse, Paris, 1778.   ML 50.2.R4M3

Merula, Tarquinio.
La finta savia, Venetia, 1643 (only partly by him, Crivelli,
and Ferrari, mostly by Laurenzi).   Schatz 5474

Meucci, Giovanni Vincenzo.
Telemaco nell' isola di Calipso, Firenze, 1773.   Schatz 6400

Micheli, Antonio.
Cesare nella Brettagna, Lucca, 1779. *See* M. Curzio in Title
catalogue.
Roma liberata dalla congiura di Catilina, Lucca, 1775. *See*
M. Curzio in Title catalogue.

Micheli, Benedetto.
Il marchese di Spartivento ovvero Il cabalista ne sa' men del
caso, Roma, 1747 (principally by Auletta).   ML 50.2.M37A9

Micheli, Girolamo.
Il giuramento alla vendetta, Venezia, 1744.   Schatz 6482
Zenobia, Venezia, 1746.   Schatz 6481

Michl, Joseph, 1745–1810.
Der baron vom Vesten thurme (Muenchen) 1777. Tr. of his
Il barone di Torre forte.   Schatz 6488
Fremore und Meline, Frankfurt a. M., 1778.   Schatz 6484
Milton und Elmire, Frankfurt und Leipzig, 1775.   Schatz 6486
— same, Augsburg, 1780.   Schatz 6487
— same, n. pl., 1782.   Schatz 6487a
Il trionfo di Clelia—Der sieg der Clelia, Monaco (1776).   Schatz 6489

Mile, *musikdirektor.* *See* Mühle.

Miller.
Télémaque dans l'isle de Calipso, Paris, 1790.   ML 48.B2

Miller, Julius.
Der freybrief, Berlin, 1788.   Schatz 4610a

Millico, Giuseppe, *b.* 1730 *or* 1739.
The princess of Tarento, pasticcio. *See* Title catalogue.
La Zelinda, Napoli (1786).   Schatz 6499

Minissari, Francesco.
L'amante del cielo, Roma, 1699.   Schatz 6520

Minoja, Ambrogio, 1752–1825.
Tito nelle Gallie, Milano (1787).   Schatz 6519

Minuti, Lorenzo.
Lo scialaquatore, Lucca, 1763.   Schatz 6521

Misliweczek, Joseph, 1737–1781 (*called* Il Boëmo).
    Adriano in Siria, Pavia (1777).   Schatz 6533
    Armida, Milano (1780).   ML 48.A5 v.9
    Il Bellerofonte (Siena, 1767).   Schatz 6532
    Il Demofoonte, Venezia, 1769.   Schatz 6529
    Il gran Tamerlano, Milano (1772).   Schatz 6530
    Il trionfo di Clelia, Torino (1768).   Schatz 6531

Mitscha, Franz Adam, *ritter* von, 1746–1811.
    Adrast und Isidore oder Die nachtmusik, Wien, 1780.   Schatz 6535

Molinari, Pietro.
    Le barbarie del caso, Venetia, 1664.   Schatz 6548

Monari, Clemente.
    L'Aretusa, Venezia, 1709.   Schatz 6549
    Teuzzone. *See* Zeno's Poesie drammatiche.

Mondonville, Jean Joseph Cassanea de, 1711–1772.
    L'Amour et Psyché. *See his* Bacchus et Érigone.
    Bacchus et Érigone—L'Amour et Psyché, n. i., n. d. (1769)   ML 52.2.B105M6
    Daphnis et Alcimaduro, Paris, 1778.   ML 50.2.D25M6
    L'Himen et l'Amour. *See his* Les projets de l'Amour.
    Jupiter et Calisto. *See his* Les projets de l'Amour.
    Mirzele. *See his* Les projets de l'Amour.
    Les projets de l'amour (Paris) 1771.   ML 52.2.P75
    Thesée (Paris) 1765 (Journal des spectacles, t. ii, Paris, 1766).   ML 48.J7
    Titon et L'Aurore, Paris, 1763.   ML 50.2.T59M7
    Titon et L'Aurore, Marseille, 1775.   ML 50.2.T59M73

Moneta, Giuseppe, *b.* 1761.
    Le bugie hanno le gambe corte. A. T. of his Il conte Policronio.
    Il capitan Tenaglia o sia La muta per amore, Firenze, 1784.   Schatz 6556
    Il conte Policronio o sia Le bugie hanno le gambe corte,
        Firenze, 1791.   Schatz 6551
    Le due orfane e i due tutori innamorati, Firenze, 1792.   Schatz 6552
    La muta per amore. A. T. of Moneta's Il capitan Tenaglia.
    L'Oreste, Pisa (1798).   Schatz 6555
    I pastori delle Alpi, Gorizia (1780).   Schatz 6557
    Il trionfo di Gedeone, Firenze (1798).   Schatz 6553
    L'Urano, Firenze, 1788.   (Is a cantata.)   Schatz 6554

Monopoli. *See* Insanguine.

Monsigny, Pierre Alexandre, 1729–1817.
  See also Catalogue of 19th cent. librettos.
    Aline, reine de Golconde. O. T. of his La reine de Golconde.
    Les aveux indiscrets, Paris, 1759.   ML 50.2.A95M7
    La bella Arsena, Augsburg, 1781. Tr. of his La belle Arsène. Schatz 6565
    La belle Arsène, Paris, 1775 (four-act version).   Schatz 6562
    La belle Arsène, n. i., n. d. (1775) (Theatre de M. Favart,
        Paris, Duchesne, 1763–77, t. x) (four-act version).   ML 49.A2F1
    Den besnaerede cadi, n. i., n. d. Tr. of his Le cadi dupé. Schatz 6568
    Le cadi dupé, Paris, 1761.   ML 50.2.C2M7
    Le cadi dupé, Paris, 1766.   Schatz 11725
    Le cadi dupé, Paris, 1782.   Schatz 6567
    Daphne and Amintor, pasticcio. *See* Title catalogue.

Monsigny, Pierre Alexandre—Continued.

The deserter, London, 1773. Tr. of his Le déserteur, with
additional music by Dibdin and Philidor.   Longe 13

The deserter (Collection of the most esteemed farces, Edinburgh, 1792, t. iv).   Schatz 11753d

Le déserteur, Paris, 1769.   Schatz 6569

Le deserteur, Paris, 1770.   ML 50.2.D45

Der deserteur, Frankfurt am Mayn (1773). **Tr. of the above.** Schatz 6570

L'enfant trouvé. A. T. of his Félix.

Le faucon, Paris, Herissant, 1772 (48 p.).   Schatz 11726

Le faucon, Paris, Herissant, 1772 (32 p.).   Schatz 6573

Félix ou L'enfant trouvé, Paris, 1777.   ML 50.2.F25M7

Félix ou L'enfant trouvé, Paris, 1784.   Schatz 6574

Felix, oder Der findling, Riga, 1790. Tr. of the above.   Schatz 6575

Den forstilte tvistighed, n. i., n. d. (Copenhagen, 1777).   Schatz 6585

Le génie Asouf ou Les deux coffrets, Paris, an VIII (1799–
1800). (Pasticcio, music partly by the above.)   Schatz 10591

The golden pippin. See Title catalogue.

L'isle sonnante, Paris, 1768.   Schatz 6576

L'isle sonnante, Paris, 1771.   Schatz 11727

Der koenig und der pachter, Frankfurt und Leipzig, 1766.
Tr. of his Le roi et le fermier.   Schatz 6581

Der koenig und der pachter, Frankfurt am Mayn, 1773.   Schatz 6582

Maid of the mill, pasticcio. See Title catalogue.

Le maître en droit, Paris, 1762.   ML 50.2.M31M6

Le maître en droit, Paris, 1764.   Schatz 6577

Man sieht niemals alles voraus, Frankfurt am Mayn, 1772.
Tr. of: Schatz 6579

On ne s'avise jamais de tout, Avignon, 1764.   Schatz 6578

On ne s'avise jamais de tout (Dresde, 1766).   Schatz 11729

On ne s'avise jamais de tout, Paris, 1775.   Schatz 11728

La reine de Golconde, Paris, 1772. L. T. of his Aline, reine
de Golconde.   Schatz 6587

Le roi et le fermier, Bruxelles, 1765.   ML 50.2.R7M7

Le roi et le fermier (Dresde, 1766).   Schatz 11732

Le roi et le fermier, Paris, 1768.   Schatz 11730

Le roi et le fermier, Paris, 1779.   Schatz 6580

Roschen und Colas, Frankfurt am Mayn, 1772. Tr. of his: Schatz 6584

Rose et Colas, Paris, 1764.   ML 50.2.R74M6

Rose et Colas, Paris, 1770.   Schatz 6583

Rose et Colas, Paris, 1779.   Schatz 11733

Die schoene Arsene, Frankfurt am Mayn, 1776. Tr. of his
La belle Arsène.   Schatz 6563

Die schoene Arsene, Hamburg, 1780.   Schatz 6564

De schoone Arsène, Amsteldam, 1789.   Schatz 6586

Den skiønne Arsene, n. i., n. d. (Copenhagen, 1781). Tr. of
his La belle Arsène.   Schatz 6566

Monteclair, Michel Pignolet de, 1666–1737.

Ascanio. Ballet music for Pollaroli's opera.

Les festes de l'été (Recueil général des opéra, Paris, 1734, t.
xii).   Schatz 6589

Jephté, Paris, 1738.   ML 50.2.J3M6

Jephté (Recueil général des opera, Paris, 1739, t. xv).   Schatz 6590

Monteverdi, Claudio Giovanni Antonio, 1567–1643.

    L'Adone, Venetia, 1640.   Schatz 6594

    L'Arianna, Mantova, 1608.   Schatz 6595

    L'Arianna, Venetia, 1640.   Schatz 6592

    L'incoronatione di Poppea, Venetia, 1656.   Schatz 6593

    Le nozze d'Enea con Lavinia (Ms.).   Schatz 6596

Monti, Gaetano, *ca.* 1740–1816.

    L'Adriano in Siria, Modena (1775).   Schatz 6605

    Le donne vendicate, Napoli, 1796.   Schatz 6601

    La fuga, Napoli, 1777.   Schatz 6603

    Il molaforbici, Napoli, 1782.   Schatz 6602

    La scuffiara: (One aria by him in Tritto's opera, Napoli, 1784.)

    Lo sposalizio per dispetto, Venezia (1782).   Schatz 6600

    Lo studente, Napoli, 1783.   Schatz 6604

Montuoli, Giuseppe, 1667–1739.

    Lucio Giunio Bruto primo consolo di Roma, Lucca, 1735.

        See M. Curzio in Title catalogue.

Monza, Carlo, 1744–1801.

    Antigono, Roma (1772).   Schatz 6620

    Aristo e Temira, Bologna, 1771.   Schatz 3934

    Cajo Mario, Venezia, 1777.   Schatz 6617

    Il cavalier parigino, Milano (1774).   L. T. of his Il finto cava-

        liere parigino.   Schatz 6619

    Cleopatra, Torino (1776).   Schatz 6613

    Enea in Cartagine, Alessandria (1784).   Schatz 6618

    Erifile, Torino (1786).   Schatz 6614

    Germanico in Germania, Roma, 1770.   Schatz 6609

    Ifigenia in Tauride, Milano (1784).   Schatz 6610

    La Nitteti, Milano, 1771.   Schatz 6615

    Oreste, Torino (1766).   Schatz 6611

    Sesostri rè d'Egitto, Milano, 1759.   Schatz 6612

Moorehead, John, *d.* 1804.

    See also Catalogue of 19th cent. librettos.

    The naval pillar, London, 1799.   Longe 258

Morange, L.

    Les qui proquo nocturnes, Paris, 1798.   Schatz 6627

Moratelli, Sebastiano.

    La gemma Ceraunia d'Ulissipone hora Lisbona, Heydelberga, 1687.   ML 50.2.G25

    I giochi olimpici overo Che fingendo si prova un vero affetto (Düsseldorf, 1694).   Schatz 6628

Moreira, Antonio Leal.

    See also Catalogue of 19th cent. librettos.

    Artemisia, regina di Caria (Lisbona, 1787).   Schatz 6629

    Ascanio in Alba (Lisbon, 1785).   Schatz 6633

    Gli eroi Spartani (Lisbona, 1788).   Schatz 6630

    L'eroina lusitana, Lisbona, 1795.   Schatz 6635

    L'Imenei di Delfo (Lisbon, 1785).   Schatz 6631

    Il natale augusto, Lisbona, 1783.   Schatz 6637

    Siface e Sofonisba (Lisbon, 1783).   Schatz 6632

    A vingança da Cigana, Lisboa (1794).   Schatz 6634

Morgan.

The comical history of Don Quixote, London, 1729. *See* Title catalogue. LONGE 168

Morin, Jean Baptiste, *ca.* 1677–1745.

La chasse du cerf (*In* the score publ. Paris, Ballard, 1709). M 1520.M8C4

Moro Lin, Francesco.

La fedeltà riconosciuta, Venezia, 1798. SCHATZ 6674

Mortellari, Michele, *b.* 1750.

Alessandro nell' Indie, Lucca (1783). SCHATZ 6683
Antigona, Venezia, 1776. SCHATZ 6679
Arsace, Venezia, 1775. SCHATZ 6685
Le astuzie amorose, Venezia (1775). SCHATZ 6688
Il baron di Lago Nero, Venezia, 1776. SCHATZ 6689
Don Salterio Civetta, Venezia, 1776. SCHATZ 6690
La fata benefica, Venezia (1783). SCHATZ 6680
Il finto pazzo per amore, Venezia, 1779. SCHATZ 6681
La governante, Roma, 1777. SCHATZ 6686
Lucio Silla, Torino (1779). SCHATZ 6682
La muta per amore, Venezia, 1781. SCHATZ 6693
Li rivali ridicoli, Venezia (1780). SCHATZ 6691
Semiramide, Milano (1785). SCHATZ 6692
Telemaco·nell' isola Ogigia (Venice, 1782). Is a cantata. SCHATZ 6684
Troja distrutta, Milano (1778). SCHATZ 6687

Mosca, Luigi, 1775–1824.

See also Catalogue of 19th cent. librettos.
L'impresario burlato, Napoli, 1797. ML 50.2.I49M6
La sposa tra le imposture, Napoli, 1798. SCHATZ 6725

Moulds, John.

The fugitive or Happy recess, London (1790). LONGE 207

Moulinghen, Jean-Baptiste.

Les nymphes de Diane, Paris, Aux dépens de la compagnie, 1755. ML 50.2.N9M6
Les nymphes de Diane, Paris, Duchesne, 1755 (Théâtre de M. Favart, Paris, Duchesne, 1763–77, t. viii). ML 49.A2F1
Les nymphes de Diane, Paris, 1766. Schatz 11502
La servante justifiée. *See* Title catalogue.

Mouret, Jean Joseph, 1682–1738.

Les amours de Ragonde (Lyon, 1742). SCHATZ 6738
Les amours des dieux (Recueil général del opéra, t. xiv, Paris, 1734). SCHATZ 6739
Les amours des dieux, Paris, 1757. ML 52.2.A5
Ariane, Paris, 1717. ML 50.2.A739M6
Ariane (Recueil général des opéras, t. xii, Paris, 1734). SCHATZ 6694
Le ballet des sens (Recueil général des opéras, t. xv, Paris, 1739). SCHATZ 6744–6746
La critique des Festes de Thalie. *See his* Les festes de Thalie.
Les festes de Thalie (Recueil général des opéra, t. xi, Paris, 1720). SCHATZ 6741–6742
Fragments, composés du prologue des Amour des dieux . . . (Paris) 1765 (the other fragments by Dauvergne and Rameau). ML 48.J7

Mouret, Jean Joseph—Continued.

Les Graces (Recueil général des opéra, Paris, 1745, t. xvi). ML 48.R4

Le jaloux puni (Le nouveau théâtre italien, Paris, 1753, t. iii). ML 48.N6

Le jeune vieillard (Le théâtre de la foire, Paris, 1724, t. v). ML 48.L2 v

Le joueur (Les parodies du Nouveau théâtre italien, Nouv. éd., Paris, 1738, t. iv). ML 48.P3

Pirithous (Recueil général des opéra, t. xiii, Paris, 1734) Schatz 6743

La Provençale (Paris, 1755). *See his* Les festes de Thalie. ML 52.2.F3

Le triomphe des sens. *See his* Le ballet des sens.

Le triomphe de Thalie. *See his* Les festes de Thalie.

Mozart, Johann Chrysostomos Wolfgang Amadeus, 1756–1791.

See also Catalogue of 19th cent. librettos.

Gli amanti folletti—Die verliebten poltergeister, Dresda, 1794. (Made up from his Il Dissoluto punito, Le nozze di Figaro and La clemenza di Tito). Schatz 6748

Belmonte und Konstanze, Berlin, 1788. L. T. of his Entführung aus dem Serail. ML 50.2.E5M8

Belmonte und Konstanze, Berlin, 1798. Schatz 6812

Caernarvon Castle. *See* Title catalogue.

Cosi fan tutte o sia La scuola degli amanti, Vienna (1790). Schatz 6762

Cosi fan tutte, o sia La scuola degli amanti—Eine wie die andere oder Die schule der liebhaber, Dresda, 1791. Schatz 6763

Il dissoluto punito, o sia Il Don Giovanni, Praga (1787). Schatz 6788

Don Juan, Frankfurt, 1789. Tr. of the above. Schatz 6789

Don Juan, oder Die redende statue, n. pl., 1793. Another Tr. Schatz 6859

Don Juan oder Der steinerne gast, n. pl., 1795. Another Tr. Schatz 6790

Eine ist wie die andere, oder Die schule der liebhaber. Tr. of his Cosi fan tutte, Dresda, 1791. Also A. T. of his Die schule der liebhaber. Schatz 6763

Eine machts wie die andere oder Die schule der liebhaber, Breslau (1792). Tr. of his Cosi fan tutte. Schatz 6764

Eine wie die andere oder Die schule der liebhaber. Tr. of Cosi fan tutte, Dresda, 1791. Schatz 6763

Elskernes skole. A. T. of his Veddemaalet.

Die entfuehrung aus dem serail, Wien, 1782. Schatz 6811

Die entführung aus dem serail, Warschau (1783). Schatz 6856

Figaro's heyrath, Hamburg, 1791. Tr. of his Le nozze di Figaro. Schatz 11396

Figaro's hochzeit, oder List über list, Passau, 1793. Tr. of his Le nozze di Figaro. Schatz 6860

Figaro's hochzeit oder Der tolle tag. Tr. of his Le nozze di Figaro, Berlino, 1790. Schatz 6827

Il flauto magico (Dresda) 1794. Tr. of his Die zauberflöte. Schatz 6858

La folle giornata. A. T. of his Le nozze di Figaro.

Der freybrief, Berlin, 1788 (music selected from Haydn, Mozart, and von Weber). Schatz 4610a

Der freybrief (Nürnberg?) 1797. Two-act version of the above. Schatz 4610

Die hochzeit des Figaro, Wien, 1798. Tr. of his Le nozze di Figaro. Schatz 6828

Die hochzeit des Figaro, Leipzig, 1794. Schatz 6829

Idomeneo—Idomeneus, Monaco (1781). Schatz 6818

List über list. A. T. of his Figaro's hochzeit, Passau, 1793.

Mozart, Johann Chrysostomos Wolfgang Amadeus—Contd.

Maedchen list und liebe. A. T. of his Die wette.

Die maedchen sind von Flandern. A. T. of his Weibertreue.

Le nozze di Figaro, Vienna (1786). Schatz 6826

Le nozze di Figaro, o sia La folle giornata—Figaro's hochzeit oder Der tolle tag, Berlino, 1790. Schatz 6827

The mariners, pasticcio. *See* Title catalogue.

The prisoner. *See* Title catalogue.

Die redende statue. A. T. of his Don Juan.

Der schauspieldirektor, Liegnitz, 1792 (detached from Stephanie's Singspiele, with separate title page). Schatz 6840

Die schule der liebhaber oder Eine ist wie die andere, Augsburg, 1794. Tr. of his Cosi fan tutte. Schatz 6765

La scuola degli amanti. A. T. of his Cosi fan tutte.

Der steinerne gast. A. T. of his Don Juan.

Titus, Cassel, 1797. Tr. of his La clemenza.di Tito. ML 50.2.C58M77

Der tolle tag. A. T. of his Figaro's hochzeit.

Veddemaalet eller Elskernes skole, Kiøbenhavn, 1798. Tr. of his Cosi fan tutte. Schatz 6768

Die verliebten poltergeister. Tr. of his Gli amanti folletti, Dresda, 1794. Schatz 6748

Weibertreue, oder Die maedchen sind von Flandern, Leipzig, 1794. Tr. of his Cosi fan tutte. Schatz 6766

Die wette, oder Maedchen list und liebe, Hamburg (1796). Tr. of his Cosi fan tutte. Schatz 6767

Die zauberfloete, n. i., 1794. ML 50.2.Z25M7

Die zauberflöte, Leipzig (1794). Schatz 6849

Mühle, Nicolaus.

Lindor und Ismene (Anspach, 1773?). Schatz 6873

Mit dem glockenschlag: zwoelf!, Anspach, 1781. Schatz 6871

Die singschule oder Drei heirathen an einem tage, Koenigsberg, 1794. Schatz 6872

Müller, Wenzel, 1767–1835.

See also Catalogue of 19th cent. librettos.

Der alte ueberall und nirgends, Wien, 1796 (I ter theil). Schatz 6906

—— Wien, 1796 (II ter theil). Schatz 6907

Das aufgeboth. A. T. of his Die getreuen Oesterreicher.

Buerger freuden, Wien (1797). Schatz 6914

Der fagottist oder Die zauberzither, Wien, 1791. Schatz 6920

Het feest der Brahminen, Amsterdam, 1798. Tr. of his Das sonnenfest der Braminen. Schatz 6966

Die getreuen Oesterreicher, oder Das aufgeboth, Wien, 1797. Schatz 6929

Der invalide (Wien, 1786). Schatz 6934

Die löwenjagd. A. T. of his Die verschwoerung der Odaliken.

Das Neusonntagskind, Wien, 1794. Schatz 6947

Das neue Sonntagskind, Berlin (1796). L. T. of this. Schatz 6949

Pizichi, oder Fortsetzung des Fagottisten, Wien, 1793. Schatz 6956

Das schlangenfest in Sangora, Wien, 1797. Schatz 6959

Die schoene marketenderinn, Wien, 1795. Schatz 6961

Die schoene marketenderin (Wien) 1798. Schatz 6961a

Die schwestern von Prag, Wien, 1794. Schatz 6963

Das sonnenfest der Braminen, Wien, 1790. Schatz 6965

Das sonntagskind, Hamburg, 1798. L. T. of his Das Neusonntagskind. Schatz 6948

Müller, Wenzel—Continued.

Der sturm, Wien, 1798.	Schatz 6967
Taddaedl, der dreyssigjaehrige A. B. C. schuetz, Wien, 1799.	Schatz 6968
Die verschwoerung der Odaliken, oder Die loewenjagd, Wien, 1792.	Schatz 6974
Wer den schaden hat, darf fuer den spott nicht sorgen, Wien, 1798.	Schatz 6976
Die zauberinsel. L. A. T. of his Der sturm.	
Die zauberzither (Wien) 1795. L. T. of his Der fagottist.	Schatz 6921
Die zauberzither, oder Der fagottist, Rostock, 1796.	Schatz 6922
Die zauberzither, Prag, 1796. L. T. of his Der fagottist.	Schatz 11714
Die zwoelf schlafenden jungfrauen (II ter theil) Wien, 1798.	Schatz 6979

Mugnes, Giuseppe.

Fernando Cortes conquistator del Messico, Firenze, 1789.	Schatz 6864
L'impostura, Napoli, 1796.	Schatz 6863

Nasolini, Sebastiano, 1768–*ca.* 1816.

See also Catalogue of 19th cent. librettos.

Adriano in Siria, Milano (1790).	Schatz 6998
Andromaca, Venezia, 1790.	Schatz 6999
La Calliroe, Firenze, 1792.	ML 48.A5 v.22
Cleopatra, regina d'Egitto, Genova (1795).	Schatz 7023
Eugenia, Venezia, 1792.	Schatz 7000
Eugenia—Eugenie, Dresda, 1794.	Schatz 7001
Le feste d'Iside, Venezia, 1799.	Schatz 7002
Gl'Indiani, Venezia, 1796.	Schatz 7004
Ines de Castro, Venezia, 1795 (with Bianchi, Gerace and Cervellini).	Schatz 1012
Gli innamorati, Venezia, 1793 (with V. Trento).	Schatz 7031
Melinda, Venezia, 1798.	Schatz 7022
Merope, Venezia, 1796.	Schatz 7005
La morte di Cleopatra. *See his* Cleopatra, regina d'Egitto.	
La morte di Semiramide ossia La vendetta di Nino, Trieste (1795).	Schatz 7013
I raggiri fortunati, Venezia, 1795.	Schatz 7029
Teseo a Stige, Firenze, 1791.	Schatz 7021
Timoleone, Reggio (1798).	Schatz 7026
Tito e Berenice, Venezia, 1793.	Schatz 7017
Il trionfo di Clelia, Milano (1799).	Schatz 7028
Gli umori contrari, Venezia (1798).	Schatz 7030
Vasco di Gama, pasticcio. *See* Title catalogue.	
La vendetta di Nino. A. T. of his La morte di Semiramide.	
Zaira, Venezia, 1797.	Schatz 7018

Naumann, Johann Gottlieb, 1741–1801.

See also Catalogue of 19th cent. librettos.

Alles aus liebe. Tr. of his Tutto per amore, Dresda, 1785.	Schatz 7057
Amore giustificato—Die gerechtfertigte liebe, Dresda, 1792.	Schatz 7037
Amphion, Leipzig (*ca.* 1790).	Schatz 7038
Armida, Venezia, 1773.	Schatz 7039
Armide (Leipzig, 1782). Tr. of this.	Schatz 7040
Die burg Hymens. Tr. of his La reggia d'Imenèo, Dresda, 1787.	Schatz 7056
Cora, Leipzig, 1781.	Schatz 7042
Cora (Dresden, 1781).	Schatz 7042a

Naumann, Johann Gottlieb—Continued.

Cora, Danzig (17—).	Schatz 7042b
Li creduti spiriti, Venezia, 1764 (with others).	Schatz 7064
La dama soldato—Die dame als soldat, Dresda, 1791.	Schatz 7043
Elisa—Elise, Dresda, 1781.	Schatz 7047
Elskovs magt, Kiøbenhavn, 1791.　Tr. of his Tutto per amore.	Schatz 7063
Der eyfersuechtige bauer.　Tr. of his Il villano geloso.	
Die gerechtfertigte liebe.　Tr. of his Amore giustificato.	
Die gestoehrte hochzeit.　Tr. of his Le nozze disturbate, Dresda, 1774.	Schatz 7059
Der hypochondriste.　Tr. of his L'ipocondriaco, Dresda, 1776.	Schatz 7050
Ipermestra, Venezia, 1774.	Schatz 7049
L'ipocondriaco—Der hypochondriste, Dresda, 1776.	Schatz 7050
L'isola disabitata, Venezia, 1775.	Schatz 7061
The midnight wanderers.　See Title catalogue.	
Le nozze disturbate—Die gestoehrte hochzeit, Dresda, 1774.　L. T. and Tr. T. of his La villanella incostante.	Schatz 7059
Orpheus og Euridice, Kiøbenhavn, 1790.	Schatz 7052
Orpheus und Euridice, Kiel und Hamburg (179–).	Schatz 7053
Osiride—Osiris, Dresda, 1781.	Schatz 7054
The picture of Paris.　See Title catalogue.	
Protesilao—Protesilaus, Berlino (1789) (1st act by Reichardt).	Schatz 8654
Protesilao—Protesilaos, Berlino (1793).	Schatz 7055
La reggia d'Imenèo—Die burg Hymens, Dresda, 1787.	Schatz 7056
Solimano, Venezia, 1773.	Schatz 7062
Tutto per amore—Alles aus liebe, Dresda, 1785.	Schatz 7057
Vasco di Gama, pasticcio.　See Title catalogue.	
La villanella incostante, Venezia, 1773.	Schatz 7058
Il villano geloso—Der eyfersuechtige bauer, Dresda, 1770.	Schatz 7060
Was trut die liebe nicht, Leipzig, 1793.　Tr. of his La dama soldato.	Schatz 7044

Navara (Navarra), Francesco.

Basilio rè Doriente [!], Venetia, 1696.	Schatz 7065
Elena rapita da Paride, Venetia, 1687 (with Freschi).　See the latter's Helena rapita da Paride.	Schatz 3358

Neefe, Christian Gottlob, 1748–1798.

Adelheit von Veltheim, Leipzig, 1781.	Schatz 7068
Adelheit von Veltheim, n. i., n. d.	Schatz 11734
Amors gukkasten, Leipzig, 1772.	Schatz 7069
Die apotheke, Leipzig, 1772.	Schatz 7070
Der einspruch, Leipzig, 1772.	Schatz 7071
Heinrich und Lyda, Leipzig, 1776.	Schatz 7073
Sophonisbe, Leipzig, 1776.	Schatz 7072
Sophonisbe, n. i., n. d. (detached).	Schatz 11724

Negri, Antonio.

Atenaide.　See Zeno's Poesie drammatiche.

Neri Bondi (Bondineri Michele, called), b. 1750.

I viaggiatori o siano I matrimoni in cantina, Pisa, 1786.	Schatz 7079

Neubauer, Franz Christian, 1760–1795.

Fernando und Yariko, Muenchen, 1784.	Schatz 7092

Niccolini, Giuseppe.　See Nicolini.

Nichelmann, Christoph, 1717–1762.
    Il sogno di Scipione—Der traum des Scipio, Berlin, 1746.   Schatz 7103

Nicolai, Johann Gottlieb, 1744–1801.
    Die wilddiebe, Muenster, 1774.   Schatz 7114

Nicolini (Niccolini), Giuseppe, 1762–1842.
    See also Catalogue of 19th cent. librettos.
    Alzira, Genova (1797).   Schatz 7153
    Artaserse, Venezia, 1795.   Schatz 7140
    La donna innamorata, Venezia, 1796.   Schatz 7142
    La famiglia stravagante, Parma (1793).   Schatz 7151
    Gli Sciti, Milano (1799).   Schatz 7133
    Il trionfo del bel sesso, Milano (1799).   Schatz 7138

Niel, Jean Baptiste.
    Le ballet des Romans, Lyon, 1742 (contains only "La Ber-
        gerie," the first entrée).   Schatz 7161
    Les romans (Recueil général des opéra, Paris, 1745, t. xvi).   ML 48.R4

Nucci, Giuseppe.
    Abduramel, ballet. *See* Nasolini's Melinda.
    Angelica e Wilton, ballet. *See* Isola's La conquista del vello
        d'oro.
    I bacchanali, ballet. *See* Farinelli's Seldano.
    I due cacciatori e la venditrice di latte, ballet. *See* Isola's
        La conquista del vello d'oro.
    L'incoronazione di Uladislao, rè di Polonia, ballet. *See*
        Isola's La conquista del vello d'oro.
    L'infausto matrimonio, ballet. *See* Portugal's La pazzia gior-
        nata.
    Oscar e Malvina, ballet. *See* Trento's Bianca de' Rossi.

Ordonez (Ordonnetz), Carlo d'.
    Diesmal hat der mann den willen! Wien, 1778.   Schatz 7291

Orefici, Antonio.
    L'amore resarciuto, Napole, 1727.   ML 50.2.A715O7
    L'Engelberta o sia La forza dell' innocenza, Napoli (1709).
        (Partly composed by Francesco Mancini).   Schatz 7294
    Melissa schernita. Intermezzo. Is part of the L'Engelberta
        libretto, and is composed either by Orefici or Mancini.
    La Rosilla, Napoli, 1733. (Partly composed by Leonardo
        Leo.)   Schatz 7293

Orgiani, Teofilo, *d. ca.* 1714.
    Armida regina di Damasco, Verona, 1711. L. T. of his Gli
        amori di Rinaldo con Armida.   Schatz 7296
    Il Dioclete, Venetia, 1687.   Schatz 7297
    Le gare dell' inganno e dell' amore, Venetia, 1689.   Schatz 7298
    L'honor al cimento, Venezia, 1703. L. T. of his Gli amori di
        Rinaldo con Armida.   Schatz 7295
    Il vitio depresso e la virtù coronata, Venetia, 1687.   Schatz 7299

Orlandini, Giuseppe Maria.
    Adelaide, Venezia, 1729.   Schatz 7326
    Adelaide, Mantova (1731).   ML 50.2.A31O7
    Antigona, Venezia, 1718.   Schatz 7327

Orlandini, Giuseppe Maria—Continued.

Arsace, Firenze (1732).	ML 48.A5v.18
` Artaserse, Napoli, 1708 (partly by Francesco Mancini).	Schatz 7328
Ataulfo rè de' Goti, ovvero La forza della virtù, Roma, 1712.	Schatz 7349
Berenice, Venezia (1725).	Schatz 7329
Il bottegaro gentiluomo, Venezia, 1739 (attributed also to Hasse).	Schatz 7350
Le bourgeois gentil-homme; or Vanesio and Larinda, London, 1737. *See his* Il bottegaro gentiluomo.	Schatz 7353
La donna nobile, Venezia, 1730.	Schatz 7340
Der ehrsuechtige Arsaces (Hamburg, 1722) (partly by Filippo Amadei).	Schatz 7354
La fedeltà coronata, Bologna, 1727. L. T. of his Antigona.	ML 50.2.A718O7
La fida ninfa (Verona, 1730) (detached copy).	ML 50.2.F4O7
La fida ninfa (Maffei, Poesie, Verona, 1752, t. ii).	PQ
La forza della virtù. A. T. of his Ataulfo rè de' Goti.	
The gamester—Il giocatore, London, 1736. Tr. and L. T. of Il marito giogatore e la moglie bacchettona.	Schatz 7339
Il giocatore—Le joueur, Paris, 1752. *See* Title catalogue.	ML 50.2.G4O7
Griselda, Venezia, 1720.	Schatz 7330
Grullo and Moschetta, London, 1737. Tr. of:	Schatz 7333
Grullo e Moschetta, Venetzia (1732).	Schatz 7332
Ifigenia in Aulide, Firenze (1732).	Schatz 7334
Ifigenia in Tauride, Venezia, 1719.	Schatz 7335
L'innocenza difesa, Roma, 1720.	Schatz 7336
Le joueur. Tr. of Il giocatore, Paris, 1752.	ML 50.2.G4O7
Lucio Papirio, Mantova (1718).	Schatz 7352
Il marito giogatore, e la moglie bacchettona, Venezia, 1719. *See* Title catalogue.	Schatz 7337
Massimiano, Venetia (1731).	Schatz 7351
Melinda e Tiburzio. O. T. of his La donna nobile (Schatz 7340).	
La Merope, Bologna (1717).	Schatz 7348●
Monsieur de Porsugnac, Venezia, 1741.	Schatz 7341
Nero (Hamburg, 1729) (partly by others). Tr. of:	Schatz 7344
Nerone, Venezia, 1721.	Schatz 7343
Paride, Venezia, 1720.	Schatz 7345
Pourceaugnac and Grilletta (Pursignacco e Grilletta) London, 1737. Tr. an L. T. of his Monsieur de Porsugnac.	Schatz 7342
La preziosa ridicola, Venezia, 1719.	Schatz 7346
Lo scialaquatore alla fiera, Venezia, 1745 (partly by others).	Schatz 7347
Serpilla e Bacocco (Monaco, 1722). L. T. of Il marito giogatore, e la moglie bacchettona. *See* Title catalogue.	Schatz 7338
Vanesio and Larinda. A. T. of his Le bourgeois gentilhomme.	
La virtù nel cimento, Mantova (1717). L. T. of his Griselda.	Schatz 7331

Oswald, James, *d.* 1769.

Love in a village, pasticcio.   *See* Title catalogue.

Ottani, Bernardo (*or* Bernardino), ca. 1735–1827.

L'amore industrioso, Dresda, 1769.	Schatz 7357
L'amore senza malizia, Venezia, 1768.	Schatz 7358
L'amore senza malizia—Die liebe ohne bossheit, Dresda, 1768.	Schatz 7359
L'amore senza malizia (Lisbona, 1774).	ML 48.C6 I
Arminio, Torino (1781).	Schatz 7363

Ottani, Bernardo—Continued.

Calipso, Torino (1777).   Schatz 7360

La Didone, Forlì (1779).   Schatz 7364

Fatima, Torino (1779).   Schatz 7361

Il fumo villano, Venezia, 1766.   (Interpolations for Piccinni's
opera.)   Schatz 8156

Le industrie amorose (Venetia, 1778).   Schatz 7365

Die liebe ohne bossheit.   Tr. of his L'amore senza malizia,
Venezia, 1768.   Schatz 7359

Le nozze della Bita, Firenze, 1778.   Schatz 7362

Ottoboni, *cardinal* **Pietro.**

Il Colombo, overo L'India scoperta, Roma, 1690.   Schatz 7371

Pacelli, Antonio.

Il finto Esaù, overo Gli odii fraterni, Venetia, 1698.   Schatz 7377

Paci, Francesco Maria.

La schiava per amore, Roma, 1746.   Schatz 7379

Pack, *colonel.*

The comical history of Don Quixote, London, 1729.   *See* Title
catalogue.   Longe 68

Pär, Ferdinando.   *See* Paër.

Paër, Ferdinando Francesco, 1771–1839.

See also Catalogue of 19th cent. librettos.

L'amante servitore, Venezia, 1796.   Schatz 7478

Il Cinna, Padova (1795).   Schatz 7560

Circe, Venezia, 1792.   Schatz 7487

I due sordi.   L. A. T. of his Il matrimonio improviso.

Ero e Leandro, Napoli, 1794.   Schatz 7551

Der fuerst von Taranto.   Tr. of his Il principe di Taranto,
Dresda, 1798.   Schatz 7524

Geld ist die loosung.   Tr. of his L'oro fa tutto, Dresda, 1795.   Schatz 7522

L'intrigo amoroso, Venezia, 1795.   Schatz 7505

L'intrigo amoroso, Lisboa, 1798.   Schatz 7559

L'intrigo amoroso—Die liebesintrigue, Dresda, 1799.   Schatz 7506

Laodicea.   O. T. of his Tegene e Laodicea.

Il matrimonio improvviso (Venice) 1794.   Schatz 7563

Il matrimonio improviso, o I due sordi, Barcellona, 1798.   Schatz 7564

Os moleiros, Lisboa, 1795.   Tr. of his: Schatz 7558

I molinari, Venezia, 1794.   Schatz 7515

Il nuovo Figaro, Parma (1794).   Schatz 7565

L'oro fa tutto, Milano (1793).   Schatz 7521

L'oro fa tutto—Geld ist die loosung, Dresda, 1795.   Schatz 7522

Orphée et Euridice (Parma) 1791.   Schatz 7550

I pretendenti burlati, Medesano, 1793.   Schatz 7566

Il principe di Taranto—Der fuerst von Taranto, Dresda, 1798.   Schatz 7524

La Rossana, Milano, 1795.   Schatz 7561

Saed ossia Il serraglio, Torino (1798).   Schatz 7507

Tegene e Laodicea, Firenze, 1799.   Schatz 7508

Il tempo fa giustizia a tutti, Milano (1797).   Schatz 7537

La testa riscaldata, Venezia, 1799.   Schatz 7540

La virtù al cimento, Parma (1798).   Schatz 7545

Paganelli, Giuseppe Antonio.

Artaserse, Venezia (1742). SCHATZ 7572

Barsina, Venezia, 1742. SCHATZ 7573

La caduta di Leone, imperator d'Oriente, Venezia (1732). SCHATZ 7571

Engelberta, Venezia, 1743. SCHATZ 7354

Rosmira, Firenze, 1746. SCHATZ 7575

Tigrane, Venezia (1733). SCHATZ 7570

Pagliardi, Giovanni Maria.

Il Caligola, Roma, 1674. L. T. of: SCHATZ 7586

Caligula delirante, Venetia, 1672. SCHATZ 7582

Lisimaco, Venetia, 1674. SCHATZ 7583

Numa Pompilio, Venetia, 1674. SCHATZ 7584

Il tiranno di Colco, Firenze, 1688. SCHATZ 7585

Il tiranno di Colco (G. A. Moniglia, Poesie drammatiche, parte
seconda, Firenze, 1690). ML 49.A2M7

Paisiello, Giovanni, 1741-1816.

See also Catalogue of 19th cent. librettos.

Die abenteurer. Tr. of his Gli avventurieri, Dresda, 1791. SCHATZ 7654

Gli amanti comici o sia D. Anchise Campanone, Napoli, 1794. SCHATZ 7588

L'amor contrastato, Venezia, 1788. O. T. of his La molinara, SCHATZ 7590a
La molinara astuta, etc.

L'amor contrastato—Die streitig gemachte liebschaft, Dresda,
1790. SCHATZ 7591

L'amore in ballo, Venezia, 1765. SCHATZ 7587

Amore ingegnoso o sia La giovane scaltra, Padova (1775). SCHATZ 7694

L'amore ingegnoso, Roma (1785). ML 50.2.A693P2

L'amore ingegnoso—Die erfinderische liebe, Dresda, 1786. SCHATZ 7597

L'amore ingegnoso, (Lisbona, 1790). SCHATZ 7596

L'Andromaca, Venezia (1798). SCHATZ 7598

Annibale in Torino, Torino (1771). SCHATZ 7692

L'Arabo cortese, Napoli, 1776 (several arias by Cimarosa). SCHATZ 7665

Gli astrologi imaginari. O. T. of his I filosofi immaginari.

Le astuzie amorose, Firenze, 1777. SCHATZ 7675

L'avaro deluso—Der verspottete geitzige, Dresda, 1776. L. T. SCHATZ 7608
of his La discordia fortunata.

L'avaro deluso—Der betrogene geizhals (Praga) 1784. SCHATZ 7609

Gli avventurieri—Die abenteurer, Dresda, 1791. SCHATZ 7654

Le barbier de Séville, Amsterdam, 1786. Tr. of his Il barbiere di Siviglia. SCHATZ 7600

Der barbier von Sevilla oder Die unnütze vorsicht, Koeln,
1786. Tr. of his: SCHATZ 7601

Il barbiere di Siviglia, Pietroburgo (1782). ML 50.2.B25P2

Der betrogene geizhals. Tr. of his L'avaro deluso (Praga)
1784. SCHATZ 7609

Der betrogene geizige, oder: Wer das glueck hat, Leipzig,
1794. Tr. of his La discordia fortunata. SCHATZ 7610

Die beyden fluechtlinge, Hamburg, 1791. Tr. of his Le gare
generose. SCHATZ 7628

O casamento inesperado. A. T. of his O marquez de Tulipano.

Il credulo deluso, Napoli, 1776. SCHATZ 7666

Dal finto il vero, Napoli, 1776. SCHATZ 7604

Dal finto il vero—Das ist er ja selbst, Dresda, 1782. SCHATZ 7605

Paisiello, Giovanni—Continued.

Il Demofoonte, Venezia, 1775.	SCHATZ 7698
La Didone, Firenze, 1795.	SCHATZ 7699
La discordia fortunata, Venezia, 1775.	SCHATZ 7607
La disfatta di Dario, Firenze, 1776.	SCHATZ 7664
La disfatta di Dario, Genova (1782).	SCHATZ 7664a
The doctor and the apothecary. *See* Title catalogue.	
Don Anchise Campanone (Vienna, 1775).	SCHATZ 7589
D. Chisciotte della Mancia, Napoli, 1769.	SCHATZ 7611
Don Quischott von Mancia, Wien (1771). (Third act and several arias by Florian Gassmann.)	SCHATZ 7612
Die drei pucklichen, Hamburg, 1780.	SCHATZ 7663
Le due contesse, Roma, 1776.	ML 50.2.D76P2
Le due contesse, Parma (1777).	SCHATZ 7613
Le due contesse—Die zwey comtessinnen, Dresda, 1781.	SCHATZ 7614
Le duel comique, Paris, 1776. French version of his Il duello.	ML 50.2.D8P19
Le duel comique (Paris) 1777. Tr. with added music by Méreaux of:	ML 50.2.D8P2
Il duello, Napoli, 1774.	SCHATZ 7676
Der edle wettstreit. Tr. of his Le gare generose, Dresda, 1793.	SCHATZ 7627
Der eingebildete Sokrates. *See his* Socrate immaginario, Dresda, 1781.	SCHATZ 7658
Die eingebildeten philosophen (Wien) 1781. Tr. of his I filosofi immaginari.	SCHATZ 7617
L'Elfrida, Firenze, 1795.	ML 48.A5 v.14
Elfrida, Venezia (1796).	SCHATZ 7615
L'Elfrida, Parma, 1798.	SCHATZ 7703
Elvira (Naples, 1794).	SCHATZ 7695
Die erfinderische liebe. *See his* L'amore ingegnoso, Dresda, 1786.	SCHATZ 7597
Il fanatico in berlina, Torino (1792). L. T. of his La locanda.	SCHATZ 7635
La fata benefica, ballet (partly music by Ercolano). *See* Cimarosa's I nemici generosi.	
Fedra, Napoli, 1788.	SCHATZ 7668
Figaro als barbier zu Sevilla, Passau, 1796. Tr. of his Il barbiere di Siviglia.	SCHATZ 7603
I filosofi immaginari, Napoli, 1784.	SCHATZ 7616
I filosofi immaginarii—Os filosofos imaginarios, Lisboa, 1790.	ML 48.C6‖II
La finta amante, Napoli, 1788.	SCHATZ 7669
I Francesi brillanti, Lisbona (1765).	SCHATZ 7687
La Frascatana, Siena (1776).	SCHATZ 7620
La Frascatana—Die Frascatanerin, Dresda, 1776.	SCHATZ 7621
La Frascatana—Landsbye-pigen fra Frascati, Kiøbenhavn, 1776.	SCHATZ 7623
La Frascatana oder Das maedchen von Fraskati, n. i., 1782.	SCHATZ 7624
La Frascatana, n. i., 1782. (German Tr.)	ML 50.2.F84P2
La Fraschetana, London, 1776.	SCHATZ 7622
Il furbo malaccorto, Napoli, 1782.	SCHATZ 7677
Le gare generose, Napoli, 1786.	SCHATZ 7679
Le gare generose—Der edle wettstreit, Dresda, 1793	SCHATZ 7627
Le gare generose ossia Gli schiavi per amore, Parma, 1796.	SCHATZ 7626

Paisiello, Giovanni—Continued.

Der geadelte landmann. A. T. of his Das witzige land-
maedchen.

Le génie Asouf, ou Les deux coffrets, Paris, an VIII [1799]
(pasticcio, music partly by the above).   Schatz 10591

La giovane scaltra. A. T. of his Amore ingegnoso.

I giuochi d'Agrigento, Venezia, 1792.   Schatz 7629

Ginochi d'Agrigento, Lisbona, 1799.   ML 50.2.G45P2

Die glueckliche unschuldige. Tr. of his L'innocente fortunata, Dresda (1780).   Schatz 7633

La grotta di Trofonio, Napoli, 1785.   Schatz 7680

The haunted tower, pasticcio. *See* Title catalogue.

L'idolo cinese, Napoli, 1783.   Schatz 7670

L'infante de Zamora, La Haye, 1783. (French version of his
La Frascatana.)   ML 50.2.F84P22

L'innocente fortunata, Firenze, 1774.   Schatz 7631

L'innocente fortunata—Die glueckliche unschuldige, Dresda
(1780).   Schatz 7633

L'inutile precauzione, Venezia, 1787. L. T. of his Il barbiere
di Siviglia.   Schatz 7602

Ipermestra, Padova (1791).   Schatz 7702

L'isola disabitata, Lisbona, 1799.   Schatz 7693

Der koenig Theodor (n. pl.), 1792. Tr. of his Il rè Teodoro
in Venezia.   Schatz 7683

Der koenig Theodor in Venedig, Koeln, 1785.   Schatz 7651

Koenig Theodor in Venedig, Hamburg, 1788.   Schatz 7653

Der koenig Theodor zu Venedig, Stuttgart, 1785.   Schatz 7682

Landsbye-pigen fra Frascati. *See his* La Frascatana, Kiøbenhavn, 1776.   Schatz 7623

La locanda, Vienna, 1792.   Schatz 7634

La locanda, London, 1792.   Schatz 7672

Lock and key. *See* Title catalogue.

Lucio Papirio dittatore (Lisboa, 1775).   Schatz 7674

Das maedchen von Fraskati. Tr. of his La Frascatana, n. i.,
1782.   Schatz 7624

Das maedchen von Fraskati, Luebeck, 1785. Tr. of his La
Frascatana.   Schatz 7625

Il marchese di Tulipano o sia Il matrimonio inespetato—O
marquez de Tulipano o O casamento inesperado, Lisbona,
1790. L. T. of his Il matrimonio inaspettato.   Schatz 7688

Il matrimonio inaspettato (St. Petersburg, 1779?).   Schatz 7636

Le mbroglie de le bajasse. O. T. of his La serva fatta padrona.

The midnight wanderers. *See* Title catalogue.

La modista ossia La scuffiaja, Gorizia (1790). L. T. of his: Schatz 7643

La modista raggiratrice, Napoli, 1787.   Schatz 7642

La molinara o sia L'amor contrastato—Die müllerin oder Die
streitig gemachte liebe, Berlino (n. d.). L. T. and Tr. of
his L'amor contrastato.   Schatz 7593

Il mondo della luna, Napoli (1792). L. T. of his Il credulo
deluso.   Schatz 7667

Die muellerin, Hamburg (1793). Tr. of his L'amor contrastato.   Schatz 7595

Paisiello, Giovanni—Continued.

Die müllerin oder Die streitig gemachte liebe. Tr. of his La molinara, Berlino (n. d.). Schatz 7593

Netley Abbey. *See* Title catalogue.

Nina o sia La pazza per amore, Napoli, 1790. Schatz 7645

Nina, o sia La pazza per amore—Nina, oder Wahnsinn aus liebe, Dresda, 1791. Schatz 7646

Nitetti—Nitetis, St. Pietroburgo (1788). ML 50.2.N46P2

Le nozze disturbate, Venezia, 1766. Schatz 7696

La pazza per amore. A. T. of his Nina.

Die phantasten. *See his* I visionari, Dresda, 1793. Schatz 7619

Die philosophen (n. i., n. d.). Tr. of his I filosofi immaginari. Schatz 7618

Il re Teodoro in Venezia, Milano (1788). ML 50.2.R3P22

Il rè Teodoro in Venezia—Le roi Théodore à Venise, Paris, 1789. ML 50.2.R3P27

Le roi Théodore à Venise, Versailles, 1787. French version of his Il rè Teodoro in Venezia. ML 50.2.R3P25

Gli schiavi per amore, Torino (1791). L. T. of his Le gare generose. Schatz 7700

Die schoene muellerin, Berlin (1793). Tr. of his L'amor contrastato. Schatz 7594

La scuffiaja. A. T. of his La modista.

La semplice fortunata, Napoli, 1773. Schatz 7632

La serva fatta padrona, Napoli, 1769. Schatz 7671

The siege of Belgrade. *See* Title catalogue.

Il Sismano nel Mogol, Cremona (1785). Schatz 7697

Socrate immaginario—Der eingebildete Sokrates, Dresda, 1781. Schatz 7658

Lo strambo in berlina, Lisbona, 1795. L. T. of his La locanda. Schatz 7685

Die streitig gemachte liebe. A. T. of his Die müllerin.

Die streitig gemachte liebschaft. Tr. of his L'amor contrastato, Dresda, 1790. Schatz 7591

Il tamburo, Napoli, 1784. Schatz 7659

Il tamburo notturno, Parma, 1778. L. T. of this. Schatz 7660

Il tamburo notturno (Vienna, 1774). Schatz 7661

Theodor in Venedig, Berlin, 1799. Tr. of his Il re Teodoro in Venezia. Schatz 7652

Le trame per amore, Napoli, 1783. Schatz 7681

Die Trofonius-hoehle (Wien, 1787?). Tr. of his La grotta di Trofonio. Schatz 7704

Die unnütze vorsicht. A. T. of his Der barbier von Sevilla.

La vallée de Montmorency ou Jean-Jacques Rousseau dans son hermitage, pasticcio. *See* Title catalogue.

Le vane gelosie, Milano (1791). Schatz 7701

Vasco di Gama, pasticcio. *See* Title catalogue.

Der verspottete geitzige. Tr. of his L'avaro deluso, Dresda, 1776. Schatz 7608

I visionari—Die phantasten, Dresda, 1793. L. T. of his I filosofi immaginari. Schatz 7619

Wahnsinn aus liebe. A. T. of his Nina.

Wer das glueck hat. A. T. of his Der betrogene geizige.

Das witzige landmaedchen, Nuernberg, 1787. Tr. of his Il matrimonio inaspettato. Schatz 7638

Paisiello, Giovanni—Continued.

Zorilan, ballet. (Music selected from his works.) *See* Cimarosa's L'impegno superato.

Die zwey comtessinnen. Tr. of his Le due contesse, Dresda, 1781.   Schatz 7614

Palella, Antonio.

Il chimico, Napoli, 1742.   Schatz 7711

L'incanti per amore, Napoli, 1741.   Schatz 7712

Origille, Venezia, 1744 (with others).   Schatz 7713

Tigrane, Napoli (1745). (Only the overture, some recitatives, and designated arias. Otherwise by Hasse.)   Schatz 4584

Pallavicini, Vincenzo.

Lo speziale, Venezia, 1755 (with Domenico Fischietti).   Schatz 7714

Lo speziale—Der apotheker, Dresden, 1755.   Schatz 7715

Pallavicino, Carlo, 1630–1688.

L'Alvida, regina de Goti. A. T. of his L'Amazone corsara.

L'Amazone corsara, overo L'Alvilda regina de Goti, Venetia, 1686.   Schatz 7716

Le Amazoni nell' Isole Fortunate, Padova (1679).   Schatz 7717

Amore inamorato, Venetia, 1686.   Schatz 7718

L'Aureliano, Venetia, 1666.   Schatz 7719

Bassiano, overo Il maggior impossibile, Venetia, 1682.   Schatz 7720

Carlo rè d'Italia, Venetia, 1682.   Schatz 7733

Il Demetrio, Venetia, 1666.   Schatz 7735

La Didone delirante, Venetia, 1686.   Schatz 7736

Diocletiano, Venetia, 1685.   Schatz 7721

Elmiro, rè di Corinto, Venetia, 1686.   Schatz 7722

Enea in Italia, Venetia, 1675.   Schatz 7723

Galieno, Venetia, 1676.   Schatz 7724

La Gierusalemme liberata, Venetia, 1687.   Schatz 7725

Licinio imperatore, Venetia, 1684.   Schatz 7726

Il maggior impossibile. A. T. of his Bassiano.

Massimo Puppieno, Venetia, 1685.   Schatz 7727

Il Meraspe. A. T. of his Il tiranno humiliato.

Messalina, Venetia, 1680.   Schatz 7728

Il Nerone, Venetia, 1679.   Schatz 7729

Penelope la casta, Venetia, 1685.   Schatz 7730

Il rè infante, Venetia, 1683.   Schatz 7734

Ricimero, rè di Vandali, Venetia, 1684.   Schatz 7731

Il tiranno humiliato d'amore, overo Il Meraspe, Venetia, 1667.   Schatz 7737

Il Vespasiano, Venetia, 1678.   Schatz 7732

Palma, Silvestro di, 1762–1834.

See also Catalogue of 19th cent. librettos.

Gli amanti della dote, Cremona (1794).   Schatz 7747

Gli amanti ridicoli, Napoli, 1797.   Schatz 7746

Chi mal fa mal aspetti ovvero Lo scroccatore smascherato, Venezia, 1792.   Schatz 7748

La finta matta, Napoli, 1789.   Schatz 7741

Le nozze in villa, Roma (1792).   ML 50.2.N72P2

La pietra simpatica, Napoli, 1796.   ML 50.2.P4P2

Palomino, José.

Il ritorno di Astrea in terra, Lisbona, 1785.   Schatz 7751

Pampani, Antonio Gaetano, *d.* 1769 (*possibly identical with* Antonio Pampino).

Artaserse, Venezia (1750).	Schatz 7754
Astianatte, Venezia, 1755.	Schatz 7755
La caduta d'Amulio, Venezia, 1747.	Schatz 7757
La clemenza di Tito (Venezia, 1748).	Schatz 7758
Il Demetrio, Venezia, 1768.	Schatz 7761
Demofoonte, Venezia, 1764.	Schatz 7752
Eurione, Venezia, 1754.	Schatz 7760
L'Olimpiade, Venezia, 1767 (with P. Guglielmi and G. F. Brusa).	Schatz 4316
Venceslao (Venezia, 1752).	Schatz 7759

Pampino, Antonio (*possibly identical with* Gaetano Antonio Pampani).

L'Anagilda, Venezia, 1735.	Schatz 7756
Artaserse Longimano, Venezia, 1737.	Schatz 7753

Paneck, Johann Baptist.

Die christliche Judenbraut, Augsburg, 1793.	Schatz 7762

Paradies, Maria Theresia, 1759–1824.

Rinaldo und Alcina, Koenigsberg, 1794.	Schatz 7770

Paradies, Pietro Domenico, 1710–1792.

Love in a village, pasticcio. *See* Title catalogue.

Parke, William Thomas, 1762–1847.

Lock and key. *See* Title catalogue.

Netley Abbey. *See* Title catalogue.

Partenio, Giovanni Domenico, *d.* 1701.

La costanza trionfante, Venetia, 1673.	Schatz 7777
Dionisio overo La virtù trionfante del vizio, Venetia, 1681 (acts II–III; act I by Franceschini).	Schatz 3319
Flavio Cuniberto, Venetia, 1682.	Schatz 7778
Flavio Cuniberto, Firenze, 1702.	ML 50.2.F6P2
Iphide Greca, Venetia, 1671 (second act by D. Freschi; third by G. Sartorio).	Schatz 7779

Pasque (Pasqua), Giuseppe.

L'albergia smascherata o sia Il cittadino rinnobilito, Vienna (1767).	Schatz 7782
Arianna e Teseo, Torino (1764).	Schatz 7781

Pasquini, Bernardo, 1637–1710.

La donna ancora è fedele, Roma, 1676.	ML 50.2.D6P2

Pattoni, Giovanni Battista.

Nicoraste rè di Tracia, Venezia, 1745.	Schatz 7785

Paulati, Andrea.

I veri amici, Venezia, 1713.	Schatz 7786

Paxton, Stephen, 1735–1787.

Fontainebleau. *See* Title catalogue.

Rosina. *See* Title catalogue.

Pè, Ferdinando. *See* Paër.

Pellegrini, Domenico.

Amor tiranno, Bologna, 1649.	Schatz 7859

Pellegrini, Pietro.
　Cirene, Venezia, 1742.　　　　　　　　　　　　　SCHATZ 7860

Pepusch, John Christopher, 1667–1752.
　Achilles. *See* Title catalogue.
　The beggar's opera, London, 1728 (1st ed.). Ballad opera
　　arr. by P.　　　　　　　　　　　　　　　　ML 50.5.B3
　The beggar's opera, London, 1729.　　　　　　ML 50.5.B33
　The beggar's opera, 5th ed., London, 1742.　　AC 901 M5　v.519
　The beggar's opera, London, 1765.　　　　　　ML 50.5.B35
　The beggar's opera, London, 1777.　　　　　　SCHATZ 7864
　The beggar's opera (J. Bell, British theatre, London, 1791–97,
　　t. 2).　　　　　　　　　　　　　　　　　　PR 1241.B4
　The beggar's opera, London, Cooke (before 1800?).　PR 3473.B4C6
　The country-wedding and Skimmington, London, 1729. Same
　　as his The wedding.　　　　　　　　　　　LONGE 275
　Myrtillo. *See his* Venus and Adonis, London, 1736.
　Perseus and Andromeda with The rape of Colombine or The
　　flying lovers, London, 1728.　　　　　　　LONGE 191
　Perseus and Andromeda, 4th ed., London, 1730.　LONGE 40
　Polly, London, 1729. Ballad opera arr. by P.　ML 50.5.P74
　Polly, London, n. d.　　　　　　　　　　　ML 50.5.B3
　Polly, London, 1777.　　　　　　　　　　　SCHATZ 7865
　Thomyris, queen of Scythia, pasticcio. *See* Title catalogue.
　Venus and Adonis . . . and Myrtillo, London, 1736.　ML 52.2.V47
　The wedding, London, 1729. Ballad opera arr. by P.　LONGE 33
　The wedding, London, 1734 (2d ed.).　　　　LONGE 306

Per, Pèr, Pér, Për, Ferdinando. *See* Paër.

Perez, David, 1711–1778.
　Alessandro nell' Indie, Lisbona, 1755.　　　SCHATZ 7882
　Arminio, London, 1760 (and others).　　　　ML 50.2.A77
　La Berenice, Verona, 1762.　　　　　　　　SCHATZ 7879
　The captive, pasticcio. *See* Title catalogue.
　Creusa in Delfo (Lisbona, 1774).　　　　　SCHATZ 7880
　Demetrio, Venezia, 1751.　　　　　　　　　SCHATZ 7876
　L'eroe coronato (Lisbona, 1775).　　　　　SCHATZ 7881
　Farnace, Torino (1751).　　　　　　　　　SCHATZ 7878
　Lucio Vero, Verona (1754).　　　　　　　　SCHATZ 7873
　Merope, Venezia (1750).　　　　　　　　　SCHATZ 7874
　Solimano, Lisbona (1768).　　　　　　　　SCHATZ 7877
　La Semiramide riconosciuta—A Semiramis reconhecida, Lis-
　　bona (1765).　　　　　　　　　　　　　SCHATZ 7875
　Zenobia (Lisbona, 1765).　　　　　　　　　ML 50.2.Z37P3

Pergolesi, Giovanni Battista, 1710–1736.
　See also Catalogue of 19th cent. librettos.
　Die als magd gewordene frau. Tr. of his La serva padrona,
　　Braunschweig (1749).　　　　　　　　　SCHATZ 7894
　Amor fa l'uomo cicco. *See* Title catalogue.
　Les Chinois. *See* Title catalogue.
　La contadina astuta. *See his* Livietta e Tracollo.
　La finta Polacca. *See his* Livietta e Tracollo.
　Il finto pazzo, Brunsviga (1749). L. T. of his Livietta e Tra-
　　collo o sia La contadina astuta.　　　　SCHATZ 7891

Pergolesi, Giovanni Battista—Continued.

Lo frate nnammorato, Napole (1734).   Schatz 7903

Il geloso schernito, Venezia, 1746.   *   Schatz 7905

Il giocatore, pasticcio. *See* Il marito giogatore.

Il ladro convertito per amore, Venezia, 1750. L. T. of: Schatz 7906

Livietta e Tracollo o sia La contadina astuta. O. T. of his
    La contadina astuta, La finta Polacca, Il finto pazzo, Tra-
    collo, Il ladro convertito per amore, etc.

Il maestro di cappella—Der kapellmeister, Berlino, 1756 (a
    very much altered version of his Il maestro di musica).   Schatz 5468

Love in the city, pasticcio. *See* Title catalogue.

Die magd als frau im hause (Dresden, 1740). Tr. of his La
    serva padrona.   Schatz 7893

Maid of the mill, pasticcio. *See* Title catalogue.

Le maître de musique, Bruxelles, 1758. Parody of his Il
    maestro di musica.   ML 50.2.M3P3

Le maître de musique, Paris, 1784.   Schatz 5467

De meid meesteres. A. T. of his Pandolfus en Zerbina.

L'Olimpiade, Venezia, 1738.   Schatz 7904

Orazio, Venezia, 1743 (mostly by Latilla, though the text is
    based on Pergolesi's Il maestro di musica).   Schatz 5466

Pandolfus en Zerbina of De meid meesteres, Amsteldam, 1793.
    Tr. of his La serva padrona.   Schatz 7896

La serva padrona, Venezia, 1748.   Schatz 7892

La serva padrona—Die als magd gewordene frau, Braun-
    schweig (1749).   Schatz 7894

La serva padrona (Frankfurt a/M, 1755). (Soralli's *rifacimento*
    of the text.)   Schatz

La servante maitresse, Paris, 1754. Parody of his La serva
    padrona.   Schatz 7895

La servante maîtresse, La Haye, 1755.   ML 48.A4

La servante maîtresse, Bruxelles, n. d.   ML 50.2.S51P3

La servante maîtresse, Paris, 1771.   Schatz 7895a

Tom Jones, pasticcio. *See* Title catalogue.

Tracollo. L. T. of his Livietta e Tracollo o sia La contadina
    astuta.

Peri, Jacopo, 1561–1633.

La Dafne, Firenze, 1600.   Schatz 7918

L'Euridice, Fiorenza, 1600.   Schatz 7919

Il Medoro, Fiorenza, 1623 (mostly by Marco da Gagliano).   ML 48.M2F

Il natal d'Ercole, Firenze, 1605.   Schatz 7920

Perillo, Salvatore (Salvador).

The accomplis'd maid. *See* Title catalogue.

Berenice, Venezia, 1759.   Schatz 7925

La buona figliuola, Venezia, 1760.   Schatz 7921

La donna Girandola, Venezia, 1763.   Schatz 7924

L'erede riconosciuta, Venezia, 1771. (Interpolations for
    Piccinni's opera.)   Schatz 8104

La finta semplice, Venezia, 1764.   Schatz 7926

Li tre vagabondi, Venezia, 1776.   Schatz 7927

Il viaggiator ridicolo, Venezia, 1761.   Schatz 7922

La villeggiatura di Mestre, Venezia (1770).   Schatz 7923

Perti, Giacomo Antonio, 1661–1756.

Atide, Bologna (1679). (Act III only, act I by G. F. Tosi, act II by Pietro degli Antoni.)   SCHATZ 10381
Brenno in Efeso, Venetia, 1690.   SCHATZ 7947
Dionisio re di Portogallo, Firenze, 1707.   ML 50.2.D57P3
Dionisio Siracusano, Parma (1689).   SCHATZ 7955
Fausta restituita all' impero, Roma, 1697.   SCHATZ 7959
La forza della virtù, Bologna, 1694.   SCHATZ 7948
Il furio Camillo, Mantova (1700).   ML 50.2.F9P3
Il fratricida innocente, Bologna (1708).   SCHATZ 7949
Il furio Camillo, Bologna, 1693.   SCHATZ 7950
L'inganno scoperto per vendetta, Venetia, 1691.   SCHATZ 7956
Laodicea e Berenice, Venetia, 1695.   SCHATZ 7951
Martio Coriolano, Venetia, 1683.   SCHATZ 7957
Nerone fatto Cesare, Venetia, 1693.   SCHATZ 7952
Il Pompeo, Genova, 1691.   SCHATZ 7958
Il rè infante, Bologna (1694).   SCHATZ 7953
La Rosaura, Venetia, 1689.   SCHATZ 7954

Pescetti, Giovanni Battista, 1704–*ca.* 1766.

Alessandro nell' Indie, Venetia (1732).   SCHATZ 7960
Demetrius—(Demetrio) London, 1737.   SCHATZ 7964
Dorinda, Venezia (1729) (with Galuppi).   SCHATZ 7967
Ezio (Venezia, 1747).   SCHATZ 7965
Ezio, London, 1764–5 (pasticcio from above and Bach, Galuppi, etc.).   ML 48.M2N
Farnace, Firenze, 1749.   SCHATZ 7966
Sabrina, London, 1737 (with others).   SCHATZ 8859
Sabrina (Rolli, Componimenti poetici, Nuova ed., Verona, 1744 (and other composers)   ML 49.A2R7
Tamerlano, Venezia (1754) (second act only; first by Cocchi; third by both).   SCHATZ 2054
I tre difensori della patria, Venezia, 1729. L. T. of: SCHATZ 7961
Tullo Ostilio, Venezia, 1740.   SCHATZ 7962
Tropotipo, Venezia, 1726.   SCHATZ 7963

Pfeiffer, Jean Michel.

Amore in puntiglio, Venezia, 1773.   SCHATZ 8001

Phanty.

Don Sylvio von Rosalva oder Der sieg der natur ueber die schwaermerey (Schleswig, 1796?).   SCHATZ 8004

Pher, Ferdinando. *See* Paër.

Philidor, François André Danican, 1726–1795.

L'amant déguisé ou Le jardinier supposé, Paris, 1769 (Theatre de M. Favart, Paris, Duchesnè, 1763–77, t. x).   ML 49.A2F1
L'amant déguisé ou Le jardinier supposé, Paris, veuve Duchesne, 1772 (35 p.).   SCHATZ 8005 and YUDIN PQ
L'amant déguisé ou Le jardinier supposé, Paris, 1785.   SCHATZ 11735
Antoine Masson. O. T. of his Le bon fils.
La belle esclave ou Valcour et Zéila, Paris, 1787.   ML 50.2.B3P3
Blaise le savetier, Paris, 1759.   ML 50.2.B39P4
Blaise le savetier, Paris, 1769.   SCHATZ 8007
Blaise le savetier, Paris, 1771.   SCHATZ 11736
Le bon fils, Paris, 1773.   SCHATZ 8009

Philidor, François André Danican—Continued.

Le bucheron ou Les trois souhaits, Paris, 1763.   SCHATZ 8010

Le bucheron ou Les trois souhaits, Copenhague, 1767.   YUDIN PQ

Le bucheron ou Les trois souhaits, Paris, 1771.   SCHATZ 11736

Le bucheron ou Les trois souhaits, Paris, 1782.   SCHATZ 11737

The deserter. *See* Monsigny's Le déserteur in Title catalogue.

Le diable à quatre ou La double métamorphose, La Haye, 1757.   ML 50.2.D52P4

Die drey wuensche. A. T. of his Der holzhauer.

Ernelinde, Paris, 1767.   ML 50.2.E65P3

Les fausses infidélités. A. T. of his Zémire et Mélide.

Les femmes vengées ou Les feintes infidélités, Paris, 1775.   SCHATZ 8014

Les femmes vengées ou Les feintes infidélités, Paris, 1782.   SCHATZ 11738

Das fest der weiblichen tugend. A. T. of his Das rosen-maedchen.

Les festes de la paix, Nouv. éd., augmentée, Paris, 1763 (Theatre de M. Favart, Paris, Duchesne, 1763–77, t. ix).   ML 49.A2F1

Der gaertner von Sidon, Frankfurt am Mayn, 1773. Tr. of his Le jardinier de Sidon.   SCHATZ 8016

The golden pippin. *See* Title catalogue.

Hanns der schufflicker, Frankfurt am Mayn, 1772. Tr. of his Blaise le savetier.   SCHATZ 8008

Der holzhauer oder Die drey wuensche, Frankfurt am Mayn, 1773. Tr. of his Le bucheron.   SCHATZ 8011

Der hufschmied, Frankfurth und Leipzig, 1772, and   SCHATZ 8019

Der hufschmied, Riga, 1785. Both Trs. of his Le maréschal ferrant.   SCHATZ 8020

L'huitre et les plaisirs ou Le tribunal de la chicane, Paris, 1761.   SCHATZ 8036

Le jardinier de Sidon, Paris, 1768.   SCHATZ 8015

Le jardinier de Sidon, Paris, 1770.   SCHATZ 11739

Le jardinier et son seigneur, Paris, 1769.   SCHATZ 11740

Le jardinier et son seigneur, Paris, 1785.   SCHATZ 8017

Le jardinier supposé. A. T. of his L'amant déguisé.

Maid of the mill, pasticcio. *See* Title catalogue.

The maid of the oaks. *See* Title catalogue.

Le marechal ferrant, Seconde éd., Paris, 1761.   YUDIN PQ

Le maréchal ferrant, Paris, 1765.   SCHATZ 8018

Le maréchal ferrant, Paris, 1785.   SCHATZ 11741

Melide oder Der schiffer, Frankfurt, 1778, and   SCHATZ 8034

Melide oder Der schiffer, Riga (1786). Both Trs. of his: SCHATZ 8035

Mélide ou Le navigateur, Paris, 1774.   SCHATZ 8033

La nouvelle école des femmes, Paris, 1770.   SCHATZ 8021

Das rosenmaedchen oder Das fest der weiblichen tugend, Frankfurth am Mayn, 1772. Tr. of his, Blaise and Duni's La rosière de Salenci.   SCHATZ 2860

La rosiere de Salenci, Paris, veuve Duchesne, 1770 (Theatre de M. Favart, Paris, Duchesne, 1763–77, t. x) (with Blaise and Duni).   ML 49.A2F1

Sancho Pança dans son isle, Avignon, 1768.   ML 50.2.S2P4

Sancho Pança dans son isle, Paris, 1771.   SCHATZ 8022

Sanko Panssa, Halberstadt, 1776. Tr. of the above.   SCHATZ 8023

Der schiffer. A. T. of his Melide.

Skovhuggeren eller De tre ønsker (Copenhagen, 1782).   SCHATZ 8013

Philidor, François Andrè Danican—Continued.

Der soldat als zauberer, Mannheim, 1772. Tr. of:	SCHATZ 8025
Le soldat magicien, Paris, 1760.	ML 50.2.S68P4
Le soldat magicien, Paris, 1775.	SCHATZ 8024
Le sorcier, Copenhague, 1767.	YUDIN PQ
Le sorcier, Paris, 1770.	SCHATZ 8027
Thémistocle (Paris) 1785.	ML 50.2.T4P3
Tom Jones, Paris, 1766.	SCHATZ 11742
Tom Jones, Paris, 1769.	ML 48.M2N
Tom Jones, Florence, 1776.	ML 48.M2F
Tom Jones, Paris, 1778.	SCHATZ 8029
Tom Jones, Frankfurt am Mayn, 1773. Tr. of the above, as are:	SCHATZ 8030
Tom Jones, Hamburg (1779).	SCHATZ 8031
Tom Jones, Oels (n. d.).	SCHATZ 8032
De tre ønsker. A. T. of his Skovhuggeren.	
Le tribunal de la chicane. A. T. of his L'huitre et les plaideurs.	
Les trois souhaits. A. T. of his Le bucheron.	
Valcour et Zéila. A. T. of his La belle esclave.	
Der verkleidete liebhaber oder Der verstellte gaertner, Frankfurt am Mayn, 1774. Tr. of his L'amant déguisé.	SCHATZ 8006
Der verstellte gaertner. A. T. of his Der verkleidete liebhaber.	
Der zauberer, Frankfurt am Mayn, 1772. Tr. of his Le sorcier.	SCHATZ 8028
Der zaubernde soldat (n. i., n. d.). Tr. of his Le soldat magicien.	SCHATZ 8026
Zémire et Mélide, ou Les fausses infidélités. O. T. of his Mélide ou Le navigateur.	

Piccinni, Luigi, 1766–1827.

L'amante statua, Venezia, 1794.	SCHATZ 8062

Piccinni, Niccolò, 1728–1800.

See also Catalogue of 19th cent. librettos.

The accomplis'd maid, London, 1767. Tr. of his La buona figliuola.	LONGE 32
The accomplish'd maid, Philadelphia, 1777. Tr. of his La buona figliuola.	ML 50.6.A2
Alessandro nell' Indie, Firenze (1777).	SCHATZ 8137
L'amante ridicolo deluso, Lisbona (1763).	SCHATZ 8063
Amelia, pasticcio. *See* Title catalogue.	
L'Americano, Venezia, 1779.	SCHATZ 8064
Der Amerikaner, Bamberg, 1791. Tr. of the above.	SCHATZ 8065
L'amor perfetto. A. T. of his I servo padrone.	
L'astratto ovvero Il giocator fortunato, Venezia, 1772.	SCHATZ 8066
L'astratto ovvero Il giuocatore fortunato, Pisa, 1773.	SCHATZ 8066a
L'astrologa, Torino (1762).	SCHATZ 8147
Atys, Paris, 1780.	SCHATZ 8067
Atys, Paris, 1783.	SCHATZ 11743
Die ausschweifenden, Mannheim, 1771. Tr. of his Gli stravaganti.	SCHATZ 8113
Il barone di Torreforte—Der baron von Starckenthurm, Dresda, 1766.	SCHATZ 8068
Il barone di Torreforte, Firenze (1768).	ML 48.A5 v.24

Piccinni, Niccolò—Continued.

La bella verità, n. i., n. d. *See also* Goldoni's Opere teatrali. SCHATZ 8069

The birth-day, or, The prince of Arragon, London, 1783 (only
two arias). LONGE 164

Bondehovmod eller Kiøbmanden som adelsmond og bondepigen som frøken. Tr. of his Il fumo villano, Kiøbenhavn, 1769. SCHATZ 8082

La buona figliuola, Roma, 1760. ML 50.2.B9P4

La buona figliuola, Vienna (1768). SCHATZ 8070

La buona figliuola—Den fromme pige, Kiøbenhavn, 1770. SCHATZ 8071

La buona figliuola, Paris, Didot l'aîné, 1771 (p. 47–48 "Ari-
ette"). SCHATZ 8073

La buona figliuola, Paris, Didot l'aîné, 1771 (p. 47–48 text). ML 48.M2M

La buona figliuola, Paris, veuve Duchesne, 1772 (56 p.). YUDIN PQ

La buona figliuola, Napoli, 1778. SCHATZ 8131

La buona figliuola—Das gute maedel, Dresda, 1781. SCHATZ 8074

La buona figliuola maritata, Vienna (1764). SCHATZ 8135

La buona figliola maritata, Roma (1769). SCHATZ 8136

La capricciosa, Roma, 1776. ML 50.2.C267P4

La capricciosa—Die eigensinnige, Dresda (1777). SCHATZ 8077

Cato in Utica, Mannheim (1770). SCHATZ 8079

Catone in Utica, Mannheim (1770). SCHATZ 8078

Der cavalier durch die liebe. Tr. of his Il cavaliere per
amore, Dresda, 1766. SCHATZ 8081

Il cavaliere Ergasto. L. T. of his La molinarella.

Il cavalier per amore e la contadina dama. A. T. of his Il
fumo villano.

Il cavaliere per amore, Vienna (1766). SCHATZ 8080

Il cavaliere per amore—Der cavalier durch die liebe, Dresda
(1766). SCHATZ 8081

Cesare in Egitto, Milano, 1770. SCHATZ 8083

Il conclave del MDCCLXXIV—Das conclave von
MDCCLXXIV, Roma (1775). (Satire with fictitious
composer name.) SCHATZ 8084

Das conclave von MDCCLXXIV, Rom (1775). SCHATZ 8085

Il conclave del 1774, Venezia (1797). SCHATZ 8132

Le contadine bizzarre, Vienna (1767). SCHATZ 8086

La contessina, Verona, 1775. SCHATZ 8149

La Corsala, Napoli, 1771. SCHATZ 8121

Il curioso del suo proprio danno, Napoli, 1756. SCHATZ 8141

Daphne and Amintor, pasticcio. *See* Title catalogue.

Dido, Berlin, 1799. Tr. of: SCHATZ 8089

Didon, Paris, 1783. SCHATZ 8088

La direttrice prudente, Napoli, 1767. SCHATZ 8122

La donna vana, Napoli, 1764. SCHATZ 8123

Le donne dispettose, Napoli, 1754. SCHATZ 8124

Le donne vendicate, Roma, 1763. SCHATZ 8090

Le donne vendicate, Venezia, 1764. SCHATZ 8091

Le due finte gemelle, Venezia, 1783. L. T. of his Le finte
gemelle. SCHATZ 8157

Der eifersuechtige (Komische opern der Italiener, 1782). SCHATZ 8119

Die eigensinnige. Tr. of his La capricciosa, Dresda (1777). SCHATZ 8077

L'equivoco, Napoli, 1764. SCHATZ 8125

Ercole al Termedonte, Napoli, 1793. SCHATZ 8126

Piccinni, Niccolò—Continued.

L'erede riconosciuta, Venezia, 1771. L. T. of his La pescatrice, with interpolations by Salvador Perillo.   SCHATZ 8104

L'esclave ou Le marin généreux, Paris, 1774. Tr. of his Gli
stravaganti.   SCHATZ 8114

Le faux lord, Paris, 1783.   SCHATZ 8092

Le finte gemelle, Firenze, 1771.   SCHATZ 8094

Le finte gemelle, Lisbona (1773).   SCHATZ 8093

Das fischermaedchen, Regensburg, 1777. Tr. of his La
pescatrice.   SCHATZ 8105

Den fromme pige. Tr. of his La buona figliuola, Kiøbenhavn, 1770.   SCHATZ 8071

Il fumo villano, Venezia, 1766 (with interpolations by Bernardino Ortani). L. T. of his Il cavaliere per amore.   SCHATZ 8156

Il fumo villano o sia Il cavalier per amore—Bondehovmod
eller Kiøbmanden som adelsmand og bondepigen som
frøken, Kiøbenhavn, 1769.   SCHATZ 8082

La furba burlata, Napoli, 1762 (with interpolations by Nicola
Logroscino and Giacomo Insanguine).   SCHATZ 8159

I furbi burlati, Napoli, 1773.   SCHATZ 8127

Die gefangene. Tr. of his La schiava, Dresda, 1765.   SCHATZ 8110

Il giocator fortunato, and Il giuocatore fortunato. Both A. T.
of his L'astratto.

Der glueckswechsel oder Mutter Natur in ihren kindern
(Komische opern der Italiener, Leipzig, 1782). Tr. of
his Le vicende della sorte.   SCHATZ 8120

La Griselda, Venezia, 1793.   SCHATZ 8095

La Griselda (Vienna, 1794).   SCHATZ 8096

Der grossmuethige seefahrer (n. i., n. d.). Tr. of his Gli
stravaganti.   SCHATZ 8117

Das gute maedchen, Leipzig, 1783. Tr. of his La buona
figliuola.   SCHATZ 8075

Das gute maedchen, Hamburg, 1791.   SCHATZ 8076

Das gute maedel. Tr. of his La buona figliuola, Dresda, 1781.   SCHATZ 8074

Das gute maegdchen, Mannheim (1769). Tr. of his La buona
figliuola.   SCHATZ 8072

L'incognita perseguitata, Venezia, 1764.   SCHATZ 8097

L'incognita perseguitata, Lisboa (1766).   ML 48.C6 I

L'incognita perseguitata—Die verfolgte unbekannte, Dresda,
1768.   SCHATZ 8098

L'incostante (Lisbona, 1775).   SCHATZ 8138

Iphigénie en Tauride, Paris, 1783.   ML 50.2.I65P3

Love in the city, pasticcio. *See* Title catalogue.

Kiøbmanden som adelsmand, og bondepigen som frøken.
A. T. of his Bondehovmod.

La locandiera di spirito, Napoli, 1768.   SCHATZ 8128

Madama Arrighetta, Bologna, 1760.   SCHATZ 8150

Maid of the mill, pasticcio. *See* the Title catalogue.

Le marin généreux. A. T. of his L'esclave

La molinara. O. T. of:

La molinarella (Lisbona, 1773).   SCHATZ 8099

Das mondenreich. Tr. of his Il regno della luna, Dresda, 1773.   SCHATZ 8107

Monsieur Petitone. O. T. of his Madama Arrighetta.

Piccinni, Niccolò—Continued.

Mutter Natur in ihren kindern. A. T. of his Der glueckswechsel.

Die nacht, Hamburg (ca. 1780). Tr. of his Notte critica.	Schatz 8101
Li Napoletani in America, Lisbona (1775).	Schatz 8133
Notte critica, Lisbona (1767).	Schatz 8100
La pescatrice ovvero L'erede riconosciuta, Firenze, 1772.	Schatz 8102
La pescatrice, Vienna (1769).	Schatz 8103
Phaon (Paris, 1778).	Schatz 8158
Il regno della luna, Milano, 1770.	Schatz 8106
Il regno della luna—Das mondenreich, Dresda, 1773.	Schatz 8107
Roland, Paris, 1778.	ML 50.2.R65P3
La scaltra letterata, Lisbona (1772).	Schatz 8139
La scaltra spiritosa, Torino (1761). L. T. of the above.	Schatz 8148
La schiava, Vienna (1765) and	Schatz 8151
La schiava—Die gefangene, Dresda, 1765, and	Schatz 8110
La schiava riconosciuta, Reggio (1770) and	Schatz 8109
La schiava, London, 1772, and	ML 50.2.S85P4
La schiava riconosciuta—Die wiedererkannte sclavin (Regens- burg, 1777). All L. T. of his Gli stravaganti.	Schatz 8111
La sciocchezza in amore, Venezia, 1764. L. T. of his Le con- tadine bizzarre.	Schatz 8087
Der schlosser, n. i., 1793.	Schatz 11756
Die sclavin und der grossmuethige seefahrer, Mannheim, 1773, and	Schatz 8115
Die sclavinn und der grossmuethige seefahrer, Wien, 1781. Both Trs. of his Gli stravaganti.	Schatz 8116
La serva onorata, Napoli, 1792.	Schatz 8129
Il servo padrone ossia L'amor perfetto, Venezia, 1794.	Schatz 8152
I sposi perseguitati, Napoli, 1782.	Schatz 8140
Lo sposo burlato, Vienna (1770).	Schatz 8153
Lo stravagante, Napoli, 1764.	Schatz 8130
Gli stravaganti, Lisbona (1765).	Schatz 8144
Gli stravaganti, Napoli, 1772.	Schatz 8112
The summer's tale, pasticcio. *See* Title catalogue.	
Tigrane, Torino (1761).	Schatz 8118
Il vagabondo fortunato, Napoli, 1773.	Schatz 8142
Die verfolgte unbekannte. Tr. of his L'incognita persegui- tata, Dresda, 1768.	Schatz 8098
I viaggiatori, Napoli, 1776.	Schatz 8134
Le vicende della sorte, Torino (1764).	Schatz 8154
Le vicende della sorte, Lisbona (1766).	Schatz 8143
La villeggiatura, Torino (1764).	Schatz 8155
Vittorina. *See* Goldoni's Opere teatrali.	
Il volubile, Roma, 1768. L. T. of his L'incostante.	ML 50.2.V75P3
Die wiedererkannte sclavin. Tr. of his La schiava ricono- sciuta (Regensburg, 1777).	Schatz 8111
Zophilette. *See* Title catalogue.	

Pichl, Wenzel, 1741–1807.

La caravana del Cairo, Milano, 1795. (Additional numbers for Grétry's opera.)	Schatz 4200
Raol de Crequi, ballet (with P. v. Winter). *See* the latter's Belisa.	

Pierotti, Giovanni Domenico, *d.* 1767.

Lucio Giunio Bruto primo consolo di Roma, Lucca, 1735.   *See*
M. Curzio in Title catalogue.

Solone, Lucca, 1741.   *See* M. Curzio in Title catalogue.

Teramene, Lucca, 1744.   *See* M. Curzio in Title catalogue.

Pietragrua, Carlo Luigi (*called also* Grua, Carlo Pietro.

La fede ne' tradimenti, Venezia, 1721. SCHATZ 8165

Meride, Mannheim (1742). SCHATZ 8167

Il pastor fido, Padoa, 1721. SCHATZ 8164

Romolo e Tazio, Venezia, 1722. SCHATZ 8166

Pignatta, Pietro Romolo.

L'Asmiro, rè di Corinto, Venetia, 1696. SCHATZ 8168

La costanza vince il destino, Venetia, 1695. SCHATZ 8169

Il Paolo Emilio, Venetia (1699). SCHATZ 8170

Sigismondo primo al diadema, Venetia, 1696. SCHATZ 8171

Pio, Antonio.

Demofoonte, Modena (1783). ML 48.A5 v.30

D. Taddeo in Barcellona, Napoli, 1774. SCHATZ 8185

Medonte rè di Epiro, Milano (1790). SCHATZ 8187

Nettuno ed Egle, Venezia, 1783. SCHATZ 8188

Piombanti, Francesco.

Alcina e Leone, ballet.   *See* Rust's Alessandro nell' Indie.

Enea e Lavinia, ballet.   *See* Caruso's L'Artaserse.

Pippo.   *See* Mattei, Filippo.

Pisani, Antonio.

Alfea reverente, Pisa, 1639. SCHATZ 8191

Pistocchi, Francesco Antonio, 1659–1717 (*called also* Pisto-
chino).

Gl'amori fatali, Venetia, 1682.   L. T. of his Il Leandro. SCHATZ 8199

Das gelaechter des Democritus.   Tr. of his Le risa di Democrito, Wien, 1737. SCHATZ 8200

Il Girello, Venetia, 1682. SCHATZ 8198

Il Leandro, Venetia, 1679. SCHATZ 8196

Il Narciso, Anspach (1697). SCHATZ 8197

Le risa di Democrito—Das gelaechter der Democritus, Wien
(1737). SCHATZ 8200

Piticchio, Francesco.

Gli amanti alla prova—Die liebhaber auf der probe, Dresda,
1784. SCHATZ 8201

Bertoldo, Wien, 1787. SCHATZ 8202

Il militare amante, Roma (1781). ML 50.2.M66P4

Pitterlin, Friedrich Adolf, *ca.* 1760–1804.

See also Catalogue of 19th cent. librettos.

Der fuerst und sein volk, Leipzig (1791).   (Pasticcio made up
of new music by him and music taken from Dittersdorf
and Bertoni.) SCHATZ 8204

Der fuerst und sein volk, n. i., 1794. SCHATZ 11613

Plantade, Charles Henri, 1764–1839.

See also Catalogue of 19th cent. librettos.

Palma ou Le voyage en Grèce, Paris, an VII (1798–99). ML 50.2.P2P4

Platania, Ignazio.
    Berenice, Torino (1771).   Schatz 8214

Platone (Platoni), Luigi.
    Amor non ha riguardi, Napoli, 1787.   Schatz 8218
    Li matrimonj per sorpresa, Roma (1788).   ML 50.2.M46P4

Pleyel, Ignaz Joseph, 1757–1831.
    Le génie Asouf ou Les deux coffrets, Paris, an VIII (1799)
        (pasticcio, partly music by the above).   Schatz 10591
    The haunted tower, pasticcio.   *See* Title catalogue.
    Le jugement de Paris, ballet, Paris, an VI (1797–98) (pasticcio
        of music by the above, Haydn, and Méhul).   ML 52.2.J9
    No song no supper, pasticcio.   *See* Title catalogue.
    Zulima o sia La famiglia riunita, ballo pantomimo.   *See* Fari-
        nelli's Il nuovo savio della Grecia.

Poggio, Lelio Ignazio, 1735–1787.
    La confederazione de i Sabini con Roma, Lucca, 1765.   *See*
        M. Curzio in Title catalogue.
    L'esilio di M. T. Cicerone, Lucca, 1768.   *See* M. Curzio in
        Title catalogue.

Polani, Girolamo.
    Berengario rè d'Italia, Venezia, 1709.   Schatz 8248
    Chi la fà, l'aspetta, Venezia, 1717.   Schatz 8249
    La costanza nell' Honore.   O. T. of his La vendetta disarmata
        dall' amore.
    Creso tolto a le fiamme, Venezia, 1705.   Schatz 8250
    Prassitele in Gnido, Venetia, 1707.   Schatz 8255
    La Rosilda, Venezia, 1707.   Schatz 8251
    Il tradimento premiato, Venetia, 1709.   Schatz 8252
    La vendetta disarmata dall' amore, Venezia, 1704.   (L. T. of
        his La costanza nell' Honore.)   Schatz 8253
    Vindice la pazzia della vendetta, Venezia, 1707.   Schatz 8254
    La virtù trionfante d'amore vendicativo, Venezia, 1708.   Schatz 8256

Polarolli, Orazio.
    Orlando furioso, Mantova (1725).   Schatz 8257

Pollaroli, Antonio, *d*. 1746.
    L'Aristeo, Venezia, 1700.   Schatz 8260
    Cosroe, Roma, 1723.   Schatz 8267
    Demetrio e Tolomeo, Venezia, 1702.   Schatz 8258
    Griselda, Venezia, 1701.   Schatz 8266
    Irene, Venetia, 1695.   Schatz 8299
    Leucippe e Teonoe, Venezia, 1719.   Schatz 8262
    Lucio Papirio dittatore, Venezia, 1721.   Schatz 8259
    Nerina, Venezia, 1728.   Schatz 8263
    Plautilla, Venezia, 1721.   Schatz 8264
    Sulpizia fedele, Venezia (1729).   Schatz 8261
    Turia Lucrezia, Venezia, 1726.   Schatz 8265

Pollaroli (Polaroli), Carlo Francesco, 1653–1722.
    L'Alboino in Italia, Venetia, 1691 (with G. F. Tosi).   Schatz 10382
    L'Alciade overo La violenza d'amore (originally overo L'eroico
        amore) Milano, 1709.   Schatz 3597
    Alfonso Primo, Venetia, 1694.   Schatz 8268

Pollaroli (Polaroli), Carlo Francesco—Continued.

Almansore o sia Il pregiudizio che nasce dal mancare di parola.
O. T. of his:

L'Almansore in Alimena, Venetia (1703).	Schatz 8269
Amage, regina de' Sarmati, Venetia, 1694.	Schatz 8270
L'amante impazzito, Venetia (1714). L. T. of his L'Alciade.	Schatz 3598
Gl'amici rivali, Venezia (1714). L. T. of his L'enigma disciolto.	Schatz 8283
Amor e dover, Venezia, 1697.	Schatz 8271
Ariodante, Venezia, 1716.	Schatz 8272
L'Arminio, Venezia, 1722.	Schatz 8273
Ascanio, Milano, 1702.	Schatz 8274
Gli avvenimenti d'Erminia e di Clorinda sopra il Tasso, Venetia, 1693.	Schatz 8275
Catone Uticense, Venetia, 1701.	Schatz 8276
Il cieco d'acuta vista. A. T. of his Il Licurgo.	
Circe abbandonata da Ulisse, Venetia, 1697.	Schatz 8324
Il colore fà la regina, Venetia, 1700.	Schatz 8277
Il Costantino, Roma, 1710.	Schatz 8278
Creonte tiranno di Tebe, Napoli, 1699. L. T. of his La forza della virtù, with interpolations by Scarlatti.	ML 50.2.C78P7
Il Dafni, Venezia, 1705.	Schatz 8279
Il delirio comune, per la incostanza de' genii, Venezia, 1701.	Schatz 8280
Il demone amante, overo Giugurta, Venetia, 1686.	Schatz 8281
L'enigma disciolto, Brescia (1708).	Schatz 8282
Ercole in cielo, Venetia, 1696.	Schatz 8284
Il falso Tiberino, Venezia, 1708.	Schatz 8285
Faramondo, Venetia, 1699.	Schatz 8286
Faramondo, Firenze, 1699.	Schatz 8325
Farnace, Venezia, 1718.	Schatz 8287
La fede ne tradimenti, Venezia, 1705.	Schatz 8288
Filippo rè della Grecia, Venezia, 1706.	Schatz 8289
Flavio Bertarido rè de Longobardi, Venezia, 1706.	Schatz 8290
La fortuna per dote, Venezia, 1704.	Schatz 8291
La forza d'amore, Venezia, 1697.	Schatz 8292
La forza della virtù, Venezia, 1693.	Schatz 8293
Il Germanico, Venezia, 1716.	Schatz 8294
Il giorno di notte, Venezia, 1704.	Schatz 8295
Giugurta. A. T. of his Il demone amante.	
L'Ibraim sultano, Venetia, 1692.	Schatz 8296
L'infedeltà punita, Venezia, 1712 (with Antonio Lotti).	Schatz 8326
Gl'inganni felici, Venezia, 1696.	Schatz 8297
L'innocenza riconosciuta, Venezia, 1717.	Schatz 8298
Iole, regina di Napoli, Venetia, 1692.	Schatz 8323
Irene, Venetia, 1695.	Schatz 8299
L'Irene, Napoli, 1704 (partly by Dom. Scarlatti).	Schatz 9539
Il Licurgo, overo Il cieco d'acuta vista, Venetia, 1686.	Schatz 8300
Lucio Vero, Venezia, 1700.	Schatz 8301
Marsia deluso, Venezia (1714).	Schatz 8302
Marzio Coriolano, Venezia, 1698.	Schatz 8303
L'odio e l'amor, Venezia, 1703.	Schatz 8304
Onorio in Roma, Venetia, 1692.	Schatz 8305
L'Oreste in Sparta, Reggio, 1697.	Schatz 8306
Ottone, Venetia, 1694.	Schatz 8307

Pollaroli (Polaroli), Carlo Francesco—Continued.

La pace fra Tolomeo e Seleuco, Venetia, 1691.   Schatz 8308

Il pastore d'Anfriso, Venetia, 1695.   Schatz 8310

Le pazzie degl' amanti, Venezia, 1712.   Schatz 8311

Peribea in Salamina, Padova, 1712.   Schatz 8312

Il pregiudizio che nasce dal mancare di parola.   A. T. of his Almansore.

Publio Cornelio Scipione, Venetia (1712).   Schatz 8313

I regii equivoci, Venezia, 1697.   Schatz 8314

Il ripudio d'Ottavia, Venetia, 1699.   Schatz 8315

Rosimonda, Venetia, 1696.   Schatz 8316

La schiavitù fortunata, Venetia, 1694.   Schatz 8317

Il Seleuco, Roma, 1693.   L. T. of his La pace fra Tolomeo e Seleuco.   Schatz 8309

Semiramide, Venezia, 1714.   Schatz 8318

Spurio Postumio, Venezia (1712).   Schatz 8320

Tetide in Sciro, Vicenza, 1715.   Schatz 8319

Tito Manlio, Firenze, 1696.   Schatz 8321

Venceslao, Venezia, 1703.   Schatz 8322

La violenza d'amore.   A. T. of his L'Alciade.

Pollarolo, Antonio and **Carlo Francesco.**   *See* Polaroli and Pollaroli.

Ponzo, Giuseppe.

Artaserse, Venezia (1761).   Schatz 8355

Demetrio, Torino (1762).   Schatz 8354

Porfiri, Pietro.

Zenocrate ambasciatore a' Macedoni, Venetia, 1687.   Schatz 8356

Porpora, Nicola Antonio, 1686–1766.

Adelaide, Roma, Bernabò, 1723.   Schatz 8376

Adelaide, Roma, Ferri, 1723.   ML 50.2.A31P6

L'Angelica.   *See* Metastasio's Opere drammatiche.

Annibale, Venezia, 1731.   Schatz 8368

Arianna e Teseo, Venezia, 1727.   Schatz 8369

Arianna in Naxo (Rolli, Componimenti poetici, Nuova ed., Verona, 1744)   ML 49.A2R7

Dorilla e Nesso, Intermezzi in the following:

Enea nel Lazio (Rolli, Componimenti poetici, Nuova ed., Verona, 1744)   ML 49.A2R7

Eumene, Roma, 1721.   Schatz 8366

Ezio, Venezia (1728).   Schatz 8370

Filandro—Philander (Dresda, 1747).   Schatz 8357

Die flucht des Aeneas nach Latien.   A. T. of his and Telemann's Der streit der kindlichen pflicht und der liebe.

Germanico in Germania, Roma (1732).   Schatz 8358

The honest Yorkshire-man.   *See* Title catalogue.

Imeneo in Atene, Venezia, 1726.   Schatz 8359

Ifigenia in Aulide (Rolli, Componimenti poetici, Nuova ed., Verona, 1744)   ML 49.A2R7

Lucio Papìrio, Venezia, 1737.   Schatz 8371

Meride e Selinunte, Venezia, 1726   Schatz 8372

Mitridate, Roma (1730).   Schatz 8373

Porpora, Nicola Antonio—Continued.

Le nozze d'Ercole e d'Ebe, Venezia, 1744.   Schatz 8374

Orfeo, pasticcio. *See* Title catalogue.

Gli orti Esperidi. *See* Metastasio's Opere drammatiche.

Philander. *See his* Filandro.

Polifemo (Rolli, Componimenti poetici, Nuova ed., Verona,
     1744)   ML 49.A2R7

Rosbale, Venezia (1737).   Schatz 8360

Semiramide riconosciuta, Venezia (1729).   Schatz 8361

Siface, Venezia, 1726.   Schatz 8362

Siroe, rè di Persia, Roma (1727).   ML 50.2.S64P6

Statira (Venezia, 1742).   Schatz 8364

Der streit der kindlichen pflicht und der liebe oder Die flucht
     des Aeneas nach Latien (Hamburg) 1731. (Recitatives
     by Telemann.) Tr. of his Didone abbandonata.   Schatz 8365

Syphax (Hamburg, 1727). Tr. of his Siface.   Schatz 8363

Tamerlano, Torino (1730).   Schatz 8375

Porsile, Giuseppe, 1672–1750.

Meride e Selinunte. *See* Zeno's Poesie drammatiche.

Spartaco, Vienna (1726).   Schatz 8377

Porta, Giovanni, *ca.* 1690–1755.

Agide rè di Sparta, Venezia (1725).   Schatz 8387

Aldiso, Venezia, 1726.   Schatz 8383

L'amor di figlia, Venezia, 1718.   Schatz 8395

L'amor tirannico, Venezia, 1722 (acts I–II by Chelleri).   Schatz 1819

Amore di sangue, Venezia (1729). L. T. of the following: Schatz 8386

Amore e fortuna, Venezia, 1727.   Schatz 8385

Antigono tutore di Filippo rè della Macedonia, Venezia, 1724
     (with Albinoni).   Schatz 133

L'Argippo, Venezia, 1717.   Schatz 8388

La caduta de Decemviri, Milano, 1723.   Schatz 8389

La costanza combattuta in amore, Venezia, 1716.   Schatz 8390

Doriclea ripudiata da Creso, Venezia, 1729.   Schatz 8378

Farnace, Monaco (1740).   Schatz 8379

Die heldenmuethige schaefer Romulus und Remus (Ham-
     burg, 1724). Recitatives and some arias by Johann Paul
     Kuntzen. Tr. of Porta's Numitore, also known as Rhea
     Sylvia.   Schatz 8381

Ifigenia in Aulide, Monaco (1738).   Schatz 8380

L'Issipile, Venezia (1732).   Schatz 8391

La Mariane, Venezia (1724). (Four arias from Albinoni's Gl'
     eccessi della gelosia.)   Schatz 117

La Mariane, Firenze (1726) (partly by Albinoni and others).   ML 48.A5 v.18

Nel perdono la vendetta, Venezia, 1728.   Schatz 8384

Numitore (Rolli, Componimenti poetici, Nuova ed., Verona,
     1744)   ML 49.A2R7

Li sforzi d'ambizione e d'amore, Venezia (1724).   Schatz 8392

Teodorico, Venezia, 1720.   Schatz 8393

Il trionfo di Flavio Olibrio, Venezia, 1726.   Schatz 8382

Ulisse, Venezia (1725).   Schatz 8394

Porta, Giuseppe della.

L'Eurillo overo La costanza negl' amori fra' pastori, Roma,
     1697.   Schatz 2477

Portugal, Marcos Antonio da Fonseca (*called* Portogallo).

See also Catalogue of 19th cent. librettos, 1762–1830.

Alceste, Venezia (1799).   Schatz 8396

O amor conjugal, Lisboa, 1789.   Schatz 8434

Il barone spazzacamino, Lisbona, 1799. L. T. of his Spazza-camino principe.   Schatz 8433

Die beiden angefuehrten thoren. A. T. of his Die schlaue wittwe.

Die buckeligen. A. T. of his Die taeuschende aehnlichkeit.

Il chiamantesi filosofo. A. T. of his Non irritare le donne.

Le confusioni della somiglianza ossiano I due gobbi. O. T. of his La somiglianza ossiano I gobbi.

Demofoonte, Milano (1794).   Schatz 8403

La donna di genio volubile, Venezia, 1796.   Schatz 8404

La donna di genio volubile—Die wankelmuethige, Dresda, 1798.   Schatz 8405

La donna di genio volubile, Lisbona, 1798.   ML 48.C6 iv

Le donne cambiate—Die verwandelten weiber, Dresda, 1799.   Schatz 8406

I due gobbi, Padova (1793). L. T. of his La confusione della somiglianza ossiano I due gobbi.   Schatz 8445

I due sciocchi delusi. A. T. of his La vedova raggiratrice.

Fernando nel Messico, Venezia, 1798.   Schatz 8409

I gobbi. A. T. of his La somiglianza.

L'inganno poco dura, Napoli, 1796.   Schatz 8426

O lunatico illudido, Lisboa, 1791.   ML 50.2.L95P7

Il matrimonio di Figaro. A. T. of his La pazza giornata.

A noiva fingida, Lisboa, 1790.   Schatz 8431

Non irritare le donne ovvero Il chiamantesi filosofo, Venezia, 1799.   Schatz 8438

Gli Orazi e I Curiazi, Venezia (1798).   Schatz 8442

La pazza giornata ovvero Il matrimonio di Figaro, Venezia, 1799.   Schatz 8439

Rinaldo d'Aste, Venezia, 1794.   Schatz 8428

Rinaldo d'Aste, Lisbona, 1799.   Schatz 8429

Die schlaue wittwe oder Die beiden angefuehrten thoren. Tr. of his La vedova raggiratrice, Dresda, 1795.   Schatz 8421

Der schorsteinfeger Peter oder Das spiel des ohngefaehrs, Pirna, 1799. Tr. of his Lo spazzacamino principe.   Schatz 8419

La somiglianza ossiano I gobbi—Die taeuschende aehnlichkeit oder Die buckeligen, Dresda, 1793. L. T. of his La con-fusione della somiglianza ossiano I due gobbi.   Schatz 8400

Lo spazzacamino, Dresda, 1794. L. T. of his: Schatz 8418

Lo spazzacamino principe, Venezia, 1794.   Schatz 8417

Das spiel des ohngefaehrs. A. T. of his Der schorsteinfeger Peter.

Die taeuschende aehnlichkeit oder Die buckeligen. Tr. of his La somiglianza ossiano I gobbi, Dresda, 1793.   Schatz 8400

La vedova raggiratrice o siano I due sciocchi delusi—Die schlaue wittwe oder Die beiden angefuehrten thoren, Dresda, 1795.   Schatz 8421

Die verwandelten weiber. Tr. of his Le donne cambiate, Dresda, 1799.   Schatz 8406

Verwirrung durch aehnlichkeit (Berlin) 1795. Tr. of his Le confusioni della somiglianza ossiano I due gobbi.   Schatz 8401

Portugal, Marcos Antonio da Fonseca—Continued.
Die wankelmuethige. Tr. of his La donna di genio volubile,
    Dresda, 1798.   Schatz 8405
Zulima, Firenze, 1796.   ML 48.A5 v.14

Potenza.
Amelia, pasticcio. *See* Title catalogue.
The school for fathers, pasticcio. *See* Lionel and Clarissa in
    Title catalogue.
The summer's tale, pasticcio. *See* Title catalogue.

Prati, Alessio, 1750–1788.
Armida abbandonata—Die verlassene Armide (Monaco), 1785. Schatz 8450
Demofoonte, Venezia, 1787.   Schatz 8454
L'Ifigenia in Aulide, Firenze, 1784.   Schatz 8451
La morte di Semiramide, Venezia, 1791. L. T. of his La ven-
    detta di Nino.   Schatz 8453
Vasco di Gama, pasticcio. *See* Title catalogue.
La vendetta di Nino, Firenze, 1786.   Schatz 8452
Die verlassene Armide. Tr. of his Armida abbandonata
    (Monaco) 1785.   Schatz 8450

Predieri, Luca Antonio, 1688–1769 *or* 1770.
Astrea placata. *See* Metastasio's Opere.
Eurene, Milano (1729).   ML 48.A5 v.3
Il fratricida innocente. *See* Title catalogue.
L'Ipermestra, Vienna (1744). (Only the licenza, with final
    chorus. Otherwise by Hasse.)   Schatz 4542
Lucio Papirio, Venezia, 1715.   Schatz 8457
La pace fra la virtù e la bellezza. *See* Metastasio's Opere.
Scipione il giovane, Venezia (1731).   Schatz 8458
Il sogno di Scipione. *See* Metastasio's Opere.
Tito Manlio, Firenze, 1720.   ML 48.A5 v.18
La Zoe, Venezia, 1736.   Schatz 8459
Zenobia. *See* Metastasio's Opere.

Preu, Friedrich.
Adrast und Isidore oder Die serenate (Bretzner, Operetten,
    bd. i, Leipzig, 1779).   Schatz 11680
Adrast und Isidore oder Die serenate (Bretzner, Operetten,
    1779, Leipzig). Detached.   Schatz 8462
Bella und Fernando oder Die satire (Vulpius, Operetten,
    Baireuth, 1790).   Schatz 8463
Der irrwisch oder Endlich fand er sie (Bretzner, Operetten,
    Leipzig, 1779).   Schatz 11680
Der irrwisch, Leipzig, 1788.   Schatz 8464
Die puzmacherinn, Baireuth, 1790.   Schatz 8465
Die satire. A. T. of his Bella und Fernando.
Die serenate. A. T. of his Adrast und Isidore.

Prot, Félix Jean, *d.* 1823.
Le printemps, Paris, 1784.   Schatz 8471

Prota, Gabriele, *ca.* 1754–1843.
Le donne dispettose, Napoli, 1793.   Schatz 8473
Le furberie deluse, Napoli, 1793.   Schatz 8474
I studenti, Napoli, 1796.   Schatz 8472

Prota, Ignazio.

La vedova ingegnosa—Die listige wittwe (Dresda, 1747).
    (Doubtful, also attributed to Leo and Sellitti.)   Schatz 5554

La vedova ingegnosa (Dresda, 1747). (Italian text only.)   ML 50.2.V25L2

Prudent.

Les jardiniers, Paris, 1772.   Schatz 8475

Puccini, Antonio Benedetto Maria, 1747–1832.

Bruto, Lucca, 1789. *See* M. Curzio in Title catalogue.

Il Castruccio, Lucca, 1781. *See* M. Curzio in Title catalogue.

Cesare nella Brettagna, Lucca, 1779. *See* M. Curzio in Title catalogue.

L'Emilio, Lucca, 1785. *See* M. Curzio in Title catalogue.

Leonida rè di Sparta, Lucca, 1783. *See* M. Curzio in Title catalogue.

Lucca liberata, Lucca, 1787. *See* M. Curzio in Title catalogue.

M. Curzio, Lucca, 1791. *See* Title catalogue.

Marco Manlio Capitolino, Lucca, 1777. *See* M. Curzio in Title catalogue.

Il Narsete, generale di Giustiniano imperatore, Lucca, 1770. *See* M. Curzio in Title catalogue.

Puccini, Giacomo, 1712–1781.

La confederazione de i Sabini con Roma, Lucca, 1765. *See* M. Curzio in Title catalogue.

L'esilio di M. T. Cicerone, Lucca, 1768. *See* M. Curzio in Title catalogue.

Marco Manlio Capitolino, Lucca, 1755. *See* M. Curzio in Title catalogue.

Marco Manlio Capitolino, Lucca, 1777. *See* M. Curzio in Title catalogue.

Il Narsete, generale di Giustiniano imperatore, Lucca, 1770. *See* M. Curzio in Title catalogue.

Roma liberata dalla signoria de' re, Lucca, 1760. *See* M. Curzio in Title catalogue.

Solone, Lucca, 1741.. *See* M. Curzio in Title catalogue.

Teramene, Lucca, 1744. *See* M. Curzio in Title catalogue.

Pündter, Ludwig Bartholomaeus.

Iphigenia (Augsburg, 1779).   Schatz 8514

Pugnani, Gaetano, 1731–1798.

Achille in Sciro, Torino (1785).   Schatz 8505

Demetrio a Rodi, Torino (1789).   Schatz 8503

Demofoonte, Torino (1788).   Schatz 8504

Issea, Torino (1771).   Schatz 8507

Orpheus ed Euridice, ballet. *See* Gazzaniga's La disfatta de' Mori.

Tamas Kouli-Kan nell' India, Torino (1772).   Schatz 8506

Pullaroli, Giovanni Battista.

L'Irene, Napoli, 1704 (partly by Dom. Scarlatti).   Schatz 9539

Pulli, Pietro.

Caio Marzio Coriolano, Venezia (1747).   Schatz 8513

La mogliere fedele, Napoli, 1731. (Interpolations in Vinci and Sellitti's opera.)   Schatz 10755

Purcell, Daniel, *d.* 1717.

Brutus of Alba: or, Augusta's triumph, London, 1697.   ML 50.2.B85

Cinthia and Endimion, or, The loves of the deities, London, 1697.   Longe 224

The grove or Love's paradice, London, 1700.   Longe 79

The island princess or The generous Portuguese, London, 1724 (with Clarke and Leveridge).   Longe 75

The world in the moon, London, 1697 (with Clarke).   Longe 180

Purcell, Henry, 1658 *or* 1659–1695.

Amphitryon, or, The two Sosias, London, 1691 ("The songs," 1690).   ML 50.2.A705P9

Amphitryon or The two Sosias, London, 1756. (His music apparently not used.)   PR 3415.A5   1756

Bonduca, or, The British heroine, London, 1696.   Longe 208

The British worthy. A. T. of his King Arthur.

The comical history of Don Quixote, London, 1729 (3 parts, with Courteville, Akeroyd, Eccles, and others).   Longe 68

The fairy-queen, London, 1692.   ML 50.2.F145

A fool's preferment or The three dukes of Dunstable (London) 1688.   M 3.3.P9 ɪɪ,11

— 2d copy, lacking the music.   Longe 132

The history of Dioclesian. A. T. of his The prophetess.

King Arthur or The British worthy, London, 1691.   ML 50.2.K54

King Arthur or The British worthy, London, 1781. (Text altered from Dryden; the additional music by Th. A. Arne.)   Longe 251

The prophetess or The history of Dioclesian, London, 1690.   ML 48.M2D

The three dukes of Dunstable. A. T. of his A fool's preferment.

The two Sosias. A. T. of his Amphitryon.

Quagliattini, Giacinto.

Il D. Tifone, Roma, 1751.   ML 50.2.D595Q2

La finta Astrea, Roma, 1754.   ML 50.2.F43Q2

Quesnada, Francesco.

La Gelidaura, Venezia, 1692.   Schatz 8525

Quilici, Domenico, 1757–1831.

Bruto, Lucca, 1789. *See* M. Curzio in Title catalogue.

Il Castruccio, Lucca, 1781. *See* M. Curzio in Title catalogue.

Lucca liberata, Lucca, 1787. *See* M. Curzio in Title catalogue.

Quinault, Jean Baptiste Maurice, *d. ca.* 1744.

Les amours des Déesses (Recueil général des opéra, t. xiv, Paris, 1734).   Schatz 8530

Quintavalle, Antonio.

Il trionfo d'amore, Mantova (1704).   ML 50.2.T81Q3

Radicchi, Giuseppe, *d.* 1799.

Medonte re di Epiro, Venezia, 1778.   Schatz 8539

Rameau, Jean Philippe, 1683–1764.

Anacréon. Entrée in Les fêtes liriques, Paris, 1766.   ML 52.2.F46

Arnéris ou Les Isies. Entrée in his Les fêtes de l'Himen et de l'Amour.

Rameau, Jean Philippe—Continued.

Canope. Entrée in his Les fêtes de l'Himen et de l'Amour.

Castor et Pollux (Paris) 1737.	ML 50.2.C29R2
Castor et Pollux (Recueil général des opéra, Paris, 1745, t. xvi).	ML 48.R4
Castor et Pollux—Castore e Polluce (Parma, 1758).	Schatz 8589
Castor et Pollux, Paris, 1764.	Schatz 8590
Castor et Pollux, Bordeaux, 1782.	ML 48.M2L
Castor et Pollux, Paris, Roullet, an V (1796–97) (31 p.).	Schatz 8586
Castor et Pollux, Paris, Roullet, an V (1796–97) (29 p.).	Schatz 11751

La danse. *See* Fragments, composés . . . de l'acte . . . de

Dardanus, Paris, 1761. ML 50.2.D27R2

Les dieux d'Egipte. A. T. of his Les fêtes de l'Himen et de l'Amour.

Les fêtes d'Hébé ou Les talens lyriques (Paris) 1739.	ML 52.2.F4R1
Les fêtes d'Hébé, ou Les talens lyriques, Paris, 1756.	ML 52.2.F4R2
Les fêtes de l'Himen et de l'Amour ou Les dieux d'Egipte, Paris, 1765.	ML 52.2.F42R2
Les fêtes de l'Hymen et de l'Amour, Paris, 1778.	ML 52.2.F42R3

Les fleurs. Entrée in his Les Indes galantes.

Hippolyte et Aricie (Paris) 1733.	ML 50.2.H4R2
Hipolyte et Aricie (Recueil général des opéra, t. xv, Paris, 1739).	Schatz 8587
Hippolyte et Aricie, Lyon, 1743.	Schatz 8587a
Gl'Incà del Perù, Parma (1757). Tr. of his Les Incas du Pérou.	Schatz 8588

Les Incas du Pérou. Entrée in his Les Indes galantes (1743).

Les Incas du Perou (Paris) 1765. (Journal des spectacles, Paris, 1766, t. i.)	ML 52.5.I5
Les Indes galantes (Paris) 1743.	ML 52.2.I4R2
Les Indes galantes (Recueil général des opéra, Paris, 1745, t. xvi).	ML 48.R4
Naïs, Paris, 1764.	ML 52.2.N22

Osiris. Entrée in his Les fêtes de l'Himen et de l'Amour.

Platée (Paris) 1745.	ML 52.2.P5
La princesse de Navarre (Paris, 1745).	ML 52.2.P7
Prologue des Indes galantes (Paris) 1765 (Journal del spectacles, Paris, 1766, t. i).	ML 48.J7

Les sauvages. Entrée in his Les Indes galantes.

Les sauvages (Paris) 1765 (Journal des spectacles, Paris, 1766, t. i). (Entrée in his Les Indes galantes.) ML 48.J7

Les talens lyriques. A. T. of his Les fêtes d'Hébé.

Le temple de la glorie (Paris) 1745. ML 50.2.T38R2

Le turc généreux. Entrée in his Les Indes galantes.

Zoroastre (Paris) 1749. ML 50.2.Z7R2

Zoroastro, Dresda (1752). (Only overture and chorus from his Zoroastre, otherwise by Adam.) Schatz 55

Rampini, Domenico, *d.* 1816.

L'impresario di Smirne (Trieste, 1798). Schatz 8592

Rampini, Giacomo.

Armida in Damasco, Venezia, 1711.	Schatz 8595
La gloria trionfante d'amore, Venezia, 1712.	Schatz 8596

Rasetti, Alessio.

Caccia di Diana, ballet. *See* Gius. Scarlatti's Partenope.

La clemenza di Tito. Incidental ballet music for Araja's opera.

La conquista del vello d'oro. Incidental ballet music for this opera by Sordella.

Demetrio. Ballet music for Hasse's opera, Torino, 1748.

Germanico. Ballet music for Bernasconi's opera.

Issipile. Ballet music for Galuppi's opera, Torino, 1737.

Lucio Papirio, Torino, 1753. Ballet music for Balbi's opera.

L'Olimpiade. Ballet music for Brivio's opera, Torino, 1737.

Poro. Ballet music for Gluck's opera.

Siroe. Ballet music in Gius. Scarlatti's opera, Torino, 1750.

Tito Manlio. Ballets for Jommelli's opera, Turin, 1743.

Rauzzini, Matteo, *d.* 1810.

Li due amanti in inganno, Venezia, 1775 (acts I and III by Giacomo Rust).　　　SCHATZ 9181

L'opera nuova, Venezia (1781).　　　SCHATZ 8613

Rava, Domenico.

Adelaide di Ghesclino, ballo eroico. *See* Fabrizj's opera L'amore per interesse.

Raymond, B. Louis.

L'amateur de musique, Paris, 1785.　　　SCHATZ 8617

Re, Giuseppe.

Ipermestra, Alessandria (1755).　　　SCHATZ 8618

Reali, Giovanni.

Il regno galante, Venezia, 1727.　　　SCHATZ 8619

Rebel, François, 1701–1775.

Amour pour amour, intermèdes (Journal des spectacles, Paris, 1766, t. i).　　　ML 48.J7

Les Augustales, Paris, 1744 (with Francoeur).　　　SCHATZ 8621

Ismène. *See* Francoeur.

Pirame et Thisbé. *See* Francoeur.

Scanderberg. *See* Francoeur.

Tarsis et Zelie. *See* Francoeur.

Telemaque, pasticcio. *See* Title catalogue.

Rebel, Jean Ferry, 1661–1746 *or* 1747.

Ulysse (Recueil général des opéra, t. viii, Paris, 1706).　　　SCHATZ 8622

Reeve, William, 1757–1815.

See also Catalogue of 19th cent. librettos.

The apparition, London, 1794.　　　LONGE 239

The apparition of the cliffs. A. T. of his The Sicilian romance.

Benevolent tar. A. T. of his The purse.

Both sides of the water. A. T. of his The raft.

Blue Beard, or, The flight of Harlequin, London, 1791.　　　LONGE 218

British fortitude and Hibernian friendship, or, An escape from France, London, 1794.　　　LONGE 308

An escape from France. A. T. of his British fortitude and Hibernian friendship.

The hall of Fingal. A. T. of his Oscar and Malvina.

Harlequin forrester. A. T. of his Merry Sherwood.

Reeve, William—Continued.

Harlequin Mungo; or A peep into the tower, London (1789). Longe 102

Merry Sherwood or Harlequin forrester, London, 1795. Longe 234

Oscar and Malvina or The hall of Fingal, 3d ed., London, 1791
(finished Shield's score). Longe 218

A peep into the tower. A. T. of his Harlequin Mungo.

The purse or Benevolent tar, London, 1794. Longe 227

The raft or Both sides of the water, London, 1798. Longe 246

The Sicilian romance or The apparition of the cliffs, London,
1794. Longe 239

The turnpike gate, London, 1799 (with Mazzinghi). Longe 258

Reichardt, Johann Friedrich, 1752–1814.

See also Catalogue of 19th cent. librettos.

Andromeda, Berlino (1788). Schatz 8634

Brenno-Brennus, Berlino, 1789. ML 50.2.B8R3

Brennus, Berlin, 1798. Tr. of his Brenno. (Abbreviated for
concert purposes.) Schatz 8637

Cephalus und Prokris. (O. T. of his Procris et Cephale.)
(Theater-journal, Gotha, 1778.) Schatz 11754

Claudine von Villa Bella, Berlin, 1789. Schatz 8640

Die geisterinsel, Berlin, 1798. Schatz 8641

Ino, Leipzig, 1790. ML 52.2.I5

Ino (Brandes, Melodramen, Pilsen, 1791). Schatz 8643

L'Olimpiade—Die Olympiade, Berlino, 1791. Schatz 8649

Procris et Cephale, Berlin, 1777. Tr. of his Cephalus und
Prokris. Schatz 8639

Orfeo—Orpheus, Berlin (1788). (Only the additions to Bertoni's opera.) Schatz 917

Protesilao—Protesilaus, Berlino (1789). (2d act by Naumann.) Schatz 8654

Reinagle, Alexander, 1758–1809.

Columbus, or The discovery of America, Boston, 1794. E 120.M885

Slaves in Algiers or A struggle for freedom, Philadelphia, 1794. PR 1241.D7   v.9

Rendeux, Engelbert (Engelberto Rendeut).

Li due gobbi rivali, Roma, 1752. ML 50.2.D77R2

Resta, Natale.

Li tre Cicisbei ridicoli, Venezia, 1748. Schatz 8692

Reutter (Reuter), Johann Adam Joseph Carl Georg, 1707–
or 8–1772.

L'Amor prigioniero. *See* Metastasio's Opere.

Archidamia, Vienna d'Austria (1727). Schatz 8695

Le Cinesi. *See* Metastasio's Opere.

La gara. *See* Metastasio's Opere.

Il palladio conservato. *See* Metastasio's Opere.

Il Parnaso accusato e difeso. *See* Metastasio's Opere.

La rispettosa tenerezza. *See* Metastasio's Opere.

Il sogno, Pisa (1757). Schatz 8696

Tributo di rispetto e d'amore. *See* Metastasio's Opere.

Zenobia, Vienna d'Austria (1732). ML 48.M2C

Rey, Jean Baptiste, 1734–1810.

Arvire et Evelina, Paris, 1788. (Finished this opera by Sacchini.) Schatz 9207

Richter.

    Amelia, pasticcio.   *See* Title catalogue.

    The summer's tale, pasticcio.   *See* Title catalogue.

Rigel, Henri Joseph, 1741–1799.

    Blanche et vermeille, Paris, 1781.   ML 50.2.B4R3

    Le savetier et le financier (Paris, 1778).   ML 50.2.S3R3

Righini, Vincenzo, 1756–1812.

  See also Catalogue of 19th cent. librettos.

    Aeneas in Latium.   Tr. of his Enea nel Lazio, Berlino (1793).   Schatz 8782

    Armida—Armide, Berlino (1797).   Schatz 8778

    Atalanta e Meleagro—Athalante und Meleager, Berlino (1797).   Schatz 8779

    — Same, Berlino (1799).   Schatz 8780

    Il convitato di pietra o sia Il dissoluto, Venezia (1777).   Schatz 8789

    Il convitato di pietra, o sia Il dissoluto—Das steinerne gast-

        mahl oder Der ruchlose, Praga, 1777.   Schatz 8781

    Il dissoluto.   A. T. of his Il convitato di pietra.

    Enea nel Lazio—Aeneas in Latium, Berlino (1793).   Schatz 8782

    Der ruchlose.   A. T. of his Das steinerne gastmahl.

    Das steinerne gastmahl oder Der ruchlose.   Tr. of his Il con-

        vitato di pietra o sia Il dissoluto, Praga, 1777.   Schatz 8781

    Il trionfo d'Arianna—Der triumph der Ariadne, Berlino, 1796.   Schatz 8788

    Vasco di Gama, pasticcio.   *See* Title catalogue.

    La vedova scaltra, Brescia (1778).   Schatz 8790

Rinaldo di (da) Capua.

    Adriano in Siria, Roma (1758).   ML 50.2.A36R4

    L'Ambizione delusa, Venezia (1744).   L. T. of his La com-

        media in commedia.   Schatz 8802

    La Bohémienne, La Haye, 1758.   Parodied from La Zingara.   Schatz 8797

    La Bohémienne, Paris, Duchesne, 1759 (Theatre de M. Favart,

        Paris, 1763–77, t. ii).   ML 49.A2F1

    Il bravo burlato, Gubbio (1757).   Schatz 8801

    Il cavalier Mignatta, Lucca, 1763.   Schatz 8800

    La Chiarina, Roma, 1754.   ML 50.2.C46R3

    Ciro riconosciuto, Roma, 1737.   Schatz 8795

    La commedia in commedia, Venezia, 1749.   Schatz 8803

    Farnace, Venezia, 1739.   Schatz 8796

    La forza della pace, Roma, 1751.   ML 50.2.F75R3

    La libertà nociva, Venezia (1744).   Schatz 8798

    Il ripiego in amore, Roma, 1751.   ML 50.2.R49R4

    La serva sposa, Roma (1753).   ML 50.2.S5R4

    La smorfiosa, Roma, 1756.   ML 50.2.S66R4

    La smorfiosa, Lucca, 1762.   Schatz 8799

    La Zingara.   (Not in L. of C.)   O. T. of his La Bohémienne.

Rispoli, Salvatore.

    Idalide, Torino (1786).   Schatz 8814

    Ipermestra, Milano (1786).   Schatz 8815

    Nitteti, Torino (1783).   Schatz 8812

    Il trionfo de' pupilli oppressi, Napoli, 1782.   Schatz 8813

Ristori, Giovanni Alberto, 1692–1753.

    Arianna, Dresda (1736).   Schatz 8816

    Le fate, Dresda (1736).   Schatz 8817

    Orlando furioso, Venezia, 1713.   Schatz 8818

    Pallade trionfante in Arcadia, Venezia, 1714.   Schatz 8819

Ritter, Peter, 1763–1846.
    See also Catalogue of 19th cent. librettos.
        Die bezauberte insel. A. T. of his Der sturm.
        Der eremit auf Formentara (Mannheim?) 1790.   Schatz 8822
        Die geister-burg (Mannheim?) 1799.   Schatz 8823
        Die lustigen weiber (Mannheim) 1792.   Schatz 8825
        Der sclavenhaendler, Mannheim, 1790.   Schatz 8830
        Der sturm oder Die bezauberte insel, Cassel, 1798.   Schatz 8831

Riva, Giulio.
        L'Adelaide regia principessa di Susa, Venetia, 1670.   Schatz 8833

Roberto (Ruberto), Costantino.
        La cantarina, Napole, 1728 (acts 2–3, act 1st by Caballone).   ML 50.2.C265C2
        Lo co. de Scrignano, Napoli (1729). (2d act only, the two
            others anonymous.)   Schatz 8837

Robuschi, Ferdinando, *b.* 1765.
        Attalo rè di Bitinia (Lisboa, 1791).   Schatz 8842
        Briseide, Napoli, 1791.   Schatz 8839
        Castrini, padre e figlio, Venezia, 1787.   Schatz 8840
        Chi sta bene non si muova, Firenze, 1787.   Schatz 8843
        La nuova Gianetta, Parma (1787).   Schatz 8841
        Li raggiri fortunati, Bologna (1792). L. T. of his Castrini,
            padre e figlio.   Schatz 8846
        Riccardo cor di Leone, Venezia, 1789.   Schatz 8844
        I tre rivali in amore, Roma (1789).   Schatz 8845

Rochar (=de Rochet?).
        Les jeunes mariés. *See* Title catalogue.

Rochefort, Jean Baptiste, 1746–1819.
        Bacchus et Ariane, Paris (1791).   ML 52.2.B1R6
        L'inconnue persécutée, Paris, 1776. French version with
            additional music of Anfossi's L'incognita perseguitata.   ML 50.2.I55A6

Rodolphe (Rudolph), Jean Joseph, 1730–1812.
        Amore e Psiche—Amor und Psyche, ballet. *See* Jommelli's
            Semiramide.
        Amore vincitore dell' indifferenza, ballet. (If not by him,
            then composed by Deller.) *See* Jommelli's L'isola dis-
            abitata.
        L'aveugle de Palmyre, Paris, 1767 (54 p.)   Schatz 11752
        L'aveugle de Palmyre, Paris, 1767 (39 p.)   Schatz 8851
        L'aveugle de Palmyre, Paris, 1776.   ML 48.M2M
        Ipermestra—Hipermenestre, ballet. *See* Jommelli's Demo-
            foonte.
        Medea e Giasone—Medée et Jason, ballet. *See* Jommelli's La
            Didone abbandonata.
        La morte d'Ercole—Der tod des Hercules, ballet. *See* Jom-
            melli's Semiramide.
        Nanine, sœur de lait de la reine de Golconde, Genève, 1773.   ML 50.2.N2R7
        Il riconoscimento inaspettato, ballet. (If not by him, then
            composed by Deller.) *See* Jommelli's L'isola disabitata.

Roellig, Carl Leopold, *d.* 1804.
        Clarisse oder Das unbekannte dienstmaedgen, Leipzig, 1772.   Schatz 8856

Rolle, Johann Heinrich, 1718–1785.
        Abraham auf Moria, n. i., 1779.   Schatz 11392

Romanogli, Deifebo, *d.* 1813.
Il Pub°. Scipione, Ms., 1789.   ML 48.A5   v.32

Romberg, Jacob Andreas, 1767–1821.
See also Catalogue of 19th cent. librettos.
Der rabe, Hamburg, 1794.   SCHATZ 8870

Roncaglia, Bernardino, *d.* 1692.
La nave d'Argo, Lucca, 1654. *See* M. Curzio in Title cata-
logue.
La pace, Lucca, 1657. *See* M. Curzio in Title catalogue.
Il trionfo del ben pubblico, Lucca, 1678. *See* M. Curzio in
Title catalogue.

Rossetti, Antonio.
Colombo nell' Indie, ballet. *See* Tritto's L'Artenice.
D. Pedro, infante di Portogallo, ballet. *See* Sacchini's Lucio
Vero.
Olimpiade, Milano (1778).   SCHATZ 8885
Il più bel dono, inutile (Venezia, 1779).   SCHATZ 8884
I Quaqueri (Venezia, 1779).   SCHATZ 8883
Il ritorno di Rinaldo presso Armida o sia La vendetta di
Armida vinta dall' amore, ballet. *See* Bianchi's Cajo
Mario.
La vendetta di Armida vinta dall' amore. A. T. of his ballet
Il ritorno di Rinaldo presso Armida.

Rossetto, Il. *See* Bisoni, Antonio.

Rossi, Francesco.
La Corilda overo L'amore trionfante della vendetta, Venezia,
1688.   SCHATZ 8887
La ninfa Apollo, Venezia, 1726.   SCHATZ 8888
La pena degl' occhi, Venezia, 1688.   SCHATZ 8889

Rossi, Giuseppe, *b.* 1761.
Pietro il Grande ossia Il trionfo dell' innocenza, Venezia, 1793.   SCHATZ 8893

Rossi, Lorenzo.
Ifigenia in Aulide, Genova (1784).   SCHATZ 8918

Rousseau, Jean Jacques, 1712–1778.
See also Catalogue of 19th cent. librettos.
The cunning man, London, 1766. Tr. of his Le devin du
village.   LONGE 257
The cunning man, London, 1766 (2d éd.).   LONGE 26
The cunning man (Collection of the most esteemed farces,
Edinburgh, 1792, t. ii).   SCHATZ 11753B
Daphnis et Chloé (2 p. l. in the score of his "Fragmens de
Daphnis et Chloé," Paris, 1779.   M 1500.R89
Le devin du village, Genève, 1760.   ML 50.2.D515R6
Le devin du village, Genève, 1796.   ML 50.2.D515R7
The maid of the oaks. *See* Title catalogue.
Pigmalion, n. i., 1772 (largely by Coignet).   ML 50.2.P41R7
Pygmalion, Genève (Lyon) 1786.   SCHATZ 2095
Pygmalion, Mannheim, 1778. Tr. of the above.   SCHATZ 2096
La vallee de Montmorency ou Jean-Jacques Rousseau dans
son hermitage, pasticcio. *See* Title catalogue.

Rovetta, Giovanni, *d.* 1668.
    Ercole in Lidia, Venetia, 1645.   Schatz 9105
    Argiope, Venezia, 1649 (with A. Leardini, but doubtful, if
        such a joint setting was performed).   Schatz 9106

Rovettino (Giovanni Battista Volpe, *called*), *d.* 1692.
    Gli amori d'Apollo e di Leucotoe, Venetia, 1663.   Schatz 9107
    La costanza di Rosmonda, Venetia, 1659.   Schatz 9108
    La costanza di Rosmonda, Milano (1675).   Schatz 11744
    La Rosilena, Venetia, 1664.   Schatz 9109

Royer, Joseph Nicolas Pancrace, *d.* 1755.
    Pirrhus (Recueil général des opéra, t. xiv, Paris, 1734).   Schatz 9110
    Zaïde, reine de Grenade, Lyon, 1749.   ML 52.2.Z2R7

Ruberto, Costantino. *See* Roberto.

Rudolph, Jean Joseph. *See* Rodolphe.

Rugali (Rugarli), Gaspare, *d.* 1799.
    Il doppio equivoco, Parma (1794).   Schatz 9128

Ruggi, Francesco, 1767–1845.
    See also Catalogue of 19th cent. librettos.
    La guerra aperta, Napoli, 1795.   Schatz 9144
    L'ombra di Nino ossia L'impostore scoverto, Palermo (1796). Schatz 9145

Ruggeri, Giovanni Maria.
    Amar per vendetta, Venezia, 1702.   L. T. of his La Clotilde. Schatz 9136
    Arato in Sparta, Venezia, 1709.   Schatz 9130
    Armida abbandonata, Venezia, 1707.   Schatz 9133
    Armida abbandonata. Mantova (1711).   ML 48.A5v.3
    Arrenione, Venezia, 1708.   Schatz 9131
    Arrenione, Mantova (1711).   ML 50.2.A775R9
    Arsinoe vendicata, Venezia, 1712.   Schatz 9134
    La Clotilde, Venetia, 1696.   Schatz 9135
    Elisa, Venetia, 1711.   Schatz 9129
    Le gare di politica e d'amore, Venezia, 1711.   Schatz 9137
    L'ingannator ingannato, Venezia, 1710.   Schatz 9138
    La Mariamme, Venetia, 1696.   Schatz 9139
    Milziade, Venetia, 1699.   Schatz 9140
    Non son quella, è la difesa, Venezia, 1710.   Schatz 9132
    La saggia pazzia di Giunio Bruto, Venetia, 1698. Schatz 9141

Ruloffs, Bartholomaeus, *ca.* 1730–1801.
    De twee standbeelden, Amsteldam, 1798.   Schatz 9150

Runcher, Giovanni Battista.
    Achille in Sciro (Venezia, 1747).   Schatz 9151

Ruprecht, Stephan.
    Die dorfhaendel oder Bund ueber eck, Wien, 1785. Schatz 9163
    Was erhält die männer treu? Wien, 1780.   Schatz 9161
    Das wuetende heer, oder Das maedchen im thurme (Wien,
        1787).   Schatz 9162

Rush, George.
    Amintas, London, 1769. Alteration of his The royal shep-
        herd, with interpolation of music by Guglielmi, etc. Longe 37

Rush, George—Continued.

Amintas (Collection of the most esteemed farces, Edinburgh,
1792, t. vi).   SCHATZ 11753

The capricious lovers, London, 1765.   LONGE 26

The royal shepherd, London, 2d ed. (176–).   LONGE 37

The royal shepherd, London, 3d ed. (176–).   LONGE 192

The statesman foil'd, London, 1768.   LONGE 37

Russell.

The summer's tale, pasticcio.   *See* Title catalogue.

Rust (Rusti), Giacomo, 1741–1786.

Adriano in Siria, Torino (1782).   SCHATZ 9166

A Aldeana em corte.   Tr. of his La contadina in corte.   SCHATZ 9180

Alessandro nell' Indie, Venezia, 1775.   SCHATZ 9175

L'amor bizzarro o sia La gelosa di se stessa, Venezia, 1775.   SCHATZ 9167

Gli antiquari in Palmira, Milano (1780).   SCHATZ 9176

Artaserse, Perugia (1781).   ML 50.2.A8R8

Artaserse, Firenze, 1783.   SCHATZ 9165

Il baron di Terra Asciuta, Venezia, 1776.   SCHATZ 9168

La caccia d'Enrico IV, Venezia, 1783.   SCHATZ 9177

La Calliroe, Venezia (1776).   SCHATZ 9173

Li cavalieri lunatici, Venezia, 1774.   SCHATZ 9169

La contadina in corte—A aldeana em corte, Lisboa, (1765).   SCHATZ 9180

Il conte Baccelone, Venezia, 1774.   SCHATZ 9178

Li due amanti in inganno, Venezia, 1775 (act II by Matteo
Rauzzini).   SCHATZ 9181

La gelosa di se stessa.   A. T. of his L'amor bizzarro.

Il Giove di Creta, Venezia, 1776.   ▸ SCHATZ 9171

L'idolo cinese, Venezia, 1773.   SCHATZ 9179

L'incognita fortunata, Napoli, 1782.   SCHATZ 9172

L'isola capricciosa, Venezia, 1780.   SCHATZ 9174

. Il Socrate immaginario, Venezia, 1776.   SCHATZ 9170

Il talismano, Milano, 1785 (first act by Salieri).   SCHATZ 9336

Rustici, Giuseppe.

Bruto, Lucca, 1789.   *See* M. Curzio in Title catalogue.

L'Emilio, Lucca, 1785.   *See* M. Curzio in Title catalogue.

Leonida rè di Sparta, Lucca, 1783.   *See* M. Curzio in Title
catalogue.

Rutini, Ferdinando, *ca.* 1767–1827.

Il matrimonio per industria o sia Il servo astuto.   O. T. of his:

Il matrimonio per industria, Milano (1793).   SCHATZ 9184

La prova del dramma serio, Firenze, 1797.   SCHATZ 9185

I vendemmiatori ovvero I due sindaci, Livorno, 1790.   ML 48.A5   v.13

Rutini, Giovanni Marco, *èa.* 1730–1797.

L'amore industrioso, Venezia, 1765.   SCHATZ 9186

De bedragne formynder eller De under masken sluttede giftermaale.   Tr. of his Il tutore burlato, Kiøbenhavn, 1768.   SCHATZ 9188

Die eheverbindung in der maske.   Tr. of his Il matrimonio in
maschera (Dresda, 1767).   SCHATZ 9187

I matrimoni in maschera, Venezia, 1765.   SCHATZ 9192

Il matrimonio in maschera—Die eheverbindung in der maske
(Dresda, 1767).   L. T. of the above.   SCHATZ 9187

L'Olandese in Italia, Lisbona (1766).   SCHATZ 9190

Rutini, Giovanni Marco—Continued.

Sicotencal, Torino (1776).   SCHATZ 9191

Il tutore burlato o sia I matrimonii in maschera—Den bedragne formynder eller De under masken sluttede giftermaale, Kiøbenhavn, 1768. L. T. and Tr. of his I matrimoni in maschera.   SCHATZ

Zulima, Firenze (1777).   SCHATZ 9189

Sabadini, Bernardo.

Demetrio, Parma, 1694.   SCHATZ 9193

Didio Giuliano, Parma, 1687.   SCHATZ 9199

Diomede punito da Alcide, Parma, 1691.   SCHATZ 9194

Eraclea, Venetia, 1696.   SCHATZ 9195

L'Ercole trionfante, Parma, 1688 (a few arias, it seems, having been retained from Antonio Boretti's setting of Moniglia's "L'Ercole in Tebe" before its textual revision under the above title by Aureli).   SCHATZ 9196

Il favore de gli Dei, Parma, 1690.   ML 50.2.F237S2

La gloria d'amore, Parma, 1690.   SCHATZ 9198

Hierone tiranno di Siracusa, Parma, 1688.   SCHATZ 9197

Olimpia placata, Parma, 1687 (with G. D. Freschi. *See* the latter's Olimpia vendicata).   SCHATZ 3359

Teseo in Atene, Parma, 1688. Only additional arias for Zannettini's opera.   SCHATZ 11143

Sabatini, Nicolo.

Arsace, Napoli, 1754.   SCHATZ 9201

Cleante, Roma (1752).   SCHATZ 9200

Sacchini, Antonio Maria Gasparo, 1734–1786.

See also Catalogue of 19th cent. librettos.

Adriano in Siria, Venezia, 1771.   SCHATZ 9204

Alessandro nell' Indie, Venezia, 1763.   SCHATZ 9243

Alessandro nell' Indie, Torino (1766).   SCHATZ 11746

Alessandro Severo, Venezia, 1763.   SCHATZ 9241

L'amore soldato ou L'amour soldat, Paris, 1779.   ML 50.2.A697S2

L'amour soldat. *See* preceding entry.

Armida, Milano (1772).   SCHATZ 9205

Armida, Piacenza (1786).   SCHATZ 11745

Artaserse, Roma (1768).   ML 50.2.A8S2

Arvire et Evelina, Paris, 1788 (finished by J. B. Rey).   SCHATZ 9207

Arvire og Evelina, Kiøbenhavn (1799). Tr. of the above.   SCHATZ 9208

L'avaro deluso, London, 1778.   SCHATZ 9209

Die baeurinn bey hofe, Wienn (1767). Tr. of his La contadina in corte.   SCHATZ 9214

Das bauren-maedgen. Tr. of his La contadina in corte, Stuttgard, 1771.   SCHATZ 9213

Calliroe (Stuttgart), 1770.   SCHATZ 9210

Chimene ou Le Cid, Paris, 1783. French version of his Il Cidde.   SCHATZ 9224

Der chinesische held. Tr. of his L'eroe cinese, Monaco (1771).   SCHATZ 9219

Den chinesiske helt. Tr. of his L'eroe cinese, Kiøbenhavn, 1773.   SCHATZ 9220

Le Cid. A. T. of his Chimene.

Il Cid, London, 1773.   SCHATZ 9246

Il Cidde (Lisbona, 1773).   SCHATZ 9223

Sacchini, Antonio Maria Gasparo—Continued.

La colonie, Paris, 1776. French version of his L'isola d'amore.	SCHATZ 9228
Die colonie, Hamburg, 1780. Tr. of his L'isola d'amore.	SCHATZ 9230
La contadina in corte, Vienna (1770).	SCHATZ 9211
La contadina in corte—Das bauren-maedgen, Stuttgart, 1771.	SCHATZ 9213
Creso, Venezia, 1770.	SCHATZ 9215
Creso, London, 1767.	SCHATZ 9216
Dardanus, Paris, 1784 (4 acts).	SCHATZ 9217
Dardanus, Paris, 1786 (3 acts).	SCHATZ 9248
Didone abbandonata, London (1775/76) (partly by others).	SCHATZ 11321
Il Don Calandrano, Firenze, 1781. L. T. of his L'avaro deluso.	SCHATZ 9218
Enea e Lavinia, London, 1779.	SCHATZ 9218
Erifile regina di Lacinto (Sassari, 1784).	SCHATZ 9244
L'eroe cinese—Der chinesische held, Monaco (1771).	SCHATZ 9219
L'eroe cinese—Den chinesiske helt, Kiøbenhavn, 1773.	SCHATZ 9220
Evelina. Score title of Arvire et Evelina.	
Eumene, Roma, 1765.	ML 50.2.E85S2
Il finto pazzo per amore. O. T. of his Il soldato per forza impazzito per amore.	
Die geadelte baeuerinn, Prag (1774). Tr. of his La contadina in corte.	SCHATZ 9212
Die insel der liebe, Mannheim (1772). Tr. of his L'isola d'amore.	SCHATZ 9226
Die insel der liebe. Tr. of his L'isola d'amore, Ratisbona, 1775.	SCHATZ 9227
Die insel der liebe, Regensburg, 1781. (Altered and expanded by baron Theodor von Schacht.)	SCHATZ 9231
L' isola d'amore, Mannheim (1772).	ML 50.2.I73S3
L'isola d'amore (Lisbona) 1774.	SCHATZ 9225
L'isola d'amore—Die insel der liebe, Ratisbona, 1775.	SCHATZ 9227
Die kolonie, Frankfurt a. Mayn, 1778. Tr. of his L'isola d'amore.	SCHATZ 9229
Lucio Vero, Napoli, 1785.	SCHATZ 9242
Motezuma, London, 1775.	SCHATZ 9232
Nicoraste, Venezia, 1769.	SCHATZ 9233
The noble peasant. See Title catalogue.	
Oedip zu Colonos, Berlin, 1798. Tr. of his Oedipe à Colone.	SCHATZ 9235
Oedipe à Colone (Paris, ca. 1792).	SCHATZ 9234
L'Olimpiade, Venezia, 1786.	SCHATZ 9238
L'Olympiade ou Le triomphe de l'amitié, Paris, 1777. French version of the above.	SCHATZ 9239
Renaud, Paris, 1783. French version of Armida.	SCHATZ 9206
Renaud, Bruxelles, 1783.	ML 50.2.R38S2
Renaud, Paris, 1786.	ML 50.2.R38S3
Rosina. See Title catalogue.	
Scipione in Cartagena—Scipio in Kartagena, Monaco (1770).	SCHATZ 9240
Il soldato per forza impazzito per amore, Pavia (1774 or 1775).	SCHATZ 9221
Le triomphe de l'amitié. A. T. of his L'Olympiade.	
Der verstellte narr aus liebe, Wien, 1779. Tr. of his Il soldato per forza impazzito per amore.	SCHATZ 9222

Sacrati, Francesco Paolo, *d.* 1650.

Il Bellerofonte, Venetia, 1642.	SCHATZ 9252
La Delia o sia La sera sposa del sole, Venetia, 1639.	SCHATZ 9256

Sacrati, Francesco Paolo—Continued.
La finta pazza, Venetia, 1641.   Schatz 9253
L'isola d'Alcina, Bologna, 1648.   Schatz 9250
La Semiramide in India, Venetia, 1648.   Schatz 9254
La sera sposa del sole. A. T. of his La Delia.
L'Ulisse errante, Venetia, 1644.   Schatz 9255
Venere gelosa, Padova, 1643.   Schatz 9251

Saggioni, Giuseppe Fedeli.
The temple of love, London, 1706.   Longe 294

Saint-Amans, Louis Joseph, 1749–1820.
L'acteur dans son ménage, Paris, an VIII (1799–1800).   ML 48.M2L

St. Germain, count (*real name* Giovannini).
The summer's tale, pasticcio. *See* Title catalogue.

Saint-Pierre, de.
La fête du château. *See* Title catalogue.

Sajon, Carlo.
Il Don Chissiot della Mancia, Venetia, 1680.   Schatz 9264
L'Ermelinda, Venetia, 1679.   Schatz 9263

Salari, Francesco, 1758–1828.
L'amore rammingo, Venezia, 1777.   Schatz 9266
Il marchese Carbonaro, Venezia (1776).   Schatz 9267

Sales, Pietro Pompeo, *ca.* 1729–1797.
Antigono-Antigonus, Monaco (1769).   Schatz 9269
Das hochzeitsfest des Amors und der Norizia, Monaco (1765).
    Tr. of his Le nozze di Amore e di Norizia.   Schatz 9268

Salieri, Antonio, 1750–1825.
See also Catalogue of 19th cent. librettos.
Apollo placato, ballet (with Luigi de Baillou.) *See* Salieri's
    Europa riconosciuta.
Armida, n. i., n. d.   Schatz 9274
Armida (Cramer's Magazin der Musik, 1783) Cramer's Tr.   ML4.M2
Armida, Lueneburg, 1786. Tr. from the Italian.   Schatz 9275
Axur, koenig von Ormus, Wien, 1788. Tr. of his Axur, rè
    d'Ormus.   Schatz 9327
Axur, koenig von Ormus, Pressburg, 1788.   Schatz 9328
Axur, koenig von Ormus. Tr. of his Axur, rè d'Ormus,
    Dresda, 1789.   Schatz 9329
Axur koenig von Ormus, Hamburg und Altona, 1799. Tr. of
    his Axur rè d'Ormus.   Schatz 9332
Axur, koenig von Ormus, n. i., n. d. (after 1800?).   Schatz 9334
Axur re d'Ormus, Praga (1788). Italian version of his Tarare.   Schatz 9326
Axur re d'Ormus-Axur, koenig von Ormus, Dresda, 1789.   Schatz 9329
Axur re d'Ormus, Milano (1792).   Schatz 9331
La calamita de cuori (Vienna) 1774.   Schatz 9276
La calamita de cuori—Der magnetstein der herzen, Dresda,
    1776.   Schatz 9277
La cifra, Milano (1790).   Schatz 9281
La cifra, Lisbona, 1796.   ML 48.C6 ii
Daliso e Delmita (Vienna, 1776). L. T. of his Delmita e
    Daliso.   ML 48.A5   v.45

Salieri, Antonio—Continued.

La dama pastorella. O. T. of his La cifra.	
Les Danaides, Paris, 1784.	SCHATZ 9285
Don Chisciotte alle nozze di Gamace, Vienna, 1770.	SCHATZ 9286
Le donne letterate (Vienna) 1770.	SCHATZ 9335
Dreymahl angefuehrt. A. T. of his Falstaff.	
Die entzifferung (n. i.) 1795. Tr. of his La cifra.	SCHATZ 9283
Eraclito e Democrito—Heraclit und Democrit, Berlino (1796).	SCHATZ 9287
A escola dos ciosos, Lisboa, 1795. Tr. of his La scola de' gelosi.	SCHATZ 9318
Europa riconosciuta, Milano (1778).	SCHATZ 9288
Fallstaff, Berlin, 1799. Tr. of his:	SCHATZ 9290
Falstaff o sia Le tre burle—Falstaff oder Dreymahl angefuehrt, Dresda, 1799.	SCHATZ 9289
La fiera di Venezia—Der markt von Venedig, Dresda, 1775.	SCHATZ 9293
La fiera di Venezia—Markedet i Venedig, Kiøbenhavn (1777).	SCHATZ 9295
La fiera di Venezia, Milano (1779).	SCHATZ 9291
Die gastwirthinn. Tr. of his La locandiera, Dresda, 1776.	SCHATZ 9301
Der geraubte eymer, Mannheim, 1774. Tr. of his La secchia rapita.	SCHATZ 9320
Der geraubte eymer. Tr. of his La secchia rapita, Dresda, 1775.	SCHATZ 9321
La grotta di Trofonio—Die hoehle des Trophonius, Dresda, 1786.	SCHATZ 9297
La grotta di Trofonio, Parma (1791).	SCHATZ 9296
Die haeuslichen zwistigkeiten. A. T. of his Die mode.	
Heraclit und Democrit. Tr. of his Eraclito e Democrito, Berlino (1796).	SCHATZ 9287
Die hoehle des Trophonius. Tr. of his La grotta di Trofonio, Dresda, 1786.	SCHATZ 9297
Les Horaces (Paris) 1786.	ML 50.2.H6S2
Der jahrmarkt zu Venedig, Berlin, 1799. Tr. of his La fiera di Venezia.	SCHATZ 9294
Das kaestchen mit der chiffer, Berlin, 1793. Tr. of his La cifra.	SCHATZ 9282
La locandiera—Die gastwirthinn, Dresda, 1776.	SCHATZ 9301
Der magnetstein der herzen. Tr. of his La calamita de cuori, Dresda, 1776.	SCHATZ 9277
Markedet i Venedig. Tr. of his La fiera di Venezia, Kiøbenhavn (1777).	SCHATZ 9295
Der markt von Venedig. Tr. of his La fiera di Venezia, Dresda, 1775.	SCHATZ 9293
Die messe zu Venedig, Mannheim, 1772. Tr. of his La fiera di Venezia.	SCHATZ 9292
Die mode oder Die haeuslichen zwistigkeiten (Wien), 1771 (pasticcio principally from S.).	SCHATZ 9337
Il moro—Der mohr, Dresda, 1797.	SCHATZ 9303
Palmira, Stuttgart, 1797. Tr. of his Palmira, regina di Persia.	SCHATZ 9307
Palmira, koenigin von Persien. Tr. of his Palmira, regina di Persia, Dresda, 1797.	SCHATZ 9306
Palmira, regina di Persia, Vienna (1795).	SCHATZ 9305
Palmira, regina di Persia—Palmira, koenigin von Persien, Dresda, 1797.	SCHATZ 9306
La partenza inaspettata, Roma, 1779.	ML 50.2.P28S2

Salieri, Antonio—Continued.

La partenza inaspettata, Milano (1781). SCHATZ 9310

La partenza inaspettata—Die unerwartete abreise, Dresda, 1781. SCHATZ 9311

Der rauchfangkehrer oder Die unentbehrlichen verraether ihrer herrschaften aus eigennutz, Wien, 1781. SCHATZ 9313

Die schule der eifersucht, Koeln am Rheine, 1787. Tr. of his La scola de' gelosi. SCHATZ 9316

Die schule der eifersuechtigen, Hamburg, 1787. Another Tr. SCHATZ 9317

Die schule der eifersuechtigen. Tr. of his La scola de gelosi, Brunsvic, 1782. SCHATZ 9315

La scola de' gelosi (Venezia, 1779?). SCHATZ 9314

La scola de' gelosi—Die schule der eifersuechtigen, Brunsvic, 1782. SCHATZ 9315

La scuola de' gelosi, Verona (1780). ML 50.2.S46S2

La secchia rapita (Vienna) 1772. SCHATZ 9319

La secchia rapita—Der geraubte eymer, Dresda, 1775. SCHATZ 9321

Semiramide—Semiramis (Munich, 1782). ML 50.2.S48S2

The siege of Belgrade. *See* Title catalogue.

Der talisman, Wien, 1789. Tr. of his Il talismano. SCHATZ 9322

Der talisman (n. i.) 1790. SCHATZ 9323

Der talismann, Berlin, 1798. SCHATZ 9324

Il talismano, Milano (1785) (acts 2–3 by Giacomo Rust). SCHATZ 9336

Tarar, Hamburg, 1791. Tr. of his Axur rè d'Ormus. SCHATZ 9330

Tarare, Amsterdam, 1787. SCHATZ 9325

Tarare, London, 1787. English Tr. of his Tarare. LONGE 299

Le tre burle. A. T. of his Falstaff, Dresda, 1799.

Trofons zauberhoele, Riga, 1794. Tr. of Salieri's La grotta di Trofonio. SCHATZ 9299

Die unentbehrlichen verraether ihrer herrschaften aus eigennutz. A. T. of his Der rauchfangkehrer.

Die unerwartete abreise. Tr. of his La partenza inaspettata, Dresda, 1781. SCHATZ 9311

Die zauberhoele des Trofonius (Wien), 1789. Tr. of his La grotta di Trofonio. SCHATZ 9298

Die zigenner. A. T. of his Der talisman.

Salomon, *d.* 1731.

Medée et Jason (Recueil général des opéra, t. x, Paris, 1714). SCHATZ 9343

Theonoé, Paris, 1715. ML 50.2.T43S2

Théonoé (Recueil général des opéra, t. xi, Paris, 1720). SCHATZ 9344

Salomon, Johann Peter, 1745–1815.

Windsor castle or The fair maid of Kent, London, 1795 (partly by Spofforth). LONGE 231

Salvi, Giacomo Mioto Antonio.

Il Bertarido, rè de Longobardi. Ballet music for Boniventi's opera.

Sammartini (San Martino), Giovanni Battista, 1704–1774.

L'Agrippina, moglie di Tiberio, Milano, 1743. ML 48.A5 v.18

Sances, Giovanni Felice, *ca.* 1600–1679.

Apollo deluso, Vienna, 1669 (a large part of the music by the emperor, Leopold I). ML 48.M2D

Aristomene Messenio, Vienna (1670). SCHATZ 9367

Sander, F. Sigismund.

Don Sylvio von Rosalva oder Der sieg der natur ueber die
schwaermerey, Koenigsberg, 1795.   SCHATZ 9371

Die regata zu Venedig oder Die liebe unter den gondolieren,
Koenigsberg, 1795.   SCHATZ 9372

Santi, Alfonso.

Le baruffe chiozzote, ballet. *See* Robuschi's Castrini, padre
e figlio.

Il marito indolente (Venezia, 1778).   SCHATZ 9393

La sposa bizzarra, Venezia (1781).   SCHATZ 9394

Santos, Luciano Xavier dos.

Ati e Sangaride (Lisboa, 1779).   SCHATZ 9398

Ercole sul Tago (Lisbona, 1785).   SCHATZ 9395

Gli orti Esperidi, Lisbona (1764).   SCHATZ 9396

Il palladio conservato, Lisbona (1771).   SCHATZ 9397

Palmira di Tebe (Lisbona) 1781.   SCHATZ 9399

Santucci, Marco, 1762–1843.

M. Curzio, Lucca, 1791. *See* Title catalogue.

Sarro (Sarri), Domenico.

Alessandro Severo, Napoli, 1719.   SCHATZ 9412

Armida al campo, Napoli, 1718.   SCHATZ 9413

Arsace, Napoli, 1718.   SCHATZ 9414

Barillotto, Venezia, 1712.   SCHATZ 9421

La Calisto.   Intermezzi in:

Candaule re di Lidia, Napoli, 1706.   SCHATZ 9417

Didone abandonata, Napoli, 1724.   ML 50.2.D55S2

Didone abbandonata, Venetia (1730).   SCHATZ 9422

La fede ne' tradimenti, Napoli (1718).   SCHATZ 9415

L'impresario—The master of the opera, Londra, 1737.   SCHATZ 9411

Moschetta e Grullo.   Intermezzi in his Siroe, rè di Persia.

La Rosaura, Napoli, 1736.   SCHATZ 9419

Siroe, rè di Persia, Napoli, 1727.   SCHATZ 9420

Sarti, Giuseppe, 1729–1802.

See also Catalogue of 19th cent. librettos.

Adriano in Siria, Roma, 1779.   SCHATZ 9470

Aglae eller Støtten (Copenhagen, 1774).   SCHATZ 9423

Alessandro e Timoteo, Parma, 1782.   SCHATZ 9424

L'ambizione delusa, Torino (1780).   SCHATZ 9471

Astrea placata ovvero La felicità della terra—Astrea tilfredsstillet eller Jordens lyksalighed, Copenhagen, 1760.   SCHATZ 9426

Attalo rè di Bitinia, Venezia, 1783.   SCHATZ 9472

Cesare in Egitto—Julius Caesar i Aegypten, Kiøbenhavn
(1763).   SCHATZ 9427

Cleomene, Bologna (1789).   SCHATZ 9428

Cleomene, Perugia, 1791.   ML 48.A5   v.7

I contrattempi, Milano (1781).   SCHATZ 9429

I contratempi—Die zwischenfälle, Dresda, 1781.   SCHATZ 9430

I dei del mare (Venezia, 1776).   SCHATZ 9477

Didone abbandonata—Den forladte Dido, Kiøbenhavn (1762). SCHATZ 9432

I due litiganti, Padova (1792).   L. T. of his Fra i due litiganti
il terzo gode.   SCHATZ 9456

Sarti, Giuseppe—Continued.

Eifersucht auf dem lande.   Tr. of his Le gelosie vilane, Berlino, 1791.   Schatz 9437

Gli equivoci svelati, Padova, 1786.   L. T. of his I contratempi.   Schatz 9431

Die erdichteten lehnserben.   Tr. of his I finti eredi, Dresda, 1787.   Schatz 9434

Die eyfersucht der bauern.   Tr. of his Le gelosie villane, Dresda, 1778.   Schatz 9436

Farnace, Venezia, 1776.   Schatz 9473

La felicità della terra.   A. T. of his Astrea placata.

I finti eredi—Les héritiers supposés, Pietroburgo (1785).   Schatz 9433

I finti eredi—Die erdichteten lehnserben, Dresda, 1787.   Schatz 9434

I finti eredi, Lisbona, 1794.   Schatz 9467

Der fischer im trueben, Stuttgardt, 1785.   Tr. of his Fra i due litiganti il terzo gode.   Schatz 9458

Den forladte Dido.   Tr. of his Didone abbandonata, Kiøbenhavn (1762).   Schatz 9432

Fra i due litiganti il terzo gode.   O. T. of his I pretendenti delusi and Le nozze di Dorina.

Fra i due litiganti il terzo gode—Unter zwey streitenden siegt der dritte, Dresda, 1784.   Schatz 9457

Fra i due litiganti il terzo gode, Lisbona, 1793.   Schatz 9468

Fra i due litiganti il terzo gode, Milano (1795).   Schatz 9454

Le gelosie villane—Die eyfersucht der bauern, Dresda (1778).   Schatz 9436

Le gelosie villane, Napoli, 1784.   Schatz 9435

Le gelosie vilane—Eifersucht auf dem lande, Berlino, 1791.   Schatz 9437

La giardiniera brillante (Lisbona, 1773).   Schatz 9469

Giulio Sabino, Venezia, 1781.   Schatz 9438

Giulio Sabino, Genova (1781).   Schatz 9440

Giulio Sabino—Julius Sabinus, Vienna, 1785.   Schatz 9439

Giulio Sabino, Firenze, 1785.   Schatz 11747

Giulio Sabina, London, 1788.   Schatz 9441

Giulio Sabino, Lisbona, 1798.   ML 48.C6 xxii

Il gran Tamerlano—Den store Tamerlan, Kiøbenhavn (1764).   Schatz 9445

The haunted tower.   *See* Title catalogue.

Les héritiers supposés, Pietroburgo (1785).   Tr. of his I finti eredi.   Schatz 9433

L'Idalide o sia La vergine del sole, Firenze, 1788.   Schatz 9444

Im trueben ist gut fischen, Hamburg (1785).   Tr. of his Fra i litiganti il terzo gode.   Schatz 9459

Im trueben ist gut fischen, Koeln am Rhein, 1786.   Schatz 9460

Jordens lyksalighed.   A. T. of his Astrea tilfredsstillet.

Julius Caesar i Aegypten.   Tr. of his Cesare in Egitto, Kiøbenhavn (1763).   Schatz 9427

Julius Sabinus.   Tr. of his Giulio Sabino, Vienna, 1785.   Schatz 9439

Julius Sabinus, Pressburg, 1785.   Schatz 9442

Julius Sabinus, Nuernberg, 1791.   Schatz 9479

Kierligheds-brevene, Kiøbenhavn, 1774.   Schatz 9446

Mahmoud, pasticcio.   *See* Title catalogue.

Medonte, Napoli, 1783.   (First performed 1777 as Medonte, rè di Epiro.)   Schatz 9447

Il militare bizzaro, Venezia, 1778.   Schatz 9448

Mitridate a Sinope (Firenze, 1779) (6 p. l., 50 p.).   ML 48.A5v.30

Sarti, Giuseppe—Continued.

Mitridate a Sinope (Firenze, 1779) (7 p. l., 52 p.).   SCHATZ 9449
Il Narciso—Narcissus, Kiøbenhavn (1763).   SCHATZ 9450
Il naufragio di Cipro—Skibbruddet ved Cypren, Kiøbenhavn
  (1764).   SCHATZ 9451
La Nitteti—Nitetis, Kiøbenhavn (1761).   SCHATZ 9452
La Nitteti, Venezia (1765).   SCHATZ 9475
Le nozze di Dorina, Torino (1796).   L. T. of his I pretendenti
  delusi.   SCHATZ 9455
Le nozze di Dorina, London (1787).   L. T. of his I pretendenti
  delusi.   ML 48.M2K
I oprørt vand er godt at fiske, Kiøbenhavn, 1795.   Tr. of his
  Fra i due litiganti il terzo gode.   SCHATZ 9462
I pretendenti delusi, Venezia (1782).   SCHATZ 9453
Il re pastore, Venezia, 1753.   SCHATZ 9466
Scipione, Venezia, 1778.   SCHATZ 9474
Semiramide—Semiramis, Kiøbenhavn (1762).   SCHATZ 9463
Semiramide, Venezia (1768).   SCHATZ 9476
Siroe, Torino (1780).   SCHATZ 9464
Skibbruddet ved Cypren.   Tr. of his Il naufragio di Cipro,
  Kiøbenhavn (1764).   SCHATZ 9451
Den store Tamerlan.   Tr. of his Il gran Tamerlano, Kiøben-
  havn (1764).   SCHATZ 9445
Il trionfo della pace, Mantova (1783).   SCHATZ 9478
Unter zwey streitenden siegt der dritte.   Tr. of his Fra i due
  litiganti il terzo gode, Dresda, 1784.   SCHATZ 9457
Unter zwey streitenden zieht der dritte den nutzen, Salz-
  burg, 1787.   Tr. of his Fra i due litiganti il terzo gode.   SCHATZ 9461
Vasco di Gama, pasticcio.   See Title catalogue.
La vergine del sole.   A. T. of his L'Idalide.
Vologeso, Venezia (1765).   SCHATZ 9465
Vologeso, Venezia, 1769.   ML 50.2.V7S3
Zophilette.   See Title catalogue.
Die zwischenfälle.   Tr. of his I contratempi, Dresda, 1781.   SCHATZ 9430

Sartorio, Antonio.

L'Adelaide, Venetia, 1672.   SCHATZ 9488
Amore spesso inganna.   A. T. of his (?) Orfeo a torto geloso.
Gl'amori infruttosi di Pirro, Venetia, 1661.   SCHATZ 9480
Anacreonte tiranno, Venetia, 1678.   SCHATZ 9490
Antonino e Pompeiano, Venetia, 1677.   SCHATZ 9491
La caduta di Elio Seiano, Venetia, 1667.   SCHATZ 9492
I duo [!] tiranni al soglio, Venetia, 1679.   SCHATZ 9481
Ercole su'l Termodonte, Venetia, 1678.   SCHATZ 9493
L'Ermengarda regina de' Longobardi, Venetia, 1670.   SCHATZ 9482
La Flora, Venetia, 1681 (with M. A. Ziani).   SCHATZ 9495
Giulio Cesare in Egitto, Venetia, 1677.   SCHATZ 9489
Massenzio, Venetia, 1673.   SCHATZ 9494
L'Orfeo, Venetia, 1673.   SCHATZ 9483
Orfeo a torto geloso overo Amore spesso inganna, Bologna, 1697.
    (According to Schatz a *rifacimento* of the above, which
    it certainly is not, though it may be by Sartorio.)   SCHATZ 9485
Orpheus, Braunschweig, 1690.   Tr. of his L'Orfeo.   SCHATZ 9484
La prosperità di Elio Seiano, Venetia, 1667.   SCHATZ 9486
Seleuco, Venetia, 1668.   SCHATZ 9487

Sartorio, Gasparo.
 L'Erginda, Venetia, 1652. SCHATZ 9496
 Iphide Greca, Venetia, 1671 (first act by G. D. Partenio,
  second by D. Freschi, third only by Sartorio). SCHATZ 7779
 Orithia, Venetia, 1650. SCHATZ 9497

Sbacci, Guglielmo.
 Zenobia, Venezia (1740). SCHATZ 9512

Scalabrini, Paolo.
 Adelaide—Adelheid, Hamburg (1744) (with Finazzi and
  others). SCHATZ 3101
 Anagilda, Kiøbenhavn, 1772. SCHATZ 9514
 Artaserse—Artaxerxes, Copenhagen (1752) (with others). SCHATZ 9515
 Demetrio—Demetrius, Hamburg, 1744 (with others). SCHATZ 9516
 Oraklet (Copenhagen, 1776). SCHATZ 9517
 Venceslao—Wenceslaus, Hamburg, 1744 (with others). SCHATZ 9518

Scannavino, Giovanni.
 La distruzione d'Aquileja fatta da Attila rè degli Unni, ballet.
  See Guglielmi's Enea e Lavinia.
 La Nina pazza per amore, ballet. *See* Guglielmi's Enea e
  Lavinia.

Scarlatti, Alessandro, 1659–1725.
 L'amor volubile e tiranno. A. T. of his La Dorisbe.
 Amore innamorato. A. T. of his La Psiche.
 Arminio, Roma, 1722. ML 50.2.A77S2
 Bassiano overo Il maggior impossibile, Napoli, 1694. SCHATZ 9533
 La caduta de' Decemviri, Napoli, 1697. SCHATZ 9523
 Cambise, Napoli, 1719. SCHATZ 9526
 Creonte tiranno di Tebe, Napoli, 1699. Interpolations only
  in Pollaroli's opera. ML 50.2.C78P7
 Despina e Niso, Venezia (1724). SCHATZ 9534
 La Dorisbe overo L'amor volubile e tiranno, Roma, 1711. SCHATZ 9531
 Gli equivoci in amore overo La Rosaura, Roma, 1690. SCHATZ 9535
 Gl'equivoci nel sembiante, Roma, 1679. SCHATZ 9527
 L'errore innocente. L. A. T. of his Gl'equivoci nel sembiante.
 Il figlio delle selve, Torino, 1699. SCHATZ 9530
 L'humanità nelle fere, Napoli (1708) (partly by G. Vignola). SCHATZ 9538
 Il Mitridate Eupatore, Venezia, 1707. SCHATZ 9524
 Il Muzio Scevola, Napoli, 1698 (but doubtful). SCHATZ 9528
 Il Pompeo, Ravenna, 1685. ML 48.A5 v.3
 Porsenna, Napoli, 1713 ("Musica del Signor Antonio Lotti,
  accomodata . . . dal Sig. Alessandro Scarlatti"). SCHATZ 5711
 Il prigioniero fortunato, Napoli, 1698. SCHATZ 9529
 Il prigioniero fortunato (Mantova, 1699). ML 50.2.P65S2
 La Psiche o vero Amore innamorato, Napoli, 1683. ML 50.2.P78S2
 Pyrrhus and Demetrius, London, 1709. His Pirro e Demetrio,
  with new music by Haym. ML 50.2.P95
 La Rosaura. A. T. and L. T. of his Gli equivoci in amore.
 Scipione Affricano, Roma, 1671. SCHATZ 9537
 La Statira, Roma, 1690. SCHATZ 9536
 Telemaco, Roma, 1718. SCHATZ 9532
 Thomyris queen of Scythia, pasticcio. *See* Title catalogue.
 Il trionfo della libertà, Venezia, 1707. SCHATZ 9525

Scarlatti, Alessandro—Continued.

Vespetta e Milo, Dresde, 1717. (First and second intermezzo only; the third by Francesco Conti. The libretto (unpaged, 19cm) forms part of the libretto of Antonio Lotti's Giove in Argo.)   SCHATZ 5719

Vespetta e Milo, Dresde, 1717. (31 p., 15cm; otherwise same as above.)   SCHATZ 9522

Scarlatti, Domenico, 1685–1757.

L'Irene, Napoli, 1704. (Partly by Giov. Batt. Pullaroli.)   SCHATZ 9539

Scarlatti, Giuseppe, 1718–1777.

L'Adriano in Siria (Venezia, 1752).   SCHATZ 9540

L'amor geloso, Vienna, 1770.   SCHATZ 9560

Artaxerxes, Wien (1763). Tr. of his Artaserse.   SCHATZ 9541

Bajazet, Verona (1765).   SCHATZ 9558

La clemenza di Tito, Venezia, 1760.   SCHATZ 9542

De gustibus non est disputandum, Venezia, 1754.   SCHATZ 9543

Demetrio, Padova, 1752.   SCHATZ 9544

Ezio, Venezia (1754).   SCHATZ 9545

Hypsipile (Wien, 1760). Tr. of his Issipile.   SCHATZ 9549

L'isola disabitata, Venezia, 1757.   SCHATZ 9546

L'isola disabitata—Die unbewohnte insel, Dresda (1767).   SCHATZ 9547

L'Issipile, Vienna (1760).   SCHATZ 9548

Maid of the mill, pasticcio. *See* the Title catalogue.

Il mercato di Malmantile, Venezia, 1758.   SCHATZ 9550

La moglie padrona, Vienna (1768).   SCHATZ 9559

Partenope, Torino (1749).   SCHATZ 9556

Pelopida, Torino (1763).   SCHATZ 9551

Pompeo in Armenia, Venezia, 1747.   SCHATZ 9552

I portentosi effetti della madre Natura, Venezia, 1752.   SCHATZ 9554

I portentosi effetti della madre Natura, Monaco (1758).   SCHATZ 9553

La serva scaltra, Venezia, 1749.   SCHATZ 9555

Siroe, Torino (1750).   SCHATZ 9557

Die unbewohnte insel. Tr. of his L'isola disabitata (Dresda, 1767).   SCHATZ 9547

Scarpari, Pietro.

L'Iffide greca, Venezia, 1722.   SCHATZ 9561

Schacht, Theodor, *freiherr* **von,** *b.* 1748.

Artaserse—Artaxerxes (Ratisbona, 1785).   SCHATZ 9562

La festa interotta o sia Il trionfo della virtù—Das unterbrochene fest oder der triumph der tugend, Regensburg (*ca.* 1780).   SCHATZ 9563

Die insel der liebe, Regensburg, 1781 (additional music for his version of Sacchini's "L'isola d'amore").   SCHATZ 9231

Il tutore deluso o sia La semplice—Der betrogene vormund oder Das einfaeltige maedgen, Regensburg (*ca.* 1780).   SCHATZ 9564

Schack, Benedict (*recte* Cziak), *d.* 1826.

See also Catalogue of 19th cent. librettos.

Die beiden Antone oder Der name thut nichts zur sache, Leipzig, 1797. L. T. of his Anton der dumme gärtner oder Der name thut nichts zur sache.   SCHATZ 9566

Die drey ringe, oder Kaspar der mundkoch (Regensburg, 1796).   SCHATZ 9568

Schack, Benedict—Continued.

Der dumme gaertner, Augsburg, 1793. L. T. of his Anton der
    dumme gaertner.   Schatz 9567

Die geplagten ehemaenner, Hamburg, 1792. L. T. of his Der
    fall ist noch viel seltener oder Die geplagten ehemaenner. Schatz 9569

Der stein der weisen oder Die zauberinsel, Frankfurt am Main,
    1796.   Schatz 9570

Die zaubertrommel oder Der wohlthaetige derwisch, Augs-
    burg, 1793. L. T. of his Der wohlthaetige derwisch oder
    Die schellenkappe.   Schatz 9571

Schall, Claus, 1756–1835.

See also Catalogue of 19th cent. librettos.

Aftenen, Kiøbenhavn, 1795.   Schatz 9581

Chinafarerne (n. i., n. d.).   Schatz 9583

Claudine af Villa Bella, Kiøbenhavn (1787).   Schatz 9584

Schenck, Johann Baptist, 1761–1836.

See also Catalogue of 19th cent. librettos.

Achmet und Almanzine (Wien) 1795.   Schatz 9591

Der dorfbarbier, Hamburg, 1799.   Schatz 9592

Im finstern ist nichtgut tappen (Wien) 1787.   Schatz 9596

Die jagd, Wien, 1799.   Schatz 9597

Ein singspiel ohne titel (n. i., before 1800?).   Schatz 9594

Schiassi, Gaetano Maria.

Demetrio—Demetrio, Bologna, 1739.   ML 50.2.D37S3

Demofoonte, Venezia (1735).   Schatz 9600

Schieferdecker, Johann Christian, 1679–1732.

Der koenigliche printz Regnerus (Hamburg) 1702.   Schatz 9602

Der siegreiche koenig der Gothen Alaricus, Hamburg (1702). Schatz 9603

Victor, hertzog der Normannen (Hamburg, 1702). (Only act
    I; Joh. Mattheson composed act II, and Georg Bronner
    act III.)   Schatz 9605

Der von dem ackers-pflug zu den thron erhabene kaeyser
    Justinus (Hamburg, 1706).   Schatz 9604

Schmelzer, Anton Andreas, *d.* 1700.

Gli stratagemi di Biante (Kriegsliste der Bias) 1682, dances.
    See Draghi's opera.

Schmelzer, Johann Heinrich, *ca.* 1630–1680.

Achille riconosciuto, Vienna, 1668 (only the ballet airs). ML 50.2.A29D7

Chi più sà manco l'intende. Ballet music for Draghi's opera.

La lanterna di Diogene. Ballet music for Draghi's opera.

Il ratto delle Sabine. Ballet music for Draghi's opera.

Schmidt, Johann Christoph, 1664–1728.

Les quatre saisons, Dresde (1719).   Schatz 9641

Schmittbauer (Schmittbaur), Joseph Aloysius, 1718–1809.

Arkadien (Soden von Sassanfart's Schauspiele, bd. i, Berlin,
    1788). L. T. of his Lindor und Ismene.   Schatz 9659

Ein grab in Arkadien, Leipzig, 1779. L. T. of his Lindor und
    Ismene.   Schatz 9658

Herkules auf dem Oeta, Leipzig, 1772.   Schatz 9656

Lindor und Ismene (n. i., 1771).   Schatz 9657

Schröter, Corona Elisabeth Wilhelmine, *d.* 1803.
Die fischerinn, n. i., 1782.   SCHATZ 9696

Schürer, Johann Georg, *d.* 1786.
Astrea placata ovvero La felicità della terra, Dresda (1753).   SCHATZ 9730
Doris (Dresden, 1747).   SCHATZ 9731
Ercole sul Termodonte—Hercules am Thermodon, Dresda (1747).   SCHATZ 9732

Schuhbauer (Schubaur), Lucas, *b.* 1753.
Die dorfdeputirten, Berlin, 1796.   SCHATZ 9710
Das lustlager, Muenchen, 1784.   SCHATZ 9711
Die treuen koehler, Muenchen (1786).   SCHATZ 9712

Schubert, Joseph, 1757–1833.
Rosalia, Gotha, 1777.   SCHATZ 9704

Schulz, Johann Abraham Peter, 1747–1800.
Aline, dronning i Golconda, Kiøbenhavn, 1789. Tr. of his Aline, reine de Golconde.   SCHATZ 9717
Aline, königinn von Golconda (Cramer's musik, 1789).   ML 4.M3
Die Angelsachsen. A. T. of his Minona.
Athalia, Kiel, n. d. Tr. of his Athalie.   SCHATZ 9719
Athalia, Kiøbenhavn, 1790. Another Tr.   SCHATZ 9720
Das erndte-fest, Altona, 1795. Tr. of his Høst-gildet.   SCHATZ 9722
Høst-gildet, Kiøbenhavn, 1790.   SCHATZ 9721
Indtoget (Heiberg's Skuespil, 3. bind).   SCHATZ 9723
Minona oder Die Angelsachsen, Hamburg, 1785.   SCHATZ 9724
Das opfer der Nymphen, Berlin (1774).   SCHATZ 9725
Peters Bryllup, Kiøbenhavn, 1793.   SCHATZ 9726

Schuster, Joseph, 1748–1812.
See also Catalogue of 19th cent. librettos.
Der alchymist, Hamburg, 1779.   SCHATZ 9742a
L'amor artigiano (Venetia, 1776).   SCHATZ 9759
L'amor perfetto. A. T. of his Il servo padrone.
Gli avari in trappola—Die geizigen in der falle, Dresda, 1787.   SCHATZ 9743
Die befreyte sklavinn. Tr. of his La schiava liberata, Dresda, 1777.   SCHATZ 9754
Die befreyte sklavin (Kaffka, Sammlung auslaendischer theaterstuecke, 1784).   SCHATZ 9755
Il bon ton, Venezia (1780).   SCHATZ 9761
Creso in Media (Livorno, 1780).   SCHATZ 9744
Demofoonte, Pavia (1777).   SCHATZ 9760
Er soll und muss ein narr sein. Tr. of his Il pazzo per forza, Dresda, 1783.   SCHATZ 9751
Der geist des widerspruchs. Tr. of his Lo spirito di contraddizione, Dresda, 1785.   SCHATZ 9757
Die geizigen in der falle. Tr. of his Gli avari in trappola, Dresda, 1787.   SCHATZ 9743
Der gleichgueltige ehemann. Tr. of his Il marito indolente, Dresda, 1782.   SCHATZ 9747
Der gleichgueltige ehemann, Hamburg, 1788. Another Tr.   SCHATZ 9748
Der herr als bedienter oder Die wahre liebe. Tr. of his Il servo padrone ossia L'amor perfetto, Dresda, 1792.   SCHATZ 9756
Il marito indolente—Der gleichgueltige ehemann, Dresda, 1782.   SCHATZ 9747

Schuster, Joseph—Continued.

Orfeo, ballet. *See* Paisiello's La disfatta di Dario.

Il pazzo per forza—Er soll und muss ein narr sein, Dresda, 1783.   SCHATZ 9751

Rübenzahl o sia Il vero amore—Ruebenzahl oder Die wahre liebe, Dresda, 1789.   SCHATZ 9752

La schiava liberata—Die befreyte sklavinn, Dresda, 1777.   SCHATZ 9754

Il servo padrone ossia L'amor perfetto—Der herr als bedienter oder Die wahre liebe, Dresda, 1792.   SCHATZ 9756

Lo spirito di contraddizione—Der geist des widerspruchs, Dresda, 1785.   SCHATZ 9757

Il vero amore. A. T. of his Rübenzahl.

Die wahre liebe. A. T. of his Der herr·als bedienter.

Die wahre liebe. A. T. of his Ruebenzahl.

Die wueste insel, Leipzig, 1778.   SCHATZ 9758

Schwanberg, Johann Gottfried, *d.* 1804.

Romeo e Giulia—Romeo und Julie, Brunsviga, 1778.   SCHATZ 9766

Romeo e Giulia—Romeo und Julie (Berlino, 1780).   SCHATZ 9766a

Il trionfo della costanza, Bronsvic, 1790.   SCHATZ 9767

Schwartzendorf, Johann Paul Aegidius (*called* Martini, Jean Paul Egide).

Schweitzer, Anton, 1737–1787.

Alceste (Weimar) 1773.   SCHATZ 9768

Alceste, n. i,, n. d. (detached from an ed. of Wieland's works).   SCHATZ 9768a

Apollo unter den hirten (Hannover, 1770).   SCHATZ 9769

Die dorfgala, Gotha, 1774.   SCHATZ 9770

Die dorfgalla, Hamburg, 1778.   SCHATZ 9771

Elysium (Hannover, 1770).   SCHATZ 9772

Das fest der Thalie (Gotha) 1775.   SCHATZ 9773

Das fest der Thalie (Litteratur und Theater Zeitung, Berlin, 1783).   SCHATZ 4772

Das maedgen im thurme. A. T. of his Das wuetende heer.

Man kann es ja probieren. A. T. of his Walmir und Gertraud.

Die neuen Amazonen (Theater Journal fuer Deutschland, Gotha, 1778, 5tes St.).   SCHATZ 11754

Polyxena, Weimar, 1793.   SCHATZ 11757

Polyxena, Hamburg, 1794.   SCHATZ 9778

Rosamund, Mannheim, 1778.   SCHATZ 9774

Die wahl des Herkules, n. i., n. d. (Detached from a probably 19th cent. ed. of Wieland's works.   SCHATZ 9775

Walmir und Gertraud, oder Man kann es ja probieren, n. i., n. d. (Apparently detached from an ed. of Michaelis works).   SCHATZ 9776

Das wütende heer oder Das mädchen im thurme (Bretzner, Operetten, Leipzig, 1779, bd. I).   SCHATZ 11680

Das wuetende heer, oder Das maedgen im thurme, Leipzig, 1788.   SCHATZ 9777

Schwindel (Schwindl), Friedrich, *d.* 1786.

Das liebesgrab, Heydelberg, 1779.   SCHATZ 9779

Sciroli, Gregorio, 1725–*ca.* 1793.

Alessandro nell' Indie, Bologna (1764).   SCHATZ 9781

Madama Prudenza, Roma, 1749.   ML 50.2.M2S2

Sciroli, Gregorio—Continued.

Li nnamorate correvate, Napoli, 1752. (Quite a few arias
    were not by him.)   SCHATZ 9785
Le nozze in campagna, Venezia, 1768.   SCHATZ 9782
L'Olimpiade, Venezia, 1760.   SCHATZ 9783
La smorfiosa, Roma, 1748.   ML.50.2.S66S2
Solimano, Venezia, 1766.   SCHATZ 9784

Scolari, Giuseppe, *d.* 1769.

Adriano in Siria, Venezia (1754).   SCHATZ 9802
Alessandro nell' Indie, Venezia, 1759.   SCHATZ 9786
L'Andromaca, Milano (1757).   SCHATZ 9803
L'Arcifanfano, Lisbona (1768).   SCHATZ 9801
Artaserse, Venezia, 1758.   SCHATZ 9787
L'avaro burlato—Den beskaemmede gnier, Kiøbenhavn (1762)
    (pasticcio, but principally by the above).   SCHATZ 9792
Cajo Fabricio, Roma (1755).   SCHATZ 9804
Cajo Mario, Milano, 1765.   SCHATZ 9788
La cascina, Venezia (1756).   SCHATZ 9789
La cascina—Der meyerhof, Berlino, 1763.   SCHATZ 9790a
La cascina, Lisbona (1766).   ML 50.2.C27S2
Chi tutto abbraccia nulla stringe, Venezia, 1753.   SCHATZ 9791
Il ciarlatano, Venezia, 1759.   SCHATZ 9793
La conversazione, Venezia, 1758.   SCHATZ 9794
La Didone abbandonata, Ferrara (1763).   SCHATZ 9806
La famiglia in scompiglio—Die in virwirrung lebende familie
    (Dresda, 1766).   SCHATZ 9795
La fata meravigliosa, Venezia, 1746 [recte 1745].   SCHATZ 9796
Die in verwirrung lebende familie. Tr. of his La famiglia in
    scompiglio (Dresda, 1766).   SCHATZ 9795
Lionel and Clarissa, pasticcio. *See* Title catalogue.
Der meyerhof. Tr. of his La cascina, Berlino, 1763.   SCHATZ 9790a
L'Olimpiade, Venezia, 1747.   SCHATZ 9797
Il Pandolfo, Venezia, 1745.   SCHATZ 9798
La schiava riconosciuta, Venezia, 1766.   SCHATZ 9805
The school for fathers, pasticcio. *See* Lionel and Clarissa in
    Title catalogue.
Statira, Venezia (1756).   SCHATZ 9799
Il vello d'oro, Venezia, 1749.   SCHATZ 9800
Il viaggiatore ridicolo, Lisbona (1770) (some arias by others).   ML 50.2.V42S2

Scolart, Jacopo.

Seila, Faenza (1787).   SCHATZ 9807

Sebenico, Giovanni.

Leonida in Sparta, Torino, 1689.   SCHATZ 9812

Seedo.

See the ballad-operas:
The boarding-school, London, 1733.   LONGE 50
The boarding school (Collection of the most esteemed farces,
    Edinburgh, 1792).   SCHATZ 11753E
The devil of a duke, London, 1732.   LONGE 120
The devil to pay, or, The wives metamorphos'd, London, 1732.   ML 50.5.D37
The devil to pay . . ., London, 1748.   ML 50.5.D39
The devil to pay . . ., London, 1771.   LONGE 69

Seedo—Continued.
 The devil to pay . . . (Collection of the most esteemed farces,
  Edinburgh, 1792, t. ii).   SCHATZ 11753B
 The lottery, 3d ed., London, 1732.   ML 50.5.L68
 The lottery (Collection of the most esteemed farces, Edin-
  burgh, 1792, t. ii).   SCHATZ 11753B
 The mock doctor or The dumb lady cur'd, 4th ed., London,
  1753.   ML 50.5.M58

Sellitti, Giuseppe.
 Amor d'un ombra, e gelosia d'un aura, Napoli, 1725.   SCHATZ 9829
 Le caprice amoureux ou Ninette à la cour. *See* Title cata-
  logue.
 Les Chinois, Paris, 1759 (Theatre de M. Favart, Paris, Du-
  chesne, 1763–77, t. iii). (Only three of the ariettes paro-
  died from his "Il Cinese rimpatriato;" the others from
  Pergolesi and Cocchi, etc.)   ML 49.A2F1
 Les Chinois, Amsterdam, 1760.   SCHATZ 9825
 Le Chinois poli en France, Paris, 1754. Another parody of
  his Il Cinese rimpatriato.   SCHATZ 9828
 Ginevra, Venezia (1733).   SCHATZ 9826
 Die listige wittwe. Tr. of his La vedova ingegnosa (Dresda,
  1747).   SCHATZ 5554
 La mogliere fedele, Napoli, 1731. (His and music by Tro-
  jano, Pulli, Leo interpolated in Vinci's opera.)   SCHATZ 10755
 Nitocri, Venezia (1733).   SCHATZ 9827
 La vedova ingegnosa—Die listige wittwe (Dresda, 1747) (also
  attributed to Leo and Prota).   SCHATZ 5554
 La vedova ingegnosa (Dresda, 1747). (Italian text only).   ML 50.2.V25L2

Seydelmann, Johann Nikolaus Franz, 1748–1806.
 Amor per oro—Liebe aus haabsucht, Dresda, 1790.   SCHATZ 9840
 Arsene, Leipzig, 1778.   SCHATZ 9841
 Arsene, n. i., n. d.   SCHATZ 9842
 Arsene (Meissner, Operetten, 1778).   ML 49.A2M3
 Arsene, n. i., n. d.   SCHATZ 11748
 Il capriccio corretto—Der eigensinn der liebe, Dresda, 1783.   SCHATZ 9843
 Der lahme husar, Dresden und Leipzig, 1784.   SCHATZ 9845
 Il mostro ossia Da gratitudine amore—Das ungeheuer oder
  Liebe aus dankbarkeit, Dresda, 1786.   SCHATZ 9846

Seyfried, Ignaz Xav(i)er, *ritter* von, 1776–1841.
 See also Catalogue of 19th cent. librettos.
 Liebe macht kurzen prozess oder Die heyrath auf gewisse art
  (Leipzig, 1799) (with Henneberg, Woelfl, and others).   SCHATZ 4633
 Orion oder Der fuerst und sein hofnarr, Wien, 1798.   SCHATZ 9858

Shalon.
 Daphne and Amintor, pasticcio. *See* Title catalogue.

Shaw, Thomas.
 The island of St. Marguerite, London, 1789.   LONGE 203
 The mariners, pasticcio. *See* Title catalogue.

Sheeles, John.
 The generous Free-mason. *See* Title catalogue.

Shield, William, 1748–1829.

See also Catalogue of 19th cent. librettos.

Abroad and at home, London, 1796.	LONGE 237
Arrived at Portsmouth, London, 1794.	LONGE 228
Blunders at Brighton. A. T. of his The Irish mimic.	
The British recruit. A. T. of his To arms.	
The choleric fathers, London, 1785.	LONGE 96
The cobler of Castlebury, London, n. d. (a few airs by Gehot).	LONGE 125
The cottagers, London, 1788.	LONGE 119
The Czar, London, 1790. (First called The Czar Peter, and finally The fugitive.)	LONGE 204
The farmer, Dublin, 1788.	LONGE 149
The farmer, 7th ed., London, 1789.	ML 50.2.F18S3
The farmer, London, 1791.	SCHATZ 7672
The farmer, Dublin, 1792.	SCHATZ 9866
A flight from Lapland. A. T. of his Lord Mayor's day.	
The flitch of bacon, Dublin, 1779.	LONGE 118
Fontainebleau or Our way in France, Dublin, 1787.	LONGE 148
The fugitive. *See his* The czar.	
The hall of Fingal. A. T. of his Oscar and Malvina.	
Hartford-Bridge or The skirts of the camp, London, 1793.	LONGE 222
The highland reel, London, 1789 (5th ed.).	PR 1241.D7
The highland reel, Dublin, 1790.	SCHATZ 9869
The Irish mimic or Blunders at Brighton, London, 1795.	LONGE 229
Lock and key, London, 1796.	LONGE 238
Lord Mayor's day or A flight from Lapland, London, 1783.	ML 52.2.L6
The midnight wanderers, London, 1793.	LONGE 221
The mysteries of the castle, London, 1795.	LONGE 229
Netley Abbey, London, 1794.	LONGE 229
The noble peasant, London, 1784 (partly selected from Cooke, Smith, Duni, Sacchini).	LONGE 93
Oscar and Malvina or The hall of Fingal, 3d ed., London, 1791 (finished by Reeve).	LONGE 218
Our way in France. A. T. of his Fontainebleau.	
Patrick in Prussia or Love in a camp, Dublin, 1786. L. T. of his Love in a camp or Patrick in Prussia.	LONGE 148
The picture of Paris. Taken in the year 1790, London, 1790.	LONGE 207
The poor soldier, Dublin, 1785 (largely ballad opera).	LONGE 168
The poor soldier, Dublin, 1791.	PR 1269.V6
Robin Hood or Sherwood forest, London, 1784.	LONGE 93
Robin Hood or Sherwood forest, 5th ed., London, 1787.	ML 50.2.R62S3
Rosina, London, 1783.	LONGE 91
The Shamrock or Revels on St. Patrick's Day. O. T. of his The poor soldier.	
The shamrock or The anniversary of St. Patrick. Earlier T. of his The poor soldier.	
Sherwood forest. A. T. of his Robin Hood.	
The siege of Gibraltar, London, 1780.	LONGE 95
The skirts of the camp. A. T. of his Hartford-Bridge.	
Sprigs of laurel, London, 1793.	LONGE 225
Sprigs of laurel, London, 1794.	ML 50.2.S74S3
To arms! or The British recruit, London, 1793 (with Giordani).	LONGE 221
The travellers in Switzerland, London, 1794.	LONGE 227
The woodman, Songs, duets, etc., London, 1791.	LONGE 218
The woodman, London, 1791.	LONGE 215

Sighizzelli, Giuseppe, *d.* 1826.
    Arianna, ballet. *See* Colla's Sicotencal.

Silva, Alberto Giuseppe Gomes da.
    Il geloso (Lisbona, 1775).   Schatz 9880

Silva, Antonio da.
    Cadmo (Lisboa, 1784).   Schatz 9881

Silva, João Cordeiro da.
    L'Arcadia in Brenta (Lisbona, 1764).   Schatz 9885
    Archelao (Lisboa, 1785).   Schatz 9887
    Bauce e Palemone (Lisboa, 1789).   Schatz 9883
    Edalide e Cambise (Lisboa, 1780).   Schatz 9886
    Lindane e Dalmiro (Lisboa, 1789).   Schatz 9882
    Il ratto di Proserpina (Lisboa, 1784).   Schatz 9884

Siri, Giacomo.
    Ricimero, Napoli, 1789.   Schatz 9896

Smelzer, Giovanni Enrico. *See* Schmelzer.

Smith, John Christopher, 1712–1795.
    The enchanter, or, Love and magic, London, 1760.   Longe 306
    The fairies, London, 1755.   ML 50.2.F14
    The fairies, 2d ed., London, 1755.   ML 50.2.F142
    A fairy tale, London, 1777, pasticcio. *See* Title catalogue.   Longe 243
    The noble peasant (possibly by **John Stafford Smith**). *See*
        Title catalogue.
    Rosalinde, London, 1740.   ML 50.2.R72
    Teraminta (Henry Carey, **Dramatick works**, London, 1743).   ML 49.A2C2

Smith, John Stafford, 1750–1836.
    The noble peasant (possibly by John Christopher). *See* Title
        catalogue.

The Society of the Temple of Apollo.
    Robin Hood, London, 1751 (Grove attributes the music to
        Burney).   AC 901.M5   v.519

Sodi, Carlo.
    Baiocco et Serpilla, Paris, 1771. (Parody of Il marito gioga-
        tore e la moglie bacchettona.)   Schatz 9929
    Baiocco et Serpilla, Nouv. ed., Paris, 1760 (Theatre de M.
        Favart, Paris, 1763–77, t. ii).   ML 49.A2F1

Soffi, Pasquale Antonio, *ca.* 1732–1810.
    L'Emilio, Lucca, 1785. *See* M. Curzio in Title catalogue.
    Lucca liberata, Lucca, 1787. *See* M. Curzio in Title cata-
        logue.
    M. Curzio, Lucca, 1791. *See* Title catalogue.
    Marco Manlio Capitolino, Lucca, 1755. *See* M. Curzio in Title
        catalogue.
    Marco Manlio Capitolino, Lucca, 1777. *See* M. Curzio in Title
        catalogue.
    Roma liberata dalla signoria de' re, Lucca, 1760. *See* M.
        Curzio in Title catalogue.

Solié. (Solier, Jean Pierre, 1755–1812, *called.*)
    Le Franc Breton ou Le négociant de Nantes, Paris, 1791
        (with Kreutzer).   ML 50.2.F8K7
    Le jockei, Paris, an IV (1796).   ML 50.2.J6S6

Sordella, Giuseppe.
La conquista del vello d'oro, Torino, 1745.   SCHATZ 9961

Spagnoletto.   *See* Garcia, Francesco Saverio.

Spanò, Gasparo.
Elisa, Roma (1738) (with the intermezzi "Corisca e Satiro")   ML 50.2.E3S7

Spinazzari, Alessandro.
L'Alcatrasso geloso, Vicenza, 1672.   SCHATZ 9975

Spindler, Stanislaus Franz Xaver, *d.* 1819.
Die liebe in der Ukräne oder Hier gehen die maedchen auf die
    freierei aus, Frankfurt am Main, 1786.   SCHATZ 9976
Piramus und Tisbe, n. i., 1788.   ·SCHATZ 9977

Spofforth, Reginald, 1770–1827.
Windsor castle or the fair maid of Kent, London, 1795 (mainly
    by Salomon).   LONGE 231

Spontini, Gaspare Luigi Pacifico, 1774–1851.
See also Catalogue of 19th cent. librettos.
Adelina Senese o sia L'amore secreto, Venezia (1797).   SCHATZ 9991

Spontoni, Carlo.
Il fanatico per la musica, Bologna (1782) (with Caruso).   SCHATZ 1667
Il tempio della gloria—O templo da gloria, Lisboa, 1790.   SCHATZ 10017

Stabingher (Stabinger, Staubingher), Mathias, *ca.* 1750–1815.
Alessandro nell' Indie, ballet (music principally his). *See*
    P. Guglielmi's Enea e Lavinia.
L'astuzie di Bettina, Venezia, 1784.   SCHATZ 10019
Le avventure d'Ircana, ballet. *See* Salieri's La fiera di
    Venezia.
La disfatta di Dario. A. T. of his ballet Il trionfo di Ales-
    sandro.
La morte di Arrigo Sesto, rè d'Inghilterra, ballet. *See* G.
    Giordani's Elpinice.
La pastorella fedele, ballet. *See* Bianchi's La villanella ra-
    pita.
La prigionia di Dario. A. T. of his ballet Il trionfo di Ales-
    sandro.
La sconfitta delle Amazoni, ballet. *See* Salieri's La fiera de
    Venezia.
Il trionfo di Alessandro o sia La disfatta di Dario, ballet. *See*
    Cimarosa's Oreste.
Il trionfo di Alessandro o sia La disfatta di Dario, ballet. *See*
    Sarti's Medonte.
Il trionfo di Alessandro o sia La prigionia di Dario, ballet. *See*
    Piticchio's Il militare amante.
Il trionfo di Alessandro o sia La prigionia di Dario, ballet. *See*
    Zanetti's Didone abbandonata.

Staggins, Nicholas, *d.* 1705.
Calisto, or, The chaste nimph, London, 1675.   LONGE 106

Standfuss, Johann.
Der lustige schuster oder Der zweyte theil vom Teufel ist los,
    n. i., n. d. (detached copy of libretto of Hiller's singspiel,
    based on that of the above).   SCHATZ 4733

Standfuss, Johann—Continued.

Der lustige schuster (Weisse, Komische opern, Carlsruhe, 1778).   ML 49.A2W2

Die verwandelten weiber oder Der teufel ist los, Leipzig, 1772. (Hiller's revision and partly recomposition of his Der teufel ist los oder Die verwandelten weiber.)   Schatz 4732

— [same title] Riga, 1794.   Schatz 4732a

Die verwandelten weiber oder Der teufel ist los (Weisse, Komische opern, Carlsruhe, 1778, t. ii).   ML 49.A2W2

Stanley, John, 1713–1786.

Amelia, pasticcio. *See* Title catalogue.

Arcadia; or, The shepherd's wedding, London, 1761.   Longe 52

The lover his own rival, ballad opera. *See* Title catalogue.

The summer's tale, pasticcio. *See* Title catalogue.

Starzer, Joseph, 1726–1787.

Agamemnon vengé (Vienne, 1771) ballet.   ML 52.2.A2

Artaserse. Ballet music for Gius. Scarlatti's opera, Vienna, 1763.

Steffani, Agostino, 1654–1728.

Alarico il Baltha, cioè l'Audace, rè de Gothi, Monaco (1687).   Schatz 10036

Der grossmuethige Roland (Hamburg, 1695). Tr. of his Orlando generoso.   Schatz 10034

Niobe, koenigin in Thebe (Muenchen, 1688). Tr. of his Niobe, regina di Thebe.   Schatz 10033

Il triumfo del fato oder Das maechtige geschick bei Lavinia und Dido (Hamburg, 1699). Tr. of his Il trionfo del fato o Le glorie d'Enea.   Schatz 10037

Thomyris, queen of Scythia, pasticcio. *See* Title catalogue.

Die vereinigten mit-buhler oder Die siegende Atalanta (Hamburg, 1698). Tr. of his Le rivali concordi.   Schatz 10035

Stegmann, Carl David, 1751–1826.

See also Catalogue of 19th cent. librettos.

Furcht und hoffnung, Hamburg, 1798.   Schatz 10038

Heinrich der Löwe, n. i., 1792.   Schatz 10039

Der kaufmann von Smirna, Hamburg, 1792.   Schatz 10040

Die recrouten auf dem lande, Wittenberg und Zerbst, 1781. (O. T. was "Die rekruten auf dem lande.")   Schatz 10041

Schach Wampum oder Die wuensche, Hamburg, 1792. L. T. of: Schatz 10043

Sultan Wampun oder Die wuensche, n. i., 1794.   Schatz 10042

Sultan Wampun oder Die wuensche, n. i., n. d. (detached).   Schatz 11749

Der triumpf der liebe, Hamburg, 1796.   Schatz 10044

Stegmayer, Matthäus.

See also Catalogue of 19th cent. librettos.

Die zwölf schlafenden jungfrauen, Wien, 1798.   Schatz 10052

Liebe macht kurzen prozess oder Die heyrath auf gewisse art (Leipzig, 1799) (with Henneberg, Woelfl, and others).   Schatz 4633

Steibelt, Daniel, 1765–1823.

Roméo et Juliette, Paris, an II (1793).   ML 50.2.R68S8

Roméo et Juliette, Paris, an III (1794–95).   ML 50.2.R68S82

72251°—VOL 2—14——29

Steudle.
   Die liebe fuer den Kaiser, Kaufbeuren, 1790.   SCHATZ 10062

Stevens, Richard John Samuel, 1757–1837.
   The deserter of Naples. *See* Title catalogue.

Stiava, Domenico, *d.* 1708.
   Hercole perseguitato, Lucca, 1657. *See* M. Curzio in Title
      catalogue.
   Il porto della libertà, Lucca, 1654. *See* M. Curzio in Title
      catalogue.

Stoelzel, Gottfried Heinrich, 1690–1749.
   L'amore vince l'inganno (Gotha, 1736).   SCHATZ 10076

Storace, Stephen, 1763–1796.
   See also Catalogue of 19th cent. librettos.
   La cameriera astuta, London, 1788.   SCHATZ 10078
   The Cherokee, London, 1795.   LONGE 233
   The Doctor and the apothecary, London, 1788. Adaptation
      of Dittersdorf's Der apotheker und der doctor.   SCHATZ 2586
   Gli equivoci, Vienna (1787).   SCHATZ 10079
   Gli equivoci—Die irrthuemer, Dresda, 1797.   SCHATZ 10080
   The haunted tower, London, 1789.   LONGE 203
   The haunted tower, London, 1791.   LONGE 218
   The haunted tower, Dublin, n. d.   SCHATZ 10081
   The iron chest, London, 1796.   LONGE 236
   Lodoiska, London (1794) (pasticcio from the above, Cherubini,
      Kreutzer, and Andreozzi).   LONGE 228
   Mahmoud (London) 1796 (posthumous work, finished by Kelly
      and partly selected from Sarti, Haydn, etc.).   LONGE 234
   My grandmother, n. i., 1794.   LONGE 233
   No song no supper, n. i., 1790 (partly selected from Pleyel,
      Grétry, Dr. Harington, Giordani, Gluck, etc.).   LONGE 206
   No song no supper, Dublin, 1792.   SCHATZ 10085
   The pirates, London, 1792.   LONGE 220
   The prize or 2, 5, 3, 8, Dublin, 1793.   LONGE 233
   The siege of Belgrade, London, 1791 (partly utilizing Martin
      y Soler's Una cosa rara).   LONGE 207
   The siege of Belgrade, Dublin (179–).   SCHATZ 6021 and LONGE 233
   The siege of Belgrade, London (*ca.* 1796).   LONGE 263

Striggio, Alessandro, *d.* 1587.
   Descrizione dell' apparato . . . [Psiche ed Amore, intermedii]
      Fiorenza, 1566 (with Corteccia).   ML 52.2.D3
   Descrizione de gl'intermedii . . . [Psiche ed Amore] Firenze,
      1593 (with Corteccia).   PQ

Strozzi, Pietro.
   Il rapimento di Cefalo, Firenze, 1600 (mainly by Caccini, with
      some music by the above, Venturi del Nibbio, and Bati). SCHATZ 1449

Stuck, Jean Batistin, *d.* 1755.
   Manto la fée (Recueil général des opéra, t. x, Paris, 1714).   SCHATZ 10123
   Méléagre (Recueil général des opéra, t. x, Paris, 1714).   SCHATZ 10124
   Polidore (Recueil général des opéra, t. xiii, Paris, 1734).   SCHATZ 10125

Süssmayr (Süssmayer), Franz Xaver, 1766–1803.
   See also Catalogue of 19th cent. librettos.
     Der besiegte zauber. Tr. of his L'incanto superato, Dresda,
       1795.   Schatz 10179
     Die drei sultaninnen. A. T. of his Soliman der Zweite.
     Die edle rache, n. i, n. d.   Schatz 10177
     L'incanto superato—Der besiegte zauber, Dresda, 1795.   Schatz 10179
     Die koenigin der Schwarzen inseln, n. i., 1797.   ML.50.2.K7S9
     Liebe macht kurzen prozess oder Die heyrath auf gewisse art
       (Leipzig, 1799) (with Henneberg, Woelfl, and others).   Schatz 4633
     Die neuen Arkadier, Weimar, 1796. L. T. of his Der spiegel
       von Arkadien.   Schatz 10184
     Soliman der Zweite oder Die drei sultaninnen, Wien, 1799. Schatz 10182
     Der spiegel von Arkadien (Wien) 1796.   Schatz 10183
     Der wildfang (Wien) 1797.   Schatz 10185

Suett, Richard.
     The female duellist, London, 1793.   Longe 225
     The smugglers. *See* Title catalogue.

Szerelemhegyi, András.
     A'lantosok, vagy-is: A'vig nyomorúság, Pesten, 1793.   Schatz 11530

Tarchi, Angelo, 1760–1814.
   See also Catalogue of 19th cent. librettos.
     Ademira, Venezia, 1787.   Schatz 10211
     Adrasto rè d'Egitto, Milano (1792).   Schatz 10233
     Alessandro nell' Indie (Livorno, 1791).   Schatz 10228
     Antioco, Milano (1788).   Schatz 10234
     L'apoteosi d'Ercole, Venezia, 1790.   Schatz 10212
     L'Archetiello, Napoli, 1778.   Schatz 10223
     Ariarate, Palermo (1787).   Schatz 10213
     L'Arminio, Mantova (1785).   Schatz 10230
     Bacco ed Arianna, Torino (1784).   Schatz 10226
     La congiura Pisoniana, Milano (1797).   Schatz 10215
     Il conte di Saldagna, Milano (1787).   Schatz 10216
     Le Danaidi, Milano (1794).   Schatz 10217
     Demofoonte, Milano (1786).   Schatz 10218
     Il disertore, Genova, Anno II (1799).   Schatz 10235
     Dorval e Virginia, Venezia, 1792.   Schatz 10219
     Ezio, Vicenza (1792).   Schatz 10239
     Giulio Sabino, Torino (1790).   Schatz 10220
     Ifigenia in Aulide, Padova (1785).   Schatz 10231
     Ifigenia in Tauride, Venezia, 1786.   Schatz 10221
     L'impostura poco dura, Milano (1795).   Schatz 10236
     Il matrimonio per contrattempo, Livorno (1785). Schatz 10237
     Il rè alla caccia, Napoli, 1780.   Schatz 10224
     Lo spazzacamino principe, Milano (1790).   Schatz 10238
     Il trionfo di Clelia, Torino (1787).   Schatz 10222
     La Virginia, Livorno (1786).   Schatz 10232
     I viluppi amorosi, Napoli, 1778.   Schatz 10227

Tavelli, Luigi.
     Amore e sdegno, Venezia, 1726.   Schatz 10253

Telemann, Georg Philipp, 1681–1767.

Adelheid (Hamburg, 1727). The O. T. had as A. T. Die ungezwungene liebe.   SCHATZ 10254

Aesopus bey hofe (Hamburg, 1729).   SCHATZ 10255

Die aus der einsamkeit in die welt zurueckgekehrte opera (Hamburg, 1729).   SCHATZ 10269

Basilio und Quiteria, n. i., n. d.   SCHATZ 10256

Belsazer. A. T. of his Das ende der babylonischen monarchie.

Der beschluss des carnevals (Hamburg, 1724) (partly based on Campra's L'Europe galante. T.'s act, the third, was called Il capitano).   SCHATZ 1564

Calypso oder Sieg der weissheit (Hamburg, 1727).   SCHATZ 10257

Il capitano (Hamburg, 1726). *See also his* Der beschluss des carnevals.   SCHATZ 10270

La capricciosa e il credulo—Die geliebte eigensinnige und der leicht glaeubige liebhaber (Hamburg, 1725).   SCHATZ 10271

Cleofida, koenigin von Indien. A. T. of his Triumph der grossmuth und treue.

Emma und Eginhard. A. T. of his Die last-tragende liebe.

Das ende der babylonischen monarchie cder Belsazer (Hamburg, 1723).   SCHATZ 10258

— Same. 2ter theil (Hamburg, 1723).   SCHATZ 10259

Flavius Bertaridus, koenig der Longobarden (Hamburg, 1729).   SCHATZ 10260

Der gedultige Socrates, Hamburg (1721).   SCHATZ 10261

Die geliebte eigensinnige und der leicht-glaeubige liebhaber (Hamburg, 1725). (Libretto headed with the title of the Italian original by unknown author "La capricciosa e il credulo.")   SCHATZ 10271

Judith, gemahlin kayser Ludewigs des Frommen oder Die siegende unschuld, Hamburg (1732). (Furnished only the recitatives for this combination of Händel's Lotario and Chelleri's L'innocenza difesa.)   SCHATZ 4481

Die last-tragende liebe, oder Emma und Eginhard (Hamburg, 1728).   SCHATZ 10262

Margaretha, koenigin in Castilien (Hamburg, 1730).   SCHATZ 10263

Der misslungene braut-wechsel oder Richardus I, koenig von England (Hamburg) 1729. (Only the German words, the Italian by Händel.)   SCHATZ 4488

Das neu-beglueckte Sachsen, Hamburg (1730).   SCHATZ 10272

Der neu-modische liebhaber Damon (Hamburg, 1724).   SCHATZ 10264

Omphale (Hamburg, 1724).   SCHATZ 10265

Riccardus I, koenig von England. A. T. of his and Händel's Der misslungene brautwechsel.

Sancio oder Die siegende grossmuth (Hamburg, 1727).   SCHATZ 10266

Sieg der schoenheit, Hamburg (1722). Only his alterations in Conradi's opera.   SCHATZ 2180

Sieg der weissheit ueber die liebe. A. T. of his Calypso.

Die siegende grossmuth. A. T. of his Sancio.

Die siegende unschuld. A. T. of his Judith, gemahlin kayser Ludewigs des Frommen.

Telemann, Georg Philipp—Continued.

Der streit der kindlichen pflicht und der liebe oder Die flucht
    des Aeneas nach Latien (Hamburg) 1731. Recitatives
    only for this Tr. of Porpora's Didone abbandonata.   SCHATZ 8365

Tamerlan (Hamburg, 1725). (Only an intermezzo in Händel's
    opera.)   SCHATZ 4492

Triumph der grossmuth und treue oder Cleofida, koenigin von
    Indien, Hamburg (1732). (Recitatives only, for this
    opera by Händel.)   SCHATZ 4487

Die ungleiche heyrath zwischen Vespetta und Pimpinone
    (Hamburg, 1725).   SCHATZ 10273

Die ungezwungene liebe. A. T. of his Adelheid.

Die verkehrte welt (Hamburg, 1728).   SCHATZ 10267

Der weiseste in Sidon, Hamburg (1733).   SCHATZ 10268

Tenducci, Giusto Ferdinando, *d.* 1790.

The castle of Andalusia, Dublin, 1783. (Additional songs
    only.)   LONGE 148

Pharnaces or The revenge of Athridates, 3d ed., Edinburgh,
    1769 (adapted and selected music for this pasticcio).   LONGE 277

Teofilo Fedele. *See* Treu.

Terradellas (Terradeglias), Domingo Miguel Barnabas,
    1711–1751.

Artaserse (Venezia, 1744).   SCHATZ 10283

La Cerere, Roma, 1740.   ML 50.2.C36T2

Didone, Torino, 1750.   SCHATZ 10285

Imeneo in Atene, Venezia (1750).   SCHATZ 10284

Sesostri rè d'Egitto, Roma (1751).   ML 50.2.S55T2

Terziani, Pietro, 1765–1831.
    See also Catalogue of 19th cent. librettos.

Creso, Venezia, 1788.   SCHATZ 10289

Teyber (Teuber), Franz, 1756–1810.
    See also Catalogue of 19th cent. librettos.

Die dorfdeputierten, n. i., 1792.   SCHATZ 10295

Theobald. Teobaldo di Gatti, *called*

Tiepolo, Marc' Antonio.

Teseo in Sicilia, Venezia, 1754.   SCHATZ 10352

Tiraboschi, Antonio.

Alessandro nell' Indie, Vicenza, 1750.   SCHATZ 10355

Toeschi, Alessandro.

Meride, ballet music. *See* Pietragrua's Meride.

Toeschi, Carlo Giuseppe, 1722 *or* 1724–1788.

Acis und Galatea, ballet. *See* J. Chr. Bach's Lucius Silla.

Cephal und Procris, ballet. (The libretto mentions as com-
    posers of this and "Reinald und Armide" "Cannabich
    und Toeschi.") *See* Holzbauer's Hadrian in Syrien.

Reinald und Armide, ballet. (The libretto mentions as com-
    posers of this and "Cephal und Procris" "Cannabich
    und Toeschi.") *See* Holzbauer's Hadrian in Syrien.

Rogerius auf der insel der Alcine, ballet. *See* Bach's Temis-
    tocle.

Telemaco. Ballet music for Grua's opera, Monaco, 1780.

Tomasi, Giovanni Battista.
    Sesto Tarquinio, Venetia, 1679.   SCHATZ 10359

Tomeoni, Florido, 1755–1820.
    Roma liberata dalla congiura di Catilina, Lucca, 1775. *See*
      M. Curzio in Title catalogue.

Tomeoni, Pellegrino.
    Il Narsete, generale di Giustiniano imperatore, Lucca, 1770.
      See M. Curzio in Title catalogue.

Torri, Pietro, *d.* 1737.
    Eumene, Monaco (1720).   SCHATZ 10364
    Griselda, Monaco (1735).   SCHATZ 10365
    Lucio Vero, Monaco (1720).   SCHATZ 10366
    Venceslao (Muenchen, 1725).   SCHATZ 10367

Tortona, Isidoro.
    L'Andromeda, Piacenza (1662).   SCHATZ 10374

Tosi, Giuseppe Felice.
    L'Alboino in Italia, Venetia, 1691 (with C. F. Pollaroli).   SCHATZ 10382
    Amulio e Numitore, Venetia, 1689.   SCHATZ 10375
    Atide, Bologna (1679).   (First act only; act II by Pietro degli
      Antoni; act III by G. A. Perti.)   SCHATZ 10381
    L'idea di tutte le perfezioni, Piacenza, 1690.   SCHATZ 10379
    L'incoronazione di Serse, Venetia, 1691.   SCHATZ 10376
    Orazio, Venetia, 1688.   SCHATZ 10377
    Pirro e Demetrio, Venetia, 1690.   SCHATZ 10378
    Traiano, Venetia, 1684.   SCHATZ 10380

Touchemolin, Joseph, 1727–1801.
    I furori di Orlando—Die rasereyen der Rolands (Ratisbona,
      1777).   SCHATZ 10383

Tozzi, Antonio.
    La morte di Dimone o sia L'innocenza vendicata, Venezia,
      1763.   SCHATZ 10385
    Rinaldo, Venezia, 1775.   SCHATZ 10386
    Tigrane, Venezia, 1762.   SCHATZ 10387
    Zenobia, Monaco (1773).   SCHATZ 10384

Traetta (Trajetta), Tommaso Michele Francesco Saverio,
      1727–1779.
    Amore in trappola, Venezia, 1768.   SCHATZ 10405
    Antigono, Padova, 1764.   SCHATZ 10406
    Armida, Vienna, 1760.   SCHATZ 11382
    Armida, Venezia, 1767.   SCHATZ 10407
    Buovo d'Antona, Venezia, 1759.   SCHATZ 10388
    Il cavaliere errante, Parma (1780).   SCHATZ 10389
    Il cavaliero errante—Der irrende ritter (Dresda, 1780).   SCHATZ 10390
    Demofoonte, Mantova (1770).   SCHATZ 10408
    Didone abbandonata, Venezia, 1757.   SCHATZ 10402
    La disfatta di Dario, Venezia, 1778.   SCHATZ 10409
    Egle.   *See his* Le feste d'Imenco.
    Enea e Lavinia (Firenze, 1768).   SCHATZ 10399
    Enea nel Lazio, Torino (1760).   SCHATZ 10391
    Ezio, Padova (1765).   SCHATZ 10410

Traetta (Trajetta), Tommaso, Michele Francesco Saverio—
 Continued.

Le feste d'Imeneo (Parma, 1760) (consists of the prologue "Il
 trionfo d'amore" and the acts "Iride," "Saffo," "Egle"). Schatz 10392

La Francese a Malghera, Venezia, 1764. Schatz 10411

Ifigenia in Aulide, Napoli (1753). Interpolated arias in Jommelli's opera. Schatz 4861

Ifigenia in Tauride, Vienna (1763). Schatz 10393

Ifigenia in Tauride, Livorno, 1763. Schatz 10393a

Ifigenia in Tauride, Mantova (1777). ML 48.A5 v.24

Iride. *See his* Le feste d'Imenco.

Der irrende ritter. Tr. of his Il cavaliero errante (Dresda,
 1780). Schatz 10390

L'isola disabitata, Bologna (1768). Schatz 10394

L'isola disabitata—Den ubeboede øe, Kiøbenhavn, 1772. Schatz 10395

La Merope, Milano (1776). Schatz 10412

La Nitteti, Reggio (1757). Schatz 10403

Olimpiade, Verona (1758). Schatz 10404

Olimpiade (Firenze, 1767). Schatz 10396

Saffo. *See his* Le feste d'Imenco.

Semiramis, Venezia, 1765. Schatz 10413

Le serve rivali, Venezia, 1767. Schatz 10397

Siroe—Siroes, Monaco (1767). ML 50.2.S6T8

I Tintaridi (Firenze, 1768). Schatz 10400

Il tributo campestre, Mantova, 1768. Schatz 10401

Il trionfo d'amore. *See his* Le feste d'Imenco.

Den ubeboede øe. Tr. of his L'isola disabitata, Kiøbenhavn,
 1772. Schatz 10395

Zenobia, Roma, 1762. Schatz 10398

Zophilette. *See* Title catalogue.

Travenol, Louis, *ca.* 1698–1783.

Les petites maisons (Le Théâtre de la foire, Paris, 1737,
 t. ix, 2). ML 48.L2**X**

Trento, Santi.

Alzira. Ballets for Giuseppe Nicolini's opera.

Trento, Vittorio, *b.* 1761 *or* 1765.

See also Catalogue of 19th cent. librettos.

Ahtor ed Erma, ballet. *See* G. Nicolini's Artaserse.

Ahtor ed Erma, ballet. *See* Prota's I studenti.

Alfredo il Grande, rè degli Anglo-Sassoni, ballet. *See* Bianchi's Selenco.

Gli amori di Clodio e Pompea, ballet. *See* F. Bianchi's
 Alonso e Cora.

Gli amori d'Igor primo Zar di Moscovia, ballet. *See* Tarchi's
 Ifigenia in Tauride.

Il baron di Lago Nero. Ballet music for Mortellari's opera.

Bianco de' Rossi, Venezia, 1797. Schatz 10418

Bianca de' Rossi, ballet. *See* P. Guglielmi's La pupilla
 scaltra.

Bianca de' Rossi, ballet. *See* Tarchi's Dorval e Virginia.

I capricci (Venezia, 1795). Schatz 10442

La distruzione di Cartagine, ballet. *See* Andreozzi's Amleto.

Le donne invidiose ossia L'onestà trionfante, ballet. *See*
 Bianchi's La sposa in equivoco.

Trento, Vittorio—Continued.

Enrichetta, ballet. *See* Bianchi's La sposa in equivoco.

L'equivoco, ballet. *See* Paër's Cinna.

L'esilio di Tarquinio il Superbo, vii. rè di Roma, ballet. *See* Zingarelli's La morte di Mitridate.

Fallaride, tirannide d'Agricento, ballet. *See* Andreozzi's La principessa filosofa.

La finta amalata, Venezia, 179 .   SCHATZ 10432

Giorgio principe della Servia, ballet. *See* Portugal's Gli Orazi e I Curiazi.

Gli innamorati, Venezia, 1793 (2d act, 1st act by Nasolini).   SCHATZ 7031

Kildar, ballet. *See* Zingarelli's Il ratto delle Sabine.

Mario e Felice, ballet. *See* Bianchi's Ines de Castro.

Mastino della Scala, ballet. *See* Paër's L'oro fa tutto.

La morte di Pirro, ballet. *See* Bertoni's Nitteti.

Obert e Melina, ballet. *See* J. S. Mayr's cantata Temira e Aristo (Schatz 6203).

Odervik, ballet. *See* Marinelli's Issipile, 1796.

Odoacre, primo rè d'Italia, ballet. *See* Piccinni's Il servo padrone.

L'onestà trionfante. A. T. of his ballet Le donne invidiose.

Padre e figlio rivali sconosciuti. A. T. of his ballet Tamar e Selimo.

La pescatrice in Jassa, ballet. *See* Gardi's Il contravveleno.

Il ratto delle castellane fatto dai Triestini, ballet. *See* Andreozzi's La principessa filosofa.

La serva padrona, Venezia, 1795.   SCHATZ 10429

Tamar e Selimo ossia Padre e figlio rivali sconosciuti, ballet. *See* Isola's Lisandro.

Treu, Daniel Gottlieb, 1695–1749 (*called* Teofilo Fedele).

Ulisses (Breslau, 1726).   SCHATZ 10444

Trial, Jean Claude, 1732–1771.

Renaud d'Ast (Paris) 1765. (Journal des spectacles, t. i, 1766) (with Vachon).   ML 48.J7

Silvie (Paris) 1765 (Journal des spectacles, t. ii, 1766) (with P. M. Berton).   ML 48.J7

Triebensee, Joseph.

Liebe macht kurzen prozess oder Die heyrath auf gewisse art (Leipzig, 1799) (with Henneberg, Woelfle and others).   SCHATZ 4633

Tritto (Tritta), Giacomo, 1733–1824.

See also Catalogues of 19th cent. librettos.

Gli amanti in puntiglio, Napoli, 1794.   SCHATZ 10465

Gli amanti riuniti. A. T. of his La donna sensibile.

Apelle e Campaspe, Milano (1796).   SCHATZ 10452

L'Arminio, Roma, 1786.   SCHATZ 10454

L'Artenice, Napoli, 1784.   SCHATZ 10455

Le astuzie in amore, Napoli, 1790.   SCHATZ 10460

Le avventure galanti, Genova (1789).   L. T. of his Le vicende amorose.   SCHATZ 10482

Il barone in angustie, Napoli, 1797.   SCHATZ 10459

La Bellinda, Napoli, 1781.   SCHATZ 10461

Il Cartesiano fantastico, Napoli, 1790.   SCHATZ 10467

La creduta selvaggia, Roma (1792).   ML 50.2.C76T7

Tritto (Tritta), Giacomo—Continued.

Li disprezzatori delle donne, sia Le vicende amorose—Die
veraechter der schoenen, oder Der wechsel in der Liebe,
Dresda, 1793. L. T. of his Le vicende amorose. SCHATZ 10458

D. Procopio in corte del Pretejanni, Napoli, 1782. SCHATZ 10468

La donna sensibile o sia Gli amanti riuniti, Napoli, 1798. SCHATZ 10469

Li due gemelli e La scuffiara, Napoli, 1784 (two operas; in
the second interpolations by Monti). SCHATZ 10456

L'equivoco, Napoli (1791). SCHATZ 10462

La fedeltà nelle selve, Venetia, 1792. SCHATZ 10484

La fedeltà tra le selve, Napoli, 1796. SCHATZ 10470

La Francese di spirito, Napoli, 1781. SCHATZ 10471

L'impostore smascherato, Napoli, 1794. SCHATZ 10472

L'impresario in angustie con farsa Il convitato di pietra Napoli,
1793. (The second by Tritto, the first by Cimarosa.) SCHATZ 10466

La molinara spiritosa, Napoli, 1787. SCHATZ 10476

Nicaboro in Jucatan, Napoli, 1799. SCHATZ 10463

Le nozze in garbuglio, Napoli, 1793. SCHATZ 10473

La pruova reciproca, Napoli, 1789. SCHATZ 10474

I raggiri d'amore, Trieste (1793). L. T. of his Le vicende
amorose. SCHATZ 10480

I raggiri scoperti, Barcell., 1792. ML 50.2.R17T8

La scaltra avventuriera, Napoli, 1788. SCHATZ 10477

La scuffiara, Napoli, 1784. (Published together with his Li
due gemelli.) (One aria by Monti.) SCHATZ 10456

La scuola degli amanti, Napoli, 1783. SCHATZ 10478

Le trame spiritose, Genova (1793). SCHATZ 10475

Die veraechter der schoenen oder Der wechsel der liebe. Tr.
of his Li disprezzatori delle donne, o sia Le vicende amorose, Dresda, 1793. SCHATZ 10458

La vergine del sole, Napoli, 1786. SCHATZ 10464

Le vicende amorose, Lisbona, 1797. O. T. of his Li disprezzatori delle donne o sia Le vicende amorose and of his Le
avventure galanti and of his I raggiri d'amore. SCHATZ 10483

Der wechsel in der liebe. A. T. of his Der veraechter der
schoenen.

Trojano, Angelo Antonio.

La mogliere fedele, Napoli, 1731. (His and music by Sellitti,
Pulli and Leo interpolated in Vinci's opera.) SCHATZ 10755

Tuczek, Vincenz Ferdinand,[1] *d.* 1820.

See also Catalogue of 19th cent. librettos.

Hanns Klachl oder Das rendezvous in der neuen alee, n. pl.,
1797. SCHATZ 10500

Hanns Klachl's zweyter theil, n. pl., 1797. SCHATZ 10501

Der travestirte Hamlet (Vienna) 1799. SCHATZ 10506

Tuerk, Daniel Gottlob, 1756–1813.

Pyramus und Thisbe, Halle, 1787. SCHATZ 10512

Turner William, 1651–1740.

Presumptuous love, London (1716). LONGE 138

---

[1] So Schatz. Eitner and Grove have Franz, Riemann has Vincenz Franz, and
others have Vincenz Ferrarius.

Ulbrich, Maximilian, *ca.* 1752–1814.
 Der blaue schmetterling oder Der sieg der natur ueber die
  schwaermerey, Wien, 1782.   Schatz 10522

Umlauf (Umlauff), Ignaz, *ca.* 1756–1796.
 See also Catalogue of 19th cent. librettos.
 Die apotheke, Wien, 1778.   Schatz 10523
 Die bergknappen, Wien, 1778.   Schatz 10524
 Endlich fand er sie. A. T. of his Das irrlicht.
 Die gluecklichen jaeger (Gottl. Stephanie d. jüng., Sing-
  spiele, Liegnitz, 1792).   Schatz 10525
 Das irrlicht, oder Endlich fand er sie, Wien, 1785.   Schatz 10526
 Der irrwisch oder Endlich fand er sie, Riga (1786).   Schatz 10527
 Die puecefarbnen schuhe oder Die schoene schusterinn,
  Wien, 1779.   Schatz 10529
 Der ring der liebe oder Zemirens und Azors ehestand, Wien,
  1786.   Schatz 10533
 Die schoene schusterinn (Gottl. Stephanie d. jüng., Sing-
  spiele, Liegnitz, 1792). L. T. of his Die puecefarbnen
  schuhe.   Schatz 10530
 Die schoene schusterinn oder Die schuhe à la Marlborough,
  Berlin, 1794. Another L. T.   Schatz 10531
 Welche ist die beste nation? Wien, 1782.   Schatz 10528
 Zemirens und Azors ehestand. A. T. of his Der ring der liebe.

Uttini, Francesco Antonio Baldassare, 1723–1795.
 Thetis och Pelee, Stockholm, 1773.   Schatz 10550
 Zenobia—Zenobia, Kiøbenhavn. 1770.   Schatz 10551

Vachon, Pierre, *d.* 1802.
 Les femmes et le secret, Avignon, 1768.   ML 50.2.F25V22
 Les femmes et le secret, Paris, 1770.   Schatz 10570
 Les femmes et le secret, Paris, 1779.   Schatz 11750
 Renaud d'Ast (Paris) 1765 (Journal des spectacles, t. i, 1766)
  (with Trial).   ML 48.J7
 Sara ou La fermière écosaise, Paris, 1774.   Schatz 10571

Vagenzail. *See* Wagenseil.

Valentini, Giovanni.
 Il capriccio dramatico, Venezia (1787). (A pasticcio, to which
  Valentini perhaps contributed.)   Schatz 10580
 I castellani burlati, Venezia (1785).   Schatz 10581
 L'innocenza protetta. A. T. of his Rosina consolata.
 L'isola della luna, Venezia, 1780.   Schatz 10585
 Le nozze in contrasto, Venezia (1779).   Schatz 10582
 Le nozze in contrasto—Die streitige heurath, Dresda, 1782.   Schatz 10583
 Le nozze in contrasto, Firenze, 1785.   ML 48.A5 v.24
 Rosina consolata ossia L'innocenza protetta, Venezia, 1781.   Schatz 10584
 Le sorelle rivali, Milano (1782) (with others who are not men-
  tioned). L. T. of his La statua matematica.   Schatz 10586

Valentini, Michel Angelo.
 Solimano, Torino (1756).   Schatz 10587

Vanbenbroeck, Othon Joseph.
 Le génie Asouf, ou Les deux coffrets, Paris, an VIII (1799).
  (Pasticcio, partly music by the above.)   Schatz 10591

Vandini, Lotavio, *fictitious name of* Macari, Giacomo.

Vanhall (Wanhal), Johann Baptist, 1739–1813.
The princess of Tarento, pasticcio. *See* Title catalogue.

Vannucci, Luigi.
Bruto, Lucca, 1789. *See* M. Curzio in Title catalogue.

Varischino (Varischini), Giovanni.
L'amante fortunato per forza, Venetia, 1684.   Schatz 10594
L'Odoacre, Venetia, 1680.   Schatz 10593

Vento, Mattia, *ca.* 1736–1776.
The captive, pasticcio. *See* Title catalogue.
The castle of Andalusia, pasticcio. *See* Title catalogue.
La conquista del Messico—The conquest of Mexico, London,
1767.   ML 50.2.C65V2
Daphne and Amintor, pasticcio. *See* Title catalogue.
L'Egiziana, Venezia, 1763.   Schatz 10610
L'Egiziana, Milano (1763).   ML 48.A5 v.3
Ezio, London, 1764–5 (pasticcio from above and Pescetti,
Bach, etc.).   ML 48.M2N
Lionel and Clarissa. *See* Title catalogue.
Love in the city, pasticcio. *See* Title catalogue.
The school for fathers, pasticcio. *See* Lionel and Clarissa in
Title catalogue.
La Zingara, Vienna, 1769 (his L'Egiziana, with music by
Gassmann).   Schatz 10611
La Zingara (Firenze, 1771). Same as this last.   Schatz 10612

Ventura, Santo.
Chi più sà manco l'intende, 1669, ballet. *See* Draghi's opera.

Venturi del Nibbio, Stefano.
Il rapimento di Cefalo, Firenze, 1600 (mainly by Caccini, with
some music by the above, Bati and Strozzi).   Schatz 1449

Veracini, Francesco Maria, 1685–1750.
The clemency of Titus—[La clemenza di Tito] London, 1737. Schatz 10618

Vernizzi (Vernici), Ottavio.
La coronatione d'Apollo per Dafne conversa in lauro. Forms
part of "Trattenimento musicale d'Apollo con il Reno,"
Bologna, 1621, and is practically identical with the next
entry.   ML52.2.T7
La coronatione d'Apollo per Dafne conversa in lauro, Bologna,
1623.   Schatz 10715
Stratira, Bologna, 1617.   Schatz 10714

Vernon, Joseph, *d.* 1782.
The summer's tale, pasticcio. *See* Title catalogue.

Verocai, Giovanni.
Achille in Sciro—Achilles in Sciro, Wolffenbüttel (1746). Schatz 10717
Il Ciro riconosciuto—Der wiedererkannte Cyrus, Braun-
schweig (1746).   Schatz 10718
Demofoonte—Demophoon, Wolffenbuttel (1742).   Schatz 10719

Viganò, Giulio.
La figlia dell' aria o sia L'innalzamento di Semiramide, ballet
(with Salvatore Viganò). *See* Righini's Armida.

Viganò, Salvatore, 1769–1821.

Cefalo e Procri, ballet. *See* Tritto's L'Arminio.

La creduta vedova o sia La sposa costante, Roma (1786).　　ML 50.2.C763V3

La figlia dell' aria o sia L'innalzamento di Semiramide, ballet (with Giulio Viganò). *See* Righini's Armida.

Raul, signore di Crechi o sia La tirannide repressa—Raoul, herr von Crequi, oder Die verhinderte grausamkeit, ballet. *See* Himmel's Semiramide.

La sposa costante. A. T. of his La creduta vedova.

Vignati, Giuseppe.

I rivali generosi, Venezia, 1726.　　Schatz 10724

Vignola, Giuseppe.

La fede tradita e vendicata, Napoli, 1707. (Additional music only for Gasparini's opera.)　　Schatz 3567

L'humanità nelle fere overo Il Lucullo, Napoli (1708) (mostly by Al. Scarlatti).　　Schatz 9538

L'inganno vinto dalla ragione, Napoli, 1708 (only the buffo scenes and added arias, the opera mainly by Lotti).　　Schatz 5727

Le Regine di Macedonia, Napoli, 1708. (Additional arias and all the buffo scenes for this altered version of Gasparini's Statira.)　　Schatz 3583

Vilderer, Joh. Ugo. *See* Wilderer.

Villeneuve, André Jacques.

La princesse d'Elide (Recueil général des opéra, t. xiv, Paris, 1734.　　Schatz 10738

Vinacese, Benedetto, *d.* 1719.

Gli amanti generosi, Venetia, 1703.　　Schatz 10739

L'innocenza giustificata, Venetia, 1699.　　Schatz 10740

L'innocenza giustificata, Mantova (1700).　　ML 50.2.I58

Vinci, Leonardo, 1690 (?) –1730.

Artaserse, Roma (1730).　　Schatz 10743

Artaserse—Artaxerxes (Dresda, 1746).　　Schatz 10744

Catone in Utica, Roma, 1728.　　Schatz 10746

Alessandro nell' Indie, Roma (1730).　　Schatz 10742

Alessandro nell' Indie, Monaco (1735).　　Schatz 11297

La caduta de' decemviri, Napoli, 1727.　　ML 50.2.C23V4

Le caprice amoureux ou Ninette à la cour. *See* Title catalogue.

The captive, pasticcio. *See* Title catalogue.

Il Catone in Utica (Venezia, 1747). (Some arias by Jommelli and other anonymous composers.)　　Schatz 10754

La contesa de' Numi. *See* Metastasio's Opere.

Demofoonte, Lucca (1741).　　Schatz 10745

Didone abbandonata, Roma (1726).　　ML 50.2.D55V4

Gismondo rè di Polonia, Roma (1727).　　Schatz 10747

Il giocatore. *See* Il marito giogatore e la moglie bacchettona in Title catalogue.

Ifigenia in Tauride, Venezia (1725).　　Schatz 10750

Macrina e Carfoglio. Intermezzi in his Medea riconosciuta.

Maid of the mill, pasticcio. *See* the Title catalogue.

Medea riconosciuta—Die wiedererkannte Medea, Wien (1735).

L. T. of his Medo.　　Schatz 10753

Vinci, Leonardo—Continued.

Medo, Parma, 1728.	Schatz 10748
La mogliere fedele, Napoli, 1731. (Some of the music by Sellitti, Trojano, Pulli, Leo.)	Schatz 10755
Orfeo, pasticcio. *See* Title catalogue.	
La Rosmira fedele, Venezia (1725).	Schatz 10751
The school for fathers, pasticcio. *See* Lionel and Clarissa in Title catalogue.	
Semiramide riconosciuta, Roma (1729).	Schatz 10752
Serpilla e Bacocco. *See* Il marito giogatore e la moglie bacchettona in Title catalogue.	
Siroe, rè di Persia, Venetia, 1731.	Schatz 10749
Il Siroe—Der Siroes (Bronsevigo, 1767) pasticcio. *See* Title catalogue.	Schatz 11365
Die wieder erkannte Medea. Tr. of his Medea riconosciuta, Wien (1735).	Schatz 10753

Vitali, Angelo.

Tomiri, Venetia, 1680.	Schatz 10758

Vivaldi, Antonio, *d.* 1743.

Armida al campo d'Egitto, Venetia, 1718.	Schatz 10759
Arsilda, regina di Ponto, Venezia, 1716.	Schatz 10760
Artabene rè di Persia, Venezia, 1718. L. T. of his:	Schatz 10762
La costanza trionfante degl' amori e degl' odii, Venezia, 1716.	Schatz 10761
La Candace o'siano Li veri amici, Mantova (1720).	ML 50.2.C26V3
Cunegonda, Venezia, 1726.	Schatz 10764
Dorilla in Tempe, Venezia, 1726.	Schatz 10765
Ercole su'l Termidonte, Roma, 1723.	ML 50.2.E61V4
Emelinda, 1750. *See* this under Galuppi.	
Farnace, Venezia, 1726.	Schatz 10766
La fede tradita e vendicata, Venezia, 1726.	Schatz 10767
Feraspe, Venezia, 1739.	Schatz 10768
Filippo rè di Macedonia, Venezia, 1721 (only third act, first and second by Boniventi).	Schatz 1196
Giustino, Roma, 1724.	Schatz 10769
The golden pippin, pasticcio. *See* Title catalogue.	
Griselda, Venezia, 1735.	Schatz 10770
L'incoronazione di Dario, Venezia, 1717.	Schatz 10771
L'inganno trionfante in amore, Venezia, 1725.	Schatz 10772
Motezuma, Venezia (1733).	Schatz 10773
L'odio vinto dalla costanza, Venezia, 1731. L. T. of his La costanza trionfante degl' amori e degl' odii (with new music by Galeazzi).	Schatz 10763
L'Olimpiade, Venezia, 1734.	Schatz 10774
L'oracolo in Messenia, Venezia, 1738.	Schatz 10775
Orlando, Venezia, 1727.	Schatz 10776
Orlando finto pazzo, Venetia (1714).	Schatz 10777
Rosilena ed Oronta, Venezia, 1728.	Schatz 10778
Rosmira, Venezia, 1738.	Schatz 10779
Il Siroe (Bronsevigo, 1767) pasticcio. *See* Title catalogue.	
Siroe, rè di Persia, Reggio, 1727.	Schatz 10780
Tieteberga, Venezia, 1717.	Schatz 10781
La verità in cimento, Venezia, 1720.	Schatz 10782

Viviani, Giovanni Bonaventura.
    Astiage, Venetia, 1677.   SCHATZ 10783
    Scipione Africano, Venetia, 1678 (mainly by Cavalli).   SCHATZ 1754

Vogel, Johann Christoph, 1756–1788.
    Démophon, Paris, de Lormel, 1789.   ML 50.2.D4V6
    Démophon, Paris, Ruault, 1789.   ML 50.2.D4V62
    La toison d'or, Paris, 1786.   ML 50.2.T67V7

Vogler, Georg Joseph, 1749–1814.
    See also Catalogue of 19th cent. librettos.
        Albert der Dritte von Bayern (Stuttgart) 1781.   SCHATZ 10791
        Castore e Polluce (Monaco) 1788.   SCHATZ 10800
        Gustaf Adolph och Ebba Brahe (Kellgren's Saml. Skrift:,
             bd. I). (Before 1800 ?)   SCHATZ 10795
        Der kaufmann von Smyrna, Mannheim, 1771.   SCHATZ 10797
        Lampedo, Darmstadt (1779).   SCHATZ 10798

Vogler, Johann Caspar, 1696–*ca.* 1765.
    Ulysses (Hamburg, 1721).   SCHATZ 10801

Volpe, Giambattista, *called* Rovettino.

Wagenseil, Christian Jacob, 1756–1839.
    Die belohnte rechtschaffenheit (Kaufbeuren, 1785).   SCHATZ 10814
    Der beschaemte geizhals, Kaufbeuren, 1787.   SCHATZ 10815

Wagenseil, Georg Christoph, 1715–1777.
    Ariodante (Venezia, 1745).   SCHATZ 10816
    Il Demetrio, Lodi (1764).   ML 48.A5   v.10
    Il Siroe (Bronsevigo, 1767) pasticcio. *See* Title catalogue.

Walter, Ignatz (*real name* von Penz), 1759–1822.
    See also Catalogue of 19th cent. librettos.
        Die boese frau (Herklots' Operetten, Berlin, 1792.)   SCHATZ 10858
        Doktor Faust, n. i., n. d. (Bremen, 1797?).   SCHATZ 10859
        Fuenf und zwanzig tausend gulden. A. T. of his Im dunkeln
             ist nicht gut munkeln.
        Graf von Waltron oder Die subordination, Hamburg, 1792.   SCHATZ 10860
        Die harfe, Offenbach und Brede, 1793. O. T. of his Die
             zauberharfe.   SCHATZ 10861
        Im dunkeln ist nicht gut munkeln oder Fuenf und zwanzig
             tausend gulden, n. i., n. d.   SCHATZ 10862
        Der spiegelritter, Hamburg, 1795.   SCHATZ 10865
        Der spiegelritter, n. i., n. d.   SCHATZ 10865a
        Die subordination. A. T. of his Graf von Waltron.
        Die zauberharfe, Offenbach, 1798. L. T. of his Die harfe.   SCHATZ 11664

Walter, Thomas Christian.
    Soliman den Anden (Copenhagen, 1778).   SCHATZ 10867

Waigel, Giuseppe. *See* Weigl, Joseph.

Wanhal. *See* Vanhall.

Weber, Christian Gottfried, *b.* 1758.
    Die totale mondfinsterniss, Stuttgart, 1786.   SCHATZ 10915

Weber, Edmund Caspar Johann Joseph Maria, *freiherr* **von,**
        1766–1828.
    See also Catalogue of 19th cent. librettos.
        Der transport im Koffer, Hamburg, 1791.   SCHATZ 10916

Weber, Fridolin Stephan Johann Maria Andreas, *freiherr* von, *b.* 1761.

Der freybrief, Berlin, 1788: music selected from Haydn, Mozart, and the above. Schatz 4610a

Der freybrief (Nuernberg?) 1797. Two-act version of the above. Schatz 4610

Wedel, Søren.

Serenaden eller De sorte naeser, Kiøbenhavn, 1795. Schatz 10919

Weigl, Joseph, 1766–1846.

See also Catalogue of 18th cent. librettos.

L'amor marinaro—Die liebe im matrosenkleide, Dresda, 1798. Schatz 10926

Die betrogne arglist, Wien, 1783. One-act version of his Das unnütze bestreben. Schatz 10959

La caffettiera bizzarra—Die launige kaffeeschenkinn, Dresda, 1796. Schatz 10930

La contessa di Amalfi—Die graefinn von Amalfi, Dresda, 1794. L. T. of his La princepessa di Amalfi. Schatz 10945

Das dorf im gebuerge, Wien (1798). Schatz 10932

Giulietta e Pierotto, Vienna (1794). Schatz 10934

Giulietta e Pierotto—Julchen und Peter, Dresda, 1796. Schatz 10935

Die graefinn von Amalfi. Tr. of his La contessa di Amalfi, Dresda, 1794. Schatz 10945

Ein gutes herz ziert jeden stand. A. T. of his Der lumpensammler.

Julchen und Peter. Tr. of his Giulietta e Pierotto, Dresda, 1796. Schatz 10935

Die launige kaffeeschenkinn. Tr. of his La caffettiera bizzarra, Dresda, 1796. Schatz 10930

Die liebe im matrosenkleide. Tr. of his L'amor marinaro. Schatz 10926

Der lumpensammler oder Ein gutes herz ziert jeden stand (Wien, 1792). Schatz 10940

Das Petermaennchen, Erster theil, Wien, 1794. Schatz 10942

—, Zweiter theil, Wien, 1794. Schatz 10943

La principessa di Amalfi. O. T. of his La contessa di Amalfi.

La principessa di Amalfi, Berlino (1796). Schatz 10946

Riccardo cuor di Lione, ballet. *See* Andreozzi's Olindo e Sofronia.

Das unnütze bestreben (Schmidel's Theatralische werke, Wien & Leipzig, 1785). Schatz 10958

Weigl, Thaddaus, 1774 *or* 1776–1844.

See also Catalogue of 19th cent. librettos.

Die marionettenbude oder Der jahrmarkt zu Gruenwald, Salzburg, 1797. ML 50.2.M455W3

Weimar, Georg Peter, 1734–1800.

Die schadenfreude (Der kinderfreund, Tuebingen, 1778). Schatz 10963

Weissflog, Christian Gotthilf, 1732–1804.

Das fruehstueck auf der jagd, oder Der neue richter, Sorau und Leipzig, 1785. Schatz 10983

Weldon, John, 1676–1736.

Love in a village, pasticcio. *See* Title catalogue.

Wessely, Carl Bernhard, 1768–1826.

Psyche, Berlin, 1789. Schatz 10990

Wich, Johann von.

Amphytrion [Hamburg, 1725]. (Composed several new arias
  for his German version of Francesco Gasparini's An-
  fitrione.)   SCHATZ 3560

Wicht, *citoyen.*

La vallée de Montmorency ou Jean-Jacques Rousseau dans son
  hermitage, pasticcio. *See* Title catalogue.

Wilderer, Johann Hugo.

Giocasta—Giocasta, Dusseldorf (1696) (partly by Krafft).   SCHATZ 11014

Il giorno di salute ovvero Demetrio in Athene—Der tag des
  heyls oder Demetrius in Athen, Dusseldorf (1697) (the
  incidental ballets by Krafft).   SCHATZ 11015

Winter, Peter von, 1754–1825.

See also Catalogue of 19th cent. librettos.

Armida und Rinaldo, Wien, 1793. L. T. of his Reinald und
  Armida.   SCHATZ 11050

Belisa ossia La fedeltà riconosciuta, Milano (1795).   SCHATZ 11020

Bellerofon, Muenchen, 1785.   SCHATZ 11022

Der bettelstudent oder Das donnerwetter, n. i., 1789.   SCHATZ 11023

Die brueder als nebenbuhler. Tr. of his I fratelli rivali,
  Dresda, 1795.   SCHATZ 11033

Die brueder als nebenbuhler, Frankfurt am Main, 1798. Another Tr.   SCHATZ 11034

Catone in Utica, Venetia, 1791.   SCHATZ 11027

Das donnerwetter. A. T. of his Der bettelstudent.

I due vedovi—Der wittwer und die wittwe, Dresda, 1798.   SCHATZ 11029

La fedeltà riconosciuta. A. T. of his Belisa.

Das fest der freundschaft. A. T. of his Das lindenfest.

I fratelli rivali, Venezia, 1793.   SCHATZ 11032

I fratelli rivali—Die brueder als nebenbuhler, Dresda, 1795. SCHATZ 11033

Helena und Paris, Muenchen, 1782.   SCHATZ 11035

Helena und Paris, Berlin, 1797.   SCHATZ 11036

Das hirtenmaegdchen, Muenchen, 1784.   SCHATZ 11037

Kora und Alonzo (München, 1781).   SCHATZ 11038

Lenardo und Blandine (Augsburg, 1785).   SCHATZ 11040

Das lindenfest oder Das fest der freundschaft, n. i., 1790. SCHATZ 11041

Marie von Montalban oder Lanassa's zweyter theil, n. i., 1794. SCHATZ 11633

Myrrha und Elvira oder Das opferfest, Hamburg, 1797. L. T.
  of his Das unterbrochene opferfest.   SCHATZ 11060

Ogus o sia Il trionfo del bel sesso—Ogus oder Der triumph des
  schoenen geschlechts, Dresda, 1796.   SCHATZ 11058

Das opferfest. A. T. of his Myrrha und Eloira. (L. T. of
  his Das unterbrochene opferfest.)

Das opferfest, Hamburg (1798). The same version, with this
  as main title.   SCHATZ 11062

Raol de Crequi, ballet (with Pichl). *See his* Belisa.

Reinold und Armida. O. T. of his Armida und Rinaldo.

Il sacrifizio interrotto, Dresda, 1798. Tr. of his Das unterbrochene opferfest.   SCHATZ 11061

Scherz, list und rache, Leipzig, Göschen, 1790 (ed. with "Es
  ist bitter," on p. 37).   GOETHE COLL.

Il trionfo del bel sesso. A. T. of his Ogus.

Der triumph des schoenen geschlechts. A. Tr. T. of his Ogus.

Winter, Peter von—Continued.

Das unterbrochene opferfest. O. ed. of Wien, 1796, not in the
L. of C.

Das unterbrochene opferfest. German text added to his Il
sacrifizio interrotto, Dresda, 1798. SCHATZ 11061

Der wittwer und die wittwe. Tr. of his I due vedovi, Dresda,
1798. SCHATZ 11029

Wittrock, G. H. L.

Die kleine aehrenleserin (Luebeck, 1785). SCHATZ 11068

Woelfl, Joseph, 1772–1812.

See also Catalogue of 19th cent. librettos.

Der kopf ohne mann, Wien, 1798. SCHATZ 11106

Liebe macht kurzen prozess, oder Die heyrath auf gewisse art
(Leipzig, 1799) (with Henneberg, Stegmayer, and others). SCHATZ 4633

Wolaneck, Anton, *b.* 1761.

Der schusterfeierabend (Augsburg, 1794). SCHATZ 11073

Wolf, Ernst Wilhelm, 1735–1792.

Der abend im walde, Weimar, 1774. SCHATZ 11075
Ceres (Hannover, 1773). SCHATZ 11076
Die dorfdeputirten, Weimar, 1773. SCHATZ 11077
Die dorfdeputirten, Riga, n. d. SCHATZ 11077a
Ehrlichkeit und liebe, Kaufbeuren, 1781. SCHATZ 11078
Der Eremit auf Formentara (Regensburg, 1790). SCHATZ 11081
Eremiten paa Formentara, Kiøbenhavn, 1791. SCHATZ 11082
Das gaertner-maedchen, Weimar, 1771. SCHATZ 11079
Das grosse loos, Weimar, 1774. SCHATZ 11080
Das rosenfest, Weimar, 1774. SCHATZ 11083
Das rosenfest (Weimar) 1776. ML 50.2.R75W6
Der schleyer, Hamburg, 1788. SCHATZ 11084
Der schleier (Vulpius, Opern, Baireuth & Leipzig, 1790). SCHATZ 11084a
Die treuen koehler, Weimar, 1773. SCHATZ 11085

Wranitzky, Paul, 1756–1808.

See also Catalogue of 19th cent. librettos.

Die gute mutter (Wien) 1795. SCHATZ 11110
Oberon oder Koenig der elfen, Hamburg, 1792. SCHATZ 11112

Zanetti, Antonio.

Tito Manlio (Venezia, 1746). Interpolated arias according to
SCHATZ, in Jommelli's opera. SCHATZ 4900

Zanetti (Zannetti) Francesco.

Le cognate in contesa, Venezia (1780). SCHATZ 11137
La Didone abbandonata, Perugia (1781). ML 48.A5 v.5
Die waescherinnen (Dresden, 1779). Tr. of his Le lavaran-
dine. SCHATZ 11139
Die waeschermaedchen (Komische opern der Italiener, hrsg.
von Bock, Leipzig, 1781). Another Tr. SCHATZ 11138

Zannettini, Antonio, *sometimes called* Giannettini.

Artaserse, Venezia, 1705. SCHATZ 11141
L'Aurora in Atene, Venetia, 1678. SCHATZ 11146
Irene e Costantino, Venetia, 1681. SCHATZ 11142
Medea in Atene, Venetia, 1678. SCHATZ 11144

Zannettini, Antonio—Continued.

Temistocle in bando, Venetia, 1683.   Schatz 11147

Teseo in Atene, Parma, 1688. L. T. of his Medea in Atene
(but with additional arias by Sabadini).   Schatz 11143

Virginio consolo, Venetia, 1704.   Schatz 11145

Zeller, Georg Bernhard Leopold, 1728–1803.

Der ehrliche raeuber, Neubrandenburg, 1785.   Schatz 11164

Das fest Germaniens, Neustrelitz, 1789.   Schatz 11165

Ziani, Marc' Antonio, 1653–1715.

L'Alcibiade, Venetia, 1680.   Schatz 11177

Alessandro Magno in Sidone, Venetia, 1679.   Schatz 11178

Alessandro Magno in Sidone, Vicenza, 1681.   ML 50.2.A515Z3

L'amante eroe, Venetia, 1691.   Schatz 11198

L'amore figlio del merito, Venetia, 1694.   Schatz 11179

Gl'amori ministri della fortuna, Milano (1694).   Schatz 11208

Gl'amori tra gl'odii, o sia Il Ramiro in Norvegia, Venetia,
1699.   Schatz 11199

L'Atanagilda, regina di Gottia. A. T. of his L'inganno regnante.

Atenaide. *See* Zeno's Poesie drammatiche.

Chilonida, Vienna (1710).   Schatz 11204

La costanza in trionfo, Venezia, 1697.   Schatz 11180

Creonte, Venetia, 1691.   Schatz 11181

Damira placata, Venetia, 1680.   Schatz 11200

Il Domizio, Venetia, 1696.   Schatz 11182

Il duello d'amore e di vendetta, Venezia, 1700.   Schatz 11183

L'Egisto rè di Cipro, Venetia, 1698.   Schatz 11184

L'Esopo, Vienna, 1703.   Schatz 11185

Eumene, Venezia, 1697.   Schatz 11201

La Falsirena, Venetia, 1690.   Schatz 11196

La finta pazzia d'Ulisse, Venetia, 1696.   Schatz 11186

La Flora, Venetia, 1681 (with A. Sartorio).   Schatz 9495

La fuga dell' invidia (Vienna, 1701).   Schatz 11187

Il Gordiano Pio, Vienna d'Austria (1700).   Schatz 11188

Il gran Tamerlano, Venetia, 1689.   Schatz 11189·

L'inganno regnante overo L'Atanagilda, Venetia, 1688.   Schatz 11205

Leonida in Tegea, Venice, 1776 (altered version of Draghi's
opera).   Schatz 2799

Il Macedone continente. A. T. of his La virtù sublimata dal
grande.

Marte deluso, Venetia, 1691. L. T. of his La Falsirena.   Schatz 11197

Il Meleagro, Brescia, 1710.   Schatz 11202

La moglie nemica, Venetia, 1694.   Schatz 11203

La ninfa bizzarra, Modona, 1701.   Schatz 11190

Odoardo, Venezia, 1698.   Schatz 11191

La pace generosa, Venetia, 1700.   Schatz 11192

Il Ramiro in Norvegia. A. T. of his Gl'amori tra gl'odii.

I rivali generosi, Venetia, 1697.   Schatz 11206

Il Romolo, Vienna d'Austria (1702).   Schatz 11193

La Rosalinda, Venetia, 1693.   Schatz 11210

La schiava fortunata, Venetia, 1674 (mainly by Cesti).   Schatz 1782

Temistocle. *See* Zeno's Poesie drammatiche.

Il Teodosio, Venezia, 1699.   Schatz 11194

Ziani, Marc' Antonio—Continued.

Tullo Ostilio, Venetia, 1685. SCHATZ 11195

La virtù sublimata dal grande ovvero Il Macedone continente,
Venetia, 1683. L. T. of his Alessandro Magno in Sidone. SCHATZ 11209

La virtù trionfante dell' amore e dell' odio, Venetia, 1681. SCHATZ 11207

Ziani, Pietro Andrea, *ca.* 1630–1711.

L'Alciade, Venetia, 1667. SCHATZ 11211

L'amor guerriero, Venetia, 1663. SCHATZ 11220

L'Annibale in Capua, Venetia, 1661. SCHATZ 11225

L'Antigona delusa da Alceste, Milano, 1662. SCHATZ 11212

Attila, Venetia, 1672. SCHATZ 11213

Candaule, Venetia, 1680. SCHATZ 11219

Etio. A. T. of his L'innocenza risorta.

L'Eupatra, Venetia, 1655. SCHATZ 11214

Le fatiche d'Ercole per Deianira, Venetia, 1662. SCHATZ 11221

Le fortune di Rodope e Damira, Bologna, 1658. SCHATZ 11215

La guerriera Spartana, Venetia, 1654. SCHATZ 11216

L'Heraclio, Venetia, 1671. SCHATZ 11217

L'incostanza trionfante overo Il Theseo, Venetia, 1658. SCHATZ 11222

L'innocenza risorta overo Etio, Venetia, 1683. SCHATZ 11224

Gli scherzi di fortuna, Venetia, 1662. SCHATZ 11218

La Semiramide, Venetia, 1671. SCHATZ 11223

Il Theseo. A. T. of his L'incostanza trionfante.

Zimmermann, Anton, 1741–1781.

Andromeda und Perseus, Wien, 1780. SCHATZ 11234

Zingarelli, Nicola Antonio, 1752–1837.

See also Catalogue of 19th cent. librettos.

Alsinda, Milano (1785). SCHATZ 11264

Andromeda (Venezia, 1796)? SCHATZ 11265

Annibale in Torino, Torino (1792). SCHATZ 11239

Antigono, Mantova (1786) ML 50.2.A72Z4

Apelle (Venezia, 1793). SCHATZ 11266

Apelle e Campaspe, Bologna (1795). L. T. of above. SCHATZ 11267

Artaserse, Milano (1794). SCHATZ 11240

Carolina e Mexicow, Venezia (1798). SCHATZ 11268

Il conte di Saldagna, Venezia, 1795. SCHATZ 11242

Der geraubte eimer. Tr. of his La secchia rapita, Dresda,
1795. SCHATZ 11259

Gerusalemme distrutta, Firenze, 1794. SCHATZ 11244

Giulietta e Romeo, Milano (1796). SCHATZ 11247

Giulietta e Romeo, Lisboa, 1798. ML 50.2.G43Z3

Ifigenia in Aulide, Milano (1787). SCHATZ 11250

Ifigenia in Aulide, Barcellona (1799). ML 48.A5 v.16

Julie und Romeo, Botzen (1798). Tr. of his Giulietta e
Romeo. SCHATZ 11248

Meleagro, Milano (1798). SCHATZ 11254

Il mercato di Monfregoso, Milano (1792). ML 50.2.M55Z2

Il mercato di Monfregoso, Lisbona, 1795. ML 50.2.M55Z3

La morte di Cesare, Milano (1791). SCHATZ 11263

La morte di Mitridate, Venezia (1797). SCHATZ 11269

Il Pirro, Parma (1799). L. T. of: SCHATZ 11253

Pirro, rè di Epiro, Milano (1792). SCHATZ 11261

Quinto Fabio (Livorno, 1794). SCHATZ 11255

Zingarelli, Nicolla Antonio—Continued.
    Il ratto delle Sabine, Venezia, 1799.   SCHATZ 11256
    Il ritratto, Milano (1799).   SCHATZ 11257
    La secchia rapita (Milano, 1793).   SCHATZ 11258
    La secchia rapita—Der geraubte eimer, Dresda, 1795.   SCHATZ 11259

Zink (Zinck), Hardenak Otto Conrad, 1746–1832.
    Selim og Mirza, Kiøbenhavn, 1790.   SCHATZ 11272

Zoppis, Francesco.
    Il Vologeso (Lipsia, 1753).   SCHATZ 11284

Zuccari, Giovanni.
    Seleuco, Venezia (1725).   SCHATZ 11286

Zucchini, Marco.
    Cimene, Venezia, 1721 (with G. Bassani).   SCHATZ 637

Zumsteeg, Johann Rudolph, 1760–1802.
    See also Catalogue of 19th cent. librettos.
    Armide, Stuttgart (1786).   SCHATZ 11292.
    Der betrug aus liebe, oder Der schuss von Gaensewiz, Stutt-
        gart, 1780.   SCHATZ 11293
    Die geisterinsel, Altona, n. d.   SCHATZ 11294
    Tamira, Tuebingen, 1791.   SCHATZ 11295

ARIA INDEX

1639

ARIA INDEX.

ARIAS INCIDENTALLY MENTIONED.

It is advisable to refer back to the Title Catalogue in every instance, since the composer's name added to an aria in this Index by no means always signifies that the aria was composed by him.

à, a, be, ce, qu . . . Oh diavolo: Cocchi's La maestra.

A cenni tuoi sovrani: Händel's Agrippina.

A fool enjoys the sweets: Arne's An hospital for fools.

A forze di mortello: Caruso's Il matrimonio in commedia.

A gli oltraggi della sorte: Zeno's Ornospade text; also in Fischietti and Porpora's Siface.

A l'amour tout est possible: Le confident heureux.

A l'armi, a l'armi: Aldrovandini's L'odio e l'amore.

A lottery is a taxation: Seedo in The lottery.

A ma soeur, en douceur: Le docteur Sangrado.

A me tu chiami bestia: Leo and Gomes' Il nuovo D. Chisciotte.

A morire, a morir: Pollaroli's Irene.

A présent j'nons: Les amours de Bastien et Bastienne.

A quella che t'adora: Pergolesi's La contadina astuta and Tracollo medico ignorante.

A quels maux il me livre: Grétry's L'amitié à l'épreuve.

A questa pellegrina: Il giocatore (Paris, 1752).

A questa pellegrina: Il marito giogatore e la moglie bacchettona.

A questa pellegrina: Orlandini's Il giocatore.

A questa pellegrina: Vinci's Bacocco e Serpilla. *See* Il marito giogatore e la moglie bacchettona.

A questo bel segno: Anfossi's La pescatrice fedele.

A rascal, a hussy: Dibdin in The school for fathers.

A Serpina pensarete: Pergolesi's La serva padrona.

A shepherd, though I am: Rush's The royal shepherd.

A soldier is free: Gehot in The cobler of Castlebury.

A svenare il mostro: Vivaldi's Motezuma.

A tant de charmes: Lasalle d'Offemont's Bertholde à la ville.

A tanto giubilo: M. A. Bononcini's Il trionfo di Camilla, regina de' Volsci.

A telle qui t'engage: Le maître de musique.

A tout le monde: Longchamps in Comment fairec.

A trente ans jadis: Les jeunes mariés.

A un gusto da stordire: Pergolesi's Il maestro di musica.

A un sleale un traditore: Porta and Albinoni's La Mariane.

A una povera Polacca: Pergolesi's Livietta e Tracollo.

A votre âge, ce langage: Piccinni's L'esclave.

A Zerbine laissez par grace: Pergolesi's La servante maîtresse.

Abbiam penato, è ver: Hasse's Ipermestra.
Accourez, garçons joyeux: La Ruette's Le medecin de l'amour.
Ach! Ich fleh: Philidor's Tom Jones.
Ach ja, eifersucht: Grétry's Der praechtige freygebige.
Ad un povero Polacco: Pergolesi's Livietta e Tracollo and all its L. T.
Ah! ma tante, je vous prie: Philidor's Tom Jones.
Ach! mein kummervoller stand: La Borde's Die muellerin.
Ach! vergesset alle schmerzen: Monsigny's Der deserteur.
Ach! welche quaal! ach!: Grétry's Zemire und Azor.
Ach! wie ist das pferd: Grétry's Der praechtige freygebige.
Ad ogni bel diletto: Galuppi's Il paese della Cuccagna.
Ad un amante savio: Cipolla in Cimarosa's Il barone burlato.
Ad un povero Tracollo: Pergolesi's Tracollo.
Adoré, poursuivi des belles: Duni's L'école de la jeunesse.
Adzooks, old Crusty: Arnold's Two to one.
Affetti del mio sposo: Nero (Hamburg).
Aga! ces gens la faut: La nouvelle Bastienne.
Agitato dallo sdegno: Paisiello's L'idolo cinese.
Agitato gelo, e tremo: Galuppi's Il filosofo di campagna.
Ah! ah! ma cassette: Sodi's Baiocco et Serpilla.
Ah! c'est un superbe cheval: Grétry's Le magnifique.
Ah! cette ligne désigne: Rinaldo di Capua's La Bohémienne.
Ah che ne mal verace: Metastasio's Demofoonte text.
Ah che ne mal verace: Hasse's Demofoonte.
Ah d'ascoltar già parmi: Piccinni's La sciocchezza in amore.
Ah dalla gioja oppresso: Insanguine's La vedova capricciosa.
Ah! dans ces fêtes: Grétry's L'ami de la maison.
Ah! dans le siècle: Grétry's Les événements imprévus.
Ah! dans quel état: Laruette's Cendrillon.
Ah! how delightful the morning: Dibdin's School for fathers.
Ah, how sweet the rural scene: Dibdin in The captive.
Ah il flebil suono: Storace's Gli equivoci.
Ah, ma honte en est extrême: Sacchini's La colonie.
Ah meschinella, che deggo far: G. Scarlatti's L'isola disabitata.
Ah! mon coeur soupire: La maître de musique.
Ah! mon ours a pris la fuite: Rinaldo di Capua's La Bohemienne.
Ah non più gelas mi sento: pasticcio Arminio (Perez).
Ah, padre adorato: pasticcio Arminio (Perez).
Ah Pallante Pallante: Händel's Agrippina.
Ah! perfide, barbare: Sodi's Baiocco et Serpilla.
Ah! più di te confusa: Hasse's Partenope.
Ah poi che pietà: Galuppi in Ciampi's Bertoldo.
Ah! pry'thee spare me: Galuppi in Dibdin's The school for fathers.
Ah! que le sort d'une femme: Monsigny's Le cadi dupé.
Ah quel martire: Pergolesi in Le maître de musique.
Ah! quel plaisir hors: Philidor's Le diable à quatre.
Ah! quel tourment d'être sensible: Grétry's Zémire et Azor.
Ah! qu'il est affreux: La fontaine de Jouvence.
Ah! qu'une fillette: Monsigny's Félix.
Ah sposina mia carina: Boroni in Laurenti's La pupilla rapita.
Ah sta un esercito: Piccinni's Il regno della luna.
Ah Teseo! Ah del mio cor: Jommelli's Il giuoco di picchetto.
Ah think, my Lord: Seedo in The lottery.
Ah! v'là tous nos bouquets: Martini's L'amoureux de quinze ans.

Ah what avails: Fisher in Dibdin's The seraglio.

Ahi che non son sicuri: Capello's L'Eudamia.

Ahi, che parlar non posso: Piccinni's I sposi perseguitati.

Ahi que l'amour: Duni's La fee Urgele.

Ajuto buona gente: Perillo in Piccinni's L'erede riconoscinta.

Al cader di ria: Albinoni and Porta's La Mariane.

Al canto, al ballo: Caccini's Euridice.

Al caro Nume appresso: Maggiore's Statira.

Al foco d'amore: Sartorio's Orfeo a torto geloso.

Al mio ben sè tu dirai (Goldoni's Il filosofo di campagna): Garcia's La pupilla.

Al mon do qui conto: Logroscino and Barbella's L'Elmira generosa.

Al pensier de torti: Latilla's Madama Ciana.

Al tuo pensier richiama: pasticcio Il rè pastore.

Al vezzeggiar d'un volto: Cortona's Farnace.

Al zelo, che m'accendi: M. Curzio.

Alas! my Lord: Seedo in The lottery.

Alessandro, che pensi: Cesti and Bigongiari's Alessandro il vincitor di se stesso.

Alles, was ich nur erblicke: Monsigny's On ne s'avise jamais de tout.

Alme amanti, a voi ritorno: M. Curzio.

Almen la sorte arrida: Galuppi's Il Muzio Scevola.

All' amoroso ardore: Guglielmi's Il disertore.

Alla guerra, che questo: Latilla's L'isola d'amore.

Alla selva, al prato: Duni's La buona figliuola.

Alle gioie, a i diletti: Cesti's L'Argia.

Alle selve, alle campanne: Gazzaniga's La vendemmia.

Aller welt blut: Monsigny's Der deserteur.

Allons, cette heureuse journée: Darcis' La fausse peur.

Als mir das schicksal: Philidor's Der zauberer.

Altho' this humble garb: Rust and Guglielmi's Amintas.

Am baum dort: Philidor's Der zauberer.

Amant fidelle & sensible: Monsigny's Le cadi dupé.

Amata Oronta: M. A. Ziani's Il Gordiano Pio.

Ami, laisse là: Monsigny's Le roi et le fermier.

Ami, qu'en mes bras: Philidor's Tom Jones.

Amico, in questa alpestre: Ciampi's Bertoldo in corte.

Amo te sola: Hasse's Cleonice.

Amo te sola: Metastasio's Clemenza di Tito text.

Amor di marito: Leopold I in Draghi's Sulpitia.

Amor discenda: Ciampi's Bertoldo in corte.

Amor e gelosia: Nero (Hamburg).

Amor, oh che diletto: Rinaldo di Capua's La Zingara.

Amor per te mi stimola: Gassmann's Gli uccellatori.

Amor spietato arciere: Sartorio's Orfeo a torto geloso.

Amor tu reggimi: Partenio and others' Flavio Cuniberto.

Amor vien sù gli occhi: Pollaroli's L'enigma disciolto.

Amore è un ragazzo: Mayr's Labino e Carlotta.

Amore nel mio core: M. A. Bononcini's Camilla, regina de' Volsci.

Amori fuggite: Cesti's L'Argia.

Amori volate: Cesti's La Dori.

Amour, dont je ressens: Laruette's Cendrillon.

Amour, entends ma voix: Laruette's Le Guy de Chesne.

Amour, que tu me fais: La Borde's La meuniere de Gentilly.

Amusés vos jeunes: Favart's La rosiere de Salenci.

Anche da te lontano: Gasparini and Lapis' La fede in cimento.

Ancor io pensai d'amore: Hasse's Siroes, king of Persia.
And silence reigns within: Kelly's Blue-beard.
And when we come: The quaker's opera.
Angenehmstes leben: Keiser's Orpheus.
Annette au bois: Philidor's Der holzhauer.
Arcieri alati / Sù brillate: Freschi's Helena rapita da Paride.
Ardo per te d'amore: Hasse's Semiramide riconosciuta.
Arsa d'interno adore: Resta's Li tre cicisbei ridicoli.
Aspettare e non venire: Pergolesi's La serva padrona.
Assise sur le bord: Le caprice amoureux.
Astolfo poveretto: Scolari's Il viaggiatore ridicolo.
Au fond d'ma poitrine: Duni in Le docteur Sangrado.
Au milien du cours: Vadé's text Il etoit tems.
Au piège il va: Rinaldo di Capua's La Bohémienne.
Au secours. Ah! je tremble: Rinaldo di Capua's La Bohémienne.
Au sein des alarmes: Le caprice amoureux.
Auf einmal ward entzündet: Duni's Der verliebte maler.
Auprès d'Annette: Les trompeurs trompés.
Auprès d'un tendron: Audinot and Gossec's Le tonnelier.
Aure amene che spirate: Leo and Gomes's Il nuovo D. Chisciotte.
Aure belle: Vignola in Gasparini's Le regine di Macedonia.
Aure, fonti, erbetti: Mancini in Lotti's Artaserse rè di Persia.
Aurette cortesi: Franceschini's Arsinoe.
Aurimena, la tua pena: Sances's Apollo deluso (this aria by Leopold I).
Autrefois à sa maîtresse: Les amours de Bastien et Bastienne.
Autrefois la jeune Thérèse: Les amours de Bastien et Bastienne.
Aux spectateurs indulgens: Le depart de l'Opéra comique.
Avant d'obtenir ma bergère: Laruette's Le Guy de Chesne.
Avec adresse, à ta maîtresse: Sellitti in Les Chinois.
Avec moi viens: Le docteur Sangrado.
Avec soin j'ai sçu: Le docteur Sangrado.
Avec une epouse chérie: Gossec's Toinon et Toinette.
Avete trovato sto: Piccinni, Logroscino, and Insanguine's La furba burlata.
Away with the fables philosophers hold: Purcell's Amphitryon.
Away with tyrant laws: Arnold in Dibdin's The seraglio.
Ay, ay, ay: Dezède's Julie.
Bannissons le soupçon jaloux: Kohault's Le serrurier.
Barbare stelle infide: Buini's Le frenesie d'amore.
Basta cosi, t'intendo: Resta's Li tre cicisbei ridicoli.
Basta dir che la mia: Albinoni and Porta's La Mariane.
Basti a lei, che per: Orlandini and Mancini's Artaserse.
Be by your friends advised: Midas.
Be still, you monsters: Sheeles in The generous free-mason.
Bel gioia, gioia soave: See Il rè infante, Intermezzi.
Bel visino graziosino: Galuppi's La forza d'amore.
Believe me dear aunt: Arne in Love in a village.
Bell' alme innamorate: Leo in Orefici's La Rosilla.
Bella dea, che al sol nascente: Franceschini's Arsinoe.
Bella destra: Nero (Hamburg).
Bella mano, or: Cocchi's La maestra.
Bella mi parto: Vignola in Gasparini's Le regine di Macedonia.
Bella mia, se son tuo sposo: Pergolesi's Il maestro di musica, also in his Il finto pazzo.
Bella mia, se son tuo sposo: Pergolesi in Galuppi's Il mondo nella luna.
Bella ninfa fugitiva: Corsi's Dafne (text by Rinuccini).

Bella prova de la mia fede: A. Scarlatti's Il prigioniero fortunato.

Bella tu sei di questo core: Jommelli's I rivali delusi.

Belle catene: D. Scarlatti in his and Pullaroli's L'Irene.

Belle rose, que j'arrose: La fête du château.

Beltà costante: *See* Il rè infante, Intermezzi.

Ben mio tù non vedrai: A. Scarlatti's Il prigioniero fortunato.

Benchè innocente sia: Jommelli's Demofoonte (1753).

Bendato arcier: interpolated in Keiser's Der sich raechende Cupido.

Bene mio, ca già: Fischietti in Le chiajese cantarine.

Bey meinem lieben topf: Neefe's Adelheit von Veltheim.

Bey meiner schwarzen seele: Dittersdorf's Hokus Pokus.

Bey mir wancken: Keiser's Orpheus.

Bien loin d'oser douter: Fridzeri's Les souliers mors-dorés.

Bien que nous courrious: Cambefort in Le ballet du temps.

Bin ich gleich vom bauernstande: Dittersdorf's Hieronimus Knicker.

Birbante cò creanza: Piccinni, Logroscino and Insanguine's La furba burlata.

Bouquet pour Annette: Les trompeurs trompés.

Bramar di perdere: Hasse's Artaserse.

Bring, ye tedious hours: Piccinni's The accomplish'd maid.

Brooks to your sources: Corri in Fontainebleau.

But pr'ythee spare me: Dibdin in The captive.

By Masons art: Carey in The generous free-mason.

C'est bien dit: La Ruette's Le medecin de l'amour.

C'est cependant le cours: Audinot-Gossec's Le tonnelier.

C'est dans le bois: Kohault's La bergère des Alpes.

C'est ici que Rose respire: Monsigny's Rose et Colas.

C'est pour jamais: Les amants trompés.

C'est pour le dieu du vin: Audinot-Gossec's Le tonnelier.

C'est un traître: Sodi's Baiocco et Serpilla.

C'est une misère: Duni's La fée Urgele.

Ça ira: Shield's The picture of Paris.

Caduca fiamma: Caccini's Il rapimento di Cefalo.

Candorn soll: Duni's Die schnitter.

Cangia il cielo: A. Scarlatti's Il prigioniero fortunato.

Cantan lieti: interpolated in Keiser's Der sich raechende Cupido.

Capace di più amarti: Leo and Gomes' Il nuovo D. Chisciotte.

Cara Drusilla: Cocchi's La maestra and its L. T. La scaltra governatrice.

Cara, se un core amante: Jommelli's Ezio.

Care luci, che regnate: pasticcio Arminio.

Care pupille amate: Gluck's Tigrane.

Care selve amiche piante: Fioravanti in Bianchi's La fedeltà tra le selve.

Cari occhietti vezzosetti: Guglielmi's L'inganno amoroso.

Cari sassi: Vignola in Gasparini's Le regine di Macedonia.

Caro . . . l'affanno mio: Hasse's Partenope.

Caro mio bene addio: Pescetti in the pasticcio Ezio.

Caro perdonami, placa: Pergolesi's Livietta e Tracollo and its L. T.

Caro signor maestro: Pergolesi's Il maestro di musica.

Caro sposo, amata speme: pasticcio Arminio (Perez).

Ce cher Bailli: Champein's Le poète supposé.

Ce n'est plus à Cythère: La nouvelle école des femmes.

Ce que je dis est la vérité: Monsigny's Le roi et le fermier.

Celia mia, meglio: Logroscino in Sciroli's Li nnamorate correvate.

Certi amorini asciutti: Latilla's Polipodio e Rucchetta.

Cerco invano in questo: Sarti's Gli equivoci svelati.

Ces oiseaux de passage: Duni's Le milicien.

Cet étang, qui s'étend: Favart's La rosiere de Salenci text.

Ch'v'à schiaffato ncanna: Piccinni, Logroscino and Insanguine's La furba burlata.

Chante un dieu: La nouvelle Bastienne.

Chanter pour l'aimable Annette: Les trompeurs trompés.

Chantez, dansez, amusez-vous: Grétry's La rosière de Salenci.

Chantez, sautez: L'amour impromptu.

Chantons deux époux: Grétry's Lucile.

Chantons le dieu qui règne: Rousseau's Le devin du village (Geneva, 1796 ed.).

Charmant espoir qui nous: in Pergolesi's La servante maitresse.

Charmant objet de ma flâme: Philidor's Le maréchal ferrant.

Che bella cosa ch'è: Fabrizi and others' I tre gobbi rivali.

Che d'è chesto: Pulli in Vinci's La mogliere fedele.

Che del cor son dolce amore: Orlandini and Mancini's Artaserse.

Che giorno di contento: Fioravanti in Bianchi's La fedeltà tra le selve.

Che legge tiranna: Jommelli's Tito Manlio.

Che mai risponderti: Metastasio's text Demofoonte.

Che mai risponderti: Jommelli's Demofoonte.

Che orror, che spavento: Rinaldo di Capua's La Zingara.

Che pena, che affanno: Monza's Sesostri rè d'Egitto.

Che piacere che diletto: Gasparini's Pollastrella & Parpagnacco.

Che sia cortese e placido: Piccinni, Logroscino, and Insanguine's La furba burlata.

Che siate maledette: Capello's L'Eudamia.

Che smania . . . che affanno: Cimarosa's La villana riconosciuta.

Cher Bacchus, c'est assez: Mondonville's Bacchus et Erigone.

Cher Lubin, si tu m'aimes: Vachon's Les femmes et le secret.

Chez l'étranger, ou apprécie: Fridzeri's Les souliers mors-dorés.

Chi cade dint' all' acqua: Pulli in Vinci's La mogliere fedele.

Chi da un bel volto: Porta's L'Issipile.

Chi è rubello ad amor: Pollaroli's L'Oreste in Sparta.

Chi llo birbo malenato: Logroscino in Sciroli's Li nnamorate correvate.

Chi mai provò in amore: Vinci, Jommelli, and others' Il Catone in Utica.

Chi mai saper desia: Marchi's La generosità politica.

Chi non prova d'Amor: Cesti's La Dori.

Chi non sa, che gran: Hasse's Demetrio (1748).

Chi non sà che sia: Chelleri's Temistocle.

Chi t'ama comprendi: Vivaldi and Galeazzi's L'odio vinto dalla costanza.

Chi troppo ad amor crede: Galuppi's Il mondo alla roverscia.

Chi và a prender la consorte: Galuppi's La lavandara.

Chiama l'amante fido: Albinoni's Gl'eccessi della gelosia.

Ciascun mi dice: Ciampi's Bertoldo, Bertoldino e Cacasenno.

Ciel più tranquillo: Orlandini's Adelaide.

Climène, au cabaret: Audinot-Gossec's Le tonnelier.

Co i lacci del tuo amor: Vignola in Gasparini's Le regine di Macedonia.

Colà sul praticello: Latilla's La finta cameriera.

Colà sul praticello: Latilla in Pergolesi's Le maître de musique.

Colin a des yeux charmants: Philidor's Der holzhauer.

Colin revient à sa bergère: Rousseau's Le devin du village.

Colin un jour sur la: Fridzeri's Les deux miliciens.

Colins augen sind sehr schön: Philidor's Der holzhauer.

Collà sul praticello: Hasse's Don Tabarrano.

Combattono a vicenda: Orlandini and Mancini's Artaserse.

Come al Polo si rivolge: See Il rè infante, Intermezzi.

Come all' amiche arene: Metastasio's Semiramide text (original version).

Come all' amiche arene: Jommelli's Semiramide.

Come chi giocca alle palle: Pergolesi's Il maestro di musica.

Come hither my country 'Squire: Carey's The honest Yorkshire-man.

Come learn by this: Carey's The honest Yorkshire-man.

Come nave in mezzo: Porpora's Siface.

Come sento in un momento: Gasparini and others' L'Alciade.

Come then, pining: Ciampi in Dibdin's The school for fathers.

Comme! chisso che dice: Cimarosa's La baronessa Stramba.

Comme ou voit notre moulin: La servante justifiée.

Con fiemma io ve lo dico: Piccinni's L'astratto.

Con la mia villanella: Rust's La contadina in çorte.

Con la scorta de la vendetta: Freschi's Helena rapita da Paride.

Con la speme del goder: Rinaldo di Capua's La Zingara.

Con tanto stranutare: Il giocatore.

Con tanto stranutare: Il vecchio pazzo in amore.

Con voi divide: Paisiello's Nina.

Confusi i miei pensieri: Jommelli's Tito Manlio.

Conservati fedele: Orlandini's Adelaide.

Contento tu sarai: Pergolesi's La serva padrona, also in his Il ladro convertito per amore and in Il giocatore (Paris, 1752).

Conti-con voi: Paisiello's Nina.

Contro di quell' audace: Salieri's La calamita de' cuori.

Contro l'idolo adorato: Porpora's Adelaide.

Cor mio inzuccherato: Leo and Gomes' Il nuovo D. Chisciotte.

Coronato il crin d'alloro: Palella in Hasse's Tigrane.

Corpo di Bacco Son Parpagnacco: Goldoni's Favola de' tre gobbi text.

Corpo di Bacco Son Parpagnacco: Fabrizi and others' I tre gobbi rivali.

Così fugge e spaventosa: Ciampi's Bertoldo in corte (Paris, 1753).

Così per terra: Rinaldo di Capua's La smorfiosa.

Costei, per quanto scorgo: Guglielmi's L'inganno amoroso and Le due gemelle.

Courir les bois: Monsigny's Félix.

Cours à ta belle: La fausse aventuriere.

Creder à femine è vanità: Cesti's Orontea, regina d'Egitto.

Credi mi nel suo petto: Vinci, Jommelli and others' Il Catone in Utica.

Cricca mio, colla cognata: Cipolla in Cimarosa's Il barone burlato.

Crude stelle più serene: Perez' Demetrio.

Crudel tiranno ingrato: Cimarosa's La baronessa Stramba.

Cueillons ces cerises: Wicht in the pasticcio La vallée de Montmorency.

Cupid, sure, of cunning: Shield's The choleric fathers.

Custodite per mia figlia: Gasparini's Tamerlano.

D'amore nella rete: Rinaldo di Capua's La serva sposa.

D'antico Amor le faci:̈ Nero (Hamburg).

D'aversa sorte: Jommelli's La Didone abbandonata (1747).

D'ogni amator la fede: Hasse's Siroe.

D'ogni core la bellezza: Latilla's Madama Ciana.

D'ogni timor già sento: Piccinni's La scaltra spiritosa.

D'un faraut de note quartier: Les racoleurs.

D'un infelice amante: Jommelli's Il giuoco di picchetto.

Da me che più volete: Cesti's Orontea, regina d'Egitto.

Da me che vorresti: Jommelli and Zanetti's Tito Manlio.

Da noi il ciel più: Pietragrua's Il pastor fido.

Da più affetti combattuta: Albinoni's L'Ardelinda.

Da questa linea: Gasparini's Parpagnacco.

Da tanti affanni oppressa: Paisiello's L'idolo cinese.

Daignés donc m'apprendre: Le mauvais plaisant.

Dal suo gentil sembiante: Hasse's Demetrio.

Dal tuo costante amore: Perillo in Piccinni's L'erede riconosciuta.

Dal tuo gentil sembiante: Vinci's Medea riconosciuta.

Dalle pupille della mia bella: Vignola in Gasparini's Le regine di Macedonia.

Dangers unknown impending: Sarti in The haunted tower.

Dans ces floeurs je vois: Piccinni's La buona figliuola.

Dans l'espérance du plaisir: Rinaldo di Capua's La Bohémienne.

Dans l'excès de sa tendresse: Les amants trompés.

Dans la brûlante saison: Grétry's Der hausfreund.

Dans le sein de la liberté: Philidor's Le sorcier.

Dans ma cabane obscure: Rousseau's Le devin du village.

Dans ma cabane obscure: Rousseau in the pasticcio La vallée de Montmorency.

Dans mon coeur: Piccinni's La buona figliuola.

Dans mon coeur s'élève: parody Hippolite et Aricie.

Dans nos bals: Jadin in Comment faire?

Dans un nouveau parentage: Rousseau's Daphnis et Chloé.

Dans un verger Colinette: Audinot and Gossec's Le tonnelier.

Das schicksal bringt mich: Gluck's Die unvermuthéte zusammenkunft.

De ce linge que je repasse: Philidor's Le sorcier.

De ce qui n'est pas: Coignet's Pigmalion.

De ce volage Colas: Les amours de Bastien et Bastienne.

De cori e del' alme: Perti's Il furio Camillo.

De dolci affetti miei: Piccinni's La scaltra letterata.

De l'amour je sens la flamme: Duni's Le peintre amoureux de son modèle.

De l'ordre exprès: Méreaux's La ressource comique.

De la gloria e de l'amor: Pollaroli's Irene.

De la richesse l'éclat: Gossec's Les pêcheurs.

De même qu'une étincelle: Le trompeur trompé.

De Phaeton la fin: Boyer's Les étrennes de l'amour.

De tes froideurs: Boyer's Les étrennes de l'amour.

De tes pleurs, tendre turore: Le bouquet du roi.

De tous les coeurs: Le trompeur trompé.

De tous nos projets: Grétry's La garde passe.

Dear Sir, be not: Seedo in The lottery.

Deggio credesti o gelosia: Partenio's Flavio Cuniberto.

Deh concedi, o caro padre: Perillo in Piccinni's L'erede riconosciuta.

Deh lasciami in pace: Vivaldi's Artabano rè de Parti.

Deh non lasciarmi, ingrata: Pergolesi's Il ladro convertito per amore.

Deh perdona, o padre: Hasse's Demofoonte.

Deh placati al fine: Jommelli in his, Vinci and others' Il Catone in Utica.

Deh respirar lasciatemi: Hasse's Artaserse.

Deh scendi Amore dal carro: Piccinni's Le finte gemelle.

Deh ti plachi: Hasse's Don Tabarrano.

Del cielo sdegnato: Hasse's Demofoonte.

Del destin non vi lagnate: Metastasio's Olimpiade text.

Del destin non vi lagnate: Jommelli's Il giuoco di picchetto.

Del destino invan: Gazzaniga's La vendemmia.

Del mio tradito core: Sacchini's Creso.

Delizie de l'alma: Pollaroli's L'Oreste in Sparta.

Dell' aurora al primo albore: Chelleri's Temistocle.

Della gran bucina: Jommelli's Fetonte.

Della mia sorte altera: Fischietti's Siface.

Delle donne il core: Perillo in Piccinni's L'erede riconosciuta.

Denken hast Du mich gelehret: Grétry's Die freundschaft auf der probe.
Der milord wies mir: Monsigny's Der koenig und der pachter.
Des biens que votre main: Duni's Les moissonneurs.
Des bouquets le plus simple: Les trompeurs trompés.
Dès ce soir l'hymen: Sacchini's La colonie.
Des reichtums pracht: Monsigny's Der koenig und der pachter.
Des rigueurs d'un cruel destin: Laruette's Cendrillon.
Désormais, je sçaurai mieux: Le maître de musique.
Destrier che all' armi: Cocchi's La scuola moderna.
Destrier, che all' armi usato: Piccinni's Le contadine bizzarre.
Deviez vous m'éclaircir: La Ruette's Le medecin de l'amour.
Di galanti cicisbei: Vento and Gassmann's La Zingara.
Di morte non cura: Vignola in Gasparini's Le regine di Macedonia.
Di occulto arcano: Händel's Agrippina.
Di pena si forte: Metastasio's Ipermestra text.
Di pena si forte: Jommelli's Demofoonte (1753).
Di potermi vendicar: Il giocatore (Paris, 1752).
Di qua vedi un milordino: Guglielmi's La pastorella nobile.
Di re si possente: Brunetti's Bertoldo e Bertoldino.
Di sdegno m'accende: Scolari's Il viaggiatore ridicolo.
Di Venere il monte: Gasparini's L'astrologo.
Dice benissimo: Anfossi's Gli amanti canuti.
Dich hab ich, Dich: Philidor's Tom Jones.
Dico bene—certo adore: Fabrizi in I tre gobbi rivali.
Die liebe fordert: Philidor's Der hufschmied.
Die prinzessin zu entdecken: Hiller's Lisuart und Dariolette.
Die wache zieht schon vorbey: Grétry's Die beiden geizigen.
Dieser teich malet: Das rosenmaedchen.
Dieu d'amour, en ce jour: Grétry's Les mariages samnites.
Dieu! quel paix: Lasalle d'Offemont's Bertholde à la ville.
Digli, che peni e frema: Jommelli's Bajazet.
Dille pur che il suo: Hasse's Siroes, king of Persia.
Dimmi a me: Pergolesi's Il finto pazzo.
Dimmi Amor, che t'hò fatt' io: Cesti's Orontea, regina d'Egitto.
Dirai all' idol mio: Gluck's L'Ipolito.
Dirai per mè: Albinoni's L'amor di figlio non conosciuto.
Dirò che fida sei: Jommelli's Didone abbandonata.
Disperato quisto core: Vignola in Gasparini's Le regine di Macedonia.
Disprezzata, abbandonata: Latilla's Madama Ciana.
Divertirsi a spese d'altri: Jommelli's I rivali delusi.
Do not ask me if: The devil of a duke.
Doit être belle: Coignet's Pigmalion.
Doje note solamente: Logroscino in Le chiajese cantarine.
Dolce ben mio: Leo in Orefici's La Rosilla.
Dolce mia vita: Keiser's Orpheus.
Dolce stral del dio: Mancini's Perichetta e Bertone.
Donn' moi ta main: La nouvelle Bastienne.
Donna son, ma non m'inganno: Paisiello's La semplice fortunata.
Donna, vi lascio il cor: G. Scarlatti's I portentosi effetti della Madre Natura.
Donne belle avete il vanto: Fischietti's Il signor dottore.
Donne belle che bramate: Amor mascherato (see Pergolesi's La servante maîtresse).
Dormiva il mio pastore: Guglielmi's La villanella ingentilita.
Dov'e Dorina: Paisiello's Gli avventurieri and Il re Teodoro.
Dove spero aver la sorte: Leo in Orefici's La Rosilla.

Dovea svenarti allora: Metastasio's Catone in Utica text.

Dovea svenarti allore: Hasse's Siroes, king of Persia.

Dread parent of despair: Sarti in The haunted tower.

Dre's l'instant que je vis: Dezède's Les trois fermiers.

Drusillina: Cocchi's La scaltra governatrice.

Du grausame schoene: Keiser's Claudius.

Du jeune objet que j'adore: Le poirier.

Du moment qu'on aime: Grétry's Zémire et Azor.

Du printemps qui vient: Duni's La clochette.

E destin troppo infelice: Sarti's I pretendenti delusi.

È follia, se nascondete (paraphrased from Metastasio's Catone in Utica): Vinci in the pasticcio Orfeo (Rolli)

E gran felicità goder: Cesti's La Dori.

E gran pena amar: Freschi's Giulio Cesare trionfante.

E n'ancunia sto core: Leo in Vinci's La mogliere fedele.

E nemico e non amante: Sciroli's La smorfiosa.

E' no scuoglio chisto core: Sellitti in Vinci's La mogliere fedele.

È prezzo leggero: Fiorillo's Alessandro nell' Indie.

E se dippiù ti chiedi: Piccinni, Logroscino, and Insanguine's La furba burlata.

E' soccorso d'incognita mano: Metastasio's Demofoonte text.

E specie di tormento: Metastasio's Temistocle text.

E specie di tormento: Rinaldo di Capua's La Zingara.

E tu malantrino: Piccinni, Logroscino, and Insanguine's La furba burlata.

E un dolce tesoro: Galuppi's Il mondo alla roversa.

E un grandissimo piacere: Fischietti's Il signor dottore.

E vero che oppresso: Metastasio's text Adriano in Siria (Original version).

Ecco Alceo guerrier novello: Cesti's L'Argia.

Ecco disciolti i lacci: Il giocatore (Paris, 1752).

Ecco il povero Tracollo: Pergolesi's Livietta e Tracollo and its L. T.

Edler friede sey willkommen: Keiser's Der bey dem allgemeinen welt-friede . . . geschlossene tempel des Janus.

Egli è ver che son: Gazzaniga's La vendemmia.

Eh bien! Finiras tu?: in Pergolesi's La servante maîtresse.

Eh Madame qu' attendez-vous: Vadé's text Il étoit tems.

Eh, mais ne fait-il pas?: Pergolesi's La servante maîtresse.

Ei d'amor quasi delira: Hasse's La Semiramide riconosciuta.

Eifersucht, argwohn und verdacht: Kohault's Der schlosser.

Ein alter mann von euren jahren: Audinot and Gossec's Der fassbinder.

Ein büttner alt: Audinot and Gossec's Der fassbinder.

Ein gärtner ist: Philidor's Der verkleidete liebhaber.

Ein solches herz zu kränken: Monsigny's Der deserteur.

Einen bach, der fliesst: Gluck's Die unvermuthete zusammenkunft.

Einen weinstock: Audinot and Gossec's Der fassbinder.

El io più nõ appare: A. Scarlatti's Bassiano.

Ella può credermi: Rinaldo di Capua's La Zingara.

En amour un tel hommage: Piccinni's L'esclave.

En grand silence: Philidor's Le diable à quatre.

En tourbillon, un papillon: Le caprice amoureux.

En revenant de Clarenton: Audinot-Gossec's Le tonnelier.

Endlich singt der gott der liebe: Duni's Der verliehte maler.

Enfans voilà votre: Philidor's Le bon fils.

Enfin j'ai découvert: parody Hippolite et Aricie.

Entends ma voix: Dezède's Blaise et Babet.

Epouse aimante: Sellitti and others' Les Chinois.

Er hat längst diesen trieb: Grétry's Silvain.

Es war einst ein vogel: Monsigny's Roschen und Colas.

Escimi tutto in lagrime: Albinoni and Porta's La Mariane.

Esprit farouche, rien: La nouvelle Bastienne.

Euch ihr schoenen augen: in Keiser's Die ueber die liebe triumphirende weissheit.

Examinez sa grace: =Tre giorni son che Nina in Rinaldo di Capua's La Bohémienne.

Ey, Sie müssen sich ja schämen: Dittersdorf's Hieronimus Knicker.

Fabrizio amabile, io parto: Galuppi's L'Arcadia in Brenta.

Faengt der stahl: Philidor's Der zauberer.

Farewell, my Lapstone: Shield in The cobler of Castlebury and in Love in a village.

Farewell ye hills: Seedo in The lottery.

Farò vendetta si: Albinoni and Porta's La Mariane.

Faut attendre avec patience: Dezède's Les trois fermiers.

Felice ai dì sereni: Araja in the pasticcio Orfeo (Rolli)

Fell war: Carter's Just in time.

Femme qu' on offense: Philidor's Le soldat magicien.

Feriteme, piagatemi: Galuppi's Il mondo alla roversa.

Fia quel semplice augelletto: Cortona's Farnace.

Fidi amanti fortunati: Maggiore's Statira.

Fiero addio: Vignola in Gasparini's Le regine di Macedonia.

Fiero Pluto de l'Inferno: See Il rè infante, Intermezzi.

Figlia, amico, io vado: Jommelli in his, Vinci and others' Il Catone in Utica.

Figlia, il cielo ti destina: Paisiello's Gli avventurieri and Il re Teodoro.

Figlia presto monta: Galuppi's La forza d'amore.

Fill ev'ry man his cup: F. Giardini in The two misers.

Fille à mon âge: Le docteur Sangrado.

Fin a tanto che uscrete: Tritto's Li due gemelli.

Finche suona il ritornello: Pergolesi's Il maestro di cappella.

Fiume, ch'alterno abbonda: Cocchi's La maestra.

Fiume che altero: Latilla's L'ambizione delusa.

Fiumicel, soave erbetta: Guglielmi's Li fratelli Pappamosca.

Flagellate: A. Scarlatti's Il prigioniero fortunato.

Fled is my love: A fool's preferment.

Fly, Cupid, fly: The devil of a duke.

Folli amanti: A. Scarlatti's Il prigioniero fortunato.

For fortune's like: Arnold in Hunt the slipper.

For moments to view: Paisiello in Shield's Lock and key.

For when I dwelt in Boston bay: "Yankee Doodle" tune in Dibdin's A match for a widow.

Forte, e lieto a morte: Gasparini's Il Bajazet.

Fortunati miei pensieri: Pollaroli's L'Ibraim sultano.

Fra buttiello fortantiello: Logroscino and Barbella's L'Elmira generosa.

Fra dubbiosi affetti miei: Piccinni's L'astratto.

Fra i dolci affetti miei: Traetta in Jommelli's Ifigenia in Aulide.

Fra il tumulto de' pensieri: Hasse's Demetrio (1748).

Fra lo splendor nel trono: Jommelli's Didone abbandonata (1747).

Fra noi scende Imeneo: Cocchi's La scaltra governatrice.

Fra tante mie pene: Bernardini's La schiava astuta.

Frà tanti pensieri di regno: Hasse's Demetrio (1740).

Frà tue ritorte: Martinengo's L'Arsiade.

Fratello Sesto mio: Guglielmi's Li fratelli Pappamosca.

Frema pur avverso il fato: Sarti's Giulio Sabino.

Fremi e pensa: Vivaldi and Galeazzi's L'odio vinto dalla costanza.

Friendship claims the name: Bertoni in Shield's Robin Hood.

From clime to clime: Arne in The summer's tale.

Fu di rè comando: Orlandini's Antigona.

Fugge e vola: Lotti and Vignola's L'inganno vinto dalla ragione.

Fugge, e vola: Orlandini and Mancini's Artaserse.

Fuggi . . . che fò . . . s'arresta: Cimarosa's La baronessa Stramba.

Fuggi dagli occhj miei: pasticcio Arminio (Perez).

Gelosia, non posso più: Freschi and Navarra's Elena rapita da Paride.

Gelosia non tormentarmi: Freschi's Helena rapita da Paride.

Geneigtes geschicke: Keiser's Der hochmuethige . . . Croesus.

Già colmo di piacer: Sellitti's Cinese rimpatriato.

Già della morte il gelo: Perez' Demetrio.

Già fucina è questo petto: Jommelli's Il giuoco del picchetto.

Già la vittima fatale: Traetta in Jommelli's Ifigenia in Aulide.

Già mi fà Galeno: Sciroli's La smorfiosa.

Già tutto valore: Nero (Hamburg).

Gieb, grausames geschick: Hiller's Lisuart und Dariolette.

Gioja mia, devo partire: Goldoni's Amor fà l'uomo cieco text.

Giovani cari amanti: Cocchi's La scuola moderna.

Giove vieni: interpolated in Keiser's Der sich raechende Cupido.

Giovinetti lascivi: Cesti's Orontea, regina d'Egitto.

Give me back my heart: Arnold in The summer's tale.

Glaube mir, was ich: Grétry's Silvain.

Glaubt, die meisten freunde: Philidor's Der gaertner von Sidon.

Gli armenti suoi raccoglie: Paisiello's Nina.

Gli sbirri: Cocchi's La mascherata and La scaltra governatrice.

Glücklich ist der, den: Philidor's Der gaertner von Sidon.

Go, and, on my truth: Vento in Dibdin's The school for fathers.

Go, naughty man: Arne in Love in a village.

Grace, sois plus traitable: Pergolesi in Le maître de musique.

Grandi, e ver son: Leo's Olimpiade in Ciampi's Bertoldo in corte (Paris, 1753).

Grata sono al tuo bel: Jommelli in his, Vinci, and others' Il Catone in Utica.

Grazia ad amore: Cocchi's La maestra.

Great Amurath all hearts: Charke in The generous free-mason.

Grida vendetta Amor: Orlandini and Mancini's Artaserse.

Groves and woods: Eccles in Wonders in the sun.

Guardami in volto, e poi: Galuppi's Il marchese villano.

Guerra, guerra, voglio guerra: D. Scarlatti in his and Pullaroli's Irene.

Guillot un jour: Dezède's L'erreur d'un moment.

Ha un gusto da morire: Latilla and Pergolesi's Orazio.

Hark! I hear the midnight owl: Lampe's Dragoness.

Hé comment ne pas le chérir: Grétry's Silvain.

He found me in a country: "Yankee Doodle" tune in Dibdin's A match for a widow.

Heaving of the lead: Shield's Hartford-Bridge.

Hélas, j'ai répandu mon lait: Duni's Les deux chasseurs et la laitière.

Hélas! Tu t'en vas: Les amours de Bastien et Bastienne.

Hence with caution: Lionel and Clarissa.

Henry cull'd the flowrets: Sacchini in Shield's Rosina.

Herr! Sie werden übel fahren: Dittersdorf's Hieronimus Knicker (Vulpius version)

Heureuse paix, tranquille indifférence: Destouches' Issé.

Heureuse paix, tranquille indifférence: Destouches in Jommelli's La critica, La conversazione and Il giuoco di picchetto.

Hier ist das kleine milchmädchen: Duni's Das milchmaedchen und die beiden jaeger.

Hier wohnt sie: Monsigny's Roschen und Colas.

Hist, soft; let's hear: Dibdin in The school for fathers.

Hò ragione, si signor: Rinaldo di Capua's La Zingara.

Hoert, wenn ihr wollt: Gassmann in his and Paisiello's Don Quischott von Mancia.

Hoffe noch, gekraencktes herz: Keiser's Der hochmuethige . . . Croesus.

Holde goettin glimmer hertzen: Keiser's Die verdammte staatsucht.

Honneur au docteur Sangrado: La Ruette in Le docteur Sangrado.

How brimful of nothing: Carey in The coffee-house.

How can you inhuman: Dibdin's The school for fathers.

How cursedly vext: Arne in Dibdin's The school for fathers.

How much superior beauty awes: Howard in Love in a village.

How hapless is: Seeds in The lottery.

How smoothly glides: Arne's An hospital for fools.

How stands the glass around: Shield's The siege of Gibraltar.

How sweet! how fresh: Paxton in Fontainebleau.

I am in truth: Carey's The honest Yorkshire-man.

I can't for my life: Philidor in Dibdin's The deserter.

I'd have you to know: Dibdin's The deserter.

I found my Caelia: The fool turn'd critick.

I simply wait for your commands: Arnold in Dibdin's The seraglio.

I'll fly these groves: Dibdin's The deserter.

I'll lay me down: A fool's preferment.

I'll range around: Damon and Phillida and Love in a riddle.

I'll sail upon the dog-star: A fool's preferment.

I've often heard: Seedo in The lottery.

I wonder, I'm sure: Dibdin's The school for fathers.

Ich bin ein musikant: Jommelli's La critica.

Ich geh gern: Duni's Die schnitter.

Ich weiss nicht, ob die schwester-liebe: Grétry's Silvain.

If a rival thy character: Carey in Midas.

If in the courts your suit: Midas.

If life can yield: Arne's An hospital for fools.

If thou wilt give: The fool's preferment.

If 'tis true, that once: The village opera.

If to me: Anfossi in Shield's Robin Hood.

Ihr, die ihr meint: Monsigny's On ne s'avise jamais de tout.

Ihr herren, ihr verlangt: Gassmann in his and Paisiello's Don Quischott von Mancia.

Ihr männer, die ihr: Philidor's Der holzhauer.

Il cor mi sento: Galuppi's La forza d'amore.

Il dardo di Cupido: Ziani's Marte deluso.

Il destin già s'è placato: M. A. Ziani in Draghi's Leonida in Tegea.

Il Dio d'amore: Orlandini and Mancini's Artaserse.

Il étoit un oiseau gris: Monsigny's Rose et Colas.

Il étoit une fille: Blaise's Annette et Lubin.

Il faut cesser d'être sévère: Darcis' La fausse peur.

Il fiero mi tormenta: Galuppi's Berenice.

Il fuggir, cara mia vita: pasticcio Arminio (Perez).

Il m'a démis l'alouette: Les Chinois.

Il mio cor non si spaventa: Gasparini's L'amor generoso.

Il mio core ingelosito: Albinoni's Gl'eccessi della gelosia.

Il modo è questo: Latilla's Madama Ciana.

Il n'est pis que l'eau: La Borde's La meuniere de Gentilly.

Il nochiero coraggioso: Vivaldi's Motezuma.

Il padre amante contro: Orlandini's La fedeltà coronata.

Il punto tuo finale: Cimarosa's La baronessa Stramba.

Il Signor conte che venga: Piccinni's L'incostante and Il volubile.

Il suo leggiadro viso: Jommelli's Demofoonte.

Il vincitore: Lascia: Leo in Orefici's La Rosilla.

Im wankenden kahne: Grétry's Das rosenfest zu Salenci.

Immortal pow'rs protect me: Lionel and Clarissa.

Imparare non voglio: Galuppi's Il paese della Cuccagna.

In che ti offende: Jommelli in his, Vinci and others' Il Catone in Utica.

In emblem I am: Dibdin in The captive.

In libertate lasciami: Leo in Orefici's La Rosilla.

In mezzo a mille straggi: Galuppi's La forza d'amore.

In mezzo a tanti affanni: pasticcio Il rè pastore.

In quel volto siede: Galuppi's Il mondo alla roverscia.

In questo minuto: Paisiello's La grotta di Trofonio.

In sen più non scintilla: pasticcio Stratonica.

In tanti affanni miei: Piccinni's La buona figliuola.

In throng from all parts: Spofforth in Salomon's Windsor castle.

In un mar di tante pene: Sarti's Mitridate a Sinope.

In vain you attempt: Arne in The summer's tale.

In vain you mention: Carey's The honest Yorkshire-man.

In yonder cowslip: A fool's preferment.

Indeed, forsooth: Scolari in Dibdin's The school for fathers.

Indulgent pow'rs, if ever: Lionel and Clarissa.

Ineffabile ardore: Caccini's Il rapimento di Cefalo.

Infelice e sventurato: Metastasio's Didone abbandonata text (Original version).

Ingegnoso è pur amore: Buini and Chelleri's La pace per amore.

Ingrat, je romps ma chaîne: Le maître de musique.

Ingrata mi sprezzi: Predieri's Scipione il giovane.

Ingrate, tu me fuis: Sodi's Baiocco et Serpilla.

Innocente sai, che sono: Galuppi's Il paese della Cuccagna.

Io cchiù nesciuno: Piccinni, Logroscino, and Insanguine's La furba burlata.

Io conosco d'ogni amante: Scolari's Il viaggiatore ridicolo.

Io già sento: Il marito giogatore e la moglie bacchettona.

Io già sento: Orlandini's Il geocatore.

Io già sento: Vinci's Bacocco e Serpilla. See Il marito giogatore e la moglie bacchettona.

Io ho un vespaio: Galuppi's Il mondo nella luna.

Io mi sento dal diletto: Cocchi's La scuola moderna.

Io mi sento in mezzo al core: Piccinni's L'astratto.

Io non so cangiar amor: Leopold I in Draghi's Leonida in Tegea.

Io pensavo innamorarmi: Cesti's L'Argia.

Io però non son di quelle: Mancini's Perichetta e Bertone.

Io so qual pena: F. Giardini in the pasticcio Cleonice.

Io sono guerriero: Gasparini's L'astrologo.

Io sono stata in Ascoli: Jommelli's Il giuoco del picchetto.

Io sono un uomo docile: Scolari's Il viaggiatore ridicolo.

Io sono una donzella: Sellitti's Cinese rimpatriato.

Io sono una ragazza: Cocchi's La maestra.

Io tradirti! e con qual cuore: Maraucci in Le chiajese cantarine.

Io·veggo in lontananza: Fischietti's Siface (from Metastasio's Semiramide text).

Io veggo un' astro splendore: Insanguine's La vedova capricciosa.

Io vorria, bellezza cara: Logroscino in Le chiajese cantarine.

Ist die liebe vergnügt: Duni's Der militz.

Ist sie eine coquette: Duni's Der verliebte maler.

J'ai fait un rêve: Gluck's La rencontre imprévue.

J'aime la ville: Philidor's L'amant déguisé.

J'avois un petit oiseau: Le depart de l'Opéra comique.

J'étois gissant à cette place: Duni's Les deux chasseurs et la laitière.

J'ons pardu mon ami: Les amours de Bastien et Bastienne.

Ja ich war ein maedchen: Duni's Der verliebte maler.

Ja, meine schoene: Telemann's Das ende der babylonischen monarchie.

Je compare les amis: Philidor's Der gaertner von Sidon.

Je devine a ces yeux: Pergolesi's La servante maîtresse.

Je le compare avec Louis: Dezède's Les trois fermiers.

Je le sçais bien: La Ruette's Cendrillon.

Je le veux, et cela suffit: Méreaux' La ressource comique.

Je m'en revenais chantant: Philidor's Sancho Pança dans son isle.

Je me mets à peine: Le bal de Strasbourg.

Je n'en puis plus: Rinaldo di Capua's La Bohémienne.

Je ne puis plus durer: Sodi's Baiocco et Serpilla.

Je ne sçais pas si ma soeur: Grétry's Silvain.

Je perds san ressource: Rinaldo di Capua's La Bohémienne.

Je quitte à regret: St. Amans. *See* L'acteur dans son ménage.

Je rêve en vain: Les trompeurs trompés.

Je suis d'une bonne pâte: Piccinni's La buona figliuola.

Je suis de vous très mécontente: Grétry's L'ami de la maison.

Je suis percé jusq'aux os: Duni's Les deux chasseurs et la laitière.

Je suis un officier nouveau: La couronne de roses.

Je suis un seigneur: La couronne de roses.

Je vais, grace à ma fille: Sellitti in Les Chinois.

Je vais revoir ma chère: Philidor's Sancho Pança dans son isle.

Je vais seulette: Philidor's Sancho Pança dans son isle.

Je vends des bouquets: Duni's La fee Urgele.

Je vieux bien m'en fier: Audinot-Gossec's Le tonnelier.

Je veux qu'on m'aime: Philidor's La nouvelle école des femmes.

Je veux tirer vengeance: Le caprice amoureux.

Je veux tout bas: Pergolesi in La maître de musique.

Je vois Lucas tous les jours: Vachon's Les femmes et le secret.

Je vous aime: Le mauvais plaisant.

Je vous aimois: Le bal de Strasbourg.

Je vous obtiens: Philidor's Tom Jones.

Jene geister, womit: Grétry's Zemire und Azor.

Jeune fillette: Philidor's Le sorcier.

Jour heureux, douce espérance: Grétry's Le magnifique.

Joys that wordly mortals: Arnold in Shield's The poor soldier.

Junge maedchen sind: Monsigny's On ne s'avise jamais de tout.

Kätchen hat mir dumm geschienen: Das rosenmaedchen.

Komm, ach komm zurück: Philidor's Der hufschmied.

L'âge en vain sembloit: Gossec's Les pêcheurs.

L'amant délicat: Les amants trompés.

L'amato, bene: Hasse's L'Ipermestra.

L'amitié vive et pure: Grétry's La double épreuve.

L'amo tanto, che per lei: Paisiello's Nina.

L'amour d'un trait vainqueur: Le chinois poli en France.

L'amour naissant n'a pas encore: Grétry's Le Huron.

L'amour se plaît: Philidor's Le maréchal ferrant.

L'ardente mia fiamma: Predieri's Scipione il giovane.

L'argent seul fixe: Philidor's Blaise le savetier.

L' augellino imprigionato: Il giuoco del picchetto.

L'autre jour à coups de pomme: La couronne de roses.

L'avez-vous vu mon bien aimé: Duni's La fee Urgele.

L'eclat est le moyen: Alexandre's Le petit-maître en province.

L'esempio de chesta vedè: Piccinni, Logroscino and Insanguine's La furba burlata.

L'espoir qui t'enflamme: Rodolphe's L'aveugle de Palmyre.

L'hymen est à craindre: Philidor's Le soldat magicien.

L'idol mio tu fosti: Latilla's Madama Ciana.

L'umore e il cervello: Paisiello's La grotta di Trofonio.

L'ussignol col mesto canto: Paisiello's L'idolo cinese.

La beauté dans vos yeux: Philidor's Le jardinier et son seigneur.

La carozza ci sarà: Goldoni's Amor fà l'uomo cieco text.

La carozza ci sarà: Pergolesi's Amor fa l'uomo cieco.

La donna ch'è amante: Gazzaniga's La costanza in amor, rende felice.

La donna ch'è amante: Gazzaniga's La vendemmia.

La donna è sempre istabile: Sarti's Der fischer im trueben.

La donna onorata: Ciampi's Bertoldo, Bertoldino e Cacasenno.

La fauvette avec ses petits: Grétry's Zémire et Azor.

La garde d'une fille: La Borde's La meuniere de Gentilly.

La garde passe: Grétry's Les deux avares.

La luce del mio foco: Martinengo's Arsiade.

La lumière la plus pure: Rodolphe's L'aveugle de Palmyre.

La meschina nel mio seno: Storace's Gli equivoci.

La mia Bella m'ha detto: Sarti's I contrattempi.

La mia cara, la mia bella: Sarti's I finti eredi.

La mia fiamma và: Buini and Chelleri's Il nemico amante.

La nostra signorina: Cipolla in Cimarosa's Il barone burlato.

La pauvre fillette a beau faire: Philidor's Tom Jones.

La pietà del core augusto: Orlandini's Adelaide.

La plus vive reconnaissance: Gossec's Toinon et Toinette.

La pudeur qui me guide: Sellitti in Le maître de musique.

La reine des fleurs: La couronne de roses.

La signorina mia: Orlandini and Mancini's Artaserse.

La smarrita tortorella: Orlandini and Mancini's Artaserse.

La speranza d'un core: D. Scarlatti in his and Pullaroli's L'Irene.

La speranza di quest' alma: Goldoni's Il finto principe text.

La tendresse et la sagesse: Piccinni's La buona figluola.

La tua diletta figlia: Jommelli's Ifigenia in Aulide.

La tua diletta figlia: Traetta in Jommelli's Ifigenia in Aulide.

La tua fortuna, o bella: Orlandini's Adelaide.

La tua nemica e mia: Capello's L'Eudamia.

La voici . . . tôt décampons: Les amours de Bastien et Bastienne.

Ladies, pray admire: Dibdin in The school for fathers.

Laissez la grandeur: Philidor's Le jardinier et son seigneur.

Laisser là mon jardin: Philidor's Le jardinier de Sidon.

Languire, oh Dio! vi sento: Jommelli's Tito Manlio.

Lascia cadermi in volto: Hasse's Artaserse.

Lasciami in abbandono: Sarti's Mitridate a Sinope.

Lasciate fare, non dubitare: Sciroli's La smorfiosa.

Lass Dich nicht mehr: Grétry's Die beiden geizigen.

Lasst uns schaaf: Monsigny's Der koenig und der pachter.

Laure a de la beauté: La nouvelle école des femmes.

Lavorando Nina mia: Latilla's L'isola d'amore.

Le badinage, l'humeur: Le maître de musique.

Le briquet frappe la pierre: Duni's Les deux chasseurs et la laitière.

Le ciel va rendre: Lasalle d'Offemont's Bertholde à la ville.

Le dieu d'amour, le dieu du vin: Vachon's Sara.

Le donne col cervello: Boroni in Laurenti's La pupilla rapita.

Le feu me monte: Pergolesi in Le maître de musique.

Le grand philosophe Panglose: Duni's L'école de la jeunesse.

Le mariage est une envie: Grétry's Les fausses apparences.

Le mariage où l'on m'engage: La Ruette's Le medecin de l'amour.

Le mylord m'offre: Monsigny's Le roi et le fermier.

Le plaisir succède: Dézède's Julie.

Le tendre coeur de ta bergère: Kohault's Le serrurier.

Le vin est un mortel venin: Le docteur Sangrado.

Le virtuose che son famose: Pergolesi's Il maestro di musica.

Le zèle ardent: Les racoleurs.

Learn all from me: Burgess in The coffee-house.

Leon ne la foresta: Porta's L'Issipile.

Les amantes qui sont fidèles: See Il rè infante, Intermezzi.

Les dehors les plus seduisants: Alexandre's Le petit-maître en province.

Les esprits dont on nous a fait: Grétry's Zémire et Azor.

Les jolis, les petits marquis: Le bouquet du roi.

Les premiers moments d'une belle: Alexandre's Le petit-maître en province.

Les yeux vers moi tournés: Laruette's Cendrillon.

Let prudes and coquets: Carey's The honest Yorkshire-man.

Letzthin erzählte auf: Fridzeri's Les deux miliciens.

Levarsi dopo il Sole: Ciampi's Il negligente.

Liebe fraegt nach keinem stande: Dittersdorf's Hieronymus Knicker (Vulpius version)

Lieto parto amato: Albinòni and Porta's La Mariane.

Like me, the tender dove: Stanley in The lover his own rival.

Lise chantoit dans la prairie: Dezède's Blaise et Babet.

Lise kann nicht mehr: Monsigny's On ne s'avise jamais de tout.

Lo conosco a quelli occhietti: Pergolesi's La serva padrona.

Lo voglio scannare: Pergolesi's La contadina astuta and Tracollo.

Loin d'imiter son inconstance: Les amants trompés.

Loin de l'objet aimé: Le confident heureux.

Loin de l'objet de ma tendresse: Philidor's Le sorcier.

Loin de son berger: Piccinni's L'esclave.

Longtemps attendre: Pergolesi's La servante maîtresse.

Lontan da tuoi bei rai: interpolated in Keiser's Der sich raechende Cupido.

Look back, behold: Arnold in The summer's tale.

Lors d'ici, et vous aussi: Le confident heureux.

Lorsqu' Annette est avec Lubin: Blaise's Annette et Lubin.

Lorsque deux coeurs: Les amants trompés.

Lorsque j'avois du chagrin: Prudent's Les jardiniers.

Lorsque l'amour dans ses nœuds: Jommelli's Il giuoco di picchetto.

Louis que le ciel: L'impromptu du coeur.

Love and drink, merry mortal: The coffee-house.

Love does so run: Th. A. Arne in Fontainebleau.

Love from the heart: Martini in The haunted tower.

Love's a gentle generous passion: Carey's The honest Yorkshire-man.

Lubin aime sa bergere: Blaise's Annette et Lubin.

Luci care, luci belle: Garcia's La pupilla.

Lungi del caro bene: Sarti's Giulio Sabino.

Lurk, lurk, o'er the green: Arnold's The battle of Hexham.

Lustig seyn die Schwobemaidle: Philidor's Der verkleidete liebhaber.

M'ama il bell' idol mio: Traetta in Jommelli's Ifigenia in Aulide.

M'ha detto la mia mama: = Son coeur d'abord in Sellitti and others' Les Chinois.

M'ha sturbata Ciommetella: Logroscino and Barbella's L'Elmira generosa.

M'incatena: A. Scarlatti's Il prigioniero fortunato.

M'involi il mio tesoro: Vinci, Jommelli and others' Il Catone in Utica.

M'offendi; e pur conviene: unknown composer's Didone abbandonata.

Ma barque flottante: Grétry's La rosière de Salenci.

Ma chesto soccede: Piccinni, Logroscino and Insanguine's La furba burlata.

Ma démarche est légère: Duni's Les moissonneurs.

Ma femme fait: Sodi's Baiocco et Serpilla.

Ma fille, ma chere fille: Cocchi in Les Chinois.

Ma non avreste appetito: Paisiello's La grotta di Trofonio.

Ma non gli affetti miei: Leo in Orefici's La Rosilla.

Ma peine vous rend: Les amours de Bastien et Bastienne.

Ma vive tendresse: Les amants trompés.

Madam' lasciatemi: Resta's I trè cicisbei ridicoli. *See also* Rinaldo di Capua's La Bohémienne.

Madre non più languir: Ottoboni's Il Colombo.

Mädchen, lasst euch die freude: Das rosenmaedchen.

Maggior follia non v'è: Metastasio's Semiramide text (original version).

Maggior follia non v'è: Hasse's La Semiramide riconosciuta.

Maledetti quanti siete: Ciampi's Bertoldo, Bertoldino e Cacasenno; *see also* Rinaldo di Capua's La Bohémiennes.

Mamma mia: Latilla's L'isola d'amore.

Man giebt uns den unterricht: Das rosenmädchen.

Maris qui croyez: Vadé's text Il etoit tems.

Maris, qui querrellez sans cesse: Philidor's Der holzhauer.

Me conzola no penziero: Pulli in Vinci's La mogliere fedele.

Me seras-tu fidèle: Pergolesi's La servante maîtresse.

Meglio rifletti al dono: Metastasio's Antigono text.

Meglio rifletti al dono: Piccinni's Il regno della luna.

Mein bester Sancio: Gassmann in his and Paisiello's Don Quischott von Mancia.

Mein Onkel ist ein halber narr: Dittersdorf's Hieronimus Knicker (Vulpius version)

Mein Onkel ist ein harter mann: Dittersdorf's Hieronimus Knicker.

Mein schäferstab war: Monsigny's Der deserteur.

Mein schatz, mein ergoetzen: Keiser's Der angenehme betrug.

Meinen garten will: Philidor's Der gaertner von Sidon.

Mentisca pure: *See* Cocchi's La maestra di scuola.

Mercè de la mia fè: *See* Il rè infante, Intermezzi.

Merope bella: Ruggeri's Arreninone.

Mes enfants, après la pluie: Les amours de Bastien et Bastienne.

Mes trois femmes: Blaise's Annette et Lubin.

Mi corrono d'intorno: Fabrizi in I tre gobbi rivali.

Mi dona, mi renda: Pescetti in the pasticcio Ezio.

Mi fà guerra: Aldrovandini's L'odio e l'amore.

Mi fai gioire: Duni's Demophontes, king of Thrace.

Mi promette al 'or la calma: Jommelli's Tito Manlio.

Mi stà d'accanto: Sellitti's Cinese rimpatriato.

Mi tormenta: A. Scarlatti's Il prigioniero fortunato.

Mia Drusilla, all 'or che: Cocchi's La maestra.

Misera rondinella: Duni's La buona figliula.

Misera tortorela: Hasse's Cajo Fabricio.

Misero pargoletto: Cimarosa's La villana riconoscinta.

Mit Ihnen bin ich unzufrieden: Grétry's Der hausfreund.

Mme sapisse a ddi: Piccinni, Logroscino, and Insanguine's La furba burlata.

Mo è no tiempo: Logroscino in Le chiajese cantarine.

Mon Bastien va perir: La nouvelle Bastienne.

Mon bonheur est extrême: Sodi's Baiocco et Serpilla.

Mon coeur jouit: Duni's Les moissonneurs.

Mon coeur, o cher Calcante: Pergolesi in Rinaldo di Capua's La Bohémienne.

Mon sort rendoit: Mondonville's L'Amour et Psyché.

Mormora il ruscelletto: Paisiello's Nina.

Munter sieht man: Grétry's Zemire und Azor.

Muove si dolce: Caccini's Il rapimento di Cefalo.

My fathers before me: Suett in Attwood's The smugglers.

My life's three parts: Philidor in Dibdin's The deserter.

My name's Tippy Bob: Reeve's Blue Beard.

My Nancy, I love you dear: The cobler of Castebury.

N'est-il, n'est-il donc: Les amants trompés.

Ne bell' occhi le Grazie: Sellitti's Amor d'un ombra e gelosia d'un aura.

Ne crois pas qu'un long ménage: Grétry's Silvain.

Ne donnones jamais: Philidor's Les femmes vengées.

Ne l'amante son gran: Pollaroli's Irene.

Ne lisons jamais: Les Troyennes en Champagne.

Ne me parle plus d'Emilie: Les amants trompés.

Ne vla-t-il pas: La nouvelle Bastienne.

Neigt sich ein hitziger tag: Grétry's Der hausfreund.

Nel cor mio pensier: Hasse's Siroes, King of Persia.

Nel giardin di piante: Buini and Chelleri's Il nemico amante.

Nel mio core poverino: Latilla's L'isola d'amore.

Nel mirar la bella dama: Sarti's I finti eredi.

Nel morir se mi vuoi: Jommelli's Tito Manlio.

Nel pensar al gran cimento: pasticcio Arminio (Perez).

Nel seno amante: See Il rè infante, Intermezzi.

Nel tuo dono: Duni's Demophontes, King of Thrace.

Nella crudel mia sorte: Orlandini's La virtù nel cimento.

Nelson flieht, mich zu verlassen: Grétry's Die freundschaft auf der probe.

Nelson part, Nelson me laisse: Grétry's L'amitié à l'épreuve.

Neptune from all ills: Sheeles in The generous free-mason.

Nicole a l'air: Favart's La rosiere de Salenci.

Nina cara, Nina bella: Galuppi's Il marchese villano.

No Don Framinio: Piccinni, Logroscino, and Insanguine's La furba burlata.

No, nò non ti lagnar: Hasse's Cajo Fabricio.

Nò, non andrà l'indegna: Anfossi's La pescatrice fedele.

No: non dicesti il vero: Jommelli's Il giuoco di picchetto.

No, non mi muove a sdegno: Cocchi's La maestra.

No, non vedrete mai: Galuppi's Issipile.

No, non vedrete mai: Piccinni's La scaltra letterata.

No place shall conceal 'em: Lampe's Dragoness.

Nobil fiamma del mio Sole: Freschi's Cesare trionfante.

Nocchier che al porto: Piccinni's L'astratto.

Noi sole semplicette: Vento and Gassmann's La Zingara.

Non condannarmi, amico: Hasse's Alessandro nell' Indie.

Non curi la mia pianta: Corsi's Dafne (text by Rinuccini).

Non dubitate o cara: Latilla's L'isola d'amore.

Non dubiti, signora: Guglielmi's L'inganno amoroso.

Non è colpa del cor: Orlandini's Griselda.

Non è sempre la femmina: Sarti's I contratempi.

Non è terribile: Porta's L'Issipile.

Non fa, ch'io porri: Leo in Orefici's La Rosilla.

Non goda quell' infida: Cocchi's La maestra and its L. T. La scaltra governatrice.

Non hà pena l'amor: D. Scarlatti in his and Pullaroli's L'Irene.

Non ha ragione ingrato: Monti's L'Adriano in Siria.

Non, infidele, cours: Les amours de Bastien et Bastienne.

Non, je n'aimerai jamais: Nicaise.

Non, je ne puis plus: Rodolphe's Nanine.

Non, je suis trop en colère: Pergolesi in Le maître de musique.

Non ma mère: Philidor's Le sorcier.

Non, ma reine, sois certaine: Monsigny's Le cadi dupé.

Non mi burli: Latilla's Madame Ciana.

Non mi parlar d'amore: Gluck's Tigrane.

Non mi state a infastidire: Garcia's La pupilla.

Non nieghi la sorte: Pollaroli's L'Ibraim sultano.

Non, non, je n'ai peur: La caprice amoureux.

Non serve cchiu: Sellitti in Vinci's La mogliere fedele.

Non si credano mai: Latilla's Madama Ciana.

Non si dà fra l'umane: Hasse's Demofoonte.

Non si faccia più rumore: Bertati's text La donna instabile.

Non si faccia più rumore: Borghi's Gli tre pretendenti.

Non si move, non rifiata: Goldoni's Amor fà l'uomo cieco text.

Non si muove, non rifiata: Pergolesi's Livietta e Tracollo and its L. T.

Non si presto il suo colore: Vivaldi's Siroe, rè di Persia.

Non si stracqus: Pulli in Vinci's La mogliere fedele.

Non si vanti di beltà: Gasparini's Parpagnacco.

Non so dir se pena sia: F. Giardini in the pasticcio Cleonice.

Non so se m'intendete: Latilla's L'isola d'amore.

Non son bella—non son vezzosa: G. Scarlatti's I portentosi effetti della Madre Natura.

Non son piccina: Cocchi's La scaltra governatrice.

Non sperar ch'io faccia: Scolari's Il viaggiatore ridicolo.

Non temer, che avanti: G. Scarlatti's I portentosi effetti della Madre Natura.

Non vi piacque, ingiusti Dei: Metastasio's Siroe text.

Non vi piacque, ingiusti Dei: Piccinni's Il regno della luna.

Non voglio imbrogli: Soralli's Il negligente text.

Nos coeurs cessent de s'entendre: Grétry's Silvain.

Nos plus beaux jours: Rodolphe's Nanine.

Note d'moiselle a dit: Martini's L'amoureux de quinze ans.

Notre bonheur nous fait: Le bal de Strasbourg.

Nous allons ici: Duni's La fée Urgèle.

Nous avons dans notre jeune age: La Borde's La meunière de Gentilly.

Now gossip strike home: Hayes in The two misers.

Now, now, my fairest, let: Dibdin in The captive.

Now fortune is past: Carey's The honest Yorkshire-man.

Now I'm seated: Midas.

Nur das geld kann: Philidor's Hanns der schuhflicker.

Nur in der stadt: Philidor's Der verkleidete liebhaber.

Nur meinem schatze: Grétry's Die beiden geizigen.

O bella costanza: Leopold I in Draghi's Sulpitia.

O bliss unexpected: Dibdin's The school for fathers.

O che gioja, o che contento: Hasse's Don Tabarrano.

O ciel! quel air: Grétry's Le magnifique.

O dell' Egitto Nume: Rinaldo di Capua's La Zingara.

O Dieux! qu'elle est belle: L'amour impromptu.

O dry those tears: Lionel and Clarissa.

O eifersucht! o eifersucht: Dittersdorf's Der schiffspatron.

O'er the rude rocks: A trip to the Nore.

O guerriero: Pollaroli's L'Ibraim sultano.

O Johnny, thou hast: The quaker's opera.

O le bon temps: Duni's Les moissonneurs.

O London is a dainty place: Carey's The honest Yorkshire-man.

O nel sen di qualche stella: Jommelli in his, Vinci and others' Il Catone in Utica.

O nuit! charmante nuit: Blaise's Isabelle et Gertrude.

O placido il mare: Hasse's Siroe.

O quanti maestri: Cocchi's La scaltra governatrice.

O su gli estivi ardori: Hasse's Alessandro nell' Indie.

O voi possenti Numi: Rinaldo di Capua's La Zingara.

O vous démons celèbres: Rinaldo di Capua's La Bohémienne.

O! wie erfreut die erndte-zeit: Duni's Die schmitter.

O! wie quälet doch die liebe: Fridzeri's Die beiden militzen.

O! wie schön sind doch: Duni's Die schnitter.

Occhi non giova: Lotti's Teuzzone.

Occhi non giova: Lotti and Vignola's L'inganno vinto dalla ragione.

Off, my lord, pray forbear: Piccinni's The accomplish'd maid.

Oft, wenn im haus: Philidor's Tom Jones.

Ogni amante che si sposa: Guglielmi's Il disertore.

Ogni amator suppone: Metastasio's Didone abbandonata text (Original version).

Ogni Nume, ed ogni Diva: Hasse's Demetrio (1740).

Ogni procella infida: Hasse's Cleonice.

Ogni procella infida: Hasse's Demetrio (1740).

Ogni tromba, ogni tamburo: Rinaldo di Capua's La Zingara.

Oh che bile: Boroni in Laurenti's La pupilla rapita.

Oh che fussi ammazzata: Guglielmi's La villanella ingentilita.

Oh che giorno di contento: Perillo in Piccinni's L'erede riconoscinta.

Oh che gusto che sente: Fischietti in Le chiajese cantarine.

Oh che risa, oh che piacere: Buini in Il giocatore (Paris, 1752).

Oh che sorte, oh che piacere: Goldoni's Amor fà l'uomo cieco text.

Oh che sproposito: Auletta in Pergolesi's Il maestro di musica.

Oh come sei bello: Goldoni's Amor fà l'uomo cieco text.

Oh! come to my arms: Carey in The generous free-mason.

Oh had I been by fate: Howard in Love in a village.

Oh la puissante querelle: Le maître de musique.

Oh! laissez donc mon coeur: Rinaldo di Capua's La Bohémienne.

Oh quanto è mai felice: Gazzaniga's L'amore costante.

Ohimè, dov'è: Cesti and Bigongiari's Alessandro il vincitor di se stesso.

On dit qu'à quinze ans: Grétry's Lucile.

On n'a dans l'mariage: Les amours de Bastien et Bastienne.

On n'a jamais vu: Sodi's Baiocco et Serpilla.

On nous donne des leçons: Favart's La rosiere de Salenci.

One conduct'r for both: Dibdin's The deserter.

On scait bien qu'il faut: Duni's L'école de la jeunesse.

On trouve un objet charmant: Grétry's La double épreuve.

Or che ballar degg' io: Monti in Tritto's Li due gemelli .

Or che Pallante è vinto: Händel's Agrippina.

Or con l'immagine: Latilla's L'isola d'amore.

Or son tutto contento: Capello's L'Eudamia.

Orinda mia crudel: Pollaroli's Gl'amici rivali.

Ornò la mia diletta: Porpora's Adelaide.

Orso, bifolco, ingrato: Cimarosa's Li amanti comici.
Orsù compresi il vostro: Paisiello's La grotta di Trofonio.
Orsù sentimi bene: Cimarosa's La baronessa Stramba.
Où peut-on être mieux: Grétry's Lucile.
Où suis-je transporté?: Rodolphe's Nanine.
Oui je crois cela: Le docteur Sangrado.
Oui, la nature est la mère: Kohault's La bergère des Alpes.
Oui, nos chanteuses: Pergolesi in Le maître de musique.
Oui, oui, je veux en sortir: Philidor's Le diable à quatre.
Oui, oui, vous le pouvez: Le mauvais plaisant.
Oui, vous serez sans cesse: Rinaldo di Capua's La Bohémienne.
Our folly is our neighbour's gain: Arne's An hospital for fools.
Ov'è Lisetta: Paisiello's Gli avventurieri and Il rè Teodoro.
Pace con un laccio: Doletti's Le joueur.
Pace si, si, dolce mia vita: Hasse's Don Tabarrano.
Padre perdona, oh pene: Hasse's Demofoonte (1749).
Padre, tiranno, barbaro: pasticcio Arminio (Perez).
Pallido il Sole: Orlandini's Adelaide.
Par le trou de la serrure: Piccinni's La buona figliuola.
Par un beau soir: L'impromptu du coeur.
Parce per carità: Monti in Tritto's Li due gemelli.
Parlar potesse il cuore: Partenio and others' Flavio Cuniberto.
Parti, deh! fuggi: Mazzoni's L'Issipile.
Parto dunque, o mia diletta: Goldoni's Amor fa l'uomo cicco text.
Parto: ma so che degno: Hasse's L'Olimpiade.
Parto mio ardore: M. A. Ziani in Draghi's Leonida in Tegea.
Pauvre Annette, quelle pitié: Piccinni's La buona figliuola.
Pauvre Colas: Monsigny's Rose et Colas.
Pauvre Nise! Tu chéris: Cocchi in Rinaldo di Capua's La Bohémienne.
Pensa che fost'e sei: interpolated in Keiser's Der sich raechende Cupido.
Pensa che l'amor mio: Hasse's Artaserse.
Pensa, che sei crudele: Hasse's Demetrio (1740).
Pensieri funesti: Sarti's Giulio Sabino.
Pensieri non v'atterrite: Sances's Apollo deluso (this aria by Leopold I).
Per il mio bene: Jommelli in his, Vinci and others' Il Catone in Utica.
Per le svele erra: M. A. Ziani's Il Gordiano Pio.
Per lei fra l'armi: Jommelli's Demofoonte.
Per mancar a te: Jommelli in his, Vinci and others' Il Catone in Utica.
Per pietà bell' idol mio: Sacchini's Artaserse.
Per pietà, bell' idol mio: Vinci's Artaserse.
Per pietà, chi mai m'insegna: Goldoni's Amor fa l'uomo cieco text.
Per questo dolce amplesso: Hasse's Artaserse.
Per salvarti, idolo mio: Porpora's Adelaide.
Per servir vi e cortegiar: Fabrizi in I tre gobbi rivali.
Per te io hò (or hò io) nel core: Pergolesi's Flaminio also in replicas of his **Livietta e** Tracolla and in his La serva padrona.
Per te io hò nel core: *See also* Rinaldo di Capua's La Bohémienne.
Per te sospiro: Gassmann's Gl'uccellatori.
Perch'io veggo se son tradito: Partenio's Flavio Cuniberto.
Perchè e sicuro pegno: Piccinni, Logroscino and Insanguine's La furba burlata.
Perchè l'altrui misura: Mazzoni's L'Issiple.
Perché mai luci adorate: Ziani's La Falsirena.
Perchè mai t'ò fatto: Guglielmi's La pastorella nobile.
Perchè son bella, perchè son cara: Cocchi's Le nozze di Monsù Fagotto.

Perdono al crudo acciaro: Hasse's Ipermestra.

Perfidi, che volete: Rinaldo di Capua's La Zingara.

Perfido amico ingrato: Leo's La clemenza di Tito.

Perfido non parlarmi: Palella in Hasse's Tigrane.

Petits maîtres sans cervelle (=Zerbinetti d'oggidì in Sellitti's Il Cinese rimpatriato): Le Chinois poli en France.

Picarone, a un cavaliero: Logroscino's in Sciroli's Li nnamorate correvate.

Pien d'ardir, costante: Goldoni's Il finto principe text.

Più celar non si può: Cesti and Bigongiari's Alessandro il vincitor di se stesso.

Più che preghi: Pollaroli's L'Oreste in Sparta.

Più cori, più vite: interpolated in Keiser's Der sich raechende Cupido.

Più non chiamo ingiusto: Cocchi's La maestra.

Più non sento gli anni: Perillo in Piccinni's L'erede riconosciuta.

Più rimiro quel visino: Rinaldo di Capua's La serva sposa.

Più sono in amore: Rinaldo di Capua's La serva sposa.

Più temer non deve: Fischietti's Siface.

Più temer non posso ormai: Fischietti's Siface (from Metastasio's Ipermestra text).

Plein de la plus vive ardeur: Leger in Ziste et Zeste.

Plus d'une fois: Philidor's Tom Jones.

Plus de dépit, plus de tristesse: Grétry's Les deux avares.

Plus matin que l'aurore: Les amours de Bastien et Bastienne.

Po fa la Ddea: Leo in Orefici's La Rosilla.

Poi che gli eterni imperi: Caccini's L'Euridice.

Poor panting heart: Dibdin in the Captive.

Poor panting heart: Dibdin in the school for fathers.

Poro, se sull' Idaspe: Händel's Porus.

Porto è vero il sen: Porpora's Siface.

Potria fra tanto: Fischietti's Siface (from Metastasio's Achille in Sciro text).

Pour Colette, que j'adore: La fête du château.

Pour d'autres instans: Nicaise.

Pour guérir toute maladie: Duni in Le docteur Sangrado.

Pour la beauté: Jadin in La lettre.

Pour l'objet qui règne: Les amants trompés.

Pour les amans et les belles: Philidor's L'amant déguisé.

Pour leur grosseur: Wicht in the pasticcio La vallée de Montmorency.

Pour me plaire il faut: Le poirier.

Pour nous est fait: Blaise's Isabelle et Gertrude.

Pour voir accueillir: Le naufrage au port.

Povera pecorella: Pulli in Vinci's La mogliere fedele.

Povere donne; che s'ha da far: G. Scarlatti's L'isola disabitata.

Poverina! ha freddo: Cocchi's La maestra.

Poverina, innocentina: Puccinni's L'incostante and Il volubile.

Pray now John: Lully in Wonders in the sun.

Prendi l'estremo addio: Sarti's Medonte.

Prendi uno sposo: Orlandini's Adelaide.

Prenez au village: L'amour impromptu.

Près de moi, dans la boutique: Audinot and Gossec's Le tonnelier.

Pretextant une bonne affaire: Le poirier.

Principessa adorata: Jommelli's Alessandro nell' Indie.

Priva del caro bene: Gluck's Tigrane.

Proverai di che fiere: Händel's Der in cronen erlangte glueckswechsel.

Pupille del mio bene: Vignola in Gasparini's Le regine di Macedonia.

Pupillette vezzosette: Latilla's L'ambizione delusa.

Pur cangia i suoi rigori: Cesti's La Dori.

Qu' espère un amant: Le maître de musique.

Qu'est-ce done vous arrête: Sacchini's La colonie.

Qu'il a de gentillesse: Le caprice amoureux.

Qu'il est cruel d'aimer: Grétry's Les événements imprévus.

Qu'il m'est doux: Blaise in Les jeunes mariés.

Qu'il tombe, qu'il meure: Pergolesi in Les Chinois.

Qu'importe à quel prix: Le confident heureux.

Qu'une fête pour ce soir: Pergolesi in Les Chinois.

Qu'on est heureux de faire: L'impromptu.

Qual colomba innamorata: Sciroli's La smorfiosa.

Qual doppo insano: Pergolesi's Il maestro di musica.

Qual Pino errante: Vivaldi's La costanza trionfante degl' amori, e degl' odii.

Qual solinga tortorella: interpolated in Keiser's Der sich raechende Cupido.

Qual trascorrendo: Caccini's Il rapimento di Cefalo.

Qualora un galantuomo: Galuppi's Il vecchio geloso.

Quand' era giovanetta: Leopold I in Draghi's Leonida in Tegea.

Quand il bell' anno: Caccini's Il rapimento di Cefalo.

Quand j'avons engagé: La nouvelle Bastienne.

Quand j'étois jeunette: Duni's Le peintre amoureux de son modèle.

Quand je reviens: Vachon's Les femmes et le secret.

Quand je vois Fanchette: Audinot-Gossec's Le tonnelier.

Quand l'amour est content: Duni's Le milicien.

Quand l'amour fait: Jerosme et Fanchonette.

Quand le feu de la guerre: Duni's L'école de la jeunesse.

Quand le hasard, ensemble: Lasalle d'Offemont's Bertholde à la ville.

Quand on se rend: Le trompeur trompé.

Quand Paris, sur le mont Ida: Philidor's Les lemmes vengées.

Quand pour nous rendre: La Borde's La meunière de Gentilly.

Quand un ayme: *See* Ii rè infante, Intermezzi.

Quand un tendron viant: Les amours de Bastien et Bastienne.

Quando amore à servo: Leo's La clemenza di Tito.

Quando arricchito: Buini and Chelleri's La pace per amore.

Quando il cuor non: Vento and Gassmann's La Zingara.

Quando l'amore insegna: Palella in Hasse's Tigrane.

Quando sciolto avrò: Pergolesi's Il maestro di musica.

Quando sento spirarmi: Leo's Se mai senti spirarti in Ciampi's Bertoldo in corte (Paris, 1753).

Quando vedi il Damerino: Galuppi's Il vecchio geloso.

Quant' è buono il cioccolato: Scolari's Il viaggiatore ridicolo.

Quanta furie scatenate: Sellitti in Vinci's La mogliere fedele.

Quanto Amore è tristarello: Leo and Gomes's Il nuovo D. Chisciotti.

Quanto comanda, si ubbidirò: Pergolesi's Il maestra di cappella.

Quanto è grave il mio: Albinoni and Porta's La Mariane.

Quanto mi vien da ridere: Goldoni's Amor fà l'nomo cieco text.

Quanto sarei beata: A. Scarlatti's Il prigioniero fortunato.

Quanto son pazze: Latilla's Ciana.

Que c'est un plaisir: Le maître de musique.

Que j'avions d'impatience: Martini's L'amoureux de quinze ans.

Que je baise cette main: Sellitti in Les Chinois.

Que la campagne est un séjour: Philidor's L'amant déguisé.

Que le soleil dans la plaine: Monsigny's Der koenig und der pachter.

Que mille plaisirs: Le maître de musique.

Que Rosine est touchante: Duni's Les moissonneurs.

Que t'importe que je reste: Rinaldo di Capua's La Bohémienne.

Que tes yeux sont charmans: Le Clair in Nouvelle chasse du cerf.
Que tout le hameau: Blaise's Annette et Lubin.
Que votre dessein: Boyer's Les étrennes de l'amour.
Quei lumi, quel labro: Ottoboni's Il Colombo.
Quel basso vapore: Fischietti's Siface, also Porpora's.
Quel beau jour se dispose: Grétry's La rosière de Salenci.
Quel core altero: Capello's L'Eudamia.
Quel délice ne trouve: Pergolesi in Le maître de musique.
Quel éclat brille: Darcis's La fausse peur.
Quel est mon embarras: Pergolesi's La servante maîtresse.
Quel labbro adorato: Galuppi in the pasticcio Cleonice.
Quel labbro adorato: Hasse's Demetrio (1740).
Quel nobil core: Mayr's Lodoiska.
Quel piacer d'esservi sposa: Boroni in Laurenti's La pupilla rapita.
Quel plaisir, quelle volupté: Piccinni's La buona figliuola.
Quel povero coro: Ottoboni's Il Colombo.
Quel sort t'amène: Sacchini's La colonie.
Quell' alma feroce: Perez' Farnace.
Quell' amor, che nel cimento: Leo in Orefici's La Rosilla.
Quell' ardore: A. Scarlatti's Il prigioniero fortunato.
Quella è Sibari al certo: Zannettini's Temistocle in bando.
Quella fiamma, che v'accende: Astaritta's Il curioso accidente.
Quella stizza lascia: Perillo in Piccinni's L'erede riconosciuta.
Quelle cruauté! Si l'inconstant: Les amants trompés.
Quelle folie extrême: La fausse aventurière.
Quest è quel uomo: Il giocatore (Paris, 1752).
Questa del sesso nostro: Salieri's La calamita de' cuori.
Queste spoglie, o invitta Roma: Pescetti's I tre difensori della patria.
Questo di logore: A. Scarlatti's Bassiano.
Questo è quell' uomo: Il marito giogatore e la moglie bacchettona.
Questo è quell' uomo: Orlandini's Il giocatore.
Questo è quell' uomo: Vinci's Bacocco e Serpilla.   *See* Il marito giogatore e la moglie bacchettona.
Questo foglio, questa carta: Pergolesi's La contadina astuta and Tracollo medico ignorante.
Qui la vipera soggiorna: Gasparini and others' L'Alciade.
Qui mieux que moi: Boyer's Les étrennes de l'amour.
Qui non si dice: Galuppi's Il nemico delle donne.
Quitte la plaine: L'amour impromptu.
Rammenta alfin chi sono: Cimarosa's La villana ricconosciuta.
Rear'd midst the war-empurpled plain: The American Indian.
Recagli quell' arciero: Pescetti in the pasticcio Ezio.
Recht schöne blumen: Duni's Die fee Urgele.
Rendimi i lacci miei: Fischietti's Siface, also Porpora's.
Rentrez chez nous: La Ruette in Le docteur Sangrado.
Répondez, je respire: L'amour impromptu.
Revenez cher amant: Les amants trompés.
Reviens amours: Le bal de Strasbourg.
Ricerca il caro bene: Cocchi's La scaltra governatrice.
Riches de la terre: Philidor's La belle esclave.
Richezza non chiede: Hasse's Cajo Fabricio.
Ricordati, cor mio: Orlandini's Adelaide.
Rien ne peut bannir: Philidor's Le sorcier.
Rissolvi ò cor tradito: *See* Il rè infante, Intermezzi.

Ritorna al tuo sovrano: Jommelli in his, Vinci and others' Il Catone in Utica.

Roccolina bella, bella: Gassmann's Gli uccellatori.

Rose chérie, aimable fleur: Grétry's Zémire et Azor.

Rule, Britannia: Arne's Alfred.

S'ha pietà delle mie pene: Albinoni and Porta's La Mariane.

Sa lei Signor marchese: Guglielmi's L'impostore punito.

Sa tendresse pour moi: Gluck's L'ivrogne corrigé.

Sa tendresse pour moi: La Ruette's L'yvrogne corrigé.

Sai che abbiamo: Galuppi's Il matrimonio per inganno.

Sag, wie dir das gefällt: Duni's Das milchmaedchen und die beiden jaeger.

Sai, ch'un ombra è: Mancini in Lotti's Artaserse rè di Persia.

Sanft schlief einst: Dezède's Julie.

Sans cesse auprès de mon trésor: Grétry's Les deux avarse.

Sans chien et sans houlette: Monsigny's Rose et Colas.

Sans fin, sans cesse: Pergolesi's La servante maitresse.

Sans l'espérance du retour: Gluck's La rencontre imprévue.

Sans un petit brin: Dezède's Les trois fermiers.

Sapessi almen dov'è: Aldrovandini's L'odio e l'amore.

Sapessi almen se barbaro: Paisiello's L'idolo cinese.

Saprò svenar con l'armi: A. Scarlatti's Il prigioniero fortunato.

Sarà vezzosa e bella: Hasse's Cajo Fabricio.

Sarai contento: Orlandini and Mancini's Artaserse.

Sbagliate Sor conte: Rinaldo di Capua's La serva sposa.

Scelerata a me rispondi: Cocchi's La maestra and its L. T. La scaltra governatrice.

Scende dal monte il fonte: Palella in Hasse's Tigrane.

Scherza il nocchier tallora: Metastasio's Demetrio text.

Scherza il nocchier tallora: Galuppi's Il conte Caramella.

Scherza il nocchier tal' ora: Hasse's Alessandro nell' Indie.

Scherza in mar la navicella: Orlandini's Adelaide.

Scherza l'ape sù: Orlandini and Mancini's Artaserse.

Scherza ridi: Vignola in Gasparini's Le regine di Macedonia.

Schöner ort, glückseelge felder: Keiser's Orpheus.

Sdegno, pietade e amor: Orlandini and Mancini's Artaserse.

Se a cantar mi metto: Accorimboni's Le virtuose bizzarre.

Se a un bel canto: Rinaldo di Capua's La smorfiosa.

Se al labbro mio: pasticcio Arminio.

Se alla mia fè: See Cocchi's La maestra di scuola.

Se ardire, e speranza: Metastasio's Demofoonte text.

Se brami mia bella: Orlandini's Adelaide.

Se chisto affritto core: Trojano in Vinci's La mogliere fedele.

Se col labro vi licon: Goldoni's Il finto principe text.

Se costante è la mia bella. See Il rè infante, Intermezzi.

Se da voi non posso: Ottani in his and Piccinni's Il fumo villano.

Se dalle stelle tu non sei: Jommelli's Didone abbandonata.

Se del fiume altera l'onda: Duni's La buona figliuola.

Se fossi in Italia: Galuppi's L'inimico delle donne.

Se giammai da speco: Pergolesi's Il maestro di musica.

Se quacci: The devil of a duke.

Se i miei strali: Leo in Orefici's La Rosilla.

Se il mio paterno amore: Hasse's Siroe.

Se il foco mi accende: Soralli's Il negligente text.

Se intende sì poco: Metastasio's Semiramide text (both versions).

Se intende sì poco: Hasse's La Semiramide riconosciuta.

Se l'amor mio t'è caro: Gasparini's La fede tradita e vendicata.

Se l'amor tuo: pasticcio Arminio (Perez).

Se l'illustrissima dicono: Latilla's Polipodio e Rucchetta.

Se la bella per via: Sarti's I finti eredi.

Se lento ancora: Händel's Der in cronen erlangte gluECkswechsel.

Se libera non sono: Hasse's Demetrio (1740).

Se mai perdete: Latilla's Madama Ciana.

Se mai s'inalza: Accorimboni's Le virtuose bizzarre.

Se mai senti spirarti: Leo's Clemenza di Tito.

Se mai turbo il tuo riposo: Jommelli's Alessandro nell' Indie.

Se mai vi vedi andar: Cocchi's La maestra.

Se mi trovo in campo: Accorimboni's Le virtuose bizzarre.

Se mi volete oppressa: Galuppi's Le nozze di Paride.

Se ne avesse mille intorno: Galuppi's Il paese della Cuccagna.

Se nessuno ora non c'è: Goldoni's Il mercato di Malmantile text; also in Ciampi's
  Bertoldo.

Se non basta: Sances's Apollo deluso (this aria by Leopold I).

Se non credi alle parole: Hasse's Don Tabarrano.

Se non posso su quel trono: Hasse's Demetrio (1732).

Se non prendo un pò: Paisiello's Nina.

Se non scocasse Amor: Vinacese's L'innocenza giustificata.

Se non ti moro allato: Metastasio's text Adriano in Siria (original version).

Se oppresso l'indegno: Sarti's Mitridate a Sinope.

Se par ch'io serbi: Ruggeri's Arrenione.

Se per dispetto io piango: Galuppi's La forza d'amore.

Se peut-il que l'on propose: La couronne de roses.

Se più il mio core: F. Giardini in the pasticcio Cleonice.

Se placate un dì: Scolari's Il viaggiatore ridicolo.

Se possono tanto: Sciroli's Alessandro nell' Indie.

Se povero il ruscello: Jommelli's Ezio.

Se quel ciglio ancor: Guglielmi's Il disertore.

Se sciogliere non vuoi: Jommelli in his, Vinci and others' Il Catone in Utica.

Se si mette una pedina: Cocchi's Le nozze di Monsù Fagotto.

Se si potesse amar: Vinacese's L'innocenza giustificata.

Se son ragazza tenera: Jommelli's I rivali delusi.

Se spunta amica face: Palella in Hasse's Tigrane.

Se spunta amica stella: Gluck's Tigrane.

Se state alla sua cura: Paisiello's L'avaro deluso.

Se t'invioli ò mia tiranna: Ottoboni's Il Colombo.

Se tal' un mi dice: G. Scarlatti' I portentosi effetti della Madre Natura.

Se ti scopro il foco mio: Porpora's Siface.

Se tronca in ramo: Jommelli's Demofoonte.

Se tu mi sei fedele: Latilla's Madama Ciana.

Se un' alma amante: Sacchini's Creso.

Se un bell' ardire: Jommelli's Ezio.

Se vaporetto in nuvoletto: Orlandini's Antigona and its L. T. La fedeltà coronata.

Se vedi il caro bene: Sacchini's Alessandro nell' Indie.

Se vi guardo ben: Fabrizi and others' I tre gobbi rivali.

Se vi guardo ben: Goldoni's Favola de' tre gobbi text.

Se voi, ch'io t'ami: Ottoboni's Il Colombo.

Se vuol mirarti esangue: Fiorillo's Alessandro nell' Indie.

Segni d'un bel valore: A. Scarlatti's Il prigioniero fortunato.

Seguaci di Cupido: Händel's Partenope.

Sei un ridicolo: Guglielmi's Le due gemelle.

Sei vago, sei vezzoso: *See* Il rè infante, Intermezzi.

Seiner arbeit abzuwarten: Audinot and Gossec's Der fassbinder.

Sembra riso, ed è sol pianto: *See* Il rè infante, Intermezzi.

Semplicetta contadina: Cipolla in Cimarosa's Il barone burlato.

Sempre attorno qual palomba: Pergolesi's Livietta e Tracollo.

Sempre in contrasti: Pergolesi's La serva padrona.

Sempre in soglio: Fischietti's Siface, also Porpora's.

Senti . . . non sarà mai: Pergolesi's Il finto pazzo and Il ladro convertito per amore.

Sento al cor la dolce: Sarti's Medonte.

Sento cangiarsi in lagrime: Latilla's Madama Ciana.

Sento che a poco: Gasparini and others' L'Alciade.

Sento in gabbia innargentata: Astaritta's Il curioso accidente.

Sento la speme: Leo in Orefici's La Rosilla.

Sento nel petto mio: Orlandini and Mancini's Artaserse.

Sento una forza in petto: D. Scarlatti in his and Pullaroli's L'Irene.

Senza il caro mio tesoro: Paisiello's Nina.

Senza sentir il danno: Ciampi's Il negligente.

Serait-il vrai, jeune bergère: Le cercle.

Serpilla diletta: Il giocatore (Paris, 1752).

Serpilla diletta: Il marito giogatore e la moglie bacchettona.

Serpilla diletta: Orlandini's Il giocatore.

Serpilla diletta: Vinci's Bacocco e Serpilla. *See* Il marito giogatore e la moglie bacchettona.

Seu tanto benedetti: Fabrizi and others' I tre gobbi rivali.

Sexe dangereux, trompeur: La fausse aventuriere.

Shades of Windsor: Spofforth in Salomon's Windsor castle.

Si c'est une coquette: Duni's Le peintre amoureux de son modèle.

Sì, caro ben sarete: Rinaldo di Capua's La Zingara.

Si con giudizio: Latilla's Madama Ciana.

Si d'une ame propice: Pergolesi in Le maître de musique.

Si despera il mio core: Gluck's Tigrane.

Si discioglie e si sconnette: Cipolla in Cimarosa's Il barone burlato.

Si godi, o cor: Vignola in Gasparini's Le regine di Macedonia.

Si jamais je fais: Philidor's Les femmes vengées.

Si je pense, c'est: Grétry's Die freundschaft auf der probe.

Si l'amant qui vous rend: La fileuse.

Si la tempesta vide: Fischietti in Le chiajese cantarine.

Si les talents & les graces: Kohault's La bergère des Alpes.

Si mia bella, si mia cara: Telemann's Das ende der babylonischen monarchie.

Si ravviva nel mio core: Il giocatore (Paris, 1752).

Si ravviva [nel mio core]: Rinaldo di Capua's La Bohémienne.

Si scordi i suoi tiranni: Sarti's La Nitteti.

Si, si, consolami: Vignola in Gasparini's Le regine di Macedonia.

Si, si maledetta: Il giocatore (Paris, 1752).

Si, si maledetta: Il marito giogatore e la moglie bacchettona.

Si, si maledetta: Orlandini's Il giocatore.

Si, si maledetta: Vinci's Bacocco e Serpilla. *See* Il marito giogatore e la moglie bacchettona.

Si, si rapide correte: Ziani's Marte deluso.

Si signore, io lo farò: Leo and Gomes' Il nuovo D. Chisciotte.

Si tant de mes confrères: Duni in Le docteur Sangrado.

Si votre flamme est trahie: Monsigny's Le cadi dupé.

Sie schlaeft die schoene: Gassmann in his and Paisiello's Don Quischott von Mancia.

Sieh doch den schmerz: Philidor's Der holzhauer.

Siehst Du, wie ich mich quäle: Grétry's Die freundschaft auf der probe.

Signor giudice: Il marito giogatore e la moglie bacchettona.

Signor giudice: Orlandini's Il giocatore.

Signor giudice: Vinci's Bacocco e Serpilla.

Signor tenente Non: Rinaldo di Capua's La smorfiosa.

Signor tutore, non dubitare (Goldoni's La pupilla text): Garcia's La pupilla.

Signorina mia carina: Piccinni's L'incostante and Il volubile.

Since you mean to hire: Midas.

Since you whom I lov'd: Seedo in The lottery.

Singet und tanzet: Grétry's Das rosenfest zu Salenci.

Sive Bertoldo mio garbato: Ciampi's Bertoldo.

Sò che gl'uomini han: Scolari's Il viaggiatore ridicolo.

Sò, che non hò fortuna: Orlandini and Mancini's Artaserse.

Sò chi t'accese: Jommelli's Ezio.

So kommt, so kommt: Gluck's Die unvermuthete zusammenkunft.

So lang die jugend: Gassmann in his and Paisiello's Don Quischott von Mancia.

So n'astritto rescegnuolo: Pulli in Vinci's La mogliere fedele.

So profound an impression: Bach in The summer's tale.

Sobald es tagt: Fridzeri's Les deux miliciens.

Soccorso bramate: Latilla's L'isola d'amore.

Soffri costante: Lotti's Teuzzone and his and Vignola's L'inganno vinto dalla ragione.

Softer than the breath of May: Fairbank in The village opera.

Sogle donne amar: Gasparini's Parpagnacco.

Sogna il guerrier: Sacchini's Artaserse.

Sois favorable à nos désirs: La fontaine de Jouvence.

Sol mi basta, che talora: Jommelli in his, Vinci, and others' Il Catone in Utica.

Sol ver poi fogli: See Il rè infante, Intermezzi.

Solo effetto era d'amore: Jommelli's Demofoonte (1753).

Some men with artful praise: Piccinni's The accomplish'd maid.

Son amante e non son figlia: Gasparini and Lapis' La fede in cimento.

Son coeur d'abord: Sellitti and others' Les Chinois.

Son già trè dì che Nina: Anfossi, Guglielmi and Gassmann's Lo sposo di trè e marito di nessuno. See also Tre giorni son che Nina.

Son imbrogliato io già: Pergolesi's La serva padrona.

Son modestina: Cipolla in Cimarosa's Il barone burlato.

Sonnata per quegl'occhi: A. Scarlatti's Il prigioniero fortunato.

Son pellegrin errante: Fischietti's Siface, also Porpora's.

Son rimasta vedovella: Bertoni's La vedova accorta.

Son stordita via tacete: Galuppi's La forza d'amore.

Son tradita: Piccinni's La buona figliuola.

Sono allegra, son contenta: Ciampi's Bertoldo.

Sono allegra, son contenta: Goldoni's La buona figliuola maritata text.

Sono ancor giovane: Accorimboni's Le virtuose bizzarre.

Sospira, si lamenta: Piccinni, Logroscino and Insanguine's La furba burlata.

Sospirate: Caccini's L'Euridice.

Sous ces gazons: Kohault's La bergère des Alpes.

Sous votre empire: Cocchi in Les Chinois.

Sovra la preda esangue: Gluck's L'Ipolito.

Sovvengati che sei: Gasparini and Vignola's La fede tradita e vendicata.

Sovvengati, spietata: Mancini in Lotti's Artaserse rè di Persia.

Sparger non vo più lagrime: Gasparini's L'amor generoso.

Spera fors' anch' un di: Doletti's La joueur.

Speri forse anche un di: Il giocatore (Paris, 1752).

Sperai vicino il lido: Metastasio's Demofoonte text.

Sperai vicino il lido: Hasse's Demofoonte.
Sperai vicino il lido: Jommelli's L'Ifigenia.
Sperai vicino il lido: Vinci, Jommelli, etc., Il Catone in Utica.
Speranza dolce e cara: Ziani's La Falsirena.
Speranza è il più bel dono: Galuppi's Il conte Caramella.
Speranze gradite: Ziani's Marte deluso.
Spesso in un core: Orlandini and Mancini's Artaserse.
Spezza lo stral piagato: Jommelli's Tito Manlio.
Spielten wir in den jungen: La Borde's Die muellerin.
Spirti fieri a la vendetta: Partenio's Flavio Cuniberto.
Spirti invisibili: Paisiello's La grotta di Trofonio.
Spirto eccelso, con valore: Nero (Hamburg).
Splenda fra noi seren: Pergolesi's Il maestro di musica.
Splenda fra noi seren: Latilla and Pergolesi's Orazio.
Sprezza il furor del vento: pasticcio La Merope.
Sprezza il furor del vento: Metastasio's Adriano in Siria text.
Spring nur, spring du Lumpenhund: Gassmann in his and Paisiello's Don Quischott von Mancia.
Sta in quell' abito: Guglielmi's L'impostore punito.
Staremo allegramente: Sarti's I finti eredi.
State zitte, non parlate: Anfossi's Gli amanti canuti.
Stets geliebt und verfolgt: Duni's Die schule der jugend.
Still in hopes to get the better: Arne in Love in a village.
Stille wasser gruenden schlecht: La Borde's Die muellerin.
Stizzoso, mio: Pergolesi's La serva padrona.
Strappami il core: Hasse's Don Tabarrano.
Su, bel bello, adagio: Gazzaniga's La vendemmia.
Sù, che fate: Sances's Apollo deluso (this aria by Leopold I).
Sù le piume de' sospiri: Maraucci in Le chiajese cantarine.
Su le sponde del torbido Lete: Hasse's Artaserse.
Su, miei spirti: Partenio and others' Flavio Cuniberto.
Su quest' Olmo: Capello's L'Eudamia.
Suis-je bien pour une actrice: Pergolesi in Le maître de musique.
Suis-je digne: Méreaux' La ressource comique.
Sul mio crin di sdegno: Gasparini and others' L'amante impazzito.
Superba; vedrai: Mancini in Lotti's Artaserse rè di Persia.
Sur les gazon: Philidor's Le sorcier.
Sveglia in sen: Freschi's Cesare trionfante.
Svenasti il padre: Galuppi's Issipile.
T'amo a segno: Piccinni's La scaltra letterata.
T'amo a segno: Piccinni's La scaltra spiritosa.
T'inganna il tuo pensier: pasticcio Stratonica.
T'intendo ingrata: Metastasio's Demofoonte text.
T'intendo ingrata: Hasse's Demofoonte.
T'intendo ingrata: Jommelli's Demofoonte.
T'intendo si mio cor: Gasparini and others' L'amante impazzito.
Ta voix au noir séjour: Rinaldo di Capua's La Bohémienne.
Tacerò se tu lo brami: Unknown's composer's Didone abbandonata.
Taci, amor, nel seno mio: Galuppi's Il filosofo di campagna.
Taci crudel: Martinengo's Arsiade.
Taci, o core: Leopold I in Draghi's Sulpitia.
Talk not to me: Vento in Dibdin's The school for fathers.
Tall'or il cacciator: Vivaldi's Artabano rè de Parti.
Tall'or il cacciator: Vivaldi's La costanza trionfante degl' amori e degl' odii.

Tandis que, du matin au soir: Kohault's Le serrurier.

Tandis que tout sommeille: Grétry's Les fausses apparences.

Tant qu'on verra: La nouvelle Bastienne.

Te fa i buono: Piccinni, Logroscino and Insanguine's La furba burlata.

Tel qu'un petit oiseau: Lasalle d'Offemont's Bertholde à la ville.

Tell me, Philly, tell me: Damon and Phillida and Love in a riddle.

Temo in un punto: Jommelli's Demofoonte (first version).

Tendre Amour reçois: La fontaine de Jouvence.

Tendres amants si vous voulez: Boyer's Les étrennes de l'amour.

Tergi'l bel ciglio, o cara: Guglielmi's Il disertore.

That all ride their hobbies: Reeve's Blue Beard.

That man who best: Carey's The honest Yorkshire-man.

That the world is a lottery: The lottery.

The age is refin'd: The fool turn'd critick.

The blush of Aurora: Shield in The cobler of Caslebury.

The face which frequently displays: Linley in Dibdin's The quaker.

The morn returns: Paxton in Shield's Rosina.

The nymph who in my bosom: Dibdin's The deserter.

The stag through the forest: Harington in Shield's Robin Hood.

The swain I adore: Lampe's Dragoness.

The tongue is a dangerous weapon: Lampe's Dragoness.

The whims of folk in love: Dibdin's The deserter.

There lies your road: Arnold in The summer's tale.

There's nought can surpass: Gehot in The cobler of Castlebury.

This marriage article: Paisiello in Dittersdorf-Storace's Doctor and apothecary.

Tho' dangers allarm me: Carey in The generous free-mason.

Tho' pity I cannot deny: Pleyel in The haunted tower.

Thou only darling: Carey's The honest Yorkshire-man.

Thus the sun at morn: Piccinni's The accomplish'd maid.

Ti lascierò se vuoi: Pollaroli's L'Ibraim sultano.

Tiens, tu me fais pitié: Philidor's Blaise le savetier.

Tiranna la sorte: Händel's Porus.

To fear a stranger: Dibdin in The school for fathers.

To happy ignorance: Midas.

To ramble from taverns: The fool turn'd critick.

To rob them of strength: Dibdin's The school for fathers.

To tell you the truth: Dibdin's The school for fathers.

Toedtliche eyffersucht: Keiser's Die verdammte staat-sucht.

Toi, que mon coeur adore: Monsigny's Le cadi dupé.

Torbida notte, e fosca: Freschi's L'incoronatione di Dario.

Tornerai nel fido amante: Hasse's Ipermestra.

Tortorella abbandonata: Sarti's I contrattempi.

Toujours ainsi: Paisiello in the pasticcio La vallée de Montmorency.

Toujours preste, toujours leste: Rinaldo di Capua's La Bohémienne.

Toujours suivre avec uniformité: Favart in La ressource des théâtres.

Tous les voeux d'une fillette: Philidor's Le soldat magicien.

Tout ici partage: Le bal de Strasbourg.

Tout suit dans l'univers: Rochar in Les jeunes marié's.

Toute fille en Provence: Philidor's L'amant déguisé.

Tre giorni son che Nina (see also Son già trè dì): See Rinaldo di Capua's Examinez sa grace in his La Bohémienne.

Tremola qual la fonda: Leo's La clemenza di Tito.

Trionfa mia core: Cesti's Orontea, regina d'Egitto.

Trionfi Giuliva: Perti's Il furio Camillo.

Trofonio, Trofonio, filosofo: Paisiello's La grotta di Trofonio.

Trop heureux qui peut: Philidor's Le jardinier de Sidon.

Trop occupé de mon ouvrage: Audinot-Gossec's Le tonnelier.

Trübe tage stiller klage: Naumann's Cora.

Tu, che il tenor già sai: Sacchini's Alessandro nell' Indie.

Tu del mio regno sei: Vinci's Medo.

Tu ne sçais pas beauté: Philidor's Mélide.

Tu ne songes guère: Rinaldo di Capua's La Bohémienne.

Tu non pensi: Rinaldo di Capua's La Zingara.

Tu parti mio: Bertoni in the pasticcio Cleonice.

Tu sai chi son: Metastasio's Demofoonte text.

Tu sai cupido: Gassmann's Gli uccellatori.

Tu sei troppo scelerato: Pergolesi's La contadina astuta and Tracollo, medico ignorante.

Tutta ricci, tutta nei: Piccinni's L'incostante and Il volubile.

Tutta rigore: Orlandini and Mancini's Artaserse.

Um vergnügt zu leben: Philidor's Hanns der schuhflicker.

Un' alma fedele ti chiama: Orlandini and Mancini's Artaserse.

Un amant dans ses beaux discours: Gluck's L'ivrogne corrigé.

. Un amant dans ses beaux discours: La Ruette's L'yvrogne corrigé.

Un amant doit-il: Vadé's text Il etoit tems.

Un amante rispettoso: Perillo in Piccinni's L'erede riconosciuta.

Un avanzo di pietà: Orlandini and Mancini's Artaserse.

Un bon Gaillard joyeux: Le confident heureux.

Un certo non sò che: Albinoni and Porta's La Mariane.

Un chanteur n'est pas: Monsigny's On ne s'avise jamais de tout.

Un consorte sciagurato: Il marito giogatore e la moglie bacchettona.

Un consorte sciagurato: Orlandini's Il giocatore.

Un consorte sciagurato: Vinci's Bacocco e Serpilla.   *See* Il marito giogatore.

Un dolce contento: Sarti's Giulio Sabino.

Un dolcissimo sorriso: Cesti's Orontea, regina d'Egitto.

Un instant a fait naître: Duni's Le peintre amoureux de son modèle.

Un jardinier est un grand homme: Philidor's L'amant déguisé.

Un militaire semillant: Boyer's Les étrennes de l'amour.

Un pensier mi nasce: Perillo in Piccinni's L'erede riconosciuta.

Un pilote battu: Le maître de musique.

Un tonnelier vieux: Audinot and Gossec's Le tonnelier.

Una damina nobile: Petrosellini's Il cavaliere per amore text.

Una ragazza semplice: Bernardini's La schiava astuta.

Une fille est un oiseau: Monsigny's On ne s'avise jamais de tout.

Une jeune danseuse: Folette ou L'enfant gâté.

Ungluecks-triebe: Keiser's Der hochmuethige . . . Croesus.

Unsern jungen leuten: Duni's Die fee Urgele.

Unsre liebe bleibt bestaendig: Keiser's Der angenehme betrug.

Va cantando l'augellino: Garcia's La pupilla.

Va dal crudel tiranna: Jommelli's Bajazet.

Va, je te rens: Les amours de Bastien et Bastienne.

Va superba ed ostinata: Orlandini's Adelaide.

Vadan li rei felloni: Hasse's Alessandro nell' Indie.

Vado con alma sorte: Vivaldi's Siroe, rè di Persia.

Vado, vado (*or* a morte), ed avrai core: Pergolesi's Livietta e Tracollo and its L. T.

Vaga stella pallidita: Porpora in the pasticcio Orfeo.

Vaghi rai del mio: *See* Il rè infante, Intermezzi.

Vainement en filant: La Borde's La meuniere de Gentilly.

Vane alla ingrata: pasticcio La Merope.

Ve', ve' di Florido: Piccinni's Il regno della luna.

Vedo l'aria che s'imbruna: Pergolesi's Livietta e Tracollo and its L. T.

Vedo quel bel l'occhietto: Pergolesi's Il maestro di musica.

Vedovella poverella: Cocchi's La scaltra governatrice.

Vedovella, poverella: Cocchi's La scaltra governatrice in Rinaldo di Capua's La Bohémienne.

Vedrai con tuo periglio: Hasse's Alessandro nell' Indie.

Veggo nel gran cimento: Galuppi's Il Muzio Scevola.

Vendetta, vendetta: Cesti's L'Argia.

Vergönne, dass ich weine: Philidor's Tom Jones.

Vezzi, lusinghe e sguarde: Gluck's Tigrane.

Vezzosa gradita: Fabrizi and others' I tre gobbi rivali.

Vezzose gradita: Goldoni Favola de' tre gobbi text.

Vezzosetto nume alato: Pollaroli's L'Oreste in Sparta.

Vi prego di core: Goldoni's Favola de' tre gobbi text.

Vi prego di core: Fabrizi and others' I tre gobbi rivali.

Vi stò ben? Vi comparisco: Goldoni's Amor fa l'uomo cieco text.

Vi stò ben? Vi comparisco: Pergolesi's Livietta e Tracollo and its L. T.

Vi vuol altro che bravati: Perillo in Piccinni's L'erede riconosciuta.

Via buon zitello: Bernardini's La schiava astuta.

Viel lieber an einem fädchen: Monsigny's Roschen und Colas.

Viens calmer ma douleur: Le depart de l'Opéra comique.

Vil trofeo d'un' alma imbelle: Hasse's Alessandro nell' Indie.

Vincerai, non paventar: Leo in La Rosilla.

Vinse Marte pugnando: Orlandini and Mancini's Artaserse.

Viverò se tu lo vuoi: Rinaldo di Capua's La Zingara.

Vò che cada trafitto: Albinoni's L'Ardelinda.

Vò dir lo basso: Pergolesi's Il maestro di musica.

Vo girando qual colomba: Cimarosa's La baronessa Stramba.

Vo mostrarvi alla francese: Boroni in Laurenti's La pupilla rapita.

Voce, che flebile: Rinaldo di Capua's La Zingara.

Vögeln ländeln und spielen: Duni's Der militz.

Voglio, che mora: Freschi's Helena rapita da Paride.

Voglio un marito: Piccinni's L'astratto.

Voglio vendetta sì: Albinoni and Porta's La Mariane.

Voi altre femmine: Perillo in Piccinni's L'erede riconosciuta.

Voi, che pietà provate: Bertoni's La vedova accorta.

Voi che tanto ne vedete: A. Scarlatti's Bassiano.

Voi la spada: Galuppi's La forza d'amore.

Voi piangete ò luci belle: Aldrovandini's L'odio e l'amore.

Voi quì, bella tiranna: Guglielmi's L'equivoco amoroso.

Voi semplici amanti: Paisiello's Gli avventurieri and Il rè Teodoro.

Voi vedrete in una sala: Cimarosa's Il credulo.

Voici tout mon projet: Duni's Les deux chasseurs et la laitière.

Voilà la petite laitière: Duni's Les deux chasseurs et la laitière.

Volez, tendres Zéphirs: Fago in Nouvelle chasse du cerf.

Volgi à me gli affetti: Hasse's Cajo Fabricio.

Vorrei pria esanime: Jommelli's Didone abbandonata (1747).

Votre coeur en vain: Lasalle d'Offemont's Bertholde à la ville.

Vous êtes le mon cher coeur: Scolari's Il viaggiatore ridicolo.

Vous, gentilles jeunes filles: Pergolesi's La servante maitresse.

Vous jaloux, que viens-je: La Ruette's Le medecin de l'amour.

Vous jugerez de mon ivresse: Lebrun's Le bon fils.

Vous me charmez: Grétry's Le Huron.

Vous n'me connoissez pas: Duni's La clochette.

Vous ne devez rien menager: Les amants trompés.

Vous, qu'amour brûle: Monsigny's Le cadi dupé.

Vous qui cherchez à mériter: Favart's La rosière de Salenci text.

Vous qui croyez que des tendres: Monsigny's On ne s'avise jamais de tout.

Vous, qui voyez un coeur: Grétry's Les mariages Samnites.

Vuò soffrire a un certo segno: Sarti's I pretendenti delusi.

Was thut man nicht: Dittersdorf's Hokus Pokus.

We all say the man: Dibdin in The school for fathers.

Well come let us hear: Arne in Love in a village.

Wenn der stein den stahl: Duni's Das milchmaedchen und die beiden jaeger.

Wenn des wilden krieges: Duni's Die schule der jugend.

Wenn man liebt, ist man: Duni's Die fee Urgele.

Wenn mich armen mann: Kohault's Der schlosser.

What blest hours: Linley in The haunted tower.

What dire misfortune: Burgess in The coffee-house.

What pleasures a coffee-house: Carey in The coffee-house.

What shall I do: Arnold in Dibdin's The seraglio.

When a freak has got in: Arne in The summer's tale.

When Arthur first: Arnold's The battle of Hexham.

When beauty our courage: Charke in The lover's opera.

When Britain first at Heaven's command: Arne's Alfred.

When Britain first her flag: Callcott in Moorehead's The naval pillar.

When cruel parents: Hayes in Arnold's Two to one.

When love gets into a youthful brain: Lionel and Clarissa.

When love is lodg'd: Seedo in The lottery.

When the candidate: Seedo in The lottery.

When the lads: Johnstone in Carter's Just in time.

When the sergeant: Arne in Shield's The poor soldier.

Where the banner of glory: Mozart in Attwood's The prisoner.

Whither my love: Paisiello in The haunted tower.

Who'er to a wife: The Yorkshire-man.

Why, Jack, my fine fellow: Dibdin's A trip to the Nore.

Why with sighs: Ciampi in Dibdin's The school for fathers.

Wie? heilig graues recht: Naumann's Cora.

Wie sich die blauen flammen: Keiser's Die verdammte staatsucht.

Wie stark ist Deine macht: Philidor's Tom Jones.

With head thrown back: Hook in The snuff box.

Wo kann man besser seyn: Grétry's Lucile.

Wond'rous timber: Midas.

Wretched is a wife's condition: Lampe's Margery.

Ye gloomy thoughts: Dibdin's The school for fathers.

Ye Gods! you gave to me: Seedo in The devil to pay.

Yes, marriage sure must: Carey in The coffee-house.

Zerbinetti d'oggidì:Sellitti's Cinese rimpatriato.

Zuerne was hin: Händel's Der in cronen erlangte glueckswechsel.